Annotated Instructor's Edition

 W9-BAO-463

Intermediate Algebra

John Tobey

Jeffrey Slater

North Shore Community College
Beverly, Massachusetts

Prentice Hall, Englewood Cliffs, NJ 07632

Library of Congress Cataloging-in-Publication Data

TOBEY, JOHN, 1943–
    Intermediate algebra/John Tobey, Jeffrey Slater,
        p.   cm.
    Includes index.
    ISBN 0-13-466624-0
    1. Algebra.   I. Slater, Jeffrey, 1947–   II. Title.
QA154.2.T634 1991
512.9—dc20

90-25616
CIP

Editorial/production supervision: Tom Aloisi
Acquisition editor: Priscilla McGeehon
Development editor: Steve Deitmer
Interior design: Judith A. Matz-Coniglio
Cover design: Judith A. Matz-Coniglio
Prepress buyer: Paula Massenaro
Manufacturing buyer: Lori Bulwin
Page layout: Karen Noferi
Photo editor: Lori Morris-Nantz
Photo research: Barbara Scott
Cover photo: Laima Druskis

Photo credits: 1, Jim Pickerell/TSW-Click/Chicago Ltd. ● 39, Art Attack/Photo Researchers ● 41, Frank Siteman/Stock, Boston ● 68, Anglo-Australian Telescope Board/ PH Photo Archives ● 75, Bob Daemmrich/Stock, Boston (Image Works) ● 80, John Coletti/ Stock, Boston ● 99, Cynthia Matthews/Stock Market ● 104, Annie Griffiths Belt/West Light ● 106, Lawrence Migdale/Stock, Boston ● 127, Rhoda Baer/Folio ● 150, William James Warren/West Light ● 181, Jon Feingersh/Uniphoto ● 191, Bob Daemmrich/Stock, Boston ● 197, Wendy Ledis/Uniphoto ● 234, Tony Freeman/Photoedit ● 243, David Stoecklein/Uniphoto ● 270, Daniel Grogan/Uniphoto ● 273, Bill Ross/West Light ● 284, Gabe Palmer/The Stock Market ● 293, Alon Reininger/Contact/Woodfin Camp ● 304, Gabe Palmer/The Stock Market ● 337, Harry Wilks/Stock, Boston ● 343, Ted Horowitz/The Stock Market ● 350, Photri San/The Stock Market ● 367, David Aronson/Stock, Boston ● 372, Charles Krebs/The Stock Market ● 391, John Bova/ Photo Researchers ● 397, Jan Halaska/Photo Researchers ● 411, NASA ● 416, Ron Jautz/Folio Inc. ● 417, NASA ● 425, J. Barry O'Rourke/The Stock Market ● 463, David Ryan/Uniphoto ● 470, Ned Gillette/Stock Market ● 477, Irene E. Springer/PH Photo Archives ● 513, John De Waele/Stock, Boston ● 520, Jeff Perkell/Stock Market ● 522, James Cook/Folio Inc. ● 525, Les Moore/Uniphoto ● 530, PH Photo Archives.

© 1991 by Prentice-Hall, Inc.
A Division of Simon & Schuster
Englewood Cliffs, New Jersey 07632

Printed in the United States of America
10 9 8 7 6 5 4 3 2 1

ISBN   0-13-466632-1

Prentice-Hall International (UK) Limited, *London*
Prentice-Hall of Australia Pty. Limited, *Sydney*
Prentice-Hall Canada Inc., *Toronto*
Prentice-Hall Hispanoamericana, S.A., *Mexico*
Prentice-Hall of India Private Limited, *New Delhi*
Prentice-Hall of Japan, Inc., *Tokyo*
Simon & Schuster Asia Pte. Ltd., *Singapore*
Editora Prentice-Hall do Brasil, Ltda., *Rio de Janeiro*

Contents

5

Fractional Algebraic Expressions and Equations *243*

6

Rational Exponents and Radicals *293*

7

Quadratic Equations *337*

8

Graphs and Functions *391*

Preface to the Annotated Instructor's Edition

The ability to use mathematics has become an essential skill for succeeding in today's world. To meet the demands that you as an instructor place on a college algebra textbook, we must provide your students with a strong foundation of mathematical skills, and we must make the text interesting and relevant.

In *Intermediate Algebra* we emphasize the importance of mathematics to students through our chapter-opening photographs, which present a diverse set of occupations that use mathematics in their everyday performance. Our applied examples and illustrations throughout the text help bring mathematics alive. We encourage students to think beyond the surface procedures they have learned and to develop problem-solving skills and reasoning abilities along with the new mathematical concepts. We support students' efforts by providing direction on improving their studying habits. A direct writing style makes exposition clear.

We have written *Intermediate* for college students taking a one-semester or two-quarter course in Algebra. Our writing style aims to speak clearly and directly to students. We hope that our tone encourages them. This text has a mathematical prerequisite of basic algebra.

Intermediate Algebra is a text/workbook. Students progress naturally from the text's full explanations and worked-out examples and parallel Practice Problems to writing their answers to exercises directly on the workbook page. The workbook format accommodates those students taking the course through classroom (lecture) instruction as well as students in a self-paced lab setting.

We believe—and academic reviewers confirm—that *Intermediate Algebra* offers students the soundest foundation for learning the topics important in this course. To enhance student learning, we have included many valuable pedagogical features.

Pedagogical Highlights

Chapter Outline. This feature lists the chapter's topical sections on the first page of every chapter. The Chapter Outline serves as a road map of the chapter's coverage.

Pretest. How well do students know the material covered in a particular chapter? Instructors may assign the Pretest in full or by section to evaluate their students' abilities in and familiarity with the topics in a given chapter. In a self-paced course, students may then be able to skip some sections or chapters and concentrate on those areas where their skills need improvement. Similarly, students can test themselves to assess their own skills. The Pretest also serves as a "post-test"—that is, students can take the Pretest after studying the chapter to confirm their mastery of the subject matter.

Learning Objectives. We introduce each chapter section with a number of student goals, or Learning Objectives. The number of the appropriate learning objective appears next to the text or example in each section where that concept is introduced.

Developing Your Study Skills. These boxes give students suggestions on how to get the most out of class time and homework assignments and how best to prepare for tests.

Examples and Matched Practice Problems. This text offers an abundance of worked-out sample examples. Each Example is numbered and is followed immediately by a corresponding Practice Problem. The Practice Problem gives students the chance to solve an exercise similar to the worked-out sample example on their own. The worked-out *solutions* to odd-numbered Practice Problems appear a few pages later, at the end of corresponding exercise set. *Answers* to even-numbered Practice Problems also appear here.

Extra Practice: Exercises. Faculty members often find that they need additional problems of a certain type to assign to the entire class or to one student who needs work in a particular area. For each chapter section we offer extra additional practice problems to solve at the end of the chapter.

To Think About. Throughout the book you will see To Think About sections, which look at interesting topics in a way designed to spark student curiosity, challenge student thinking, foster student writing, and promote interesting points for classroom discussion. There are often parallel To Think About exercises in the following exercise set.

Exercise Sets. Each section ends with an exercise set for homework assignment. In addition to multiple exercises for each topic, students are offered special types of problems.

* To Think About problems. These are designed to develop reasoning and problem-solving skills and tie back to the preceding To Think About section in the text.

* Cumulative Review Problems. These problems review the content of previous chapters and refresh students' understanding of important topics covered earlier.

* Calculator Problems. A calculator icon signals optional problems best handled with a calculator.

Putting Your Skills to Work. This feature, which appears in selected chapters, takes students beyond the classroom and shows them how to apply the lessons just learned.

Chapter Organizer. This unique chapter-ending feature summarizes the chapter material in an easily accessible grid. The first column lists a key topic and the page number within the chapter where discussion of that topic begins. The second column outlines the procedure appropriate to understanding the key topic. The third column gives the student a step-by-step worked-out example of the key topic. The Chapter Organizer is an ideal tool for students to use in reviewing the chapter material for a test and working the end-of-chapter assignment material.

Review Problems. Grouped by section, Review Problems give students still more practice in testing their comprehension of the chapter's coverage.

Practice Quizzes. Each chapter has two Practice Quizzes, each covering one-half of the chapter's material. Instructors may assign the Practice Quiz as homework or use it as an in-class test because it can easily be removed from the book. Of course, students may use the Practice Quizzes on their own as measures of their mastery of the chapter and as preparation for tests.

Chapter Test. Each chapter has a Chapter Test. The test pages are perforated so they may easily be torn out and handed in.

Cumulative Tests. Every chapter following Chapter 1 concludes with a Cumulative Test. One-half of this test is based on the content of the chapter in which it appears. The other half is based on the content of all previous chapters. The Cumulative Test affords instructors the opportunity to test their students' retention of previously learned material as well as the content of the particular chapter.

Glossary. At the end of the text is a full glossary of important terms used in the book. Each entry presents the definition and an example of how the text treats the term.

A Note on the Problem Material

Whenever possible, we give students realistic application problems designed to raise their interest and minimize their anxiety. We include a broad range of consumer mathematics problems of particular interest to college students. Word problems are fully integrated into the assignment material, as appropriate. In addition, where appropriate, students are shown how to estimate answers, to round off answers to an appropriate level of accuracy, and to determine if a calculated answer is reasonable.

Supplements

The *Annotated Instructor's Edition* includes not only the complete student text, but also (in blue), worked-out solutions to end-of-section and end-of-chapter exercises, answers to Practice Problems, Extra Practice Exercises, Quizzes and Tests; teaching tips in the margin; and articles about teaching basic mathematics in the front of the book.

The *Supplements Guide with Instructor's Disk* (by Lea Pruet Campbell) is a comprehensive, detailed instructor's reference for teaching and for using supplements in and out of the classroom. This handy guide contains a sample syllabus, detailed lecture outlines including suggested homework assignments, and correlations to TASP, ELM, and CLAST competencies. The material is also available on an ASCII-code disk, allowing you to edit and personalize syllabus, assignments, and so on.

The *Instructor's Manual with Tests* (by Marie Clark) includes nine tests per chapter (five are standard-answer format, four are multiple-choice), ready to be photocopied and used in your classroom or lab.

Computerized Testing/Prentice Hall Test Manager contains a bank of over 3,000 test questions in short-answer and multiple-choice format. Our state-of-the-art program allows the instructor to access questions from the computerized Test Item File and personally prepare and print out tests. It includes an editing feature that allows questions to be added or changed. A Function Plotter is also included. Available on IBM $5\frac{1}{4}$ or $3\frac{1}{2}$-inch format.

The *Instructor's Solutions Manual* (by Pat Traxler) is a comprehensive collection of worked-out solutions to even-numbered exercises in the text. (Worked-out solutions to the odd-numbered exercises are provided in the Student Solutions Manual.)

The *Student Solutions Manual* (by Helen Burrier) contains worked-out solutions for all odd-numbered exercises in the text, for sale to students who want extra support through the course.

The *Study Guide* provides chapter summary material, practice exercises with additional examples, self-tests, and an answer key to the tests and exercises.

Videotapes, available with a qualified adoption of 100 or more copies of the book, are a set of 40–48 important lecture topics that present and solve examples of progressive difficulty.

Interactive Algebra Tutor is user-friendly, menu-driven software for both IBM and MacIntosh personal computers. For every section of the text, it presents a (1) Summary of Key Concepts page-referenced to the text; (2) Practice Exercises with diagnostic feedback and full solutions, page-referenced to the text; and (3) a Simulated Quiz with scoring capability. A classroom management feature allows the student to print out a score with his and her name. Available on adoption.

Teamwork

Each of us has twenty years' experience teaching at the college level, but the guidance and enthusiasm we received from many people have been invaluable in getting down on paper, our vision of the best possible basic mathematics book.

In several full-day reviewer conferences, our academic peers examined the manuscript page by page and point by point. The detailed observations of these reviewers helped us immensely in shaping the manuscript.

Every page of every draft was reviewed by academic peers for accuracy and clarity. We read your insights and recommendations enthusiastically. To all the conference participants and reviewers who helped us write this book, thank you.

Barbara A. Jur, University of Tennessee at Chattanooga
Judy Kasabian, El Camino College
Ara B. Sullenberger, Tarrant County Junior College
Ben Zirkle, Virginia Western Community College
Shelba J. Morman, North Lake College
Diane Trimble, Collin County Community College
Howard Penn, El Centro College
Linda Kyle, Tarrant County Junior College
William A. Neal, Fresno City College
Larry Blevins, Tyler Junior College
Louis Hoelzle, Bucks County Community College
Louis P. Pushkarsky, Trenton Junior College
James W. Newsom, Tidewater Community College
Michael A. Contino, California State University, Hayward
Ann S. Bretscher, University of Georgia
Phyllis Jore, Valencia Community College
Sheldon Kovitz, University of Massachusetts at Boston
Robert Gesell, Cleary College
Linda Kyle, Tarrant County Junior College
Helen Burrier, Kirkwood Community College
Marie Clarke, North Shore Community College
Jamie King, Orange Coast College
Pat Cross, University of Oklahoma
Richard Semmler, Northern Virginia Community College
Tom Rourke, North Shore Community College

We thank, as well, the following supplements authors:

Pat Traxler, Southern Illinois University at Edwardsville, *Instructor's Solution Manual*
Marie Clarke, North Shore Community College, *Instructor's Manual with Tests*
Lea Pruet Campbell, Lamar University, *Supplements' Guide with Instructor's Disk*
Helen Burrier, Kirkwood Community College, *Student Solutions Manual*

Accuracy

As instructors we are acutely aware of how important it is to have full confidence in the textbook we use. We have taken many steps to ensure that *Intermediate Algebra* is error-free. In addition to careful proofreading, we asked several instructors who teach this course to read every word and every number and relay to us any error they uncovered. We are grateful to Pat Cross, Richard Semmler, Jamie King, Myrna Mitchell, and Jim Keefe. Of course, the checking process gave us additional insights on how to improve our text to reach full technical accuracy. We believe that these painstaking efforts have helped us give you a book on which you can depend.

Development Editing

Prentice Hall assigned the Managing Editor of College Book Editorial Development to this project. Every draft of every chapter received full analysis and word-by-word editing to help us bring your students a clearly written, accessible, and consistent book. Special thanks to Steve Deitmer and Tom Whipple for their hard work.

Acknowledgments

Finally, we would like to thank all those people at Prentice Hall whose hard work and encouragement made this book possible, including Tom Aloisi and Barbara DeVries, Production; Judith Matz-Coniglio, Design; Alison Munoz, Supplements Editor; and Priscilla McGeehon, Editor.

We have been greatly helped by a supportive group of colleagues who not only teach at North Shore Community College but who have provided a number of ideas as well as extensive help on all of our mathematics books. So a special word of thanks to Marie Clark, Hank Harmeling, Tom Rourke, Wally Hersey, Bob McDonald, Judy Carter, Kathy LeBlanc, Bob Oman, Keth Piggott, Russ Sullivan, and Rick Ponticelli who gave help in a variety of ways as this book was being completed. Joan Peabody patiently typed and retyped the entire manuscript. Her cheerful dedication to doing a long job and doing it well have been an invaluable contribution in the task of preparing this book.

Book writing is impossible for us without the support of our families. Our deepest thanks to Nancy, Johnny, Marcia, Melissa, Shelly, Rusty, and Abby. You have patiently waited, quietly assisted, and given words of encouragement when greatly needed. Finally, we thank God for the strength and energy to write and the opportunity to help others through this textbook.

John Tobey
Jeff Slater

WHO ARE THE DEVELOPMENTAL MATHEMATICS STUDENTS? WHAT CAN WE DO TO HELP THEM?

Ara B. Sullenberger
Tarrant County Junior College, Fort Worth, Texas

This article is designed to assist the teacher who is new to teaching developmental mathematics courses in college. The students who are not yet prepared for the university parallel courses in mathematics are very special people whom we shall attempt to identify and describe. We will also offer some suggestions for helping these students.

There are many reasons for students to be required to take developmental or remedial mathematics courses in college: they may need to refresh their knowledge of high school mathematics that is long-forgotten through years of being away from school entirely; they may have never been exposed to high school mathematics courses for one reason or another; they may suffer from what we call "Math Anxiety;" or perhaps they cannot read well enough to understand the questions asked of them on placement tests, much less work out the solutions to those questions. In addition, some of the students we will find in developmental courses are there strictly by choice, having preferred to begin their college mathematics with the very beginning course.

The primary reason students often give for their deficiencies in mathematics is that it has been too long since they took any mathematics courses. Sometimes "too long" is translated by students to be "two or three years." They contend that when they were in high school the farthest thing from their minds was continuing their education beyond high school. The main goal at that time was to "just get out of high school." The study of algebra frequently was not required for high school graduation; and if it did happen to be a requirement, the students seldom could see the need for retention of the algebraic skills and did not apply themselves. Now, perhaps as many as twenty years later for some, those same students have been made aware that they are not allowed to enroll in the mathematics course required for their chosen majors until they learn the skills developed in a course on the level of the one for which this text is designed. We have found that these returning students are the most successful of all our developmental students, for they are quite highly motivated once introduced to the material. Teaching that group of students is a joy, for they strive for perfection.

A second group, the eighteen-year-old students who were forced (for whatever reason) to leave high school early or were never enrolled in a true algebra course in high school, are not as rare as one might suppose today. Those students actually fall into two categories: one group is excited about learning algebra and is quite successful (each one thriving on the success s/he is having, much as the returning student described above); the other group appears to be a bit bewildered, hanging on to the idea that only smart people can learn algebraic concepts, thus lacking the confidence each student needs to be successful. The former type needs no particular attention, but the latter does—each individual in that group needs encouragement as often as one can bestow it. The rewards of having both these kinds of student in class are great, for they appreciate the instructor's efforts, once they get acquainted with the subject.

The developmental mathematics course often attracts another type of eighteen-year-old that needs a bit of attention here: the recent high school graduates in the class who have been sent to college against their will or who resent having been placed in a remedial course. Our job is to make the learning of mathematics fun for them so that they will forget to disrupt the class. Fortunately that type is rare and seldom returns after one semester, for those individuals disappear one way or another: they catch on to becoming real "students" or they drop out. Our concern in this article is not really about that kind of student, but one needs to be aware in advance that the type does exist.

Another group of developmental students is the one that consists of people who typically suffer from the disease we call "Math Anxiety" and perhaps there are many reasons for this anxiety. They have developed a real fear of mathematics usually derived from some earlier experience with the subject that turned out to be disagreeable for one reason or another. The most vocal of these people are usually female and they usually eventually finish the course with good grades. A study conducted in 1983 at Tarrant County Junior College showed a predominance of "math anxiety" among young male students who did *not* finish the developmental mathematics sequence, perhaps because they were not vocal enough. This anxious student, whether male or female, needs special care on the part of the teacher, for feelings are easily hurt and the fear returns quickly, sometimes daily. Lots of personal encouragement is necessary for each of these anxious students to feel that s/he can succeed where failure prevailed before.

Today, more and more students are coming to college with deficiencies in all areas of their education, for whatever reason. Reading difficulties often surface as the major hurdle for students in developmental mathematics courses. Often some of the students are not able to read above the third grade level when they reach their first mathematics course. Those persons are going to need as much extra help as one can possibly give them in translating the words in the mathematics text to ideas that are meaningful to them, at least until they can progress far enough in developmental reading courses to raise their level of reading. Sometimes the solution to the problem of what to do with the students hindered in their math by a lack of reading skills is to arrange for each one to have some peer tutoring if at all possible. This tutoring needs to be obtained either from a special center on campus that furnishes such tutoring, or the instructor might ask one of the classmates to help each one outside of class for a while. The instructor should have a role in making students aware of any possible tutoring that is available on campus, prescribing the type of tutoring that he feels will help the most.

In dealing with all developmental mathematics students, one must bear in mind that they are all special, even though the difficulties are similar. The developmental mathematics class group is seldom homogeneous, thus one of the most helpful things that can be done for this type of student is to keep class size down to about thirty if at all possible. Another thing that can be done is for the instructor to arrange for small study groups to meet after class in a vacant classroom, preferably with a qualified assistant to help. Sometimes schools have facilities for a "math lab" in which para-professionals with good mathematics backgrounds can assist in getting individual students or small groups over rough spots in their work. These math labs appear to be useful in assisting the remedial student.

Computer-assisted instruction is often helpful, too. Several commercial companies market tutorial type software for use on microcomputers. We would suggest that the instructor preview this material carefully before it is purchased, for there is some software being sold in which unclear mathematical techniques and language are used.

There are also audio and video types and workbooks available commercially that attempt to assist the developmental student. I suggest that the instructor carefully preview these materials as well. The ideal situation would involve the use of the student manual designed for use with this textbook.

It has been our finding that developmental students profit greatly from short tests given daily to reinforce the skills as they are learned. Frequent brief testing on topics from previous chapters is another way to improve the instructor's success rate with developmental classes. Major exams for these developmental courses usually do not need to differ in format or amount of coverage from those in college algebra or other university mathematics courses.

Generally, the developmental mathematics students are very different from the students taking university parallel mathematics courses, for more motivation on the part of the instructor is needed with them. Just as each person is different, an instructor will find that each of the developmental mathematics students may have one or more of the characteristics mentioned. Some are returning to school or mathematics after many years away from study, some are totally overwhelmed in any learning program by lack of reading skills, others have the "Math Anxiety" disease while still others simply may not want to be in that remedial class. Whatever special problems these students have, the developmental mathematics students are people who need more individual attention than the amount given the average student in a university parallel course.

TEACHING WORD PROBLEMS

H. Joan Dykes
Edison Community College, Fort Myers, Florida

As you prepare to teach a section involving word problems, try to realize that the day's lesson is not just about a particular type of problem. Problem-solving strategies involve many different skills aside from the particular algebraic skill needed to solve the equation or equations that arise from the problems. You are asking the students to read a problem, translate English into symbols and variables, draw a diagram, picture, or box that is properly labeled or filled in, decide on an algorithm that fits the situation (perhaps $D = rt$), solve this equation (in itself no small feat!) and check the answer or answers for reasonableness as well as accuracy! We often *assume* that we only need to show them the algorithm and *its* solution. If you can break your teaching into as many different steps as necessary, and discuss each step, your students will have a better chance of learning each of these steps. For example, consider teaching a typical $D = rt$ problem.

One car leaves Miami traveling at 60 mph. A second car leaves Orlando traveling at 40 mph. If Miami and Orlando are 400 miles apart, and the cars travel the same route toward each other, when will they meet?

After the students read the problem to themselves, and you discuss what you are looking for, you might try to organize the information in a table. Rather than just place a table on the board, try discussing with the class what type of columns would make sense for the table. Discuss how the columns should be labeled so that it makes sense to someone else looking at it as well as the themselves when they refer back to it. We often show our students tables, but we don't really teach them why we use a particular table. So take this opportunity to teach them this skill. The table now probably looks like:

	Rate	Time	Distance
Miami Car	60 mph	x hours	60x miles
Orlando Car	40 mph	x hours	40x miles

Notice that the units are stated in the table. This emphasis on the type of units with each measurement will help make the data meaningful. (Students often try to tell me that the 60 mph is time!) Teaching them what units belong with each quantity will also help them with their future courses in chemistry, biology and physics. At this point, the students probably need to reread the problem to decide what to do with the data. A discussion about whether the distances should be added or set equal to each other should follow. This discussion should eventually lead to:

$$60x + 40x = 400$$

which can be solved for $x = 4$. At this point, you will need to discuss two aspects of checking. First, was the algebra performed properly thus leading to an accurate answer, and second, was the answer reasonable in terms of the original problem? Students who write an incorrect equation to solve a word problem can check the x value in the equation and get the answer to "check." But you should also teach your students to check the answer in the context of the original problem to see if it makes "sense." In this case, cars traveling for 4 hours toward each other over a distance of 400 miles should seem reasonable.

After teaching all the different skills necessary to work the particular type of applicable, you will need to test your students' mastery of these skills. Although it's important to expect a student to work a problem from set up to solution to check, their failure at *one* of these skills doesn't mean they haven't learned. By testing the different skills you can determine more precisely what has been mastered. The following test questions demonstrate this concept.

1. Restate this problem in your own words.
2. Letting $x = \dots$, write an equation to solve for x.
3. Fill in this table with data from the problem (and provide the table).
4. Draw a picture (construct a table) and label it to organize the data from the problem.

5. Given this problem, decide whether this answer is reasonable.

Although you can ask for several of these steps from one stated problem, remember that this will increase the difficulty of the task and may lead to testing something which you are not interested in testing—working a problem with parts A, B, C, etc.

As you test these applications skills you may want to test horizontal transfer skills as well as vertical transfer skills. Horizontal transfer problems require the same or similar strategies as you have taught while vertical transfer problems require one or more additional strategies. For example, a horizontal transfer problem based on the $D = rt$ problem stated previously would be:

A car left Richmond traveling 45 mph. A second car left Richmond headed in the opposite direction at 55 mph. How many hours would they travel before they were 600 miles apart?

A vertical transfer problem might be:

A car left Miami traveling 60 mph at 8 a.m. heading for Orlando. A car left Orlando at the same time traveling 55 mph heading for Miami. What time did the cars meet?

Notice in the vertical transfer problem the students would first have to compute the number of hours before the cars would meet, and would then have to compute the elapsed time from 8 a.m. When you test, be careful that you test what you mean to test. A vertical transfer problem is harder and may not be appropriate in the time frame of your classroom test.

When I have asked my students what types of word problems interest them, they always list "real-life problems." You can enhance the problems in your textbook with a little research to tailor the problems to your location. For example, consult your local banks for current interest rates when you teach the $I = Prt$ type of problems. The $D = rt$ problems seem more realistic when your own local landmarks are used. Distances between towns can easily be checked with a map. A word of caution here about using "real" data. Changing the solutions from integers to decimals requires an extra skill. If you want to use horizontal transfer skills, approximate the data to obtain the same types of answers as you have demonstrated.

In addition to tailoring the data to your own geographic locale, you can often tailor the problems to the majors of the students in your class. Blood alcohol problems may be more interesting to a class of nursing students. If many of the students are going to take trigonometry, geometry problems can be stressed. Even if you are not currently teaching calculus, a glance through the textbook will help you determine the types of problems your students may see again. A discussion with the physics and chemistry instructors will alert you to applications the students are likely to see again. It's also important to realize that current areas of concern should be brought into the classroom. If you are reading about robotics, introduce some of the formulas to the class. As you read the newspaper and discover an article on the decrease in percentage of rainfall and destruction of the ozone layer, jot down some data and share this extra tidbit as a word problem.

A particularly useful exercise at the beginning of the semester is to have the students write their own rules for tackling word problems. This should be a general strategy written in their own words. Although it will often start with "The first thing I do is panic...," there may also be very useful ideas listed. By reading these strategies and keeping them on file, you can help students on a very individualized basis when they come for help. Sometimes referring to what was written in a relaxed state helps them calm down as they panic over word problems. Also, attempting to work problems using their train of thought will often help both you and the student to develop a successful plan for solving a problem. If their plan has flaws, together you can adjust it and then make use of it.

One technique for involving students in the word problems is to have them write their own problems. Consider imposing some rules on them to help this become a truly valuable learning situation. For example, have the students write problems in small groups of two, three or four students, and have the groups exchange problems after the writing session to solve them. Students tend to be more reasonable with their writing when they know that others in the class will have to work on their problems. If the word problems are written individually for extra credit, establish rules for acceptable problems. Be sure to include a rule that the problem must be solvable by whatever technique is currently under study. If turned loose in this manner without rules, students will often write problems that cannot be solved at all, or must be solved with techniques too advanced for the level of the class. One more advantage to having students write their own problems is that they truly have to think through the translation of English into mathematics. Students who translate an addition problem into a multiplication problem when given a problem to solve tend to be forced to think through the meaning of the words when writing their own problems.

Every time I enthusiastically announce to my classes "Tomorrow we'll do word problems," the groan that arises is loud, disheartening, and in unison. Perhaps the student's attitude is what leads many of us to leave out those sections. Perhaps it's the pressure to complete so many other topics that we're *certain* the students can't live without that causes us to skip these sections. Perhaps teaching these applications is so difficult because they are so easy for you, so hard for them, and so unrewarding when it comes to grading the results. Regardless of what the reason for wanting to skip a particular word-problem section, resist the temptation. Teaching mathematics without applications is like teaching someone to put the parts of a television together and never letting them turn it on to see the magnificent aspects of their work. The techniques mentioned in this paper will improve your attitude and the attitudes of your students. Work on your involvement and their involvement and you'll both benefit from the experience. There is a bibliography, not exhaustive by any means, at the end of this paper that will help you broaden your knowledge in the area of applications.

BIBLIOGRAPHY

Feynman, R. (1986). *Surely You're Joking, Mr. Feynman*. New York: Bantam Press.

Gadanidis, G. (1988). Problem solving: the third dimension in mathematics teaching. *Mathematics Teacher* 81(1), 16–21.

Greeno, J.G. (1978). Natures of problem solving abilities. In W.K. Estes (Ed.), *The Handbook of Learning and Cognitive Processes, Vol. 5, Human Information Processing.* New York: Erlbaum Basic Books.

National Council of Teachers of Mathematics. (1979). *Applications in School Mathematics.* Reston, Va: The National Council of Teachers of Mathematics.

National Council of Teachers of Mathematics. (1980). *An Agenda for Action: Recommendations for School Mathematics for the 1980s.* Reson, Va: The National Council of Teachers of Mathematics.

Newell, A., & Simon, H.A. (1972). *Human Problem Solving.* Englewood Cliffs, N.J.: Prentice-Hall.

Rebovich, R. (1986). Processes and strategies employed by algebra students in the solution of textbook word problems. (University of South Florida, 1986). *Dissertation Abstracts International.* 47A: 4011; May 1987.

Skinner, B.F. (1966). An operant analysis of problem solving. In B. Kleinmuntz (Ed.), *Problem Solving: Research, Method and Theory.* New York: Wiley.

WRITING IN MATHEMATICS

Agnes Azzolino, *Asst. Prof. of Mathematics*
Middlesex County College

"How do you graph a function?" Most of my second semester computer science students couldn't answer this question the first time they tried. Some learned they didn't know the answer. Some completed many rewrites. All were eventually able to answer the question. Though these college-able students had never before been asked to write about mathematics, they came to appreciate their ability to learn more thoroughly through writing. Remedial math students are no different.

Writing is a valuable way to learn mathematics. Writing assignments provide students with opportunities to: (1) translate and decode mathematical notation; (2) emote or focus on feelings, frustrations, and successes; (3) record and retain content; (4) experiment and "create" mathematics; (5) relate, associate, and organize ideas and concepts; (6) practice literacy; (7) personalize, assimilate, and accommodate content; and (8) discover (Azzolino, c].

Additionally, the instructor can: (1) improve instruction; (2) diagnose and remediate students' weaknesses and misunderstandings; (3) require the student to take even more responsibility for his education; and (4) collect evidence for research.

This article will not attempt to prove the above, but will illustrate some ways writing might be used to teach the remedial algebra student. Some theory will be considered before example strategies and sample problems are presented.

Writing As Thinking

As we write, teach, or speak, we think. Have you ever introduced yourself to someone and learned something about yourself as you spoke? Have you ever written to a friend explaining a problem or dilemma and solved your problem as you wrote? This kind of writing parallels first-order thinking [Elbow, 1983].

When using first-order thinking we just write. We write without censoring or restricting ourselves. We brainstorm. We fantasize. First-order thinking often happens quickly and the product might surprise even its author.

Second-order thinking is much slower. When rewriting, editing, or writing guarded texts, we use second-order thinking. The judge and critic in us surfaces. [For those interested in first-order and second-order thinking, the Peter Elbow article is highly recommended!]

While problem-solving, first-order thinking generates strategy or hypothesizes about a solution, then second-order thinking checks to see if the hypothesis has merit. One might alternate between first and second, and finish with second-order thinking's scrutiny.

When writing technically, even on subjects about which one is very familiar, second-order thinking is necessary. Asking students to write a definition in a non-test, perhaps out-of-class situation is an excellent exercise. Second-order thinking can be practiced. On a test, asking a student to write a definition without prior-to-test practice is unfair. Second-order thinking must occur and that takes time.

Advice On Assigning Student Writing

Experiment. Build upon existing successful assignments. Let your writing assignments be an extension of your teaching. Use the writing exercises, problems, and assignments you already have and extend other assignments to include writing. Determine your goal; recognize your students' backgrounds; and then create the assignment to achieve the goal.

Keep Assignments Short!!! Make assignments short and frequent. Frequent, even short, practice is preferable to little or no practice. Keeping assignments short increases the opportunities to practice writing.

Don't Read Everything Your Students Write. Just as it is not necessary for an instructor to examine all student assignments, it is not necessary for an instructor to read all student writings.

Grade a Paper More for Correctness of Content and Ability to Communicate an Idea Than for Grammar, Syntax, or Spelling. Consider using only "C," "I," and "R" as grades: "C" or "OK" for correct or acceptable; an "I" for incomplete; or an "R" for "redo, something is wrong." Make suggestions and edit. Praise good thoughts and wording.

Many different writing assignments are possible in mathematics. Our-of-class assignments are the easiest to incorporate into an instructor's style. (See [Azzolino, a].) In-class writing takes more practice on the part of the instructor [Azzolino, b], but is very worthwhile. The major differences between in-class and out-of-class writing assignments are the length of time required to complete the assignment and the type of thinking required—first order or second order.

In-Class Writing

The in-class assignments that I use include: completion, rewording, wordbank, lead sentence, non-thought warmups, and debriefing [Azzolino, b]. These can be used either in or out of class, but because these formats tend to make assignments easier, they can be used in-class. Here wordbanks and debriefing are considered.

Wordbank. Given a list or bank of words, write a sentence or paragraph using two, three, . . . , or all of the words [Azzolino, b]. This technique is handy for writing definitions, relating two ideas (Geeslin, 1977), writing paragraph-long explanations, theorizing about related or apparently unrelated thoughts. Following are some possible formats.

Problems:

1. Use the terms *abscissa* and *slope* in the same sentence.
2. Use the words *coefficients*, *variables*, and *exponents* to write a definition of "like terms."
3. Write a question that includes the words factor, prime, or determine.
4. "Free write" about four or five key words on the board (Sanders, 1985).
5. Write a paragraph using the words *rectangle* and *square* but without using the word *always*.
6. Write a paragraph that includes as many of the wordbank words as possible.
7. Write a paragraph relating two ideas (Geeslin, 1977).

Debriefing. Complete a procedure, reading, or lecture. Then have the students list important ideas, list the steps in the procedure, state the most important idea, or list new words [Azzolino, b].

Problems:

1. After completing a procedure or algorithm, ask students to explain or state what you did in a specific step.
2. After completing a procedure or algorithm, ask students to list the steps needed to complete the algorithm.
3. Have students summarize the lecture in a standard format:
   Title of Lecture: _____ Date: _____
   This lesson taught me: _____
   or
   Title of Lecture: _____ Date: _____
   List the major topics of the lecture.
   List two key words in each topic.
4. List the mistakes you made on the homework, last test, or in class.
5. List four different topics examined in this chapter.
6. Write a cheat sheet for the test on this chapter.

It should be noted that this sort of summarizing can be habit forming and beneficial. It truly forces one to reconsider. It doesn't replace taking notes. It does help organize material presented.

Before considering more specific writing exercises, here's an example of how debriefing can work. Please debrief yourself by listing at least three words or terms presented above. Then, state 1 idea or thought which is worth remembering.

Presenting Opportunities to Practice Literacy

Students often demonstrate symbolic literacy. To build written literacy, people must be given written and spoken words, and places to use them.

Example: Assign a section of the text as a reading. Experiment with assigning study guide questions before the reading, after the reading, or not at all.

Once a person learns to read texts he stands a good chance of succeeding in mathematics courses.

Write words—not just symbols—on the board. Write the title of the lecture. Write the verb or the directions with the problem. Instead of just solving an equation, write the word "solve," then solve the equation. Perhaps go so far as writing expressions like, "clear the radical by squaring each side" or "the product of the sum and difference of two numbers."

Sure, it takes more time. But the time it takes to write on the board increases clarity and helps students catch up with the lecture. Consider writing both an equation or expression and the words or phrase it represents.

Example: When introducing solving equations by factoring, instead of just writing the equations (as on the right, below), consider writing the sentences first, then (as on the left, below) the equations.

If the product of two numbers is zero, $\qquad$ $AB = 0$
then one or both of the numbers is zero. $\qquad$ $A = 0$ or $B = 0$

Ask students to draw . . . , write . . . , state symbolically . . . .
Example: On the board, draw two concentric circles, or some other figure of having more than one shape. Ask students to describe on paper, in words, what they see. Solicit volunteers to read their descriptions. Once a student has something written, he is likely to be willing to share it. Some students are unable to describe figures except in nonmathematical terms. Concentric circles might appear as a cross section of a pipe, a pie plate, or two circles with the same center but with different diameters.

As contributions are read, create a wordbank by recording the real world or mathematical terms generating a wordbank. Discuss the terminology you wish to emphasize. Then, ask students to write a mathematically stated description. Time or interest permitting, draw another figure and repeat the process, or divide the class into teams of two where one person on each team describes (even verbally) the given figure so the other half of each team can draw it.

Problems:

1. State the equation of a line
   a) parallel to $y = -4x + 8$;
   b) intersecting $y = -4x + 8$.
2. Draw circle *C*. Draw inscribed right triangle *ADB* in which *AB* is a diameter. Label minor arc *DA* with a measure of 30 degrees. Label the measures of all other angles and arcs. (Notice that all computation can be done mentally. The drawing and labeling is the important part.)

Emote and Focus on Feelings, Frustrations, and Successes

For remedial students who have not found success, providing an acceptable way of channeling feelings is desirable. Perhaps this is not the job of a college mathematics professor. Perhaps it is. There are reasons to use writing about feelings in a mathematics class. If frustration is felt about a certain skill, that frustration can be recognized with writing; once recognized, it can be addressed and remediated. Feelings of frustration about certain skills can be focused, localized, and not generalized to create negative feelings about "all mathematics." Students who are shy or who choose not to extol verbally the beauty of mathematics may do so personally through their writing [Azzolino, c].

Example: During the fall of 1987, I required, with other out-of-class writing assignments, a sequence of letters. With these I attempted to help remedial Algebra I students to focus on their self-perceptions and goals in hopes that frequent self-evaluation and reflection would stimulate positive change. The letters were singled out as being different because of their format and content and because they were turned in on NCR paper so that both the student and the instructor would have a copy [Azzolino, b]. This exercise was valuable and did achieve in part its goal.

Problems:

1. Complete: The problem I had with . . . was _____. (Watson 1980)
2. Complete: When I'm home doing my math homework, I feel _____.
3. Complete: I think this lesson taught some really beautiful ideas. For example, _____.
4. Complete: The reason math is so great is _____.
5. Complete: The reason this part of math is a real pain is _____.
6. First Night's Questionbook question: Write a letter to me, your instructor (Aggie), telling me who you, the mathematics student, are. Tell me of your strengths, weaknesses, fears, and goals. Tell me who you, the mathematics student, want to be after this semester's final exam.

    Tell me what other worlds you are a part of and how these worlds and your roles in these other worlds affect your role as a mathematics student. Tell me how your mathematics background affects you at present and how it affects your plans for your future.

Recording and Retaining

I think we hope keeping notebooks does this job but realize that is not always the case. Notes are important communications but not always finished products. Summarizing assignments or listing assignments can be extremely productive.

Consider asking things like [Azzolino, c]:

1. List the steps or procedures required to square a binomial. You may use an example to help illustrate your explanation.
2. How do you find _____?
3. List the sequence of calculator buttons used to compute $3^{-1/5}$.
4. Write a set of directions for _____.
5. If _____, why does _____?

6. Explain one way of _____.
7. Show another way of doing the same thing.
8. How do you mentally simplify $4^{-1/2}$?
9. In one sentence, explain how to raise x cubed to the fifth power. In other words, how do you simplify: $(x^3)^5$?
10. The line $y = 5x - 4$ may be graphed quickly by a method called slope-intercept. In words, in five or fewer steps, state how this method is completed.

Relating, Associating, and Organizing Ideas and Concepts

Example: Consider assigning the following sort of assignment prior to a test.
You have been given the points $(3, -4)$ and $(2, 6)$.

1. List at least three things the prof might ask you to do on the next test using these two points.
2. Using one activity described above, write the question or problem on this task as your teacher would ask it.
3. Using this same question, change the wording of the question so the question sounds different but means exactly the same thing.
4. Don't answer the question. List some things you must remember when answering this type question or doing this type problem.
5. Using another one of the activities described in number 1, answer questions 2, 3, and 4.

Problems:

1. Page 186 in your textbook has lovely problems on it. What makes all these problems the same type of problem? In one or two sentences, explain how to do this kind of problem.

BIBLIOGRAPHY

Azzolino, Agnes (a) and Roth, Robert G. "Questionbooks: Using Writing to Learn Mathematics." *The AMATYC Review* 9 (Fall/Winter 1987): 41–49.

———, (b). "In-Class Writing Assignments in the Content Areas" c 1988.

———, (c). *HOW TO USE WRITING TO TEACH MATHEMATICS* Keyport, NJ. Mathematical Concepts, 1987.

———, (d). "Dear Aggie: Letters in Remedial Algebra" c 1988.

Birken, Marcia. "Teaching Students How to Study Mathematics: A Classroom Approach," *The Mathematics Teacher* 79 (September 1986): 410–413.

Costa, Arthur L. and Marzano, Robert. "Teaching the Language of Thinking." *Educational Leadership* 45 (October 1987): 29–33.

Davison, David M. and Pearce, Daniel L. "Using Writing Activities to Reinforce Mathematics Instruction." *The Arithmetic Teacher* 35 (April 1988): 42–45.

Elbow, Peter. "Teaching Thinking by Teaching Writing." *Change* (September 1983): 37–40.

Fulwiler, Toby (a). "Showing, Not Telling, at a Writing Workshop" *College English* 43 (January 1981): 55–63.

———, (b). "Journals across the Disciplines." *English Journal* 69 (December 1980): 14–19.

Geeslin, William E. "Using Writing About Mathematics As A Teaching Technique." *The Mathematics Teacher* 70 (February 1977): 112–115.

Herrington, Anne J. "Writing to Learn: Writing Across the Disciplines" *College English* 43 (April 1981): 379–387.

Nahrgang, Cynthia l. and Petersen, Bruce T. "Using Writing to Learn Mathematics." *The Mathematics Teacher* ** (September 1986): 461–465.

Mett, Coreen L., "Writing as a Learning Device in Calculus." *The Mathematics Teacher* 80 (October 1987): 534–537.

Myers, John W. *Writing to Learn Across the Curriculum.* Bloomington, In. Phi Delta Kappa Educational Foundation, 1984.

Raths, James. "Enhancing Understanding Through Debriefing." *Educational Leadership* 45 (October 1987): 24–27.

Sanders, Arlette. "Learning Logs: A Communication Strategy for All Subject Areas." *Educational Leadership* 42 (February 1985): 7.

Watson, Margaret. "Writing Has a Place in a Mathematics Class." *Mathematics Teacher* 73 (October 1980): 518–519.

PLACEMENT OF STUDENTS IN MATHEMATICS

Dick J. Clark
Portland Community College

Proper placement might be defined as the enrollment of a student in a mathematics course in which the student will be challenged and yet can be successful without undue stress. There have been many attempts to accomplish this elusive ideal, and yet a plethora of difficulties awaits the school or instructor setting up such a program.

The most common tool utilized for placement is, of course, a placement test. (The author of this book has provided one for use by adopters.) After reviewing a number of standardized placement tests, I have found the College Board Computer Placement Test (CPT) to be, in my mind, the closest to our elusive ideal. In this case, the student sits at a computer terminal and answers informational questions which determine the level at which the student begins. Then, as the student is tested on arithmetic or basic algebra, the questions get more or less difficult according to how well s/he is able to answer them correctly. Theoretically, the student will seek the level of competency for proper placement. Although this system works well, the basic problems with this exam are (1) that it does not place students at all levels; (2) the cost per student is prohibitive for many math programs; and (3) some students may find the computer intimidating.

The January 1988 issue of *MAPS Update* published a report entitled "Computer Assisted Assessment Center Established at Santa Fe Community College," based on that college's report from February 1987. In this study, all students enrolled in mathematics classes took the algebra test, while only those enrolled in the basic college preparatory classes and in elementary algebra took the arithmetic test. A high correlation of 0.8362 was found between the CPTs Sentence Skills percentile and scores from the students' ACT English Test. However, when comparing the CPTs Algebra percentile to scores on the ACT Mathematics Test, the correlation dropped to 0.4863.

The MAPS report also indicated that "... almost two-thirds of the students taking the CPTs felt no pressure to complete the test quickly. Over four-fifths of the students felt the directions given by the computer were clear and easy to follow ... more than two-thirds of the students said they preferred a computer-administered test (over a pencil and paper test.)" Encouragingly, this issue of MAPS also reported that the tests for Intermediate Algebra and Functions and Graphs will be available for Fall 1988.

In the meantime, the Polaroid Company has taken this form of testing to a higher level, bringing it yet closer to the ideal. The Polaroid test will lead the individual to the proper level of competency by testing its employees for every level from arithmetic to calculus.

Such a placement/diagnostic test would be useful at a community college as well as at the high school level. At a large community college such as Portland Community College, with virtually year-round registration, students could come in at their leisure and be properly placed at all levels. This would help reduce the anxiety of many students caused by forced placement exams crowded into registration. Because many of our students are working, they must register during their lunch break or take time off from work. Another large segment of our students is of foreign extraction and has difficulty with the English language rather than the mathematical concepts. Rarely can either of these two groups perform at its best on placement exams under these circumstances.

Properly designed placement testing has the potential to do much more for students than place them in a course. Instructors and math lab monitors could use placement/diagnostic exams to help diagnose the problems a particular student may have, providing them with concentrated help needed to master a particular concept. Random generation of numbers would allow an unlimited number of exams and/or worksheets to be generated as well, so that memorization or passing of answers from one student to another would not invalidate the placement of a student.

At Portland Community College, we are currently using the Comparative Guidance and Placement Program Test of the College Board. This form of placement exam shares some basic difficulties which seem to be inherent in most placement tests. Its greatest advantage is that it is cheaper than most tests. Unfortunately, however, according to a survey and study done on our campus, most students felt that they were misplaced. Some were so angered by the test and testing procedure that their responses on the questionnaire were not used as it was felt they would invalidate the study. Others, especially foreign students and minorities, felt handicapped because of the verbiage and form of the tests. Another disadvantage is that these tests really do not cover all of our needs, as they only test through intermediate algebra. Thus this test cannot help place the student who must be ready to enter calculus in order to be admitted to the engineering program. Students also complain of lack of preparation, that they must take the test "cold" without warning as to what is on the test, what it is, what is expected, etc. To help, the Mathematics Department has prepared an information sheet about the tests.

In hopes of solving the many problems with standardized placement exams, many schools have developed their own methods and forms of placement. One has a list of problems of increasing difficulty. The student looks at the problems and decides at which point s/he begins to have difficulty. At that point, the student is asked to work some of the problems—going backward or forward as his or her ability indicates. Then the student is placed according to predetermined department criteria. Another method I have heard about is based on the same concept but has more formalized department exams with ten problems each.

Because of inherent difficulties, Portland Community College has also experimented with teacher placement, using placement exams only as a last resort. Some claim, however, that this invalidates the exams. Recently we have initiated two other methods of trying to place students. We have developed a brochure for each course. The first page is informational, listing prerequisite courses and courses that can be taken afterward. Inside is a quiz of the types of problems a student should be able to solve in order to be successful in this course, with the answers. The last page is a summary of the topics taught in the course. These brochures have answered a host of student questions and have helped students recognize their level of ability. The second method we are trying is to use high school teachers to help place their students into college courses through an articulated course alighment which compares each high school course with an appropriate community college course.

In trying to correlate the different methods of placement to student success at Portland Community College, research was difficult due to the number of variables. The study produced did point out that students have more success if they take sequential courses as soon as possible, especially for those courses taught out of the same book. The study also recommended standard tests and grading procedures for the pre-college courses. These courses also were recommended to have five contact hours per week. A further study under more controlled circumstances where the students, instructor, term, course, etc. were held constant would be more fruitful. Students in participating classes would be given the various tools for testing. These would be correlated with student success.

Karen Brown and Bella Wang from the Mathematics Department of the Metro Campus of Cuyahoga Community College in Cleveland, Ohio, reported their own student tracking program at the 13th annual AMATYC conference in Kansas City, Missouri, in 1987. This system was designed to "provide accurate and timely prerequisite information about each student currently enrolled in a mathematics course. This includes information about a student's past performance in math courses and results of the placement test." This information is given to the instructor early enough in the term so that student counseling and movement, where necessary, may still take place without drastically hindering the student. Tracking also helps to validate placement tests or any other form of placement.

It has been suggested that the problem objectives of mathematics need to be laid out in sequence, and that each course then take up its own share from this string of objectives. This, it would seem, would take care of the problems of place-

ment. If a student could not demonstrate a working knowledge of previous objectives, that student certainly would not be prepared for that particular class even if s/he "successfully" passed the prerequisite course. However, like a meal, there are too many variables for this proposition to work. How hungry is the individual (motivation); what craving does s/he have (purpose for taking the course); what are the nutritional needs (requirements for a particular program); how leisurely can the meal be (time constraints such as when does the course have to be finished, or how much time can the student devote to studying); who is preparing the meal (resources to help the student supplement class time)? These are just a few of the myriad of influences that enhance or detract from a student's success.

Another ladle in the mixture (to extend the metaphor) is the constantly changing curriculum dictated by advancing technology, such as we have seen with the calculator and computer of late. These have made all but obsolete such topics as logarithmic tables, interpolation for greater accuracy in logarithms, square root and cube root algorithms, table of powers, etc. Technology has enhanced other methods of evaluating functions and has taken the drudgery out of learning, opening the possibility of rediscovering the beauty of mathematics.

Proper placement of students will continue to be a problem only to the degree that we allow it to be. We need to determine how important placement is for our students and how best to meet their needs, in order to improve our systems. Computerization of placement will improve greatly over what we have used in the past. By incorporating a variety of solutions which I have listed here—randomization of numbers, diagnosis of specific problems and generation of worksheets designed to correct those problems, tracking of student progress as well as accurate and timely information about a student's background—we can hope to reach the ideal system.

BIBLIOGRAPHY

(1) *MAPS Update*, The College Board, January, 1988. The reports states that a complete Santa Fe Community College report can be obtained by contacting L. J. Abernathy, Director, MAPS, The College Board 45 Columbus Avenue, New York, New York 10023-6992, (212) 713-8057.

(2) *DO YOU KNOW WHO YOUR STUDENTS ARE? COMPUTERIZED STUDENT TRACKING*, American Mathematical Association of Two Year Colleges, 13th Annual Convention, Kansas City, Missouri, October 29–November 1, 1987, presented by Karen J. Brown and Bella Wang of the Mathematics Department, Metro Campus, Cuyahoga Community College, Cleveland, Ohio 44115 (216) 987-4554 on 30 October, 1987.

USING VIDEODISC TECHNOLOGY IN DEVELOPMENTAL MATHEMATICS

Every developmental student learns differently. Each student has his or her own preferences in regard to study schedule, speed of learning, and learning environment. Likewise, students learn according to their individual learning styles—through visual, verbal or auditory materials; in a lecture or an individualized program; and through the use of different media in different combinations.

Interactive Videodisc technology is the logical successor to the two most revolutionary educational tools created in this century—television and the computer. It has been proven to help increase retention, significantly decrease actual learning time, and virtually ensure a positive learning experience. Interactive Videodisc technology is learner-controlled and self-paced, readily accessible at the student's convenience.

Ferranti Educational Systems and Prentice Hall, Inc. have joined forces to provide you and your students with the most beneficial package of teaching/learning materials for your mathematics learning laboratory, combining the best and most advanced techniques of mathematics education and technology.

Together, Prentice Hall's book by John Tobey and Jeffrey Slater, and Ferranti's videodisc courseware form a strong, unified and effective teaching/learning system which incorporates all the learning styles of a diverse student population.

Ferranti's *Interactive Mathematics* courseware utilizes the power of multimedia, while enhancing classroom teaching. Student can proceed in a sequential, self-paced, individualized approach from arithmetic through intermediate algebra. This interactive videodisc-based course has achieved measurable results, while relating mathematics to real-life situations.

Below, we have listed a correlation between the content of this book and the modules of Ferranti's *Interactive Mathematics* courseware, which will help you to integrate it into your course.

A special discount on Ferranti's *Interactive Mathematics* courseware will be avilable for a limited time only to adopters of Slater/Tobey's *Basic College Mathematics*. Tobey/Slater's *Beginning Algebra, Second Edition.* Tobey/Slater's *Intermediate Algebra.* Call your Prentice Hall representative for details.

CORRELATION BETWEEN TOBEY AND SLATER'S INTERMEDIATE ALGEBRA AND FERRANTI EDUCATIONAL SYSTEMS' INTERACTIVE MATH COURSES

* [ALL MODULE REFERENCES ARE FROM INTERACTIVE MATH II COURSE.]

Ferranti Interactive Mathematics	Module*	Tobey/Slater Intermediate Algebra
		1. BASIC CONCEPTS
A1	Rational Numbers and Their Properties	1.1 The Real Number System
A6	Real Numbers and Their Properties	
B1	Addition/Subtraction/Multiplication/Division of Rational Numbers	1.2 Operations with Signed Numbers
B1	Addition/Subtraction/Multiplication/Division of Rational Numbers	1.3 Powers, Square Roots, and the Order of Operations of Signed Numbers
B2	Combining and Simplifying Exponential Equations	
A2	Integral Exponents and Scientific Notation	1.4 Integer Exponents and Scientific Notation
B2	Combining and Simplifying Exponential Equations	
D1	Solving Equations Using Rational Numbers	1.5 Operations with Variables and Grouping Symbols
D2	Formulas and Equations Using Scientific Notation and Exponents	
D3	Linear Equations	
D1	Solving Equations Using Rational Numbers	1.6 Evaluating Variable Expressions and Formulas
D2	Formulas and Equations Using Scientific Notation and Exponents	
D3	Linear Equations	
D1	Solving Equations Using Rational Numbers	1.7 First Degree Equations With One Unknown
D2	Formulas and Equations Using Scientific Notation and Exponents	
D3	Linear Equations	
D1	Solving Equations Using Rational Numbers	1.8 Literal Equations
D2	Formulas and Equations Using Scientific Notation and Exponents	
D3	Linear Equations	
		2. APPLICATIONS OF LINEAR EQUATIONS
E3	Using Algebra in Problem Solving	2.1 Graphing Linear Equations with Two Unknowns
		2.2 The Slope of a Line
D3	Linear Equations	2.3 The Equations of a Line
E1	Using Algebra in Problem Solving	2.4 Using Equations to Solve Word Problems
E2	Using Algebra in Problem Solving	

CORRELATION BETWEEN TOBEY AND SLATER'S INTERMEDIATE ALGEBRA AND FERRANTI EDUCATIONAL SYSTEMS' INTERACTIVE MATH COURSES

* [ALL MODULE REFERENCES ARE FROM INTERACTIVE MATH II COURSE.]

Ferranti Interactive Mathematics	Module*	Tobey/Slater Intermediate Algebra
E3	Using Algebra in Problem Solving	
E1	Using Algebra in Problem Solving	2.5 Solving More Involved Word Problems
E2	Using Algebra in Problem Solving	
E3	Using Algebra in Problem Solving	
		3. SYSTEMS OF LINEAR EQUATIONS
		3.1 Systems of Equations in Two Variables
		3.2 Systems of Equations in Three Variables
		3.3 Applications of Systems of Linear Equations
		3.4 Determinants
		3.5 Cramer's Rule (Optional)
		4. POLYNOMIALS
A5	Polynomials	4.1 Addition, Subtraction, and Multiplication of Polynomials
B5	Simplifying Polynomials	
		4.2 Division of Polynomials
		4.3 Synthetic Division (Optional)
B6	Polynomial Products and Factors	4.4 Removing Common Factors: Factoring by Grouping
B6	Polynomial Products and Factors	4.5 Factoring Trinomials
B6	Polynomial Products and Factors	4.6 Special Cases of Factoring
B6	Polynomial Products and Factors	4.7 Completely Factoring a Polynomial
		5. FRACTIONAL ALGEBRAIC EXPRESSIONS AND EQUATIONS
A3	Rational Expressions	5.1 Reducing Algebraic Fractions
B3	Operations on Rational Expressions	
B3	Operations on Rational Expressions	5.2 Multiplication and Division of Algebraic Fractions
B3	Operations on Rational Expressions	5.3 Addition and Subtraction of Algebraic Fractions
		5.4 Simplifying Complex Fractions
E3	Using Algebra in Problem Solving	5.5 Solving Fractional Equations
E3	Using Algebra in Problem Solving	5.6 Applications: Formulas and Ratio Problems
		6. RATIONAL EXPONENTS AND RADICALS
A4	Radicals and Rational Exponents	6.1 Rational Exponents
A4	Radicals and Rational Exponents	6.2 Radical Expressions
B4	Computing with Radicals and Rational Exponents	6.3 Simplifying, Adding and Subtracting Radicals
B4	Computing with Radicals and Rational Exponents	6.4 Multiplying and Dividing Radicals
		6.5 Complex Numbers
		7. QUADRATIC EQUATIONS
		7.1 Solving Quadratic Equations by Factoring
		7.2 Solving Quadratic Equations by Taking Square Roots or by Completing the Square
		7.3 The Quadratic Formula
		7.4 Radical Equations

CORRELATION BETWEEN TOBEY AND SLATER'S INTERMEDIATE ALGEBRA AND FERRANTI EDUCATIONAL SYSTEMS' INTERACTIVE MATH COURSES

* [ALL MODULE REFERENCES ARE FROM INTERACTIVE MATH II COURSE.]

Ferranti Interactive Mathematics	Module*	Tobey/Slater Intermediate Algebra
		7.5 Equations that can be Transformed to Quadratic Form
		7.6 Formulas and Applications
		8. GRAPHS AND FUNCTIONS
		8.1 The Distance Formula and the Circle
		8.2 The Parabola
		8.3 The Ellipse
		8.4 The Hyperbola
		8.5 Functions
		8.6 The Inverse of a Function
		8.7 Nonlinear Systems of Equations
		9. EXPONENTIAL AND LOGARITHMIC FUNCTIONS
		9.1 The Exponential Functions
		9.2 The Logarithmic Function
		9.3 Properties of Logarithms
		9.4 Logarithms to Different Bases
		9.5 Exponential and Logarithmic Equations
		10. INEQUALITIES
		10.1 Linear Inequalities
		10.2 Compound Inequalities
		10.3 Absolute Value Inequalities
		10.4 Quadratic Inequalities
		10.5 Linear Inequalities in Two Variables
		10.6 Systems of Inequalities in Two Variables

Intermediate Algebra

John Tobey

Jeffrey Slater

North Shore Community College
Beverly, Massachusetts

Prentice Hall, Englewood Cliffs, NJ 07632

Library of Congress Cataloging-in-Publication Data

TOBEY, JOHN, 1943–
    Intermediate algebra/John Tobey, Jeffrey Slater,
       p.   cm.
    Includes index.
    ISBN 0-13-466624-0
    1. Algebra. I. Slater, Jeffrey, 1947–   . II. Title.
QA154.2.T634 1991
512.9—dc20

90-25616
CIP

Editorial/production supervision: Tom Aloisi
Acquisition editor: Priscilla McGeehon
Development editor: Steve Deitmer
Interior design: Judith A. Matz-Coniglio
Cover design: Judith A. Matz-Coniglio
Prepress buyer: Paula Massenaro
Manufacturing buyer: Lori Bulwin
Photo editor: Lori Morris-Nantz
Photo research: Barbara Scott
Cover photo: Laima Druskis

Photo credits: 1, Jim Pickerell/TSW-Click/Chicago Ltd. ● 39, Art Attack/Photo Researchers ● 41, Frank Siteman/Stock, Boston ● 68, Anglo-Australian Telescope Board/PH Photo Archives ● 75, Bob Daemmrich/Stock, Boston (Image Works) ● 80, John Coletti/Stock, Boston ● 99, Cynthia Matthews/Stock Market ● 104, Annie Griffiths Belt/West Light ● 106, Lawrence Migdale/Stock, Boston ● 127, Rhoda Baer/Folio ● 150, William James Warren/West Light ● 181, Jon Feingersh/Uniphoto ● 191, Bob Daemmrich/Stock, Boston ● 197, Wendy Ledis/Uniphoto ● 234, Tony Freeman/Photoedit ● 243, David Stoecklein/Uniphoto ● 270, Daniel Grogan/Uniphoto ● 273, Bill Ross/West Light ● 284, Gabe Palmer/The Stock Market ● 293, Alon Reininger/Contact/Woodfin Camp ● 304, Gabe Palmer/The Stock Market ● 337, Harry Wilks/Stock, Boston ● 343, Ted Horowitz/The Stock Market ● 350, Photri San/The Stock Market ● 367, David Aronson/Stock, Boston ● 372, Charles Krebs/The Stock Market ● 391, John Bova/Photo Researchers ● 397, Jan Halaska/Photo Researchers ● 411, NASA ● 416, Ron Jautz/Folio Inc. ● 417, NASA ● 425, J. Barry O'Rourke/The Stock Market ● 463, David Ryan/Uniphoto ● 470, Ned Gillette/Stock Market ● 477, Irene E. Springer/PH Photo Archives ● 513, John De Waele/Stock, Boston ● 520, Jeff Perkell/Stock Market ● 522, James Cook/Folio Inc. ● 525, Les Moore/Uniphoto ● 530, PH Photo Archives.

 © 1991 by Prentice-Hall, Inc.
A Division of Simon & Schuster
Englewood Cliffs, New Jersey 07632

Printed in the United States of America
10 9 8 7 6 5 4 3 2 1

ISBN   0-13-466624-0

Prentice-Hall International (UK) Limited, *London*
Prentice-Hall of Australia Pty. Limited, *Sydney*
Prentice-Hall Canada Inc., *Toronto*
Prentice-Hall Hispanoamericana, S.A., *Mexico*
Prentice-Hall of India Private Limited, *New Delhi*
Prentice-Hall of Japan, Inc., *Tokyo*
Simon & Schuster Asia Pte. Ltd., *Singapore*
Editora Prentice-Hall do Brasil, Ltda., *Rio de Janeiro*

This book is dedicated to
John Tobey III, Marcia Yvonne Tobey, Melissa Dawn Tobey
who patiently waited and quietly studied

Contents

5

Fractional Algebraic Expressions and Equations 243

6

Rational Exponents and Radicals 293

7

Quadratic Equations 337

8

Graphs and Functions 391

Preface

To the Student

Mathematics becomes more important each year as our society—and the global society of which we are a part—grows and changes with new technologies. Perhaps you do not believe that you need algebra to handle your every-day life and advance in your job. Farmers, elementary school teachers, bus drivers, laboratory technicians, nurses, telephone operators, photographers, pharmacists, salespeople, doctors, architects and so many others who perhaps believed that they needed little if any mathematics are finding that basic mathematical skills can help them. Algebra, you will find, can help you too.

People who enter college have a variety of mathematical backgrounds. Many of you may be looking forward to this course. We hope that our book keeps your enthusiasm high. Others of you have never enjoyed math and may never have done too well in it. You may be quite anxious about taking this course. We hope that our book delivers the assistance and supports that helps you develop an interest in this most important field.

To show you how mathematics may affect your life and how you can put it to work for yourself, this book draws a great number of examples and problems from every-day situations—maintaining a budget, using a checking account, figuring mileage on a trip, and so on. Also, we explore the mathematical side of situations taken from many different jobs and professions such as astronomer, lab technician, photographer, environmentalist, and many more. Learning mathematics is more enjoyable if you can see how people put it to use.

Special Features

- To Think About, in text as well as incorporated into exercises, challenges you to think in a logical, organized way and exposes you to the power of mathematical ideas.
- Developing Your Study Skills, scattered throughout the first few chapters, provides practical advice to ensure personal success in the course.
- Pretests begin each chapter, diagnosing in advance your strengths and weaknesses in the upcoming material.
- Examples and matched Practice Problems gives you a chance to solve an exercise similar to the preceding example on your own. Answers and solutions appear a few pages later.
- Four-color photos show the mathematics at work in real-life applications and occupations, answering the question "When will I ever need to use this course?"
- Chapter Organizers summarize key concepts, provide additional examples for brief review, and give a page reference for further study—all, in a compact grid format.

- Calculator Problems encourage you to take advantage of this modern technology.
- Practice Quizzes reinforce concepts half-way through each chapter.
- Practice Chapter Tests provide tests that can be used as preparation or as actual tests in a math lab.
- Cumulative Review Problems review the content of previous chapters within exercises sets.
- Cumulative Tests, at the end of each chapter (except the first), cover content from the preceding chapters.
- Extra Practice at the end of every chapter provides the additional drill for those of you who want more than the exercise sets provide.
- Glossary at the end of the book presents both a definition and an example of the term.

This book is the last of a series of three developmental math books. In a tightly coordinated sequence of books, the first text, *Basic College Mathematics*, is followed by *Beginning Algebra* and *Intermediate Algebra*. We would like to thank our editors at Prentice Hall: Priscilla McGeehon, Steve Deitmer, and Tom Aloisi, for their advice, support, time and persistence. Without their insight, suggestions, and creative thinking we surely would have had a difficult time finishing this book.

We have been greatly helped by a supportive group of colleagues who not only teach at North Shore Community College but who have provided a number of ideas as well as extensive help on all of our mathematics books. So a special word of thanks to Marie Clark, Hank Harmeling, Tom Rourke, Wally Hersey, Bob McDonald. Judy Carter, Kathy LeBlanc, Bob Oman, Keith Piggott, Russ Sullivan, and Rick Ponticelli who gave help in a variety of ways as this book was being completed. Joan Peabody patiently typed and retyped the entire manuscript. Her cheerful dedication to doing a long job and doing it well have been an invaluable contribution in the task of preparing this book.

We extend our thanks and appreciation to the following reviewers:

Barbara A. Jur, University of Tennessee at Chattanooga
Judy Kasabian, El Camino College
Ara B. Sullenberger, Tarrant County Junior College
Ben Zirkle, Virginia Western Community College
Shelba J. Morman, North Lake College
Diane Trimble, Collin County Community College
Howard Penn, El Centro College
Linda Kyle, Tarrant County Junior College
William A. Neal, Fresno City College
Larry Blevins, Tyler Junior College
Louis Hoelzle, Bucks County Community College
Louis P. Pushkarsky, Trenton Junior College
James W. Newsom, Tidewater Community College
Michael A. Contino, California State University, Hayward
Ann S. Bretscher, University of Georgia
Phyllis Jore, Valencia Community College
Sheldon Kovitz, University of Massachusetts at Boston
Robert Gesell, Cleary College
Linda Kyle, Tarrant County Junior College
Helen Burrier, Kirkwood Community College
Marie Clarke, North Shore Community College
Jamie King, Orange Coast College
Pat Cross, University of Oklahoma
Richard Semmler, Northern Virginia Community College
Tom Rourke, North Shore Community College

We thank, as well, the following supplements authors:

Pat Traxler, Southern Illinois University at Edwardsville, *Instructor's Solutions Manual*
Marie Clarke, North Shore Community College, *Instructor's Manual with Tests*
Lea Pruet Campbell, Lamar University, *Supplements' Guide with Instructor's Disk*
Helen Burrier, Kirkwood Community College, *Student Solutions Manual*

Book writing is impossible for us without the support of our families. Our deepest thanks to Nancy, Johnny, Marcia, Melissa, Shelly, Rusty, and Abby. You have patiently waited, quietly assisted, and given words of encouragement when greatly needed. Finally, we thank God for the strength and energy to write and the opportunity to help others through this textbook.

John Tobey

Jeffrey Slater

Beverly, Massachusetts

Basic Concepts

Modern laboratory technicians solve mathematical problems daily as part of lab procedures.

1

PRETEST CHAPTER 1

If you are familiar with the topics in this chapter, take this test now. Check your answers with those in the back of the book. If an answer was wrong or you couldn't do a problem, study the appropriate section of the chapter.

If you are not familiar with the topics in this chapter, don't take this test now. Instead, study the examples, work the practice problems, and then take the test.

This test will help you identify those concepts that you have mastered and those that need more study.

Section 1.1 For the set $\left\{\pi, \sqrt{3}, 2, -2, \dfrac{6}{-2}, 0, \dfrac{1}{5}, 0.333, \ldots\right\}$:

1. List the irrational real numbers. $\pi, \sqrt{3}$ **2.** List the whole numbers. 2, 0

3. What is the property of real numbers that justifies the following equation?

$$(x + y) + 0 = x + y \qquad \text{Identity property for addition}$$

Section 1.2 Simplify.

4. $20 \div (-5) - 6 + 3(-2)$ -16

5. $\dfrac{\dfrac{1}{2} - \dfrac{1}{3}}{-\dfrac{1}{4}}$ $-\dfrac{2}{3}$

Section 1.3 Evaluate.

6. $2^3 + \sqrt{4(-2) + 12}$ 10

7. $(-4)^3 + 2(3)^2 - 2^2$ -50

Section 1.4 Simplify each expression. You may leave negative exponents in your answers for problems 8–11.

8. $(-6xy^2)(-3xy^0z)(2x^{-3})$ $36x^{-1}y^2z$

9. $\dfrac{(5x^{-2}y)^3}{(2x^3y^2)^2}$ $\dfrac{125}{4x^{12}y}$

10. $\dfrac{6x^2y^5}{-18x^3y^{-2}}$ $\dfrac{y^7}{-3x}$ y^9

11. $\left(\dfrac{4a^{-4}b^{-1}}{3a^{-3}b^2}\right)^2$ $\dfrac{16}{9a^2b^6}$

12. $(-3x^2y^{-3})^{-3}$ $-27x^6$

13. Write 0.0000000723 in scientific notation. 7.23×10^{-8}

Section 1.5 Simplify.

14. $-7x^2 - 2x + 3x^3 - 5x - 7x^2$ $3x^3 - 14x^2 - 7x$

15. $5x^2y(-2x^2 + 3xy - 1)$ $-10x^4y + 15x^3y^2 - 5x^2y$

16. $-3\{x + 2[y - 4(x + y)]\}$ $21x + 18y$

Section 1.6

17. Evaluate $3y^2 + 2xy - 5x$ when $y = -2$ and $x = 5$. -33

18. Find the area of a circle if its radius is 6 meters. (Use $\pi \approx 3.14$.)
113.04 sq. meters

Section 1.7 Solve for x.

19. $\dfrac{1}{3}(2x - 1) = 4(x + 3)$ $x = -3.7$

20. $\dfrac{x - 2}{4} = \dfrac{1}{2}x + 4$ $x = -18$

21. $15x - 2 = -38$ $x = -2.4$

Section 1.8

22. Solve for y: $5x - 8y = 15$. $\dfrac{15 - 5x}{-8}$ or $\dfrac{5x - 15}{8}$ or $-\dfrac{15 - 5x}{8}$

23. Solve for a: $5ab - 2b = 16ab - 3(8 + b)$. $a = \dfrac{b + 24}{11b}$

24. (a) Solve for r: $A = P + Prt$. $\quad r = \dfrac{A - P}{Pt}$

(b) Find r when $P = 100$, $t = 3$, and $A = 118$. $\quad r = \dfrac{3}{50} = 0.06$

Section 1.9 Solve for x.

25. $|3x - 2| = 7$ $\quad x = 3 \quad x = -\dfrac{5}{3}$

26. $|8 - x| - 3 = 1$ $\quad x = 4 \quad x = 12$

27. $\left|\dfrac{2x + 3}{4}\right| = 2$ $\quad x = 2.5 \quad x = -5.5$

28. $|5x - 8| = |3x + 2|$ $\quad x = 5 \quad x = 0.75$

1.1 THE REAL NUMBER SYSTEM

1 Sets of Numbers

A **set** is a collection of objects called **elements**. A set of numbers is simply a listing, within braces { }, of the numbers (elements) in the set. For example,

$$S = \{1, 3, 5, \ldots\}$$

is the set of positive odd numbers. The three dots (called an ellipsis) mean that the set is *infinite;* in other words, we haven't written all the possible elements of the set.

Some important sets of numbers that we will study are the

- Natural numbers
- Whole numbers
- Integers
- Rational numbers
- Irrational numbers
- Real numbers

After studying this section, you will be able to:

1 *Identify what subsets of the real numbers a given set belongs to*

2 *Identify which property of the real numbers is used in a given equation*

Definition

The **natural numbers** N (also called the *positive integers*) are the counting numbers:

$$N = \{1, 2, 3, \ldots\}$$

The **whole numbers** W are the natural numbers plus 0:

$$W = \{0, 1, 2, 3, \ldots\}$$

The **integers** I are the whole numbers plus the *negative* of all natural numbers:

$$I = \{\ldots, -3, -2, -1, 0, 1, 2, 3, \ldots\}$$

The **rational numbers** Q include the integers and all *quotients* of integers (but division by zero is not allowed):

$$Q = \left\{\dfrac{a}{b} \,\middle|\, a \text{ and } b \text{ are integers but } b \neq 0\right\}$$

TEACHING TIP Although all the students in this course should have seen set notation in previous math courses, they will not all remember it. Emphasize the use of the braces and the idea that a set is merely a listing—not an ordered listing—of the elements in the set.

The foregoing expression means "the set of all fractions a divided by b, such that a and b are integers but b is not equal to zero." (The $|$ is read "such that.") The letters a and b are **variables**; that is, they can represent different numbers.

A rational number can be written as a **terminating decimal**[†] (for example, $\dfrac{1}{8} = 0.125$) or as a **repeating decimal** (for example, $\dfrac{2}{3} = 0.6666\ldots$). For repeating decimals we often use a bar over the repeating digits. Thus, we write $0.232323\ldots$ as $0.\overline{23}$ to show that the digits 23 repeat indefinitely.

However, some numbers in decimal notation are nonterminating *and* nonrepeating—in other words, we can't write them as quotients of integers. Such numbers are called irrational.

[†] A terminating decimal has a definite number of digits. A repeating decimal goes on forever, but the digits repeat in a definite pattern.

> The **irrational numbers** are numbers whose decimal forms are nonterminating and nonrepeating.

For example, $\sqrt{3} = 1.7320508\ldots$ can be carried out to an infinite number of decimal places with no repeating pattern of digits. In Chapter 6 we study irrational numbers extensively.

Now we can describe the set of real numbers.

> The set R of **real numbers** is the set of all numbers that are rational or irrational.

In other words, *every* number that we study is a real number.[‡]

The figure below will help you see the relationships among all of these sets of numbers that we have described.

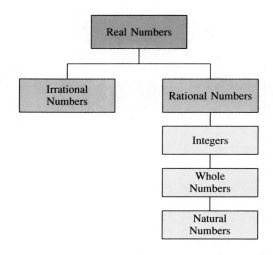

The figure shows that the natural numbers are contained within the set of whole numbers (or we could say that the set of whole numbers contains the set of natural numbers). If all the members of one set are also members of another set, then the first set is a **subset** of the second set. The whole numbers are a subset of the integers, and so on. You need to realize that the natural numbers are also a subset of the integers, rational numbers, and real numbers.

TEACHING TIP Students often have difficulty in determining which numbers are rational and which are irrational if they are in decimal form. Emphasize the fact that irrational numbers in decimal form must be both nonterminating and nonrepeating. Thus, $1.896896896\ldots$ is rational, but $1.896789667896\ldots$ is irrational.

Example 1 Name the sets to which the following numbers belong.

(a) 5   **(b)** $0.2666\ldots$ **(c)** $1.4371826138526\ldots$

(d) 0   **(e)** $\dfrac{1}{9}$

(a) 5 is a natural number, a whole number, an integer, a rational number, and a real number.
(b) $0.2666\ldots$ is a repeating decimal, so it is a rational number and a real number.
(c) $1.4371826138526\ldots$ doesn't have any repeating pattern. Therefore, it is an irrational number and a real number.
(d) 0 is a whole number, an integer, a rational number, and a real number.
(e) $\dfrac{1}{9}$ can be written as $0.111\ldots$ (or $0.\overline{1}$), so it is a rational number and a real number.

■

Practice Problem 1 Name the sets to which the following numbers belong.

(a) 1.26   **(b)** 3   **(c)** $\dfrac{3}{7}$ **(d)** -2 **(e)** $5.182671\ldots$

■

[‡] There is an even larger set of numbers, called *complex numbers*, but we aren't concerned with them now.

2 Properties of Real Numbers

A *property* of something is a characteristic that we know is true. For example, one property of water is that it freezes at 32°F.

Real numbers also have properties. In other words, there are some characteristics of real numbers that we have found to be true. For example, we know we can add real numbers and that it makes no difference in what *order* we add them: $6 + 8 = 8 + 6$. Mathematicians fall this property of numbers the **commutative property**. Since all real numbers have this characteristic, we can write the property using letters:

$$a + b = b + a$$

where a and b are any real numbers.

Another property is called **closure**. This property means that the set of real numbers is *closed*. That is, if we add two real numbers, we get another real number. In symbols, we write

$$\text{If } a, b \in R, \text{ then } a + b \in R$$

R, of course, means the set of real numbers. The symbol $\in$ means "belongs to."

A third property is the **associative property**. This property tells us that we can group real numbers in any manner and their sum will not change.

$$(a + b) + c = a + (b + c) = (a + c) + b$$

The **identity property** states that if we add a unique real number (called an *identity element*) to any other real number, that number is not changed. Unique means only one such number has this property. For addition, zero (0) is the identity element. Thus,

$$99 + 0 = 0 + 99 = 99$$

and, in general,

$$a + 0 = 0 + a = a$$

The last property we describe is the **inverse property**. For any real numbers a there is a unique real number $-a$ such that if we add them we obtain the identity element.

$$a + (-a) = 0$$

We have described the properties of real numbers only for addition. You should be able to see how these properties apply to multiplication also. We will use these properties to simplify expressions and solve equations. They are summarized in the table below. Note that the dot $\cdot$ indicates multiplication. Thus $3 \cdot 5$ means multiply 3 and 5; $a \cdot b$ means multiply a and b.

PROPERTIES OF REAL NUMBERS
(FOR ALL REAL NUMBERS a, b, c)

Addition	Property	Multiplication
$a + b$ is a real number	Closure properties	$a \cdot b$ is a real number
$a + b = b + a$	Commutative properties	$a \cdot b = b \cdot a$
$a + (b + c) = (a + b) + c$	Associative properties	$a \cdot (b \cdot c) = (a \cdot b) \cdot c$
$a + 0 = a = 0 + a$	Identity properties	$a \cdot 1 = a = 1 \cdot a$
$a + (-a) = 0 = (-a) + a$	Inverse properties	$a \cdot \dfrac{1}{a} = 1 = \dfrac{1}{a} \cdot a$ when $a \neq 0$

Distributive property of multiplication over addition

$$a(b + c) = a \cdot b + a \cdot c$$

Example 2 State the name of the property that justifies each statement.

(a) $3 + 12$ is a real number

(b) $12 + 0.6 = 0.6 + 12$

(c) $5 + (7 + 1) = (5 + 7) + 1$

(d) $\pi + 0 = \pi$

(e) $\dfrac{1}{5} + \left(-\dfrac{1}{5}\right) = 0$

(a) Closure property of addition
(b) Commutative property of addition
(c) Associative property of addition
(d) Identity property of addition
(e) Inverse property of addition ■

Practice Problem 2 State the name of the property that justifies each statement.
(a) $9 + 8 = 8 + 9$

(b) $17 + 0 = 17$

(c) $-4 + 4 = 0$

(d) $19 + 26$ is a real number

(e) $7 + (3 + 4) = (7 + 3) + 4$ ■

We will now look at an example that illustrates each of the properties of multiplication.

Example 3 State the name of the property that justifies each statement.

(a) $5 \cdot 7 = 7 \cdot 5$

(b) $6 \cdot \dfrac{1}{6} = 1$

(c) $\dfrac{1}{5} \cdot \dfrac{1}{7}$ is a real number

(d) $12 \cdot (3 \cdot 5) = (12 \cdot 3) \cdot 5$

(e) $56 \cdot 1 = 56$

(a) Commutative property of multiplication
(b) Multiplicative inverse property
(c) Closure property of multiplication
(d) Associative property of multiplication
(e) Identity property of multiplication ■

Practice Problem 3 State the name of the property that justifies each statement.
(a) $\dfrac{1}{3} \cdot \dfrac{2}{7}$ is a real number

(b) $4 \cdot \dfrac{1}{4} = 1$

(c) $6 \cdot (2 \cdot 8) = (6 \cdot 2) \cdot 8$

(d) $76 \cdot 1 = 76$

(e) $4 \cdot 15 = 15 \cdot 4$ ■

Example 4 Verify the distributive property by showing that you get the same result on both sides of the expression.

$$5(2 + 7) = 5 \cdot 2 + 5 \cdot 7$$

Simplify both sides of the equals sign to show that you get the same result.

$$5(2 + 7) = 5 \cdot 2 + 5 \cdot 7$$
$$5(9) = 10 + 35$$
$$45 = 45 \quad ■$$

Practice Problem 4 Verify the distributive property by showing that you get the same result when simplifying both sides of the equals sign:

$$7(3 + 9) = 7 \cdot 3 + 7 \cdot 9 \quad ■$$

TEACHING TIP The properties that are infrequently referred to—the closure properties for addition and multiplication—are the two properties that students tend to forget or confuse. Sometimes it is helpful to involve the class in a discussion such as: Are the integers closed under addition? Multiplication? Under the operation of taking a square root? Under the operation of raising to a power? (Answers are: yes, yes, no, yes.) Although the last two operations are not binary, it helps students focus on the idea of closure.

Check the column(s) to which the number belongs.	*Natural Numbers*	*Whole Numbers*	*Integers*	*Rational Numbers*	*Irrational Numbers*	*Real Numbers*
1. $\dfrac{2}{3}$				✓		✓
2. 0		✓	✓	✓		✓
3. -15			✓	✓		✓
4. $\dfrac{105}{3}$	✓	✓	✓	✓		✓
5. $0.\overline{16}$				✓		✓
6. $2.713713\ldots$				✓		✓
7. $\dfrac{\pi}{6}$					✓	✓
8. $\sqrt{2}$					✓	✓
9. 0.86				✓		✓
10. $1.314278619\ldots$ (no discernible pattern)					✓	✓

Problems 11–18 refer to the set $\left\{-25, -\dfrac{18}{5}, -\pi, -0.763, -0.333\ldots, 0, \dfrac{1}{10}, \dfrac{2}{7}, \dfrac{\pi}{4}, \sqrt{3}, 9, \dfrac{283}{5}, 52.8\right\}.$

11. List the rational numbers.
$-25, -\dfrac{18}{5}, -0.763, -0.333\ldots, 0, \dfrac{1}{10}, \dfrac{2}{7}, 9, \dfrac{283}{5}, 52.8$

12. List the negative integers.
-25

13. List the counting numbers.
9

14. List the whole numbers.
$0, 9$

15. List the negative real numbers.
$-25, -\dfrac{18}{5}, -\pi, -0.763, -0.333\ldots$

16. List the irrational numbers.
$-\pi, \dfrac{\pi}{4}, \sqrt{3}$

17. List the positive integers.
9

18. List the negative rational numbers.
$-25, -\dfrac{18}{5}, -0.763, -0.333\ldots$

List all the elements of each set.

19. $\{a \mid a$ is a counting number less than 8$\}$
$1, 2, 3, 4, 5, 6, 7$

20. $\{b \mid b$ is an even integer$\}$
$\ldots -4, -2, 0, 2, 4 \ldots$

21. $\{x \mid x$ is a negative integer between -5 and $-1\}$
$-4, -3, -2$

22. $\{x \mid x$ is a whole number less than 10$\}$
$0, 1, 2, 3, 4, 5, 6, 7, 8, 9$

Indicate whether the statement is true or false.

23. All integers are rational numbers.

True

24. All counting numbers are whole numbers.

True

25. Every rational number is a real number.

True

26. Every integer is an irrational number.

False

Name the property that justifies each statement. All variables represent real numbers.

27. $(6 + 1) + 3 = 6 + (1 + 3)$

Associative property for addition

28. $5 + 1.8$ is a real number

Closure property for addition

29. $\dfrac{1}{7} \cdot 7 = 1$

Inverse property for multiplication

30. $3\left(7 + \dfrac{1}{2}\right) = 3 \cdot 7 + 3 \cdot \dfrac{1}{2}$

Distributive property for multiplication over addition

31. $26 + 0 = 26$

Identity property for addition

32. $9 + (-9) = 0$

Inverse property for addition

33. $\dfrac{5}{3} \cdot \dfrac{7}{8} = \dfrac{7}{8} \cdot \dfrac{5}{3}$

Commutative property for multiplication

34. $\dfrac{1}{16} \cdot 1 = \dfrac{1}{16}$

Identity property for multiplication

35. $\sqrt{2} \cdot 15$ is a real number

Closure property for multiplication

36. $8 \cdot (3 \cdot 6) = (8 \cdot 3) \cdot 6$

Associative property for multiplication

37. $7 + 3 = 3 + 7$

Commutative property for addition

38. $0 + 56 = 56$

Identity property for addition

39. $x \cdot \dfrac{1}{x} = 1$

Inverse property for multiplication

40. $5 + x$ is a real number

Closure property for addition

41. $4 \cdot (3 \cdot x) = (4 \cdot 3) \cdot x$

Associative property for multiplication

42. $2(x + 5) = 2 \cdot x + 2 \cdot 5$

Distributive property of multiplication over addition

43. $(x + y) + 7 = x + (y + 7)$

Associative property for addition

44. $8 \cdot x = x \cdot 8$

Commutative property for multiplication

45. $x + \pi = \pi + x$

Commutative property for addition

46. $y + 0 = y$

Identity property for addition

47. $5 \cdot x$ is a real number

Closure property for multiplication

48. $x \cdot 1 = x$

Identity property for multiplication

49. $(-x) + x = 0$

Inverse property for addition

50. $\sqrt{3}(x + 2) = \sqrt{3} \cdot x + \sqrt{3} \cdot 2$

Distributive property of multiplication over addition.

❓ To Think About

51. List the numbers in the set

$$\left\{-82, -\dfrac{156}{3}, -\sqrt{3}, -\dfrac{5}{7}, -0.\overline{16}, -\dfrac{1}{10}, 0, 2, 4, \dfrac{55}{3}, 26.13214\ldots, 156.\overline{3}\right\}$$

that satisfy *all* of the following properties: rational, not negative irrational, not positive integers, not positive real.

$-82, -\dfrac{156}{3}, -\dfrac{5}{7}, -0.\overline{16}, -\dfrac{1}{10}, 0$

$\left.\begin{array}{c}(-\sqrt{3}, 26.13214) \text{ not rational} \\ \left(2, 4, \dfrac{55}{3}, 156.\overline{3}\right) \text{ positive reals}\end{array}\right\}$ Do not satisfy requirements

52. Write the property of real numbers that justifies each of the following steps. Treat the brackets as parentheses.

$$[\sqrt{3} + (\pi + 6) \cdot x][x + y] = [\sqrt{3} + x \cdot (\pi + 6)][x + y] \qquad \text{Commutative property of multiplication}$$

$$= [x \cdot (\pi + 6) + \sqrt{3}][y + x] \qquad \text{Commutative property of addition}$$

$$= [x \cdot \pi + x \cdot 6 + \sqrt{3}][y + x] \qquad \text{Distributive property of multiplication over addition}$$

$$= [y + x][x \cdot \pi + \sqrt{3} + x \cdot 6] \quad \begin{matrix} \text{Two} \\ \text{properties} \end{matrix} \quad \begin{cases} \text{Commutative property of multiplication} \\ \text{Commutative property of addition} \end{cases}$$

$$= [y + x][\pi \cdot x + 6 \cdot x + \sqrt{3}] \quad \begin{matrix} \text{Two} \\ \text{properties} \end{matrix} \quad \begin{cases} \text{Commutative property of addition} \\ \text{Commutative property of multiplication} \end{cases}$$

For Extra Practice Exercises, turn to page 60.

Solutions to Odd-Numbered Practice Problems

1. (a) 1.26 is a rational number and a real number. **(b)** 3 is a natural number, whole number, integer, and a real number.
(c) $\frac{3}{7}$ is a rational number and a real number. **(d)** -2 is an integer, a rational number, and a real number.
(e) 5.18267134 . . . has no repeating pattern. Therefore, it is an irrational number and a real number.
3. (a) The product $\frac{1}{3} \cdot \frac{2}{7}$ will give a real number answer. This is the closure property of multiplication.

(b) $4 \cdot \frac{1}{4} = 1$ is the multiplicative inverse property. **(c)** $6 \cdot (2 \cdot 8) = (6 \cdot 2) \cdot 8$ is the associative property of multiplication.
(d) $76 \cdot 1 = 76$ is the identity property of multiplication. **(e)** $4 \cdot 15 = 15 \cdot 4$ is the commutative property of multiplication.

Answers to Even-Numbered Practice Problems

2. (a) Commutative property of addition **(b)** Identity property of addition **(c)** Additive inverse property
(d) Closure property of addition **(e)** Associative property of addition
4. $7(12) = 21 + 63$
$84 = 84$

1.2 OPERATIONS WITH SIGNED NUMBERS

☐ After studying this section, you will be able to:

1 The Real Number Line and Absolute Value

We can think of real numbers as points on a line, called the *real number line*, where positive numbers lie to the right of zero, and negative numbers lie to the left.

The number line helps us to understand the important concept of absolute value, and lets us see how to add and subtract signed numbers.

1 *Find the absolute value of any real number*

2 *Add, subtract, multiply, and divide signed numbers*

3 *Perform mixed operations of addition, subtraction, multiplication, and division in the proper order.*

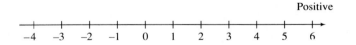

Positive

$$-4 \quad -3 \quad -2 \quad -1 \quad 0 \quad 1 \quad 2 \quad 3 \quad 4 \quad 5 \quad 6$$

Definition

The **absolute value** of a number x, written $|x|$, is its distance from 0 on the number line.

For example, 5 is located 5 units from 0 on the number line. Therefore, its absolute value is 5, and we write $|5| = 5$. But -5 is also located 5 units from 0 on the number line, so its absolute value is also 5: $|-5| = 5$. Even though -5 is located in the opposite direction from 5, we are concerned *only* with distance, which is always positive. (We don't say, for instance, that we traveled -10 miles.) Therefore, we see that the absolute value of any number is *always* positive or zero.

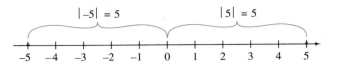

We formally define absolute value like this:

$$|x| = \begin{cases} x & \text{if } x > 0 \\ 0 & \text{if } x = 0 \\ x & \text{if } x < 0 \end{cases}$$

The $>$ symbol means "is greater than"; the $<$ symbol means "is less than."

Example 1 Evaluate.

(a) $|6|$ **(b)** $|-8|$ **(c)** $|0|$ **(d)** $|5 - 3|$

(a) $|6| = 6$ **(b)** $|-8| = 8$

(c) $|0| = 0$ **(d)** $|5 - 3| = |2| = 2$ ∎

Practice Problem 1 Evaluate.

(a) $|-4|$ **(b)** $|3.16|$ **(c)** $|0|$ **(d)** $|12 - 7|$ ∎

◪ Addition of Signed Numbers

Addition of signed numbers can be pictured on the number line. For example, to add $+6$ and $+5$, we start at 6 on the number line and move 5 units in the positive direction (to the right).

To add two negative numbers, say -4 and -3, we start at -4 and move 3 units in the negative direction (to the left). In other words, we add their absolute values. We state this procedure as a rule.

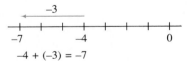

Rule 1.1

To add two real numbers with the *same* sign, add their absolute values. The sum takes the common sign.

Example 2 Add.

(a) $-5 + (-0.6)$ **(b)** $-\dfrac{1}{2} + \left(-\dfrac{1}{3}\right)$ **(c)** $\dfrac{2}{5} + \dfrac{3}{7}$

We apply Rule 1.1 to all three problems.

(a) $-5 + (-0.6) = -5.6$

(b) $-\dfrac{1}{2}+\left(-\dfrac{1}{3}\right)=-\dfrac{3}{6}+\left(-\dfrac{2}{6}\right)=-\dfrac{5}{6}$

> Obtain a common denominator before adding.

(c) $\dfrac{2}{5}+\dfrac{3}{7}=\dfrac{14}{35}+\dfrac{15}{35}=\dfrac{29}{35}$ ■

Practice Problem 2 Add.

(a) $3.4+2.6$　　　　**(b)** $\left(-\dfrac{3}{4}\right)+\left(-\dfrac{1}{6}\right)$　　　　**(c)** $(-5)+(-37)$ ■

What do we do if the numbers have different signs? Let's add -4 and 3. Again using our number line, we start at -4 and move 3 units in the positive direction. Thus, the rule is

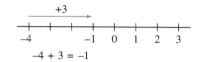

$$-4+3=-1$$

> **Rule 1.2**
>
> To add two real numbers with different signs, find the difference of their absolute values. The answer takes the sign of the number with the larger absolute value.

Example 3 Add.

(a) $12+(-5)$　　　**(b)** $-12+5$　　　**(c)** $-\dfrac{1}{3}+\dfrac{1}{4}$　　　**(d)** $8+(-8)$

(a) $12+(-5)=7$　　　　　　　　　**(b)** $-12+5=-7$

(c) $-\dfrac{1}{3}+\dfrac{1}{4}=-\dfrac{4}{12}+\dfrac{3}{12}=-\dfrac{1}{12}$　　　**(d)** $8+(-8)=0$ ■

Practice Problem 3 Add.

(a) $26+(-18)$　　　**(b)** $24+(-30)$　　　**(c)** $-\dfrac{1}{5}+\dfrac{2}{3}$　　　**(d)** $-8.6+8.6$

■

TEACHING TIP Emphasize the understanding of the word "opposite." Ask them if they can think of another word for "opposite" of a number. Usually, someone in the class will correctly suggest "additive inverse."

Notice part (d) that if you add two numbers that are opposites, the answer will *always* be zero. The **opposite** of a number is the number with the same absolute value but a different sign. The opposite of -6 is 6. The opposite of $\dfrac{2}{3}$ is $-\dfrac{2}{3}$.

The opposite of a number is also called the **additive inverse**. Do you see why?

Subtraction of Signed Numbers

We define subtraction in terms of addition and use our rules for adding signed numbers. So, actually you already *know* how to subtract if you understood how to add numbers with opposite signs.

> **Rule 1.3**
>
> To subtract b from a, add the opposite (inverse) of b to a. Thus, $a - b = a + (-b)$.

Example 4   Use Rule 1.3 to subtract.

(a) $5 - 7$ (b) $-8 - 2$ (c) $8 - 6$
(d) $-3 - (-4)$ (e) $-12 - (-3)$

(a) $5 - 7 = 5 + (-7) = -2$ (b) $-8 - 2 = -8 + (-2) = -10$
(c) $8 - 6 = 8 + (-6) = 2$ (d) $-3 - (-4) = -3 + 4 = 1$
(e) $-12 - (-3) = -12 + 3 = -9$ ■

Practice Problem 4   Use Rule 1.3 to subtract.
(a) $9 - 2$ (b) $-8 - (-3)$ (c) $-5 - (-14)$

(d) $18 - 26$ (e) $\dfrac{1}{2} - \left(-\dfrac{1}{4}\right)$ ■

Multiplication and Division of Real Numbers

Multiplication and division can be written in several ways. Here are five ways to write 3 times 5:

$$3 \cdot 5 \quad (3)(5) \quad 3 \times 5 \quad 3(5) \quad (3) \cdot (5)$$

Usually, we write $(3)(5)$ or $3(5)$. Here are three ways to write 3 divided by 5:

$$\frac{3}{5} \quad 3/5 \quad 3 \div 5$$

Recall that the product or quotient of two positive numbers is positive. For example,

$$(2)(5) = (+2)(+5) = 2 + 2 + 2 + 2 + 2 = 10$$

and

$$\frac{+10}{+2} = +5 \quad \text{because } (+5)(+2) = +10$$

But suppose that the signs of the numbers we want to multiply or divide are different. What will be the sign of the answer? We can again use repeated addition to help us find out. Let's multiply 5 and -2:

$$(-2)(5) = (-2) + (-2) + (-2) + (-2) + (-2) = -10$$

Similarly,

$$(2)(-5) = (-5) + (-5) = -10$$

Therefore, we must have

$$\frac{-10}{2} = -5$$

So we can see that multiplying or dividing a negative number with a positive number gives a negative answer.

It takes a bit more work to show that multiplying or dividing two negative numbers gives a positive answer. In other words, for any integers a and b,

$$(-a)(-b) = ab$$

We can prove this by using the familiar properties of real numbers. We just showed that

$$-a(b) = -ab$$

since

$$-a(0) = 0^\dagger$$

we can write

$$-a(0) = -a(-b + b) \qquad \text{Additive inverse}$$

$$(-a)(-b + b) = (-a)(-b) + (-a)(b) \qquad \text{Distributive property}$$

But the left side of this equation is $(-a)(0) = 0$, and the second term on the right side is $-ab$. Thus, for the equation to be true, $(-a)(-b)$ must equal ab, so that we have $ab + (-ab) = 0$. Therefore, we have proved the following rules:

Rule 1.4

When you multiply or divide two signed numbers with like signs, the answer is positive.

Rule 1.5

When you multiply or divide two signed numbers with different signs, the answer is negative.

Example 5 Evaluate.

(a) $(-8)(-2)$

(b) $\dfrac{-3}{-5} \cdot \dfrac{-2}{11}$

(c) 12×5

(d) $(-6) \div (-12)$

(e) $\dfrac{-15}{-3}$

(f) $\dfrac{2}{3} \div \dfrac{5}{7}$

(a) $(-8)(-2) = 16$

(b) $\dfrac{-3}{5} \cdot \dfrac{-2}{11} = \dfrac{(-3)(-2)}{(5)(11)} = \dfrac{6}{55}$

(c) $12 \times 5 = 60$

(d) $(-6) \div (-12) = \dfrac{-6}{-12} = \dfrac{1}{2}$

(e) $\dfrac{-15}{-3} = 5$

(f) $\dfrac{2}{3} \div \dfrac{5}{7} = \dfrac{2}{3} \cdot \dfrac{7}{5} = \dfrac{(2)(7)}{(3)(5)} = \dfrac{14}{15}$ ■

Practice Problem 5 Evaluate.

(a) $(-9)(-3)$

(b) 5×200

(c) $\dfrac{-20}{-2}$

(d) $-60 \div (-5)$

(e) $\left(-\dfrac{3}{7}\right) \div \left(-\dfrac{1}{5}\right)$ ■

Example 6 Evaluate.

(a) $\dfrac{12}{-6}$

(b) $5(-8)$

(c) $(-13)(2)$

(d) $(-5)\left(\dfrac{2}{17}\right)$

(e) $\dfrac{-\dfrac{1}{3}}{7}$

(a) $\dfrac{12}{-6} = -2$

(b) $5(-8) = -40$

(c) $(-13)(2) = -26$

(d) $(-5)\left(\dfrac{2}{17}\right) = \left(-\dfrac{5}{1}\right)\left(\dfrac{2}{17}\right) = -\dfrac{10}{17}$

We could write $-\dfrac{10}{17}$ as $\dfrac{-10}{17}$ or $\dfrac{10}{-17}$. In general, $-\dfrac{a}{b} = \dfrac{-a}{b} = \dfrac{a}{-b}$

---

† Why is $a \cdot 0 = 0$? Think about it. Multiplication, you know, is just repeated addition. So multiplying $a \cdot 0$ means add 0 to itself a times:

$$\underbrace{0 + 0 + 0 + \cdots + 0}_{a \text{ times}} = 0$$

Work to eliminate a negative value in the denominator.

(e) $\dfrac{-\dfrac{1}{3}}{7} = -\dfrac{1}{3} \div 7 = \left(-\dfrac{1}{3}\right)\dfrac{1}{7} = -\dfrac{1}{21}$ ∎

Practice Problem 6 Evaluate.

(a) $(-3)(7)$

(b) $\left(-\dfrac{2}{5}\right)\left(\dfrac{3}{4}\right)$

(c) $\dfrac{150}{-30}$

(d) $\dfrac{-4}{\dfrac{2}{5}}$

(e) $-36 \div (18)$ ∎

To Think About

Can you solve this division problem? $-\dfrac{5}{3} \div 0 = ?$

Let's try to solve it by changing it to a multiplication problem. (Why can we do this?)

$$-\dfrac{5}{3} = ? \times 0$$

In other words, what number multiplied by 0 gives $-\dfrac{5}{3}$? Since $a \cdot 0 = 0$ for any a, there is *no* number that can be multiplied by 0 to give $-\dfrac{5}{3}$, or any other number, for that matter. Therefore, our division problem is impossible to solve. Thus, division by 0 is not defined.

Here's another way to think about dividing by 0. We know that $-\dfrac{5}{3} \cdot 0 = 0$. It is also true that $125 \cdot 0 = 0$. Therefore, since $0 = 0$, we can write

$$125 \cdot 0 = -\dfrac{5}{3} \cdot 0$$

Then

$$\dfrac{125 \cdot 0}{0} = \dfrac{-\dfrac{5}{3} \cdot 0}{0}$$

so that $125 = -\dfrac{5}{3}$! Obviously, this is absurd. Division by 0 is impossible. ∎

❸ Order of Operations

It is very important to perform all mathematical operations in the proper order. Otherwise, you will get wrong answers. If addition, subtraction, multiplication, and division are written horizontally do the operations in the following order:

1. Do all multiplications and divisions from left to right.
2. Do all additions and subtractions from left to right.

Example 7 Evaluate: $20 \div (-4) \times 3 + 2 + 6 \times 5$.

1. Beginning at the left, we do any multiplication or division as we encounter it. Here we do division first, then multiplication.

$$20 \div (-4) \times 3 + 2 + 6 \times 5 = -5 \times 3 + 2 + 6 \times 5$$
$$= -15 + 2 + 6 \times 5$$
$$= -15 + 2 + 30$$

2. Next we add or subtract from left to right.

$$-15 + 2 + 30 = -13 + 30$$
$$= 17 \quad \blacksquare$$

Practice Problem 7 Evaluate:

$$5 + 7(-2) - (-3) + 50 \div (-2) \quad \blacksquare$$

Example 8 Evaluate.

(a) $6(-3) - 5(-7) + (-8)$ **(b)** $(-20) \div (-5)(3) + 6 - 5(-2)$

(c) $\dfrac{13 - (-3)}{5(-2) - 6(-3)}$

(a) $6(-3) - 5(-7) + (-8)$ **(b)** $(-20) \div (-5)(3) + 6 - 5(-2)$
$\quad = -18 + 35 + (-8)$ $\qquad\qquad = (4)(3) + 6 - 5(-2)$
$\quad = 17 + (-8)$ $\qquad\qquad\qquad = 12 + 6 + 10$
$\quad = 9$ $\qquad\qquad\qquad\qquad = 28$

(c) $\dfrac{13 - (-3)}{5(-2) - 6(-3)} = \dfrac{13 + 3}{-10 + 18} = \dfrac{16}{8} = 2 \quad \blacksquare$

Practice Problem 8 Evaluate.
(a) $3(-5) + 3(-6) - 2(-1)$ **(b)** $6(-2) + (-20) \div (2)(3)$

(c) $\dfrac{7 + 2 - 12 - (-1)}{(-5)(-6) + 4(-8)} \quad \blacksquare$

DEVELOPING YOUR STUDY SKILLS

KEEP TRYING

You may be one of those students who have had much difficulty with mathematics in the past and who are sure that you cannot do well in this course. Perhaps you are thinking, "I have never been any good at mathematics," or "I have always hated mathematics," or "Math always scares me," or "I have not had any math for so long that I have forgotten it all." You may even have picked up on the label "math anxiety" and attached it to yourself. That is most unfortunate, and it is time for you to reprogram your thinking. Replace those negative thoughts with more positive ones. You need to say things like, "I will give this math class my best shot," or "I can learn mathematics if I work at it," or "I will try to do better than I have done in previous math classes." You will be pleasantly surprised at the difference this more positive attitude makes!

We live in a highly technical world, and you cannot afford to give up on the study of mathematics. Dropping mathematics may prevent you from entering certain career fields that you may find interesting. You may not have to take math courses as high-level as calculus, but such courses as intermediate algebra, finite math, college algebra, and trigonometry may be necessary. Learning mathematics can open new doors for you.

Learning mathematics is a process that takes time and effort. You will find that regular study and daily practice are necessary to strengthen your skills and to help you grow academically. This process will lead you toward success in mathematics. Then, as you become more successful, your confidence in your ability to do mathematics will grow.

Perform the operations indicated. Write your answer in simplest form.

1. $5 + (-8)$
-3

2. $-6 + (-12)$
-18

3. $-7 - (-2)$
$-7 + (2) = -5$

4. $-6 - (+4)$
$-6 + (-4) = -10$

5. $5 - 6 + 2 - 4$
$7 - 10 = -3$

6. $3 - 7 - 6 + 1$
$-13 + 4 = -9$

7. $5\left(-\dfrac{1}{3}\right)$
$-\dfrac{5}{3}$ or $-1\dfrac{2}{3}$

8. $(-20) \div (-2)$
10

9. $\dfrac{-15}{-3}$
5

10. $(-16)(-2)$
32

11. $(-7)(-2)(-1)(3)$
-42

12. $(18)\left(-\dfrac{1}{2}\right)(3)(-1)$
27

13. $\dfrac{\dfrac{2}{7}}{-\dfrac{3}{5}}$
$\dfrac{2}{7} \cdot -\dfrac{5}{3} = -\dfrac{10}{21}$

14. $\dfrac{-26}{\dfrac{13}{5}}$
$-\dfrac{26}{1} \cdot \dfrac{5}{13} = -10$

15. $\dfrac{-\dfrac{3}{4}}{-24}$
$-\dfrac{3}{4} \cdot -\dfrac{1}{24} = \dfrac{1}{32}$

16. $\dfrac{-\dfrac{12}{7}}{-\dfrac{6}{11}}$
$-\dfrac{12}{7} \cdot -\dfrac{11}{6} = \dfrac{22}{7}$ or $3\dfrac{1}{2}$

17. $-8 + (6)\left(-\dfrac{1}{3}\right)$
$-8 - 2 = -10$

18. $-12 - (-3)(2)$
$-12 + (+6) = -6$

19. $5 + 6 - (-3) - 8 + 4 - 3$
$5 + 6 + (+3) - 8 + 4 - 3 = 18 - 11 = 7$

20. $12 - 3 - (-4) + 6 - 5 - 8$
$12 - 3 + (+4) + 6 - 5 - 8 = 22 - 16 = 6$

21. $\dfrac{12 - 4(3)}{2 - 6}$
$\dfrac{12 - 12}{-4} = \dfrac{0}{-4} = 0$

22. $\dfrac{5 - (-2) + 3}{6 - 4}$
$\dfrac{5 + 2 + 3}{2} = \dfrac{10}{2} = 5$

23. $9(-1) - 4(-3) + 6 - 2$
$-9 + 12 + 6 - 2 = 18 - 11 = 7$

24. $-8(-4) + 3(-2) + 5 - 7$
$32 - 6 + 5 - 7 = 37 - 13 = 24$

25. $7 + 30 \div 10 - 15(-3)$
$7 + 3 + 45 = 55$

26. $100 \div 2 \div 5 + 3(-2) - (-6)$
$10 - 6 + 6 = 10$

27. $\dfrac{1 + 49 \div (-7) - (-3)}{-1 - 2}$
$\dfrac{1 - 7 + 3}{-3} = \dfrac{-3}{-3} = 1$

28. $\dfrac{72 \div (-4) + 3(-4)}{5 - (-5)}$
$\dfrac{-18 - 12}{5 + (+5)} = -\dfrac{30}{10} = -3$

29. $(-20)\left(-\dfrac{1}{4}\right)(3)(-2)$
$(5)(3)(-2) = -30$

30. $(-15)\left(\dfrac{1}{3}\right)(-2)(0)(-1)$
0

? To Think About

31. Three numbers are multiplied $a \cdot b \cdot c = d$. The value of d is a negative number. What are the possibilities of being positive or negative for a, b, and c?

One or three of the quantities a, b, c must be negative. In other words, when multiplying an odd number of negative numbers, the answer will be negative.

32. Three numbers are multiplied $a \cdot b \cdot c = d$. The value of d is a positive number. What are the possibilities of being positive or negative for a, b, and c?

Either two quantities are negative or all are positive. In other words, when multiplying an even number of negative numbers, the answer will be positive. When all the quantities being multiplied are positive, the answer will be positive.

Perform the operations indicated. Reduce your answer.

33. $\dfrac{(-60) \div (-3)(-2) + 5 - (-7) + 3}{81 \div (-9) + 5(-3) + 2 - (-2)}$

$\dfrac{-40 + 5 + 7 + 3}{-9 - 15 + 2 + 2} = \dfrac{-25}{-20} = \dfrac{5}{4}$ or $1\dfrac{1}{4}$

34. $\dfrac{(-3)(-2)(-1)(4)(-1) - (-6)}{20 \div (-5) + 2(-6) - 5 + 1}$

$\dfrac{24 + 6}{-4 - 12 - 5 + 1} = \dfrac{30}{-20} = -\dfrac{3}{2}$ or $-1\dfrac{1}{2}$

Cumulative Review Problems

Name the property illustrated by each equation.

35. $5 + 17 = 17 + 5$

commutative property for addition

36. $4 \cdot (3 \cdot 6) = (4 \cdot 3) \cdot 6$

associative property for multiplication

Calculator Problems

37. $\dfrac{1.63482 - 2.48561}{(16.05436)(0.07814)}$

-0.678197169

38. $(1.783)(2.5725) - (1.0526)(-5.9812)$

10.88257862

For Extra Practice Exercises, turn to page 61.

Solutions to Odd-Numbered Practice Problems

1. (a) $|-4| = 4$ **(b)** $|3.16| = 3.16$ **(c)** $|0| = 0$ **(d)** $|12 - 7| = |5| = 5$

3. (a) $26 + (-18) = 8$ **(b)** $29 + (-30) = -6$ **(c)** $-\dfrac{1}{5} + \dfrac{2}{3} = -\dfrac{3}{15} + \dfrac{10}{15} = \dfrac{7}{15}$ **(d)** $-8.6 + 8.6 = 0$

5. (a) $(-9)(-3) = 27$ **(b)** $5 \times 200 = 1000$ **(c)** $\dfrac{-20}{-2} = 10$ **(d)** $-60 \div (-5) = 12$

(e) $\left(-\dfrac{3}{7}\right) \div \left(-\dfrac{1}{5}\right) = \left(-\dfrac{3}{7}\right) \cdot \left(-\dfrac{5}{1}\right) = \dfrac{15}{7}$ or $2\dfrac{1}{7}$

7. $5 + 7(-2) - (-3) + 50 \div (-2) = 5 + (-14) - (-3) + (-25) = 5 + (-14) + (+3) + (-25) = -31$

Answers to Even-Numbered Practice Problems

2. (a) 6.0 **(b)** $-\dfrac{11}{12}$ or $\dfrac{-11}{12}$ **(c)** -42 **4. (a)** 7 **(b)** -5 **(c)** 9 **(d)** -8 **(e)** $\dfrac{3}{4}$

6. (a) -21 **(b)** $-\dfrac{3}{10}$ or $\dfrac{-3}{10}$ **(c)** -5 **(d)** -10 **(e)** -2 **8. (a)** -31 **(b)** -42 **(c)** 1

1.3 POWERS, SQUARE ROOTS, AND THE ORDER OF OPERATIONS OF SIGNED NUMBERS

After studying this section, you will be able to:

1 *Raise a number to an integer power*

2 *Find square roots of numbers that are perfect squares*

3 *Evaluate expressions by using the proper order of operations*

1 Raising a Number to a Power

Repeated multiplication is usually expressed in exponential notation. For example, we write $6 \cdot 6 \cdot 6 \cdot 6$ as 6^4. The number 6 is called the **base** and tells us what value is being multiplied. The **exponent** 4 tells us how many factors of the base 6 occur. The number

$$\underset{\text{base of 2}}{2^5} = \underbrace{2 \cdot 2 \cdot 2 \cdot 2 \cdot 2}_{\text{5 factors}}$$

has base 2 and exponent 5, which tells us that there are five factors.

Exponential Notation

If x is a real number and n is a positive integer, then

$$x^n = \underbrace{x \cdot x \cdot x \cdot x \cdots}_{n \text{ factors}}$$

Example 1 Write in exponential notation.

(a) $3 \cdot 3 \cdot 3 \cdot 3 \cdot 3 \cdot 3 \cdot 3$

(b) $(-2)(-2)(-2)(-2)(-2)$

(c) $x \cdot x \cdot x \cdot x \cdot x \cdot x \cdot x \cdot x$

(d) $(a + b)(a + b)(a + b)$

(a) $3 \cdot 3 \cdot 3 \cdot 3 \cdot 3 \cdot 3 \cdot 3 = 3^7$

(b) $(-2)(-2)(-2)(-2)(-2) = (-2)^5$

(c) $x \cdot x \cdot x \cdot x \cdot x \cdot x \cdot x \cdot x = x^8$

(d) $(a + b)(a + b)(a + b) = (a + b)^3$ (the base is $a + b$) ■

Practice Problem 1 Write in exponential notation.

(a) $(-4)(-4)(-4)(-4)$

(b) $z \cdot z \cdot z \cdot z \cdot z \cdot z \cdot z$ ■

Example 2 Evaluate.

(a) 4^3 **(b)** $(-2)^4$ **(c)** 3^5 **(d)** $(-5)^3$ **(e)** -2^4

(a) $4^3 = 4 \cdot 4 \cdot 4 = 64$

(b) $(-2)^4 = (-2)(-2)(-2)(-2) = (4)(-2)(-2) = (-8)(-2) = 16$

(c) $3^5 = 3 \cdot 3 \cdot 3 \cdot 3 \cdot 3 = 243$

(d) $(-5)^3 = (-5)(-5)(-5) = (25)(-5) = -125$

(e) $-2^4 = -(2 \cdot 2 \cdot 2 \cdot 2) = -16$

Notice that in part (b) we are raising -2 to the fourth power. In (e) we are raising 2 to the fourth power. That is, in (b) the base is -2, but in (e) the base is 2. Be careful; you must use parentheses to clearly indicate the base. ■

Practice Problem 2 Evaluate.

(a) $(-3)^5$ **(b)** $(-3)^6$ **(c)** 2^5 **(d)** $(-4)^4$ **(e)** -4^4

■

TEACHING TIP Ask students to do the following problems at their seats: Evaluate $(-3)^4$ and -3^4. Stress the absolute necessity of having parentheses around the entire number -3 if you want to raise a negative number to a power. (The answers $(-3)^4 = 81$ and $-3^4 = -81$ will emphasize that point.)

Square Roots

The square root of a number is one of the number's two equal factors. That is, $4 \cdot 4 = 4^2 = 16$. Thus, 4 is a square root of 16. Since $(-4) \cdot (-4) = 16$, the square root of 16 is also -4. Every positive real number, therefore has a positive square root and a negative square root. The positive square root is called the **principal square root**. The principal square root of a is written $\sqrt{a}$, where a is called the **radicand** and $\sqrt{}$ is called the **radical**. We summarize these remarks by the following definition.

2

If x is an integer and a is a positive real number such that $a = x^2$, then x is a **square root** of a, and a is a **perfect square**.

Example 3 Find the square roots of 25. What is the principal square root?

Since $(-5)^2 = 25$ and $5^2 = 25$, the square roots of 25 are 5 and -5. The principal square root is 5. ■

Practice Problem 3 What are the square roots of 49? What is the principal square root of 49? ■

Example 4   Find the principal square roots.

(a) $\sqrt{36}$ **(b)** $\sqrt{81}$ **(c)** $\sqrt{0}$ **(d)** $-\sqrt{25}$ **(e)** $-\sqrt{49}$

(a) $\sqrt{36} = 6$ because $6^2 = 36$ **(b)** $\sqrt{81} = 9$ because $9^2 = 81$
(c) $\sqrt{0} = 0$ because $0^2 = 0$ **(d)** $-\sqrt{25} = -(\sqrt{25}) = -(5) = -5$
(e) $-\sqrt{49} = -7$ because $(-7)^2 = 49$
Remember: A principal square root is *positive*.   ∎

Practice Problem 4   Find the principal square root.

(a) $\sqrt{100}$ **(b)** $\sqrt{1}$ **(c)** $-\sqrt{100}$ **(d)** $-\sqrt{36}$ **(e)** $\sqrt{0}$ ∎

TEACHING TIP   Students often have trouble remembering that the square root sign $\sqrt{}$ indicates a principal square root which is NEVER negative. They have trouble remembering that the square roots of 121 are $+11$ and -11, but that the $\sqrt{121}$ is only $+11$.

Since our definition said that the radicand was real, we can find square roots of rational numbers as well.

Example 5   Evaluate.   **(a)** $\sqrt{0.04}$ **(b)** $\sqrt{\dfrac{25}{36}}$

(a) $(0.2)^2 = (0.2)(0.2) = 0.04$. Therefore, $\sqrt{0.04} = 0.2$

(b) We know that $\left(\dfrac{5}{6}\right)^2 = \left(\dfrac{5}{6}\right)\left(\dfrac{5}{6}\right) = \dfrac{25}{36}$. Therefore, $\sqrt{\dfrac{25}{36}} = \dfrac{5}{6}$.   ∎

Practice Problem 5   Evaluate.   **(a)** $\sqrt{0.09}$ **(b)** $\sqrt{\dfrac{4}{81}}$ ∎

So far, we have been able to evaluate square roots exactly. But can we always *exactly* evaluate the square root of a signed number? Let's try to evaluate exactly $\sqrt{7}$ and $\sqrt{-4}$. The key word here is "exactly." By definition, we are looking for two numbers that, when multiplied, give us $\sqrt{7}$. But $\sqrt{7}$ is an irrational number, so there is no integer. We can square to get 7. Since $2^2 = 4$ and $3^2 = 9$, we know that the value of $\sqrt{7}$ must be between 2 and 3. To find the *approximate* value, we could use a calculator with a $\boxed{\sqrt{}}$ button; or we could use Table B-1 at the back of the book. To three decimal places, $\sqrt{7} \approx 2.646.$[†] Therefore, we cannot always evaluate a square root exactly.

But what about $\sqrt{-4}$? Well, our definition says that the radicand must be positive. Hence, we cannot find $\sqrt{-4}$ because there is no real number that we can square to obtain -4. [It's true that $2(-2) = 4$, but $2 \neq -2$.] Therefore, $\sqrt{-4}$ *is not a real number*. A number that is not real is called **imaginary**. We discuss these numbers in Section 7.3.

❸ Order of Operations of Signed Numbers

Parentheses are used as symbols of grouping. The group symbols contain the expression to be evaluated first.

Example 6   Evaluate.

(a) $5(2 + 3 + 6)$ **(b)** $(2 + 8)(7 - 12)$

(a) $5(2 + 3 + 6) = 5(11)$ Combining numbers inside grouping symbol.
$\qquad\qquad\quad = 55$ Multiplying 5 by 11.
(b) $(2 + 8)(7 - 12) = (10)(-5)$ Combining numbers inside the parentheses.
$\qquad\qquad\qquad = -50$ Multiplying 10 by -5.   ∎

Practice Problem 6   Evaluate.
(a) $6(2 - 8 - 4)$ **(b)** $(5 - 7)(2 + 12)$ ∎

The fraction bar acts like a grouping symbol. We must evaluate the expressions above and below the fraction bar before we divide.

The symbol $\approx$ means "approximately equal to."

Example 7 Evaluate $\dfrac{(5)(-2)(-3)}{6-8+4}$.

The numerator is $\qquad (5)(-2)(-3) = (-10)(-3) = 30$

The denominator is $\qquad 6 - 8 + 4 = -2 + 4 = 2$

Thus, $\qquad\qquad\qquad \dfrac{(5)(-2)(-3)}{6-8+4} = \dfrac{30}{2} = 15$ ∎

Practice Problem 7 Evaluate: $\dfrac{5 + 2(-3) - 10 + 1}{(1)(-2)(-3)}$. ∎

A radical or absolute value symbol groups the quantities within it. Thus, we evaluate the terms within the grouping symbol before we find the square root or the absolute value.

Example 8 Evaluate.

(a) $\sqrt{(-3)^2 + (4)^2}$ $\qquad\qquad\qquad$ **(b)** $|5 - 8 + 7 - 13|$

(a) $\sqrt{(-3)^2 + (4)^2} = \sqrt{9 + 16} = \sqrt{25} = 5$

(b) $|5 - 8 + 7 - 13| = |-9| = 9$ ∎

Practice Problem 8 Evaluate.

(a) $\sqrt{(-5)^2 + 12^2}$ $\qquad\qquad\qquad$ **(b)** $|-3 - 7 + 2 - (-4)|$ ∎

When many arithmetic operations or grouping symbols are used, we use the following order of operations:

Order of Operations for Calculations

1. Combine numbers inside grouping symbols.
2. Raise numbers to a power and take any indicated roots.
3. Multiply and divide numbers from left to right.
4. Add and subtract numbers from left to right.

Example 9 Evaluate: $(4 - 6)^3 + 5(-4) + 3$.

$(4 - 6)^3 + 5(-4) + 3$

$\qquad = (-2)^3 + 5(-4) + 3 \qquad$ Combining the $4 - 6$ inside parentheses.

$\qquad = -8 + 5(-4) + 3 \qquad$ Cubing -2.

$\qquad = -8 - 20 + 3 \qquad$ Multiplying $5(-4)$.

$\qquad = -25 \qquad$ Combining $-8 - 20 + 3$. ∎

Practice Problem 9 Evaluate: $-7 - 2(-3) + 4^3$. ∎

TEACHING TIP After discussing example 10 or a similar problem, have them try the following problem for classwork:

$(-3)(5) - (-2) + 3\sqrt{12 - 3}$

This example will help them remember to combine numbers inside a radical first, and also to multiply the number immediately preceeding a radical by the value of the radical. (Answer: -4.)

Example 10 Evaluate: $2 + 66 \div 11 \cdot 3 + 2\sqrt{36}$.

$2 + 66 \div 11 \cdot 3 + 2\sqrt{36}$

$\qquad = 2 + 66 \div 11 \cdot 3 + 2 \cdot 6 \qquad$ Evaluating $\sqrt{36}$.

$\qquad = 2 + 6 \cdot 3 + 2 \cdot 6 \qquad$ Dividing $66 \div 11 = 6$.

$\qquad = 2 + 18 + 12 \qquad$ Multiplying $6 \cdot 3$ and $2 \cdot 6 = 12$.

$\qquad = 32 \qquad$ Adding 2, 18, and 12. ∎

Practice Problem 10 Evaluate: $5 + 6 \cdot 2 - 12 \div (-2) + 3\sqrt{4}$. ∎

Example 11 Evaluate: $\dfrac{2 \cdot 6^2 - 12 \div 3}{4 - 8}$.

We evaluate the numerator first.

$2 \cdot 6^2 - 12 \div 3$

$= 2 \cdot 36 - 12 \div 3$ Raising to a power.

$= 72 - 4$ Multiplying and dividing from left to right.

$= 68$ Subtracting.

Next we evaluate the denominator.

$$4 - 8 = -4$$

Thus,

$$\frac{2 \cdot 6^2 - 12 \div 3}{4 - 8} = \frac{68}{-4} = -17 \quad \blacksquare$$

Practice Problem 11 Evaluate: $\dfrac{2(3) + 5(-2)}{1 + 2 \cdot 3^2 + 5(-3)}$. ∎

DEVELOPING YOUR STUDY SKILLS

CLASS ATTENDANCE

A student of mathematics needs to get started in the right direction by choosing to attend class every day, beginning with the first day of class. Statistics show that class attendance and good grades go together. Classroom activities are designed to enhance learning, and therefore, you must be in class to benefit from them. Vital information and explanations are given each day that can help you in understanding concepts. Do not be deceived into thinking that you can just find out from a friend what went on in class. There is no good substitute for firsthand experience. Give yourself a push in the right direction by developing the habit of going to class every day.

CLASS PARTICIPATION

People learn mathematics through active participation, not through observation from the sidelines. If you want to do well in this course, be involved in classroom activities. Sit near the front where you can see and hear well, where your focus is on the instruction process and not on those students around you. Ask questions, be ready to contribute toward solutions, and take part in all classroom activities. Your contributions are valuable to the class and to yourself. Class participation requires an investment of yourself in the learning process, which you will find pays huge dividends.

EXERCISES 1.3

Write in exponential form.

1. $2 \cdot 2 \cdot 2 \cdot 2 \cdot 2 \cdot 2 \cdot 2 \cdot 2$

2^8

2. $5 \cdot 5 \cdot 5 \cdot 5 \cdot 5 \cdot 5 \cdot 5 \cdot 5 \cdot 5$

5^9

3. $x \cdot x \cdot x \cdot x \cdot x \cdot x$

x^6

4. $y \cdot y \cdot y \cdot y \cdot y \cdot y \cdot y$

y^7

5. $(-6)(-6)(-6)(-6)(-6)$

$(-6)^5$

6. $(-8)(-8)(-8)$

$(-8)^3$

Evaluate.

7. 3^4
81

8. 2^5
32

9. $(-4)^3$
-64

10. $(-5)^2$
25

11. -8^2
$-(8)^2 = -64$

12. -2^4
$-(2)^4 = -(16) = -16$

13. 6^3
216

14. 4^4
256

15. $(-3)^4$
81

16. $(-4)^4$
256

? **To Think About**

17. When a negative number is raised to an odd power, is the result positive or negative?
negative

18. When a negative number is raised to an even power, is the result positive or negative?
positive

Find each principal square root, if it exists.

19. $\sqrt{25}$
5

20. $\sqrt{36}$
6

21. $\sqrt{81}$
9

22. $\sqrt{49}$
7

23. $-\sqrt{16}$
-4

24. $-\sqrt{64}$
-8

25. $\sqrt{\dfrac{25}{49}}$
$\dfrac{5}{7}$

26. $\sqrt{\dfrac{1}{100}}$
$\dfrac{1}{10}$

27. $\sqrt{-100}$
Does not exist

28. $\sqrt{-4}$
Does not exist

29. $\sqrt{0.09}$
0.3

30. $\sqrt{0.25}$
0.5

31. $\sqrt{|-49|}$
$\sqrt{49} = 7$

32. $\sqrt{|-81|}$
$\sqrt{81} = 9$

Evaluate.

33. $8 \div 4 \cdot 3 - 6$
$6 - 6 = 0$

34. $5 \cdot 2 - 3(-4)$
$10 + 12 = 22$

35. $\sqrt{16} + 8(-3)$
$4 - 24 = -20$

36. $27 \div 3 \cdot 2 - (-1)$
$18 + (+1) = 19$

37. $(5 + 2 - 8)^3 - (-7)$
$(-1)^3 + (+7) = (-1) + (7) = 6$

38. $\sqrt{(-3)^2 + (2)^2 + 3}$
$\sqrt{9 + 4 + 3} = \sqrt{16} = 4$

39. $2(-4)^2 + 25 \div 5 + \sqrt{9}$
$32 + 5 + 3 = 40$

40. $(8 - 6 - 7)^2 \div 5 - 6$
$(-5)^2 \div 5 - 6 = 5 - 6 = -1$

41. $(12 - 7)(3 - 2)(1 - 8)$
$(5)(1)(-7) = -35$

42. $2\sqrt{16} + (-4)^2 - 3$
$8 + 16 - 3 = 21$

43. $(4^3)(0) + 7(-2)$
$0 - 14 = -14$

44. $3\sqrt{25} + 2(0) - 8$
$15 + 0 - 8 = 7$

45. $\dfrac{7 + 2(-4) + 5}{8 - 6}$
$\dfrac{7 - 8 + 5}{2} = \dfrac{4}{2} = 2$

46. $\dfrac{2^3 + 3^2 - 5}{4}$
$\dfrac{8 + 9 - 5}{4} = \dfrac{12}{4} = 3$

47. $\dfrac{-3(2^3 - 1)}{-7}$
$\dfrac{-3(7)}{-7} = \dfrac{-21}{-7} = 3$

48. $\dfrac{4 + 2(3^2 - 12)}{-2}$
$\dfrac{4 + 2(-3)}{-2} = \dfrac{-2}{-2} = 1$

49. $\dfrac{|5 - 8 + 6 - 12|}{\sqrt{2^2 + (-3)^2 - 4}}$
$\dfrac{|-9|}{\sqrt{9}} = \dfrac{9}{3} = 3$

50. $\dfrac{\sqrt{(-5)^2 - 3 + 14}}{|19 - 6 + 3 - 25|}$
$\dfrac{\sqrt{36}}{|-9|} = \dfrac{6}{9} = \dfrac{2}{3}$

When parentheses are contained within parentheses, we can replace one set of parentheses by brackets, [ ]. *Operate on the innermost grouping symbol first.* Thus, $2[4(2 + 3) - 6]$ means first add $2 + 3$, then evaluate $2[4 \cdot 5 - 6]$ to obtain $2[14] = 28$.

Evaluate.

51. $4^3 - 2[(-4)^2 - 2^3] + 3[2(-4) + \sqrt{16} - 8 \div 2]$
$64 - 2[16 - 8] + 3[-8 + 4 - 4] = 64 - 16 - 24 = 24$

52. $\sqrt{\dfrac{(-3)^2 + 6(-4) + 12 + 28}{2[6 \cdot 5 + 12 \cdot 3 + 5(3 - 8)] + 18}}$

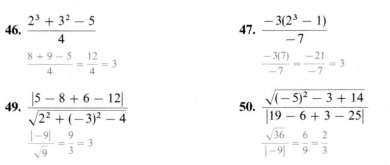

$\sqrt{\dfrac{9 - 24 + 12 + 28}{2[30 + 36 - 25] + 18}} = \sqrt{\dfrac{25}{2(41) + 18}} = \sqrt{\dfrac{25}{100}} = \sqrt{\dfrac{1}{4}} = \dfrac{1}{2}$

State the property illustrated by each equation.

53. $(7)\left(-\dfrac{2}{3}\right) = \left(-\dfrac{2}{3}\right)(7)$

Commutative property for multiplication

54. $9 + (8.6 + 2.0) = (9 + 8.6) + 2.0$

Associative property for addition

Calculator Problems

Evaluate.

55. $(5.986)^5$

7685.702373

56. $\sqrt{22{,}934{,}521}$

4789

For Extra Practice Exercises, turn to page 61.

Solutions to Odd-Numbered Practice Problems

1. (a) $(-4)(-4)(-4)(-4) = (-4)^4$ The parentheses are necessary in the answer. **(b)** $z \cdot z \cdot z \cdot z \cdot z \cdot z \cdot z = z^7$
3. (a) The two square roots of 49 are 7 and -7. **(b)** The principal square root of 49 is 7.

5. (a) $\sqrt{0.09} = 0.3$ **(b)** $\sqrt{\dfrac{4}{81}} = \dfrac{2}{9}$ **7.** $\dfrac{5 + 2(-3) - 10 + 1}{(1)(-2)(-3)} = \dfrac{5 + (-6) - 10 + 1}{6} = \dfrac{-10}{6} = -\dfrac{5}{3}$

9. $-7 - 2(-3) + 4^3 = -7 - 2(-3) + 64 = -7 + 6 + 64 = 63$

11. $\dfrac{2(3) + 5(-2)}{1 + 2 \cdot 3^2 + 5(-3)} = \dfrac{6 + (-10)}{1 + 2 \cdot 9 + 5(-3)} = \dfrac{-4}{1 + 18 + (-15)} = \dfrac{-4}{4} = -1$

Answers to Even-Numbered Practice Problems

2. (a) -243 **(b)** 729 **(c)** 32 **(d)** 256 **(e)** -256 **4. (a)** 10 **(b)** 1 **(c)** -10 **(d)** -6 **(e)** 0   **6. (a)** -60 **(b)** -28
8. (a) $\sqrt{169} = 13$ **(b)** $|-4| = 4$ **10.** 29

1.4 INTEGER EXPONENTS AND SCIENTIFIC NOTATION

☐ After studying this section, you will be able to:

1 *Evaluate products and quotients involving exponents*

2 *Raise a power to a power*

3 *Express numbers in scientific notation*

Negative Exponents

We now extend the definition of an exponent to include negative integer exponents, as well as positive ones.

> **Definition of Negative Exponents**
>
> If x is any nonzero real number
>
> $$x^{-n} = \frac{1}{x^n}$$

Example 1 Simplify. **(a)** 4^{-1} **(b)** 2^{-5} **(c)** w^{-6}

(a) $4^{-1} = \dfrac{1}{4^1} = \dfrac{1}{4}$ **(b)** $2^{-5} = \dfrac{1}{2^5} = \dfrac{1}{32}$ **(c)** $w^{-6} = \dfrac{1}{w^6}$ ∎

Practice Problem 1 Simplify.
(a) 3^{-2} **(b)** 7^{-1} **(c)** z^{-8} ∎

Example 2 Simplify. **(a)** $\left(\dfrac{2}{3}\right)^{-4}$ **(b)** $\left(\dfrac{1}{5}\right)^{-2}$

(a) $\left(\dfrac{2}{3}\right)^{-4} = \dfrac{1}{\left(\dfrac{2}{3}\right)^4} = \dfrac{1}{\dfrac{16}{81}} = (1)\left(\dfrac{81}{16}\right) = \dfrac{81}{16}$

(b) $\left(\dfrac{1}{5}\right)^{-2} = \dfrac{1}{\left(\dfrac{1}{5}\right)^2} = \dfrac{1}{\dfrac{1}{25}} = (1)\left(\dfrac{25}{1}\right) = 25$ ∎

Practice Problem 2   Simplify.   **(a)** $\left(\dfrac{3}{4}\right)^{-2}$ **(b)** $\left(\dfrac{1}{3}\right)^{-3}$ ∎

1 The Product Rule

Numbers and variables in exponential notation can be multiplied quite simply if *the base is the same.* For example, we know that

$$(x^3)(x^2) = (x \cdot x \cdot x)(x \cdot x)$$

Since the factor x appears five times, it must be true that

$$x^3 \cdot x^2 = x^5$$

Hence, we can state a general rule.

> ### Rule 1.5: Product Rule of Exponents
>
> If x is a real number and n, m are integers, then
>
> $$x^m \cdot x^n = x^{m+n}$$

Remember that we don't write an exponent of 1. Thus, $3 = 3^1$ and $x = x^1$.

Example 3   Multiply and leave your answer in exponential form.

(a) $x^5 \cdot x^8$ **(b)** $4^3 \cdot 4^{10}$
(c) $y \cdot y^6 \cdot y^3$ **(d)** $(a + b)^2(a + b)^3$

(a) $x^5 \cdot x^8 = x^{5+8} = x^{13}$ **(b)** $4^3 \cdot 4^{10} = 4^{3+10} = 4^{13}$
(c) $y \cdot y^6 \cdot y^3 = y^{1+6+3} = y^{10}$
(d) $(a + b)^2(a + b)^3 = (a + b)^{2+3} = (a + b)^5$

The base is $a + b$. ∎

Practice Problem 3   Multiply and leave your answer in exponential form.
(a) $w^5 \cdot w$ **(b)** $2^8 \cdot 2^{15}$
(c) $x^2 \cdot x^8 \cdot x^6$ **(d)** $(x + 2y)^4(x + 2y)^{10}$ ∎

Example 4   Multiply.

(a) $(3x^2)(5x^6)$ **(b)** $(2x)(3y^2)$ **(c)** $(5x^2y)(-2xy^3)$

(a) $(3x^2)(5x^6) = (3 \cdot 5)(x^2 \cdot x^6) = 15x^8$
(b) $(2x)(3y^2) = 6xy^2$ Because x and y are different bases, we cannot combine their exponents.
(c) $(5x^2y)(-2xy^3) = (5)(-2)(x^2 \cdot x^1)(y^1 \cdot y^3) = -10x^3y^4$ ∎

Practice Problem 4   Multiply.
(a) $(7w^3)(2w)$ **(b)** $(-5xy)(-2x^2y^3)$ **(c)** $(x)(2x)(3xy)$ ∎

Negative Exponents

Rule 1.5 says that the exponents are integers. Thus, they can be negative. Hence, if m and n are any integers:

$$x^m \cdot x^{-n} = x^{m+(-n)} = x^{m-n}$$

$$x^{-m} \cdot x^{-n} = x^{-m+(-n)} = x^{-(m+n)}$$

Example 5 Multiply.

(a) $(-3x^4y^{-3})(2x^{-5}y^{-6})$ **(b)** $(8a^{-3}b^{-8})(2a^5b^5)$

(a) $(-3x^4y^{-3})(2x^{-5}y^{-6}) = -6x^{4-5}y^{-3-6} = -6x^{-1}y^{-9}$
(b) $(8a^{-3}b^{-8})(2a^5b^5) = 16a^{-3+5}b^{-8+5} = 16a^2b^{-3}$ ■

Practice Problem 5 Multiply.
(a) $(2x^4y^{-5})(3x^2y^{-4})$ **(b)** $(7xy^{-2})(2x^{-5}y^{-6})$ ■

The Quotient Rule

Let's develop the rule for dividing numbers with exponents. Divide $\dfrac{x^5}{x^3}$. We know that

$$\frac{x^5}{x^3} = \frac{x \cdot x \cdot x \cdot x \cdot x}{x \cdot x \cdot x} = x \cdot x = x^2$$

But $x^2 = x^{5-3}$. Also,

$$\frac{5^4}{5^2} = \frac{5 \cdot 5 \cdot 5 \cdot 5}{5 \cdot 5} = 5^2 = 25$$

But $5^2 = 5^{4-2}$. The general rule is then

Rule 1.6: Quotient Rule of Exponents

If x is a nonzero real number and m and n are integers,

$$\frac{x^m}{x^n} = x^{m-n}$$

We can use our definition of negative exponents to find another important rule of exponents. Since

$$x^{-n} = \frac{1}{x^n}$$

it must be true that $\qquad x^{-n} \cdot x^n = 1$

But the left side is just $\qquad x^{-n} \cdot x^n = x^{-n+n} = x^0$

Therefore we conclude $x^0 = 1$.

Rule 1.8: Raising a Number to the Zero Power

For any nonzero real number x: $\qquad x^0 = 1$

Example 6 Simplify.

(a) 3^{-4} **(b)** $(3x)^0$ **(c)** $(-2x^{-5}y^3)^0$ **(d)** $\left(\dfrac{xyz}{abc}\right)^0$

(a) $3^{-4} = \dfrac{1}{3^4} = \dfrac{1}{81}$ **(b)** $(3x)^0 = 1$

(c) $(-2x^{-5}y^3)^0 = 1$ **(d)** $\left(\dfrac{xyz}{abc}\right)^0 = 1$ ■

Practice Problem 6 Simplify.
(a) 6^{-2} **(b)** $5x^2y^0$ **(c)** $(3xy)^0$ **(d)** $(5^{-3})(2a)^0$ ■

Example 7 Divide each exponential expression. Leave your answer in exponential form.

(a) $\dfrac{x^{12}}{x^3}$ **(b)** $\dfrac{5^{16}}{5^7}$ **(c)** $\dfrac{y^3}{y^{20}}$ **(d)** $\dfrac{2^{20}}{2^{30}}$ **(e)** $\dfrac{x^{10}}{x^{10}}$

(a) $\dfrac{x^{12}}{x^3} = x^{12-3} = x^9$ **(b)** $\dfrac{5^{16}}{5^7} = 5^{16-7} = 5^9$

(c) $\dfrac{y^3}{y^{20}} = y^{3-20} = y^{-17}$ **(d)** $\dfrac{2^{20}}{2^{30}} = 2^{20-30} = 2^{-10}$

(e) $\dfrac{x^{10}}{x^{10}} = x^{10-10} = x^0 = 1 \quad (x \neq 0)$ ■

Practice Problem 7 Divide each exponential expression. Leave your answer in exponential form.

(a) $\dfrac{w^8}{w^6}$ **(b)** $\dfrac{3^7}{3^3}$ **(c)** $\dfrac{x^5}{x^{16}}$ **(d)** $\dfrac{4^5}{4^8}$ **(e)** $\dfrac{7^3}{7^3}$ ■

Example 8 Divide.

(a) $\dfrac{26x^3y^4}{-13xy^8}$ **(b)** $\dfrac{-150a^3b^4c^2}{-300abc^2}$

(a) $\dfrac{26x^3y^4}{-13xy^8} = \dfrac{26}{-13} \cdot \dfrac{x^3}{x} \cdot \dfrac{y^4}{y^8} = -2x^2y^{-4}$

(b) $\dfrac{-150a^3b^4c^2}{-300abc^2} = \dfrac{-150}{-300} \cdot \dfrac{a^3}{a} \cdot \dfrac{b^4}{b} \cdot \dfrac{c^2}{c^2} = \dfrac{1}{2} \cdot a^2 \cdot b^3 \cdot c^0 = \dfrac{a^2b^3}{2}$ ■

Practice Problem 8 Divide.

(a) $\dfrac{30x^6y^5}{20x^3y^2}$ **(b)** $\dfrac{-15a^3bc^4}{3a^5b^4c^2}$ ■

Example 9 Divide.

(a) $\dfrac{3x^{-5}y^{-6}}{27x^2y^{-8}}$ **(b)** $\dfrac{2^{-4}a^3b^2c^{-4}}{2^{-5}a^{-1}b^3c^{-5}}$

(a) $\dfrac{3x^{-5}y^{-6}}{27x^2y^{-8}} = \dfrac{1}{9}x^{-5-2}y^{-6-(-8)} = \dfrac{1}{9}x^{-5-2}y^{-6+8} = \dfrac{1}{9}x^{-7}y^2$

(b) $\dfrac{2^{-4}a^3b^2c^{-4}}{2^{-5}a^{-1}b^3c^{-5}} = 2^{-4-(-5)}a^{3-(-1)}b^{2-3}c^{-4-(-5)} = 2^{-4+5}a^{3+1}b^{-1}c^{-4+5}$

$$= 2a^4b^{-1}c$$ ■

Practice Problem 9 Divide.

(a) $\dfrac{2x^{-3}y}{4x^{-2}y^5}$ **(b)** $\dfrac{5^{-3}xy^{-2}}{5^{-4}x^{-6}y^{-7}}$ ■

The Power Rule

The expression $(x^4)^3$ means that $(x^4)^3 = x^4 \cdot x^4 \cdot x^4 = x^{4+4+4} = x^{4 \cdot 3} = x^{12}$. In the same way (try it, using the definitions and rules already proven) we can show that

$$(xy)^n = x^n y^n$$

and

$$\left(\frac{x}{y}\right)^n = \frac{x^n}{y^n} \quad (y \neq 0)$$

Therefore, we have

2

Rule 1.9: Power Rules of Exponents

If x and y are any real numbers and n and m are integers,

$$(x^m)^n = x^{mn} \qquad (xy)^n = x^n y^n$$

$$\left(\frac{x}{y}\right)^n = \frac{x^n}{y^n} \qquad \text{if } y \neq 0$$

Example 10 Use the power rules of exponents to simplify.

(a) $(x^6)^5$ 　　　　　　　**(b)** $(2^8)^4$ 　　　　　　　**(c)** $[(a + b)^2]^4$

(a) $(x^6)^5 = x^{6 \cdot 5} = x^{30}$
(b) $(2^8)^4 = 2^{32}$ 　　　　　Careful. Don't change the base of 2.
(c) $[(a + b)^2]^4 = (a + b)^8$ 　　　The base is $a + b$. ∎

Practice Problem 10 Use the power rules of exponents to simplify.
(a) $(w^3)^8$ 　　　　　　**(b)** $(5^2)^5$ 　　　　　　**(c)** $[(x - 2y)^3]^3$ ∎

Example 11 Raise to the indicated power and simplify. You may leave negative exponents in your answer.

(a) $(2a^2 b^{-3} c^0)^{-4}$ 　　　　　　　**(b)** $\left(\dfrac{5xy^{-3}}{2x^{-4}yz^{-3}}\right)^{-2}$

(a) $(2a^2 b^{-3} c^0)^{-4} = (2a^2 b^{-3})^{-4} = 2^{-4} a^{-8} b^{12} = \dfrac{1}{2^4} a^{-8} b^{12} = \dfrac{1}{16} a^{-8} b^{12}$

(b) $\left(\dfrac{5xy^{-3}}{2x^{-4}yz^{-3}}\right)^{-2} = \dfrac{5^{-2} x^{-2} y^6}{2^{-2} x^8 y^{-2} z^6} = \dfrac{2^2}{5^2} x^{-2-8} y^{6-(-2)} z^{-6} = \dfrac{4}{25} x^{-10} y^8 z^{-6}$ ∎

Practice Problem 11 Raise to the power indicated and simplify. You may leave negative exponents in your answer.
(a) $(3xy^2)^{-2}$ 　　　　　　　**(b)** $\left(\dfrac{4x^2 y^{-2}}{x^{-4} y^{-3}}\right)^{-3}$ ∎

We need to derive one more rule. You should be able to follow the steps.

$$\frac{x^{-m}}{y^{-n}} = \frac{\dfrac{1}{x^m}}{\dfrac{1}{y^n}} = \frac{1}{x^m} \cdot \frac{y^n}{1} = \frac{y^n}{x^m}$$

Rule 1.10: Law of Negative Exponents

If n and m are positive integers and x and y are nonzero real numbers, then

$$\frac{x^{-m}}{y^{-n}} = \frac{y^n}{x^m}$$

Example 12 Simplify: $(-3x^2)^{-2}(2x^3 y^{-2})^3$. Express your answer with positive exponents only.

$$(-3x^2)^{-2}(2x^3 y^{-2})^3 = (-3)^{-2} x^{-4} \cdot 2^3 x^9 y^{-6}$$

$$= \frac{2^3 x^9}{(-3)^2 x^4 y^6} = \frac{8x^9}{9x^4 y^6} = \frac{8x^5}{9y^6}$$ ∎

Practice Problem 12 Simplify: $(2x^{-3})^2(-3xy^{-2})^{-3}$. Express your answer with positive exponents only. ∎

TEACHING TIP The type of problem presented in example 10 is often difficult for students to master. After presenting example 10 or a similar problem, try the following: Write the problem $(-4x^{-2})^{-2}(-2x^3 y^{-3})^2$ on the board and work through the next few steps with them.

$$(-4x^{-2})^{-2}(-2x^3 y^{-3})^2$$
$$= (-4)^{-2} x^4 \cdot (-2)^2 x^6 y^{-6}$$
$$= \frac{(-2)^2 x^4 x^6}{(-4)^2 y^6} = \frac{4x^{10}}{16y^6}$$
$$= \frac{x^{10}}{4y^6}$$

TEACHING TIP Students will sometimes incorrectly write the answer to example 10c as $a^8 + b^8$. Remind them that $(ab)^8 = a^8 b^8$ but that $(a + b)^8 \neq a^8 + b^8$.

TEACHING TIP After doing example 11 or a similar example for the class, ask them this question: If you had to change 567 and 0.0567 both into scientific notation, how would you remember which answer has ten to the power $+2$ and which answer has ten to the -2 power? Usually, the range of student comments here is helpful to the other members of the class.

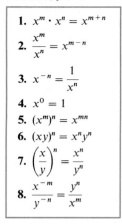

1. $x^m \cdot x^n = x^{m+n}$

2. $\dfrac{x^m}{x^n} = x^{m-n}$

3. $x^{-n} = \dfrac{1}{x^n}$

4. $x^0 = 1$

5. $(x^m)^n = x^{mn}$

6. $(xy)^n = x^n y^n$

7. $\left(\dfrac{x}{y}\right)^n = \dfrac{x^n}{y^n}$

8. $\dfrac{x^{-m}}{y^{-n}} = \dfrac{y^n}{x^m}$

The table below summarizes the laws of exponents. If you simply try to memorize these rules, you might become confused or forget some of them. However, if you have understood how we obtained the rules, you should have no trouble deriving them yourself. Every rule is based on the simple fact that $x^n = x \cdot x \cdot x \cdots x$ (n factors). These rules are highly important. They are used frequently in algebra and other branches of mathematics.

❸ Scientific Notation

Scientific notation is a convenient way to write numbers. In scientific notation, a number is written as the product of a number between 1 and 10 (including 1) and a power of 10. For example, we can write 5000 as 5×10^3 since $10^3 = 1/1000$, and we can write 0.005 as 5×10^{-3} since $10^{-3} = 1/1000$.

Definition: Scientific Notation

A positive number written in scientific notation has the form $a \times 10^n$, where
$1 \leq a < 10$ and n is an integer.

Rule 1.11: Convert from Decimal Notation to Scientific Notation

1. Move the decimal point from its original position to the right of the first non-zero digit.
2. Count the number of places that you moved the decimal point. This number is the power of 10 (that is, the exponent).
3. If you moved the decimal point to the right, the exponent is negative; if you moved it to the left, the exponent is positive.

Example 13   Write in scientific notation.

(a) 7816   (b) 15,200,000   (c) 0.0123   (d) 0.00046

(a) $7816 = 7.816 \times 10^3$ We moved the decimal point three places to the left, so the power of 10 is 3.

(b) $15,200,000 = 1.52 \times 10^7$

(c) $0.0123 = 1.23 \times 10^{-2}$ We moved the decimal point two places to the right, so the power of 10 is -2.

(d) $0.00046 = 4.6 \times 10^{-4}$ ∎

Practice Problem 13   Write in scientific notation.

(a) 128,320   (b) 476   (c) 0.0123   (d) 0.007   ∎

Any number between 1 and 10 considered to be in scientific notation. Thus 2.36, 5.8, and 9 are treated as numbers in scientific notation, because they could be written 2.36×10^0, 5.8×10^0, and 9×10^0. However, this is not commonly done.

We can also convert from scientific notation to decimal notation. We simply move the decimal point to the right or left the number of places indicated by the power of 10.

Example 14   Write in decimal form.

(a) 1.28×10^2 (b) 8.8632×10^4 (c) 6.6×10^5
(d) 6.032×10^{-2} (e) 4.4861×10^{-5}

Move the decimal point two places to the right.

(a) $1.28 \times 10^2 = 128. = 128$
(b) $8.8632 \times 10^4 = 88,632$

(c) $6.6 \times 10^5 = 660{,}000$

Move the decimal point two places to the left.

(d) $6.032 \times 10^{-2} = 0.0632$

(e) $4.4861 \times 10^{-5} = 0.000044861$ ∎

Practice Problem 14 Write in decimal form.

(a) 3×10^4 **(b)** 4.62×10^6 **(c)** 1.973×10^{-3}

(d) 6×10^{-8} **(e)** 4.931×10^{-1} ∎

Using scientific notation and the laws of exponents greatly simplifies calculations.

Example 15 Evaluate: $\dfrac{(0.000000036)(0.0002)}{0.000012}$.

Of course, we could use a calculator to solve this problem, if we had one. Or we could do the actual division. A simpler way, though, is to write the number in scientific notation:

$$\frac{(3.6 \times 10^{-8})(2.0 \times 10^{-3})}{1.2 \times 10^{-5}}$$

Now rewrite using the commutative property.

$$\frac{\overset{3}{\cancel{(3.6)}}(2.0)(10^{-8})(10^{-3})}{\underset{1}{\cancel{(1.2)}}(10^{-5})} = \frac{6.0}{1} \times \frac{10^{-11}}{10^{-5}} \quad \begin{array}{l}\text{Canceling and using} \\ \text{the laws of exponents.}\end{array}$$

$$= 6.0 \times 10^{-11-(-5)}$$

$$= 6.0 \times 10^{-6} \quad ∎$$

Practice Problem 15 Evaluate using scientific notation: $\dfrac{(55{,}000)(3{,}000{,}000)}{5{,}500{,}000}$. ∎

DEVELOPING YOUR STUDY SKILLS

WHY STUDY MATHEMATICS?

Students often question the value of mathematics, particularly algebra. They see little real use for algebra in their everyday lives. The manipulation of letters and symbols seems almost meaningless. This is understandable at the beginning or intermediate levels of algebra, because applications of algebra may not be obvious.

The extensive usefulness of mathematics becomes clear as you take higher-level courses, such as college algebra, statistics, trigonometry, and calculus. You may not be planning to take these higher-level courses now, but your college major may require you to do so.

In our present-day, technological world, it is easy to see mathematics at work. Many vocational and professional areas—such as the fields of business, statistics, economics, psychology, finance, computer science, chemistry, physics, engineering, electronics, nuclear energy, banking, quality control, and teaching—require a certain level of expertise in mathematics. Those who want to work in these fields must be able to function at a given mathematical level. Those who cannot will not make it.

So if your field of study requires you to take higher-level mathematics courses, be sure to realize the importance of mastering the basics of this course. Then you will be ready for the next one.

Simplify. Assume that all variables are nonzero. For problems 1–46, if a large numerical value is involved, leave your answer in exponential form. You may leave negative exponents in your answer.

1. $x^4 \cdot x^8$
x^{12}

2. $y^{10} \cdot y$
y^{11}

3. $x^2 \cdot x^3 \cdot x^{12} \cdot x$
x^{18}

4. $a^3 \cdot a^2 \cdot a \cdot a^5$
a^{11}

5. $3^{12} \cdot 3^5$
3^{17}

6. $2^{18} \cdot 2^{10}$
2^{28}

7. $(3x)(-2x^5)$
$-6x^6$

8. $(5y^2)(3y)$
$15y^3$

9. $(-12x^3y)(-3x^5y^2)$
$36x^8y^3$

10. $(-20a^3b^2)(5ab)$
$-100a^4b^3$

11. $(2x^0y^5z)(-5xy^0z^8)$
$(2y^5z)(-5xz^8) = -10xy^5z^9$

12. $(4^0x^2y^3)(-3x^0y^6)$
$(x^2y^3)(-3y^6) = -3x^2y^9$

13. $(3a^{-2}b)(-2a^{-1}b^{-4})$
$-6a^{-3}b^{-3}$

14. $(-4a^3b^{-2})(2a^{-3}b^2)$
$-8a^0b^0 = -8$

15. $(6x^{-3}y^{-5})(-2x^3y^{-6})$
$-12x^0y^{-11} = -12y^{-11}$

16. $(-5x^{-8}y^{-2})(3x^{-5}y^2)$
$-15x^{-13}y^0 = -15x^{-13}$

17. $\dfrac{x^{12}}{x^7}$
x^5

18. $\dfrac{y^{18}}{y^{20}}$
$\dfrac{1}{y^2}$ or y^{-2}

19. $\dfrac{a^{20}}{a^{25}}$
$\dfrac{1}{a^5}$ or a^{-5}

20. $\dfrac{x^{10}}{x^{20}}$
$\dfrac{1}{x^{10}}$ or x^{-10}

21. $\dfrac{2^8}{2^5}$
$2^3 = 8$

22. $\dfrac{3^{16}}{3^{18}}$
$\dfrac{1}{3^2} = \dfrac{1}{9}$

23. $\dfrac{2x^3}{x^8}$
$\dfrac{2}{x^5}$ or $2x^{-5}$

24. $\dfrac{4y^3}{8y}$
$\dfrac{y^2}{2}$

25. $\dfrac{20xy^3z}{5xy}$
$4y^2z$

26. $\dfrac{100ab^5c^4}{25abc}$
$4b^4c^3$

27. $\dfrac{12a^{-5}b^{-4}c}{18a^{10}b^{-3}c}$
$\dfrac{2}{3}a^{-5-10}b^{-4+3}c^0$ $\dfrac{2}{3a^{15}b}$ or $\dfrac{2}{3}a^{-15}b^{-1}$

28. $\dfrac{-15x^8yz^{-4}}{-35x^0y^5z^{-2}}$
$\dfrac{3}{7}x^{8-0}y^{1-5}z^{-4+2} = \dfrac{3x^8}{7y^4z^2}$

29. $\dfrac{-14a^{-12}b^{-10}}{8a^{-15}b^{-20}}$
$-\dfrac{7}{4}a^{-12+15}b^{-10+20} = \dfrac{-7}{4}a^3b^{10}$

30. $\dfrac{21x^{-12}y^{-3}}{-14x^{-16}y^{-8}}$
$-\dfrac{3}{2}x^{-12+16}y^{-3+8} = -\dfrac{3}{2}x^4y^5$

31. $(x^2)^8$
x^{16}

32. $(a^5)^7$
a^{35}

33. $(3a^5b)^4$
$3^4a^{20}b^4 = 81a^{20}b^4$

34. $(2xy^6)^5$
$2^5x^5y^{30} = 32x^5y^{30}$

35. $\left(\dfrac{x^2y^3}{z}\right)^6$
$\dfrac{x^{12}y^{18}}{z^6}$

36. $\left(\dfrac{x^3}{y^5z^8}\right)^4$
$\dfrac{x^{12}}{y^{20}z^{32}}$

37. $\left(\dfrac{-2x^0y^6z}{y^4}\right)^3$
$\left(\dfrac{-2y^6z}{y^4}\right)^3 = -8y^6z^3$

38. $\left(\dfrac{-5x^4yz^3}{z^2}\right)^2$
$\dfrac{25x^8y^2z^6}{z^4} = 25x^8y^2z^2$

39. $\left(\dfrac{3ab^{-2}c^3}{4a^0b^4}\right)^2$
$\dfrac{9a^2b^{-4}c^6}{16b^8} = \dfrac{9}{16}a^2b^{-4-8}c^6 = \dfrac{9a^2c^6}{16b^{12}}$

40. $\left(\dfrac{5a^3bc^0}{-3a^{-2}b^5}\right)^3$
$\dfrac{125a^9b^3}{-27a^{-6}b^{15}} = \dfrac{-125a^{15}}{27b^{12}}$

41. $\left(\dfrac{2xy^2}{x^{-3}y^{-4}}\right)^{-3}$
$\dfrac{2^{-3}x^{-3}y^{-6}}{x^9y^{12}} = \dfrac{1}{8x^{12}y^{18}}$

42. $\left(\dfrac{3x^{-4}y}{x^{-3}y^2}\right)^{-2}$
$\dfrac{3^{-2}x^8y^{-2}}{x^6y^{-4}} = \dfrac{x^2y^2}{9}$

43. $\dfrac{(x^{-2}y^{-3})^{-2}}{(3x^{-1}y^{-2})^3}$
$\dfrac{x^4y^6}{3^3x^{-3}y^{-6}} = \dfrac{x^7y^{12}}{27}$

44. $\dfrac{(x^4y^{-2})^{-3}}{(2x^{-3}y)^2}$
$\dfrac{x^{-12}y^6}{2^2x^{-6}y^2} = \dfrac{y^4}{4x^6}$

45. $\dfrac{(-4a^3b^{-5})^3}{(-2a^{-6}b^{-1})^{-2}}$
$\dfrac{(-4)^3a^9b^{-15}}{(-2)^{-2}a^{12}b^2} = \dfrac{-256}{a^3b^{17}}$

46. $\dfrac{(-5ab^3)^{-2}}{(-2a^8b^{-3})^3}$
$\dfrac{(-5)^{-2}a^{-2}b^{-6}}{(-2)^3a^{24}b^{-9}} = \dfrac{b^3}{-200a^{26}} = \dfrac{-b^3}{200a^{26}}$

Simplify. Express your answer with positive exponents only.

47. $\dfrac{2^{-3}a^2b^{-4}}{2^{-4}a^{-2}b^3}$

$2^{-3+4}a^{2+2}b^{-4-3} = \dfrac{2a^4}{b^7}$

48. $\dfrac{3^4a^{-3}b^2c^{-4}}{3^3a^4b^{-2}c^0}$

$3^{4-3}a^{-3-4}b^{2+2}c^{-4} = \dfrac{3b^4}{a^7c^4}$

49. $(3x^4y^{-2}z^0)^{-2}$

$3^{-2}x^{-8}y^4 = \dfrac{y^4}{9x^8}$

50. $(2x^{-3}y^2)^{-3}$

$2^{-3}x^9y^{-6} = \dfrac{x^9}{8y^6}$

51. $\left(\dfrac{x^{-3}}{y^{-4}}\right)^{-2}$

$\dfrac{x^6}{y^8}$

52. $\left(\dfrac{2^{-1}y^{-5}}{x^{-6}}\right)^{-2}$

$\dfrac{2^2y^{10}}{x^{12}} = \dfrac{4y^{10}}{x^{12}}$

53. $\dfrac{a^{-12}b^{-10}c^3}{a^3b^{-5}c^3}$

$a^{-12-3}b^{-10+5}c^{3-3} = \dfrac{1}{a^{15}b^5}$

54. $\dfrac{b^3c^{-5}d^2}{b^{-6}c^{-2}d^2}$

$b^{3+6}c^{-5+2}d^{2-2} = \dfrac{b^9}{c^3}$

55. $\left(\dfrac{14x^{-3}y^{-3}}{7x^{-4}y^{-3}}\right)^{-2}$

$\dfrac{14^{-2}x^6y^6}{7^{-2}x^8y^6} = \dfrac{1}{4x^2}$

56. $\left(\dfrac{25x^{-1}y^{-6}}{5x^{-4}y^{-6}}\right)^{-2}$

$\dfrac{(25)^{-2}x^2y^{12}}{(5)^{-2}x^8y^{12}} = \dfrac{1}{25x^6}$

57. $\dfrac{7^{-8}\cdot 5^{-6}}{7^{-9}\cdot 5^{-5}\cdot 6^0}$

$7^{-8+9}\cdot 5^{-6+5} = 7^1\cdot 5^{-1} = \dfrac{7}{5}$

58. $\dfrac{9^{-2}\cdot 8^{-10}\cdot 4^0}{9^{-1}\cdot 8^{-9}}$

$9^{-2+1}8^{-10+9} = 9^{-1}\cdot 8^{-1} = \dfrac{1}{72}$

Write in scientific notation.

59. 470

4.7×10^2

60. 1230

1.23×10^3

61. 1,730,000

1.73×10^6

62. 5,318,000,000

5.318×10^9

63. 0.017

1.7×10^{-2}

64. 0.093

9.3×10^{-2}

65. 0.000008346

8.346×10^{-6}

66. 0.000007116

7.116×10^{-6}

Write in decimal notation.

67. 7.13×10^5

713,000

68. 2.75×10^6

2,750,000

69. 1.863×10^{-2}

0.01863

70. 7.07×10^{-3}

0.00707

71. 9.01×10^{-7}

0.000000901

72. 6.668×10^{-9}

0.000000006668

Perform the calculations indicated.

73. $(7.2 \times 10^{-3})(5.0 \times 10^{-5})$

$(7.2)(5.0)(10^{-3})(10^{-5})$
36×10^{-8}

74. $(3.1 \times 10^{-5})(2.0 \times 10^8)$

$(3.1)(2.0)(10^{-5})(10^8)$
6.2×10^3

75. $\dfrac{4.8 \times 10^{-15}}{1.6 \times 10^{-12}}$

$3 \times 10^{-15+12} = 3 \times 10^{-3}$

76. $\dfrac{4.6 \times 10^{-12}}{2.3 \times 10^5}$

$2 \times 10^{-12-5} = 2 \times 10^{-17}$

 **To Think About**

Simplify. Assume that n is a positive integer.

77. $\left(\dfrac{-3x^{7+n}y^{-9}z^{2+5n}}{-2x^{10}y^{4n+3}z^{2n-1}}\right)^6$

$\dfrac{(-3)^6x^{42+6n}y^{-54}z^{12+30n}}{(-2)^6x^{60}y^{24n+18}z^{12n-6}} = \dfrac{729}{64}x^{42+6n-60}y^{-54-24n-18}z^{12+30n-12n+6}$

$= \dfrac{729}{64}x^{6n-18}y^{-24n-72}z^{18n+18}$

78.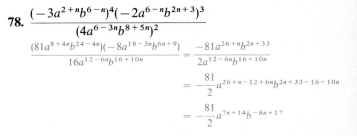

$\dfrac{(-3a^{2+n}b^{6-n})^4(-2a^{6-n}b^{2n+3})^3}{(4a^{6-3n}b^{8+5n})^2}$

$\dfrac{(81a^{8+4n}b^{24-4n})(-8a^{18-3n}b^{6n+9})}{16a^{12-6n}b^{16+10n}} = \dfrac{-81a^{26+n}b^{2n+33}}{2a^{12-6n}b^{16+10n}}$

$= -\dfrac{81}{2}a^{26+n-12+6n}b^{2n+33-16-10n}$

$= -\dfrac{81}{2}a^{7n+14}b^{-8n+17}$

Cumulative Review Problems

Evaluate.

79. $(-3)(-2)(-1)(-4)$
  24

80. $5 + 2(-3) + 12 \div (-6)$
  $5 - 6 - 2 = -3$

81. $5 - 7 + 3 - 4(2)^2$
  $5 - 7 + 3 - 16 = -15$

82. $\dfrac{5 + 3 - 4}{32 \div (-8)}$
  $\dfrac{4}{-4} = -1$

Calculator Problems

Simplify.

83. $(-3.6982x^3y^4)^7$
  $-9460.906704x^{21}y^{28}$

84. $\dfrac{1.98364 \times 10^{-14}}{4.32571 \times 10^{-16}}$
  45.8569807

For Extra Practice Exercises, turn to page 61.

Solutions to Odd-Numbered Practice Problems

1. (a) $3^{-2} = \dfrac{1}{3^2} = \dfrac{1}{9}$ **(b)** $7^{-1} = \dfrac{1}{7^1} = \dfrac{1}{7}$ **(c)** $z^{-8} = \dfrac{1}{z^8}$

3. (a) $w^5 \cdot w = w^5 \cdot w^1 = w^6$ **(b)** $2^8 \cdot 2^{15} = 2^{23}$ Do *not* multiply the first base of 2 by the second base of 2.
(c) $x^2 \cdot x^8 \cdot x^6 = x^{16}$ **(d)** $(x + 2y)^4(x + 2y)^{10} = (x + 2y)^{14}$
5. (a) $(2x^4y^{-5})(3x^2y^{-4}) = 6x^6y^{-9}$ **(b)** $(7xy^{-2})(2x^{-5}y^{-6}) = 14x^{-4}y^{-8}$

7. (a) $\dfrac{w^8}{w^6} = w^2$ **(b)** $\dfrac{3^7}{3^3} = 3^4$ **(c)** $\dfrac{x^5}{x^{16}} = x^{-11}$ **(d)** $\dfrac{4^5}{4^8} = \dfrac{1}{4^3}$ **(e)** $\dfrac{7^3}{7^3} = 1$ **9. (a)** $\dfrac{2x^{-3}y}{4x^{-2}y^5} = \dfrac{1}{2}x^{-1}y^{-4}$ **(b)** $\dfrac{5^{-3}xy^{-2}}{5^{-4}x^{-6}y^{-7}} = 5x^7y^5$

11. (a) $(3xy^2)^{-2} = (3^1x^1y^2)^{-2} = 3^{-2}x^{-2}y^{-4}$ **(b)** $\left(\dfrac{4x^2y^{-2}}{x^{-4}y^{-3}}\right)^{-3} = \dfrac{4^{-3}x^{-6}y^6}{x^{12}y^9} = 4^{-3}x^{-18}y^{-3}$

13. (a) 1.2832×10^5 **(b)** 4.76×10^2 **(c)** 1.23×10^{-2} **(d)** 7×10^{-3}

15. $\dfrac{(55,000)(3,000,000)}{5,500,000} = \dfrac{5.5 \times 10^4 \times 3 \times 10^6}{5.5 \times 10^6} = 3 \times 10^4$

Answers to Even-Numbered Practice Problems

2. (a) $\dfrac{16}{9}$ **(b)** 27 **4. (a)** $14w^4$ **(b)** $10x^3y^4$ **(c)** $6x^3y$ **6. (a)** $\dfrac{1}{36}$ **(b)** $5x^2$ **(c)** 1 **(d)** $\dfrac{1}{125}$

8. (a) $\dfrac{3}{2}x^3y^3$ **(b)** $-5a^{-2}b^{-3}c^2$ **10. (a)** w^{24} **(b)** 5^{10} **(c)** $(x - 2y)^9$ **12.** $-\dfrac{4y^6}{27x^9}$

14. (a) 30,000 **(b)** 4,620,000 **(c)** 0.001973 **(d)** 0.00000006 **(e)** 0.4931

After studying this section, you will be able to:

1 Add polynomial expression

2 Multiply polynomial expressions

3 Remove grouping symbols in their proper order to simplify polynomial expressions

1.5 OPERATIONS WITH VARIABLES AND GROUPING SYMBOLS

Basic Concepts

A collection of numerical values, variables, and signs of operations is called an **algebraic expression**. An algebraic expression usually contains the sum or difference of several *terms*. A **term** is a real number, or a variable, or a product or quotient of numbers and variables.

> Terms are *always* separated by + or − signs.

Example 1 List the terms in each algebraic expression.

(a) $5x + 3y^2$　　　　　(b) $6y^2 + 3y + 2$　　　　　(c) $5x^2 - 3xy - 7$

(a) $5x$ is a product of a real number (5) and a variable (x), so $5x$ is a term. $3y^2$ is also a product of a real number and a variable, so $3y^2$ is a term.

(b) $6y^2$ and $3y$ are products, so they are terms. 2 is a real number, so it is also a term.

(c) Note that we can write $5x^2 - 3xy - 7$ in an equivalent form: $5x^2 + (-3xy) + (-7)$. This second form helps us to identify more readily the three terms. The terms are: $5x^2$, $-3xy$, and -7. ■

Practice Problem 1 List the terms in each algebraic expression.

(a) $7x - 2w^3$　　　　　(b) $5 + 6x + 2y$ ■

　　　Any factor or group of factors in a term is called the **coefficient** of the term. In the term $-8xy$, $-8x$ is the coefficient of y, -8 is the coefficient of xy, and $-8y$ is the coefficient of x. The **numerical coefficient** of a term is the numerical value multiplied by the variables. If no numerical coefficient appears before a variable in a term, the coefficient is understood to be 1. For example, the coefficient of xy is 1.

Example 2

(a) In the expression $5x^2 - 2x + 3xy$, what is the coefficient of x^2? of y?

(b) In the expression $8x^3 - 12xy + y$, what is the numerical coefficient of each term?

(a) The coefficient of x^2 is 5, and the coefficient of y is $3x$.

(b) The numerical coefficients are 8, -12, and 1. ■

Practice Problem 2

(a) In the expression $5x^2y + 3w$, what is the coefficient of y? of w?

(b) In the expression $-7x + 6w + 5z^2$, what is the numerical coefficient of each term? ■

1 Collecting Like Terms

We can add or substract terms if they are **like terms**; that is, the terms have the same variables and the same exponents. When we collect like terms, we are using the following form of the distributive property:

$$(b + c)a = ba + ca$$

Example 3 Collect like terms by showing the use of the distributive property.

(a) $8x + 2x$　　　　　(b) $5x^2y + 12x^2y$

(a) $8x + 2x = (8 + 2)x = 10x$

(b) $5x^2y + 12x^2y = (5 + 12)x^2y = 17x^2y$ ■

Practice Problem 3 Collect like terms by showing the use of the distributive property.

(a) $9x - 12x$　　　　　(b) $4ab^2c + 15ab^2c$ ■

Example 4 Collect like terms.

(a) $5a^2b + 3ab - 8a^2b + 2ab$　　　　　(b) $7x^2 - 2x - 8 + x^2 + 5x - 12$

(a) $5a^2b + 3ab - 8a^2b + 2ab = -3a^2b + 5ab$

Note that we cannot combine $-3a^2b + 5ab$ since they are not like terms.

(b) $7x^2 - 2x - 8 + x^2 + 5x - 12 = 8x^2 + 3x - 20$

Remember that the coefficient of x^2 is 1, so you are adding $7x^2 + 1x^2$. ■

Practice Problem 4 Collect like terms: $12x^3 - 5x^2 + 7x - 3x^3 - 8x^2 + x$. ■

☑ Multiplication of Expressions with Variables

We can use the distributive property $a(b + c) = ab + ac$ to multiply more involved algebraic expressions. The kinds of expressions usually encountered are called *polynomials*. **Polynomials** are variable expressions that contain terms with *nonnegative* integer exponents. Some examples of polynomials are $6x^2 + 2x - 8$, $5a + b$, $16x^3$, and $5x + 8$.

Example 5 Use the distributive property to multiply $-2x(x^2 + 5x)$.

The distributive property tells us to multiply each term in the parentheses by the term outside the parentheses.

$$-2x(x^2 + 5x) = (-2x)(x^2) + (-2x)(5x) = -2x^3 - 10x^2 \quad ■$$

Practice Problem 5 Use the distributive property to multiply: $-3x^2(2x - 5)$. ■

There is no limit to the number of terms we can multiply. For example, $a(b + c + d + \cdots) = ab + ac + ad + \cdots$.

Example 6 Multiply.

(a) $7x(x^2 - 3x - 5)$ **(b)** $5ab(a^2 - ab + 8b^2 + 2)$

(a) $7x(x^2 - 3x - 5) = 7x^3 - 21x^2 - 35x$

(b) $5ab(a^2 - ab + 8b^2 + 2) = 5a^3b - 5a^2b^2 + 40ab^3 + 10ab \quad ■$

Practice Problem 6 Multiply: $-5x(2x^2 - 3x - 1)$. ■

☑ Removing Grouping Symbols

We also use the distributive property to remove grouping symbols.

Example 7 Remove grouping symbols by using the distributive property.

(a) $(3x^2 + 2)$ **(b)** $+(5x - 7)$ **(c)** $-(2x + 3)$ **(d)** $-4x(x - 2y)$

(a) $(3x^2 + 2) = 1(3x^2 + 2) = 3x^2 + 2$ **(b)** $+(5x - 7) = +1(5x - 7) = 5x - 7$

(c) $-(2x + 3) = -1(2x + 3) = -2x - 3$

(d) $-4x(x - 2y) = -4x^2 + 8xy \quad ■$

Practice Problem 7 Remove grouping symbols by using the distributive property.
(a) $(7x^2 - 8)$ **(b)** $+(5x^2 + 6)$
(c) $-(3x + 2y - 6)$ **(d)** $-5x^2(x + 2xy)$ ■

Example 8 Remove grouping symbols and collect like terms:
$5(x - 2y) - (y + 3x) + (5x - 8y)$.

$$5(x - 2y) - (y + 3x) + (5x - 8y)$$
$$= 5x - 10y - y - 3x + 5x - 8y$$
$$= 7x - 19y \quad ■$$

> Remember that you are really multiplying by -1, so don't forget to change this sign.

Practice Problem 8 Remove grouping symbols and collect like terms:
$-7(a + b) - 8a(2 - 3b) + 5a$. ■

To simplify an expression that contains grouping symbols within grouping symbols, work from the inside out.

Example 9 Simplify: $-2\{3 + 2[z - 4(x + y)]\}$.

$-2\{3 + 2[z - 4(x + y)]\}$

$\quad = -2\{3 + 2[z - 4x - 4y]\}$ Removing the parentheses by multiplying each term of $x + y$ by -4.

$\quad = -2\{3 + 2z - 8x - 8y\}$ Removing the brackets by multiplying each term of $z - 4x - 4y$ by 2.

$\quad = -6 - 4z + 16x + 16y$ Removing the braces by multiplying each term by -2. ■

Practice Problem 9   Simplify: $-2\{4x - 3[x - 2x(1 + x)]\}$. ■

Example 10   Simplify: $-2\{3x + [x - (3x - 1)]\}$.

$-2\{3x + [x - (3x - 1)]\}$

$\quad = -2\{3x + [x - 3x + 1]\}$ Removing the parentheses by multiplying each term of $3x - 1$ by -1.

$\quad = -2\{3x + [-2x + 1]\}$ Collecting like terms.

$\quad = -2\{3x - 2x + 1\}$ Removing the brackets.

$\quad = -2\{x + 1\}$ Collecting like terms.

$\quad = -2x - 2$ Removing the braces by multiplying by -2.

It would also be correct to leave our answer in its "factored" form, $-2\{x + 1\}$. By common practice, we would then use parentheses instead of braces and write $-2(x + 1)$. ■

Practice Problem 10   Simplify: $3\{-2a + [b - (3b - a)]\}$. ■

TEACHING TIP   After you have discussed example 10 or a similar example, ask students to do the following problem at their seats! Remove grouping symbols: $2y - 8\{6 + 2[y - 3(2 - y)]\}$ (The answer is $-62y + 48$.) Take time to go over how the answer is obtained. You may find that some students who did not collect like terms until the last step will want reassurance that it is mathematically valid to do the problem that way as well.

EXERCISES 1.5

1. What is the coefficient of y in $-5x^2y$?
$-5x^2$

2. What is the coefficient of x in $3xy^3z$?
$3y^3z$

In problems 3–8, list the numerical coefficient of each term.

3. $x^2 + 2x + 3y$
1, 2, 3

4. $x^2 + 2xy + 8y^2$
1, 2, 8

5. $5x^3 - 3x^2 + x$
5, -3, 1

6. $6x^2 - x - 6y$
6, -1, -6

7. $18x^3y^2 - 12x^2y^2 + y^3$
18, -12, 1

8. $-24a^3b^2 - 16a^2b^3 - ab$
-24, -16, -1

9. What are the terms in the expression $5x^3 - 6x^2 + 4x + 8$?
$5x^3$, $-6x^2$, $+4x$, $+8$

10. What are the terms in the expression $5x^3 + 3x^2 - 2y - 8$?
$5x^3$, $3x^2$, $-2y$, -8

Collect like terms.

11. $3ab + 8ab$
$11ab$

12. $7ab - 5ab$
$2ab$

13. $5x - 2x + 3x - 8y$
$6x - 8y$

14. $2a - 8a + 3b + 5a$
$-a + 3b$

15. $x^2 + 3x - 8x^2 + 7x$
$-7x^2 + 10x$

16. $2y^2 + 8y - 5y - 3y^2$
$-y^2 + 3y$

17. $\frac{1}{2}a + \frac{1}{3}b - \frac{1}{3}a - \frac{1}{3}b$

$a\left(\frac{1}{2} - \frac{1}{3}\right) + b\left(\frac{1}{3} - \frac{1}{3}\right) = \frac{a}{6}$

18. $\frac{1}{4}x + \frac{1}{3}y - \frac{1}{12}x + \frac{1}{6}y$

$x\left(\frac{1}{4} - \frac{1}{12}\right) + y\left(\frac{1}{3} + \frac{1}{6}\right) = \frac{x}{6} + \frac{y}{2}$

19. $\frac{1}{5}a^2 - 3b - \frac{1}{2}a^2 + 5b$

$a^2\left(\frac{1}{5} - \frac{1}{2}\right) + 2b = \frac{-3a^2}{10} + 2b$

20. $\frac{1}{2}x^2 + 6y - \frac{1}{7}x^2 - 8y$

$x^2\left(\frac{1}{2} - \frac{1}{7}\right) - 2y = \frac{5}{14}x^2 - 2y$

21. $1.2x^2 - 5.6x - 8.9x^2 + 2x$

$-7.7x^2 - 3.6x$

22. $4y^2 - 2.1y - 8.6y - 2.2y^2$

$1.8y^2 - 10.7y$

23. $-8a^2b - 2ab + 3ab^2 + 5a^2b - 12ab - 8ab^2$

$-3a^2b - 14ab - 5ab^2$

24. $12mn + 8m^2n - 6mn^2 + mn - 16m^2n - 4mn^2$

$13mn - 8m^2n - 10mn^2$

Multiply. Simplify your answer wherever possible.

25. $2x(x + y)$

$2x^2 + 2xy$

26. $5y(3x - 2)$

$15xy - 10y$

27. $-x(-x^3 + 3x^2 + 5x)$

$x^4 - 3x^3 - 5x^2$

28. $-2y(y^2 - 3y + 1)$

$-2y^3 + 6y^2 - 2y$

29. $-5(2a^2 - 3a - 8)$

$-10a^2 + 15a + 40$

30. $-6(4a + 2ab - 7b^2)$

$-24a - 12ab + 42b^2$

31. $2xy(x^2 - 3xy + 4y^2)$

$2x^3y - 6x^2y^2 + 8xy^3$

32. $4ab(a^2 - 6ab - 2b^2)$

$4a^3b - 24a^2b^2 - 8ab^3$

33. $\frac{1}{3}(2x + 6xy - 12)$

$\frac{2}{3}x + 2xy - 4$

34. $\frac{1}{4}(7x^2 - 4x + 8)$

$\frac{7}{4}x^2 - x + 2$

35. $\frac{x}{6}(x^2 + 5x - 9)$

$\frac{x^3}{6} + \frac{5x^2}{6} - \frac{3x}{2}$

36. $\frac{x}{2}(7x^2 - 4x + 1)$

$\frac{7}{2}x^3 - 2x^2 + \frac{1}{2}x$

37. $2ab(a^5 - 3a^4 + a^2 - 2a)$

$2a^6b - 6a^5b + 2a^3b - 4a^2b$

38. $5xy^2(y^3 - y^2 + 3x + 1)$

$5xy^5 - 5xy^4 + 15x^2y^2 + 5xy^2$

39. $5(x - 3y) - 2x(y - 1)$

$5x - 15y - 2xy + 2x = 7x - 2xy - 15y$

40. $8(x + 5y) - 2y(x + 1)$

$8x + 40y - 2xy - 2y = 8x - 2xy + 38y$

Remove grouping symbols and simplify.

41. $2y - 3(y + 4z)$

$2y - 3y - 12z = -y - 12z$

42. $5x + 2(-x - 6)$

$5x - 2x - 12 = 3x - 12$

43. $2(x + 3) - (x + 4) + (x + 6)$

$2x + 6 - x - 4 + x + 6 = 2x + 8$

44. $5(x - 2) + (3x - 8) - (x - 2)$

$5x - 10 + 3x - 8 - x + 2 = 7x - 16$

45. $2[x + (x - y)] - 3[x - (x - y)]$

$2[x + x - y] - 3[x - x + y] = 4x - 2y - 3y = 4x - 5y$

46. $3[2x + (y - 2x)] - 2[x - (3y - x)]$

$3[2x + y - 2x] - 2[x - 3y + x] = 9y - 4x$

47. $2\{3x - 2[x - 4(x + 1)]\}$

$2\{3x - 2[x - 4x - 4]\} = 2\{3x - 2x + 8x + 8\} = 18x + 16$

48. $-3\{3y + 2[y + 2(y - 4)]\}$

$-3\{3y + 2[y + 2y - 8]\} = -27y + 48$

49. $2(a^2 - 5) - 3[4 - a(a + 2)]$

$2a^2 - 10 - 3[4 - a^2 - 2a] = 5a^2 + 6a - 22$

50. $-5(b + a^2) - 6[a + a(-3 - a)]$

$-5b - 5a^2 - 6[a - 3a - a^2] = a^2 + 12a - 5b$

To Think About

Remove grouping symbols and simplify.

51. $3\left[\dfrac{1}{4}x^3 + \dfrac{1}{3}y^3\right] - \dfrac{1}{6}x^2 + \dfrac{1}{2}x - 2y + \dfrac{1}{9}y^3 - \dfrac{2}{5}x^3 + \dfrac{1}{4}x + 2\left[x^3 + \dfrac{1}{2}y^3\right]$

$\dfrac{3}{4}x^3 + y^3 - \dfrac{1}{6}x^2 + \dfrac{1}{2}x - 2y + \dfrac{1}{9}y^3 - \dfrac{2}{5}x^3 + \dfrac{1}{4}x + 2x^3 + y^3 = x^3\left(\dfrac{3}{4} - \dfrac{2}{5} + \dfrac{2}{1}\right) + y^3\left(\dfrac{1}{1} + \dfrac{1}{9} + \dfrac{1}{1}\right) + x\left(\dfrac{1}{2} + \dfrac{1}{4}\right) - \dfrac{1}{6}x^2 - 2y$

$= x^3\left(\dfrac{15 - 8 + 40}{20}\right) + y^3\left(\dfrac{9 + 1 + 9}{9}\right) + x\left(\dfrac{2 + 1}{4}\right) - \dfrac{1}{6}x^2 - 2y$

$= \dfrac{47}{20}x^3 + \dfrac{19}{9}y^3 + \dfrac{3}{4}x - \dfrac{1}{6}x^2 - 2y$

52. $2\{x - 4(y - 2) + 5x[x - 2y + 3(y - 1)]\} - 3\{x + 5[x^2 - 2y(x - 1)]\}$

$2\{x - 4y + 8 + 5x[x - 2y + 3y - 3]\} - 3\{x + 5[x^2 - 2xy + 2y]\}$

$= 2\{x - 4y + 8 + 5x^2 - 10xy + 15xy - 15x\} - 3\{x + 5x^2 - 10xy + 10y\}$

$= 2x - 8y + 16 + 10x^2 - 20xy + 30xy - 30x - 3x - 15x^2 + 30xy - 30y$

$= -5x^2 - 31x + 40xy - 38y + 16$

Cumulative Review Problems

Evaluate.

53. $2(-3)^2 + 4(-2)$

$2(9) - 8 = 10$

54. $4(2 - 3 + 6) + \sqrt{36}$

$4(5) + 6 = 26$

55. $\dfrac{5(-2) - 8}{3 + 4 - (-3)}$

$\dfrac{18}{10} = \dfrac{9}{5}$

56. $(-3)^5 + 2(-3)$

$-243 - 6 = -249$

Calculator Problems

Simplify.

57. $-1.982x^3 + 2.435y^3 - 20.718x^3 - 5.008y^3$

$-22.7x^3 - 2.573y^3$

58. $1.634(9.217x^2 - 3.005x - 5.915)$

$15.060578x^2 - 4.91017x - 9.66511$

For Extra Practice Exercises, turn to page 62.

Solutions to Odd-Numbered Practice Problems

1. (a) The two terms are $7x$ and $-2w^3$. **(b)** The three terms are 5, $6x$, and $2y$.

3. (a) $9x - 12x = 9x + (-12x) = [9 + (-12)]x = -3x$ **(b)** $4ab^2c + 15ab^2c = (4 + 15)ab^2c = 19ab^2c$

5. $-3x^2(2x - 5) = -3x^2[2x + (-5)]$
$= (-3x^2)(2x) + (-3x^2)(-5)$
$= -6x^3 + 15x^2$

7. (a) $(7x^2 - 8) = 1(7x^2 - 8) = 7x^2 - 8$ **(b)** $+(5x^2 + 6) = +1(5x^2 + 6) = 5x^2 + 6$

(c) $-(3x + 2y - 6) = -1(3x + 2y - 6) = -3x - 2y + 6$ **(d)** $-5x^2(x + 2xy) = -5x^3 - 10x^3y$

9. $-2\{4x - 3[x - 2x(1 + x)]\} = -2\{4x - 3[x - 2x - 2x^2]\}$ Removing parentheses.
$\qquad\qquad\qquad\qquad = -2\{4x - 3[-x - 2x^2]\}$ Collecting like terms.
$\qquad\qquad\qquad\qquad = -2\{4x + 3x + 6x^2\}$ Removing brackets.
$\qquad\qquad\qquad\qquad = -2\{7x + 6x^2\}$ Collecting like terms.
$\qquad\qquad\qquad\qquad = -14x - 12x^2$ Removing braces.

You will get the same answer if you wait until the last step to collect like terms.

$$-2\{4x - 3[x - 2x(1 + x)]\} = -2\{4x - 3[x - 2x - 2x^2]\}$$
$$= -2\{4x - 3x + 6x + 6x^2\}$$
$$= -8x + 6x - 12x - 12x^2$$
$$= -14x - 12x^2$$

Answers to Even-Numbered Practice Problems

2. (a) The coefficient of y in $5x^2$ and the coefficient of w is 3. **(b)** The coefficient of x is -7; the coefficient of w is 6; the coefficient of z^2 is 5. **4.** $9x^3 - 13x^2 + 8x$ **6.** $-10x^3 + 15x^2 + 5x$ **8.** $-18a - 7b + 24ab$ **10.** $-3a - 6b$

☐ After studying this section, you will be able to:

1 *Evaluate a variable expression when the value of the variable is given*

2 *Solve problems involving perimeters, areas, and volumes*

1.6 EVALUATING VARIABLE EXPRESSIONS AND FORMULAS

1 Evaluating an Expression

We want to learn how to evaluate—compute a numerical value for—variable expressions when we know the values of the variables.

> **Evaluating a Variable Expression**
>
> 1. Replace each variable (letter) by its numerical value. Put parentheses around the value (watch out for negative values).
> 2. Carry out each step, using the correct order of operations.

Example 1 Evaluate $5 + 2x$ when $x = -3$.

Replace x by -3 and put parentheses around it.

$$5 + 2(-3) = 5 + (-6) = 5 - 6 = -1 \quad \blacksquare$$

Practice Problem 1 Evaluate $-6 + 3x$ when $x = -5$. $\quad\blacksquare$

Example 2 Evaluate $x^2 - 5x - 6$ when $x = -4$.

$(-4)^2 - 5(-4) - 6$	Replacing x by -4 and putting parentheses around it.
$= 16 - 5(-4) - 6$	Squaring -4.
$= 16 - (-20) - 6$	Multiplying $5(-4)$.
$= 16 + 20 - 6$	Multiplying $-1(-20)$.
$= 30$	Combining $16 + 20 - 6$. $\quad\blacksquare$

Practice Problem 2 Evaluate $2x^2 + 3x - 8$ when $x = -3$. $\quad\blacksquare$

Example 3 Evaluate $(5 - x)^2 + 3xy$ when $x = -2$ and $y = 3$.

$$[5 - (-2)]^2 + 3(-2)(3)$$
$$= [5 + 2]^2 + 3(-2)(3) = [7]^2 + 3(-2)(3)$$
$$= 49 + 3(-2)(3) = 49 - 18 = 31 \quad \blacksquare$$

Practice Problem 3 Evaluate $(x - 3)^2 - 2xy$ when $x = -3$ and $y = 4$. $\quad\blacksquare$

Example 4 Evaluate when $x = -3$.

(a) $(-2x)^2$ \qquad\qquad\qquad\qquad **(b)** $-2x^2$

(a) $[-2(-3)]^2 = [6] = 36$	Multiplying $(-2)(-3)$ and *then* squaring the result.
(b) $-2(-3)^2 = -2(9)$	Squaring -3.
$\quad\quad = -18$	Multiplying by -2. $\quad\blacksquare$

Practice Problem 4 Evaluate when $x = -4$. **(a)** $(-3x)^2$ **(b)** $-3x^2$ $\quad\blacksquare$

TEACHING TIP After discussing examples 1 and 2 or similar problems, try the following as a class exercise: Write this problem on the board: Evaluate $3x^2 - 4x - 7$ when $x = -2$. Write out the first step by substitution of the value -2 for x in each place using parentheses. Ask them to finish the problem. (The answer is 13.)

Do you see the difference between (a) and (b)? The form in (a) means square everything in parentheses. But the form in (b) means square only x.

Evaluating Formulas

A *formula* is a rule for finding the value of a variable when the values of other variables in the expression are known. The word "formula" is usually applied to some physical situation, much like a recipe is. For example, we can determine the Fahrenheit temperature F for any Celsius temperature C from the formula

$$F = \frac{9}{5}C + 32$$

Example 5 Find the Fahrenheit temperature when the Celsius temperature is $-30°C$.

$F = \frac{9}{5}(-30) + 32$ Substituting the known value -30 for the variable C.

$= \frac{9}{\overset{}{\underset{1}{5}}}(\overset{-6}{\cancel{-30}}) + 32 = 9(-6) + 32$

$= -54 + 32 = -22$

Thus, when the temperature is $-30°C$, the equivalent Fahrenheit temperature is $-22°$. ∎

Practice Problem 5 The period T (the time in seconds for the pendulum to swing back and forth one time) of a pendulum is $T = 2\pi\sqrt{\dfrac{L}{g}}$ where L is the length of the pendulum and g is the acceleration due to gravity. Find the period when $L = 288$ and $g = 32$. Approximate the value cf π by 3.14. ▪

2   Area and Perimeter Formulas

In the following formulas, $A = $ area, and $P = $ perimeter, and $C = $ circumference. The "squares" in the figures like ⌐ mean that the angle formed by the two lines is $90°$.

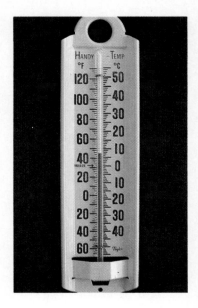

Rectangle $A = lw$
    $P = 2l + 2w$

Triangle $A = \dfrac{1}{2}ab$
    $P = b + c + d$

Parallelogram $A = ab$
    $P = 2b + 2c$

Rhombus $A = ab$
    $P = 4b$

Trapezoid $A = \dfrac{1}{2}a(b + c)$
    $P = b + c + d + e$

Circle $A = \pi r^2$
    $C = 2\pi r$ where r is radius
    $C = \pi d$ where d is diameter

In circle formulas we need to use π, which is an irrational number. Its value can be approximated to as many decimal places as we like, but we will use 3.14 because it is accurate enough for most calculations.

Volume and Surface Area Formulas

In the following formulas, V = volume and S = surface area.

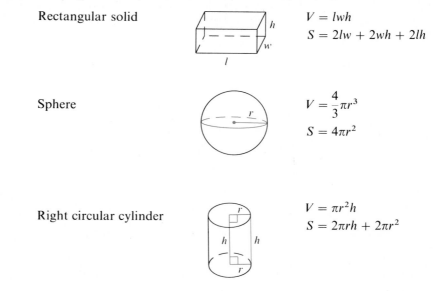

Rectangular solid

$V = lwh$

$S = 2lw + 2wh + 2lh$

Sphere

$V = \frac{4}{3}\pi r^3$

$S = 4\pi r^2$

Right circular cylinder

$V = \pi r^2 h$

$S = 2\pi rh + 2\pi r^2$

TEACHING TIP   After discussing example 6 or a similar example, ask them to find the area of a circle with radius 4 meters using 3.14 as an approximation for π in the formula $A = \pi r^2$. Then show them the steps to obtain the correct answer of $50.24m^2$. Some students may make the error of multiplying 3.14 times 4. Stress the importance of following the order of operations convention and raising to a power first BEFORE multiplying by 3.14.

Example 6   Find the area of a trapezoid that has a height of 6 meters and bases of 7 and 11 meters.

The formula is

$$A = \frac{1}{2}a(b + c)$$

We are told that $a = 6$, $b = 7$, and $c = 11$, so we put those values into the formula.

$$A = \frac{1}{2}(6)[7 + 11] = \frac{1}{2}(6)(18) = 54$$

The area is 54 *square meters* because we are multiplying the units also.   ∎

Practice Problem 6   Find the area of a triangle with an altitude of 12 meters and a base of 14 meters.   ∎

Example 7   Find the volume of a sphere with a radius of 3 centimeters.

The formula is

$$V = \frac{4}{3}\pi r^3$$

Therefore, we have

$$V = \frac{4}{3}(3.14)(3)^3 \approx \frac{4}{3}(3.14)(27)$$

$$\approx \frac{4}{\overset{}{3}}(3.14)(\overset{9}{\cancel{27}}) \approx 113.04$$

$$\underset{1}{}$$

The volume is approximately 113.04 cubic centimeters   ∎

Practice Problem 7   Find the volume of a right circular cylinder of height 10 meters and radius 6 meters.   ∎

Example 8 An amount of money invested or borrowed (not including interest) is called the *principal*. Find the amount A to be repaid on a principal p of $1000.00 borrowed at an interest rate r of 8% for a time t of two years. The formula is $A = p(1 + rt)$.

$$A = 1000[1 + (0.08)(2)] \qquad \text{Change 8\% to 0.08.}$$
$$= 1000[1 + 0.16]$$
$$= 1000(1.16) = 1160$$

Therefore, the amount to be repaid (principal plus interest) is $1160. ∎

Practice Problem 8 Find the amount to be repaid on a loan of $600.00 at an interest rate of 9% for a time of three years. ∎

TEACHING TIP After discussing example 8 or a similar example, ask students to find S in the formula

$$S = \frac{n}{2}[2a + (n - 1)d]$$

if $n = 21$, $a = 3$, and $d = -2$. (The answer is -357.) Work out each step of the problem and ask students if they have any questions.

DEVELOPING YOUR STUDY SKILLS

READING THE TEXTBOOK

Your homework time each day should begin with the careful reading of the section(s) assigned in your textbook. Usually, much time and effort has gone into the selection of a particular text, and your instructor has decided that this is the book that will help you to become successful in this mathematics class. Textbooks are expensive, but they can be a wise investment if you take advantage of them by reading them.

Reading a mathematics textbook is unlike reading many other types of books that you may find in your literature, history, psychology, or sociology courses. Mathematics texts are technical books that provide you with exercises to practice on. Reading a mathematics text requires slow and careful reading of each word, which takes time and effort.

Begin reading your textbook with a paper and pencil in hand. As you come across a new definition, or concept, underline it in the text and/or write it down in your notebook. Whenever you encounter an unfamiliar term, look it up and make a note of it. When you come to an example, work through it step-by-step. Be sure to read each word and to follow directions carefully.

Notice the helpful hints the author provides. They guide you to correct solutions and prevent you from making errors. Take advantage of these pieces of expert advice.

Be sure that you understand what you are reading. Make a note of any of those things that you do not understand and ask your instructor about them. Do not hurry through the material. Learning mathematics takes time.

EXERCISES 1.6

Evaluate each expression for the values given.

1. $3x + 4$; $x = -3$
$3(-3) + 4 = -5$

2. $2x - 6$; $x = 4$
$2(4) - 6 = 2$

3. $18 - 5x$; $x = 5$
$18 - 5(5) = -7$

4. $8x + 5$; $x = -6$
$8(-6) + 5 = -43$

5. $x^2 + 5x - 6$; $x = -3$
$(-3)^2 + 5(-3) - 6 = -12$

6. $x^2 + 7x + 12$; $x = -2$
$(-2)^2 + 7(-2) + 12 = 2$

7. $5x^2 - 3x - 4$; $x = 2$
$5(2)^2 - 3(2) - 4 = 10$

8. $-3x^2 + 5x + 2$; $x = -1$
$-3(-1)^2 + 5(-1) + 2 = -6$

9. $-2x^2 + 5x - 3$; $x = -4$
$-2(-4)^2 + 5(-4) - 3 = -55$

10. $6x^2 - 3x + 5$; $x = 5$
$6(5)^2 - 3(5) + 5 = 140$

11. $ax + by - 2a$; $a = 3$, $x = 2$, $b = -1$, $y = -4$
$3(2) + (-1)(-4) - 2(3) = 4$

12. $3ay - 2by + x$; $a = 4$, $x = 1$, $y = -1$, $b = -6$
$3(4)(-1) - 2(-6)(-1) + 1 = -23$

13. $ax^2 + bxy + y^2$; $a = 4$, $x = -1$, $b = 3$, $y = -2$
$(4)(-1)^2 + 3(-1)(-2) + (-2)^2 = 14$

14. $x^3 + ax^2 + aby$; $a = 1$, $b = -3$, $x = -2$, $y = 5$
$(-2)^3 + (1)(-2)^2 + 1(-3)(5) = -19$

15. $\sqrt{b^2 - 4ac}$; $b = 2$, $a = 1$, $c = -15$
$\sqrt{(2)^2 - 4(1)(-15)} = \sqrt{64} = 8$

16. $\sqrt{b^2 - 4ac}$; $b = -5$, $a = 2$, $c = -3$
$\sqrt{(-5)^2 - 4(2)(-3)} = \sqrt{49} = 7$

Solve each problem.

17. Find $S = \dfrac{1}{2}gt^2$ if $g = 32$ and $t = 5$.

$S = \dfrac{1}{2}(32)(5)^2 = 400$

18. Find $S = \dfrac{1}{2}gt^2$ if $g = 32$ and $t = 3$.

$S = \dfrac{1}{2}(32)(3)^2 = 144$

19. Find $z = \dfrac{Rr}{R + r}$ if $R = 36$ and $r = 4$.

$z = \dfrac{(36)(4)}{36 + 4} = \dfrac{18}{5}$

20. Find $z = \dfrac{Rr}{R + r}$ if $R = 35$ and $r = 15$.

$z = \dfrac{(35)(15)}{35 + 15} = \dfrac{21}{2}$

For problems 21 and 22, use the formula $C = \dfrac{5F - 160}{9}$.

21. Find the Celsius temperature if the Fahrenheit temperature is $122°F$.
$C = \dfrac{5(122) - 160}{9} = 50°C$

22. Find the Celsius temperature if the Fahrenheit temperature is $-40°F$.
$C = \dfrac{5(-40) - 160}{9} = -40°C$

In problems 23–34, use the geometry formulas on pages 39 and 40 to find the quantities specified.

23. Find the area of a circle with a radius of 2 inches.
$A = \pi r^2 = 3.14(2)^2 = 12.56$ sq. in.

24. Find the circumference of a circle with a diameter of 7 inches.
$C = \pi d = 3.14(7) = 21.98$ in.

25. Find the area of a triangle with a base of 12 meters and an altitude of 14 meters.
$A = \dfrac{1}{2}bh = \dfrac{1}{2}(12)(14) = 84$ sq. meters

26. Find the area of a triangle with a base of 16 centimeters and a height of 7 centimeters.
$A = \dfrac{1}{2}bh = \dfrac{1}{2}(16)(7) = 56$ sq. centimeters

27. Find the area of a parallelogram with an altitude of 5 yards and a base of 8 yards.
$A = bh = 8(5) = 40$ sq. yards

28. Find the area of a rhombus with a height of 16 centimeters and a base of 5 centimeters.
$A = bh = 5(16) = 80$ sq. centimeters

29. Find the area of a rectangle 0.5 meter long and 0.07 meter wide.
$A = lw = (0.5)(0.07) = 0.035$ sq. meters

30. Find the surface area of a rectangular solid 12.4 centimeters long, 6.7 centimeters, wide, and 1.2 centimeters high.
$S = 2lw + 4wh = 2(12.4)(6.7) + 4(6.7)(1.2)$
$= 166.16 + 32.16$
$= 198.32$ sq. centimeters

31. The base of a rhombus is 0.07 meter. Find its perimeter.
$P = 4s = 4(0.07) = 0.28$ meters

32. A trapezoid has sides 5.2, 6.1, 3.5, and 2.2 meters long. Find its perimeter.
$P = s_1 + s_2 + s_3 + s_4 = 5.2 + 6.1 + 3.5 + 2.2$
$= 17$ meters

33. A right circular cylinder has a height of 7 feet and a radius of 3 feet.
  (a) Find its volume. $V = \pi r^2 h = (3.14)(3^2)(7) = 197.82$ cu. ft.
  (b) Find its surface area.
    $S = 2\pi rh = 2(3.14)(3)(7) = 131.88$ sq. ft.

34. A sphere has a radius of 6 meters.
  (a) Find its volume.
  (b) Find its surface area.

  (a) $V = \dfrac{4}{3}\pi r^3 = \dfrac{4}{3}(3.14)(6)^3 = 904.32$ cu. meters

  (b) $S = 4\pi r^2 = 4(3.14)(6)^2 = 452.16$ sq. meters

In problems 35 and 36, use the formula $A = p(1 + rt)$.

35. Find A if $p = \$2500$, $r = 12\%$, and $t = 1.5$.
  $A = \$2500[1 + (0.12)(1.5)] = \$2950$

36. Find A if $p = \$3200$, $r = 0.07$, and $t = 2$.
  $A = \$3200[1 + (0.07)(2)] = 3200[1.14] = \$3648$

In problems 37 and 38, you need the formula $S = \dfrac{n}{2}[2a + (n - 1)d]$.

37. Find S if $n = 12$, $a = -7$, and $d = 3$.
  $S = \dfrac{12}{2}[2(-7) + (12 - 1)3] = 6(19) = 114$

38. Find S if $n = 16$, $a = 4$, and $d = -3$.
  $S = \dfrac{16}{2}[2(4) + (16 - 1)(-3)] = 8(-37) = -296$

? To Think About

39. The formula for the total resistance R of an electrical circuit containing three resistors in parallel is

$$\frac{1}{R} = \frac{1}{R_1} + \frac{1}{R_2} + \frac{1}{R_3}$$

Find R when $R_1 = \dfrac{3}{2}$ ohms, $R_2 = \dfrac{5}{3}$ ohms, and $R_3 = \dfrac{1}{4}$ ohm. See the figure.

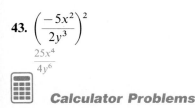

$\dfrac{1}{R} = \dfrac{1}{\frac{3}{2}} + \dfrac{1}{\frac{5}{3}} + \dfrac{1}{\frac{1}{4}}$

$\dfrac{1}{R} = \dfrac{2}{3} + \dfrac{3}{5} + \dfrac{4}{1} = \dfrac{79}{15}$ $R = \dfrac{15}{79}$ ohm

40. Find the cost of spraying a rust-resisting coating on the outside surface area of a silo shaped like a right circular cylinder. The paint costs \$4.50 per square meter, and the silo is 5.2 meters high has a radius of 2.1 meters.
  $S = 2\pi rh = 2(3.14)(2.1)(5.2) = 68.5776$ m^2
  Cost $= \$4.50(68.5776) = 308.5992$
  Cost $= \$308.60$

Cumulative Review Problems

Simplify.

41. $3x - 7x - 8x$
  $-12x$

42. $5(a - b) - 3(2a + b)$
  $5a - 5b - 6a - 3b = -a - 8b$

43. $\left(\dfrac{-5x^2}{2y^3}\right)^2$

  $\dfrac{25x^4}{4y^6}$

44. $2\{5 - 2[x - 3(2x + 1)]\}$
  $2\{5 - 2[x - 6x - 3]\}$
  $= 2\{5 - 2x + 12x + 6\}$
  $= 10 - 4x + 24x + 12$
  $= 20x + 22$

Calculator Problems

45. Evaluate $2x^2 - 5x + 6$ when $x = -3.52176$.
  48.414387

46. Find the area of a circle when the radius is 9.05263 centimeters. (Use $\pi \approx 3.1415927$ or the value of π in your calculator.)
  257.4538633

For Extra Practice Exercises, turn to page 62.

1. Evaluate $-6 + 3x$ when $x = -5$.

$$-6 + 3(-5) = -6 + (-15)$$
$$= -21$$

3. Evaluate $(x - 3)^2 - 2xy$ when $x - 3$ and $y = 4$.

$$(-3 - 3)^2 - 2(-3)(4) = (-6)^2 - 2(-3)(4)$$
$$= 36 + 24 = 60$$

5. Evaluate $T = 2\pi \sqrt{\dfrac{L}{g}}$ when $L = 288$ and $g = 32$.

$$T \approx 3.14 \sqrt{\dfrac{288}{32}}$$
$$= 3.14\sqrt{9} \qquad \text{Do the operation under the radical.}$$
$$= (3.14)(3) \qquad \text{Find the principal square root of 9.}$$
$$= 9.42$$

This answer is approximate because $\pi \approx 3.14$ is an approximation.

7. Evaluate $V = \pi r^2 h$ where $\pi = \approx 3.14$, $r = 6$ meters, and $h = 10$ meters.

$$V \approx (3.14)(6)^2(10) = (3.14)(36)(10)$$
$$= (113.04)(10) = 1130.4 \text{ cubic meters}$$

This is an approximate value.

2. 1 **4. (a)** 144 **(b)** -48 **6.** 84 square meters **8.** $762.00

1.7 FIRST-DEGREE EQUATIONS WITH ONE UNKNOWN

1 An **equation** is a mathematical statement that two quantities are equal. A **first-degree equation with one unknown** (also called a **linear** equation) is an equation in which only one kind of variable appears, and that variable has an exponent of 1. (But the variable itself may appear more than once.) The equation $-6x + 7x + 8 = 2x - 4$ is a first-degree equation with one unknown, because there is one variable (x) and that variable has an exponent of 1. Other examples are $5(6y + 1) = 2y$ and $5z + 3 = 10z$.

To Think About

Which of the following equations are *not* linear?

$$\frac{2}{x} = x + 1 \qquad 3\pi + 2 = y \qquad x^2 - 4 = 0 \qquad 2x + y = 24$$

To solve a first-degree equation with one unknown, we need to find the value of the variable that makes the equation a true mathematical statement. This value is the **solution** or **root** of the equation. ■

Example 1

(a) Is $x = 4$ a root of the equation $5x - 6 = 14$?

(b) Is $a = \dfrac{1}{3}$ a solution of the equation $2a + 5 = a + 6$?

(a) We replace x by the value 4 in the equation $5x - 6 = 14$.

$$5(4) - 6 \overset{?}{=} 14$$
$$20 - 6 \overset{?}{=} 14$$
$$14 = 14$$

Since we obtained a true statement, $x = 4$ is a root of $5x - 6 = 14$.

(b) We replace a by $\frac{1}{3}$ in the equation $2a + 5 = a + 6$.

$$2\left(\frac{1}{3}\right) + 5 \stackrel{?}{=} \frac{1}{3} + 6$$

$$\frac{2}{3} + 5 \stackrel{?}{=} \frac{1}{3} + 6$$

$$\frac{17}{3} \neq \frac{19}{3}$$

This last statement is not true. Thus, $a = \frac{1}{3}$ is not a solution of $2a + 5 = a + 6$.

Practice Problem 1

(a) Is $x = -5$ the root of the equation $2x + 3 = 3x + 8$?

(b) Is $a = 4$ a solution of the equation $3a - 2 = 5a + 6$? ■

Equations that have the same solution are said to be **equivalent**. The equations

$$7x - 2 = 12 \qquad 7x = 14 \qquad x = 2$$

are equivalent because the solution of each equation is $x = 2$.

To solve an equation, we perform algebraic operations on it to obtain a simpler, equivalent equation of the form variable = constant or constant = variable.

Properties of Equivalent Equations

1. If $a = b$, then $a + c = b + c$ and $a - c = b - c$. If the same number is added to or subtracted from both sides of an equation, the result is an equivalent equation.

2. If $a = b$ and $c \neq 0$, then $ac = bc$ and $\frac{a}{c} = \frac{b}{c}$. If both sides of an equation are multiplied or divided by the same nonzero number, the result is an equivalent equation.

To solve a first-degree equation, we isolate the variable on one side of the equation and the constants on another, using the properties of equivalent equations.

Example 2 Solve for x: $x - 8.2 = 5.0$.

$$x - 8.2 + 8.2 = 5.0 + 8.2 \qquad \text{Adding 8.2 to each side.}$$
$$= 13.2 \qquad \text{Combining.}$$

Thus, the solution is $x = 13.2$.

We must also check to see if our answer really is a valid root of the equation. Checking is especially important when we solve higher-degree equations later. We check the validity of our answer in the same way that we determined the validity of roots on page 44—we substitute the answer into the original equation.

$$\textit{Check:} \quad x - 8.2 = 5.0$$

$$13.2 - 8.2 \stackrel{?}{=} 5.0$$

$$5.0 = 5.0 \checkmark \qquad \begin{array}{l}\text{Statement is valid, so our answer}\\ x = 13.2 \text{ is root of the equation.} \quad ■\end{array}$$

Practice Problem 2 Solve for y: $y + 5.2 = -2.8$. ■

Example 3   Solve for y: $\frac{1}{3}y = -6$.

$$3\left(\frac{1}{3}\right)y = 3(-6) \qquad \text{Multiplying each side by 3 to eliminate the fraction.}$$

$$y = -18 \qquad \text{Multiplying.}$$

The solution is $y = -18$. Check this.   ■

Practice Problem 3   Solve for w: $\frac{1}{5}w = -6$.   ■

Example 4   Solve: $5x + 2 = 17$.

$$5x + 2 - 2 = 17 - 2 \qquad \text{Subtracting 2 from (or add } -2 \text{ to) both sides.}$$

$$5x = 15$$

$$\frac{5x}{5} = \frac{15}{5} \qquad \text{Dividing each side by 5 to isolate the variable } x.$$

$$x = 3$$

You should verify this.   ■

Practice Problem 4   Solve for x: $-7x - 2 = 26$. Check your answer.   ■

Example 5   Solve: $6x - 2 - 4x = 8x + 3$.

$$2x - 2 = 8x + 3 \qquad \text{Collecting like terms.}$$

$$2x - 8x - 2 = 8x - 8x + 3 \qquad \text{Subtracting } 8x \text{ from (or add } -8x \text{ to) each side.}$$

$$-6x - 2 = 3$$

$$-6x - 2 + 2 = 3 + 2 \qquad \text{Adding 2 to each side.}$$

$$-6x = 5$$

$$\frac{-6x}{-6} = \frac{5}{-6} \qquad \text{Dividing each side by } -6.$$

$$x = -\frac{5}{6}$$

$$\textit{Check: } \quad 6\left(-\frac{5}{6}\right) - 2 - 4\left(-\frac{5}{6}\right) \overset{?}{=} 8\left(-\frac{5}{6}\right) + 3 \qquad \text{Replacing } x \text{ by } -\frac{5}{6} \text{ in the } \textit{original} \text{ equation.}$$

$$-5 - 2 + \frac{10}{3} \overset{?}{=} \frac{-20}{3} + 3$$

$$\frac{-21}{3} + \frac{10}{3} \overset{?}{=} \frac{-20}{3} + \frac{9}{3}$$

$$\frac{-11}{3} = -\frac{11}{3} \checkmark$$

Thus, $x = -\frac{5}{6}$ is the solution.   ■

Practice Problem 5   Solve for w: $8w - 3 = 2w - 7w + 4$.   ■

   When the equation contains grouping symbols and fractions, use the following procedure.

TEACHING TIP   Some students, when trying to solve problems like example 5, neglect to collect like terms on the left–hand side BEFORE adding a quantity to each side of the equation. Stress the importance of collecting like terms on each side FIRST, in order to make the equation as short and simple as possible before adding something to each side.

Example 6 Solve for x: $3(3x + 2) - 4x = -2(x - 3)$.

$9x + 6 - 4x = -2x + 6$	Removing parentheses.
$5x + 6 = -2x + 6$	Collecting like terms.
$5x + 2x + 6 = -2x + 2x + 6$	Adding $2x$ to each side.
$7x + 6 = 6$	
$7x + 6 - 6 = 6 - 6$	Subtracting 6 from each side.
$7x = 0$	
$\dfrac{7x}{7} = \dfrac{0}{7}$	Dividing each side by 7.
$x = 0$	

Check: $3[3(0) + 2] - 4(0) \overset{?}{=} -2(0 - 3)$

$$3[0 + 2] - 0 \overset{?}{=} -2(-3)$$

$$6 - 0 \overset{?}{=} 6$$

$$6 = 6 \checkmark$$

Thus, $x = 0$ is the solution. ■

Practice Problem 6 Solve for a: $a - 4(2a - 7) = 3(a + 6)$. ■

Example 7 Solve: $\dfrac{x}{5} + \dfrac{1}{2} = \dfrac{4}{5} + \dfrac{x}{2}$.

The LCD is 10.

$10\left(\dfrac{x}{5}\right) + 10\left(\dfrac{1}{2}\right) = 10\left(\dfrac{4}{5}\right) + 10\left(\dfrac{x}{2}\right)$	Multiplying each term by the LCD.
$2x + 5 = 8 + 5x$	Simplify.
$2x - 2x + 5 = 8 + 5x - 2x$	Subtracting $2x$ from each side.
$5 = 8 + 3x$	
$5 - 8 = 8 - 8 + 3x$	Subtracting 8 from each side.
$-3 = 3x$	
$-\dfrac{3}{3} = \dfrac{3x}{3}$	Dividing each side by 3.
$-1 = x$	

Check: See if you can verify this solution. ■

TEACHING TIP Point out to students that steps 1 and 2 can be interchanged in the procedure to solve equations. Some students may have been taught in high school to remove the fractions first.

TEACHING TIP Ask students to do the following problem at their seats: Solve for y in the equation:

$$\frac{6y}{5} - \frac{4}{5} = \frac{3}{5}(5y + 2) - y$$

Work out the first step for the student by removing the parentheses to obtain:

$$\frac{6y}{5} - \frac{4}{5} = 3y + \frac{6}{5} - y$$

Ask them to finish the problem.

$\left(\text{The answer is: } y = -\dfrac{5}{2}.\right)$

After the class has done the problem, show them the steps to obtain the answer.

Practice Problem 7 Solve and check: $\dfrac{y}{3} + \dfrac{1}{2} = 5 + \dfrac{y-9}{4}$ ∎

EXERCISES 1.7

Solve problems 1–36. Check your solutions.

1. $-16 + x = 43$
$x = 59$ *Check:* $-16 + 59 = 43\checkmark$

2. $17 + x = -24$
$x = -41$
Check: $17 + (-41) = -24\checkmark$

3. $-5x = 35$
$x = -7$ *Check:* $-5(-7) = 35\checkmark$

4. $-12x = -48$
$x = 4$ *Check:* $-12(4) = -48\checkmark$

5. $7x - 8 = 20$
$7x = 28$ *Check:* $7(4) - 8 = 20\checkmark$
$x = 4$

6. $5x + 3 = 43$
$5x = 40$ *Check:* $5(8) + 3 = 43\checkmark$
$x = 8$

7. $5y + 8 = 4y - 2$
$y = -10$
Check: $5(-10) + 8 = 4(-10) - 2$
$-42 = -42\checkmark$

8. $8y - 3 = 2y + 3$
$6y = 6$ *Check:* $8(1) - 3 = 2(1) + 3$
$y = 1$ $5 = 5\checkmark$

9. $\dfrac{y}{4} + \dfrac{1}{2} = \dfrac{2}{3}$ $12\left(\dfrac{y}{4} + \dfrac{1}{2} = \dfrac{2}{3}\right)$ *Check:* $\dfrac{1}{4}\left(\dfrac{2}{3}\right) + \dfrac{1}{2} = \dfrac{2}{3}$
$\qquad 3y + 6 = 8$ $\dfrac{1}{6} + \dfrac{3}{6} = \dfrac{2}{3}$
$\qquad 3y = 2$ $\dfrac{2}{3} = \dfrac{2}{3}\checkmark$
$\qquad y = \dfrac{2}{3}$

10. $\dfrac{y}{3} + 2 = \dfrac{4}{5}$ $15\left(\dfrac{y}{3} + 2 = \dfrac{4}{5}\right)$ *Check:* $\dfrac{1}{3}\left(-\dfrac{18}{5}\right) + 2 = \dfrac{4}{5}$
$\qquad 5y + 30 = 12$ $-\dfrac{6}{5} + \dfrac{10}{5} = \dfrac{4}{5}$
$\qquad 5y = -18$ $\dfrac{4}{5} = \dfrac{4}{5}\checkmark$
$\qquad y = -\dfrac{18}{5}$

11. $0.7x + 3 = 0.5x + 2$
$0.2x = -1$ *Check:* $0.7(-5) + 3 = 0.5(-5) + 2$
$x = -5$ $-3.5 + 3 = -2.5 + 2$
$\qquad -0.5 = -0.5\checkmark$

12. $1.5x + 4 = 1.2x - 2$
$0.3x = -6$ *Check:* $1.5(-20) + 4 = 1.2(-20) - 2$
$x = -20$ $-30 + 4 = -24 - 2$
$\qquad -26 = -26\checkmark$

13. $3a - 5 - 2a = 2a - 3$
$a - 5 = 2a - 3$ *Check:* $3(-2) - 5 - 2(-2) = 2(-2) - 3$
$-2 = a$ $-6 - 5 + 4 = -4 - 3$
$\qquad -7 = -7\checkmark$

14. $5a - 2 + 4a = 2a + 12$
$9a - 2 = 2a + 12$ *Check:* $5(2) - 2 + 4(2) = 2(2) + 12$
$7a = 14$ $10 - 2 + 8 = 4 + 12$
$a = 2$ $16 = 16\checkmark$

15. $2(y + 3) = 3(y - 7)$
$2y + 6 = 3y - 21$ *Check:* $2(27) + 6 = 3(27) - 21$
$27 = y$ $54 + 6 = 81 - 21$
$\qquad 60 = 60\checkmark$

16. $9(y + 3) = 4(2y - 1)$
$9y + 27 = 8y - 4$ *Check:* $9(-31 + 3) = 4[2(-31) - 1]$
$y = -31$ $9(-28) = 4(-63)$
$\qquad -252 = -252\checkmark$

17. $(4x - 3) - (2x + 7) = -1(x - 6)$
$4x - 3 - 2x - 7 = -x + 6$
$2x - 10 = -x + 6$ *Check:* $\left(\dfrac{64}{3} - 3\right) - \left(\dfrac{32}{3} + 7\right) = -1\left(\dfrac{16}{3} - 6\right)$
$3x = 16$
$x = \dfrac{16}{3}$ $-\dfrac{2}{3} = -\dfrac{2}{3}\checkmark$

18. $8 - (4x - 5) = x - 7$
$8 - 4x + 5 = x - 7$ *Check:* $8 - [4(4) - 5] = 4 - 7$
$-4x + 13 = x - 7$ $8 - [11] = -3$
$20 = 5x$ $-3 = -3\checkmark$
$4 = x$

19. $\dfrac{3a}{4} - 3 = \dfrac{a}{2} + 2$
$4\left[\dfrac{3a}{4} - 3 = \dfrac{a}{2} + 2\right]$ *Check:* $\dfrac{3}{4}(20) - 3 = \dfrac{1}{2}(20) + 2$
$3a - 12 = 2a + 8$ $15 - 3 = 10 + 2$
$a = 20$ $12 = 12\checkmark$

20. $a + \dfrac{1}{2} = 1 - \dfrac{a}{3}$
$6\left[a + \dfrac{1}{2} = 1 - \dfrac{a}{3}\right]$ *Check:* $\dfrac{3}{8} + \dfrac{1}{2} = 1 - \dfrac{1}{3}\left(\dfrac{3}{8}\right)$
$6a + 3 = 6 - 2a$ $\dfrac{3}{8} + \dfrac{4}{8} = \dfrac{8}{8} - \dfrac{1}{8}$
$8a = 3$
$a = \dfrac{3}{8}$ $\dfrac{7}{8} = \dfrac{7}{8}\checkmark$

21. $5(y + 1) + 2 = y - 3(2y + 1)$
$5y + 5 + 2 = y - 6y - 3$
$5y + 7 = -5y - 3$
$10y = -10$
$y = -1$
Check: $5(-1 + 1) + 2 = -1 - 3[2(-1) + 1]$
$\qquad 5(0) + 2 = -1 - 3(-1)$
$\qquad 2 = -1 + 3$
$\qquad 2 = 2\checkmark$

22. $5 - 2(3 - y) = 2(2y + 5) + 1$
$5 - 6 + 2y = 4y + 10 + 1$
$-1 + 2y = 4y + 11$
$-12 = 2y$
$-6 = y$
Check: $5 - 2[3 - (-6)] = 2[2(-6) + 5] + 1$
$\qquad 5 - 2[9] = 2[-7] + 1$
$\qquad 5 - 18 = 14 + 1$
$\qquad -13 = -13\checkmark$

23. $0.3x + 0.4 = 0.5x - 0.8$

$1.2 = 0.2x$ Check: $0.3(6) + 0.4 = 0.5(6) - 0.8$
$6 = x$ $1.8 + 0.4 = 3.0 - 0.8$
                        $2.2 = 2.2$ ✓

24. $0.7x - 0.2 = 0.5x + 0.8$

$0.2x = 1.0$ Check: $0.7(5) - 0.2 = 0.5(5) + 0.8$
$x = 5$ $3.5 - 0.2 = 2.5 + 0.8$
                       $3.3 = 3.3$ ✓

25. $\dfrac{2}{3}(x + 6) = 1 + \dfrac{4x - 7}{3}$

$2x + 12 = 3 + 4x - 7$
$16 = 2x$
$8 = x$

Check:
$\dfrac{2}{3}(8 + 6) = 1 + \dfrac{4(8) - 7}{3}$

$\dfrac{2}{3}(14) = \dfrac{3}{3} + \dfrac{25}{3}$

$\dfrac{28}{3} = \dfrac{28}{3}$ ✓

26. $2y - 5 - \dfrac{4}{3}(2y + 6) = -\dfrac{5}{3}$

$6y - 15 - 8y - 24 = -5$ Check: $2(-17) - 5 - \dfrac{4}{3}(-34 + 6) = -\dfrac{5}{3}$
$-2y = 34$
$y = -17$

$-\dfrac{102}{3} - \dfrac{15}{3} + \dfrac{112}{3} = -\dfrac{5}{3}$

$-\dfrac{5}{3} = -\dfrac{5}{3}$ ✓

27. $\dfrac{7x}{3} + 5 = 3x + 5$

$3\left[\dfrac{7x}{3} + 5 = 3x + 5\right]$ Check: $\dfrac{7}{3}(0) + 5 = 3(0) + 5$
$7x + 15 = 9x + 15$ $5 = 5$ ✓
$0 = x$

28. $\dfrac{1}{5} - \dfrac{x}{3} = \dfrac{x - 2}{5}$

$15\left[\dfrac{1}{5} - \dfrac{x}{3} = \dfrac{x - 2}{5}\right]$ Check: $\dfrac{1}{5} - \dfrac{1}{3}\left(\dfrac{9}{8}\right) = \dfrac{1}{5}\left(\dfrac{9}{8} - 2\right)$
$3 - 5x = 3x - 6$
$9 = 8x$
$\dfrac{9}{8} = x$

$\dfrac{1}{5} - \dfrac{3}{8} = \dfrac{9}{40} - \dfrac{2}{5}$

$\dfrac{8}{40} - \dfrac{15}{40} = \dfrac{9}{40} - \dfrac{16}{40}$

$-\dfrac{7}{40} = -\dfrac{7}{40}$ ✓

29. $\dfrac{4y - 1}{10} = \dfrac{5y + 2}{4} - 4$

$20\left[\dfrac{4y - 1}{10} = \dfrac{5y + 2}{4} - 4\right]$ Check: $\dfrac{4(4) - 1}{10} = \dfrac{5(4) + 2}{4} - 4$
$2(4y - 1) = 5(5y + 2) - 80$
$8y - 2 = 25y + 10 - 80$ $\dfrac{15}{10} = \dfrac{22}{4} - \dfrac{16}{4}$
$68 = 17y$
$4 = y$ $\dfrac{3}{2} = \dfrac{3}{2}$ ✓

30. $\dfrac{y + 5}{7} = \dfrac{5}{14} - \dfrac{y - 3}{4}$

$28\left[\dfrac{y + 5}{7}\right] = 28\left[\dfrac{5}{14} - \dfrac{y - 3}{4}\right]$ Check: $\dfrac{1 + 5}{7} = \dfrac{5}{14} - \dfrac{1 - 3}{4}$
$4(y + 5) = 10 - 7(y - 3)$
$4y + 20 = 10 - 7y + 21$ $\dfrac{6}{7} = \dfrac{5}{14} + \dfrac{1}{2}$
$11y = 11$
$y = 1$ $\dfrac{6}{7} = \dfrac{5}{14} + \dfrac{7}{14}$

$\dfrac{6}{7} = \dfrac{6}{7}$ ✓

31. $4(3x + 4) + 2(5x + 1) - 2(x - 1) = 0$

$12x + 16 + 10x + 2 - 2x + 2 = 0$
$20x + 20 = 0$
$20x = -20$
$x = -1$
Check: $4(-3 + 4) + 2(-5 + 1) - 2(-1 - 1) = 0$
$4(1) + 2(-4) - 2(-2) = 0$
$0 = 0$ ✓

32. $2(x + 6) + 3(x - 1) - 4(x - 2) = 0$

$2x + 12 + 3x - 3 - 4x + 8 = 0$
$x + 17 = 0$
$x = -17$
Check: $2(-17 + 6) + 3(-17 - 1) - 4(-17 - 2) = 0$
$2(-11) + 3(-18) - 4(-19) = 0$
$-22 - 54 + 76 = 0$
$0 = 0$ ✓

33. $0.3 + 0.4(2 - x) = 6(-0.2 + 0.1x) + 0.3$

$0.3 + 0.8 - 0.4x = -1.2 + 0.6x + 0.3$
$1.1 - 0.4x = 0.6x - 0.9$
$2 = x$
Check: $0.3 + 0.4(2 - 2) = 6(-0.2 + 0.2) + 0.3$
$0.3 = 0.3$ ✓

34. $3(0.3 + 0.1x) + 0.1 = 0.5(x + 2)$

$0.9 + 0.3x + 0.1 = 0.5x + 1$
$0.3x + 1 = 0.5x + 1$
$0 = 0.2x$
$0 = x$
Check: $3(0.3 + 0) + 0.1 = 0.5(0 + 2)$
$0.9 + 0.1 = 1.0$
$1.0 = 1.0$ ✓

35. $\dfrac{1}{2}(x + 2) = \dfrac{2}{3}(x - 1) - \dfrac{3}{4}$ Check: $\dfrac{33}{4} = \dfrac{9}{1} - \dfrac{3}{4}$

$6x + 12 = 8x - 8 - 9$ $\dfrac{33}{4} = \dfrac{36}{4} - \dfrac{3}{4}$
$29 = 2x$
$\dfrac{29}{2} = x$ $\dfrac{33}{4} = \dfrac{33}{4}$ ✓

36. $x - \dfrac{5}{3}(x - 2) = \dfrac{1}{9}(x + 2)$ Check: $4 - \dfrac{5}{3}(4 - 2) = \dfrac{1}{9}(4 + 2)$

$9x - 15x + 30 = x + 2$
$-6x + 30 = x + 2$ $4 - \dfrac{10}{3} = \dfrac{2}{3}$
$28 = 7x$
$4 = x$ $\dfrac{12}{3} - \dfrac{10}{3} = \dfrac{2}{3}$

$\dfrac{2}{3} = \dfrac{2}{3}$ ✓

37. Is $x = -\dfrac{1}{2}$ a solution for $\dfrac{1}{5}(3x - 1) = 1 + \dfrac{1}{3}(x - 4)$?

$\dfrac{1}{5}\left[-\dfrac{5}{2}\right] = 1 + \dfrac{1}{3}\left(-\dfrac{9}{2}\right)$

$-\dfrac{1}{2} = 1 - \dfrac{3}{2}$ Yes

$-\dfrac{1}{2} = -\dfrac{1}{2}$

38. Is $y = \dfrac{5}{6}$ a solution for $\dfrac{1}{2}(y - 1) + 2 = y + \dfrac{1}{8}(7 + 2y)$?

$\dfrac{1}{2}\left(-\dfrac{1}{6}\right) + \dfrac{24}{12} = \dfrac{10}{12} + \dfrac{1}{8}\left[\dfrac{26}{3}\right]$

$-\dfrac{1}{12} + \dfrac{24}{12} = \dfrac{10}{12} + \dfrac{13}{12}$ Yes

$\dfrac{23}{12} = \dfrac{23}{12}$

Solve.

39. $-1(2x + 3) + \dfrac{7x - 7}{4} = -\dfrac{3}{4}(4 - x) + \dfrac{x + 1}{2}$

$-4(2x + 3) + 7x - 7 = -3(4 - x) + 2(x + 1)$
$-8x - 12 + 7x - 7 = -12 + 3x + 2x + 2$
$-x - 19 = 5x - 10$
$-\dfrac{3}{2} = x$

Check: $-1(0) + \dfrac{1}{4}\left(-\dfrac{35}{2}\right) = -\dfrac{3}{4}\left(\dfrac{11}{2}\right) + \dfrac{1}{2}\left(-\dfrac{1}{2}\right)$

$-\dfrac{35}{8} = -\dfrac{33}{8} - \dfrac{2}{8}$

$-\dfrac{35}{8} = -\dfrac{35}{8} \checkmark$

40. $8 - 4a + 3(2 - 4a) = -7[3(2a - 1) - 4(a + 1)]$

$8 - 4a + 6 - 12a = -7[6a - 3 - 4a - 4]$
$-16a + 14 = -7(2a - 7)$
$-16a + 14 = -14a + 49$
$-35 = 2a$
$-\dfrac{35}{2} = a$

Check:

$8 - 4\left(-\dfrac{35}{2}\right) + 3(2 + 70) = -7\left[3(-35 - 1) - 4\left(-\dfrac{35}{2} + 1\right)\right]$

$8 + 70 + 216 = -7[-108 + 70 - 4]$
$294 = 294 \checkmark$

Cumulative Review Problems

Simplify. Leave positive exponents in your answer.

41. $3x - 2(5x - 6) + 2(x - 4)$

$3x - 10x + 12 + 2x - 8 = -5x + 4$

42. $\left(\dfrac{3xy^2}{2x^2y}\right)^3$

$\dfrac{27x^3y^6}{8x^6y^3} = \dfrac{27y^3}{8x^3}$

43. $5\{x - 2[3 - x(4 + x)]\}$

$5\{x - 2[3 - 4x - x^2]\}$
$5\{x - 6 + 8x + 2x^2\}$
$5x - 30 + 40x + 10x^2$
$10x^2 + 45x - 30$

44. $(2x^{-2}y^{-3})^2(4xy^{-2})^{-2}$

$(4x^{-4}y^{-6})\left(\dfrac{1}{16}x^{-2}y^4\right) = \dfrac{x^{-6}y^{-2}}{4} = \dfrac{1}{4x^6y^2}$

Calculator Problems

Solve for x. Round your answer to four decimal places.

45. $9.8615x - 2.3218 = 18.0716x + 4.9862$

$x = -0.8901$

46. $2x + \dfrac{36,942}{79,603} = 5x - \dfrac{88,032}{91,264}$

$x = 0.4762$

For Extra Practice Exercises, turn to page 63.

Solutions to Odd-Numbered Practice Problems

1. (a) Is $x = -5$ the root of the equation $2x + 3 = 3x + 8$? **(b)** Is $a = 4$ a solution of the equation $3a - 2 = 5a + 6$?

$2(-5) + 3 \stackrel{?}{=} 3(-5) + 8$ $\qquad\qquad$ $3(4) - 2 \stackrel{?}{=} 5(4) + 6$

$-10 + 3 \stackrel{?}{=} -15 + 8$ $\qquad\qquad$ $12 - 2 \stackrel{?}{=} 20 + 6$

$-7 = -7 \checkmark$ $\quad$ Yes, $x = -5$ is the root. $\qquad$ $10 \neq 26$ $\quad$ No, $a = 4$ is not a solution.

3. $\dfrac{1}{5}w = -6$

$5\left(\dfrac{1}{5}w\right) = 5(-6)$ $\quad$ Multiplying each side by 5.

$w = -30$

5. $8w - 3 = 2w - 7w + 4$

$8w - 3 = -5w + 4$ $\qquad$ Collecting like terms.
$8w + 5w - 3 = -5w + 5w + 4$ $\qquad$ Adding $5w$ to each side.
$13w - 3 = 4$
$13w - 3 + 3 = 4 + 3$ $\qquad$ Adding 3 to each side.
$13w = 7$

$w = \dfrac{7}{13}$ $\qquad$ Dividing each side by 7.

7. Solve: $\frac{y}{3} + \frac{1}{2} = 5 + \frac{y-9}{4}$.

$$\frac{y}{3} + \frac{1}{2} = 5 + \frac{y}{4} - \frac{9}{4}$$

$$12\left(\frac{y}{3}\right) + 12\left(\frac{1}{2}\right) = 12(5) + 12\left(\frac{y}{4}\right) - 12\left(\frac{9}{4}\right)$$

$$4y + 6 = 60 + 3y - 27$$

$$4y + 6 = 3y + 33$$

$$y + 6 = 33$$

$$y = 27$$

Check: $\frac{27}{3} + \frac{1}{2} \overset{?}{=} 5 + \frac{27-9}{4}$

$$\frac{54}{6} + \frac{3}{6} \overset{?}{=} 5 + \frac{18}{4}$$

$$\frac{57}{6} \overset{?}{=} 5 + \frac{9}{2}$$

$$\frac{19}{2} = \frac{19}{2} \checkmark$$

Answers to Even-Numbered Practice Problems

2. $y = -8.0$ **4.** $x = -4$ **6.** $a = 1$
$$-7(-4) - 2 \overset{?}{=} 26$$
$$26 = 26 \checkmark$$

1.8   LITERAL EQUATIONS

After studying this section, you will be able to:

1 *Solve literal equations for the desired unknown*

1 A first-degree **literal equation** is an equation that has other letters in it besides the variable. When you solve for an unknown in a literal equation, the final expression will contain these other letters. We use this procedure to deal with formulas in applied problems.

Example 1   Solve for x: $5x + 3y = 2$.

     $5x = 2 - 3y$ Subtracting $3y$ from each side.

     $\dfrac{5x}{5} = \dfrac{2 - 3y}{5}$ Dividing each side by 5.

     $x = \dfrac{2 - 3y}{5}$ The solution is a fractional expression. ∎

Practice Problem 1   Solve for W: $P = 2L + 2W$.   ∎

Where possible, collect like terms as you solve the equation.

Example 2   Solve for y: $3ay + 8 = 5ay - 7$.

     $3ay - 5ay + 8 = -7$ Subtracting $5ay$ from each side.

     $-2ay = -7 - 8$ Simplifying and subtract 8 from each side.

     $-2ay = -15$ Simplifying.

     $\dfrac{-2ay}{-2a} = \dfrac{-15}{-2a}$ Dividing each side by the coefficient of y, which is $-2a$.

     $y = \dfrac{15}{2a}$ Simplifying. (Recall that a negative divided by a negative is positive.) ∎

Practice Problem 2   Solve for w: $8 + 12wx = 18 - 7wx$.   ∎

For longer problems, follow this procedure.

TEACHING TIP   After discussing examples 1 and 2 or similar examples, ask the class to solve for w in the equation $5w - 3 = -2w + 9x$. The correct solution is $w = \dfrac{9x + 3}{7}$. Point out to students that $9x + 3$ cannot be combined because these two terms are not like terms.

TEACHING TIP   After discussing example 3 or a similar example, ask students to do the following problem: Solve for a in the formula

$$B = 3\left(2x + \frac{1}{2}a - 5y\right)$$

The answer is

$$\frac{2B - 12x + 30y}{3} = a.$$

Work out the steps to the problem and ask students if they have any questions. Then ask if any student did the problem a different way. Some of their suggestions may prove interesting.

Example 3   Solve for b: $A = \frac{2}{3}(a + b + 3)$.

$A = \frac{2}{3}a + \frac{2}{3}b + 2$	Removing parentheses.
$3A = 3\left(\frac{2}{3}a\right) + 3\left(\frac{2}{3}b\right) + 3(2)$	Multiplying all terms by the LCD 3.
$3A = 2a + 2b + 6$	Simplifying.
$3A - 2a - 6 = 2b$	Subtracting $2a$ from each side. Subtracting 6 from each side.
$\frac{3A - 2a - 6}{2} = \frac{2b}{2}$	Dividing each side of the equation by coefficient of b.
$\frac{3A - 2a - 6}{2} = b$	Simplifying. ■

Practice Problem 3   Solve for a: $3(2ax - y) = \frac{1}{2}(ax + 2y)$.   ■

Example 4   Solve for x: $5(2ax + 3y) - 4ax = 2(ax - 5)$.

$10ax + 15y - 4ax = 2ax - 10$	Removing parentheses.
$6ax + 15y = 2ax - 10$	Collecting like terms.
$6ax - 2ax + 15y = -10$	Subtracting $2ax$ from each side to obtain terms containing x on one side.
$4ax = -10 - 15y$	Simplifying and subtracting $15y$ from each side.
$\frac{4ax}{4a} = \frac{-10 - 15y}{4a}$	Dividing each side by coefficient of x.
$x = \frac{-10 - 15y}{4a}$ ■	

TEACHING TIP   Points out to students that the skill of rearranging an equation or formula to solve for a particular letter is often necessary before inserting a formula in a computer program. Many computer programs require that any formula that is used be solved for the Dependent variable that will be printed out when the program is running.

Practice Problem 4   Solve for b: $-2(ab - 3x) + 2(8 - ab) = 5x + 4ab$.   ■

Example 5

(a) Solve the formula for the area of a trapezoid for c: $A = \frac{1}{2}a(b + c)$.

(b) Find c when $A = 20$ square inches, $a = 3$ inches, and $b = 4$ inches.

(a)
$$A = \frac{1}{2}ab + \frac{1}{2}ac \qquad \text{Removing parentheses.}$$

$$2A = 2\left(\frac{1}{2}ab\right) + 2\left(\frac{1}{2}ac\right) \qquad \text{Multiplying each term by 2.}$$

$$2A = ab + ac \qquad \text{Simplifying.}$$

$$2A - ab = ac \qquad \text{Subtracting } ab \text{ from each side to isolate the } ac \text{ term.}$$

$$\frac{2A - ab}{a} = c \qquad \boxed{\text{Dividing each side by } a.}$$

(b) $c = \dfrac{2A - ab}{a}$

$$= \frac{2(20) - (3)(4)}{3} \qquad \text{Substituting given values of } A, a, b \text{ to find } c.$$

$$= \frac{40 - 12}{3} = \frac{28}{3} \qquad \text{Simplifying.}$$

Thus, side $c = \dfrac{28}{3}$ inches or $9\dfrac{1}{3}$ inches ■

Practice Problem 5
(a) Solve for h: $A = 2\pi rh + 2\pi r^2$.
(b) Find h when $A = 100$, $\pi \approx 3.14$, $r = 2.0$. Round your answer to the nearest hundredth. ■

DEVELOPING YOUR STUDY SKILLS

EXAM TIME: HOW TO REVIEW

Reviewing adequately for an exam enables you to bring together the concepts you have learned over several sections. For your review, you will need to:

1. Reread your textbook. Make a list of any terms, rules, or formulas you need to know for the exam. Be sure you understand them all.
2. Reread your notes. Go over returned homework and quizzes. Redo the problems you missed.
3. Practice some of each type of problem covered in the chapter(s) you are to be tested on.
4. Use the end-of-chapter materials provided in your textbook. Read carefully through the Chapter Organizer. Do the Extra Practice sections. Take the Practice Quizzes. When you are finished, check your answers. Redo any problems you missed.
5. Get help if any concepts give you difficulty.

EXERCISES 1.8

Solve for x.

1. $3ax = 7$ $\quad x = \dfrac{7}{3a}$

2. $xy = 2h$ $\quad x = \dfrac{2h}{y}$

3. $5x - 2(x - y) = 3y$
$$5x - 2x + 2y = 3y$$
$$3x = y$$
$$x = \dfrac{y}{3}$$

4. $2a - 3(x + a) = 2x$
$$2a - 3x - 3a = 2x$$
$$\dfrac{-a}{5} = x$$

5. $5abx - 2y - 3abx = 6y$
$$2abx = 8y$$
$$x = \dfrac{4y}{ab}$$

6. $8d + 8cdx - 3d = 5cdx$
$$5d = -3cdx$$
$$-\dfrac{5}{3c} = x$$

7. $5x + 3y = 8$

$5x = 8 - 3y$

$x = \dfrac{8 - 3y}{5}$

8. $7x - 2y = 4$

$7x = 4 + 2y$

$x = \dfrac{4 + 2y}{7}$

9. $y = \dfrac{2}{3}x - 4$

$3y = 2x - 12$

$\dfrac{3y + 12}{2} = x$

10. $y = -\dfrac{1}{3}x + 2$ $3\left[y = -\dfrac{1}{3}x + 2\right]$

$3y = -x + 6$

$x = 6 - 3y$

11. $2x + a - 3b = 4x - 2a$

$3a - 3b = 2x$

$\dfrac{3a - 3b}{2} = x$

12. $3x - 4(x - 2b) = x + 4a$

$3x - 4x + 8b = x + 4a$

$-x + 8b = x + 4a$

$8b - 4a = 2x$

$4b - 2a = x$

Solve for the letter specified.

13. $d = rt$; for t

$\dfrac{d}{r} = t$

14. $I = prt$; for p

$\dfrac{I}{rt} = p$

15. $\dfrac{2}{3}(x + y) = 2(x - y)$; for y

$2(x + y) = 6(x - y)$

$2x + 2y = 6x - 6y$

$8y = 4x$

$y = \dfrac{x}{2}$

16. $\dfrac{1}{5}(a + 2b) = 3(a + 2b)$; for b

$a + 2b = 15(a + 2b)$

$a + 2b = 15a + 30b$

$-14a = 28b$

$\dfrac{-a}{2} = b$

17. $3abx + cd = 5cd - 2abx$; for b

$5abx = 4cd$

$b = \dfrac{4cd}{5ax}$

18. $-6dex + 3y = 5(dex - 3y)$; for d

$-6dex + 3y = 5dex - 15y$

$18y = 11dex$

$\dfrac{18y}{11ex} = d$

19. $\dfrac{2}{3} + y = \dfrac{2}{5}b + 3y$; for y

$10 + 15y = 6b + 45y$

$10 - 6b = 30y$

$\dfrac{10 - 6b}{30} = \dfrac{5 - 3b}{15} = y$

20. $\dfrac{1}{2}A + 3B = \dfrac{1}{3}B + 6$; for B

$3A + 18B = 2B + 36$

$16B = 36 - 3A$

$B = \dfrac{36 - 3A}{16}$

Follow the directions given.

21. **(a)** Solve for a: $A = \dfrac{1}{2}ab$.

(b) Evaluate when $A = 50$ and $b = 10$.

(a) $2\left[A = \dfrac{1}{2}ab\right]$ (b) $\dfrac{2(50)}{10} = 10 = a$

$2A = ab$

$\dfrac{2A}{b} = a$

22. **(a)** Solve for C: $F = \dfrac{9}{5}C + 32$.

(b) Evaluate when $F = 23°$.

(a) $5\left[F = \dfrac{9}{5}C + 32\right]$ (b) $\dfrac{5(23) - 160}{9} = -5° = C$

$5F = 9C + 160$

$\dfrac{5F - 160}{9} = C$

23. **(a)** Solve for n: $A = a + d(n - 1)$.

(b) Evaluate when $A = 28$, $a = 3$, and $d = 5$.

(a) $A = a + dn - d$ (b) $\dfrac{28 - 3 + 5}{5} = 6 = n$

$A - a + d = dn$

$\dfrac{A - a + d}{d} = n$

24. **(a)** Solve for t: $A = p + prt$.

(b) Evaluate when $A = 140$, $p = 100$, and $r = 0.20$.

(a) $A - p = prt$ (b) $\dfrac{140 - 100}{100(0.20)} = 2 = t$

$\dfrac{A - p}{pr} = t$

25. **(a)** Solve for a: $D = Vt + \dfrac{1}{2}at^2$.

(b) Evaluate when $D = 46$, $V = 20$, and $t = 2$.

(a) $2\left[D = Vt + \dfrac{1}{2}at^2\right]$ (b) $\dfrac{2(46) - 2(20)(2)}{2^2} = 3 = a$

$2D = 2Vt + at^2$

$2D - 2Vt = at^2$

$\dfrac{2D - 2Vt}{t^2} = a$

26. **(a)** Solve for S: $A = \dfrac{\pi r^2 S}{360}$.

(b) Evaluate when $A = 0.314$, $r = 2$, and $\pi \approx 3.14$.

(a) $360\left[A = \dfrac{\pi r^2 S}{360}\right]$ (b) $\dfrac{360(0.314)}{3.14(2)^2} = 9 = S$

$360A = \pi r^2 S$

$\dfrac{360A}{\pi r^2} = S$

27. Solve for y: $-3[2x + 3(6 - 7x)] = 18 - 5(x + 4y)$.

$-3[2x + 18 - 21x] = 18 - 5x - 20y$
$-6x - 54 + 63x = 18 - 5x - 20y$
$57x - 54 = 18 - 5x - 20y$
$\dfrac{62x - 72}{-20} = -\dfrac{31x - 36}{10} = y$

28. Solve for b: $\dfrac{2}{3}V = 3ax(b + x) + \dfrac{1}{4}(7abx - 2y)$

$8V = 36ax(b + x) + 3(7abx - 2y)$
$8V = 36abx + 36ax^2 + 21abx - 6y$
$8V = 57abx + 36ax^2 - 6y$
$\dfrac{8V - 36ax^2 + 6y}{57ax} = b$

Cumulative Review Problems

Write with positive exponents in simplest form.

29. $(2x^{-3}y)^{-2}$

$2^{-2}x^6y^{-2} = \dfrac{x^6}{4y^2}$

30. $\left(\dfrac{5x^2y^{-3}}{x^{-4}y^2}\right)^{-3}$

$\dfrac{5^{-3}x^{-6}y^9}{x^{12}y^{-6}} = \dfrac{y^{15}}{125x^{18}}$

Solve for x.

31. $3.2 + 0.7x = 0.5(8 + x)$

$3.2 + 0.7x = 4 + 0.5x$
$4 = x$

32. $0.14x + 4800 - 0.12x = 5160$

$0.02x = 360; \ x = 18{,}000$

Calculator Problems

Solve for x. Round your answer to four decimal places.

33. $A = 259.276(12.8x - 15.3)$

$x = \dfrac{A + 3966.9228}{3318.7328}$

34. $16.932x - 19.832 = 15.428 + 19.3(56x - 12)$

$x = 0.1846$

For Extra Practice Exercises, turn to page 63.

Solutions to Odd-Numbered Practice Problems

1. Solve for W: $P = 2L + 2W$

$P - 2L = 2W$ — Subtracting $2L$ from each side.

$\dfrac{P - 2L}{2} = \dfrac{2W}{2}$ — Dividing each side by 2.

$\dfrac{P - 2L}{2} = W$ — Simplifying.

3. Solve for a: $3(2ax - y) = \dfrac{1}{2}(ax + 2y)$

$6ax - 3y = \dfrac{1}{2}ax + y$ — Removing parentheses.

$2(6ax) - 2(3y) = 2\left(\dfrac{1}{2}ax\right) + 2(y)$ — Multiplying each term by 2.

$12ax - 6y = ax + 2y$ — Simplifying.
$12ax - ax = 2y + 6y$ — Subtracting ax from each side. Add $6y$ to each side.

$11ax = 8y$ — Simplifying.

$\dfrac{11ax}{11x} = \dfrac{8y}{11x}$ — Dividing each side by coefficient of a.

$a = \dfrac{8y}{11x}$ — Simplifying.

5. (a) Solve for h: $A = 2\pi rh + 2\pi r^2$

$A - 2\pi r^2 = 2\pi rh$ — Subtracting $2\pi r^2$ from each side.

$\dfrac{A - 2\pi r^2}{2\pi r} = \dfrac{2\pi rh}{2\pi r}$ — Dividing each side by coefficient of h.

$\dfrac{A - 2\pi r^2}{2\pi r} = h$ — Simplifying.

(b) Evaluate when $A = 100$, $\pi \approx 3.14$, and $r = 2$.

$\dfrac{100 - 2(3.14)(2)^2}{2(3.14)(2)} = \dfrac{100 - 2(3.14)(4)}{2(3.14)(2)}$

$= \dfrac{100 - 25.12}{12.56} = \dfrac{74.88}{12.56} \approx 5.96$ (rounded to nearest hundredth)

Answers to Even-Numbered Practice Problems

2. $w = \dfrac{10}{19x}$ **4.** $b = \dfrac{-1x - 16}{-8a}$ or $b = \dfrac{x + 16}{8a}$

1 Find the solution to absolute
value equations of the form
$|ax + b| = c$

2 Find the solution to absolute
value equations of the form
$|ax + b| + c = d$

3 Find the solution to absolute
value equations of the form
$|ax + b| = |cx + d|$

1.9 ABSOLUTE VALUE EQUATIONS

1 From Section 1.2, you know that the absolute value of a number x is the distance between 0 and x on the number line. This definition shows us how to solve equations containing absolute values.

For example, the equation $|x| = 4$ has two solutions: 4 and -4. Why? Because the distance from 0 to 4 is 4 units, and the distance from 0 to -4 is also 4 units.

Let us look at a definition for the absolute value of x in a slightly different form.

$$|x| = \begin{cases} x & \text{if } x \geq 0 \\ -x & \text{if } x < 0 \end{cases}$$

If we use that definition to solve for x in the equation

$$|x| = 4$$

we would obtain the following:

If $x \geq 0$ then $|x| = x$ If $x < 0$ then $|x| = -x$

Hence, $|x| = x = 4$ Hence, $|x| = -x = 4$

and $x = -4$.

Therefore based on this discussion, we can develop a simple procedure to solve absolute value equations of the type $|ax + b| = c$.

To solve an equation of the form $|ax + b| = c$ where $a \neq 0$ and c is a positive real number, we solve the two equations

$$ax + b = c \quad \text{or} \quad ax + b = -c.$$

Example 1 Solve $|2x + 5| = 11$ and check your solutions by using the procedure established above. We now have

$$2x + 5 = 11 \quad \text{or} \quad 2x + 5 = -11$$
$$2x = 6 \quad\quad\quad\quad 2x = -16$$
$$x = 3 \quad\quad\quad\quad x = -8.$$

The two solutions are $x = 3$ or $x = -8$. ∎

Check: if $x = 3$ if $x = -8$

$|2x + 5| = 11$ $|2x + 5| = 11$

$|2(3) + 5| \overset{?}{=} 11$ $|2(-8) + 5| \overset{?}{=} 11$

$|6 + 5| \overset{?}{=} 11$ $|-16 + 5| \overset{?}{=} 11$

$|11| \overset{?}{=} 11$ $|-11| \overset{?}{=} 11$

$11 = 11 \checkmark$ $11 = 11 \checkmark$

Practice Problem 1 Solve for x $|3x - 4| = 23$, and check your solutions. ∎

Example 2 Solve for x $\left|\frac{1}{2}x - 1\right| = 5$ and check your solutions. By using the procedure, we have the two equations

$$\frac{1}{2}x - 1 = 5 \quad \text{or} \quad \frac{1}{2}x - 1 = -5$$

If we multiply each term of each equation by 2 we will obtain

$$x - 2 = 10 \quad \text{or} \quad x - 2 = -10$$
$$x = 12 \qquad\qquad x = -8$$

Check: if $x = 12$ $\qquad\qquad$ if $x = -8$

$$\left| \frac{1}{2}(12) - 1 \right| \stackrel{?}{=} 5 \qquad\qquad \left| \frac{1}{2}(-8) - 1 \right| \stackrel{?}{=} 5$$

$$|6 - 1| \stackrel{?}{=} 5 \qquad\qquad |-4 - 1| \stackrel{?}{=} 5$$

$$|5| \stackrel{?}{=} 5 \qquad\qquad |-5| \stackrel{?}{=} 5$$

$$5 = 5 \checkmark \qquad\qquad 5 = 5 \checkmark \quad \blacksquare$$

Practice Problem 2 Solve for x and check your solutions:

$$\left| \frac{2}{3}x + 4 \right| = 2. \quad \blacksquare$$

2 Our procedure that we have developed is only valid if there is a positive real number on one side of the equation and an absolute value expression on the other side of the equation. If we encounter an equation of the form $|ax + b| + c = d$, then we will need to add the additive inverse of c to each side to make the absolute value equation conform to the standard form that we have used so far.

Example 3 Solve for x and check your solutions:

$$|3x - 1| + 2 = 5.$$

First we will get the absolute value equation in a more appropriate form by adding -2 to both sides of the absolute value equation.

$$|3x - 1| + 2 - 2 = 5 - 2$$
$$|3x - 1| = 3$$

Now we may employ the usual procedure and solve the resulting two equations.

$$3x - 1 = 3 \quad \text{or} \quad 3x - 1 = -3$$
$$3x = 4 \qquad\qquad 3x = -2$$
$$x = \frac{4}{3} \qquad\qquad x = -\frac{2}{3}$$

In our checking step we will substitute those values into the original equation.

Check: If $x = \frac{4}{3}$ $\qquad\qquad$ if $x = -\frac{2}{3}$

$$\left| 3\left(\frac{4}{3}\right) - 1 \right| + 2 \stackrel{?}{=} 5 \qquad \left| 3\left(-\frac{2}{3}\right) - 1 \right| + 2 \stackrel{?}{=} 5$$

$$|4 - 1| + 2 \stackrel{?}{=} 5 \qquad\qquad |-2 - 1| + 2 \stackrel{?}{=} 5$$

$$|3| + 2 \stackrel{?}{=} 5 \qquad\qquad |-3| + 2 \stackrel{?}{=} 5$$

$$3 + 2 \stackrel{?}{=} 5 \qquad\qquad 3 + 2 \stackrel{?}{=} 5$$

$$5 = 5 \checkmark \qquad\qquad 5 = 5 \checkmark \quad \blacksquare$$

Practice Problem 3 Solve for x and check your solution $|2x + 1| + 3 = 8$ $\quad \blacksquare$

3 Let us now consider what are the possibilities of what a and b can be if $|a| = |b|$.

Suppose $a = 5$ then $b = 5$ or -5.

If we first had $a = -5$ then $b = 5$ or -5,

To generalize if $|a| = |b|$, then $a = b$ or $a = -b$

Do you see that this allows for all the possibilities that we discussed above? We will now apply this property in solving a similar problem.

Example 4 Solve for x and check $|3x - 4| = |x + 6|$.

Since if $|a| = |b|$ then $a = b$ or $a = -b$ we can immediately write the two possible equations as:

$$3x - 4 = x + 6 \qquad \text{or} \qquad 3x - 4 = -(x + 6)$$

Now we solve each equation in the normal fashion:

$$3x - 4 = x + 6 \qquad\qquad 3x - 4 = -x - 6$$
$$3x - x = 4 + 6 \qquad\qquad 3x + x = 4 - 6$$
$$2x = 10 \qquad\qquad\qquad 4x = -2$$
$$x = 5 \qquad\qquad\qquad\quad x = -\frac{1}{2}$$

Now we will check each solution by substituting into the original equation

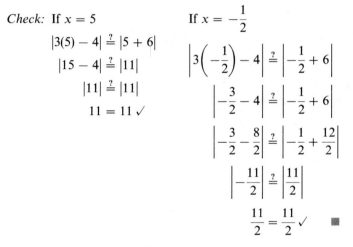

Check: If $x = 5$

$$|3(5) - 4| \overset{?}{=} |5 + 6|$$
$$|15 - 4| \overset{?}{=} |11|$$
$$|11| \overset{?}{=} |11|$$
$$11 = 11 \checkmark$$

If $x = -\frac{1}{2}$

$$\left|3\left(-\frac{1}{2}\right) - 4\right| \overset{?}{=} \left|-\frac{1}{2} + 6\right|$$
$$\left|-\frac{3}{2} - 4\right| \overset{?}{=} \left|-\frac{1}{2} + 6\right|$$
$$\left|-\frac{3}{2} - \frac{8}{2}\right| \overset{?}{=} \left|-\frac{1}{2} + \frac{12}{2}\right|$$
$$\left|-\frac{11}{2}\right| \overset{?}{=} \left|\frac{11}{2}\right|$$
$$\frac{11}{2} = \frac{11}{2} \checkmark \qquad ∎$$

Practice Problem 4 Solve for x and check:

$$|x - 6| = |5x + 8| \qquad ∎$$

There are a few special cases to consider. If we are looking at an absolute value equation of the form $|ax + b| = c$, we might wonder what to do if c is not a positive number.

If $c = 0$, obviously there would be only one equation. Thus if you wanted to solve the absolute value equation $|7x - 35| = 0$, you could immediately set up the one equation $7x - 35 = 0$ and solve to obtain the one solution $x = 5$.

When you take the absolute value of an expression, you will always obtain 0 or a positive number by the definition of absolute value. Therefore if you are asked to solve an equation of the form $|ax + b| = c$ where c is a negative number, we can immediately conclude there is no solution. To illustrate, if you were asked to solve the equation $|5x - 8 + 12x| = -4$, you would not need to do any steps but could immediately conclude that there is **no solution**.

Solve each absolute value equation.

1. $|x| = 14$

$x = 14 \qquad x = -14$

2. $|x| = 19$

$x = 19 \qquad x = -19$

3. $|x + 2| = 7$

$x + 2 = 7 \qquad x + 2 = -7$

$x = 5 \qquad\quad x = -9$

4. $|x - 3| = 6$

$x - 3 = 6 \qquad x - 3 = -6$

$x = 9 \qquad\quad x = -3$

5. $|2x - 5| = 13$

$2x - 5 = 13 \qquad 2x - 5 = -13$

$x = 9 \qquad\qquad x = -4$

6. $|2x + 1| = 15$

$2x + 1 = 15 \qquad 2x + 1 = -15$

$x = 7 \qquad\qquad x = -8$

7. $|3x + 8| = 16$

$3x + 8 = 16 \qquad 3x + 8 = -16$

$x = \dfrac{8}{3} \qquad\qquad x = -8$

8. $|3x - 7| = 23$

$3x - 7 = 23 \qquad 3x - 7 = -23$

$x = 10 \qquad\qquad x = \dfrac{-16}{3}$

9. $\left|\dfrac{1}{2}x - 3\right| = 2$

$\dfrac{1}{2}x - 3 = 2 \qquad \dfrac{1}{2}x - 3 = -2$

$x = 10 \qquad\qquad x = 2$

10. $\left|\dfrac{1}{4}x + 5\right| = 3$

$\dfrac{1}{4}x + 5 = 3 \qquad \dfrac{1}{4}x + 5 = -3$

$x = -8 \qquad\qquad x = -32$

11. $|5 - x| = 3$

$5 - x = 3 \qquad 5 - x = -3$

$2 = x \qquad\qquad 8 = x$

12. $|6 - x| = 4$

$6 - x = 4 \qquad 6 - x = -4$

$2 = x \qquad\qquad 10 = x$

13. $|2x + 3| + 3 = 20$

$|2x + 3| = 17$

$2x + 3 = 17 \qquad 2x + 3 = -17$

$x = 7 \qquad\qquad x = -10$

14. $|3x + 5| + 3 = 14$

$|3x + 5| = 11$

$3x + 5 = 11 \qquad 3x + 5 = -11$

$x = 2 \qquad\qquad x = \dfrac{-16}{3}$

15. $|4x - 5| - 8 = 3$

$|4x - 5| = 11$

$4x - 5 = 11 \qquad 4x - 5 = -11$

$x = 4 \qquad\qquad x = \dfrac{-3}{2}$

16. $|2x - 9| - 1 = 15$

$|2x - 9| = 16$

$2x - 9 = 16 \qquad 2x - 9 = -16$

$x = \dfrac{25}{2} \qquad\qquad x = \dfrac{-7}{2}$

17. $\left|1 - \dfrac{3}{4}x\right| + 4 = 7$

$\left|1 - \dfrac{3}{4}x\right| = 3$

$1 - \dfrac{3}{4}x = 3 \qquad 1 - \dfrac{3}{4}x = -3$

$x = \dfrac{-8}{3} \qquad\qquad x = \dfrac{16}{3}$

18. $\left|4 - \dfrac{5}{2}x\right| + 3 = 15$

$\left|4 - \dfrac{5}{2}x\right| = 12$

$4 - \dfrac{5}{2}x = 12 \qquad 4 - \dfrac{5}{2}x = -12$

$x = \dfrac{-16}{5} \qquad\qquad x = \dfrac{32}{5}$

19. $|x + 6| = |2x - 3|$

$x + 6 = 2x - 3 \qquad x + 6 = -2x + 3$

$9 = x \qquad\qquad x = -1$

20. $|x - 4| = |2x + 5|$

$x - 4 = 2x + 5 \qquad x - 4 = -2x - 5$

$x = -9 \qquad\qquad x = \dfrac{-1}{3}$

21. $|4x + 7| = |5x + 2|$

$4x + 7 = 5x + 2 \qquad 4x + 7 = -5x - 2$

$x = 5 \qquad\qquad x = -1$

22. $|6x - 2| = |3x + 1|$

$6x - 2 = 3x + 1 \qquad 6x - 2 = -3x - 1$

$x = 1 \qquad\qquad x = \dfrac{1}{9}$

23. $|8 - x| = |4 - 2x|$

$8 - x = 4 - 2x \qquad 8 - x = -4 + 2x$

$x = -4 \qquad\qquad x = 4$

24. $|5 + x| = |3 - 4x|$

$5 + x = 3 - 4x \qquad 5 + x = -3 + 4x$

$x = \dfrac{-2}{5} \qquad\qquad x = \dfrac{8}{3}$

25. $|3x - 1| = |6x + 4|$

$3x - 1 = 6x + 4 \qquad 3x - 1 = -6x - 4$

$x = \dfrac{-5}{3} \qquad\qquad x = \dfrac{-1}{3}$

26. $|5x + 3| = |3x - 5|$

$5x + 3 = 3x - 5 \qquad 5x + 3 = -3x + 5$

$x = -4 \qquad\qquad x = \dfrac{1}{4}$

27. $|4x - 20| = 0$

$4x - 20 = 0$

$x = 5$

28. $\left|\dfrac{1}{2}x + 3\right| = 0$

$\dfrac{1}{2}x + 3 = 0$

$x = -6$

29. $\left|\dfrac{2}{3}x + \dfrac{1}{7}\right| = -4$

No solution

30. $\left|\dfrac{3}{4}x - \dfrac{2}{3}\right| = -8$

No solution

? **To Think About**

Solve for x.

31. $\dfrac{|x + 2|}{-3} = -5$

$x + 2 = 15 \qquad x + 2 = -15$

$x = 13 \qquad\qquad x = -17$

32. $\left|\dfrac{2x - 1}{3}\right| = \dfrac{5}{6}$

$\dfrac{2x - 1}{3} = \dfrac{5}{6} \qquad \dfrac{2x - 1}{3} = \dfrac{-5}{6}$

$x = \dfrac{7}{4} \qquad\qquad x = \dfrac{-3}{4}$

Cumulative Review Problems

Solve for x.

33. $2(3x + 1) - 3(x - 2) = 2x + 5$
$x = -3$

34. $\frac{1}{2}(3x + 1) - \frac{1}{6}(7x + 3) = \frac{1}{3}(3 - x)$
$x = \frac{3}{2}$

35. $\frac{7}{3}x - \frac{6}{5} = \frac{12}{5}x - \frac{2}{3}$
$x = -8$

36. $\frac{5}{3}x + \frac{3}{2} = \frac{7}{6}x - \frac{5}{2}$
$x = -8$

Calculator Problems

Solve for x. Round to the nearest hundredth.

37. $|1.62x + 3.14| = 2.19$
$x = -0.59 \qquad x = -3.29$

38. $|-0.74x - 8.26| = 5.36$
$x = -18.41 \qquad x = -3.92$

39. $|9.63x + 1.52| = |-8.61x + 3.76|$
$x = 0.12 \qquad x = -5.18$

40. $|8.12x - 5.85| + 1.93 = 5.42$
$x = 1.15 \qquad x = 0.29$

For Extra Practice Examples, turn to page 64.

Solutions to Odd-Numbered Practice Problems

1. $3x - 4 = 23$ $\qquad$ $3x - 4 = -23$
$\qquad 3x = 27$ $\qquad\qquad 3x = -19$
$\qquad\quad x = 9$ $\qquad\qquad\quad x = -\dfrac{19}{3}$

$\qquad$ Check: $|3(9) - 4| \overset{?}{=} 23$
$\qquad\qquad\quad |27 - 4| \overset{?}{=} 23 \qquad \left|3\left(-\dfrac{19}{3}\right) - 4\right| \overset{?}{=} 23$
$\qquad\qquad\qquad\quad 23 = 23 \checkmark$
$\qquad\qquad\qquad\qquad\qquad\qquad |-19 - 4| \overset{?}{=} 23$
$\qquad\qquad\qquad\qquad\qquad\qquad\qquad |-23| \overset{?}{=} 23$
$\qquad\qquad\qquad\qquad\qquad\qquad\qquad\quad 23 = 23 \checkmark$

3. $|2x + 1| = 5$ $\qquad\qquad$ $2x + 1 = -5$
$\quad 2x + 1 = 5$ $\qquad\qquad\qquad 2x = -6$
$\qquad 2x = 4$ $\qquad\qquad\qquad\qquad x = -3$
$\qquad\quad x = 2$

$\qquad$ Check: $|2(2) + 1| \overset{?}{=} 5 \qquad |2(-3) + 1| \overset{?}{=} 5$
$\qquad\qquad\qquad\quad |4 + 1| \overset{?}{=} 5 \qquad\quad |-6 + 1| \overset{?}{=} 5$
$\qquad\qquad\qquad\qquad |5| \overset{?}{=} 5 \qquad\qquad\quad |-5| \overset{?}{=} 5$
$\qquad\qquad\qquad\qquad\quad 5 = 5 \checkmark \qquad\qquad\quad 5 = 5 \checkmark$

Answers to Even-Numbered Practice Problems

2. $x = -3$ or $x = -9$ $\qquad$ **4.** $x = -\dfrac{7}{2}$ or $x = -\dfrac{1}{3}$

EXTRA PRACTICE: EXERCISES

Section 1.1

Consider the set of numbers $\left\{-6, 0, \dfrac{1}{3}, -\dfrac{2}{5}, 3\pi, \sqrt{2}\right\}.$

1. List all the positive real numbers. $\dfrac{1}{3}, 3\pi, \sqrt{2}$

2. List all the rational numbers. $-6, 0, \dfrac{1}{3}, -\dfrac{2}{5}$

3. List all the whole numbers. 0

4. Are any elements of this set real numbers that are not rational numbers? If so, list them. $3\pi, \sqrt{2}$

5. List all the nonpositive integers. $-6, 0$

6. List all the even integers. $-6, 0$

7. List all the rational numbers that are nonintegers. $\dfrac{1}{3}, -\dfrac{2}{5}$

List all the elements of each given set.

8. $\{x \mid x$ is a counting number less than $8\}$ $\quad 1, 2, 3, 4, 5, 6, 7$

9. $\{x \mid x$ is an odd integer between -6 and $6\}$
$-5, -3, -1, 1, 3, 5$

10. $\{x \mid x \text{ is a nonnegative integer} \leq 5\}$ 0, 1, 2, 3, 4, 5

11. $\{x \mid x \text{ is an even integer} > -5\}$ $-4, -2, 0, 2, 4, 6 \ldots$

Name the property of real numbers that justifies each statement.

12. $6 + (2 + 3) = (6 + 2) + 3$ associative property for addition

13. $8 \cdot 1 = 8$ identity property for multiplication

14. $5(2 + 3) = 5 \cdot 2 + 5 \cdot 3$

15. $7(2 \cdot 3) = (7 \cdot 2)3$ associative property for multiplication

16. $(-a) + -(-a) = 0$ inverse property for addition

17. $5(x + 6) = (x + 6)5$ commutative property for multiplication

14. distributive property of multiplication over addition

18. $9 + 0 = 9$ identity property for addition

19. $6 + (8 - 2) = (8 - 2) + 6$ commutative property for addition

20. $8(6 + 4) = 8 \cdot 6 + 8 \cdot 4$

21. $8 + 7 = \text{a real number}$ closure property for addition

22. $6 + (-6) = 0 = (-6) + 6$ inverse property for addition

23. $5 \cdot 12 = \text{a real number}$ closure property for multiplication

24. $17 \cdot \dfrac{1}{17} = 1 = \dfrac{1}{17} \cdot 17$ inverse property for multiplication

25. $8(5 + 7) = 8 \cdot 5 + 8 \cdot 7$

distributive property of multiplication over addition

20. distributive property of multiplication over addition

Section 1.2

Perform the operations indicated. Simplify completely.

1. $(-8)(2)$ -16

2. $-4 + 6 - 2$ 0

3. $\dfrac{5 - 8 + 6}{-2}$ $-\dfrac{3}{2}$

4. $\dfrac{-\dfrac{2}{3}}{-\dfrac{3}{7}}$ $\dfrac{14}{9}$

5. $5(-6) + 3(-2)$ -36

6. $\dfrac{2 - (-3) + 1}{-3}$ -2

7. $18 \div (-2) + 3(4) - 6$ -3

8. $2 + 3(-4) - 6 \div 2$ -13

9. $\dfrac{\dfrac{1}{3} - \dfrac{1}{4}}{-\dfrac{2}{5}}$ $-\dfrac{5}{24}$

10. $-\dfrac{1}{3} + \dfrac{1}{4} - \dfrac{1}{2}$ $-\dfrac{7}{12}$

11. $\dfrac{3 + 20 \div 2}{6 - 7}$ -13

12. $\dfrac{5 - 8(2) + 3(4)}{2(5) - 3(2)}$ $\dfrac{1}{4}$

13. $2(-3)(1)(-4)(2)$ 48

14. $(1)(-2)(-3)(-4)(3)$ -72

15. $(-8)(0)(-4)$ 0

16. $(-6) - (-2) + (-14)$ -18

17. $(-8) + (-2)(-4)$ 0

18. $\dfrac{(-6) + (-2) - (-3)}{-5}$ 1

19. $6 - 16 \div 2 \cdot 4$ -26

20. $18 - (-17)(-1)$ 1

21. $16 \cdot 2 \div 8 + 2 \cdot 3$ 10

22. $-\dfrac{1}{8} + \dfrac{1}{4} - \dfrac{1}{16}$ $\dfrac{1}{16}$

23. $6(2 + 4) - 9 \cdot 4$ 0

24. $\dfrac{\dfrac{5}{3} - \dfrac{5}{6}}{\dfrac{1}{2}}$ $\dfrac{5}{3}$

25. $\dfrac{5 \cdot 6 - 4 \div 2}{3 + 4}$ 4

26. $(12)(-2)(-3)(0)(-4)$ 0

27. $\dfrac{8 \cdot 2 - 4 \cdot 4}{26 \div 2}$ 0

Section 1.3

Evaluate.

1. $(-2)^5$ -32

2. $\left(\dfrac{1}{2}\right)^3$ $\dfrac{1}{8}$

3. $\sqrt{\dfrac{4}{9}}$ $\dfrac{2}{3}$

4. $\sqrt{121}$ 11

5. -2^4 -16

6. $\left(\dfrac{2}{3}\right)^2$ $\dfrac{4}{9}$

7. $\sqrt{\dfrac{25}{144}}$ $\dfrac{5}{12}$

8. $(-2)^4$ 16

9. $(-6)^3$ -216

Evaluate. Be sure to follow carefully the established priority of operations.

10. $\sqrt{9 - 2 + 6 + 3}$ 4

11. $\sqrt{5(-3) + 16}$ 1

12. $2(3)^2 + 4\sqrt{9} - 6(2)$ 18

13. $5 - 3 + 2\sqrt{16} - 2(3)^2$ -8

14. $\dfrac{|3(-2) - 6|}{\sqrt{2^2 + (-3)^2}}$ $\dfrac{12}{\sqrt{13}}$

15. $2^3 + (-3)^4 - 2^2 + |-4|$ 89

16. $\sqrt{2 \cdot 3^2 - 2}$ 4

17. $\sqrt{2^4 - 4^2}$ 0

18. $\sqrt{18 \div 3 \cdot 3}$ $\sqrt{18}$

19. $10 \cdot 10^2 - 10 \div 10 \cdot 10$ 990

20. $18 - \sqrt{9} \div 3$ 17

21. $|(-2)(+3) + (-3)^2|$ 3

22. $\sqrt{\left(\dfrac{2}{3}\right)^2 - \dfrac{1}{3}}$ $\dfrac{1}{3}$

23. $\sqrt{16 + 9}$ 5

Section 1.4

In problems 1–15, you may leave negative exponents in your answer.

Multiply and simplify.

1. $(3x^{-2})(2x)(-3x^3)$ $-18x^2$

2. $(-12xy^2)(-4x^{-3}y^0)$ $\dfrac{1}{48x^{-2}y^2}$

3. $(2^3x^2y)(2^{-4}x^{-6}y^{-1})$ $\dfrac{1}{2x^4}$

4. $(-5a^{-2}b^{-4}c)(-2a^2b^0)(-3b^3c^3)$ $\dfrac{-30c^4}{b}$

5. $(4x^2y^3z^4)(6x^2y^3z^4)$ $24x^4y^6z^8$

6. $(2^4)(2^3)(2^{-5})$ 4

7. $(x^2y^{-4})(3xz^2)(-2x^3y^3z)$ $-6x^6y^{-1}z^3$

8. $(-4x^4y^4)(3x^3y^3)$ $-12x^7y^7$

Divide and simplify.

9. $\dfrac{3^4x^{-8}}{3^5x^6}$ $\dfrac{1}{3x^{14}}$

10. $\dfrac{2^{17}a^3}{2^{15}a^6}$ $\dfrac{4}{a^3}$

11. $\dfrac{36x^5y^6z}{-12x^{-3}y^{-5}z}$ $-3x^8y^{11}$

12. $\dfrac{-36ab^{-3}}{-72a^0b^{-6}}$ $\dfrac{ab^3}{2}$

13. $\dfrac{14x^{14}y^8}{2x^2y^8}$ $7x^{12}$

14. $\dfrac{2^4x^4}{2^4x^4}$ 1

15. $\dfrac{48x^{12}y^0z^6}{8x^2y^2z^3}$ $\dfrac{6x^{10}z^3}{y^2}$

Raise to the power indicated and simplify.

16. $(4x^3y)^3$ $64x^9y^3$

17. $(-2x^0yz^6)^{-4}$ $\dfrac{1}{16y^4z^{24}}$

18. $\dfrac{(3ab)^2}{(2a^3b)^3}$ $\dfrac{9}{8a^7b}$

19. $\dfrac{-5a^3bd^4}{(-5ab)^3}$ $\dfrac{d^4}{25b^2}$

20. $(-3^0x^2y^3)^2$ x^4y^6

21. $\left(\dfrac{24x^3y}{6xy^4}\right)^3$ $\dfrac{64x^6}{y^9}$

22. $\left(\dfrac{8x^2z^4}{2^2xz^2}\right)^{-3}$ $\dfrac{1}{8x^3z^6}$

Simplify each expression. Write your answer using only positive exponents.

23. $(-3x^{-2}y^3)^{-2}$ $\dfrac{x^4}{9y^6}$

24. $(5x^{-6}y^{-2})(-3x^3y^{-4})$ $\dfrac{-15}{x^3y^6}$

25. $\left(\dfrac{2x^{-4}y^{-3}}{3x^{-6}y^2}\right)^3$ $\dfrac{8x^6}{27y^{15}}$

26. $\dfrac{5^0x^3y^{-4}z}{6^{-2}x^3y^{-8}z^{-3}}$ $36y^4z^4$

27. $(3^2x^{-3}y^4)(2^{-2}x^4y^{-6})$ $\dfrac{9x}{4y^2}$

Write in scientific notation.

28. 0.0003125 3.125×10^{-4}

29. $537,210,000,000$ 5.3721×10^{11}

30. 0.0000016 1.6×10^{-6}

31. $432,000$ 4.32×10^5

Section 1.5

Collect like terms.

1. $7ab - 3ab + 2b - 5ab$ $2b - ab$

2. $x - 3y + 5x^2 - 8y - 2x$ $5x^2 - x - 11y$

3. $\dfrac{1}{2}a^2 + \dfrac{1}{3}b^2 - 2a^2 + \dfrac{1}{6}b^2$ $-\dfrac{3}{2}a^2 + \dfrac{1}{2}b^2$

4. $-1.6xy + 2y^2 - 8.3xy - 5y^2$ $-9.9xy - 3y^2$

5. $4xy - 6xy^2 + 3yx + 2y^2x$ $7xy - 4xy^2$

6. $4x^2 - 3x + 2x^2 - 5x^3$ $6x^2 - 3x - 5x^3$

7. $18x + (-2y) - 3x - 4y$ $15x - 6y$

8. $6abc - 4ab + 2abc$ $8abc - 4ab$

Multiply. Simplify your answer wherever possible.

9. $-3ab(a - 2b + 5)$ $-3a^2b + 6ab^2 - 15ab$

10. $5x^2(x^3 - 2x^2 + x - 4)$ $5x^5 - 10x^4 + 5x^3 - 20x^2$

11. $\dfrac{2}{3}(3x - 2y + 5)$ $2x - \dfrac{4}{3}y + \dfrac{10}{3}$

12. $-8x^2y(x - 2y + 3x^2)$ $-8x^3y + 16x^2y^2 - 24x^4y$

13. $2ax(4ax - 6a + 3x)$ $8a^2x^2 - 12a^2x + 6ax^2$

14. $3x^2y(2x - 3y + 4x)$ $18x^3y - 9x^2y^2$

15. $\dfrac{3}{4}xy^2(12x - 4xy + 8y^2)$ $9x^2y^2 - 3x^2y^3 + 6xy^4$

16. $0.3x(1.2x + 3.04xy)$ $0.36x^2 + 0.912x^2y$

Remove grouping symbols and simplify completely.

17. $5(x - 3y) - 2(y + 4x)$ $-3x - 17y$

18. $-2\{x + 3[y - 2(x + y)]\}$ $10x + 6y$

19. $-a\{3 - a[a + b(1 - a)]\}$ $-3a + a^3 + a^2b - a^3b$

20. $8[1 + 3(x - y)] + 2[2x - (x + y)]$ $26x - 26y + 8$

21. $3(x + 2y) - 3[x - 4(x + 2y)]$ $12x + 30y$

22. $\dfrac{1}{2}(a - b) - \dfrac{1}{3}(3a + b)$ $-\dfrac{1}{2}a - \dfrac{5}{6}b$

23. $4x(x - 3) - 2(3x + 4x^2)$ $-4x^2 - 18x$

24. $14x - 2x\{3x - x(4 - 3x) + 2x\}$ $14x - 2x^2 - 6x^3$

25. $18 - 9(2a - 3b) + 3a(b - 1)$ $18 - 21a + 27b + 3ab$

26. $\dfrac{2}{3}x^2\left(y - \dfrac{5}{2}\right) - \dfrac{1}{3}x(xy + 6x)$ $\dfrac{1}{3}x^2y - \dfrac{11}{3}x^2$

27. $0.2x(0.3x + 0.1) - 0.05(x^2 - 2x)$ $0.01x^2 + 0.12x$

Section 1.6

Evaluate.

1. $-5x + 6;\ x = 4$ -14

2. $x^2 + 3x - 2;\ x = -2$ -4

3. $x^3 - 2x^2 + x - 6;\ x = 3$ 6

4. $x^2 - 3xy + y^2;\ x = 1,\ y = -3$ 19

5. $\sqrt{b^2 - 4ac};\ b = 5,\ a = 3,\ c = -2$ 7

6. $(3x - 2)^2 - 5x;\ x = 2$ 6

7. $3x^2 - 2xz + z^2;\ x = 0,\ z = -2$ 4

8. $(3x + 2y)(3x - 2y);\ x = 2,\ y = -1$ 32

9. $(2x + 5y)^3;\ x = -3,\ y = 1$ -1

10. $\sqrt{a^2 + b^2};\ a = -3,\ b = 4$ 5

11. $52x^2yz^3;\ x = -2,\ y = 0,\ z = -3$ 0

12. $(x + 2)(x - 3)(x + 4)(x - 5);\ x = 4$ -48

13. $\dfrac{4x + 6}{2x + 3};\ x = -7$ 2

14. $\dfrac{x^2 - x - 6}{x - 3};\ x = 4$ 6

Solve using a formula.

15. Find $Z = \dfrac{Rr}{R + r}$ if $R = 18$ and $r = 2$. $\dfrac{9}{5}$

16. Find the circumference of a circle if the diameter is 5 meters. (Use $\pi \approx 3.14$.) 15.7 m.

17. Find the volume of a right circular cylinder with a height of 4 meters and a radius of 2 meters. (Use $\pi \approx 3.14$.) 50.24 cu. m.

18. Find the area of a triangle with a base of 6.1 centimeters and an altitude of 2.6 centimeters. 7.93 sq. cm.

19. Find A in the formula $A = P(1 + rt)$ if $P = \$3600$, $r = 0.05$, and $t = 3$. $\$4140$

20. Find S in the formula $S = \dfrac{n}{2}[2a + (n - 1)d]$ if $n = 14$, $a = 1$, $d = -4$. -350

21. If $A = \dfrac{1}{2}bh$, find A if $b = 12$ and $h = 13$. 78

22. If $A = \dfrac{1}{2}h(b_1 + b_2)$, find A if $h = 11$, $b_1 = 3$, and $b_2 = 5$. 44

23. If $S = \dfrac{1}{2}gt^2$, find S if $g = 32$ and $t = 5$. 400

24. If $C = \dfrac{5}{9}(F - 32°)$, find C if $F = 212°$. 100

25. If $V = \dfrac{4}{3}\pi r^3$, find V if $\pi = \dfrac{22}{7}$ and $r = 21$. 38,808

Section 1.7

Solve for x. Check your solution.

1. $5x + 6 = 41$ $x = 7$

2. $6x + 3 = 2x - 7$ $x = -\dfrac{5}{2}$

3. $4 - (2x + 3) = 12 + 9x$ $x = -1$

4. $5(x + 2) = 3x - 2(x + 1)$ $x = -3$

5. $3(2x + 1) - 2(x - 2) = 5$ $x = -\dfrac{1}{2}$

6. $6 - 2(3x - 2) = 4x$ $x = 1$

7. $3x - 8 = 16 - 4x$ $x = \dfrac{24}{7}$

8. $7x - 30 = 2x - 15$ $x = 3$

9. $8 - 3x = 2x - 2$ $x = 2$

10. $2[4 - 3(1 - 2x)] = 7$ $x = \dfrac{5}{12}$

11. $2(3x - 4) - 4(2 - x) = 18$ $x = \dfrac{17}{5}$

Solve for the unknown.

12. $\dfrac{2x}{3} = 7 - \dfrac{x}{2}$ $x = 6$

13. $\dfrac{5y}{4} - 1 = \dfrac{3y}{4} + \dfrac{1}{2}$ $y = 3$

14. $\dfrac{4w}{5} - \dfrac{2w + 3}{4} = 1$ $w = \dfrac{35}{6}$

15. $\dfrac{271 + 2x}{5} = 93$ $x = 97$

16. $2w - 3(w - 2) = \dfrac{1}{2}(w + 1)$ $w = \dfrac{11}{3}$

17. $\dfrac{1}{3}(y - 5) = y + 1 - \dfrac{1}{5}y$ $y = -\dfrac{40}{7}$

18. $\dfrac{2x - 3}{2} = \dfrac{4x - 1}{6} + \dfrac{1}{3}$ $x = 5$

19. $\dfrac{2y - 3}{4} = 1 + \dfrac{y - 5}{3}$ $y = \dfrac{1}{2}$

20. $\dfrac{8 - 4x}{4} + \dfrac{6x + 3}{3} = 1$ $x = -2$

21. $\dfrac{4a + 3}{2} = \dfrac{5a - 1}{2}$ $a = 4$

22. $0.2(x - 3) = 0.4(x + 1)$ $x = -5$

23. $0.01(2 - x) - 0.2(x + 1) = 0.04$ $x = \dfrac{-22}{21}$

24. $\dfrac{x}{45} = \dfrac{x}{9} - \dfrac{x}{5}$ $x = 0$

25. $\dfrac{36 - 2x}{2} + \dfrac{(4x - 8)}{4} = x$ $x = 16$

Section 1.8

Solve for x.

1. $7x + 3y = -5$ $x = \dfrac{-3y - 5}{7}$

2. $7y - 4x = 8$ $x = \dfrac{7y - 8}{4}$

3. $3axy + 2 = 4y$ $x = \dfrac{4y - 2}{3ay}$

4. $3w - 2(x + w) = 5w$ $x = -2w$

5. $3x + 2b + 5b = 7x - 3b$ $x = \dfrac{5b}{2}$

6. $\dfrac{3}{5}(x - a) = 2(x + a)$ $x = \dfrac{-13a}{7}$

7. $38(ax + 2) = 4a(x - 1)$ $x = \dfrac{-2a - 38}{17a}$

8. $6x + 2a = b - 3$ $x = \dfrac{b - 3 - 2a}{6}$

9. $5ax - 2bc = 3 - 2ax$ $x = \dfrac{3 + 2bc}{7a}$

10. $0.2(x - a) = 0.3(a + x)$ $x = -5a$

11. $\dfrac{5bx}{2} = \dfrac{2bx}{3} + \dfrac{1}{4}$ $x = \dfrac{3}{22b}$

12. $4x(a + b) = 4bx - 7$ $x = \dfrac{-7}{4a}$

Solve for the letter specified.

13. $7abc - 3ab - 7 = 5abc - 4ab$; for c $c = \dfrac{7 - ab}{2ab}$

14. $2(x + 3yw) = \dfrac{2}{5}(x - 2)$; for y $y = \dfrac{-4x - 2}{15w}$

15. $\dfrac{7}{8} + 2y = \dfrac{3}{4}x - 8y$; for y $y = \dfrac{6x - 7}{80}$

16. $5ab - 2x = 3b(a + 4)$; for a $a = \dfrac{x + 6b}{b}$

17. $3x + 2y = z + 2$; for y $y = \dfrac{z + 2 - 3x}{2}$

18. $C = \dfrac{5}{9}(F - 32)$; for F $F = \dfrac{9C + 160}{5}$

19. $S = \dfrac{1}{2}gt^2$; for g $g = \dfrac{2s}{t^2}$

20. $\dfrac{4}{r_1} = \dfrac{1}{r_1} + \dfrac{1}{r_2}$; for r_2 $r_2 = \dfrac{r_1}{3}$

21. $a = \dfrac{h}{2}(b_1 + b_2)$; for b_2 $b_2 = \dfrac{2a - hb_1}{h}$

Follow the directions given.

22. (a) $A = P + Prt$ Solve for t. $t = \dfrac{A - P}{Pr}$

   (b) Evaluate when $A = 260$, $P = 200$, and $r = 0.1$. $t = 3$

23. (a) $S = \dfrac{n}{2}[2a + d(n - 1)]$ Solve for a. $a = \dfrac{2S + nd - dn^2}{2n}$

   (b) Evaluate when $S = 820$, $n = 20$, and $d = 4$. $a = 3$

24. (a) $F = \dfrac{9}{5}C + 32$ Solve for C. $C = \dfrac{5F - 160}{9}$

   (b) Evaluate for $F = 212°$. $C = 100°$

25. (a) $S = \dfrac{n}{2}(a + l)$ Solve for a. $a = \dfrac{2S - nl}{n}$

   (b) Evaluate for $S = 80$, $n = 10$, and $l = 12$. $a = 4$

Solve for x.

1. $|6x - 1| = 17$ $x = 3$ $x = -\dfrac{8}{3}$

2. $|2 - x| = 8$ $x = -6$ $x = 10$

3. $\left|\dfrac{1}{3}x - 2\right| = 4$ $x = 18$ $x = -6$

4. $\left|x + \dfrac{1}{2}\right| = 3$ $x = \dfrac{5}{2}$ $x = -\dfrac{7}{2}$

5. $|2 - 3x| + 5 = 9$ $x = -\dfrac{2}{3}$ $x = 2$

6. $|4 - 9x| - 2 = 12$ $x = -\dfrac{10}{9}$ $x = 2$

7. $|2x + 5| - 3 = 5$ $x = \dfrac{3}{2}$ $x = -\dfrac{13}{2}$

8. $|2x + 9| + 5 = 6$ $x = -4$ $x = -5$

9. $|3x + 5| = |4x - 1|$ $x = 6$ $x = -\dfrac{4}{7}$

10. $|6x + 1| = |3 + 5x|$ $x = 2$ $x = -\dfrac{4}{11}$

11. $|1 - 2x| = |3 - 4x|$ $x = -1$ $x = \dfrac{2}{3}$

12. $|6 - 3x| = |5 - 2x|$ $x = 1$ $x = \dfrac{11}{5}$

13. $|-6 - 8x| = |3x - 6|$ $x = 0$ $x = -\dfrac{12}{5}$

14. $|-5 - 6x| = |2x - 5|$ $x = 0$ $x = -\dfrac{5}{2}$

CHAPTER ORGANIZER

Topic	Procedure	Examples
Closure property of addition, p. 5	For real numbers a, b, c, $a + b$ is a real number.	$5 + 7$ is a real number.
Closure property of multiplication, p. 5	$a \cdot b$ is a real number.	$7 \cdot 6$ is a real number.
Commutative property of addition, p. 5	$a + b = b + a$	$12 + 13 = 13 + 12$
Commutative property of multiplication, p. 5	$a \cdot b = b \cdot a$	$11 \cdot 19 = 19 \cdot 11$
Associative property of addition, p. 5	$a + (b + c) = (a + b) + c$	$4 + (3 + 6) = (4 + 3) + 6$
Associative property of multiplication, p. 5	$a \cdot (b \cdot c) = (a \cdot b) \cdot c$	$7 \cdot (3 \cdot 2) = (7 \cdot 3) \cdot 2$
Identity property of addition, p. 5	$a + 0 = 0 + a = a$	$9 + 0 = 0 + 9 = 9$
Identity property of multiplication, p. 5	$a \cdot 1 = 1 \cdot a = a$	$7 \cdot 1 = 1 \cdot 7 = 7$
Inverse property of addition, p. 5	$a + (-a) = (-a) + a = 0$	$8 + (-8) = -8 + 8 = 0$
Inverse property of multiplication, p. 5	If $a \neq 0$, $a\left(\dfrac{1}{a}\right) = \dfrac{1}{a}(a) = 0$	$15\left(\dfrac{1}{15}\right) = \dfrac{1}{15}(15) = 1$
Distributive property of multiplication after addition, p. 5	$a(b + c) = a \cdot b + a \cdot c$	$7(9 + 4) = 7 \cdot 9 + 7 \cdot 4$
Addition of signed numbers, p. 10	*Addition:* To add two real numbers with the *same sign*, add their absolute values and use the common sign. To add two real numbers with *different signs*, take the difference of their absolute values and the answer takes the sign of the number with the larger absolute value.	$9 + 5 = 14$ $-7 + (-3) = -10$ $-\dfrac{1}{5} + \left(\dfrac{3}{5}\right) = \dfrac{2}{5}$ $-42 + 19 = -23$
Subtraction of signed numbers, p. 12	*Subtraction:* To subtract b from a, *add the opposite* of b to a. $$a - b = a + (-b)$$	$12 - (-3) = 12 + (+3) = 15$ $-7.2 - (+1.6) = -7.2 + (-1.6) = -8.8$
Multiplication and division of signed numbers, p. 13	*Multiplication and Division:* When you multiply or divide two signed numbers with like signs, the answer is a *positive* number. When you multiply or divide two signed numbers whose signs are *different*, the answer is a *negative* number.	$(-6)(-3) = 18$ $-20 \div (-4) = 5$ $(-8)(5) = -40$ $16 \div (-2) = -8$

Topic	Procedure	Examples
Order of operations of real numbers, p. 20	For involved numerical expressions, use this order of operations. 1. Combine numbers inside grouping symbols. 2. Raise numbers to their indicated powers and take any indicated roots. 3. Multiply and divide numbers from left to right. 4. Add and subtract numbers from left to right.	Simplify: $5 + 2(5 - 8)^3 - 12 \div (-4)$. $5 + 2(-3)^3 - 12 \div (-4)$ $= 5 + 2(-27) - 12 \div (-4)$ $= 5 + (-54) - (-3)$ $= -49 + 3$ $= -46$
Rules of Exponents for multiplication and division, p. 24	If x, y are any nonzero real numbers and m, n are integers, Multiplication: $x^m x^n = x^{m+n}$ Division: $\dfrac{x^m}{x^n} = x^{m-n}$	$(2x^5)(3x^6) = 6x^{11}$ $\dfrac{15x^8}{5x^3} = 3x^5$
Negative exponents, p. 23	Transforming negative exponents $x^{-n} = \dfrac{1}{x^n} \qquad \dfrac{x^{-n}}{y^{-m}} = \dfrac{y^m}{x^n}$	$x^{-6} = \dfrac{1}{x^6} \qquad 2^{-8} = \dfrac{1}{2^8} \qquad \dfrac{x^{-4}}{y^{-5}} = \dfrac{y^5}{x^4}$
Zero Exponent, p. 25	$x^0 = 1$ when $x \neq 0$	$x^0 = 1 \qquad 5^0 = 1 \qquad (3ab)^0 = 1$
Power Rules, p. 27	$(x^m)^n = x^{mn}$ $(xy)^n = x^n y^n$ $\left(\dfrac{x}{y}\right)^n = \dfrac{x^n}{y^n}$	$(7^3)^4 = 7^{12}$ $(3x^{-2})^4 = 3^4 x^{-8}$ $\left(\dfrac{2a^2}{b^3}\right)^{-4} = \dfrac{2^{-4}a^{-8}}{b^{-12}}$
Solving first-degree (linear) equations, p. 47	1. Remove any parentheses. 2. If fractions exist, multiply all terms on both sides by the LCD of all the fractions. 3. Collect like terms is possible. 4. Add or subtract terms on both sides of the equation to get all terms with the variable on one side of the equation. 5. Add or subtract a value on both sides of the equation to get all terms not containing the variable on the other side of the equation. 6. Divide both sides of the equation by the coefficient of the variable. 7. Simplify the solution (if possible). 8. Check the solution.	Solve for x: $\dfrac{1}{3}(2x - 3) + \dfrac{1}{2}(x + 1) = 3$. $\dfrac{2}{3}x - 1 + \dfrac{1}{2}x + \dfrac{1}{2} = 3$ $6\left(\dfrac{2}{3}x\right) - 6(1) + 6\left(\dfrac{1}{2}x\right) + 6\left(\dfrac{1}{2}\right) = 6(3)$ $4x - 6 + 3x + 3 = 18$ $7x - 3 = 18$ $7x = 18 + 3$ $7x = 21$ $x = 3$ Check: $\dfrac{1}{3}[2(3) - 3] + \dfrac{1}{2}(3 + 1) \stackrel{?}{=} 3$ $\dfrac{1}{3}[3] + \dfrac{1}{2}(4) \stackrel{?}{=} 3$ $1 + 2 = 3 \checkmark$ It checks.
Linear equations and formulas with more than one variable, p. 52	If an equation or formula has more than one variable, you can solve for a particular variable by using the procedure for solving linear equations. Remember, your goal is to get all terms containing the desired variable on one side of the equation and all other terms on the opposite side of the equation.	Solve for r: $A = P(1 + rt)$. $A = P + Prt$ $A - P = Prt$ $\dfrac{A - P}{Pt} = \dfrac{Prt}{Pt}$ $\dfrac{A - P}{Pt} = r$

Topic	Procedure	Examples
Absolute value equations, p. 56	To solve an equation that involves an absolute value we rewrite the absolute value equation as two separate equations. We solve each equation. If $\lvert ax + b\rvert = c$ then $ax + b = c$ or $ax + b = -c$	Solve for x: $\lvert 4x - 1\rvert = 17$. $4x - 1 = 17$ or $4x - 1 = -17$ $4x = 17 + 1$ $4x = -17 + 1$ $4x = 18$ $4x = -16$ $x = \dfrac{18}{4}$ $x = \dfrac{-16}{4}$ $x = \dfrac{9}{2}$ $x = -4$

REVIEW PROBLEMS CHAPTER 1

1. List all the elements of the set $\{x \mid x$ is an even whole number less than 12$\}$.

0, 2, 4, 6, 8, 10

In problems 2 and 3, name the properties of real numbers that justify each statement.

2. $(2 + 3) + (7 + x) = (2 + 3) + (x + 7)$

Commutative property for addition

3. $5(2 \cdot x) = (5 \cdot 2) \cdot x$

Associative property for multiplication

4. Are all rational numbers also real numbers?

Yes

Compute.

5. $2 - 3(-4) + 6 \div (-2)$

11

6. $\dfrac{5 - 8}{2 - 7 - (-2)}$

1

7. $4\sqrt{16} + 2^3 - 6$

18

8. $4 - 2 + 6\left(-\dfrac{1}{3}\right)$

0

9. $3 - \lvert -4\rvert + (-2)^3$

-9

10. $\sqrt{(-3)^2} + (-2)^3$

-5

11. $\sqrt{\dfrac{25}{36}} - 2\left(\dfrac{1}{12}\right)$

$\dfrac{2}{3}$

12. $2\sqrt{16} + 3(-4)(0)(2) - 2^2$

4

Simplify. In Problems 13–18, you may leave negative exponents in your answer.

13. $(3xy^2)(-2x^0y)(4x^3y^3)$

$-24x^4y^6$

14. $(2^4ab)(2^{-3}a^{-5}b^6)$

$2a^{-4}b^7$

15. $\dfrac{5^{-3}x^{-3}y^6}{5^{-5}x^{-5}y^8}$

$25x^2y^{-2}$

16. $\dfrac{27ab^3c}{81a^5bc^0}$

$\dfrac{3b^2c}{4a^4}$ or $\dfrac{3}{4}a^{-4}b^2c$

17. $\left(\dfrac{-3x^3y}{2x^4z^2}\right)^4$

$\dfrac{81y^4}{16x^4z^8}$ or $\dfrac{81}{16}x^{-4}y^4z^{-8}$

18. $\dfrac{(-2a^{-3}b^{-4})^3}{(-3a^{-4}b^2c)^{-2}}$

$-\dfrac{72c^2}{a^{17}b^8}$ or $-72a^{-17}b^{-8}c^2$

19. $(2^{-1}a^2b^{-4})^3$

$\dfrac{a^6}{8b^{12}}$ or $2^{-3}a^6b^{-12}$

20. $\dfrac{3^{-2}x^5y^{-6}}{3x^{-4}y^{-5}}$

$\dfrac{x^9}{27y}$ or $3^{-3}x^9y^{-1}$

21. $\dfrac{(3^{-1}x^{-2}y)^{-2}}{(4^{-1}xy^{-2})^{-1}}$

$\dfrac{9x^5}{4y^4}$ or $\dfrac{9}{4}x^5y^{-4}$

22. $\left(\dfrac{a^5b^2}{3^{-1}a^{-5}b^{-4}}\right)^3$

$27a^{30}b^{18}$

23. Write in scientific notation: 0.00721.

7.21×10^{-3}

24. Change to scientific notation and multiply: (5,300,000)(2,000,000,000). Express your answer in scientific notation.

1.06×10^{16}

25. Collect like terms:
$2ab - 4a^2b - 6b^2 - 3ab + 2a^2b + 5b^3$

$-ab - 2a^2b - 6b^2 + 5b^3$

26. Multiply:
$-5ab^2(a^3 + 2a^2b - 3b - 4)$

$-5a^4b^2 - 10a^3b^3 + 15ab^3 + 20ab^2$

In problems 27 and 28, remove grouping symbols and simplify.

27. $3a[2a - 3(a + 4)]$

$-3a^2 - 36a$

28. $2x^2 - \{2 + x[3 - 2(x - 1)]\}$

$4x^2 - 5x - 2$

29. Evaluate $5x^2 - 3xy - 2y^3$ when $x = 2$ and $y = -1$.

28

30. A right circular cylinder has a height of 2 meters and a radius of 3 meters. Find its volume.

56.52 cu.m

Solve for x in problems 31–36.

31. $5x - 1 = -6x - 23$

$x = -2$

32. $6 - (3x + 5) = 15 - (x - 6)$

$x = -10$

33. $4(x - 1) + 2 = 3x + 8 - 2x$

$x = \dfrac{10}{3}$

34. $x - \dfrac{7}{5} = \dfrac{1}{3}x + \dfrac{7}{15}$

$x = \dfrac{14}{5}$

35. $\dfrac{x - 4}{2} - \dfrac{1}{5} = \dfrac{7x + 1}{20}$

$x = 15$

36. $\dfrac{1}{9}x - 1 = \dfrac{1}{2}\left(x + \dfrac{1}{3}\right)$

$x = -3$

37. Solve for y: $4x - 8y = 5$.

$y = \dfrac{4x - 5}{8}$

38. Solve for a: $2(3ax - 2y) - 6ax = -3(ax + 2y)$.

$a = \dfrac{2y}{-3x}$

39. (a) Solve for W: $P = 2W + 2L$. $W = \dfrac{P - 2L}{2}$
(b) Now find W when $P = 100$ meters and $L = 20.5$ meters. 29.5 m

40. (a) Solve for F: $C = \dfrac{5F - 160}{9}$. $F = \dfrac{9C + 160}{5}$
(b) Now find F when $C = 10°$. $F = 50°$

Solve for x.

41. $|x + 1| = 8$ $x = 7$
$x = -9$

42. $|x - 3| = 12$ $x = 15$
$x = -9$

43. $|4x - 5| = 7$ $x = 3$
$x = -\dfrac{1}{2}$

44. $|3x + 2| = 20$ $x = 6$
$x = -\dfrac{22}{3}$

45. $|x + 8| = |2x - 4|$ $x = 12$
$x = -\dfrac{4}{3}$

46. $|3 - x| = |5 - 2x|$ $x = 2$
$x = \dfrac{8}{3}$

47. $\left|\dfrac{1}{4}x - 3\right| = 8$ $x = 44$
$x = -20$

48. $|4 - 7x| = 25$ $x = -3$
$x = \dfrac{29}{7}$

49. $|6 - 5x| - 5 = 2$ $x = -\dfrac{1}{5}$
$x = \dfrac{13}{5}$

50. $|2x - 8| + 7 = 12$ $x = \dfrac{13}{2}$
$x = \dfrac{3}{2}$

PUTTING YOUR SKILLS TO WORK

A Formula for the Brightness Ratio of Stars

The general procedure for measuring how bright stars appear to the naked eye was developed by Hipparchus more than 2000 years ago. He created six categories of stars, ranging from sixth magnitude (the faintest stars visible to the naked eye) to the first magnitude (the brightest stars visible to the naked eye). This system is still used and has even been extended to include stars that are not visible to the naked eye.

A formula has been developed to compare the brightness of two stars. The formula is more involved than those we examined in Section 1.6 because it uses powers of 10 that are not integers. We examine this concept in more detail in Chapter 6.

For now, just realize that we can approximate values such as $10^{0.4}$ and $10^{1.6}$. These values can be obtained on a calculator with a $\boxed{y^x}$ or $\boxed{10^x}$ key or from a table. The one below is an abbreviated table of such values.

APPROXIMATE VALUES
FOR 10^x

x	10^x	x	10^x
0.0	1.00	1.0	10.0
0.1	1.26	1.1	12.6
0.2	1.58	1.2	15.8
0.3	2.00	1.3	20.0
0.4	2.51	1.4	25.1
0.5	3.16	1.5	31.6
0.6	3.98	1.6	39.8
0.7	5.01	1.7	50.1
0.8	6.31	1.8	63.1
0.9	7.94	1.9	79.4
		2.0	100.0

The formula is

$$\frac{B_2}{B_1} = 10^{0.4(M_1 - M_2)}$$

where M_1 and M_2 are the magnitudes of two stars, and B_1 and B_2 are their measures of brightness. B_2/B_1 is the ratio of the brightness of star 2 to that of star 1.

For example, the star Polaris has a magnitude of 1.99 and the star Archernar has a magnitude of 0.51. Thus,

$$\frac{B_2}{B_1} = 10^{0.4(1.99 - 0.51)}$$
$$= 10^{0.4(1.48)} = 10^{0.592} \approx 10^{0.6}$$

From the table we find that $10^{0.6} \approx 3.98$. Therefore, Archernar is approximately 3.98 times as bright as Polaris.

A Challenge For You!

Use Table 1.3 (or a calculator with a $\boxed{y^x}$ key) to answer these questions.

1. How much brighter is Rigel (magnitude 0.14) than Castor (magnitude 1.97)?

2. How much brighter is Sirius (magnitude -1.47) than Alnilam (magnitude 1.79)?

Answers

1. Approximately 5.01 times brighter
2. Approximately 20 times brighter

For the set $\left\{-2\sqrt{3}, -\dfrac{1}{3}, 0, \dfrac{1}{5}, \pi, \dfrac{12}{3}, 5.676767, \ldots, 18.62\right\}$:

1. List the integers.   **2.** List the irrational numbers.

3. True or false: All rational numbers are real numbers.

Name the property that justifies each statement.

4. $(18 + x) + 0 = 18 + x$ **5.** $(16 + x) \cdot y = (x + 16) \cdot y$

Evaluate.

6. $(-3)^2 + 4^3 + |-2|$.   **7.** $3\sqrt{16 - 7} + 2\sqrt{(5)(7) + 1}$.

8. $\dfrac{-3(2)(-4) + 6(-1)}{(-2)^3 - 2^2}$

Simplify each expression. You may leave negative exponents in your answer.

9. $2^{-18} \cdot 2^{20} \cdot 2^{30} \cdot 2^0$ **10.** $\dfrac{x^{-15}}{6x^{-10}}$

1. $0, \dfrac{12}{3}$

2. $-2\sqrt{3}, \pi$

3. True

4. Identity property for addition

5. Commutative property for addition

6. 75

7. 21

8. $-\dfrac{3}{2}$

9. 2^{32}

10. $\dfrac{1}{6x^5}$ or $\dfrac{x^{-5}}{6}$

11. $-30x^3$ _____

12. $\dfrac{3y^4}{5xz}$ or $\dfrac{3}{5}x^{-1}y^4z^{-1}$ _____

13. $\dfrac{1}{81x^8y^4}$ or $\dfrac{1}{81}x^{-8}y^{-4}$ _____

14. $\dfrac{1}{8x^{24}y^{15}}$ or $\dfrac{1}{8}x^{-24}y^{-15}$ _____

15. $-\dfrac{x^{10}}{32y^{15}}$ _____

16. $\dfrac{a^2}{b^4c^{10}}$ _____

17. $\dfrac{27x^2}{y^{13}}$ _____

18. $\dfrac{16}{a^{22}b^2}$ _____

19. 3.13×10^{-7} _____

20. $\dfrac{(3 \times 10^9)(2.14 \times 10^7)}{= 6.42 \times 10^{16}}$ _____

---

11. $(5x^{-3})(-2x^6)(3x^0)$

12. $\dfrac{-15x^3y^{-2}}{-25x^4y^{-6}z}$

13. $(-3x^2y)^{-4}$

14. $\left(\dfrac{7x^{-2}y^{-3}}{14x^6y^2}\right)^3$

Simplify problems 15–18. Use only positive exponents in your answer.

15. $(-2x^{-2}y^3)^{-5}$

16. $(a^{-8}b^2c^{-4})(a^{10}b^{-6}c^{-6})$

17. $\dfrac{3x^{-2}y^{-7}}{3^{-2}x^{-4}y^6}$

18. $\left(\dfrac{4^{-1}a^5b^{-2}}{a^{-6}b^{-3}}\right)^{-2}$

19. Write in scientific notation: 0.000000313.

20. Change to scientific notation and multiply: ($3,000,000,000)(21,400,000). Write your answer in scientific notation.

In problems 1–6, simplify each expression.

1. $\dfrac{1}{2}x + 3x^2 - 2x + 5x^2$

2. $3ab - 2b^2 - 6ab - 7b^2 + 3ab^2$

3. $-3(x^2 - 2xy - 1)$

4. $4x^2y(-x^2 + 3x - 4)$

5. $2(a - 3b) - 6a(2 - 4b)$

6. $2 + 3\{x - 2[x + 3(x - 1)]\}$

7. Evaluate $3(x - 2)^2$ when $x = -3$.

8. Evaluate $x^3 + 3x^2 - 2xy + y^2$ when $x = -2$ and $y = 3$.

9. Find the perimeter of a parallelogram if two of the sides measure 16 centimeters and 7 centimeters.

10. Find the volume of a sphere of radius 3 feet.

1. $-\dfrac{2}{3}x + 8x^2$

2. $-3ab - 9b^2 + 3ab^2$

3. $-3x^2 + 6xy + 3$

4. $-4x^4y + 12x^3y - 16x^2y$

5. $-10a + 24ab - 6b$

6. $20 - 21x$

7. 75

8. 25

9. 46 centimeters

10. 113.04 ft³

11. -13

12. $y = 68$

13. $x = -\dfrac{11}{5}$

14. $y = \dfrac{8x + 12}{5}$

15. (a) $y = \dfrac{5H - B}{Bx}$ (b) $y = 3$

16. $x = -4$ $x = 8$

17. $x = 3$ $x = -\dfrac{9}{5}$

18. $x = 2$ $x = \dfrac{1}{3}$

11. Solve: $3 - 2(4 - x) = 2(x + 4) + x$.

12. Solve: $\dfrac{1}{3}(y - 2) = \dfrac{1}{4}y + 5$.

13. Solve: $5x - 2 = -13$.

14. Solve for y: $8x - 5y = -12$.

15. (a) Solve for y: $H = \dfrac{1}{5}(B + Bxy)$.

(b) Find y if $B = 50$, $x = \dfrac{1}{2}$, and $H = 25$.

Solve for x:

16. $\left|\dfrac{x - 2}{3}\right| = 2$

17. $|5x - 3| - 4 = 8$

18. $|2x + 1| = |4x - 3|$

For the set $\left\{16, 13, \dfrac{8}{2}, \dfrac{15}{15}, 0, -\pi, -\dfrac{2}{3}, -1.67236723\ldots, \sqrt{7}, 3\sqrt{2}\right\}$:

1. List the real numbers that are not rational.

2. List the whole numbers.

3. Name the property that justifies this statement: $(8 \cdot x)3 = 8(x \cdot 3)$.

In problems 4–23, you may leave negative exponents in your answer.

4. Evaluate:
$(3 - 2)^3 + 12 \div (-4) + 2\sqrt{8 + 1}$.

5. Evaluate: $\dfrac{2 - 3\sqrt{16} - 2^3}{|2 - 11|}$.

6. Simplify: $(6a^{-6}b^{-2})(-2ab)(3a^4b^0)$.

7. Simplify: $\dfrac{16x^{-3}y^4z^{-5}}{-20x^{-2}y^3z^8}$.

8. Simplify: $\left(\dfrac{5a^{-3}b^{-4}}{-15a^2b^{-6}}\right)^{-2}$.

9. Simplify:
$5x + 7x^2 - 6x - 8x^2 - 15x$.

10. Simplify:
$2a - 3b - 5a^2 - 8b - 6a + 3a^2$.

11. Simplify: $2ab^2(3a + 2b - 6a^3)$.

12. Simplify: $2\{3x - 2[x - 3(x + 5)]\}$.

13. Evaluate $2x^2 - 3x - 6$ when $x = -4$.

---

1. $-\pi, \sqrt{7}, 3\sqrt{2}$

2. $16, 13, \dfrac{8}{2}, \dfrac{15}{15}, 0$

3. Associative property for multiplication

4. 4

5. -2

6. $-36a^{-1}b^{-1}$ or $\dfrac{-36}{ab}$

7. $-\dfrac{4}{5}x^{-1}yz^{-13}$ or $\dfrac{-4y}{5xz^{13}}$

8. $9a^{10}b^{-4}$ or $\dfrac{9a^{10}}{b^4}$

9. $-x^2 - 16x$

10. $-2a^2 - 4a - 11b$

11. $6a^2b^2 + 4ab^3 - 12a^4b^2$

12. $14x + 60$

13. 38

14. 9 _____

15. 78 sq. m _____

16. 113.04 sq. m _____

17. $x = 1$ _____

18. $x = \dfrac{1}{2}$ _____

19. $x = -5$ _____

20. $n = \dfrac{L - a + d}{d}$ _____

21. $C = \dfrac{5F - 160}{9}$ _____

22. $C = -40°$ _____

23. $r = \dfrac{4H - 12b + 1}{2}$ _____

24. 2.186×10^{-6} _____

25. $x = -7 \qquad x = \dfrac{39}{5}$ _____

26. $x = 6 \qquad x = -18$ _____

14. Evaluate $5x^2 + 3xy - y^2$ when $x = 3$ and $y = -3$.

15. Find the area of a trapezoid with an altitude of 12 meters and bases of 6 and 7 meters.

16. Find the area of a cricle with a diameter of 12 meters.

17. Solve: $\dfrac{1}{3}(x - 1) + 4 = 4(3x - 2)$.

18. Solve: $3(7 - 2x) = 14 - 8(x - 1)$.

19. Solve: $3x + 2 = -13$.

20. Solve for n: $L = a + d(n - 1)$.

21. Solve for C: $F = \dfrac{9}{5}C + 32$.

22. Use your answer for problem 21 to evaluate C when $F = -40°$.

23. Solve for r: $H = \dfrac{1}{2}r + 3b - \dfrac{1}{4}$.

24. Write in scientific notation: 0.000002186.

Solve for x:

25. $|5x - 2| = 37$

26. $\left|\dfrac{1}{2}x + 3\right| - 2 = 4$

Applications of Linear Equations

The rate at which people learn a foreign language varies from person to person and can be determined by a bilingual leader using a mathematical formula.

2

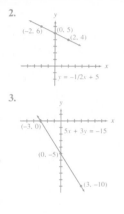

80 gms @ 77% pure copper,
20 gms @ 92% pure copper

PRETEST CHAPTER 2

If you are familiar with the topics in this chapter, take this test now. Check your answers with those in the back of the book. If an answer was wrong or you couldn't do a problem, study the appropriate section of the chapter.

If you are not familiar with the topics in this chapter, don't take this test now. Instead, study the examples, work the practice problems, and then take the test.

This test will help you identify those concepts that you have mastered and those that need more study.

Section 2.1

1. Find the value of a if $(a, 6)$ is a solution of $5x + 2y = -12$. $a = -\dfrac{24}{5}$

Plot three points and graph the lines of these equations.

2. $y = -\dfrac{1}{2}x + 5$

3. $5x + 3y = -15$

Section 2.2

4. Find the slope of the line passing through the points $(2, 8)$ and $(-1, -6)$. $m = \dfrac{14}{3}$

5. Find the slope of the line *perpendicular* to the line passing through the points $(5, 0)$ and $(-13, -4)$. $m_\perp = -\dfrac{9}{2}$

Section 2.3

6. Write the equation of a line of slope -2 that passes through $(7, -3)$. $2x + y = 11$

7. Write the equation of a line passing through $(-1, -2)$ and perpendicular to $2x + 4y = -7$. $y = 2x$

Section 2.4 Use an algebraic equation to find a solution for the problems.

8. The perimeter of a rectangle is 64 centimeters. Its length is 4 centimeters less than three times its width. Find the rectangle's dimensions. 9 cm × 23 cm

9. Eastern Bank charges its customers a flat fee of $6.00 per month for a checking account plus 12¢ for each check. The bank charged Jose $9.12 for his checking account last month. How many checks did he use? 26

Section 2.5 Use an algebraic equation to find a solution for the problems.

10. A technician needs 100 grams of an alloy that is 80% pure copper (Cu). She has one alloy that is 77% pure Cu and another that is 92% pure Cu. How many grams of each alloy should she use to obtain 80% pure Cu?

11. A retired couple earned $4725 in simple interest last year from two investments. They deposited part of their $40,000 life savings in an account bearing 10% interest. They invested the rest of their money in a mutual fund earning 15% interest. How much did they deposit? How much did they invest?
    $25,500 @ 10%, $14,500 @ 15%

☐ After studying this section, you will be able to:

1 *Graph a linear equation in two variables*

2 *Use x- and y-intercepts to graph a linear equation*

2.1 GRAPHING LINEAR EQUATIONS WITH TWO UNKNOWNS

To form a rectangular (two-dimensional) coordinate system,[†] we construct two real number lines—one horizontally and one vertically—that intersect. The horizontal line is the **x-axis** (or **abscissa**), and its equation is $y = 0$. The vertical line is the **y-axis**

[†] A rectangular coordinate system is also called a *Cartesian coordinate system*, after its inventor René Descartes

(or **ordinate**), and its equation is $x = 0$. The axes intersect at the **origin** (or zero point). The two number lines divide the rectangular coordinate system into four areas called **quadrants**, which are labeled I, II, III, and IV. (The points of the axes do not belong to the quadrants.)

To graph an ordered pair of real numbers on a rectangular coordinate system, we begin at the origin. For example, we plot (locate) the point (a, b), $a, b > 0$, by moving a units to the right of the origin and b units up. Pay attention to the word *ordered*. The order of the coordinates is important; $(a, b) \neq (b, a)$. The figure below shows plots of $(3, 4)$ and $(4, 3)$.

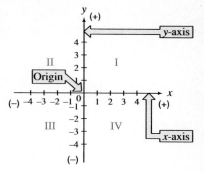

Example 1 Graph the ordered pairs $A(3, 2)$, $B(0, -4)$, $C(-2, -1)$, $D(-5, -4)$, and $E(-3, 4)$ on a rectangular coordinate system.

The points are graphed as shown:

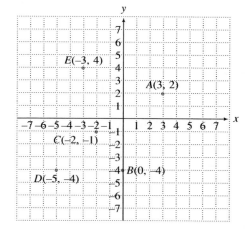

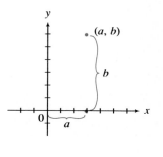

Practice Problem 1 Graph the ordered pairs $A(-4, 1)$, $B(2, -3)$, $C(0, 5)$, $D(-4, -2)$, and $E(4, 0)$ on a rectangular coordinate system. ■

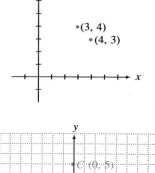

1 Graphing Linear Equations

A **solution of an equation** in two variables is an ordered pair of real numbers that *satisfies* the equation. In other words, when we substitute the values of the coordinates into the equation, we get a true statement. For example, $(0, -4)$, $(3, 0)$, and $(6, 4)$ are solutions to $4x - 3y = 12$.) Let's see why. The ordered pairs $(6, 4)$ means that $x = 6$ and $y = 4$. We substitute these numbers into the equation:

$$4x - 3y = 12$$
$$4(6) - 3(4) = 12$$
$$24 - 12 = 12$$
$$12 = 12$$

Since we obtained an identity (that is, a true statement), the point $(6, 4)$ satisfies the equation. Verify that $(0, -4)$ and $(3, 0)$ are also solutions.

An equation of the form $Ax + By = C$, where A, B, C are constants, is called the **standard form of a linear equation in two unknowns**. The graph of a linear equation is a straight line. To graph it, we find three solutions (sets of points) to the equation, plot them, and connect them with a straight line. (We only need two points to draw a straight line, but we plot the third one for accuracy.)

Example 2 Graph the equation $y = -3x + 2$.

We choose three values of x and then solve the equation to find the corresponding values of y. Let's choose $x = -1$, $x = 1$, and $x = 2$. For $x = -1$,

$$y = -3(-1) + 2 = 3 + 2 = 5$$

so the first point, or solution, is $(-1, 5)$. For $x = 1$,

$$y = -3(1) + 2 = -3 + 2 = -1$$

and for $x = 2$,

$$y = -3(2) + 2 = -6 + 2 = -4$$

Therefore, the second and third points are $(1, -1)$ and $(2, -4)$. We can condense this procedure by using a table like this

x	y
-1	5
1	-1
2	-4

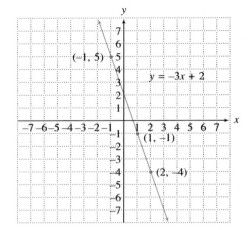

to help us construct a graph.

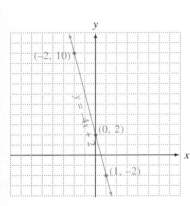

Practice Problem 2   Graph the equation $y = -4x + 2$. ■

2 Graphing a Linear Equation by Using Intercepts

We can quickly graph a straight line by using the x- and y-intercepts. A straight line that is not vertical or horizontal has these two intercepts. In the figure below, the x-intercept is $(a, 0)$ and the y-intercept is $(0, b)$.

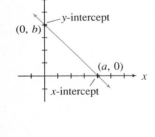

> **Definition**
>
> The **x-intercept** of a line is the point where the line crosses the x-axis (that is, where $y = 0$). The **y-intercept** of a line is the point where the line crosses the y-axis (that is, where $x = 0$).

Example 3   Use intercepts to graph the equation $4x - 3y = -12$.
We find the x-intercept by setting $y = 0$:

$$4x - 3(0) = -12$$

$$4x = -12$$

$$x = -3$$

so the x-intercept is $(-3, 0)$.
We find the y-intercept by setting $x = 0$:

$$4(0) - 3y = -12$$

$$-3y = -12$$

$$y = 4$$

so the y-intercept is $(0, 4)$.

We can now pick any value of x or y to find our third point. Let's pick $y = 2$:

$$4x - 3(2) = -12$$
$$4x - 6 = -12$$
$$4x = -12 + 6$$
$$4x = -6$$
$$x = -\frac{6}{4} = -\frac{3}{2}$$

Hence, the third point on the line is $\left(-\frac{3}{2}, 2\right)$.

The figure below shows the graph of the equation that corresponds to the following table of values:

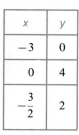

x	y
-3	0
0	4
$-\dfrac{3}{2}$	2

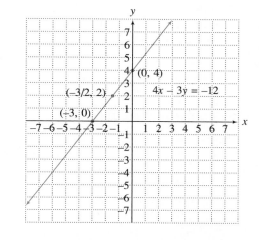

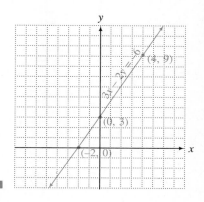

Practice Problem 3   Use intercepts to graph the equation $3x - 2y = -6$. ■

Horizontal and Vertical Lines

The linear equation $Ax + By = C$ reduces to $Ax = C$ if $B = 0$. Solving for x, we get

$$x = \frac{A}{C}$$

But $\dfrac{A}{C}$ is just a constant, so let's rename it a, for convenience. The equation then becomes

$$x = a$$

Its graph is a vertical line.
    Similarly, if $A = 0$, we get $y = b$, which is a horizontal line.

Example 4   Graph each equation.

(a) $x = -3$ **(b)** $2y - 4 = 0$

(a) The equation $x = -3$ is equivalent to the equation $x + 0 \cdot y = -3$. We can assign any value to y and the x-value will always be -3. The graph of $x = -3$ is therefore a vertical line which crosses the x axis 3 units to the left of the origin.

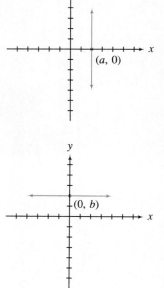

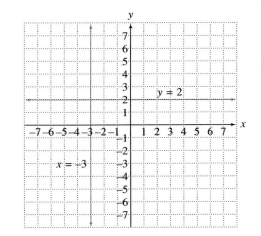

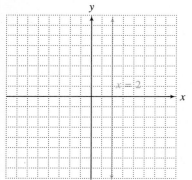

(b) Solving the equation $2y - 4 = 0$ gives $y = 2$, which is equivalent to the equation $0 \cdot x + y = 2$. We can assign any value to x and the y value will always be 2. Therefore, this line is a horizontal line crossing the y-axis 2 units above the origin. ■

Practice Problem 4   Graph the equation $5x + 8 = 9x$. ■

Using Different Scales for the Axes

By common convention, each square on the graph indicates 1 unit, so we don't need to use a marked scale on each axis. But sometimes a different scale is more appropriate. This new scale must then be clearly labeled on each axis.

Example 5   A company's finance officer has determined that the monthly cost in dollars for leasing a photocopy machine is $C = 100 + 0.002n$, where n is the number of copies produced in a month in excess of a specified number. Graph the equation using $n = 0$, 30,000, and 60,000. Let the n-axis be the horizontal axis.
The table of values is

n	C
0	100
30,000	160
60,000	220

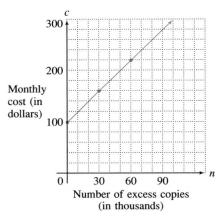

Since n varies from 0 to 60,000 and C varies from 100 to 200, we need a different scale on each axis. We let each square on the horizontal scale represent 10,000 excess copies, and each square on the vertical scale represents $20. ■

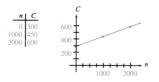

Practice Problem 5   The cost of a product is given by $C = 300 + 0.15n$. Graph the equation using an appropriate scale. ■

STEPS TOWARD SUCCESS IN MATHEMATICS

Mathematics is a building process, mastered one step at a time. The foundation of this process is built on a few basic requirements. Those who are successful in mathematics realize the absolute necessity for building a study of mathematics on the firm foundation of these six minimum requirements.

1. Attend class every day.
2. Read the textbook.
3. Take notes in class.
4. Do assigned homework every day.
5. Get help immediately when needed.
6. Review regularly.

EXERCISES 2.1

Find the missing coordinate.

1. $(-2, \underline{\hspace{1cm}})$ is a solution of $y = 3x - 7$.
$y = 3(-2) - 7; \; y = -13$

2. $(-3, \underline{\hspace{1cm}})$ is a solution of $y = 4 - 3x$.
$y = 4 - 3(-3); \; y = 13$

3. $(\underline{\hspace{1cm}}, 1)$ is a solution of $7x + 14y = -21$.
$7x + 14(1) = -21; \; x = -5$

4. $(\underline{\hspace{1cm}}, 2)$ is a solution of $6x - 24y = 12$.
$6x - 24(2) = 12; \; x = 10$

5. $(0, \underline{\hspace{1cm}})$ is a solution of $7x - 12y = 24$.
$7(0) - 12y = 24; \; y = -2$

6. $(0, \underline{\hspace{1cm}})$ is a solution of $-6x + 3y = 15$.
$-6(0) + 3y = 15; \; y = 5$

7. $(\underline{\hspace{1cm}}, 3)$ is a solution of $2x - 2y = 1$. $2x - 2(3) = 1; \; x = \dfrac{7}{2}$

8. $(\underline{\hspace{1cm}}, 1)$ is a solution of $2x - 4y = -3$.
$2x - 4(1) = -3; \; x = \dfrac{1}{2}$

First simplify each equation. Then graph each equation.

9. $y = 3x - 3$

x	y
0	-3
1	0
2	3

10. $y = -2x + 1$

x	y
-2	5
0	1
2	-3

11. $y = 4 - 2x$

x	y
-1	6
0	4
1	2

12. $y = -5x - 2$

x	y
-1	3
0	-2
1	-7

13. $y = \dfrac{2}{3}x - 4$

x	y
-3	-6
0	-4
3	-2

14. $y = \dfrac{3}{5}x + 2$

x	y
-5	-1
0	2
5	5

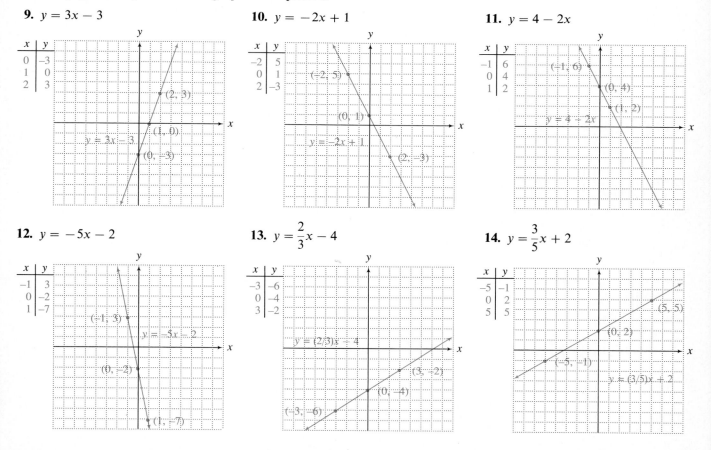

15. $3x - 2y = 6$

x	y
0	-3
2	0
4	3

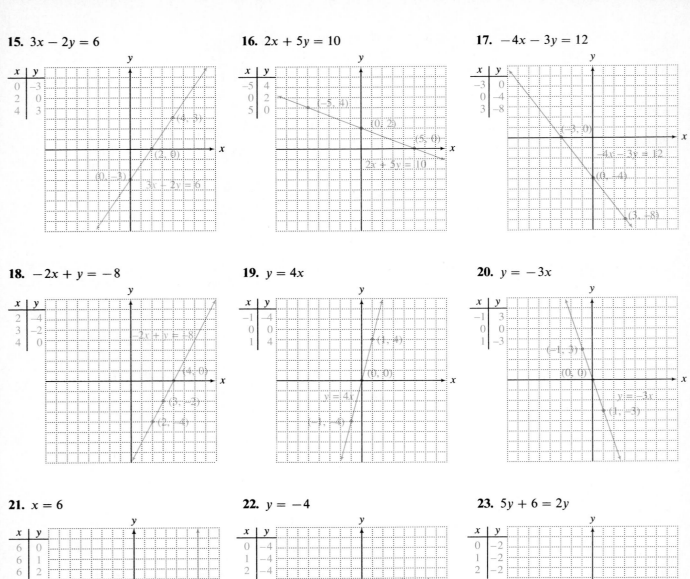

16. $2x + 5y = 10$

x	y
-5	4
0	2
5	0

17. $-4x - 3y = 12$

x	y
-3	0
0	-4
3	-8

18. $-2x + y = -8$

x	y
2	-4
3	-2
4	0

19. $y = 4x$

x	y
-1	-4
0	0
1	4

20. $y = -3x$

x	y
-1	3
0	0
1	-3

21. $x = 6$

x	y
6	0
6	1
6	2

22. $y = -4$

x	y
0	-4
1	-4
2	-4

23. $5y + 6 = 2y$

x	y
0	-2
1	-2
2	-2

24. $-2x + 5 = 3x$

x	y
1	0
1	1
1	2

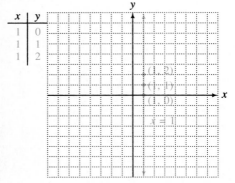

25. $8x + 3 = 4y + 3$

x	y
0	0
1	2
2	4

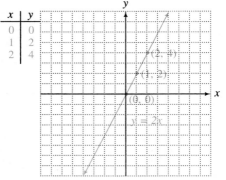

26. $-2x + 5y - 6 = -6$

x	y
-5	-2
0	0
5	2

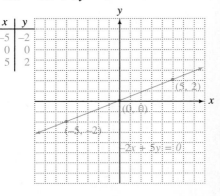

27. $y = -x$

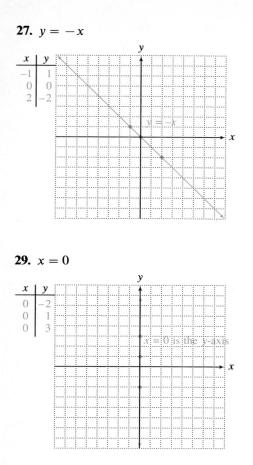

x	y
−1	1
0	0
2	−2

$y = -x$

28. $y = x$

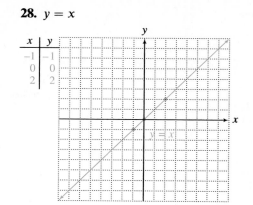

x	y
−1	−1
0	0
2	2

$y = x$

29. $x = 0$

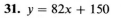

x	y
0	−2
0	1
0	3

$x = 0$ is the y-axis

30. $y = 0$

x	y
−2	0
0	0
3	0

$y = 0$ is the x-axis

Graph each equation. Use an appropriate scale.

31. $y = 82x + 150$

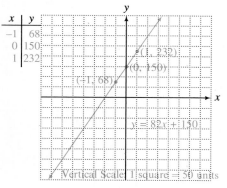

x	y
−1	68
0	150
1	232

(1, 232)
(0, 150)
(−1, 68)
$y = 82x + 150$
Vertical Scale: 1 square = 50 units

32. $y = 0.06x - 0.04$

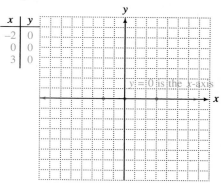

x	y
0	−.04
1	.02
2	.08

(2, .08)
(1, .02)
Vertical Scale:
1 square = 0.01 unit
(0, −.04)
$y = 0.06x - 0.04$

33. If an object is thrown vertically upward from the ground, its velocity V (feet per second) after T seconds is $V = 120 - 32T$.
   (a) Find V for $T = 0, 1, 2, 3,$ and 4.
   (b) Graph the equation.

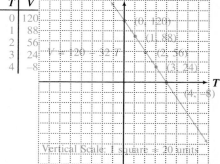

T	V
0	120
1	88
2	56
3	24
4	−8

(0, 120)
(1, 88)
(2, 56)
(3, 24)
$V = 120 - 32T$
(4, −8)
Vertical Scale: 1 square = 20 units

34. A full storage tank contains 900 gallons. Gasoline is then pumped from the tank at a rate of 15 gallons per minute. The equation is $G = 900 - 15m$, where G is the number of gallons of gasoline in the tank and m is the number of minutes since the pumping started.

(a) Find G for $m = 0$, 10, 20, 30, and 60.

(b) Graph the equation.

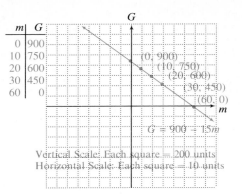

m	G
0	900
10	750
20	600
30	450
60	0

Vertical Scale: Each square = 200 units
Horizontal Scale: Each square = 10 units

To Think About

35. Simplify the expression $5(x - y) + 3(2x + 4y) = 6(y - 2x) - 12$ and graph it.

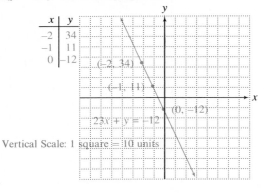

x	y
−2	34
−1	11
0	−12

Vertical Scale: 1 square = 10 units

36. Pick an appropriate scale and graph the equation $P = 14.7 - 0.0005d$ for $d = 0$, 1000, 2000, 3000, 9000, and 15,000. (This equation predicts the atmospheric pressure in pounds per square inch at d feet above sea level.)

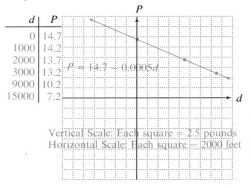

d	P
0	14.7
1000	14.2
2000	13.7
3000	13.2
9000	10.2
15000	7.2

Vertical Scale: Each square = 2.5 pounds
Horizontal Scale: Each square = 2000 feet

Cumulative Review Problems

Solve for the variable.

37. $\dfrac{x}{7} - \dfrac{1}{2} = \dfrac{x}{4} - \dfrac{5}{7}$

$4x - 14 = 7x - 20$
$6 = 3x \quad x = 2$

38. $\dfrac{y}{3} - 1 + y = -\dfrac{1}{2}$

$2y - 6 + 6y = -3$
$8y = 3 \quad y = \dfrac{3}{8}$

39. $\dfrac{1}{6}(w - 7) + \dfrac{1}{2} = 0$

$2(w - 7) + 6 = 0$
$2w = 8$
$w = 4$

40. $3x - 5(x - 2) = \dfrac{1}{3}(x + 2)$

$9x - 15(x - 2) = x + 2$
$-6x + 30 = x + 2$
$4 = x$

Calculator Problems

Find three points on the line determined by the following equation. Use the values $x = 1$, $x = 2$, and $x = 3$.

41. $y = -5.97132x + 8.18205$

(1, 2.21073)
(2, −3.76059)
(3, −9.73191)

42. $1.9823x + 5.7614y = 18.9312$

(1, 2.94180)
(2, 2.59774)
(3, 2.25367)

For Extra Practice Exercises, turn to page 112.

Solutions to Odd-Numbered Practice Problems

1.

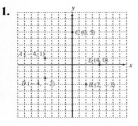

3. $3x - 2y = -6$. We'll use the intercept method.

Choice	Compute			Ordered Pair
Let $x = 0$	$3(0) - 2y = -6$	$-2y = -6$	$y = 3$	$(0, 3)$
Let $y = 0$	$3x - 2(0) = -6$	$3x = -6$	$x = -2$	$(-2, 0)$
Let $x = 4$	$3(4) - 2y = -6$	$12 - 2y = -6$	$y = 9$	$(4, 9)$

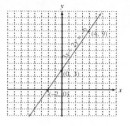

5. Let $n = 0$, 1000, and 2000. We then have

n	C
0	300
1000	450
2000	600

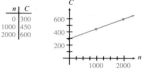

Answers to Even-Numbered Practice Problems

2.

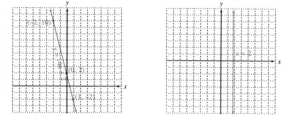

4. The graph is a vertical line; $5x + 8 = 9x$ is equivalent to $2 = x$.

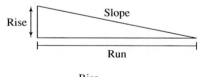

2.2 THE SLOPE OF A LINE

After studying this section, you will be able to:

1 *Find the slope of any nonvertical straight line if two points are known.*

2 *Determine if two lines are parallel or perpendicular by comparing their slopes.*

The concept of slope is one of the most useful in mathematics and in practical applications. A carpenter needs to figure the slope (or pitch) of a roof (you may have heard someone say that a roof has a 5:12 pitch). Road engineers must determine the proper slope (or grade) of a roadbed. If the slope is steep, you feel like you're driving almost straight up. And, perhaps most familiar to everyone, is "ski slope"—the steeper the slope, the faster the skier goes downhill.

Simply put, slope is a variation from the horizontal. That is, slope measures vertical change (*rise*) versus horizontal change (*run*).

$$\text{Slope} = \frac{\text{Rise}}{\text{Run}}$$

Mathematically, we define slope as follows:

1

> The **slope of a straight line** with points (x_1, y_1) and (x_2, y_2) is
>
> $$\text{slope} = m = \frac{y_2 - y_1}{x_2 - x_1} \qquad (x_2 \neq x_1)$$

In each sketch, we see that the rise is $y_2 - y_1$ and the run is $x_2 - x_1$.

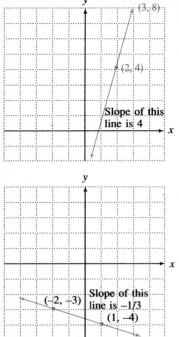

Example 1 Find the slope of a line passing through

(a) (2, 4) and (3, 8)   **(b)** $(-2, -3)$ and $(1, -4)$

(a) Let $(x_1, y_1) = (2, 4)$ and $(x_2, y_2) = (3, 8)$. Thus,

$$m = \frac{y_2 - y_1}{x_2 - x_1} = \frac{8 - 4}{3 - 2} = \frac{4}{1} = 4$$

(b) Let $(x_1, y_1) = (-2, -3)$ and $(x_2, y_2) = (1, -4)$. Thus,

$$m = \frac{y_2 - y_1}{x_2 - x_1} = \frac{-4 - (-3)}{1 - (-2)} = \frac{-4 + 3}{1 + 2} = \frac{-1}{3} = -\frac{1}{3} \quad ∎$$

Practice Problem 1 Find the slope of a line passing through the points $(-6, 1)$ and $(-5, -2)$. ∎

It doesn't matter which point you call (x_1, y_1) or (x_2, y_2). To see this, let's redo part (b) of Example 1. This time let (x_1, y_1) be $(1, -4)$, and let (x_2, y_2) be $(-2, -3)$. Then

$$m = \frac{-3 - (-4)}{-2 - (1)} = \frac{-3 + 4}{-3} = \frac{1}{-3} = -\frac{1}{3}$$

From the sketches we have made we can learn some basic facts about the slope of a line.

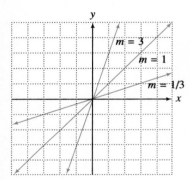

1. Lines sloping upward to the right have positive slopes.
2. Lines sloping downward to the right have negative slopes.

For any two points (x_1, y_1) and (x_2, y_2) in a horizontal line, because the line is horizontal (or parallel to the x-axis), then $y_1 = y_2$. Therefore, its slope is

$$m = \frac{y_2 - y_1}{x_2 - x_1} = \frac{y_2 - y_2}{x_2 - x_1} = \frac{0}{x_2 - x_1} = 0$$

Thus all lines that are horizontal have a slope of zero.

If a line is vertical (or parallel to the y-axis), then $x_1 = x_2$. Therefore, we cannot use the formula

$$m = \frac{y_2 - y_1}{x_2 - x_1}$$

because division by zero is not defined.

Thus, we say that a vertical line has no slope or the slope is undefined.

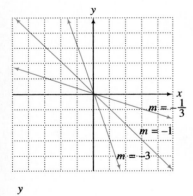

We can use slopes to determine if lines are parallel or perpendicular. *Parallel lines* are straight lines that never intersect. Therefore, their slopes must be equal (see the bottom figure). We can use this fact to define parallel lines.

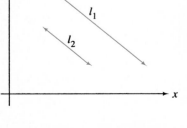

2

Definition: Parallel Lines

Two different lines with slopes m_1, and m_2, respectively, are *parallel* if $m_1 = m_2$.

Example 2 A line k passes through the points $(-1, 3)$ and $(2, -1)$. A second line h passes through the points $(-1, -4)$ and $(-4, 0)$. Is line k parallel to line h?

The slope of line k is

$$m_k = \frac{y_2 - y_1}{x_2 - x_1} = \frac{-1 - 3}{2 - (-1)} = \frac{-4}{2 + 1} = -\frac{4}{3}$$

The slope of line h is

$$m_h = \frac{y_2 - y_1}{x_2 - x_1} = \frac{0 - (-4)}{-4 - (-1)} = \frac{0 + 4}{-4 + 1} = \frac{4}{-3} = -\frac{4}{3}$$

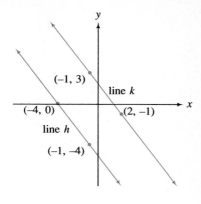

Since both lines are distinct (that is, different) and have the same slope, they are parallel. ■

Practice Problem 2 Line k passes through $(7, -2)$ and $(-5, -3)$. Find the slope of a line *parallel* to line k. ■

By definition, two lines are perpendicular if they intersect at right angles (a right angle is an angle of 90°).

If two non-vertical lines have slopes m_1 and m_2 the lines are perpendicular if $m_1 m_2 = -1$. We can write this as $m_1 = -\dfrac{1}{m_2}$.

Definition: Perpendicular Lines

Two lines with slopes m_1 and m_2, respectively, are *perpendicular* if $m_1 = -\dfrac{1}{m_2}$ $(m_1, m_2 \neq 0)$.

Example 3 Find the slope of a line that is perpendicular to a line l that passes through $(4, -6)$ and $(-3, -5)$.

The slope of line l is

$$m_l = \frac{-5 - (-6)}{-3 - 4} = \frac{-5 + 6}{-7} = \frac{1}{-7} = -\frac{1}{7}$$

The slope of a line perpendicular to line l must have a slope of $-1 \div (-\frac{1}{7}) = 7$. ■

Practice Problem 3 If a line l passes through $(5, 0)$ and $(6, -2)$, what is the slope of a line h that is *perpendicular* to l? ■

Example 4 Without plotting any points, show that the points $A(-5, -1)$, $B(-1, 2)$, and $C(3, 5)$ lie on the same line.

First we find the slopes of a line segment from A to B and a line segment from B to C.

$$m_{AB} = \frac{2 - (-1)}{-1 - (-5)} = \frac{2 + 1}{-1 + 5} = \frac{3}{4}$$

$$m_{BC} = \frac{5 - 2}{3 - (-1)} = \frac{3}{3 + 1} = \frac{3}{4}$$

Since the slopes are equal, we must have one line or two parallel lines. But the line segments have a point (B) in common, so all three points lie on the same line. ■

Practice Problem 4 Without plotting the points, show that $A(1, 5)$, $B(-1, 1)$, and $C(-2, -1)$ lie on the same line. ■

DEVELOPING YOUR STUDY SKILLS

WHY IS HOMEWORK NECESSARY?

Mathematics is a set of skills that you learn by practicing, not by watching someone else do it. Your instructor may make solving a mathematics problem look very easy, but for you to learn the necessary skills, you must practice them over

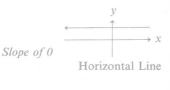

and over again, just as your instructor once had to do. There is no other way. Learning mathematics is like learning to play a musical instrument, to type, or to play a sport. No matter how much you watch someone else do it, how many books you may read on "how to" do it, or how easy it may seem to be, the key to success is practice on a regular basis.

Homework provides this practice. The amount of practice varies for each individual, but usually students need to do most or all of the exercises provided at the end of each section in the text. The more problems you do, the better you get. Some problems in a set are more difficult than others, and some stress different concepts. Only by working all the problems will you understand the full range of difficulty and coverage.

EXERCISES 2.2

In problems 1–8, find the slope of a line passing through each pair of points.

1. $(0, 5)$ and $(1, -2)$

$m = \dfrac{5 - (-2)}{0 - 1} = -7$

2. $(-3, 6)$ and $(2, 5)$

$m = \dfrac{6 - 5}{-3 - 2} = \dfrac{-1}{5}$

3. $(-7, -2)$ and $(3, 4)$

$m = \dfrac{4 - (-2)}{3 - (-7)} = \dfrac{3}{5}$

4. $(2, -1)$ and $(-6, 3)$

$m = \dfrac{-1 - 3}{2 - (-6)} = -\dfrac{1}{2}$

5. $\left(\dfrac{1}{2}, 3\right)$ and $(1, 5)$

$m = \dfrac{5 - 3}{1 - \dfrac{1}{2}} = 4$

6. $(6, 1)$ and $\left(0, \dfrac{1}{3}\right)$

$m = \dfrac{1 - \dfrac{1}{3}}{6 - 0} = \dfrac{1}{9}$

7. $(-7, 6)$ and $(2, 6)$

$m = \dfrac{6 - 6}{-7 - 2} = 0$

8. $(-2, -8)$ and $(5, -8)$

$m = \dfrac{-8 - (-8)}{5 - (-2)} = 0$

9. Does the line passing through $(-3, -7)$ and $(-3, 5)$ have a slope? Give a reason for your answer.

$m = \dfrac{-12}{0}$ no, division by zero is undefined

10. It is correct to say that "the slope of *any* straight line can be found by using the formula $m = \dfrac{y_2 - y_1}{x_2 - x_1}$?"

no, $x_2 - x_1$ can equal zero, thus no slope. The formula only works for non-vertical straight lines.

11. Let $(x_1, y_1) = (-6, -3)$ and $(x_2, y_2) = (-4, 5)$. Find

$$\dfrac{y_2 - y_1}{x_2 - x_1} \quad \text{and} \quad \dfrac{y_1 - y_2}{x_1 - x_2}$$

Are the results the same? Why or why not?

$\dfrac{-3 - 5}{-6 - (-4)} = \dfrac{5 - (-3)}{-4 - (-6)} = m$

$4 = 4$ yes

12. Repeat the directions for problem 11, using $(x_1, y_1) = (0.3, 1.6)$ and $(x_2, y_2) = (0.4, 2.2)$.

$\dfrac{1.6 - 2.2}{0.3 - 0.4} = \dfrac{2.2 - 1.6}{0.4 - 0.3}$

$6 = 6$ yes

In problems 13–18, find the slope of a line parallel *to a line that passes through the points.*

13. $(7, 1)$ and $(6.5, 2)$

$m = \dfrac{2 - 1}{6.5 - 7} = -2$

14. $(3, 5)$ and $(2.8, 6)$

$m = \dfrac{6 - 5}{2.8 - 3} = -5$

15. $(-7, 1)$ and $(-4, -3)$

$m = \dfrac{1 - (-3)}{-7 - (-4)} = \dfrac{4}{3}$

16. $(2, -6)$ and $(-5, -8)$

$m = \dfrac{-8 - (-6)}{-5 - 2} = \dfrac{2}{7}$

17. $(-6, -3)$ and $(4, -3)$

$m = \dfrac{-3 - (-3)}{-6 - 4} = 0$

18. $(2, -5)$ and $(2, 16)$

$\dfrac{-5 - 16}{2 - 2} = $ No slope

In problems 19–24, find the slope of a line perpendicular *to a line that passes through the points.*

19. $(1, 2)$ and $(3, 5)$

$\dfrac{5 - 2}{3 - 1} = \dfrac{3}{2}$ $m_\perp = -\dfrac{2}{3}$

20. $(-2, 5)$ and $(1, 3)$

$m = \dfrac{5 - 3}{-2 - 1} = -\dfrac{2}{3}$ $m_\perp = \dfrac{3}{2}$

21. $(3, -3)$ and $(1, 5)$

$m = -4$ $m_\perp = \dfrac{1}{4}$

22. $(-5, -2)$ and $(-3, 4)$

$m = 3$ $m_\perp = -\dfrac{1}{3}$

23. $(-8, 0)$ and $(0, 6)$

$m = \dfrac{3}{4}$ $m_\perp = -\dfrac{4}{3}$

24. $(0, -5)$ and $(-2, 0)$

$m = -\dfrac{5}{2}$ $m_\perp = \dfrac{2}{5}$

25. Do the points $A(-1, -2)$, $B(2, -1)$, and $C(8, 1)$ lie on a straight line? Explain.

$m_{AB} = \dfrac{-2 - (-1)}{-1 - 2} = \dfrac{1}{3}$

$m_{BC} = \dfrac{-1 - 1}{2 - 8} = \dfrac{1}{3}$ Since $m_{AB} = m_{BC}$ and B is a common point, then all the points lie on one straight line

26. Do the points $A(1, -5)$, $B(-2, -3)$, and $C(-8, 1)$ lie on a straight line? Explain.

$m_{AB} = \dfrac{-5 - (-3)}{1 - (-2)} = \dfrac{-2}{3}$

$m_{BC} = \dfrac{-3 - 1}{-2 - (-8)} = \dfrac{-2}{3}$ Yes, see explanation problem 25

27. Show that $ABCD$ is a parallelogram if the four vertices are $A(2, 1)$, $B(-1, -2)$, $C(-7, -1)$, and $D(-4, 2)$.

(*Hint:* A parallelogram is a four-sided figure with opposite sides parallel.)

$$m_{AD} = m_{BC} = -\frac{1}{6}$$

$$m_{AB} = m_{CD} = 1$$

28. Is $ABCD$ a parallelogram if the four vertices are $A(6, 2)$, $B(1, -3)$, $C(-3, 1)$, and $D(1, 5)$? Explain. (*Hint:* A parallelogram is a four-sided figure with opposite sides parallel.)

$$\left.\begin{matrix} m_{AD} = -\dfrac{3}{5} \\ m_{BC} = -1 \end{matrix}\right\} m_{AD} \neq m_{BC}$$

Thus AD is not parallel to BC and $ABCD$ is not a parallelogram

To Think About

29. Is the line l passing through points $\left(\dfrac{8}{5}, \dfrac{4}{5}\right)$ and $\left(\dfrac{1}{5}, -\dfrac{6}{5}\right)$ parallel to the line h passing through points $\left(-\dfrac{13}{5}, -\dfrac{7}{5}\right)$ and $\left(-\dfrac{6}{5}, \dfrac{3}{5}\right)$? Explain.

$$m_l = \frac{\dfrac{6}{5} - \dfrac{4}{5}}{\dfrac{1}{5} - \dfrac{8}{5}} = \frac{-\dfrac{10}{5}}{-\dfrac{7}{5}} = \frac{10}{7}$$

$$m_h = \frac{-\dfrac{7}{5} - \dfrac{3}{5}}{-\dfrac{13}{5} + \dfrac{6}{5}} = \frac{-\dfrac{10}{5}}{-\dfrac{7}{5}} = \frac{10}{7}$$

Thus $l \| h$

30. A triangle ABC is constructed with vertices $A(-0.1, 0.7)$, $B(1.7, 0.2)$, $C(-0.7, -1.4)$. Determine if it is a right triangle. Explain.

Hint: Determine if two of the sides are perpendicular.

$$m_{AB} = \frac{0.7 - 0.2}{-0.1 - 1.7} = -\frac{5}{18}$$

$$m_{BC} = \frac{-1.4 - 0.2}{-0.7 - 1.7} = \frac{2}{3}$$

$$m_{AC} = \frac{-1.4 - 0.7}{-0.7 + 0.1} = \frac{7}{2}$$

Not a right triangle $m_1 m_2 \neq -1$

Cumulative Review Problems

Evaluate.

31. $2(3 - 6)^3 + 20 \div (-10)$

$2(-3)^3 - 2 = -54 - 2 = -56$

32. $\dfrac{5 + 3\sqrt{9}}{|2 - 9|}$

$\dfrac{5 + 9}{|-7|} = \dfrac{14}{7} = 2$

Simplify.

33. $(5x^{-3}y^{-4})(-2x^6y^{-8})$

$-10x^3y^{-12} = \dfrac{-10x^3}{y^{12}}$

34. $\dfrac{-15x^6y^3}{-3x^{-4}y^6}$

$5x^{10}y^{-3} = \dfrac{5x^{10}}{y^3}$

Calculator Problems

Find the slope of a line

35. Passing through $(1923, -5218)$ and $(7219, -3154)$

0.389728097

36. Passing through $(0.02156, -0.09182)$ and $(-0.12573, 0.36991)$

-3.134836038

For Extra Practice Exercise, turn to page 113.

Solutions to Odd-Numbered Practice Problems

1. The slope of a line passing through $(-6, 1)$ and $(-5, -2)$ is given by

$$m = \frac{y_2 - y_1}{x_2 - x_1} = \frac{-2 - 1}{-5 - (-6)} = \frac{-3}{-5 + 6} = \frac{-3}{1} = -3$$

Note: If you chose the points in opposite order, you also find that

$$m = \frac{1 - (-2)}{-6 - (-5)} = \frac{1 + 2}{-6 + 5} = \frac{3}{-1} = -3$$

3. The slope of a line l passing through $(5, 0)$ and $(6, -2)$ is

$$m_l = \frac{-2 - 0}{6 - 5} = \frac{-2}{1} = -2$$

The slope of a line *h perpendicular* to *l* would have a slope $m_2 = -\left(-\dfrac{1}{2}\right) = \dfrac{1}{2}$. (If the slopes of two lines are negative reciprocals, the lines are perpendicular.)

Answers to Even-Numbered Practice Problems

2. $\dfrac{1}{12}$

4. The slope of the line from *B* to *A* is 2. The slope of the line from *C* to *B* is 2. Since the slopes are the same and have a point in common, the points lie on the same line.

After studying this section, you will be able to:

1 *Write the equation of a line using the slope-intercept form*

2 *Write the equation of a line using the point-slope form*

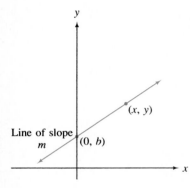

Line of slope *m*
(0, *b*)
(*x*, *y*)

2.3 THE EQUATIONS OF A LINE

Recall that the equation of a straight line is $Ax + By = C$. This is called the **standard form**. Another useful form of the equation of a straight line is called the **slope-intercept form**. The slope-intercept form immediately reveals the slope of a line and where it intercepts the *y*-axis. Since every straight line except a vertical line has a slope and crosses the *y*-axis somewhere, the slope-intercept form can be used for all nonvertical straight lines. We will now derive the equation of a line in slope-intercept form.

1 Let a straight line with slope *m* cross the *y*-axis at some point (0, *b*), where *b* is the *y*-intercept. Choose any point on the line and label it (*x*, *y*). By the definition of slope,

$$\frac{y_2 - y_1}{x_2 - x_1} = m$$

But here $x_1 = 0$ and $y_1 = b$, so

$$\frac{y_2 - b}{x_2 - 0} = m$$

Now, for convenience, let $y_2 = y$ and $x_2 = x$:

$$\frac{y - b}{x} = m$$

Now we solve this equation for *y*:

$$y - b = mx$$

$$y = mx + b$$

Slope-Intercept Form

The **slope-intercept** form of the equation of a line is $y = mx + b$, where *m* is the slope and *b* is the *y*-intercept.

Example 1 Write the equation of a line with slope $-\dfrac{2}{3}$ and *y*-intercept 5.

$$y = mx + b$$

$$y = \left(-\frac{2}{3}\right)(x) + (5)$$

$$y = -\frac{2}{3}x + 5 \qquad \blacksquare$$

Practice Problem 1 Write the equation of a line with slope 4 and *y*-intercept $-\dfrac{3}{2}$.

$\blacksquare$

Using algebraic operations, we can write *any* nonvertical line in the slope-intercept form. In this form we can identify immediately the slope and the *y*-intercept of the line.

Example 2   What is the slope and the *y*-intercept of the line $28x - 7y = 2$?

We want to isolate the *y* term so that the equation can be written as $y = mx + b$.

$$-7y = -28x + 2 \qquad \text{Subtracting } 28x \text{ from each side.}$$

$$\frac{-7y}{-7} = \frac{-28x}{-7} + \frac{2}{-7} \qquad \text{Dividing each term by } -7.$$

$$y = 4x + \left(-\frac{2}{7}\right) \qquad \text{Simplifying.}$$

$$y = 4x + \left(-\frac{2}{7}\right) \qquad y = mx + b$$

Thus, the slope is 4, the *y*-intercept is $-\frac{2}{7}$. ∎

Practice Problem 2   Write the equation $3x - 4y = -2$ in slope-intercept form. Then find the slope and the *y*-intercept. ∎

TEACHING TIP   As a class exercise after discussing example 2, ask the students to find the slope and the *y*-intercept of $3y + 4x = -6$. $\left(\text{The answer is } m = \frac{-4}{3} \text{ and } b = -2.\right)$ Emphasize the need to be able to quickly find these two quantities from a linear equation written in any form.

To Think About

As a check and for practice, let's find the slope and *y*-intercept of the line $28x - 7y = 2$ *without* using the slope-intercept form.

The *y*-intercept is the point at which the line crosses the *y*-axis, and therefore $x = 0$. So

$$28x - 7y = 2$$

$$28(0) - 7y = 2$$

$$-7y = 2$$

$$y = -\frac{2}{7}$$

This gives us the point $\left(0, -\frac{2}{7}\right)$ on the line which is the *y*-intercept. To find the slope, we need another point. One point we can use is the *x*-intercept (where $y = 0$). Thus,

$$28x - 7y = 2$$

$$28x - 7(0) = 2$$

$$28x = 2$$

$$x = \frac{2}{28} \quad \text{or} \quad \frac{1}{14}$$

So our second point is $\left(\frac{1}{14}, 0\right)$. Therefore,

$$m = \frac{y_2 - y_1}{x_2 - x_1} = \frac{-\dfrac{2}{7} - 0}{0 - \dfrac{1}{14}} = \left(-\frac{2}{7}\right)\left(-\frac{14}{1}\right) = 4 \quad \blacksquare$$

2 What happens if we know the slope of a line and a point on the line that is not the y-intercept? Let (x_1, y_1) and (x, y) be two points on a line of slope m. By definition of slope,

$$m = \frac{y - y_1}{x - x_1}$$

If we multiply each side of the equation by $x - x_1$, we obtain

$$m(x - x_1) = y - y_1$$

This is the *point-slope form* of the equation of a line.

> **Point–Slope Form**
>
> The **point–slope form** of the equation of a line is $y - y_1 = m(x - x_1)$, where m is the slope and (x_1, y_1) are the coordinates of a known point on the line.

TEACHING TIP Students sometimes ask directly, "Why are we learning another form for the straight line. We already know two other forms!" Explain that the point-slope form is the most useful form for writing the equation of the line if we are given some points, a slope and a point, or another equation and a point.

Example 3 Find the equation of a line with slope $-\frac{3}{4}$ that passes through the point $(-6, 1)$. Express your answer in standard form.

Since we don't know the y-intercept, we can't use the slope-intercept form. Therefore, we use the point-slope form.

$y - y_1 = m(x - x_1)$

$y - 1 = -\dfrac{3}{4}(x - (-6))$ Substituting the given values.

$y - 1 = -\dfrac{3}{4}x - \dfrac{9}{2}$ Simplifying. (Do you see how we did this?)

$4y - 4(1) = 4\left(-\dfrac{3}{4}x\right) - 4\left(\dfrac{9}{2}\right)$ Multiplying each term by the LCD 4.

$4y - 4 = -3x - 18$ Simplifying.

$3x + 4y = -18 + 4$ Adding $3x + 4$ to each side.

$3x + 4y = -14$ Adding like terms.

The equation in standard form is $3x + 4y = -14$. $\blacksquare$

Practice Problem 3 Find the equation of a line that passes through $(5, -2)$ and has a slope of $\frac{3}{4}$. Express your answer in slope-intercept form. $\blacksquare$

We can use the point-slope form to find the equation of a line if we are given two points.

Example 4 Find the equation of a line in standard form that passes through $(3, -2)$ and $(5, 1)$.

First find the slope.

$$m = \frac{y_2 - y_1}{x_2 - x_1} = \frac{1 - (-2)}{5 - 3} = \frac{1 + 2}{2} = \frac{3}{2}$$

Now we substitute the value of the slope and the coordinates of either point into the point-slope equation. Let's use (5, 1). Then

$$y - y_1 = m(x - x_1)$$

$$y - 1 = \frac{3}{2}(x - 5)$$ Substituting $m = \frac{3}{2}$ and $(x_1, y_1) = (5, 1)$.

$$y - 1 = \frac{3}{2}x - \frac{15}{2}$$ Removing parentheses.

$$2y - 2 = 2\left(\frac{3}{2}x\right) - 2\left(\frac{15}{2}\right)$$ Multiplying each term by 2.

$$2y - 2 = 3x - 15$$ Simplifying.

$$-3x + 2y = -15 + 2$$ Adding $2 - 3x$ to each side.

$$-3x + 2y = -13$$ Simplifying.

$$3x - 2y = 13$$ It is customary, but not necessary to have a positive value for the coefficient of x in the standard form, so we multiply each term by -1. ∎

Practice Problem 4 Find the equation of a line in standard form that passes through $(-4, 1)$ and $(-2, -3)$. ∎

Before we go further, we want to point out that these various forms of the equation of a straight line are just that—*forms* for convenience. We are *not* using different equations each time, nor should you simply try to memorize the different variations without understanding when to use them. They can easily be derived from the definition of slope, as we have seen. And remember, you can *always* use the definition of slope to find the equation of a line.

We can also use the properties of slopes of parallel and perpendicular lines to find equations of lines.

Example 5 Find the equation of a line passing through the point $(-2, -4)$ and parallel to the line $2x + 5y = 8$. Express the answer in standard form.

First find the slope of the line $2x + 5y = 8$. We do this by writing the equation in slope-intercept form.

$$5y = -2x + 8$$

$$y = -\frac{2}{5}x + \frac{8}{5}$$

The slope of the given line is $-\frac{2}{5}$. Since parallel lines have the same slope, the slope of the unknown line is also $-\frac{2}{5}$. Now we substitute $m = -\frac{2}{5}$ and the coordinates of the point $(-2, -4)$ into the point-slope form of the equation.

$$y - y_1 = m(x - x_1)$$

$$y - (-4) = -\frac{2}{5}[(x - (-2))]$$ Substituting.

$$y + 4 = -\frac{2}{5}(x + 2)$$ Simplifying.

$$y + 4 = -\frac{2}{5}x - \frac{4}{5}$$ Removing parentheses.

$$5y + 5(4) = 5\left(-\frac{2}{5}x\right) - 5\left(\frac{4}{5}\right)$$ Multiplying each term by LCD $= 5$.

$$5y + 20 = -2x - 4 \qquad \text{Simplifying.}$$

$$2x + 5y = -4 - 20 \qquad \text{Adding } 2x - 20 \text{ to each side.}$$

$$2x + 5y = -24 \qquad \blacksquare$$

Practice Problem 5   Find the equation of a line passing through $(4, -5)$ and parallel to the line $5x - 3y = 10$. $\blacksquare$

Example 6   Find the equation of a line that passes through the point $(2, -3)$ and is perpendicular to the line $3x - y = -12$.

Find the slope of the line $3x - y = -12$. Its slope-intercept form is

$$-y = -3x - 12$$

$$y = 3x + 12$$

Therefore, the slope is 3, so the slope of a line perpendicular to this line is the negative reciprocal, $-\dfrac{1}{3}$.

Now substitute the slope $m_2 = -\dfrac{1}{3}$ and the coordinates of the point $(2, -3)$ into the point-slope form of the equation.

$$y - y_1 = m(x - x_1)$$

$$y - (-3) = -\frac{1}{3}(x - 2) \qquad \text{Substituting.}$$

$$y + 3 = -\frac{1}{3}(x - 2) \qquad \text{Simplifying.}$$

$$y + 3 = -\frac{1}{3}x + \frac{2}{3} \qquad \text{Removing parentheses.}$$

$$3y + 3(3) = 3\left(-\frac{1}{3}x\right) + 3\left(\frac{2}{3}\right) \qquad \text{Multiplying each term by the LCD 3.}$$

$$3y + 9 = -x + 2 \qquad \text{Simplifying.}$$

$$x + 3y = 2 - 9 \qquad \text{Adding } x - 9 \text{ to each side.}$$

$$x + 3y = -7 \qquad \blacksquare$$

Practice Problem 6   Find the equation of a line that passes through $(-4, 3)$ and is perpendicular to the line $6x + 3y = 7$. $\blacksquare$

DEVELOPING YOUR STUDY SKILLS

APPLICATIONS OR WORD PROBLEMS

Applications or word problems are the very life of mathematics! They are the reason for doing mathematics, as they teach you how to put into use the mathematical skills you have developed. Learning mathematics without ever doing word problems is similar to learning all the skills of a sport without ever playing a game or learning all the notes on an instrument without ever playing a song.

The key to success is practice. Make yourself do as many problems as you can. You may not be able to do them all correctly at first, but keep trying. Do not give up whenever you reach a difficult one. If you cannot solve it, just try another one. Then come back and try it again later.

A misconception among students when they begin studying word problems is that each problem is different. At first the problems may seem this way, but as you practice more and more, you will begin to see the similarities, the different "types." You will see patterns in solving problems, which will enable you to solve problems of a given type more easily.

TEACHING TIP   As students go through the steps of examples 5 and 6 they sometimes get so busy with details that they miss the key point. The examples are almost exactly the same in format except that in example 5 we want to find the equation of a line PARALLEL to a given line, and in example 6 we want to find the equation of a line PERPENDICULAR to a given line.

Write each equation in standard form.

1. $y = -\frac{2}{7}x + 5$

$2x + 7y = 35$

2. $y = \frac{3}{4}x - \frac{2}{3}$

$9x - 12y = 8$

3. $y - 6 = \frac{1}{5}(x - 10)$

$x - 5y = -20$

4. $y + 5 = -\frac{2}{3}(x + 6)$

$2x + 3y = -27$

Write each equation in slope-intercept form. Then find the slope and the y-intercept for each line.

5. $y + 5x = 2$

$y = -5x + 2 \quad m = -5, b = 2$

6. $y - 3x = 4$

$y = 3x + 4 \quad m = 3, b = 4$

7. $2x - 3y = -8$

$y = \frac{2}{3}x + \frac{8}{3} \quad m = \frac{2}{3}, b = \frac{8}{3}$

8. $5x - 4y = -20$

$y = \frac{5}{4}x + 5 \quad m = \frac{5}{4}, b = 5$

9. $\frac{1}{2}x + 4y = 5$

$y = -\frac{1}{8}x + \frac{5}{4} \quad m = -\frac{1}{8}, b = \frac{5}{4}$

10. $3x + \frac{2}{3}y = -2$

$y = -\frac{9}{2}x - 3 \quad m = -\frac{9}{2}, b = -3$

11. $7x + 11y = -10$

$y = -\frac{7}{11}x - \frac{10}{11} \quad m = -\frac{7}{11}, b = -\frac{10}{11}$

12. $5x + 13y = 17$

$y = -\frac{5}{13}x + \frac{17}{13} \quad m = -\frac{5}{13}, b = \frac{17}{13}$

Find the equation of the line that passes through the given point and has the given slope. Express your answer in slope-intercept form.

13. $(5, 6), m = 3$

$y - 6 = 3(x - 5) \quad y = 3x - 9$

14. $(-1, 2), m = 4$

$y - 2 = 4(x + 1) \quad y = 4x + 6$

15. $(-7, -2), m = 5$

$y + 2 = 5(x + 7) \quad y = 5x + 33$

16. $(8, 0), m = -3$

$y - 0 = -3(x - 8) \quad y = -3x + 24$

17. $(2, -4) \ m = -\frac{2}{3}$

$y + 4 = -\frac{2}{3}(x - 2) \quad y = -\frac{2}{3}x - \frac{8}{3}$

18. $(-3, 1), m = -\frac{1}{4}$

$y - 1 = -\frac{1}{4}(x + 3) \quad y = -\frac{1}{4}x + \frac{1}{4}$

Find the equation of a line passing through the pair of points. Write the equation in standard form.

19. $(-2, 3)$ and $(1, 4)$

$m = \frac{4 - 3}{1 + 2} = \frac{1}{3}$

$y - 4 = \frac{1}{3}(x - 1)$

$x - 3y = -11$

20. $(6, -1)$ and $(3, 2)$

$m = \frac{2 + 1}{3 - 6} = -1$

$y - 2 = -1(x - 3)$

$x + y = 5$

21. $(7, -2)$ and $(-1, -3)$

$m = \frac{-2 + 3}{7 + 1} = \frac{1}{8}$

$y + 3 = \frac{1}{8}(x + 1)$

$x - 8y = 23$

22. $(-4, -1)$ and $(3, 4)$

$m = \frac{4 + 1}{3 + 4} = \frac{5}{7}$

$y - 4 = \frac{5}{7}(x - 3)$

$5x - 7y = -13$

23. $(0, 6)$ and $(2, -7)$

$m = \frac{6 + 7}{0 - 2} = -\frac{13}{2}$

$y - 6 = -\frac{13}{2}(x - 0)$

$13x + 2y = 12$

24. $(3, -8)$ and $(-5, 0)$

$m = \frac{-8 - 0}{3 + 5} = -1$

$y - 0 = -1(x + 5)$

$x + y = -5$

25. Write the equation of a line passing through $(2, -3)$ with zero slope.

$y + 3 = 0(x - 2)$
$y + 3 = 0$
$\quad y = -3$

26. Write the equation of a horizontal line passing through $(-5, 1)$. Horizontal line

$m = 0$
$y - 1 = 0(x + 5)$
$y - 1 = 0$
$\quad y = 1$

27. Write the equation of a vertical line passing through $(-6, -3)$. Vertical line-no slope

$x = -6$

28. Write the equation of a line that has no slope and passes through $(5, -4)$. Vertical line-no slope

$x = 5$

Find the equation of the lines satisfying the conditions given. Express your answer in standard form.

29. Parallel to $3x + 4y = -12$ and passing through $(-5, 0)$

$y = -\frac{3}{4}x - 3$

$m \,(\| \text{ line}) = -\frac{3}{4}$

$y - 0 = -\frac{3}{4}(x + 5)$

$3x + 4y = -15$

30. Parallel to $2x + 3y = 5$ and passing through $(-3, 4)$

$y = -\frac{2}{3}x + \frac{5}{3}$

$m \,(\| \text{ line}) = -\frac{2}{3}$

$y - 4 = -\frac{2}{3}(x + 3)$

$2x + 3y = 6$

31. Parallel to $y + 4x = 7$ and passing through $(-8, -10)$

$y = -4x + 7$
$m\ (\parallel \text{line}) = -4$
$y + 10 = -4(x + 8)$
$4x + y = -42$

32. Parallel to $x = 3y - 8$ and passing through $(5, -1)$

$y = \frac{1}{3}x + \frac{8}{3}$ $y + 1 = \frac{1}{3}(x - 5)$

$m\ (\parallel \text{line}) = \frac{1}{3}$ $x - 3y = 8$

33. Perpendicular to $y = 5x$ and passing through $(4, -2)$

$m\ (\text{Given line}) = 5$
$m\ (\perp \text{line}) = -\frac{1}{5}$
$y + 2 = -\frac{1}{5}(x - 4)$
$x + 5y = -6$

34. Perpendicular to $y = -\frac{2}{3}x$ and passing through $(-3, 1)$

$m\ (\text{Given line}) = -\frac{2}{3}$
$m\ (\perp \text{line}) = \frac{3}{2}$
$y - 1 = \frac{3}{2}(x + 3)$
$3x - 2y = -11$

35. Perpendicular to $5x - 3y = -8$ and passing through $(6, 1)$

$m\ (\text{Given line}) = \frac{5}{3}$
$m\ (\perp \text{line}) = -\frac{3}{5}$
$y - 1 = -\frac{3}{5}(x - 6)$
$3x + 5y = 23$

36. Perpendicular to $x + 7y = -12$ and passing through $(-4, -1)$

$m\ (\text{Given line}) = -\frac{1}{7}$
$m\ (\perp \text{line}) = 7$
$y + 1 = 7(x + 4)$
$7x - y = -27$

37. Parallel to $x = -2$ and passing through $(5, 8)$

$x = 5$ (vertical line)

38. Parallel to $x = -3$ and passing through $(4, 6)$

$x = 4$ (vertical line)

? **To Think About**

39. Find the equation of a line passing through $\left(-\frac{2}{7}, \frac{3}{4}\right)$ and $\left(-\frac{1}{5}, -\frac{2}{3}\right)$. Express your answer in standard form.

$m = \dfrac{\frac{3}{4} + \frac{2}{3}}{-\frac{2}{7} + \frac{1}{5}} = \dfrac{\frac{17}{12}}{-\frac{3}{35}} = -\frac{595}{36}$ $y + \frac{2}{3} = -\frac{595}{36}\left(x + \frac{1}{5}\right)$

$595x + 36y = -143$

40. Find the equation of a line perpendicular to $0.5x + 1.3y = 20.6$ and passing through $(1.4, 2.3)$. Express your answer in standard form.

$m\ (\text{Given line}) = -\frac{5}{13}$
$m\ (\perp \text{line}) = \frac{13}{5} = 2.6$
$y - 2.3 = 2.6(x - 1.4)$
$2.6x - y = 1.34$

Cumulative Review Problems

Consider the set of numbers $\left\{5, -6, 2, 1.333\ldots, \sqrt{2}, -\frac{1}{4}, 0\right\}$.

41. List the rational numbers.

$5, -6, 2, 1.333\ldots, -\frac{1}{4}, 0$

42. List the whole numbers.

$0, 2, 5$

Collect like terms.

43. $\frac{1}{2}x^2 - 3xy + 5y^2 - 2x^2 - 6xy - 8y^2$

$-\frac{3}{2}x^2 - 9xy - 3y^2$

44. $2(a - 3b) - 5(2b - a)$

$7a - 16b$

▦ **Calculator Problems**

Round your final answers to the nearest thousandth.

45. Find the equation of a line passing through $(12.986, -5.321)$ and $(6.052, 8.986)$.

$y = -2.063x + 21.473$

46. Find the equation of a line parallel to $15.625x - 19.082y = 16.721$ and passing through $(9.35, 8.07)$. $y = 0.819x + 0.414$

For Extra Practice Exercises, turn to page 113.

Solution to Odd-Numbered Practice Problems

1. An equation of a line with slope 4 and y-intercept $-\dfrac{3}{2}$ is $y = 4x - \dfrac{3}{2}$.

3. $\quad y - y_1 = m(x - x_1)$

$\quad y - (-2) = \dfrac{3}{4}(x - 5)$ Substituting $m = \dfrac{3}{4}$, $(x_1, y_1) = (5, -2)$.

$\quad y + 2 = \dfrac{3}{4}(x - 5)$ Simplifying.

$\quad y + 2 = \dfrac{3}{4}x - \dfrac{15}{4}$ Removing parentheses.

$\quad y = \dfrac{3}{4}x - \dfrac{15}{4} - \dfrac{8}{4}$ Adding -2 to each side $\left(\text{recall that } \dfrac{-2}{1} = \dfrac{-8}{4}\right)$.

$\quad y = \dfrac{3}{4}x - \dfrac{23}{4}$ This is in the form $y = mx + b$.

5. $5x - 3y = 10$

$\quad 5x - 10 = 3y$

$\quad \dfrac{5}{3}x - \dfrac{10}{3} = y \quad$ or $\quad y = \dfrac{5}{3}x - \dfrac{10}{3}$

This line is in the form $y = mx + b$. The slope is $\dfrac{5}{3}$. A line parallel to this passing through $(4, -5)$ would have an equation

$$y - (-5) = \dfrac{5}{3}(x - 4)$$

$$y + 5 = \dfrac{5}{3}x - \dfrac{20}{3}$$

$$3y + 15 = 5x - 20$$

$$-5x + 3y = -35 \quad \text{or} \quad 5x - 3y = 35$$

Either answer is in standard form.

Answers to Even-Numbered Practice Problems

2. In slope-intercept form it is $y = \dfrac{3}{4}x + \dfrac{1}{2}$. The slope is $\dfrac{3}{4}$; the y-intercept is $\dfrac{1}{2}$.   **4.** $2x + y = -7$

6. $-x + 2y = 10 \quad$ or $\quad x - 2y = -10$

2.4 USING EQUATIONS TO SOLVE WORD PROBLEMS

1   In all branches of mathematics and science, we encounter written problems that can be solved by a mathematical equation. First we need to learn the algebraic equivalents of common English expressions. You should be familiar with the following list.

SYMBOLIC EQUIVALENTS OF ENGLISH PHRASES

English Phrase	Mathematical Symbol
and, added to, increased by, greater than, plus, more than, sum of	+
decreased by, subtracted from, less than, diminished by, minus, difference between	−
product of, multiplied by, of, times	· or ( )( ) or ×
divided by, quotient of, ratio of	÷ or fraction bar
equals, are, is, will be, yields, gives, makes, is the same as, has a value of	=

After studying this section, you will be able to:

1 *Translate the information contained in a word problem involving comparisons into an equivalent algebraic equation*

2 *Solve the resulting algebraic equation to find the solution or solutions of the word problem*

3 *Check the solution to verify that it satisfies all the conditions of the original word problem*

Although we often use x to represent the unknown quantity when we write equations, any letter can be used. It is a good idea to use a letter that helps us remember what the variable represents. (For example, we might use s for speed or h for hours.) We now look at some examples of writing algebraic equations.

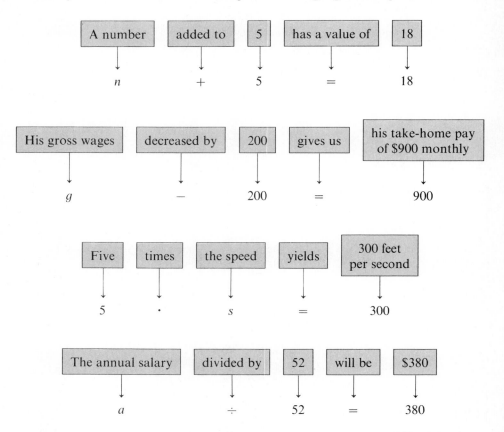

When subtraction is involved, watch carefully the order of elements of the equation. For example, "5 less than a number will be 40" is written

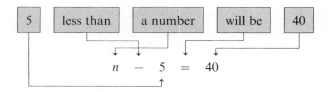

Do you see why?

2 After you determine what the variable will represent and what the equation is, solve the equation and check the answer.

Example 1 Three-fifths of a number is 150. What is the number?

Let $x =$ the number.

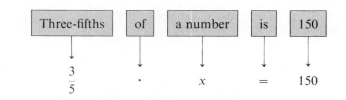

TEACHING TIP   This type of translation from an English sentence to an equation is a very useful skill for students and helps reduce anxiety about doing word problems. As a class exercise, ask them to write a math equation for each of the following sentences (Use the letter "n" as the variable):

A: The number of packages diminished by 12 yields a final result of 30.

B: The new salary is increased by $120 a week to result in $400.

C: The product of the needed amount of money and 5 yields a value of $2000.

D: The number of cars divided by 12 gives the monthly quota of 300 cars.

(Answers: A: $n - 12 = 30$.
B: $n + 120 = 400$.
C: $5n = 2000$.
D: $n/12 = 300$.)

$$\frac{3}{5} \cdot x = 150 \qquad \text{(We used the dot just for clarity. It is not necessary to write it.)}$$

$$5\left(\frac{3}{5}x\right) = 5(150) \qquad \text{Multiplying each side by 5.}$$

$$3x = 750 \qquad \text{Simplifying.}$$

$$x = 250 \qquad \text{Dividing each side by 3.}$$

Therefore, the number is 250

3 *Check:* Is three-fifths of 250 equal to 150?

$$\frac{3}{\overset{}{5}} \overset{50}{(250)} \overset{?}{=} 150$$
$$\underset{1}{} \qquad 150 = 150 \checkmark$$

Our answer is therefore correct. ■

Practice Problem 1 When three-fourths of a number is increased by 20, the result is 110. What is the number? ■

Example 2 An agency's truck rental charges are $40 per day plus 20¢ a mile. Nancy rented a truck for three days and paid the agency $177. How many miles did she drive?

Let n = the number of miles driven. We can analyze the situation in this way:

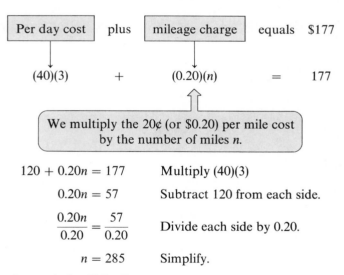

Per day cost	plus	mileage charge	equals	$177
(40)(3)	+	(0.20)(n)	=	177

We multiply the 20¢ (or $0.20) per mile cost by the number of miles n.

$$120 + 0.20n = 177 \qquad \text{Multiply (40)(3)}$$

$$0.20n = 57 \qquad \text{Subtract 120 from each side.}$$

$$\frac{0.20n}{0.20} = \frac{57}{0.20} \qquad \text{Divide each side by 0.20.}$$

$$n = 285 \qquad \text{Simplify.}$$

Nancy drove the truck for 285 miles
   Check: Can you verify this answer? ■

Practice Problem 2 Western Laboratories rents a computer terminal for $400 per month plus $8 per hour for computer use time. The bill for one year's computer use was $7680. How many hours did Western Laboratories actually use the computer? ■

Some problems involve two or more unknown quantities. We then represent one quantity as n and express the other quantities in terms of n. **Consecutive even integers** are numbers such as 2, 4, 6, . . . , n, $n + 2$, ... Each number in the sequence is larger by 2 than the preceding number. If we let n be the first unknown even integer then $n + 2$ must be the second even integer, and $n + 4$ must be the third. **Consecutive odd integers** are represented the same way. Thus we can write

$$1, 3, 5, 7, 9, 11, \ldots, n, n + 2, n + 4, \ldots.$$

Example 3   The sum of three consecutive even integers is 264. What are the integers? Since the sum of these integers is 264, we have

$$n + (n + 2) + (n + 4) = 264$$
$$3n + 6 = 264$$
$$3n = 258$$
$$n = 86$$

If $n = 86$, then

$$n + 2 = 86 + 2 = 88$$

and

$$n + 4 = 86 + 4 = 90$$

The three consecutive even integers are thus 86, 88, and 90.

  Check: $86 + 88 + 90 = 264$.   ■

Practice Problem 3   The sum of three consecutive odd integers is 195. What are the three integers?   ■

Sometimes we need a simple formula from geometry or some other science to write the original equation.

Example 4   The length of a rectangle is 3 meters more than double its width. Its perimeter is 108 meters. Find the width and length.

The formula for the perimeter P of a rectangle is $P = 2w + 2l$, where w is the width and l is the length. For this problem, let $w =$ the width. Therefore, the length is $2w + 3$. We thus have

$$P = 2w + 2l$$
$$108 = 2w + 2(2w + 3)$$
$$108 = 2w + 4w + 6$$
$$108 = 6w + 6$$
$$102 = 6w$$
$$17 = w$$

For $w = 17$, we have $2w + 3 = 2(17) + 3 = 37$. Thus, the rectangle is 17 meters wide and 37 meters long.

  Check: $P = 2w + 2l$

$$108 \overset{?}{=} 2(17) + 2(37)$$
$$108 \overset{?}{=} 34 + 74$$
$$108 = 108 \checkmark$$ ■

Practice Problem 4   The perimeter of a triangular lawn is 162 meters. The length of the first side is twice the length of the second side. The length of the third side is 6 meters shorter than three times the length of the second side. Find the dimensions of the triangle.   ■

DEVELOPING YOUR STUDY SKILLS

HOW TO SOLVE WORD PROBLEMS

There are three steps to solving word problems. You will be delighted with the success you will achieve if you follow these steps.

Step 1 Understand the Problem

- Read the problem for understanding. What does it say? Pick out all the important information and write it down.
- Draw any diagrams, charts, or pictures that will help you visualize the problem.
- Write down the question the problem is asking.

The point of Step 1 is to understand the problem. Do not be concerned about *how* to solve the problem at this time. Unfortunately, many students misunderstand or ignore this step. Instead of reading for understanding, they read the problem with the thought, "How am I going to solve this problem?" Watch out for this, as it will block your reasoning process.

Step 2 Set up the Problem

- Identify the variables to be used for the unknown quantity. Decide what you will let "*x*" be in your solution. Be specific, and include the units of measure, if applicable.
- Identify other unknown quantities if called for. Sometimes two or more quantities are to be found. Let "*x*" be one unknown and show the other in terms of "*x*."

Be careful in Step 2. Carelessness or incompleteness here leads to confusion. You need to know exactly what "*x*" *means* to understand your solutions.

Step 3 Solve the Problem

- Write the equation for the relationship that exists in the problem, using the unknowns you have identified in Step 2. Be sure that the equation makes sense and that it shows the relationship accurately.
- Solve the equation. Be careful with decimal points and negative signs—little errors here can cause *big* problems.
- Read the problem again to be sure you have found all the solutions the problem asks for.
- Check your answer. Does it work? Does it make sense? Watch for negative or fractional solutions. Can they exist?

Remember that the key to success with word problems is to practice solving them. KEEP TRYING, AND DON'T GIVE UP!

EXERCISES 2.4

Write an algebraic equation and use it to solve each problem.

1. Two-thirds of a number is 140. What is the number?

$x = \text{number} = 210$

$\frac{2}{3}x = 140$

$x = 210$

2. Four-sevenths of a number is 64. What is the number?

$x = \text{number} = 112$

$\frac{4}{7}x = 64$

$x = 112$

3. Three times a number is increased by 150 to yield a value of 219. What is the number?

$x = \text{number} = 23$

$3x + 150 = 219$

$x = 23$

4. If 50 is added to one-half of a number, the sum is 114. What is the number?

$x = \text{number} = 128$

$\frac{1}{2}x + 50 = 114$

$x = 128$

5. Bob's annual salary is $2000 less than double Wally's salary. The sum of the two men's salaries is $23,200. What is the annual salary of each man?

Wally's salary $= x$ $= \$8400$
Bob's salary $= 2x - \$2000 = \$14,800$
$(x) + (2x - \$2000) = \$23,200$
$x = \$8400$

6. The number of employees at Computer Village is 50 less than triple the number of employees at Digital Center. The number of employees at both companies is 470. How many people are employed at each company?

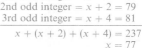

\# employees at Digital Center $= x$ $= 130$ peo[
\# employees at Computer Village $= 3x - 50 = 340$ peo[
$(x) + (3x - 50) = 470$
$x = 130$

7. The Economy Car Rental Company charges customers $22 per day and 15¢ per mile to rent a compact car. Jean rented one of their compact cars for five days. She paid $149 for the car rental. How many miles did she drive?

Number of miles $= x = 260$
$22(5) + 0.15x = 149$
$x = 260$

8. When Terry moved, he rented a small truck. The rental charge was $55 per day and 25¢ per mile. He rented the truck for four days and was charged $310. How many miles did he drive the truck?

Number of miles $= x = 360$ miles
$55(4) + 0.25x = 310$
$x = 360$

9. Western Insurance Company leases a computer terminal for $300 per month plus $12 per hour of computer use time. The company's bill for the first six months was $2760. How many hours was the computer used during that six-month period?

Number of hours $= x = 80$
$300(6) + 12x = 2760$
$x = 80$

10. Manchester Community Bank charges its customers $8.00 per month plus 10¢ per check for the use of a checking account. Sonja had a checking account there for four months and was charged $39.70 in service charges. How many checks did she write during that period?

Number of checks $= x = 77$
$8.00(4) + 0.10x = 39.70$
$x = 77$

11. The sum of three consecutive even integers is 192. What are the integers?

1st even integer $= x$ $= 62$
2nd even integer $= x + 2 = 64$
3rd even integer $= x + 4 = 66$
$x + (x + 2) + (x + 4) = 192$
$x = 62$

12. The sum of three consecutive odd integers is 237. What are the integers?

1st odd integer $= x$ $= 77$
2nd odd integer $= x + 2 = 79$
3rd odd integer $= x + 4 = 81$
$x + (x + 2) + (x + 4) = 237$
$x = 77$

13. In a set of three numbers, the first number is half of the second number, and the third number is three times the second number. The sum of the three numbers is 72. Find each number.

1st number $= \frac{1}{2}x = 8$
2nd number $= x = 16$
3rd number $= 3x = 48$
$\frac{1}{2}x + x + 3x = 72$
$x = 16$

14. In a set of three numbers, the first number is one-third of the second number, and the third number is twice the second number. The sum of the three numbers is 70. Find each number.

1st number $= \frac{1}{3}x = 7$
2nd number $= x = 21$
3rd number $= 2x = 42$
$\frac{1}{3}x + x + 2x = 70$
$x = 21$

15. A rectangular piece of land has a perimeter of 2204 meters. The length is 2 meters longer than three times the width. Find the dimensions of the land.

Width $= x$ $= 275$ meters
Length $= 3x + 2 = 827$ meters
$2(x) + 2(3x + 2) = 2204$
$x = 275$

16. An electronics firm manufactures a rectangular copper plate that has a perimeter of 166 centimeters. The length is 4 centimeters less than twice the width. Find the dimensions of the plate.

Width $= x$ $= 29$ cm
Length $= 2x - 4 = 54$ cm
$2(x) + 2(2x - 4) = 166$
$x = 29$

17. The perimeter of a triangle is 98 inches. The first side is twice as long as the second side. The third side is one-half as long as the second side. Find the dimensions of each side of the triangle.

1st side $= 2x = 56$ in
2nd side $= x = 28$ in
3rd side $= \frac{1}{2}x = 14$ in
$2x + x + \frac{1}{2}x = 98$
$x = 28$

18. The perimeter of a triangle is 66 feet. The first side is 2 feet longer than the second side. The third side is three times as long as the second side. Find the dimensions of each side of the triangle.

1st side $= x + 2 = 14.8$ ft
2nd side $= x = 12.8$ ft
3rd side $= 3x = 38.4$ ft
$(x + 2) + (x) + (3x) = 66$
$x = 12.8$

19. The sum of the angles of a triangle is 180°. The first angle is 10° less than twice the second angle. The third angle is 50° greater than the first angle. What is the size of each angle?

$$1\text{st angle} = 2x - 10 \qquad = 50°$$
$$2\text{nd angle} = x \qquad = 30°$$
$$3\text{rd angle} = (2x - 10) + 50 = 100°$$
$$\overline{(2x - 10) + (x) + (2x + 40) = 180}$$
$$x = 30$$

20. Sam's total cost for tuition, books, and room and board during his last year at the university was $11,500. His tuition was $3000 more than the cost of his room and board. His books were only one-eighth as expensive as his room and board. How much did Sam pay for tuition? for books? for room and board?

$$\text{Room and Board} = x \qquad = \$4000$$
$$\text{Tuition} = x + \$3000 = \$7000$$
$$\text{Books} = \frac{1}{8}x \qquad = \$500$$
$$\overline{x + (x + \$3000) + \frac{1}{8}x = \$11,500}$$
$$x = \$4000$$

? **To Think About**

21. Two angles are *complements* if their sum is 90°. Two angles are *supplements* if their sum is 180°. The complement of a certain angle is one-seventh of the supplement of that same certain angle. How large is the angle?

$$\text{Angle} = x = 75°$$
$$\text{Complement} = 90 - x = 15°$$
$$\text{Supplement} = 180 - x = 105°$$
$$\overline{(90 - x) = \frac{1}{7}(180 - x)}$$
$$x = 75$$

22. The sum of one-half of a number, one sixth of a number, and three-eighths of a number is 100. What is the number?

$$\text{Number} = x = 96$$
$$\overline{\frac{1}{2}x + \frac{1}{6}x + \frac{3}{8}x = 100}$$
$$x = 96$$

Cumulative Review Problems

Name the property that justifies each statement.

23. $57 + 0 = 57$

Identity property for addition

24. $(2 \cdot 3) \cdot 9 = 2 \cdot (3 \cdot 9)$

Associative property for multiplication

Simplify.

25. $5(x + 3) - 2[x - 3(x + 1)]$

$9x + 21$

26. $2\{3x - 3[x + 2(x - 1)]\}$

$-12x + 12$

▦ **Calculator Problems**

27. A man rented a car at $29.95 per day for three days. He was charged 23 cents per mile. He paid $165.06. How many miles did he drive?

327 miles

28. An electronics company uses a computer chip with a perimeter of 0.05052 centimeter. The length is double the width. Find the length and width.

Width = 8.42×10^{-3} cm
Length = 1.684×10^{-2} cm

For Extra Practice Exercises, turn to page 114.

Solutions to Odd-Numbered Practice Problems

1. Let n = the number.

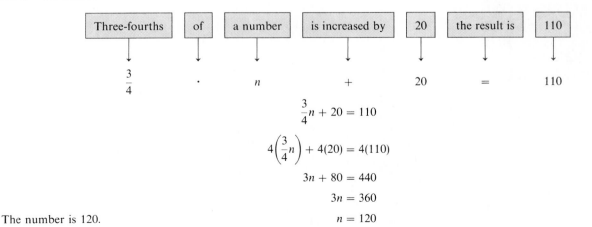

$$\frac{3}{4}n + 20 = 110$$

$$4\left(\frac{3}{4}n\right) + 4(20) = 4(110)$$

$$3n + 80 = 440$$

$$3n = 360$$

$$n = 120$$

The number is 120.

3. Let $\qquad n = $ the first odd integer

$\qquad n + 2 = $ the second consecutive odd integer

$\qquad n + 4 = $ the third consecutive odd integer

$$n + n + 2 + n + 4 = 195$$

$$3n + 6 = 195$$

$$3n = 189$$

$$n = \frac{189}{3}$$

$$n = 63$$

Thus, $n = 63$, $n + 2 = 65$, $n + 4 = 67$. The three integers are 63, 65, and 67.

Answers to Even-Numbered Practice Problems

2. The computer was used for 360 hours during the year.

4. The first side of the triangle is 56 meters, the second 28 meters, and the third 78 meters.

After studying this section, you will be able to:

1 *Solve word problems dealing with geometry, percent, or interest by using one linear equation containing one variable*

2 *Solve word problems dealing with mixtures by using one linear equation containing one variable*

2.5 SOLVING MORE-INVOLVED WORD PROBLEMS

1 To solve some word problems, we need to understand interest, percents, mixtures, or some other concept before we can use an algebraic equation as a model.

Percents and Interest

From arithmetic you know that to find a percent of a number we write the percent as a decimal and multiply the decimal by the number. Thus to find 36% of 85, we calculate $(0.36)(85) = 30.6$. If the number is not known, we can represent it by a variable.

Example 1 The Wildlife Refuge Rangers tagged 144 deer. They estimate that they have tagged 36% of the deer in the refuge. If they are correct, approximately how many deer are in the refuge?

Let $n = $ the number of deer in the refuge. We can paraphrase the central points of the problem as follows:

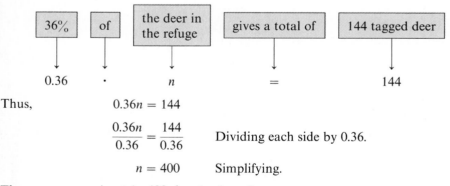

36%	of	the deer in the refuge	gives a total of	144 tagged deer
↓	↓	↓	↓	↓
0.36	·	n	=	144

Thus, $\qquad 0.36n = 144$

$$\frac{0.36n}{0.36} = \frac{144}{0.36} \qquad \text{Dividing each side by 0.36.}$$

$$n = 400 \qquad \text{Simplifying.}$$

There are approximately 400 deer in the refuge.

Check: How can you verify that 36% of 400 is 144? ■

Practice Problem 1 Technology Resources, Inc. sold 6900 computer workstations, a 15% increase in sales over the year. How many computer workstations were sold last year? (Hint: let $x = $ the amount of sales last year and let $0.15x = $ the increase in sales over last year.) ■

Adding two numbers yields a total, so we can call one of the numbers x and the other one $(\text{total} - x)$. We will use this concept in example 2.

Example 2 Bob's and Marcia's weekly salaries total $265. If they both went from part-time to full-time employment, their combined weekly income would be $655. Bob's salary would double while Marcia's would triple. How much do they make now?

Let b = Bob's part-time weekly salary. Since the total of the two part-time weekly salaries is $265, it follows that Marcia's part-time weekly salary is $265 - b$.

Now we consider the financial effect of their full-time status. We can condense the basic facts as follows:

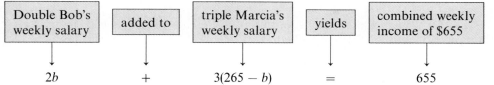

| Double Bob's weekly salary | added to | triple Marcia's weekly salary | yields | combined weekly income of $655 |

$$2b \quad + \quad 3(265 - b) \quad = \quad 655$$

Thus,

$$2b + 3(265 - b) = 655$$

$2b + 795 - 3b = 655$	Removing parentheses.
$795 - b = 655$	Simplifying.
$-b = -140$	Subtracting 795 from each side.
$b = 140$	Multiplying each side by -1.

If $b = 140$, then $265 - b = 265 - 140 = 125$. Thus, Bob's present full-time weekly salary is $140, and Marcia's present full-time weekly salary is $125

Check: Do their present weekly salaries total $265? Yes: $140 + 125 = 265$. If Bob's income is doubled and Marcia's is tripled, will their new weekly salaries total $655? Yes: $2(140) + 3(125) = 280 + 375 = 655$. ∎

Practice Problem 2 Alicia and Heather each sold several cars at Prestige Motors last month. Together they sold 43 cars. If next month Alicia doubles her sales, and Heather triples her sales, they will sell 108 cars. How many cars did each person sell this month? ∎

Simple interest is an income from investing money or a charge for borrowing money. It is computed by multiplying the amount of money borrowed or invested (called the principal) by the rate of interest by the period of time it is borrowed or invested (usually measured in years unless otherwise stated). Hence,

$$\text{interest} = \text{principal} \times \text{rate} \times \text{time}$$

$$I = prt$$

All interest problems in this chapter involve simple interest.

Example 3 Find the interest on $800 borrowed at an interest rate of 18% for two years.

$$I = prt$$
$$= (800)(0.18)(2)$$
$$= (144)(2)$$
$$= 288$$

The interest charge for borrowing $800 for two years at 18% is $288 ∎

Practice Problem 3 Find the interest on $7000 borrowed at an interest rate of 12% for four years. ∎

Investment Problems

Let's apply these concepts to a more involved problem.

TEACHING TIP After discussing example 1 or a similar example, ask students to solve the following problem: Westfield now has a population of 6160. This is a 12% increase from the population of ten years ago. What was the population ten years ago? (Answer: 5500 people.) Remind students that they can use the equation $n + 0.12n = 6160$ or they can say 112% of the population of 10 years ago is 6160 and use the equation $1.12n = 6160$ immediately.

TEACHING TIP If students seem a little unclear about example 2, you can explain in more detail using the following similar problem: Two packages (A and B) together weigh 100 pounds. Three of package A and four of package B weigh a total of 340 pounds. How much does each package weigh? (Answer: Let a = the weigh of package A. Then $100 - a$ = the weight of package B. Thus, $3a + 4(100 - a) = 340$. Solution: Package A weighs 60 pounds and package B weighs 40 pounds.)

Example 4 Maria has a job as a loan counselor in a bank. She advised a customer to invest part of his money in a 12% interest money market fund and the rest in a 14% interest investment fund. The customer had $6000 to invest. If he earned $772 in interest in one year, how much did he invest in each fund?

Let x = the amount of money invested in the 12% interest money market fund. We let the other amount be represented by (total − x). Thus, $6000 - x$ = the amount of money invested in the 14% interest investment fund. Now we look at the total investment picture.

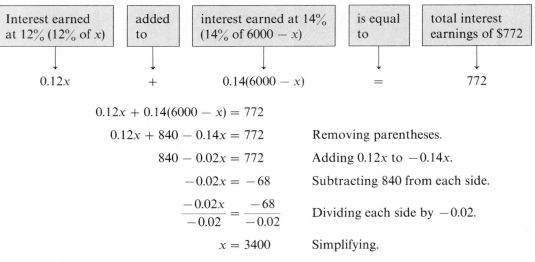

Interest earned at 12% (12% of x)	added to	interest earned at 14% (14% of 6000 − x)	is equal to	total interest earnings of $772
0.12x	+	0.14(6000 − x)	=	772

$$0.12x + 0.14(6000 - x) = 772$$

$0.12x + 840 - 0.14x = 772$	Removing parentheses.
$840 - 0.02x = 772$	Adding $0.12x$ to $-0.14x$.
$-0.02x = -68$	Subtracting 840 from each side.
$\dfrac{-0.02x}{-0.02} = \dfrac{-68}{-0.02}$	Dividing each side by -0.02.
$x = 3400$	Simplifying.

If $x = 3400$, then $6000 - x = 6000 - 3400 = 2600$. Thus $3400 was invested in the 12% interest money market fund, and $2600 was invested in the 14% interest investment fund.

Check: Can you verify that the two amounts total $6000? Can you verify that 12% of 3400 added to 14% of 2600 totals $772? ■

Practice Problem 4 Tricia received an inheritance of $5500 one year before she entered college. She invested part of it at 8% interest and the remainder at 12% interest. At the end of the year she had earned $540. How much did Tricia invest at each amount? ■

2 Mixture Problems

Sometimes we encounter a situation where two or more items are combined to form a mixture or solution. These types of problems are called *mixture problems.*

Example 5 A small truck has a radiator that holds 20 liters. A mechanic needs to fill the radiator with a solution that is 60% antifreeze. How many liters of a solution that is 70% antifreeze should he mix with a solution that is 30% antifreeze to achieve the desired mix?

A chart or table of the various quantities is most helpful in keeping track of each quantity. Let x = the number of liters of 70% antifreeze to be used. Since the total solution must be exactly 20 liters, we know that

$$20 - x = \text{the number of liters of 30\% antifreeze to be used}$$

We set up the following chart. Now we multiply the entry in column (A) by the entry in column (B) to obtain the entry in column (C).

	(A) Number of Liters of the Solution	(B) Percent Pure Antifreeze	(C) Number of Liters of Pure Antifreeze
70% antifreeze solution	x	70%	$0.70x$
30% antifreeze solution	$20 - x$	30%	$0.30(20 - x)$
Final 60% solution	20	60%	$0.60(20)$

TEACHING TIP   Students usually have some trouble finding how much of the 20 liters in example 5 is pure antifreeze. You may need to show them that 6% of 20 liters or $(0.60)(20) = 12$ liters of pure antifreeze.

Now we form an equation from the entries of column (C).

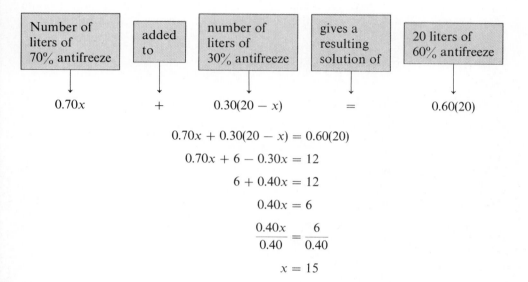

Number of liters of 70% antifreeze	added to	number of liters of 30% antifreeze	gives a resulting solution of	20 liters of 60% antifreeze
$0.70x$	+	$0.30(20 - x)$	=	$0.60(20)$

$$0.70x + 0.30(20 - x) = 0.60(20)$$

$$0.70x + 6 - 0.30x = 12$$

$$6 + 0.40x = 12$$

$$0.40x = 6$$

$$\frac{0.40x}{0.40} = \frac{6}{0.40}$$

$$x = 15$$

If $x = 15$, then $20 - x = (20 - 15) = 5$. Thus, the mechanic needs 15 liters of 70% antifreeze solution and 5 liters of 30% antifreeze solution.   ■

Practice Problem 5   A jeweler wishes to prepare 200 grams of 80% pure gold from sources that are 68% pure gold and 83% pure gold. How many grams of each should he use?   ■

Rate–Time Problems

Some problems involve the relationship distance = rate × time or $d = rt$.

Example 6   Frank drove at a steady speed for 3 hours on the turnpike. He then slowed his traveling speed by 15 miles per hour for traveling on secondary roads. The entire trip took 5 hours and covered 245 miles. What was his speed on the turnpike?

Let $x = $ speed on the turnpike in miles per hour
$x - 15 = $ speed on secondary roads in miles per hour
$d_1 = $ distance traveled on turnpike
$d_2 = $ distance traveled on secondary roads

On the turnpike, Frank traveled 3 hours at x miles per hour. Since the whole trip took 5 hours, he traveled on secondary roads 2 hours at $x - 15$ miles per hour. Thus,

$d_1 = 3x$ and $d_2 = 2(x - 15)$. Now we are given that $d_1 + d_2 = 245$. Our equation becomes

$$3x + 2(x - 15) = 245$$
$$3x + 2x - 30 = 245$$
$$5x - 30 = 245$$
$$5x = 275$$
$$x = 55$$

Thus, he traveled at an average speed of 55 miles per hour on the turnpike. ∎

Practice Problem 6   Wally drove for 4 hours at a steady speed. He slowed his speed by 10 miles per hour for the last part of the trip. The entire trip took 6 hours and covered 352 miles. How fast did he drive on each portion of the trip? ∎

EXERCISES 2.5

Write an algebraic equation for each problem and solve it.

1. 55% of what number is 1650?

Number $= x = 3000$
$$0.55x = 1650$$
$$x = 3000$$

2. 43% of what number is 2580?

Number $= x = 6000$
$$0.43x = 2580$$
$$x = 6000$$

3. Barbara is earning $14,000 this year after receiving a pay raise. The amount of increase she received was equal to 12% of last year's salary. What was her salary last year?

Last year's salary $= x = \$12{,}500$
$$x + 0.12x = \$14{,}000$$
$$x = \$12{,}500$$

4. Eastwing dormitory just purchased a new color television on sale for $340. The sale price was 80% of the original price. What was the original price of the television set?

Original price $= x = \$425$
$$0.80x = \$340$$
$$x = \$425$$

5. The dean of student activities issued 324 parking permits in August for incoming freshman. She estimated that about 60% of the commuting freshmen students came to get their parking permits in August. If her estimate is correct, how many commuting freshmen students are there?

Number of commuting freshmen students $= x = 540$
$$0.60x = 324$$
$$x = 540$$

6. The Environmental Preservation Committee found 390 dead birds on a beach contaminated by an oil slick. The committee estimated that this was only 15% of the birds that would eventually die as a result of the oil slick. If this estimate is correct, how many birds will die?

Number of dead birds $= x = 2600$
$$0.15x = 390$$
$$x = 2600$$

7. The sum of two numbers is 46. If the first number is multiplied by 3 and the second number is multiplied by 4, the sum is 163. What are the numbers?

1st number = $x = 21$
2nd number = $46 - x = 25$
$$3x + 4(46 - x) = 163$$
$$x = 21$$

8. The sum of two numbers is 88. If the first number is doubled and added to four times the second number, the result is 250. What are the numbers?

1st number = $x = 51$
2nd number = $88 - x = 37$
$$2x + 4(88 - x) = 250$$
$$x = 51$$

9. Fred Willianson had some leftover boards that were 16 feet long. He decided to use them for projects in his house. First he cut a 16-foot board into two unequal pieces. He then cut five additional 16-foot boards using exactly the same dimensions. He used all six of the longer pieces to complete a wall. He used four of the shorter pieces to case in a stairwell. In all he used 82 linear feet of boards on the two projects, and the remaining wood was left over. What were the lengths of the boards after he cut them into two pieces?

Shorter piece of board = $x = 7$ linear feet
Longer piece of board = $16 - x = 9$ linear feet
$$4x + 6(16 - x) = 82$$
$$x = 7$$

10. A hospital received a shipment of 8-milligram doses of a medicine. Each 8-milligram package was repacked into two smaller doses of unequal size and labeled packet A and packet B. The hospital then used 17 doses of packet A and 14 doses of packet B in one week. The total use of this medicine at the hospital during that week was 127 milligrams. How many milligrams of the medicine are contained in each packet A? in each packet B?

Number of milligrams in packet A = $x = 5$ mg
Number of milligrams in packet B = $8 - x = 3$ mg
$$17x + 14(8 - x) = 127$$
$$x = 5$$

11. Robert invested $3000 in two types of bonds for one year. The first type earns 6% interest, and the second type earns 9% interest. At the end of one year Robert earned $231 in interest. How much did he invest at each rate?

Amount invested @ 6% = $x = \$1300$
Amount invested @ 9% = $3000 - x = \$1700$
$$0.06x + 0.09(3000 - x) = 231$$
$$x = \$1300$$

12. An elderly lady invested her savings of $9000 in two accounts. She deposited part of her savings in a special notice account yielding 15% interest, and the rest in a regular savings account yielding 5% interest. At the end of one year she earned $1100 in interest. How much money did she deposit in each account?

Amount in sp. notice acct @ 15% interest = $x = \$6500$
Amount in regular savings acct @ 5% interest = $9000 - x = \$2500$
$$0.15x + 0.05(\$9000 - x) = \$1100$$
$$x = \$6500$$

13. A retired couple earned $4140 last year from their investments in mutual funds. They originally invested $30,000 in two types of funds. In the science investment fund they earned 12% interest. In the overseas investment fund they earned 15% interest. How much did they invest in each type of fund?

Amount in science investment @ 12% interest = $x = \$12,000$
Amount in overseas investment @ 15% interest = $30,000 - x = \$18,000$
$$0.12x + 0.15(30,000 - x) = \$4140$$
$$x = \$12,000$$

14. Ramon invested $7000 in money market funds. Part was invested at 14% interest and the rest at 11% interest. At the end of one year Ramon had earned $902 in interest. How much did Ramon invest at each amount?

Amount invested @ 14% = $x = \$4400$
Amount invested @ 11% = $7000 - x = \$2600$
$$0.14x + 0.11(\$7000 - x) = \$902$$
$$x = \$4400$$

15. A chemist has one solution of 60% hydrochloric acid and another containing 30% hydrochloric acid. How many quarts of each solution should he mix to obtain 30 quarts of a solution that is 40% hydrochloric acid?

Number qts of 60% acid = $x = 10$ qts
Number qts of 30% acid = $30 - x = 20$ qts
$$0.60x + 0.30(30 - x) = 0.40(30)$$
$$x = 10$$

16. A pharmacist has two solutions; one is 50% strength, and the other is 25% strength. How many milliliters of each should she mix to obtain 50 milliliters of a 40% strength solution?

Amount of solution @ 50% = $x = 30$ milliliters
Amount of solution @ 25% = $50 - x = 20$ milliliters
$$0.50x + 0.25(50 - x) = 0.40(50)$$
$$x = 30$$

17. A grocer at a specialty store is mixing tea worth $6.00 per pound with tea worth $8.00 per pound. He wants to obtain 144 pounds of tea worth $7.50 per pound. How much of each tea should he mix?

Amount of tea @ $6.00/lb. = $x = 36$ lbs.
Amount of tea @ $8.00/lb. = $144 - x = 108$ lbs.
$$\$6.00x + \$8.00(144 - x) = \$7.50(144)$$

18. The meat department manager at a large food store wishes to mix some hamburger with 30% fat content with some hamburger that has 10% fat content in order to obtain 100 pounds of hamburger with 25% fat content. How much hamburger of each type should she use?

Amount of hamburger @ 30% = $x = 75$ lbs.
Amount of hamburger @ 10% = $100 - x = 25$ lbs.
$$0.30x + 0.10(100 - x) = 0.25(100)$$
$$x = 75$$

19. A grocer has 200 pounds of candy worth $1.80 per pound. He also has some imported candy worth $3.00 per pound. How much imported candy should he mix with the 200 pounds in order to obtain a mixture worth $2.40 per pound?

Amount of candy @ $1.80/lb. = 200 lbs.
Amount of candy @ $3.00/lb = x

$$1.80(200) + 3.00(x) = 2.40(x + 200)$$
$$x = 200$$

He should mix 200 lbs of imported candy

20. A pharmacist has 40 liters of a 30% salt solution. He needs to cut the strength to 27%. He has on hand some 15% solution. How much of the 15% solution should the pharmacist add to the 30% solution?

Amount of salt solution @ 30% = 40
Amount of salt solution @ 15% = x = 10 liters

$$0.30(40) + 0.15x = 0.27(40 + x)$$
$$x = 10$$

21. Susan drove for 4 hours on secondary roads at a steady speed. She completed her trip by driving 2 hours on an interstate highway. Her total trip was 250 miles. Her average speed was 20 miles per hour faster on the interstate highway portion of the trip. How fast did she travel on the mountain raods?

Speed on secondary roads = x = 35 mph
Speed on interstate highway = $x + 20$ = 55 mph

$$4x + 2(x + 20) = 250$$
$$x = 35$$

22. Alice and Wendy flew a small plane for 930 miles. For the first 3 hours they flew at maximum speed. After refueling, they finished the trip at a cruising speed, which was 60 miles per hour slower than maximum speed. The entire trip took 5 hours of flying time. What is the maximum flying speed of the plane?

Speed for 1st three hours = x = 210 miles/hour
Speed for 2nd two hours = $x - 60$

$$3x + 2(x - 60) = 930$$
$$x = 210$$

23. Paul ran at 8 kilometers per hour for his morning jog. John ran for the same amount of time at 10 kilometers per hour. John ran exactly 1 more kilometer in his morning jog. How long did each of them run?

Paul's rate = 8 kph; Paul's time = $x = \dfrac{1}{2}$ hr or 30 min

John's rate = 10 kph; John's time = $x = \dfrac{1}{2}$ hr or 30 min

$$8x + 1 = 10x$$
$$x = \dfrac{1}{2}$$

24. The Clarke family went sailing on the lake. Their boat averaged 6 kilometers per hour. The Rourke family took their outboard runabout for a trip on the lake for the same amount of time. Their boat averaged 14 kilometers per hour. The Rourke family traveled 20 kilometers farther than the Clarke family. How many hours did each family spend on the boat trip?

Rate of Clarke's boat = 6 km/hr, Clarke's time = $x = 2\dfrac{1}{2}$ hrs

Rate of Rourke's boat = 14 km/hr, Rourke's time = $x = 2\dfrac{1}{2}$ hrs

$$14x - 20 = 6x$$
$$x = 2.5$$

? To Think About

25. An computer programmer earned a certain salary two years ago. He received a pay raise of 15% one year ago. This year the company was in severe financial difficulties, and all programmers received a pay cut of 22%. He now earns $26,910. How much did he earn two years ago?

programmer's salary two years ago = x = $30,000
programmer's salary one year ago = $x + 0.15x = 1.15x$
programmer's salary this year = $1.15x - 0.22(1.15x)$

$$1.15x - 0.22(1.15x) = \$26{,}910$$
$$x = \$30{,}000$$

26. Southern University held an informal student election to indicate support for its new president. Sixty percent of the students voted to support her, and 32% of the students voted not to support her. A total of 344 students did not vote. How many students are enrolled at Southern University?

Number of students enrolled = x = 4300 students

$$0.60x + 0.32x + 344 = x$$
$$x = 4300$$

Cumulative Review Problems

Evaluate.

27. $2x^2 - 3x + 1$ when $x = -2$

$2(-2)^2 - 3(-2) + 1 = 15$

28. $5a - 2b + c$ when $a = 1, b = -3, c = -4$

$5(1) - 2(-3) - 4 = 7$

29. $a + d(n - 1)$ when $a = 12, d = 2, n = 4$

$12 + 2(4 - 1) = 18$

30. $\dfrac{9}{5}C + 32$ when $C = -25$ $\quad \dfrac{9}{5}(-25) + 32 = -13$

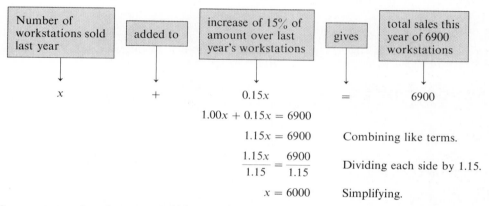
31. From 1950 to 1970 the town of Spencerville *grew* by 38.6%. From 1970 to 1990 the population *decreased* by 19%. The population in 1990 is 56,133. What was the population in 1950?

50,000

32. Tom and Linda invested $18,375 in money market funds. Part was invested at 5.9% interest and part was invested at 7.8% interest. In one year they earned $1243.25 in interest. How much did they invest at each rate?

$10,000 @ 5.9% $8375 @ 7.8%

For Extra Practice Exercises, turn to page 114.

Solutions to Odd-Numbered Practice Problems

1. Let x = the number of computer workstations sold last year. We can analyze the problem in this way.

Number of workstations sold last year	added to	increase of 15% of amount over last year's workstations	gives	total sales this year of 6900 workstations
x	$+$	$0.15x$	$=$	6900

$$1.00x + 0.15x = 6900$$
$$1.15x = 6900 \qquad \text{Combining like terms.}$$
$$\frac{1.15x}{1.15} = \frac{6900}{1.15} \qquad \text{Dividing each side by 1.15.}$$
$$x = 6000 \qquad \text{Simplifying.}$$

Therefore, 6000 computer workstations were sold last year.

Check: Can you verify that 6000 + (15% of 6000) = 6900?

3. Let I = the interest at 12% for $7000 for four years.

$$I = prt$$
$$= 7000(0.12)(4)$$
$$= (840)(4)$$
$$= 3360$$

The interest is $3360.

5. Let x = the number of grams of 68% pure gold and $200 - x$ = the number of grams of 83% pure gold. Now we multiply the entry in column (A) by the entry in column (B) to obtain the entry in column (C).

	(A) Number of Grams of the Mixture	(B) Percent Pure Gold	(C) Number of Grams of Pure Gold
68% pure gold source	x	68%	$0.68x$
83% pure gold source	$200 - x$	83%	$0.83(200 - x)$
Final 80% mixture of pure gold	200	80%	$0.80(200)$

Now we form an equation from the entries in column (C).

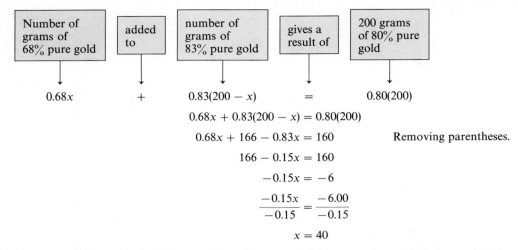

Number of grams of 68% pure gold	added to	number of grams of 83% pure gold	gives a result of	200 grams of 80% pure gold
0.68x	+	0.83(200 − x)	=	0.80(200)

$$0.68x + 0.83(200 - x) = 0.80(200)$$
$$0.68x + 166 - 0.83x = 160 \qquad \text{Removing parentheses.}$$
$$166 - 0.15x = 160$$
$$-0.15x = -6$$
$$\frac{-0.15x}{-0.15} = \frac{-6.00}{-0.15}$$
$$x = 40$$

If $x = 40$, then $200 - x = 200 - 40 = 160$. Thus, we have 40 grams of 68% pure gold and 160 grams of 83% pure gold.

Answers to Even-Numbered Practice Problems

2. Alicia sold 21 cars and Heather 22 cars this month.   **4.** $3000 is invested at 8% interest and $2500 is invested at 12% interest.
6. Wally drove for 4 hours at 62 miles per hour and then for 2 hours at 52 miles per hour.

EXTRA PRACTICE: EXERCISES

Section 2.1

Find the missing coordinate.

1. (5, _____) is a solution to $x + 4y + 3 = 0$.   (5, −2)

2. (_____, −3) is a solution to $x = \frac{2}{3}y - 6$.   (−8, −3)

3. (0, _____) is a solution to $9x - 3y = 20$. $\left(0, \frac{-20}{3}\right)$

4. (_____, ½) is a solution to $5x - 4y = 8$. $\left(2, \frac{1}{2}\right)$

5. (_____, −2) is a solution to $2x - 3y = 12$.   (3, −2)

6. (−2, _____) is a solution to $y = 3x - 7$.   (−2, −13)

7. (_____, 0.2) is a solution to $3x = 6y$.   (0.4, 0.2)

8. (_____, 0) is a solution to $4x - 3y = 12$.   (3, 0)

Simplify each equation. Graph the equation of the straight line determined by each equation. Plot three points and draw the line.

9. $5x - 2y = 0$ **9.**

10. $7x - 2y = 28$ **10.**

11. $y = \frac{2}{3}x - 4$ **11.**

12. $2(x + 4) = 3(y - 2)$ **12.**

13. $3x - 8 = 17$ **13.**

14. $5x - 2y - 3x - 10 = 0$ **14.**

15. $3x + 2y = 6$ **15.**

16. $x + y = 0$ **16.**

17. $\frac{1}{2}(4x - 6) = \frac{1}{3}(3y + 9)$ **17.**

18. $y = \frac{3x}{4} + 4$ **18.**

19. $3(y - x) = 4 - 3x$ **19.**

20. $\frac{2}{3}y - \frac{1}{2}x = 1$ **20.**

21. $0.2x + 0.4y = 1$ **21.**

Graph the straight line determined by the equation. Use an appropriate scale.

22. $y = 0.1x + 0.05$ **22.**

23. Some studies show that the ideal weight (W) in pounds for a man is given by the equation $W = 5.5d - 230$, where d is the height of the man in inches. Graph this relationship for the values of $d = 4$ feet, 10 inches; 5 feet; 5 feet, 2 inches; 5 feet, 4 inches; and 5 feet, 6 inches.

Hint: Remember to change the value of d to *inches* first.

24. Celsius temperatures are related to Farenheit temperatures by the relationship

$$C = \frac{5}{9}(F - 32°)$$

Graph this relationship for the values of $F = 32°$, $122°$, and $212°$.

23.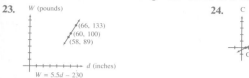

24.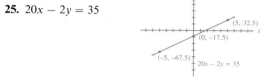

25. $20x - 2y = 35$

25.

Section 2.2

1. Find the slope of the line passing through $(7, -1)$ and $(2, -3)$. $\frac{2}{5}$

2. Find the slope of the line passing through $(-2, 4)$ and $\left(\frac{1}{2}, 3\right)$. $-\frac{2}{5}$

3. A line passes through a point $(2, 4)$ and a point $(3, b)$. Find the value of b if the slope of the line is 8.   12

4. A line has *no slope*. One point on the line is $(6, -3)$ the other point on the line is $(a, -12)$. Find the value of a.   6

5. Find the slope of a line *parallel* to a line passing through $(-4, -6)$ and $(-2, 1)$. $\frac{7}{2}$

6. One line passes through the points $(7, 2)$ and $(5, -1)$. A second line passes through $(-8, 4)$ and $(6, 25)$. Are the lines parallel? Why or why not?   Yes, m (both) $= \frac{3}{2}$

7. Find the slope of a line perpendicular to a line passing through $(5, 7)$ and $(-6, 1)$. $-\frac{11}{6}$

8. Find the slope of a line *perpendicular* to a line passing through $(0, 0.5)$ and $(-2.5, 0)$. -5

9. Do the points $(3, -8), (-1, 4)$ and $(1, -2)$ all lie on the same straight line? Explain.

10. Is $ABCD$ a parallelogram if the four vertices are $A(-2, 1)$, $B(-1, 6)$, $C(-4, 5)$, $D(-5, 0)$? Explain.
Hint: A parallelogram is a four-sided figure with opposite sides parallel.

9. Yes, $m = -3$ using pts 1 and 2
$m = -3$ using pts 2 and 3

10. Yes, $m_{AB} = m_{CD} = 5$
$m_{BC} = m_{AD} = \frac{1}{3}$

11. Find the slope of the line passing through $(6, -2)$ and $(-1, -2)$.   0

12. Find the slope of the line passing through $\left(\frac{1}{2}, \frac{1}{3}\right)$ and $\left(-\frac{1}{4}, \frac{1}{5}\right)$. $\frac{8}{45}$ **13.** $\frac{1}{25}$ or 0.04   **15.** $m = 0$

13. Find the slope of the line passing through $(0.2, 0.03)$ and $(-0.3, 0.01)$.

14. A line has a slope of 0. If it passes through $(6, -3)$ and $(-19, b)$, find b. -3

15. Find the slope of all lines perpendicular to the y-axis.

16. Find the slope of all lines parallel to the x-axis. $m = 0$

17. If one line has a slope of $\frac{a}{b}$, find, in terms of a and b, the slope of a line perpendicular to the original line. $-\frac{b}{a}$

18. Find the slope of the line that bisects quadrants I and III.

19. Find the slope of the line that bisects quadrants II and IV.

20. If line l_1 has equation $3x - 2y = 6$ and line $l_2 \parallel l_1$ and passes through the origin, find the equation of line l_2.

21. Are $(3, 5)$, $(6, 9)$, and $(-6, -7)$ collinear (all lie on one straight line)?

22. Are $3x - 2y = 6$ and $2x + 3y = -6$ perpendicular? Explain.

23. Are $3(2x - y) = 6 - 4x$ and $3y = 10x + 1$ parallel? Explain.
Yes, $m_1 = m_2 = \frac{10}{3}$

18. $m = 1$ **19.** $m = -1$ **20.** $3x - 2y = 0$ **21.** yes, $m = \frac{4}{3}$ **22.** Yes, $m_1 = \frac{3}{2}, m_2 = -\frac{2}{3}$

Section 2.3

1. Write in standard form: $y + 2 = \frac{1}{3}(x - 6)$. $x - 3y = 12$

2. (a) Write in slope-intercept form: $7x - 2y = -18$.
(b) Find the slope and the y-intercept.

3. (a) Write in the slope-intercept form: $\frac{2}{5}(x - y) = 1$.
(b) Find the slope and the y-intercept.   (Answers on p. 114.)

4. Write in standard form: $y = \frac{2}{3}x - 1$. $2x - 3y = 3$

Express the equation in standard form, *if possible.*

5. Find the equation of a line passing through $(-5, 2)$ and having a slope of $\frac{1}{2}$. $x - 2y = -9$

6. Find the equation of a *horizontal line* passing through $(-7, -2)$. $y = -2$

7. Find the equation of a *vertical line* passing through $(8, -3)$.

$x = 8$ **2.** (a) $y = \frac{7}{2}x + 9$ (b) $m = \frac{7}{2}$ $b = 9$

8. Find the equation of a line passing through $(-7, -6)$ and $(2, 1)$. $7x - 9y = 5$

9. Find the equation of a line parallel to $5x - 2y = 8$ and passing through $(0, 7)$. $5x - 2y = -14$

10. Find the equation of a line perpendicular to $7x = 2y$ and passing through $(-2, -3)$. $2x + 7y = -25$

11. A line is parallel to $5x + 6y = 8$ and passes through $(5, 1)$. It is written in the form $ax + by = 31$. Find the value of a and b. $a = 5, b = 6$

12. Find the equation of a line passing through $(6, -2)$ and perpendicular to $5x - 2 = 3$. $y = -2$

13. Find the equation of the line passing through $(6, 3)$ and parallel to $2x - 3y = 6$. $2x - 3y = 3$

14. Find the equation of the line with y-intercept $(0, -2)$ and parallel to the x-axis. $y = -2$

15. Find the equation of the line with x-intercept $(-3, 0)$ and parallel to the y-axis. $x = -3$

16. If the line $ax + by = 12$ has a y-intercept of 6 and a slope of 4, find the values of a and b. $a = -8, b = 2$

17. Find the equation of a line parallel to the x-axis and passing through $(-3, 4)$. $y = 4$

18. Find the equation of a line parallel to the y-axis and passing through $(5, -2)$. $x = 5$

19. Find the line with slope of $\dfrac{2}{3}$ and passing through $(5, -4)$.
$2x - 3y = 22$

20. Find **(a)** the x-intercept and **(b)** the y-intercept of $\dfrac{x}{4} + \dfrac{y}{3} = 1$.
x-intercept $= 4$ y-intercept $= 3$

21. Find the equation of the line perpendicular to $3x - 2y = 6$ and passing through $(2, 5)$. $2x + 3y = 19$

22. Find the equation of the line parallel to $3x - 2y = 12$ and passing through $(-3, 4)$. $3x - 2y = -17$

23. If $\dfrac{x}{a} + \dfrac{y}{b} = 1$ passes through $(6, -4)$ and $(-3, 8)$ find a and b. $a = 3$ $b = 4$

3. **(a)** $y = x - \dfrac{5}{2}$ **(b)** $m = 1$ $b = -\dfrac{5}{2}$

Section 2.4

1. Five-sevenths of a number is 40. What is the number?   56

2. If 60 is subtracted from one-fourth of a number, the result is 196. What is the number?   1024

3. The Jackson car rental company charges $30 per day and 12¢ per mile to rent a midsized car. Nancy rented a car for 8 days. She was charged $282. How many miles did she drive the car?   350

4. Ocean View Bank charges its customers $7.00 per month plus 18¢ per check for the use of a checking account. Sonja had a checking account there for four months and was charged $38.80 in service charges. How many checks did she write during that period?   60

5. Marcia's annual salary is $3000 less than double Anita's salary. The sum of the women's salaries is $46,500. What is the annual salary of each woman?   Anita: $16,500, Marcia: $30,000

6. A rectangular piece of land has a perimeter of 1600 meters. The length is 5 meters longer than triple the width. Find the dimensions of the piece of land.

7. Consider three numbers. The first number is one-third the second number. The third number is double the second number. The sum of three numbers is 60. Find each number.

8. The sum of the angles of a triangle is 180°. The first angle is 10° less than double the second angle. The third angle is 50° greater than the first angle. Find each angle of the triangle.   1st $\angle = 50°$ 2nd $\angle = 30°$ 3rd $\angle = 100°$

9. The sum of three consecutive odd integers is 393. What are the three integers?   129, 131, 133

10. The sum of one-half of a number, two-thirds of a number, and one-seventh of a number is 110. What is the number?   84

11. A rectangle is 9 feet longer than it is wide. If its perimeter is 62 feet, how wide is it?   11 ft

12. If the sum of four consecutive even integers is 108, find the largest integer.   30

13. The sum of two supplementary angles is always 180°. If one of these angles is 20 more than 3 times the smaller angle, find both angles.   40°   140°

14. If it costs $1.20 plus 40¢ an ounce to mail a package to Denver and I have to pay $3.60, how much does the package weigh?   6 ounces

15. Keith's mother is one year less than 7 times as old as Keith. If the sum of their ages is 55, how old is Keith?   7

16. If one-half of a number plus twice the number is 60, find the number.   24

17. Kevin has 35 coins. If he has twice as many dimes as nickels and three more quarters than nickels, how many nickels does he have?   8

18. If 60% of a number is 150, what is the number?   250

19. If it costs 3 times as much to make a cup as it does to make a saucer and it costs $4.80 to make one of each, how much does it cost to make a saucer? $1.20

20. If we have 4 times as many chairs as tables and 100 items altogether, how many tables do we have?   20

21. 4 is multiplied by the sum of one-fifth of a number added to one-sixth of the number. The result is 88. Find the number.   60

22. The value of a fraction is $\dfrac{2}{3}$ and its numerator is three greater than one-half its denominator. Find the fraction. $\dfrac{12}{18}$

23. Kathy has 3 times as many plums as Kerry. If each had 5 more, Kathy would have only two times as many plums. How many plums does Kerry have?   5

6. Width $= 198.75$ m   Length $= 601.25$ m   7. 1st $= 6$ 2nd $= 18$ 3rd $= 36$

Section 2.5

1. 28% of what number is 448?   1600

2. Hank is earning $12,390 this year after receiving a pay raise. The amount of increase he received was equal to 5% of last year's salary. What was his salary last year? $11,800

3. The sum of two numbers is 64. If the first number is doubled and added to 3 times the second number, the result is 169. What are the two numbers?   23, 41

4. The director of disease control for a midwestern state recently announced that 117,000 citizens over 70 years of age received a flu shot last year. She estimated that 39% of the citizens over 70 years of age received the shot. How many citizens in the state are over 70 years of age?   300,000

5. Kathy invested $5000 in money market funds. Part was invested at 14% interest, the rest at 11% interest. At the end of one year she had earned $625 in interest. How much did Kathy invest at each amount? $2500 @ 14% $2500 @ 11%

6. A chemist has two solutions, one of 50% strength and another of 75% strength. How many milliliters of each should be mixed to obtain 200 milliliters of a 60% strength solution?   120 ml @ 50%, 80 ml @ 75%

7. A manufacturer is mixing chocolate that costs $5.00 per pound with chocolate that costs $3.00 per pound. She desires to have 300 pounds of chocolate that costs $3.50 per pound. How much should she use of each type?
75 lbs. @ $5.00   225 lbs. @ $3.00

8. An alloy of zinc and copper weighing 400 kilograms contains 45 kilograms of zinc. How much zinc must be added so that 20% of the alloy will be zinc?   43.75 kg

9. A lab technician wishes to obtain a solution of 50 liters of 20% acid. How many liters of 24% acid and how many liters of 18% acid should be mixed to obtain the desired solution?

10. A certain lady invested some money in interest free bonds at 7% interest. She invested half that amount in interest free bonds at 8%. She earns $567 more per year from the 7% interest investment than the 8% interest investment. How much was invested at each amount?

11. I have 6 hours at my disposal. How far can I ride on my bicycle at 9 mph and return to the original point by walking at 3 mph?   13.5 miles

12. John and Tom made a profit of $9000 on a business venture. If John supplied 25% more of the capital, how much should John receive of the $9000? $5000

9. $16\frac{2}{3}$ liters @ 24%, $33\frac{1}{3}$ liters @ 18%

10. $18,900 @ 7%, $9,450 @ 8%

13. How much pure gold added to 180 ounces of gold 14 karats fine $\left(\frac{14}{24}\text{ pure}\right)$ will make an alloy 16 karats fine?   45 ounces

14. Gregory invested $15,000, part at 12% and the rest at 6%. If his annual return was 10% of the total investment, what amount was invested at each rate?

15. The speed of an express train is $\frac{3}{2}$ that of a freight train. The express train covers 270 miles in 3 hours less than the freight train. Find the rate of the express train.   45 mph

16. In an alloy of 100 pounds of zinc and copper there are 75 pounds of copper. How much copper must be added to make the alloy 10% zinc?   150 lbs

17. A bank invests three sums of money that are in the ratio of 1:2:3. If they are invested at 8%, 7%, and 6%, respectively, for one year, they will bring in a total of $800. How much is invested at 7%? $4000

18. A solution is 40% acid. How much water (H_2O) must be evaporated from 100 quarts of this solution to make it 50% acid?   20 qts

14. $10,000 @ 12%, 5,000 @ 6%

CHAPTER ORGANIZER

Topic	Procedure	Examples
Slope, p. 85	The *slope m* of any straight line that contains the points (x_1, y_1) and (x_2, y_2) is defined by $$m = \frac{y_2 - y_1}{x_2 - x_1} \quad \text{where } x_2 \neq x_1$$	Find the slope of a line passing through $(6, -1)$ and $(-4, -5)$. $$m = \frac{-5 - (-1)}{-4 - 6} = \frac{-5 + 1}{-4 - 6} = \frac{-4}{-10} = \frac{2}{5}$$
Parallel and perpendicular lines, p. 87	Two distinct lines with nonzero slopes m_1 and m_2, respectively, are **1.** *Parallel* if $m_1 = m_2$ **2.** *Perpendicular* if $m_1 = -\dfrac{1}{m_2}$	Find the slope of a line parallel to $y = -\frac{3}{2}x + 6$. $m = -\frac{3}{2}$ Find the slope of a line perpendicular to $y = -4x + 7$. $m = \frac{1}{4}$
Zero slope, p. 86	All horizontal lines have *zero slope*. They can be written in the form $y = b$, where b is a real number.	What is the slope of $2y = 8$? $y = 4$. It is a horizontal line; the slope is zero.
No slope, p. 86	All vertical lines have *no slope*. They can be written in the form $x = a$, where a is a real number. (p. 86)	What is the slope of $5x = -15$? $x = -3$. It is a vertical line. This line has *no slope*.
Intercepts, p. 78	The number a is the *x*-intercept of a line if the line crosses the *x*-axis at $(a, 0)$. The number b is the *y*-intercept of a line if the line crosses the *y*-axis at $(0, b)$.	Find the intercepts of $7x - 2y = -14$. If $x = 0$, $-2y = -14$ and $y = 7$. The *y*-intercept is 7. If $y = 0$, $7x = -14$ and $x = -2$. The *x*-intercept is -2.
Standard form, p. 90	The equation of a line is in *standard form* when it is written as $Ax + By = C$, where A, B, C are real numbers.	Place this equation in standard form: $y = -5(x + 6)$. $$y = -5x - 30$$ $$5x + y = -30$$
Slope-intercept form, p. 90	The *slope-intercept form* of the equation of a line is $y = mx + b$, where the slope is m and the *y*-intercept is b.	Find the slope and *y*-intercept of $y = -\frac{7}{3}x + \frac{1}{4}$. The slope $= -\frac{7}{3}$; the *y*-intercept $= \frac{1}{4}$.

Topic	Procedure	Examples
Point-slope form, p. 92	The *point-slope form* of the equation of a line is $y - y_1 = m(x - x_1)$, where m is the slope and (x_1, y_1) are the coordinates of a point.	Write the point-slope form of an equation whose slope is -4 and which passes through $(6, -1)$. $$y - (-1) = -4(x - 6)$$ $$y + 1 = -4(x - 6)$$
Solving word problems, p. 104	**1.** Read the problem carefully. Sketch the quantities or objects described in the problem to help you visualize the situation. **2.** Determine what is required and what quantity you will represent by a variable. Write an equation that indicates exactly what the variable represents. **3.** Determine the relationship between this variable and other quantities in the problem and express it algebraically. **4.** Use the variable you chose to write an equation that describes the given information. **5.** Solve this equation and determine the values asked for in the problem. **6.** Are the answers reasonable? Are the values you found close to what you estimated them to be? **7.** Make sure your answers satisfy all requirements in the problem. This usually involves at least two sets of calculations.	The perimeter of a rectangle is 88 meters. The length is 1 meter less than double the width. Find the dimensions of the rectangle. **1.** Length Width Perimeter = 88 meters **2.** We need to find the length and the width. Let w = width $2w - 1$ = length **3.** The formula for the perimeter is $P = 2w + 2l$. **4.** $88 = 2w + 2(2w - 1)$ **5.** $88 = 2w + 4w - 2$ $88 = 6w - 2$ $90 = 6w$ $\dfrac{90}{6} = w$ $15 = w$ $2w - 1 = 2(15) - 1 = 30 - 1 = 29$ *The width is 15 meters. The length is 29 meters.* Checking: **6.** We estimate our answers to be 30 meters and 15 meters. Our answer is reasonable! **7.** Is the length 1 meter less than double the width? $29 \overset{?}{=} 2(15) - 1$ $29 = 29$ ✓ Yes. Is the perimeter 88 meters? $2(29) + 2(15) = 58 + 30 = 88$ ✓ Yes.
Checking word problems, p. 105		

REVIEW PROBLEMS CHAPTER 2

1. Find the value of a if $(a, -6)$ is a solution to the equation $7x - 2y - 5 = 0$.

  -1

In problems 2 and 3, graph the equation of the straight line determined by each equation by plotting three points and drawing the line.

2. $2y - 6x + 4 = 0$

x	y
0	-2
1	1
2	4

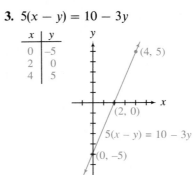

3. $5(x - y) = 10 - 3y$

x	y
0	-5
2	0
4	5

4. The profit in dollars for a microcomputer company is given by the equation $P = 140x - 2000$, where x is the number of microcomputers sold each day. How many microcomputers must be sold each day for the company to make a profit?

15 or more computers

5. Find the slope of the line connecting $(-8, -4)$ and $(2, -3)$.

$m = \dfrac{1}{10}$

6. A line passes through the points $(a, 6)$ and $(-2, 3)$. Find the value of a if $m = 2$.

$-\dfrac{1}{2}$

7. A line is perpendicular to a line of zero slope. What is its slope?

No slope

8. Find the slope of a line perpendicular to the line passing through $\left(\dfrac{2}{3}, \dfrac{1}{3}\right)$ and $(4, 2)$,

$m = -2$

9. Do the points $(3, -5)$, $(2, 1)$, and $(-2, 10)$ all lie on the same straight line? Explain.

No, slope 1st two pts $= -6$, slope 2nd two pts $= -\dfrac{9}{4}$

10. Write the equation $3x + 2y = 5x - 6$ in slope-intercept form. Find the slope and y-intercept.

$y = x - 3$, $m = 1$, $b = -3$

11. A line has a slope of $\dfrac{2}{3}$ and a y-intercept of -4. Write its equation in standard form.

$2x - 3y = 12$

12. Find the equation of a line in standard form that passes through $\left(\dfrac{1}{2}, -2\right)$ and has slope -4.

$4x + y = 0$

In problems 13–16, find the equation of a line satisfying these conditions. Write your answer in standard form.

13. A line passing through $(5, 6)$ and $\left(-1, -\dfrac{1}{2}\right)$

$13x - 12y = -7$

14. A line that has no slope passing through $(-6, 5)$

$x = -6$

15. A line parallel to $3x - 2y = 8$ and passing through $(5, 1)$.

$3x - 2y = 13$

16. A line perpendicular to $7x + 8y - 12 = 0$ passing through $(-2, 5)$.

$8x - 7y = -51$

17. Five-eighths of a number is 290. What is the number?

464

18. The number of men attending Western Tech is 200 less than twice the number of women. The number of students at the school is 280. How many men attend? How many women attend?

120 men   160 women

19. City Compacts rents cars for $30 per day plus 12¢ per mile. Juanita rented a car for two days and was charged $102. How many miles did she drive the car?

350 miles

20. The sum of three consecutive even integers is 408. What are the integers?

134, 136, 138

21. A rectangular piece of copper has a perimeter of 88 mm. The length of the rectangle is 8 mm longer than three times the width. Find the length and width.

Width = 9 mm, Length = 35 mm

22. Alice's employer withholds from her monthly paycheck $102 for federal and state taxes and for retirement. She noticed that the amount withheld for her state income tax is $13 more than that withheld for retirement. The amount withheld for federal income tax is three times the amount withheld for the state tax. How much is withheld monthly for federal tax? state tax? retirement?

Retirement = $10, State Tax = $23, Federal Tax = $69

23. Hightstown College has 12% fewer students this year than it did last year. There are 2332 students enrolled. How many students were enrolled last year?

2650

24. An auto manufacturer wants to make 260,000 sedans a year. Some will be two-door sedans; the rest will be four-door. He also wants to make three times as many four-door sedans as he does two-door sedans. How many of each type should be manufactured?

65,000 two dr. sedans, 195,000 four dr. sedans

25. Lucinda has invested $7000 in mutual funds and bonds. The mutual fund earns 12% simple interest. The bonds earn 8% simple interest. At the end of the year she earned $740 in interest. How much did she invest at each rate?

$4500 @ 12%, $2500 @ 8%

26. To make a weak solution of 24 liters of 4% acid, a lab technician has some premixed solutions: one is 2% acid; the other, 5% acid. How many liters of each type should he mix to obtain the desired solution?

8 liters @ 2%, 16 liters @ 5%

27. A local coffee specialty shop wants to obtain 30 pounds of a mixture of coffee beans costing $4.40 per pound. They have a mixture costing $4.25 a pound and a mixture costing $4.50 per pound. How much of each should be used?

12 lbs @ $4.25, 18 lbs @ $4.50

28. When Eastern Slope Community College opened, the number of students (full-time and part-time) was 380. Since then the number of full-time students has doubled, and the number of part-time students had tripled. There are now 890 students at the school. How many of the present students are full-time? part-time?

500 full-time students, 390 part-time students

1. Find the value of b if $(-3, b)$ is a solution to the equation $5x - 2y = -8$.

In problems 2 and 3, graph each line (plot three points).

2. $y = 4x - 3$

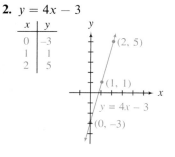

3. $5x - 2y = 4$

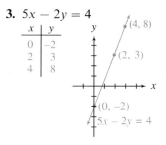

4. Find the slope of the line passing through $(-6, -1)$ and $(-2, 4)$.

5. Do the points $(-2, -4)$, $(1, 2)$, and $(-5, -8)$ all lie on the same line? Explain.

6. Write the equation $2x - \dfrac{3}{4}y + 2 = 0$ in slope-intercept form. Find the slope and the y-intercept.

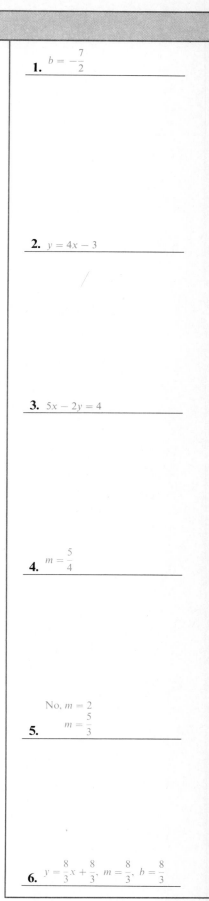

1. $b = -\dfrac{7}{2}$

2. $y = 4x - 3$

3. $5x - 2y = 4$

4. $m = \dfrac{5}{4}$

5. No, $m = 2$
$m = \dfrac{5}{3}$

6. $y = \dfrac{8}{3}x + \dfrac{8}{3}$, $m = \dfrac{8}{3}$, $b = \dfrac{8}{3}$

7. $y = -\dfrac{3}{2}x + \dfrac{7}{2}$

7. Write the equation in slope-intercept form of a line parallel to $3x + 2y = 6$ that passes through $(-1, 5)$.

8. Write the equation in standard form of a line perpendicular to $5x - 3y + 8 = 0$ that passes through $(-4, 0)$.

8. $3x + 5y = -12$

9. Find the equation in standard form of a line passing through $\left(\dfrac{1}{2}, \dfrac{1}{4}\right)$ and $\left(\dfrac{3}{2}, 2\right)$.

9. $14x - 8y = 5$

10. Write the equation of a vertical line passing through $(-1, -7)$.

10. $x = -1$

11. Graph the equation $0.03y + 6x = 2.2$ by plotting the points corresponding to $x = 1$, $x = 2$, and $x = 3$. Be sure to choose an appropriate scale.

x	y
1	$-126.\overline{6}$
2	$-326.\overline{6}$
3	$-526.\overline{6}$

$0.63y + 6x = 2.2$

$(1, -126.\overline{6})$
$(2, -326.\overline{6})$
$(3, -526.\overline{6})$

11. $0.63y + 6x = 2.2$

Use an algebraic equation to find a solution for each problem.

1. Four-fifths of a number is 148. What is the number?

2. Jeffrey rented a car for four days from Zenith Car Rental. Zenith charges 14¢ per mile and $32 per day. Jeffrey paid $163 to rent the car. How many miles did he drive?

3. The sum of the angles of a triangle is 180°. The second angle is 10° more than twice the first. The third angle is 30° more than the first. Find each angle.

1. 185

2. 250 miles

3. 1st ∡ = 35°, 2nd ∡ = 80°, 3rd ∡ = 65°

4. Ten years ago Paul's annual salary and Richard's annual salary totaled $23,500. Since that time, Paul's annual salary has tripled and Richard's annual salary has doubled. They now earn a combined annual income of $58,500. Find the current salary of each man.

5. Nancy has saved $8000 from her salary her first three years at her job. She invested part of it at 8% interest and the remainder at 14% interest. At the end of one year her investments had earned $964. How much did she invest at each rate?

6. A chemist needs to obtain a solution of 50 liters of 40% acid. She has available a solution that is 70% acid and another solution that is 30% acid. How much of each should she mix?

1. Graph the line with equation $2x + 3y = -10$. Plot at least three points.

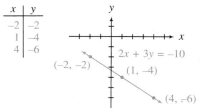

$2x + 3y = -10$

$(-2, -2)$

$(1, -4)$

$(4, -6)$

2. Find the slope of the line passing through $(2, -3)$ and $\left(\dfrac{1}{2}, -6\right)$.

3. Find the slope of the line $3x = -8y + 12$.

4. Write the equation in standard form of a line passing through $(5, -2)$ and $(-3, -1)$.

5. Write the equation in standard form of a line perpendicular to $6x - 7y - 1 = 0$ that passes through $(0, -2)$.

6. Write the equation of a horizontal line passing through $\left(-\dfrac{1}{3}, 2\right)$.

1. $2x + 3y = -10$

2. 2

3. $-\dfrac{3}{8}$

4. $x + 8y = -11$

5. $7x + 6y = -12$

6. $y = 2$

1st side = 16 meters,
2nd side = 32 meters,
7. 3rd side = 21 meters

Use an algebraic equation to find a solution.

7. A triangle has a perimeter of 69 meters. The second side is twice the length of the first side. The third side is 5 meters longer than the first side. How long is each side?

8. 900 hrs

8. The city hall leased a computer for one year. The city was billed for a one-time $200 installation fee, a monthly rental fee, and a fee for the number of actual hours the computer was used. The contract stated the monthly rental fee was $280 and the hourly charge was $10 per hour of actual computer use. The first yearly bill was $12,560. How many actual hours was the computer used?

9. Linda needs 10 gallons of solution that is 60% antifreeze. She has a mixture that is 90% antifreeze and one that is 50% antifreeze. How much of each should she use?

9. 2.5 gal @ 90%,   7.5 gal @ 50%

10. Lon Triah invested $5000 at a local bank. Part was invested at 6% interest and the remainder at 10%. At the end of one year Lon earned $428 interest. How much was invested at each rate?

10. $1800 @ 6%, $3200 @ 10%

This test is made up equally of problems from Chapters 1 and 2.

1. Consider the set of numbers $\left\{-12,\right.$ $-3, 0, \frac{1}{4}, 2.16, 2.333\ldots,$ $2.9614371823\ldots, -\frac{5}{8}, 3\left.\right\}$. List all the rational numbers.

2. Name the property that justifies $7 + (6 + 3) = (7 + 6) + 3$.

3. Evaluate: $\sqrt{49} + 3(2 - 6)^2 - (-3)$.

4. Simplify: $(-2x^{-3}y^4)^{-2}$.

5. Simplify: $\dfrac{7ab^3}{-14a^5b^{-2}}$.

6. Find the perimeter of a parallelogram if two sides measure 9 centimeters and 18 centimeters.

7. Find the area of a circle with radius 7 inches.

8. Simplify: $2x(3x - 4) - 5x^2(2 - 6x)$.

9. Solve for x: $\dfrac{1}{4}(x + 5) - \dfrac{5}{3} = \dfrac{1}{3}(x - 2)$.

10. Solve for b: $h = \dfrac{2}{3}(b + d)$.

---

1. $-12, -3, 0, \frac{1}{4}, 2.16, 2.333\ldots, -\frac{5}{8}, 3$

2. Associative property for addition

3. 58

4. $\dfrac{x^6}{4y^8}$

5. $\dfrac{b^5}{-2a^4}$

6. 54 cm

7. 153.86 square inches

8. $30x^3 - 4x^2 - 8x$

9. 3

10. $b = \dfrac{3h - 2d}{2}$

11. $4x - 6y = 10$

12. $\dfrac{1}{2}$

13. $2x + y = 11$

14. $3x + 2y = -12$

15. 1st side = 25 meters
2nd side = 35 meters
3rd side = 45 meters

16. 340 miles

17. $2000 @ 12%
$4500 @ 10%

18. 6 gals @ 80%
3 gals @ 50%

11. Graph the line $4x - 6y = 10$. Plot at least three points.

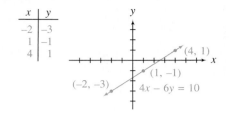

12. Find the slope of the line passing through $(6, 5)$ and $(-2, 1)$.

13. Write the equation of a line in standard form that passes through $(5, 1)$ and $(4, 3)$.

14. Write the equation of a line in standard form that passes through $(-2, -3)$ and is perpendicular to $y = \dfrac{2}{3}x - 4$.

15. A triangle has a perimeter of 105 meters. The second side is 10 meters longer than the first. The third side is 5 meters shorter than double the first. How long is each side?

16. A man rented a car for four days at a cost of $19 per day. He was billed for $154.20. He was charged 23¢ for each mile driven. How far did he drive?

17. Wendy invested $6500 for one year. She invested part at 12% interest and part at 10% interest. She earned $690 in interest. How much did she invest at each rate?

18. Hector needs 9 gallons of a solution that is 70% antifreeze. He will combine a mixture of 80% antifreeze with a mixture of 50% antifreeze to obtain the desired 9 gallons. How many gallons of each should he use?

Systems of Linear Equations

Anyone using X-ray machinery is required to learn mathematics to measure and doublecheck safety factors for a patient during an X-ray.

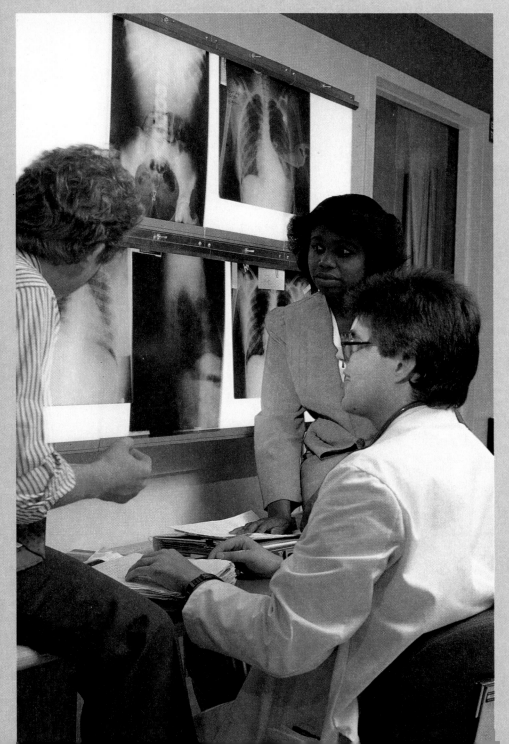

3

PRETEST CHAPTER 3

If you are familiar with the topics in this chapter, take this test now. Check your answers with those in the back of the book. If an answer was wrong or you couldn't do a problem, study the appropriate section of the chapter.

If you are not familiar with the topics in this chapter, don't take this test now. Instead, study the examples, work the practice problems, and then take the test.

This test will help you identify those concepts that you have mastered and those that need more study.

Section 3.1 Find the solution to each system of equations. If there is no single solution to a system, state the reason.

1. $7x - 2y = 3$ $x = 1, y = 2$
$2x + y = 4$

2. $5x + 7y = -11$ $x = 2, y = -3$
$\dfrac{3}{4}x - \dfrac{1}{2}y = 3$

3. $x = 2 + 3y$ Infinite number of solutions–dependent eqs.
$6y = 2x - 4$

Section 3.2 Find the solution to each system of equations.

4. $-2x + 5y + 2z = -2$ $x = 3$
$3x + 2y - 4z = 1$ $y = 0$
$-x + 3y - 3z = -9$ $z = 2$

5. $x + y + 2z = 3$ $x = 4$
$3x + 2y + 4z = 10$ $y = -3$
$2y + z = -5$ $z = 1$

Section 3.3 Use a system of linear equations to solve each of the following problems.

6. A coach purchased two shirts and three pairs of pants for his team and paid $75.00. His assistant purchased three shirts and five pairs of pants at the same store for $121.00. What is the cost for a shirt? What is the cost for a pair of pants? $12 shirts, $17 pants

7. A biologist needs to use 21 milligrams of iron, 22 milligrams of vitamin B_{12}, and 26 milligrams of niacin for an experiment. She has available packets A, B, and C to meet these requirements. Packet A contains 3 milligrams of iron, 2 milligrams of vitamin B_{12}, and 4 milligrams of niacin. Packet B contains 2 milligrams of iron, 4 milligrams of vitamin B_{12}, and 5 milligrams of niacin. Packet C contains 2 milligrams of iron, 2 milligrams of vitamin B_{12}, and 1 milligrams of niacin. How many of each packet should she use?   Packet A = 3, Packet B = 2, Packet C = 4

Section 3.4 Evaluate the determinant.

8. $\begin{vmatrix} 3 & -6 \\ 2 & -5 \end{vmatrix}$ -3

9. $\begin{vmatrix} -4 & -2 \\ -3 & 7 \end{vmatrix}$ -34

10. $\begin{vmatrix} 3 & 0 \\ 4 & 0 \end{vmatrix}$ 0

11. $\begin{vmatrix} 2 & -5 & 1 \\ 3 & 0 & 4 \\ 1 & 2 & -1 \end{vmatrix}$ -45

Section 3.5 Use Cramer's rule to solve each system of equations.

12. $2x + 7y = -1$ $x = 3, y = -1$
$5x + 6y = 9$

13. Solve for x **only:**

$2x + y + 3z = 3$ $x = -4$
$x - 2y + 2z = -2$
$3x - 4y = -20$

3.1 SYSTEMS OF EQUATIONS IN TWO VARIABLES

After studying this section, you will be able to:

1 Solve a system of two linear equations by the substitution method

2 Solve a system of two linear equations by the addition (elimination) method

3 Determine if a system of two linear equations is an inconsistent system

4 Determine if a system of two linear equations is dependent

1 In Chapter 2 we found that a linear equation containing two variables, such as $4x + 3y = 12$, has an unlimited number of ordered pairs (x, y) that satisfy it. For example, $(3, 0)$, $(0, 4)$, and $(-3, 8)$ all satisfy the equation $4x + 3y = 12$. We call two linear equations in *two* unknowns a **system of two equations in two variables**. Many such systems have exactly one solution. A **solution to a system** of two linear equations in two variables is an *ordered pair* that when substituted into *each* equation will produce an identity.

For example, the equations

$$x + 3y = -7$$
$$4x + 3y = -1$$

form a system. Its solution is $(2, -3)$. Let's verify that $(2, -3)$ is a solution to this system by substituting $x = 2$ and $y = -3$ into each equation. For the first equation,

$$2 + 3(-3) \stackrel{?}{=} -7$$
$$2 - 9 \stackrel{?}{=} -7$$
$$-7 = -7 \checkmark$$

For the second equation,

$$4(2) + 3(-3) \stackrel{?}{=} -1$$
$$8 - 9 \stackrel{?}{=} -1$$
$$-1 = -1 \checkmark$$

Since we obtain a true mathematical statement each time, $x = 2$ and $y = -3$ [that is, the ordered pair $(2, -3)$] is a solution of the system of equations.

We could verify this solution another way—by graphing. Sketch the graphs of each equation. Since the equations are linear, the graphs are straight lines. (Review Chapter 2 if you do not fully understand linear equations and how to graph them by using the x- and y-intercepts.) The lines intersect at only *one* point. That point is the solution to the system.

Later we will discuss systems that have more than one solution. Now we will learn how to solve this system of equations.

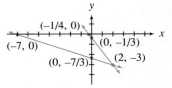

The Substitution Method

If a system of linear equations in two variables has a unique solution, we can find it by the **substitution method**. To use this method, we choose one equation and solve for one variable in terms of the other variable. Then we substitute that expression into the remaining equation. It is usually best to solve for a variable that has a coefficient of $+1$ or -1. This will avoid unnecessary fractions.

Example 1   Find the solution to the following system of equations:

$$x + 3y = -7 \qquad \boxed{1}$$
$$4x + 3y = -1 \qquad \boxed{2}$$

We can work with equation $\boxed{1}$ or equation $\boxed{2}$. Let's choose equation 1 and solve for x. This gives us equation $\boxed{3}$.

$$x = -7 - 3y \qquad \boxed{3}$$

TEACHING TIP   Sometimes students remember how to do one method from high school (either the substitution method or the addition method) and want to know why they need two methods. Tell them that when they get to study systems of non-linear equations, sometimes a particular system can be solved by only one method and they will need to know the one method that works for that system.

Now we substitute this expression for x into equation $\boxed{2}$ and solve the equation for y.

$$4x + 3y = -1 \qquad \boxed{2}$$
$$4(-7 - 3y) + 3y = -1$$
$$-28 - 12y + 3y = -1$$
$$-28 - 9y = -1$$
$$-9y = -1 + 28$$
$$-9y = +27$$
$$y = -3$$

Now we can substitute $y = -3$ into equation $\boxed{1}$, $\boxed{2}$, or $\boxed{3}$ to find x. Let's use $\boxed{3}$:

$$x = -7 - 3(-3)$$
$$= -7 + 9$$
$$= 2$$

Therefore, our solution is $x = 2$ and $y = -3$, we can also express the solution by the ordered pair $(2, -3)$.

Check: We must verify the solution in both equations.

$$
\begin{array}{ll}
x + 3y = -7 & 4x + 3y = -1 \\
2 + 3(-3) \overset{?}{=} -7 & 4(2) + 3(-3) \overset{?}{=} -1 \\
2 - 9 \overset{?}{=} -7 & 8 - 9 \overset{?}{=} -1 \\
-7 = -7 \checkmark & -1 = -1 \checkmark \quad \blacksquare
\end{array}
$$

Practice Problem 1   Use the substitution method to solve the system

$$2x - y = 7$$
$$3x + 4y = -6 \qquad \blacksquare$$

We summarize the method here.

TEACHING TIP   Remind students that they must check the solution to the system in both of the original equations in order to have a valid proof that the answers are correct. Students sometimes think that checking with one equation is sufficient.

> **How to Solve a System of Two Equations by the Substitution Method**
>
> 1. Choose one of the two equations and solve for one variable in terms of the other variable.
> 2. Substitute this expression from step 1 into the *other* equation.
> 3. You now have one equation with one variable. Solve this equation for that variable.
> 4. Substitute this value for the variable into either of the equations with two variables to obtain a value for the second variable.
> 5. Check each solution in each original equation.

Example 2   Solve the following system of equations:

$$\frac{x}{2} - \frac{y}{4} = -\frac{3}{4} \qquad \boxed{1}$$
$$3x - 2y = -6 \qquad \boxed{2}$$

First clear equation $\boxed{1}$ of fractions by multiplying each term by 4.

$$4\left(\frac{x}{2}\right) - 4\left(\frac{y}{4}\right) = 4\left(-\frac{3}{4}\right)$$
$$2x - y = -3 \qquad \boxed{3}$$

The new system is now

$$2x - y = -3 \quad \boxed{3}$$
$$3x - 2y = -6 \quad \boxed{2}$$

Step 1. Let's solve equation $\boxed{3}$ for y.

$$-y = -3 - 2x$$
$$\boxed{y = 3 + 2x}$$

Step 2. Substitute this expression for y into equation $\boxed{2}$.

$$3x - 2(3 + 2x) = -6$$

Step 3. Solve this equation for x.

$$3x - 6 - 4x = -6$$
$$-6 - x = -6$$
$$-x = -6 + 6$$
$$-x = 0$$
$$x = 0$$

Step 4. Substitute $x = 0$ into equation $\boxed{2}$ (you could also choose equation $\boxed{1}$ or equation $\boxed{3}$).

$$3(0) - 2y = -6$$
$$-2y = -6$$
$$y = 3$$

So our solution is $x = 0$ and $y = 3$, we can also write this as $(0, 3)$.

Step 5. We must verify the solution in both original equations ($\boxed{1}$ and $\boxed{2}$).

$$\frac{x}{2} - \frac{y}{4} = -\frac{3}{4} \qquad 3x - 2y = -6$$
$$\frac{0}{2} - \frac{3}{4} \overset{?}{=} -\frac{3}{4} \qquad 3(0) - 2(3) \overset{?}{=} -6$$
$$\qquad\qquad\qquad\qquad -6 = -6 \checkmark$$
$$-\frac{3}{4} = -\frac{3}{4} \checkmark \quad \blacksquare$$

Practice Problem 2   Use the substitution method to solve the system

$$\frac{x}{2} + \frac{2y}{3} = 1$$

$$\frac{x}{3} + y = -1 \quad \blacksquare$$

Now let's talk about another way to solve systems of two equations.

◪ The Addition Method (Elimination Method)

Another way to solve a system of two linear equations in two variables is to add the two equations so that a variable is eliminated. This technique is called the **addition method** or the **elimination method**. We usually have to multiply one or both of the equations by suitable factors so that we obtain the same coefficient of one variable (either x or y) in each equation.

Example 3   Solve the following system by the addition method.

$$5x + 8y = -1 \quad \boxed{1}$$
$$3x + y = 7 \quad \boxed{2}$$

We can eliminate either the x or the y variable. Let's choose y. However, if we just add the two equations, we get

$$8x + 9y = 6$$

which has an unlimited number of solutions. (Why?) So we haven't helped our situation. But now let's multiply equation $\boxed{2}$ by -8. This gives

$$-8(3x) + (-8)(y) = -8(7)$$
$$-24x - 8y = -56 \qquad \boxed{3}$$

We now add equations $\boxed{1}$ and $\boxed{3}$.

$$
\begin{array}{lr}
5x + 8y = -1 & \boxed{1} \\
-24x - 8y = -56 & \boxed{3} \\
\hline
-19x \phantom{{}- 8y} = -57 &
\end{array}
$$

Therefore,

$$x = \frac{-57}{-19} = 3$$

Now substitute $x = 3$ into equation $\boxed{2}$ (or equation $\boxed{1}$):

$$3(3) + y = 7$$
$$9 + y = 7$$
$$y = -2$$

Our solution is $x = 3$ and $y = -2$, or $(3, -2)$.

Check: Verify that this solution is correct. ■

Practice Problem 3   Use the addition method to solve the system

$$-3x + y = 5$$
$$2x + 3y = 4 \qquad ■$$

?

To Think About

Is there a way to use the addition method in example 3 to eliminate y without multiplying equation $\boxed{2}$ by -8? Yes.

Instead of multiplying equation $\boxed{2}$ by -8, we could have multiplied equation $\boxed{1}$ by $-\dfrac{1}{8}$ to eliminate y. Let's do it.

$$\left(-\frac{1}{8}\right)(5x) + \left(-\frac{1}{8}\right)(8y) = \left(-\frac{1}{8}\right)(-1)$$

$$-\frac{5}{8}x - y = \frac{1}{8} \qquad \boxed{3}$$

Our equivalent system is now

$$-\frac{5}{8}x - y = \frac{1}{8} \qquad \boxed{3}$$
$$3x + y = 7 \qquad \boxed{2}$$

Adding gives

$$\frac{19}{8}x = \frac{57}{8}$$

$$x = \frac{57}{8} \div \frac{19}{8} = \frac{57}{8} \times \frac{8}{19} = \frac{57}{19} = 3$$

Then, substitute into the original equation to find y.

$$3(3) + y = 7$$
$$y = 7 - 9 = 2$$

We obtain the same answer, although we had to work a little harder. As you gain experience, you will usually be able to tell which variable should be eliminated. ■

For convenience, we summarize the procedure here.

How to Solve a System of Two Linear Equations by the Addition (Elimination) Method

1. Arrange each equation in the form $ax + by = c$. (Remember, a, b, and c can be any real numbers.)
2. Multiply one or both equations by appropriate numbers so that either x or y is eliminated after you add the equations.
3. Add the two equations from step 2.
4. Solve this equation in one variable.
5. Substitute this value into one of the original equations and solve it.
6. Check the solution in each original equation.

Example 4 Solve the following system by the addition method:

$$3x + 2y = -8 \quad \boxed{1}$$
$$2x + 5y = 2 \quad \boxed{2}$$

To eliminate the variable x, we multiply equation $\boxed{1}$ by 2 and equation $\boxed{2}$ by -3. We now have the equivalent system

$$\begin{array}{r} 6x + 4y = -16 \\ -6x - 15y = -6 \\ \hline -11y = -22 \end{array} \qquad \text{Adding the equations.}$$

$$y = 2 \qquad \text{Solving for } y.$$

Substitute $y = 2$ into equation $\boxed{1}$.

$$3x + 2(2) = -8$$
$$3x + 4 = -8$$
$$3x = -12$$
$$x = -4$$

The solution to the system is $x = -4$, $y = 2$, or $(-4, 2)$.

Check: Verify that this solution is correct.

Note: We could have easily eliminated the variable y in Example 4 by multiplying equation $\boxed{1}$ by 5 and equation $\boxed{2}$ by -2. ■

Practice Problem 4 Use the addition (elimination) method to solve the system

$$5x + 4y = 23$$
$$7x - 3y = 15 \quad ■$$

3 **Example 5** Solve the system

$$5x - 2y = 14 \quad \boxed{1}$$
$$3x + 4y = 11 \quad \boxed{2}$$

TEACHING TIP After discussing example 4 or a similar example, ask students to solve the system by using the addition method.

$$2x + 3y = 5$$
$$7x + 4y = -2$$

(The answer is $x = -2$, $y = 3$ or $(-2, 3)$.) Usually, some students will eliminate the variable x, while others will eliminate y. It is a good time to discuss the different approaches one can take to solve a system and obtain the correct answer in each case.

It is easier to eliminate y than x. If we eliminate x, we must multiply equation $\boxed{1}$ by 3 and equation $\boxed{2}$ by -5. To eliminate y, we need only multiply equation $\boxed{1}$ by 2.

$$2(5x) - 2(2y) = 2(14)$$
$$10x - 4y = 28 \qquad \boxed{3}$$

So our system is

$$\begin{array}{r} 10x - 4y = 28 \\ 3x + 4y = 11 \\ \hline 13x = 39 \\ x = 3 \end{array}$$

Now substitute this value into equation $\boxed{1}$.

$$5(3) - 2y = 14$$
$$-2y = -1$$
$$y = \frac{1}{2}$$

The solution is $x = 3$, $y = \dfrac{1}{2}$ or it may be written as $\left(3, \dfrac{1}{2}\right)$. ■

Check: Can you verify this answer?

Practice Problem 5   Use the addition method to solve the system

$$3x + 12y = 25$$
$$2x - 6y = 12 \qquad ■$$

Systems That Do Not Have a Unique Solution

So far we have examined only systems that have one solution. But other systems must also be considered. These systems can best be illustrated by several graphs. In general, the system of equations

$$ax + by = c$$
$$dx + ey = f$$

may have one solution, no solution, or an infinite number of solutions.

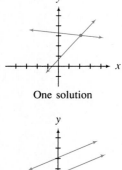

One solution

1. *One solution.* The two graphs intersect at one point, which is the solution. We say that the equations are *independent* and *consistent*. There is a point (an ordered pair) *consistent* with both equations.

No solution

■ 2. *No solution.* The two graphs are parallel and so do not intersect. We say that the system of equations is *inconsistent* because there is no point consistent with both equations.

3. *An infinite number of solutions.* The graphs of each equation yield the same line. Every ordered pair on this line is a solution to both of the equations. We say that the equations are *dependent* and *consistent.*

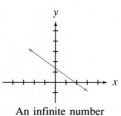

An infinite number of solutions

Example 6   If possible, solve the system:

$$2x + 8y = 3 \qquad \boxed{1}$$
$$4x + 16y = -8 \qquad \boxed{2}$$

To eliminate the variable y, we'll multiply equation $\boxed{1}$ by -2.

$$-2(2x) + (-2)(8y) = (-2)(3)$$
$$-4x - 16y = -8 \qquad \boxed{3}$$

We now have the equivalent system

$$-4x - 16y = -6 \quad \boxed{3}$$

$$4x + 16y = -8 \quad \boxed{2}$$

When we add equations $\boxed{3}$ and $\boxed{2}$, we get

$$0 = -14$$

which, of course, is false. Thus, we conclude that this system of equations is inconsistent, so there is no solution . Therefore, equations $\boxed{1}$ and $\boxed{2}$ do not intersect as we can see on the graph.

   If we had used the substitution method to solve this system, we would still obtain a false statement. When you try to solve an inconsistent system of linear equations by any method, you will always obtain a mathematical equation that is not true. ■

Practice Problem 6   If possible, solve the system:

$$4x - 2y = 6$$

$$-6x + 3y = 9 \quad ■$$

Example 7   If possible solve the system

$$0.5x - 0.2y = \quad 1.3 \quad \boxed{1}$$

$$-1.0x + 0.4y = -2.6 \quad \boxed{2}$$

   Although we could work directly with the decimals, it is easier to multiply each equation by the appropriate value (10, 100, etc.) so that the coefficients of the new system are integers. Therefore, we will multiply equations $\boxed{1}$ and $\boxed{2}$ by 10 to obtain the equivalent system

$$5x - 2y = \quad 13 \quad \boxed{3}$$

$$-10x + 4y = -26 \quad \boxed{4}$$

We can eliminate the variable y by multiplying each term of equation $\boxed{3}$ by 2.

$$
\begin{array}{rr}
10x - 4y = & 26 \quad \boxed{5} \\
-10x + 4y = & -26 \quad \boxed{4} \\
\hline
0 = & 0 \quad \text{Adding the equations.}
\end{array}
$$

This statement is always true. Hence, the two equations are dependent, and there are an infinite number of solutions . Any solution satisfying equation $\boxed{1}$ will also satisfy equation $\boxed{2}$. For example (3, 1) is a solution to equation $\boxed{3}$ (prove this). Hence it must also be a solution of equation $\boxed{4}$ (prove it). Thus the equations actually give the same line as you can see on the graph.   ■

Practice Problem 7   If possible, solve the system

$$0.3x - 0.9y = \quad 1.8$$

$$-0.4x + 1.2y = -2.4 \quad ■$$

TEACHING TIP   This is a good time to remind students that if a system of equations has fractional or decimal coefficients, each equation should be multiplied by the appropriate value in order to have integer coefficients. If a system of equations has parentheses such as

$$1 + 4(y - 2) = 1 - 2x$$

$$6y + 5 = 5 + 3(4 - x)$$

ask the students to remove the parentheses and collect like terms for this system and then identify the type of system. (Answer: the system contains dependent equations.)

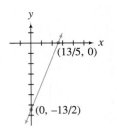

DEVELOPING YOUR STUDY SKILLS

PREVIEWING NEW MATERIAL

Part of your study time each day should consist of looking over the sections in your text that are to be covered the following day. You do not necessarily need to study and learn the material on your own, but a survey of the concepts, terminology, diagrams, and examples will help the new ideas seem more familiar as the instructor presents them. You can look for concepts that appear confusing or difficult and be ready to listen carefully for your instructor's explanations. You can be prepared to ask the questions that will increase your understanding. Previewing new material enables you to see what is coming and prepares you to be ready to absorb it.

EXERCISES 3.1

Find the solution to each system by the substitution method. Check your answers for problems 1–6.

1. $7x - 2y = 3$
$y = 4 - 2x$
$7x - 2(4 - 2x) = 3$
$x = 1$
$y = 2$

2. $2x + 3y = 9$
$x = 2 + y$
$2(2 + y) + 3y = 9$
$x = 3$
$y = 1$

3. $3x + 2y = -17$
$2x + y = 3$
$y = 3 - 2x$
$3x + 2(3 - 2x) = -17$
$x = 23$
$y = -43$

4. $5x - 2y = -19$
$x - 3y = 4$
$x = 3y + 4$
$5(3y + 4) - 2y = -19$
$x = -5$
$y = -3$

5. $-x + 3y = -10$
$2x + y = 6$
$y = 6 - 2x$
$-x + 3(6 - 2x) = -10$
$x = 4, y = -2$

6. $5x - 2y = 8$
$3x + y = 7$
$y = 7 - 3x$
$5x - 2(7 - 3x) = 8$
$x = 2, y = 1$

7. $3a + 5b = -19$
$-a + 3b = -3$
$a = 3b + 3$
$3(3b + 3) + 5b = -19$
$a = -3, b = -2$

8. $-3a + 4b = -18$
$2a + b = 1$
$b = 1 - 2a$
$-3a + 4(1 - 2a) = -18$
$a = 2, b = -3$

Remove parentheses and collect like terms first. Then solve by the substitution method.

9. $2(2 + x) - y = 3$
$3(x + y) = 5 + y$
$2x - y = -1$
$3x + 2y = 5$
$3x + 2(2x + 1) = 5$
$x = \dfrac{3}{7}, y = \dfrac{13}{7}$

10. $5(y - x) = 9 + y$
$8 - y = -3(x - 4)$
$4y - 5x = 9$
$3x - 4 = y$
$4(3x - 4) - 5x = 9$
$x = \dfrac{25}{7}, y = \dfrac{47}{7}$

11. $3(x - 1) + 2(y + 2) = 6$
$4(x - 2) + y = 2$
$y = -4x + 10$
$3x + 2(-4x + 10) = 5$
$x = 3, y = -2$

12. $2(x - 2) + 3(y + 1) = -2$
$x + 2(y - 1) = -4$
$x = -2y - 2$
$2(-2y - 2) + 3y = -1$
$x = 4, y = -3$

Find the solution to each system by the addition (elimination) method. Check your answers for problems 13–18.

13. $9x + 2y = 2$
$3x + 5y = 5$
$9x + 2y = 2$
$-9x - 15y = -15$
$x = 0, y = 1$

14. $x + 3y = 2$
$4x + 5y = 1$
$-4x - 12y = -8$
$4x + 5y = 1$
$x = -1, y = 1$

15. $a + 2b = -1$
$2a - b = 3$
$a + 2b = -1$
$4a - 2b = 6$
$a = 1, b = -1$

16. $2a + b = 3$
$a - 2b = -1$
$a - 2b = -1$
$4a + 2b = 6$
$a = 1, b = 1$

17. $6s - 3t = 1$
$5s + 6t = 15$
$5s + 6t = 15$
$12s - 6t = 2$
$s = 1, t = \dfrac{5}{3}$

18. $2s + 3t = 5$
$3s - 6t = 18$
$3s - 6t = 18$
$4s + 6t = 10$
$s = 4, t = -1$

19. $7x + 5y = -8$
$9x + 2y = 3$
$14x + 10y = -16$
$-45x - 10y = -15$
$x = 1, y = -3$

20. $4x - 3y = 12$
$3x - 4y = 2$
$16x - 12y = 48$
$-9x + 12y = -6$
$x = 6, y = 4$

21. $0.4x + 0.3y = 2.3$
$0.2x - 0.5y = 0.5$
$0.8x + 0.6y = 4.6$
$-0.8x + 2.0y = -2.0$
$x = 5, y = 1$

22. $0.9x + 0.4y = 0$
$0.5x - 0.8y = 2.3$
$0.5x - 0.8y = 2.3$
$1.8 + 0.8y = 0$
$x = 1, y = -\dfrac{9}{4}$

23. $4(x + 1) + 2(y - 1) = 4$
$x + 3(y - 2) = 2$
$2x + y = 1$
$-2x - 6y = -16$
$x = -1, y = 3$

24. $3(x + 1) + y = -7$
$2(x + 4) + 3(y + 1) = -5$
$-9x - 3y = 30$
$2x + 3y = -16$
$x = -2, y = -4$

If possible, solve each system of equations. Use any method. If there is not a unique solution to a system, say why.

25. $2x + y = 4$

$\dfrac{2}{3}x + \dfrac{1}{4}y = 2$

$-6x - 3y = -12$
$\underline{8x + 3y = 24}$
$x = 6, y = -8$

26. $2x + 3y = 16$

$5x - \dfrac{3}{4}y = 7$

$2x + 3y = 16$
$\underline{20x - 3y = 28}$
$x = 2, y = 4$

27. $0.2x = 0.1y - 1.2$
$0.2x - 1.2 = 0.3y$

$-2x + y = 12$
$\underline{2x - 3y = 12}$
$x = -12, y = -12$

28. $0.1x - 0.6 = 0.3y$
$0.3x + 0.1y + 2.2 = 0$

$-3x + 9y = -18$
$\underline{3x + y = -22}$
$x = -6, y = -4$

29. $5a + 3b = -4(1 - a)$
$2(a - 4) + 9 = 3(b + 3)$

$a + 3b = -4$
$\underline{2a - 3b = 8}$
$a = \dfrac{4}{3}, b = -\dfrac{16}{9}$

30. $5a = 4(b + 12)$
$3(a - 6) = b - 1$

$5a - 4b = 48$
$\underline{-12a + 4b = -68}$
$a = \dfrac{20}{7}, b = \dfrac{-59}{7}$

31. $8x + 9y = 13$
$6x - 5y = 45$

$40x + 45y = 65$
$\underline{54x - 45y = 405}$
$x = 5, y = -3$

32. $-9x + 6y - 10 = 0$
$6x = 4y - 8$

$-18x + 12y = 20$
$\underline{18x - 12y = -24}$
$0 = -4$
No sol.; inconsistent
system of eqs.

33. $\dfrac{4}{5}b = \dfrac{1}{5} + a$

$15a - 12b = 4$

$15a - 12b = 4$
$\underline{-15a + 12b = 3}$
$0 \neq 7$
No solution;
inconsistent system
of eqs.

34. $3a - 2b = \dfrac{3}{2}$

$\dfrac{3a}{2} = \dfrac{3}{4} + b$

$6a - 4b = 3$
$\underline{-6a + 4b = -3}$
$0 = 0$
Infinite number
of solutions:
dependent eqs.

35. $\dfrac{3}{4}x - y = 4$

$-\dfrac{1}{6}x + \dfrac{1}{3}y = -1$

$3x - 4y = 16$
$\underline{-2x + 4y = -12}$
$x = 4, y = -1$

36. $\dfrac{2}{5}x + \dfrac{3}{5}y = 1$

$x - \dfrac{2}{3}y = \dfrac{1}{3}$

$4x + 6y = 10$
$\underline{9x - 6y = 3}$
$x = 1, y = 1$

To Think About

37. Solve the system for x and y. Use the substitution method.

$$ax + by = c$$
$$x + dy = e$$

$x = e - dy$
$a(e - dy) + by = c$
$y(b - ad) = c - ae$

$y = \dfrac{c - ae}{b - ad}$

$x = \dfrac{eb - cd}{b - ad}$

38. Solve the system for x and y. Use the addition method.

$$ax + by = c$$
$$dx - ey = f$$

$aex + eby = ec$
$\underline{bdx - eby = bf}$
$x(ae + bd) = ec + bf$

$x = \dfrac{ec + bf}{ae + bd}$

$y = \dfrac{cd - af}{bd + ae}$

Let $a = \dfrac{1}{x}$ and $b = \dfrac{1}{y}$ in each system. Substitute these expressions into the original equations to find a and b. Then find x and y.

39. $\dfrac{3}{x} + \dfrac{2}{y} = \dfrac{1}{2}$

$\dfrac{5}{x} + \dfrac{1}{y} = 4$

$6a + 4b = 1$
$\underline{-20a - 4b = -16}$
$a = \dfrac{15}{14}, b = -\dfrac{19}{14}$

$x = \dfrac{14}{15}, y = -\dfrac{14}{19}$

40. $\dfrac{3}{x} + \dfrac{4}{y} = 2$

$\dfrac{5}{x} + \dfrac{6}{y} = \dfrac{19}{6}$

$-27a - 36b = -18$
$\underline{30a + 36b = 19}$
$a = \dfrac{1}{3}, b = \dfrac{1}{4}$

$x = 3, y = 4$

41. $\dfrac{7}{x} + \dfrac{5}{y} = \dfrac{11}{2}$

$\dfrac{4}{x} - \dfrac{7}{y} = \dfrac{3}{2}$

$98a + 70y = 77$
$\underline{40a - 70y = 15}$
$a = \dfrac{46}{69}, b = \dfrac{1}{6}$

$x = \dfrac{69}{46}, y = 6$

42. $\dfrac{3}{x} - \dfrac{2}{y} = -\dfrac{11}{15}$

$\dfrac{2}{x} + \dfrac{6}{y} = \dfrac{22}{5}$

$45a - 30b = -11$
$\underline{10a + 30b = 22}$
$a = \dfrac{1}{5}, b = \dfrac{2}{3}$

$x = 5, y = \dfrac{3}{2}$

Cumulative Review Problems

Graph by plotting three points.

43. $5x + y = 4$

x	y
0	4
1	−1
2	−6

44. $6x - y = 3$

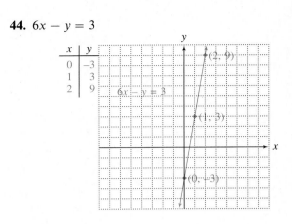

x	y
0	−3
1	3
2	9

45. $7x - 2y = -14$

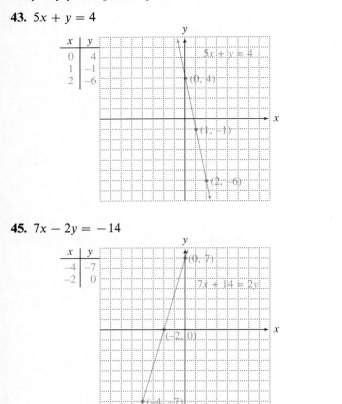

x	y
−4	−7
−2	0

46. $3x + 5y = -15$

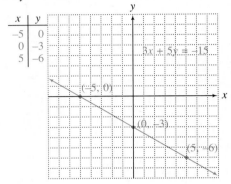

x	y
−5	0
0	−3
5	−6

Calculator Problems

Find the solution to each system. Round your answer to four decimal places.

47. $9.836x + \quad y = 12.824$
  $-8.073x - 5.982y = \ 8.913$

  $x = 1.6867$
  $y = -3.7662$

48. $0.0052x - 0.0093y = 0.1256$
  $-0.0104x + 0.0521y = 0.9315$

  $x = 87.2945$
  $y = 35.3045$

For Extra Practice Exercises, turn to page 173.

Solutions to Odd-Numbered Practice Problems

1. $2x - \ y = \ \ 7$ ⬜1
  $3x + 4y = -6$ ⬜2

Solve equation ⬜1 for y.

  $-y = \ \ 7 - 2x$
  $\quad y = -7 + 2x$ ⬜3

Substitute into equation ⬜2.

  $3x + 4(-7 + 2x) = -6$
  $\quad 11x - 28 = -6$
  $\quad\quad 11x = 22$
  $\quad\quad\quad x = 2$

3. $-3x + \ y = 5$ ⬜1
  $2x + 3y = 4$ ⬜2

Multiply equation ⬜1 by -3 and add to equation ⬜2.

$$9x - 3y = -15$$
$$\underline{2x + 3y = \quad 4}$$
$$11x \quad\quad = -11$$
$$x = -1$$

Now substitute $x = -1$ into equation ⬜1.

  $-3(-1) + y = 5$
  $\quad\quad 3 + y = 5$
  $\quad\quad\quad\quad y = 2$

1. (continued)

Substitute $x = 2$ into equation $\boxed{3}$.

$$y = -7 + 2(2) = -3$$

The solution is $x = 2$, $y = -3$.

5. $3x + 12y = 25$ $\quad\boxed{1}$

 $2x - 6y = 12$ $\quad\boxed{2}$

Multiply equation $\boxed{2}$ by 2 and add to equation $\boxed{1}$.

$$\begin{array}{r} 3x + 12y = 25 \\ 4x - 12y = 24 \\ \hline 7x = 149 \end{array}$$

$$x = 7$$

Now substitute $x = 7$ into equation $\boxed{2}$.

$$2(7) - 6y = 12$$
$$14 - 6y = 12$$
$$-6y = 12 - 14$$
$$-6y = -2$$
$$y = +\frac{1}{3}$$

The solution is $x = 7$, $y = \frac{1}{3}$.

Answers to Even-Numbered Practice Problems

2. $x = 6$, $y = -3$ $\quad$ **4.** $x = 3$, $y = 2$ $\quad$ **6.** Inconsistent system of equations; no solution

3. (continued)

The solution is $x = -1$, $y = 2$.

7. $0.3x - 0.9y = 1.8$ $\quad\boxed{1}$

 $-0.4x + 1.2y = -2.4$ $\quad\boxed{2}$

Multiply each equation by 10 to obtain a more convenient form.

$$3x - 9y = 18 \quad\boxed{3}$$
$$-4x + 12y = -24 \quad\boxed{4}$$

Let us try to eliminate x. We multiply equation $\boxed{3}$ by 4 and multiply equation $\boxed{4}$ by 3.

$$\begin{array}{r} 12x - 36y = 72 \\ -12x + 36y = -72 \\ \hline 0 = 0 \end{array}$$

These are dependent equations. There are an infinite number of solutions.

3.2 SYSTEMS OF EQUATIONS IN THREE VARIABLES

1 We are now going to study **systems of three linear equations with three variables** (unknowns). Many of these systems have exactly one solution. A **solution** to a system of three linear equations in three unknowns is an ordered triple of real numbers (x, y, z) that satisfies each equation in the system. In other words, if we substitute the values of x, y, and z into each equation, we will obtain true mathematical statements (or identities). For example, $(2, -5, 1)$ is the solution to the system

$$3x + y + 2z = 3$$
$$4x + 2y - z = -3$$
$$x + y + 5z = 2$$

How can you prove that $(2, -5, 1)$ really is the solution to this system? You must substitute $x = 2$, $y = -5$, and $z = 1$ into each equation and obtain a true statement. Let's do this. For the first equation,

$$3(2) + (-5) + 2(1) \overset{?}{=} 3$$
$$6 - 5 + 2 \overset{?}{=} 3$$
$$\boxed{3 = 3} \qquad \text{True statement.}$$

For the second,

$$4(2) + 2(-5) - 1 \overset{?}{=} -3$$
$$8 - 10 - 1 \overset{?}{=} -3$$
$$\boxed{-3 = -3} \qquad \text{True statement.}$$

After studying this section, you will be able to:

1 *Find the solution to a system of three linear equations in three variables if all coefficients are nonzero*

2 *Find the solution to a system of three linear equations in three variables if some of the coefficients are zero*

Finally,
$$2 + (-5) + 5(1) \stackrel{?}{=} 2$$
$$2 - 5 + 5 \stackrel{?}{=} 2$$
$$\boxed{2 = 2} \qquad \text{True statement.}$$

Since we obtained three true statements, the ordered triple $(2, -5, 1)$ is a solution to the system.

You can also verify the solution by graphing. We will discuss this later.

One way to solve a system of three equations with three variables is to obtain an equivalent system of two equations in two variables; in other words, we eliminate one variable from both equations. We can then use the methods of section 3.1 to solve the system. You can find the third variable (the one that was eliminated) by substituting the two variables that you have solved for into one of the original equations.

TEACHING TIP In-class practice is very helpful for students in this section. After discussing example 1 or a similar example, ask them to find the solution to the system of equations:

$$x - 2y - z = 4$$
$$2x + 3y + z = 3$$
$$x - y - 2z = -1$$

Tell them to solve the system by eliminating the variable z. (Answer $x = 3$, $y = -2$, $z = 3$. Usually, students will add equations 1 and 2 and obtain $3x + y = 7$ and then add equation 2 (multiplied by two) to equation 3 to obtain $5x + 5y = 5$. This is a good time to point out that we may divide each term of $5x + 5y = 5$ by 5 to obtain $x + y = 1$.)

Example 1 Find the solution to (that is, solve) the following system of equations:

$$-2x + 5y + z = 8 \qquad \boxed{1}$$
$$-x + 2y + 3z = 13 \qquad \boxed{2}$$
$$x + 3y - z = 5 \qquad \boxed{3}$$

Let's eliminate z because it can be easily done by adding equations $\boxed{1}$ and $\boxed{3}$.

$$\begin{array}{rr} -2x + 5y + z = 8 & \boxed{1} \\ x + 3y - z = 5 & \boxed{3} \\ \hline -x + 8y \phantom{{}+ z} = 13 & \boxed{4} \end{array}$$

Now we need to choose a *different pair* from the original equations and once again eliminate the same variable . In other words, we have to use equations $\boxed{1}$ and $\boxed{2}$ or equations $\boxed{2}$ and $\boxed{3}$ and eliminate z. Let's multiply each term of equation $\boxed{3}$ by 3 (and call it equation $\boxed{6}$) and add the result to equation $\boxed{2}$.

$$\begin{array}{rr} -x + 2y + 3z = 13 & \boxed{2} \\ 3x + 9y - 3z = 15 & \boxed{6} \\ \hline 2x + 11y \phantom{{}- 3z} = 28 & \boxed{5} \end{array}$$

We now can solve the system of two linear equations.

$$-x + 8y = 13 \qquad \boxed{4}$$
$$2x + 11y = 28 \qquad \boxed{5}$$

Multiply each term of equation $\boxed{4}$ by 2.

$$\begin{array}{r} -2x + 16y = 26 \\ 2x + 11y = 28 \\ \hline 27y = 54 \qquad \text{Adding the equations.} \\ y = 2 \qquad \text{Solving for } y. \end{array}$$

Substituting $y = 2$ into $\boxed{4}$, we have

$$-x + 8(2) = 13$$
$$-x = -3$$
$$x = 3$$

Now substitute $x = 3$ and $y = 2$ into one of the original equations (any one will do) to solve for z. Let's use $\boxed{1}$.

$$-2x + 5y + z = 8$$
$$-2(3) + 5(2) + z = 8$$
$$-6 + 10 + z = 8$$
$$z = 4$$

2 The solution to the system is therefore $x = 3$, $y = 2$, $z = 4$; or $(3, 2, 4)$.

Check: Verify that $(3, 2, 4)$ satisfies *each* of the three *original* equations. ■

Practice Problem 1 Solve the system

$$x + 2y + 3z = 4$$
$$2x + y - 2z = 3$$
$$3x + 3y + 4z = 10$$

Here's a summary of the procedure that we just used. ■

How to Solve a System of Three Linear Equations in Three Unknowns

1. Use the addition method to eliminate any variable from any pair of equations. (The choice of variable is arbitrary.)

2. Use appropriate steps to eliminate the *same variable* from a *different pair* of equations. (If you don't eliminate the same variable, you will still have three unknowns.)

3. Solve the resulting system of two equations in two variables.

4. Substitute the values obtained in step 3 into one of the three original equations. Solve for the remaining variable.

Example 2 Solve the system

$$4x + 3y + 3z = 4 \qquad \boxed{1}$$
$$3x + 2z = 2 \qquad \boxed{2}$$
$$2x - 5y = -4 \qquad \boxed{3}$$

Note that equation $\boxed{2}$ has no y term, and equation $\boxed{3}$ has no z term. Obviously, that makes our work easier. Let's work with equations $\boxed{2}$ and $\boxed{1}$ to obtain an equation that contains only x and y.

Step 1. Multiply equation $\boxed{1}$ by 2 and equation $\boxed{2}$ by -3 to obtain the system

$$\begin{aligned} 8x + 6y + 6z &= 8 \qquad \boxed{4} \\ -9x \qquad - 6z &= -6 \qquad \boxed{5} \\ \hline -x + 6y \qquad &= 2 \qquad \boxed{6} \end{aligned}$$

Step 2. This step is already done, since equation $\boxed{3}$ has no z term.

Step 3. Now we can solve the system formed by equations $\boxed{3}$ and $\boxed{6}$.

$$2x - 5y = -4 \qquad \boxed{3}$$
$$-x + 6y = 2 \qquad \boxed{6}$$

If we multiply each term of equation $\boxed{6}$ by 2, we obtain the system

$$\begin{aligned} 2x - 5y &= -4 \\ -2x + 12y &= 4 \\ \hline 7y &= 0 \qquad \text{Adding.} \\ y &= 0 \qquad \text{Solving for } y. \end{aligned}$$

Substituting $y = 0$ in equation $\boxed{6}$, we find that

$$-x + 6(0) = 2$$
$$-x = 2$$
$$x = -2$$

TEACHING TIP   After discussing example 2 or a similar example, ask students to solve the system:

$$x + y = 0$$
$$2x - 3z = -10$$
$$3y + z = 1$$

(Answer is $x = 1$, $y = -1$, $z = 4$ or $(1, -1, 4)$.)

Step 4. To find z, we substitute $x = -2$ and $y = 0$ into one of the original equations containing z. Since equation $\boxed{2}$ has only two variables, let's use it.

$$3x + 2z = 2$$
$$3(-2) + 2z = 2$$
$$2z = 8$$
$$z = 4$$

The solution to the system is $x = -2$, $y = 0$, and $z = 4$, or $(-2, 0, 4)$.

Check: Verify this solution by substituting these values into equations $\boxed{1}$, $\boxed{2}$, and $\boxed{3}$. ■

Practice Problem 2 Solve the systems

$$2x + y + z = 11$$
$$4y + 3z = -8$$
$$x - 5y = 2$$ ■

To Think About

The next example is more challenging, but don't be frightened or discouraged. We will still use the methods you already know. ■

Example 3 Solve the system

$$\frac{1}{x} - \frac{1}{y} - \frac{2}{z} + 3 = 0 \qquad \boxed{1}$$

$$\frac{3}{x} + \frac{2}{y} + \frac{1}{z} - 4 = 0 \qquad \boxed{2}$$

$$\frac{2}{x} - \frac{1}{z} = 0 \qquad \boxed{3}$$

There are two approaches we could use. We could treat $\frac{1}{x}$, $\frac{1}{y}$, and $\frac{1}{z}$ as variables (instead of x, y, z) and then solve for x, y, and z. Or we could substitute other variables for $\frac{1}{x}$, $\frac{1}{y}$, and $\frac{1}{z}$. For example, we might let $u = \frac{1}{x}$, $v = \frac{1}{y}$, and $w = \frac{1}{z}$. Then after we solve for u, v, and w, we must substitute to find x, y, and z. For convenience, we choose the second approach.

Now our system is

$$u - v - 2w = -3 \qquad \boxed{4}$$
$$3u + 2v + w = 4 \qquad \boxed{5}$$
$$2u - w = 0 \qquad \boxed{6}$$

Do you understand how we obtained these equations? Remember that $\frac{3}{x}$ is just $3\left(\frac{1}{x}\right)$. Since we let $u = \frac{1}{x}$, we replace $\frac{1}{x}$ by u and get $3u$. We obtain the other terms in a similar way.

Now we solve the new system just as we've done before. Since equation $\boxed{6}$ has the variable v eliminated already, it will be most efficient to work with equations $\boxed{4}$ and $\boxed{5}$ and eliminate v. We multiply equation $\boxed{4}$ by 2

$$2u - 2v - 4w = -6 \quad \boxed{7} \qquad \text{Multiplying } \boxed{4} \text{ by 2.}$$
$$\underline{3u + 2v + w = 4 \quad \boxed{5}}$$
$$5u - 3w = -2 \quad \boxed{8} \qquad \text{Adding.}$$

We thus have the system

$$5u - 3w = -2 \quad \boxed{8}$$
$$2u - w = 0 \quad \boxed{6}$$

Multiply $\boxed{6}$ by -3 and add the equations to get

$$-u = -2$$
$$u = 2$$

Now substitute $u = 2$ into equation $\boxed{6}$ to find w.

$$2(2) - w = 0$$
$$-w = -4$$
$$w = 4$$

Substitute $w = 4$, $u = 2$ into equation $\boxed{4}$ to get

$$2 - v - 8 = -3$$
$$-v = 3$$
$$v = -3$$

We have solved our system with variables u, v, w, but our original system was in variables x, y, z. So we must use our relations $u = \dfrac{1}{x}$, $v = \dfrac{1}{y}$, $w = \dfrac{1}{z}$ to find x, y, and z.

$$u = \frac{1}{x} \qquad v = \frac{1}{y} \qquad w = \frac{1}{z}$$
$$2 = \frac{1}{x} \qquad -3 = \frac{1}{y} \qquad 4 = \frac{1}{z}$$
$$\frac{1}{2} = x \qquad -\frac{1}{3} = y \qquad \frac{1}{4} = z$$

Thus our solution is $x = \dfrac{1}{2}$, $y = -\dfrac{1}{3}$, $z = \dfrac{1}{4}$. We can also write our solution as an ordered triple $\left(\dfrac{1}{2}, -\dfrac{1}{3}, \dfrac{1}{4}\right)$.

Check: For equation $\boxed{1}$,

$$\frac{1}{x} - \frac{1}{y} - \frac{2}{z} = -3 \quad \boxed{1}$$
$$\frac{1}{\left(\dfrac{1}{2}\right)} - \frac{1}{\left(-\dfrac{1}{3}\right)} - \frac{2}{\left(\dfrac{1}{4}\right)} \overset{?}{=} -3$$
$$2 + 3 - 8 \overset{?}{=} -3$$
$$-3 = -3 \checkmark \qquad \text{It checks.}$$

You should check the other two equations. ■

TEACHING TIP Some students find problems like example 3 very difficult. This type of problem can be omitted at the instructor's discretion, and is not referred to in later chapters. If you cover the topic, you may find it helpful to work out the following additional example for students. Solve

$$\frac{3}{x} - \frac{1}{y} + \frac{1}{z} = -2$$
$$\frac{2}{x} - \frac{3}{y} + \frac{1}{z} = -7$$
$$\frac{1}{x} + \frac{4}{y} + \frac{3}{z} = 0$$

By letting

$$u = \frac{1}{x}, \; v = \frac{1}{y}, \; w = \frac{1}{z}$$

we have

$$3u - v + w = -2 \quad \boxed{1}$$
$$2u - 3v + w = -7 \quad \boxed{2}$$
$$u + 4v + 3w = 0 \quad \boxed{3}$$

Multiply $\boxed{2}$ by -1 and add to $\boxed{1}$ to obtain

$$u + 2v = 5 \quad \boxed{4}$$

Multiply $\boxed{1}$ by -3 and add to $\boxed{3}$ to obtain

$$-8u + 7v = 6 \quad \boxed{5}$$

Solve the system of $\boxed{4}$, $\boxed{5}$, to obtain $u = 1$, $v = 2$, and then find $w = -3$. Finally $x = 1$, $y = \dfrac{1}{2}$, $z = -\dfrac{1}{3}$

Practice Problem 3 Solve the system

$$\frac{4}{x} + \frac{3}{y} + \frac{1}{z} = 10$$

$$\frac{5}{x} - \frac{4}{y} - \frac{1}{z} = 18$$

$$\frac{1}{x} + \frac{2}{y} = 1 \qquad \blacksquare$$

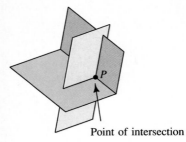

P

Point of intersection

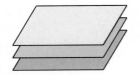

(a)

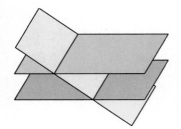

(b)

The procedure you have just learned can be used to solve systems of four equations in four unknowns. (Actually, there is no limit to the number of equations that can be solved.) However, there are other methods that are simpler, and we will study some of them.

Do you recall our discussion of consistent and inconsistent systems? Well, systems of three (or more) equations can also be inconsistent (have no solution) or have two (or more) dependent equations (have an infinite number of solutions).

A linear equation in two variables is a straight line (it is two-dimensional). But a linear equation in three variables, $ax + by + cz = d$, represents a *plane* in three-dimensional space. So a solution to a system of three equations is the point (the ordered triple) where the three planes intersect as you can see on the graph. (Recall that a solution to two linear equations in two dimensions is the point where both *lines* intersect.)

If the system has no solution, then the planes do not intersect at all or the three planes do not intersect at any point in common. If the system has an infinite number of solutions, the three planes intersect in one *line*. Each case is shown in the graphs.

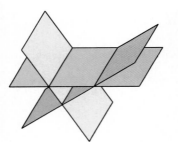

(c)

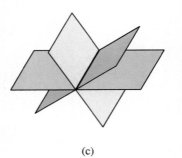

(c)

Solve each system.

1. $x + y + 2z = 0$
$2x - y - z = 1$
$x + 2y + 3z = 1$

Eliminate y:
$3x + z = 1 \Rightarrow -3x - z = -1$
$5x + z = 3 \Rightarrow 5x + z = 3$
─────────────────────
$x = 1, y = 3, z = -2$

2. $2x + y + 3z = 2$
$x - y + 2z = -4$
$x + 3y - z = 1$

Eliminate x:
$3y - z = 10 \Rightarrow -9y + 3z = -30$
$4y - 3z = 5 \Rightarrow 4y - 3z = 5$
─────────────────────
$x = -9, y = 5, z = 5$

3. $x + 2y - 3z = -11$
$-2x + y - z = -11$
$x + y + z = 6$

Eliminate z:
$7x - y = 22 \Rightarrow 14x - 2y = 44$
$-x + 2y = -5 \Rightarrow -x + 2y = -5$
─────────────────────
$x = 3, y = -1, z = 4$

4. $-5x + 3y + 2z = 1$
$x + y + z = 7$
$2x - y + z = 7$

Eliminate z:
$\boxed{1 \text{ and } 2}\ -7x + y = -13$
$\boxed{2 \text{ and } 3}\ x - 2y = 0$
─────────────────────
$-14x + 2y = -26$
$x - 2y = 0$
─────────────────────
$x = 2, y = 1, z = 4$

5. $3x - 2y + z = 4$
$x - 4y - z = 6$
$2x - y + 3z = 0$

Eliminate y:
$\boxed{1 \text{ and } 2}\ -5x - 3z = -2$
$\boxed{2 \text{ and } 3}\ -7x - 13z = 6$
─────────────────────
$-35x - 21z = -14$
$35x + 65z = -30$
─────────────────────
$x = 1, y = -1, z = -1$

6. $3x - y + 4z = 4$
$x - 2y + 2z = 4$
$2x + y - 3z = 5$

Eliminate y:
$\boxed{1 \text{ and } 2}\ -5x - 6z = -4$
$\boxed{2 \text{ and } 3}\ 5x - 4z = 14$
─────────────────────
$x = 2, y = -2, z = -1$

7. $x + 4y - z = -5$
$-2x - 3y + 2z = 5$
$3x - 2y + 3z = 11$

Eliminate x:
$\boxed{1 \text{ and } 2}\ 5y = -5$
$\boxed{1 \text{ and } 3}\ -14y + 6z = 26$
─────────────────────
$y = -1$
$14 + 6z = 26$
$x = 1, y = -1, z = 2$

8. $x - 4y + 4z = -1$
$-2x + y - 5z = -6$
$-x + 3y - z = 5$

Eliminate x:
$\boxed{1 \text{ and } 2}\ -7y + 3z = -8$
$\boxed{2 \text{ and } 3}\ -5y - 3z = -16$
─────────────────────
$x = -1, y = 2, z = 2$

9. $2x - 3y + 2z = -7$
$6x + 4y + 2z = 8$
$x + 4y - z = 10$

Eliminate z:
$\boxed{1 \text{ and } 2}\ -4x - 7y = -15$
$\boxed{2 \text{ and } 3}\ 4x + 6y = 14$
─────────────────────
$x = 2, y = 1, z = -4$

10. $-2x + y - 2z = 0$
$4x + 2y + 2z = -6$
$3x - 2y + 2z = -3$

Eliminate y:
$\boxed{1 \text{ and } 2}\ 4x + 3z = -3$
$\boxed{2 \text{ and } 3}\ 7x + 4z = -9$
─────────────────────
$-16x - 12z = 12$
$21x + 12z = -27$
─────────────────────
$x = -3, y = 0, z = 3$

11. $a = 8 + 3b - 2c$
$4a + 2b - 3c = 10$
$c = 10 + b - 2a$

Eliminate a:
$\boxed{1 \text{ and } 2}\ 14b - 11c = -22$
$\boxed{2 \text{ and } 3}\ 4b - 5c = -10$
─────────────────────
$-70b + 55c = 110$
$44b - 55c = -110$
─────────────────────
$a = 4, b = 0, c = 2$

12. $a = c - b$
$3a - 2b + 6c = 1$
$c = 4 - 3b - 7a$

Eliminate c:
$\boxed{1 \text{ and } 2}\ 9a + 4b = 1$
$\boxed{2 \text{ and } 3}\ -39a - 20b = -23$
─────────────────────
$45a + 20b = 5$
$-39a - 20b = -23$
─────────────────────
$a = -3, b = 7, c = 4$

13. $3a + 3b + 2c = -3$
$-2a + 5b + 3c = 3$
$10a - 4b - 8c = 6$

Eliminate c:
$\boxed{1 \text{ and } 2}\ 13a - b = -15$
$\boxed{2 \text{ and } 3}\ a + 2b = 3$
─────────────────────
$26a - 2b = -30$
$a + 2b = 3$
─────────────────────
$a = -1, b = 2, c = -3$

14. $4a + 2b + 3c = 9$
$3a + 5b + 4c = 19$
$9a + 3b + 2c = 3$

Eliminate c:
$\boxed{1 \text{ and } 2}\ a - b = -3$
$\boxed{1 \text{ and } 3}\ -19a - 5b = 9$
─────────────────────
$-19a - 5b = 9$
$19a - 19b = -57$
─────────────────────
$a = -1, b = 2, c = 3$

15. $-y + 2z = 1$
$x + y + z = 2$
$-x + 3z = 2$

Eliminate x:
$\boxed{2 \text{ and } 3}\ y + 4z = 4$
$\boxed{1}\ -y + 2z = 1$
─────────────────────
$x = \dfrac{1}{2}, y = \dfrac{2}{3}, z = \dfrac{5}{6}$

16. $-2x + y - 3z = 0$
$-2y - z = -1$
$x + 2y - z = 5$

Eliminate x:
$\boxed{1 \text{ and } 3}\ y - z = 2$
$\boxed{2}\ 2y + z = 1$
─────────────────────
$x = 2, y = 1, z = -1$

17. $x - 2y + z = 0$
$-3x - y = -6$
$y - 2z = -7$

Eliminate z:
$\boxed{1 \text{ and } 3}\ 2x - 3y = -7$
$\boxed{2}\ 9x + 3y = 18$
─────────────────────
$x = 1, y = 3, z = 5$

18. $x + 2z = 0$
$3x + 3y + z = 6$
$6y + 5z = -3$

Eliminate x:
$\boxed{1 \text{ and } 2}\ 3y - 5z = 6$
$\boxed{3}\ 6y + 5z = -3$
─────────────────────
$x = 2, y = \dfrac{1}{3}, z = -1$

19. $3a - b + c = 6$
$4a + 2b - c = 12$
$a + 3c = 14$

Eliminate b:
$\boxed{1 \text{ and } 2}\ 10a + c = 24$
$\boxed{3}\ -10a - 30c = -140$
─────────────────────
$a = 2, b = 4, c = 4$

20. $a + 2b + c = 5$
$4a + 2c = 10$
$-b - 5c = -6$

Eliminate a:
$\boxed{1 \text{ and } 2}\ 4b + c = 5$
$\boxed{3}\ -4b - 20c = -24$
─────────────────────
$a = 2, b = 1, c = 1$

21. $3x = 2 - 2y$
$2x = 14 + 3y + 3z$
$y = 4 + 5z - 6x$

Eliminate z:
$\boxed{2 \text{ and } 3}\ 4x + 9y = -29$
$2 \times \boxed{2 \text{ and } 3}\ 8x + 18y = -58$
$\boxed{1}\ -27x - 18y = -18$
─────────────────────
$x = 4, y = -5, z = 3$

22. $3x = 7 + 2y - 4z$
$5x = 1 + 4y$
$3z = -2 - 2y$

Eliminate z:
$\boxed{1 \text{ and } 3}\ 9x - 14y = 29$
$2 \times \boxed{1 \text{ and } 3}\ 18x - 28y = 58$
$\boxed{2}\ -35x + 28y = -7$
─────────────────────
$x = -3, y = -4, z = 2$

To Think About

Using Example 3 as a model, see if you can solve each system.

23. $\dfrac{2}{x} + \dfrac{3}{y} - \dfrac{1}{z} = -1$

$\dfrac{3}{x} \qquad - \dfrac{8}{z} = -1$

$\qquad \dfrac{5}{y} + \dfrac{7}{z} = -1$

$2a + 3b - \ c = -1$
$3a \qquad - 8c = -1$
$\qquad 5b + 7c = -1$

$\overline{a = 5, b = -3, c = 2}$
$x = \dfrac{1}{5}, y = -\dfrac{1}{3}, z = \dfrac{1}{2}$

24. $\dfrac{3}{x} + \dfrac{1}{y} + \dfrac{1}{z} = 2$

$\dfrac{2}{x} + \dfrac{1}{y} \qquad = 1$

$\qquad \dfrac{3}{y} + \dfrac{1}{z} = 0$

$3a + \ b + c = 2$
$2a + \ b \qquad = 1$
$\qquad 3b + c = 0$

$\overline{a = \dfrac{4}{7}, b = -\dfrac{1}{7}, c = \dfrac{3}{7}}$
$x = \dfrac{7}{4}, y = -7, z = \dfrac{7}{3}$

25. $\dfrac{2}{x} + \dfrac{6}{y} + \dfrac{3}{z} = \ -2$

$\dfrac{3}{x} - \dfrac{1}{y} - \dfrac{2}{z} = \ \ 1$

$\dfrac{1}{x} + \dfrac{3}{y} - \dfrac{1}{z} = -11$

$2a + 6b + 3c = \ -2$
$3a - \ b - 2c = \ \ 1$
$\ a + 3b - \ c = -11$

Eliminate b:

| 1 and 2 | $20a - 9c = \ \ 4$ |
| 2 and 3 | $10a - 7c = -8$ |

$\overline{a = 2, b = -3, c = 4}$
$x = \dfrac{1}{2}, y = -\dfrac{1}{3}, z = \dfrac{1}{4}$

26. $\dfrac{3}{x} + \dfrac{1}{y} - \dfrac{1}{z} = 11$

$\dfrac{1}{x} + \dfrac{3}{y} - \dfrac{1}{z} = 13$

$\dfrac{1}{x} + \dfrac{1}{y} - \dfrac{3}{z} = 11$

$3a + \ b - \ c = 11$
$\ a + 3b - \ c = 13$
$\ a + \ b - 3c = 11$

Eliminate c:

| 1 and 3 | $4a + b = \ \ 11$ |
| 1 and 2 | $a - b = -1$ |

$\overline{a = 2, b = 3, c = -2}$
$x = \dfrac{1}{2}, y = \dfrac{1}{3}, z = -\dfrac{1}{2}$

Try to solve the system of equations. Explain your result in each case.

27. $\quad 2x + \ y \qquad\qquad = -3$
$\qquad\qquad 2y + 16z = -18$
$-7x - 3y + \ 4z = \qquad 6$

Eliminate x:

1 and 3	$y + \ 8z = \ -9$
$2 \times$ 1 and 3	$2y + 16z = -18$
2	$2y + 16z = -18$

Infinite number of solutions–
dependent eqs.

28. $\quad 6x - 2y + 2z = \ \ 2$
$\quad 4x + 8y - 2z = \ \ 5$
$-2x - 4y + \ z = -2$

Eliminate z:

1 and 2	$10x + 6y \qquad = \ \ 7$
2 and 3	$4x + 8y - 2z = \ \ 5$
	$-4x - 8y + 2z = -4$

$\overline{\qquad\qquad\qquad 0 \neq \ 1}$

No sol.; inconsistent system of eqs.

29. $\quad 3x + 3y - 3z = -1$
$\quad 4x + \ y - 2z = \ \ 1$
$-2x + 4y - 2z = -8$

Eliminate z:

A	1 and 2	$-6x + 3y = \ -5$
B	2 and 3	$-6x + 3y = \ -9$
C	1 and 3	$-6x + 3y = -11$

$A - B: 0 \neq 4$
$B - C: 0 \neq 2$ No sol.; inconsistent system of eqs.
$A - C: 0 \neq 6$

30. Transform the following system to a system of three equations in three unknowns and solve it. Find values for all variables (x, y, w, z).

$5x - \ y - 2w - 4z = 20$
$\ x + \ y + 5w + 2z = 11$
$\ x + 2y + 4w + 2z = 12$
$2x + \ y + 3w + \ z = 12$

Eliminate z:

A	1 and 2	$7x + y + 8w = \ \ 42$
B	2 and 3	$-y + \ w = \ -1$
C	3 and 4	$-3x \qquad - 2w = -12$

Eliminate x:

| A and C | $3y + 10w = \ \ 42$ |
| $3 \times$ B | $-3y + \ 3w = -3$ |

$x = 2, y = 4, w = 3, z = -5$

Cumulative Review Problems

31. Find the slope of a line $5x + 6y = -8$.

$y = -\dfrac{5}{6}x - \dfrac{4}{3}, m = -\dfrac{5}{6}$

32. Find the equation of a line in standard form with a slope of -6 and passing through $(-3, -1)$.

$y + 1 = -6(x + 3), 6x + y = -19$

33. Find the equation of a line in standard form passing through $(1, 4)$ and $(-2, 3)$.

$m = \dfrac{4 - 3}{1 + 2} = \dfrac{1}{3}$

$y - 4 = \dfrac{1}{3}(x - 1)$

$x - 3y = -11$

34. Find the equation of a line in standard form that is perpendicular to $y = -\dfrac{2}{3}x + 4$ and passes through $(-4, 2)$.

$m(\perp \text{ line}) = \dfrac{3}{2}$

$y - 2 = \dfrac{3}{2}(x + 4)$

$3x - 2y = -16$

Find the solution for each system of equations. Round your answers to five decimal places.

35.
$$x - 4y + 4z = -3.72186$$
$$-x + 3y - z = 5.98115$$
$$2x - y + 5z = 7.93645$$

$x = 1.10551$
$y = 2.93991$
$z = 1.73307$

36.
$$4x + 2y + 3z = 9$$
$$9x + 3y + 2z = 3$$
$$2.987x + 5.027y + 3.867z = 18.642$$

$x = 0.99773$
$y = 1.99139$
$z = 3.00272$

For Extra Practice Exercises, turn to page 173.

Solutions to Odd-Numbered Practice Problems

1.
$$x + 2y + 3z = 4 \quad \boxed{1}$$
$$2x + y - 2z = 3 \quad \boxed{2}$$
$$3x + 3y + 4z = 10 \quad \boxed{3}$$

We eliminate x by multiplying equation $\boxed{1}$ by -2 and adding it to equation $\boxed{2}$.

$$\begin{array}{rl} -2x - 4y - 6z = -8 & \boxed{4} \\ 2x + y - 2z = 3 & \boxed{2} \\ \hline -3y - 8z = -5 & \boxed{5} \end{array}$$

Now we eliminate x by multiplying equation $\boxed{1}$ by -3 and adding it to equation $\boxed{3}$.

$$\begin{array}{rl} -3x - 6y - 9z = -12 & \boxed{6} \\ 3x + 3y + 4z = 10 & \boxed{3} \\ \hline -3y - 5z = -2 & \boxed{7} \end{array}$$

We now eliminate y and solve for z in the system

$$-3y - 8z = -5 \quad \boxed{5}$$
$$-3y - 5z = -2 \quad \boxed{7}$$

To do this, we multiply equation $\boxed{5}$ by -1 and add it to equation $\boxed{7}$.

$$\begin{array}{rl} 3y + 8z = 5 & \boxed{8} \\ -3y - 5z = -2 & \boxed{7} \\ \hline 3z = 3 & \\ z = 1 & \end{array}$$

Substitute $z = 1$ into equation $\boxed{8}$.

$$3y + 8 = 5$$
$$3y = -3$$
$$y = -1$$

Substitute $z = 1$, $y = -1$ into equation $\boxed{1}$.

$$x + 2(-1) + 3(1) = 4$$
$$x + 1 = 4$$
$$x = 3$$

The solution is $x = 3$, $y = -1$, $z = 1$.

3. Let $\frac{1}{x} = u$, $\frac{1}{y} = v$, $\frac{1}{z} = w$. Then the system becomes

$$4u + 3v + w = 10 \quad \boxed{1}$$
$$5u - 4v - w = 18 \quad \boxed{2}$$
$$u + 2v = 1 \quad \boxed{3}$$

Now we add equation $\boxed{1}$ and $\boxed{2}$ together to obtain

$$9u - v = 28 \quad \boxed{4}$$
$$u + 2v = 1 \quad \boxed{3}$$

If we multiply equation $\boxed{4}$ by 2, we obtain

$$\begin{array}{rl} 18u - 2v = 56 & \boxed{5} \\ u + 2v = 1 & \boxed{3} \\ \hline 19u = 57 & \\ u = 3 & \end{array}$$

Now we substitute $u = 3$ into $\boxed{3}$.

$$3 + 2v = 1$$
$$2v = -2$$
$$v = -1$$

Now we substitute $u = 3$ and $v = -1$ into $\boxed{1}$.

$$4(3) + 3(1) + w = 10$$
$$12 - 3 + w = 10$$
$$9 + w = 10$$
$$\boxed{w = 1}$$

Now $u = \frac{1}{x}$, so

$$3 = \frac{1}{x} \qquad 3x = 1 \qquad x = \frac{1}{3}$$

Also, $v = \frac{1}{y}$, so

$$-1 = \frac{1}{y} \qquad -y = 1 \qquad y = -1$$

Finally, $w = \frac{1}{z}$, so

$$1 = \frac{1}{z} \qquad z = 1$$

Our solution is $x = \frac{1}{3}$, $y = -1$, $z = 1$.

2. $x = 7$, $y = 1$, $z = -4$; can be written as the ordered triple $(7, 1, -4)$.

After studying this section, you will be able to:

1 *Solve an applied problem requiring the use of a system of two linear equations with two unknowns*

2 *Solve an applied problem requiring the use of a system of three linear equations with three unknowns*

3.3 APPLICATIONS OF SYSTEMS OF LINEAR EQUATIONS

1 We can use a system of linear equations to solve some practical problems.

Example 1   For the upcoming Kings Band concert, advance tickets cost $5 and tickets at the door cost $6. The band's manager predicts that gross ticket sales will be $4540. He also said that if ticket prices were raised to $7 and $9, respectively, then gross ticket sales would be $6560. If he is correct, how many tickets of each type can the concert's promoters expect to sell?

Since we are looking for the number of tickets sold, we let

x = number of tickets bought in advance

y = number of tickets bought at the door

If advance tickets cost $5, then the total sales will be $5x$; similarly, total sales of door tickets will be $6x$. Since the total sales of both types of tickets is $4540, we have

$$5x + 6y = 4540$$

By the same reasoning, we have

$$7x + 9y = 6560$$

Our system is thus

$$5x + 6y = 4540 \quad \boxed{1}$$
$$7x + 9y = 6560 \quad \boxed{2}$$

We now use our familiar procedure to solve the system. You should be able to follow the steps.

$$
\begin{array}{rl}
-15x - 18y = -13,620 & \boxed{3} \\
\underline{14x + 18y = 13,120} & \boxed{4} \\
-x = -500 &
\end{array}
$$

Therefore, $x = 500$. Substituting $x = 500$ into equation $\boxed{1}$ we have

$$5(500) + 6y = 4540$$
$$6y = 2040$$
$$y = 340$$

Thus, the manager predicted that 500 advance tickets and 340 door tickets would be sold.

Check: We need to check our answers. Do they seem reasonable?

Would 500 advance tickets at $7 and 340 door tickets at $9 yield $6560?

$$7(500) + 9(340) \overset{?}{=} 6560$$
$$3500 + 3060 \overset{?}{=} 6560$$
$$6560 = 6560 \checkmark$$

Would 500 advance tickets at $5 and 340 door tickets at $6 yield $4540?

$$5(500) + 6(340) \overset{?}{=} 4540$$
$$2500 + 2040 \overset{?}{=} 4540$$
$$4540 \overset{?}{=} 4540 \checkmark$$

Therefore, our solution is correct. ■

Practice Problem 1   Coach Perez purchased baseballs at $6 each and bats at $21 each last week for the college baseball team. The total cost of the purchase was $318.

TEACHING TIP   After discussing example 1 or a similar example, ask students to try to solve the following problem: Have them use p = the hourly pay for the plumber, and h = the hourly pay for his helper. A plumber worked for 2 hours on a project and his helper worked 3 hours. The plumber charged $101 for that project. Later the plumber worked for 3 hours and his helper for 7 hours on another project, and the bill was $189. How much does the plumber charge per hour for his work? How much does the plumber charge per hour for his helper? (Answer: $2p + 3h = 101$, $3p + 7h = 189$. The plumber charges $28 per hour for himself and $15 per hour for his helper.)

This week he noticed that the same items are on sale. Baseballs are now $5 each and bats are $17. He found that if he had made the same purchase this week, it would have cost only $259. How many baseballs and how many bats did he buy last week?

Example 2 An electronics firm makes two types of switching devices. Type A takes 4 minutes to make and requires $3 worth of materials. Type B takes 5 minutes to make and requires $5 worth of materials. When the production manager reviewed the latest batch, he found that it took 35 hours to make these switches with a materials cost of $1900. How many switches of each type were produced?

Let A = the number of type A devices produced

B = the number of type B devices produced

How should we construct the equations? What relationships exist between our variables (or unknowns)? According to the problem, the devices are related by time and by cost. So we set up one equation in terms of time (minutes in this case) and one in terms of cost (dollars). Each type A took 4 minutes to make, each type B took 5 minutes to make, and the total time was 2100 minutes. Each type A used $3 worth of materials, each type B used $5 worth of materials, and the total material cost was $1900, we can gather this information in a table. This will help in forming the equation.

	Type A Devices	Type B Devices	Total
Number of minutes	$4A$	$5B$	2100
Cost of materials	$3A$	$5B$	1900

$$4A + 5B = 2100$$
$$3A + 5B = 1900$$

Therefore we have the system

$$4A + 5B = 2100 \qquad \boxed{1}$$
$$3A + 5B = 1900 \qquad \boxed{2}$$

Multiplying equation $\boxed{2}$ by -1 and adding the equations, we find

$$A = 200$$

Substituting $A = 200$ into equation $\boxed{1}$, we have

$$800 + 5B = 2100$$
$$5B = 1300$$
$$B = 260$$

Thus 200 type A devices and 260 type B devices were produced. You should check these answers. ■

2 **Practice Problem 2** A furniture company makes both small and large chairs. It takes 30 minutes of machine time and 1 hour and 15 minutes of labor to build the small chair. The large chair needs 40 minutes of machine time and 1 hour and 20 minutes of labor. The company has 57 hours of labor time and 26 hours of machine time available each day. If all available time is used, how many chairs of each type can the company make? ■

In some problems we need to use a mathematical formula from geometry, physics, or science.

TEACHING TIP This type of problem seems a little more difficult to many students. You may use this additional problem as an example for the class: A car manufacturing plant makes compact cars and luxury cars. It takes 4 hours on the assembly line to make a compact car, but 7 hours to make a luxury car. The plant makes $1000 profit on each compact car made and $3000 profit on each luxury car made. The plant will be operating for 260 hours this month, and plant officials have set a profit goal of $90,000. How many of each car should be made? (Answer let c = number of compact cars made and l = number of luxury cars made. Then $1000c + 3000l = 90,000$. Also $4c + 7l = 260$. Solving $c = 30$ and $l = 20$. They must make 30 compact cars and 20 luxury cars this month.)

Example 3 An airplane travels between two cities that are 1500 miles apart. The trip against the wind takes 3 hours. The return trip with the wind takes $2\frac{1}{2}$ hours. What is the speed of the plane in still air (in other words, how fast could the plane go if there were no wind)? What is the speed of the wind?

Our unknowns are the speed of the plane in still air and the speed of the wind. Let

x = the speed of the plane in still air

y = the speed of the wind

To solve this problem, we need the distance formula $D = RT$.

Solving the distance formula gives

$$R = \frac{D}{T}$$

Going against the wind requires 3 hours to go 1500 miles. Hence,

$$R = \frac{1500}{3} = 500 \text{ mph}$$

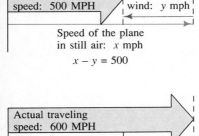

Why do we use a minus sign? The diagram shows that the wind speed *opposes* the plane's speed, so the plane's speed in still air must be *reduced* by the speed of the wind.

Going with the wind requires only $2\frac{1}{2}$ hours to go 1500 miles. Hence,

$$R = \frac{1500}{2.5} = 600 \text{ mph}$$

In this case the wind is *helping* the plane, so its speed is *added* to the plane's speed in still air. Therefore, we solve the system

$$x - y = 500$$
$$x + y = 600$$

and obtain $x = 550$ and $y = 50$. Verify these answers. Now we know that the speed of the plane in still air is 550 mph, and the speed of the wind is 50 mph. ■

Practice Problem 3 An airplane travels west from city *A* to city *B* against the wind. It takes 3 hours to travel 1950 kilometers. On the return trip the plane travels east from city *B* to city *C* a distance of 1600 kilometers in a time of 2 hours. On the return trip the plane travels with the wind. What is the speed of the plane in still air? What is the speed of the wind? ■

Example 4 A trucking firm has three sizes of trucks. The biggest trucks hold 10 tons of gravel; the next size holds 6 tons, and the smallest holds 4 tons. The firm's manager has 15 trucks available to haul 104 tons of gravel. However, to reduce fuel cost she wants to use two more of the fuel-efficient 10-ton trucks than she does the 6-tons trucks. Her assistant tells her that she has two more 10-ton trucks available than 6-ton trucks. How many trucks of each type should she use?

Since we need to know three things (the number of 10-ton trucks, 6-ton trucks, and 4-ton trucks), we need three equations. Let

x = the number of 10-ton trucks used

y = the number of 6-ton trucks used

z = the number of 4-ton trucks used

We now need to see how to relate our unknowns. We know that 15 trucks will be used; hence,

$$x + y + z = 15 \quad \boxed{1}$$

How can we get our second equation? Well, we also know the *capacity* of each truck type, and we know the total tonnage to be hauled. The first type of truck hauls 10 tons, the second type 6 tons, and the third type 4 tons, and the total tonnage is 104 tons. Hence, we can write

$$10x + 6y + 4z = 104 \quad \boxed{2}$$

We still need one more equation. What other given information can we use? The problem states that the manager wants to use two more 10-ton trucks than the number of 6-ton trucks. Thus

$$x = 2 + y \quad \boxed{3}$$

(We could have also written $y = x - 2$.) Hence our equation system is

$$
\begin{array}{rcl}
x + y + z &=& 15 \quad \boxed{1} \\
10x + 6y + 4z &=& 104 \quad \boxed{2} \\
x - y &=& 2 \quad \boxed{3}
\end{array}
$$

Equation $\boxed{3}$ doesn't contain the variable z. Now let's work with equations $\boxed{1}$ and $\boxed{2}$ to eliminate z also. First we multiply equation $\boxed{1}$ by -4 and add it to equation $\boxed{2}$.

$$
\begin{array}{rcl}
-4x - 4y - 4z &=& -60 \quad \boxed{4} \\
10x + 6y + 4z &=& 104 \quad \boxed{2} \\
\hline
6x + 2y &=& 44 \quad \boxed{5}
\end{array}
$$

Make sure you understand how we got equation $\boxed{5}$. Dividing each term of equation $\boxed{5}$ by 2 and adding to equation $\boxed{3}$ gives

$$4x = 24 \quad \text{or} \quad x = 6$$

For $x = 6$, equation $\boxed{3}$ yields

$$6 - y = 2$$
$$4 = y$$

Now, using equation $\boxed{1}$, we get

$$6 + 4 + z = 15$$
$$z = 5$$

Thus the manager needs six 10-ton trucks, four 6-ton trucks, and five 4-ton trucks.
Check: Does this answer meet all conditions of the problem? ▪

Practice Problem 4 A factory uses three machines to wrap boxes for shipment. Machines A, B, and C can wrap 260 boxes in 1 hour. If machine A runs 3 hours and machine B runs 2 hours, they can wrap 390 boxes. If machine B runs 3 hours and machine C runs 4 hours, 655 boxes can be wrapped. How many boxes per hour can each machine wrap? ▪

Example 5 Electricians plan to lay three sizes of conduits (pipes) together under the floor of a building so they can pull their wires from one end of the building to the other. The center of each pipe is labeled A, B, and C, as shown in our sketch. The distance from A to B is 15 centimeters. The distance from B to C is 13 centimeters. The distance from C to A is 16 centimeters. Find the radius of each pipe.

Again, we have three unknowns, so we need three equations. Let

$x =$ the radius of pipe A

$y =$ the radius of pipe B

$z =$ the radius of pipe C

TEACHING TIP Example 5 illustrates the type of problem situation where each of the three equations used to solve the problem does not contain all three variables. A simple example that you can quickly show to the class is the following: A watch, a calculator, and a ring together cost $225. The watch cost $50 more than the calculator. The ring cost $25 more than the watch and the calculator together. What did each item cost? (Let $w =$ the cost of the watch, $c =$ the cost of the calculator, and $r =$ the cost of the ring.) Thus we have

$$w + c + r = 225$$
$$w = 50 + c$$
$$r = 25 + w + c.$$

Solving the system we obtain $r = 125$, $c = 25$, $w = 75$. Thus, the ring cost $125, the calculator cost $25, and the watch cost $75.)

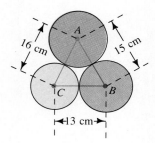

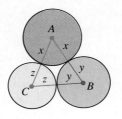

As we see in the sketch, the line joining A and B consists of the radius of pipe A and the radius of pipe B. (Why?) Thus

$$x + y = 15 \quad \boxed{1}$$

The distance from B to C is 13 centimeters. Thus,

$$y + z = 13 \quad \boxed{2}$$

The distance from C to A is 16 centimeters. Thus,

$$z + x = 16 \quad \boxed{3}$$

We therefore have the system

$$x + y \phantom{{}+z} = 15 \quad \boxed{1}$$
$$\phantom{x+{}}y + z = 13 \quad \boxed{2}$$
$$x \phantom{{}+y} + z = 16 \quad \boxed{3}$$

If we multiply equation $\boxed{3}$ by -1 and add the result to equation $\boxed{2}$, we obtain

$$-x + y = -3$$

We then solve the system

$$-x + y = -3 \quad \boxed{4}$$
$$x + y = 15 \quad \boxed{1}$$

and get $y = 6$ and $x = 9$. Substituting these values into equation $\boxed{3}$, we have $z = 7$. Thus, the radius of pipe A is 9 centimeters, the radius of pipe B is 6 centimeters, and the radius of pipe C is 7 centimeters. ∎

Practice Problem 5 An electrician places three wires next to each other inside a radio transmitter. The cross section of each wire is circular. The centers of the wires are labeled A, B, and C in this sketch. The distance between the center of A and the center of B is 13 millimeters. The distance between the center of B and the center of C is 22 millimeters. The distance from the outside edge of the wire at A to the outside edge of the wire at C is 52 millimeters, as shown in the figure. Find the radius of each wire. ∎

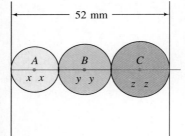

Use a system of linear equations to solve each problem.

1. A Broadway musical had a paid attendance of 530 people. Mezzanine tickets cost \$9, and orchestra tickets cost \$14. Ticket sales receipts totaled \$5870. How many tickets of each type were sold?

   # of mezzanine tickets = $x = 310$ $x + y = 530$
   # of orchestra tickets = $y = 220$ $\$9x + \$14y = \$5870$

2. An employment agency specializing in temporary construction help pays heavy equipment operators \$40 per day and general laborers \$25 per day. If 35 people were hired and the payroll was \$1115, how many heavy equipment operators were employed? How many laborers?

   # of heavy equipment operators = $x = 16$ $x + y = 35$
   # of general laborers = $y = 19$ $\$40x + \$25y = \$1115$

3. Kurt bought 25¢ stamps for letters and 15¢ stamps for postcards. He bought 146 stamps for \$27.00. How many of each type did he buy?

   # of stamps for letters = $x = 51$ $x + y = 146$
   # of stamps for postcards = $y = 95$ $\$0.25x + \$0.15y = \$27.00$

4. A tea company bought 1000 pounds of tea for \$776. India tea cost 84¢ per pound, and English tea cost 68¢ per pound. How many pounds of each type did the company buy?

   # of lbs of India Tea = $x = 600$ lbs $x + y = 1000$
   # of lbs of English Tea = $y = 400$ lbs $\$0.84x + \$0.68y = \$776.00$

5. At Western State, full-time students pay a registration fee of \$20, and part-time students pay \$14. The registrar determined that registration fees of \$9080 had to be billed to students. However, due to a programming error, the computer billed each full-time student \$15 and each part-time student \$12, for a total of \$7140. How many full-time students have registered? How many part-time students?

   # of full-time students = $x = 300$ $\$20x + \$14y = \$9080$
   # of part-time students = $y = 220$ $\$15x + \$12y = \$7140$

6. For its sales-staff the Star Sales Company rents cars each month under a package deal from a local car dealer. Last month the company rented 25 compact cars and 10 intermediate cars for \$13,750. This month, in a cost-saving move, it rented 32 compact cars and three intermediate cars for \$12,700. What is the rental cost per month for each type of car?

   av. rental for compact cars = $x = \$350$ $25x + 10y = \$13,750$
   av. rental for intermediate cars = $y = \$500$ $32x + 3y = \$12,700$

7. During a time study, a company that makes auto radar detectors found that its basic model required 3 hours to manufacture the inside components and 2 hours to manufacture the housing and controls. The advanced model needed 5 hours to manufacture the inside components and 3 hours to manufacture the housing and controls. The production division has 1050 hours available this week to manufacture inside components and 660 hours available to manufacture housing and controls. How many detectors of each type can be made?

   # of basic detectors = $x = 150$ $3x + 5y = 1050$
   # of advanced detectors = $y = 120$ $2x + 3y = 660$

8. An insurance company determined that it takes 20 hours to train a new salesperson on company procedure and 12 hours to train the salesperson on sales techniques. An experienced salesperson learns company procedure in 14 hours and sales techniques in 5 hours. Sales managers can devote 240 hours for training in sales techniques. The company extension school has 468 hours available to teach company procedure. How many experienced salespersons can be trained? How many new salespersons?

   # new salespeople = $x = 15$ $20x + 14y = 468$
   # experienced salespeople = $y = 12$ $12x + 5y = 240$

9. To provide vitamin additives for patients, a staff hospital dietician has two prepackaged mixtures available. Mixture 1 contains 5 grams of vitamin C and 3 grams of niacin; mixture 2 contains 6 grams of vitamin C and 5 grams of niacin. On an average day she needs 87 grams of niacin and 117 grams of vitamin C. How many packets of each mixture will she need?

   # packets of mixture 1 = $x = 9$ $5x + 6y = 117$
   # packets of mixture 2 = $y = 12$ $3x + 5y = 87$

10. A farmer has several packages of fertilizer for his new grain crop. The old packages contain 50 pounds of long-term-growth supplement and 60 pounds of weed killer. The new packages contain 65 pounds of long-term-growth supplement and 45 pounds of weed killer. Using past experience, the farmer estimates that he needs 3125 pounds of long-term-growth supplement and 2925 pounds of weed killer for the fields. How many old packages of fertilizer and how many new packages of fertilizer should he use?

    # of packages of old fertilizer = $x = 30$ lbs $50x + 65y = 3125$
    # of packages of new fertilizer = $y = 25$ lbs $60x + 45y = 2925$

11. With the current a motorboat can travel 84 miles in 2 hours. Against the current the same trip takes 3 hours. How fast can the boat travel in still water? What is the speed of the current?

speed of boat in still water $= x = 35$ mph

speed of the current $= y = 7$ mph

$2(x + y) = 84$
$3(x - y) = 84$

12. Against the wind a small plane flew 210 miles in 1 hour and 10 minutes. The return trip took only 50 minutes. What was the speed of the wind? What was the speed of the plane in still air?

speed of plane in still air $= x = 216$ mph

speed of wind $= y = 36$ mph

$\frac{7}{6}(x - y) = 210$
$\frac{5}{6}(x + y) = 210$

13. Against the wind a commercial airline in South America flew 630 miles in 3 hours and 30 minutes. With a tailwind the return trip took 3 hours. What was the speed of the wind? What was the speed of the plane in still air?

speed of plane in still air $= x = 195$ mph

speed of the wind $= y = 15$ mph

$\frac{7}{2}(x - y) = 630$
$3(x + y) = 630$

14. It took Linda and Alice 4 hours to travel 24 miles downstream by canoe on Indian River. The next day they traveled for 6 hours upstream for 18 miles. What was the rate of the current? What was their average speed in still water?

average speed of canoe in still water $= x = 4.5$ mph

rate of the current $= y = 1.5$ mph

$4(x + y) = 24$
$6(x - y) = 18$

15. A company packs three types of packages in a large shipping box. Package type A weighs 0.5 pound, package type B weighs 0.25 pound, and package type C weighs 1.0 pound. Seventy-five packages weighing a total of 42 pounds were placed in the box. The number of type A packages was three less than the total number of types C and B combined. How many packages of each type were placed in the box?

of A packages $= x + y - 3 = 36$

of B packages $= x = 20$

of C packages $= y = 19$

$(x + y - 3) + x + y = 75$
$0.5(x + y - 3) + 0.25x + 1.0y = 42$

16. Sunshine Fruit Company packs three types of gift boxes of oranges, pink grapefruit, and white grapefruit. Box A contains 10 oranges, 3 pink grapefruit, and 3 white grapefruit. Box B contains 5 oranges, 2 pink grapefruit, and 3 white grapefruit. Box C contains 4 oranges, 1 pink grapefruit, and 2 white grapefruit. The shipping manager has available 51 oranges, 16 pink grapefruit, and 23 white grapefruit. How many gift boxes of each type can she prepare?

of A boxes $= x = 2$

of B boxes $= y = 3$

of C boxes $= z = 4$

$10x + 5y + 4z = 51$
$3x + 2y + z = 16$
$3x + 3y + 2z = 23$

17. The Falmouth pumping station normally uses three pumps to provide drinking water for the town. When pumps A, B, and C are used for 2 hours, they can pump 74,000 gallons. The supervisor wanted to run pumps A and B for 4 hours, but pump B overheated and was shut down after 2 hours. During that time (that is, the 2 hours that pumps A and B ran, and the 2 additional hours that only pump A ran), 64,000 gallons of water were pumped. After cooling down, pump B was used for 5 hours and pump C for 4 hours to pump 120,000 gallons. How many gallons per hour can each pump handle?

gal/hour for pump $A = x = 10,000$ gal/hr

gal/hour for pump $B = y = 12,000$ gal/hr

gal/hour for pump $C = z = 15,000$ gal/hr

$2x + 2y + 2z = 74,000$
$4x + 2y = 64,000$
$5y + 4z = 120,000$

18. A mathematician needs to find the radii of three circles. Each circle is drawn so that the circles are tangent (touching at only one point) (see the figure). The circles have centers at A, B, and C, respectively. The mathematician knows that $AB = 9$ centimeters, $AC = 7$ centimeters, and $CB = 8$ centimeters. Find the radius of each circle.

Hint: Let $z =$ radius of circle C, let $y =$ radius of circle B, and let $x =$ radius of circle A.

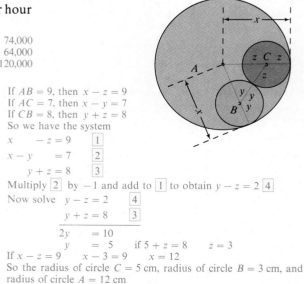

If $AB = 9$, then $x - z = 9$
If $AC = 7$, then $x - y = 7$
If $CB = 8$, then $y + z = 8$
So we have the system

$x \quad - z = 9$ [1]
$x - y \quad = 7$ [2]
$\quad y + z = 8$ [3]

Multiply [2] by -1 and add to [1] to obtain $y - z = 2$ [4]
Now solve $y - z = 2$ [4]
$\underline{\quad y + z = 8}$ [3]
$2y \quad = 10$
$y \quad = 5$ if $5 + z = 8$ $z = 3$
If $x - z = 9$ $x - 3 = 9$ $x = 12$
So the radius of circle $C = 5$ cm, radius of circle $B = 3$ cm, and radius of circle $A = 12$ cm

Use a system of four linear equations in four unknowns to solve the following problem.

19. A scientist is performing an experiment to determine how to increase the life-span of mice through a controlled diet. The mice need 134 grams of carbohydrates, 150 grams of protein, 178 grams of fat, and 405 grams of moisture during the length of the experiment. The food is available in four packets, as listed below. How many packets of each type should the scientist use?

Contents	Packet			
	A	B	C	D
Carbohydrates	42	20	0	10
Protein	20	10	20	0
Fat	34	0	10	20
Moisture	50	35	30	40

of A packages $= x = 2$ $42x + 20y + \ 0z + 10q = 134$
of B packages $= y = 1$ $20x + 10y + 20z + \ 0q = 150$
of C packages $= z = 5$ $34x + \ 0y + 10z + 20q = 178$
of D packages $= q = 3$ $50x + 35y + 30z + 40q = 405$

Cumulative Review Problems

Solve for the variable indicated.

20. $\frac{1}{3}(4 - 2x) = \frac{1}{2}x - 3$

$2(4 - 2x) = 3x - 18$
$\frac{26}{7} = x$

21. $0.06x + 0.15(0.5 - x) = 0.04$

$0.06x + 0.075 - 0.15x = 0.04$
$-0.09x = -0.035$
$x = \frac{7}{18}$

22. $2(y - 3) - (2y + 4) = -6y$

$2y - 6 - 2y - 4 = -6y$
$\frac{5}{3} = y$

▦ **Calculator Problems**

23. A recent concert had a paid audience of 987 people. Advance tickets were $9.95 and tickets at the door were $12.95. A total of $10,738.65 was collected in ticket sales. How many of each type of ticket were sold?

681 tickets @ $9.95
306 tickets @ $12.95

24. This year the state highway department purchased 256 identical cars and 183 identical trucks for official use. The purchase price was $5,791,948. Due to a budget shortfall, next year the department plans to purchase only 64 cars and 107 trucks. It will be charged the same price for each car and for each truck. Next year it plans to spend $2,507,612. How much does the department pay for each car and for each truck?

Cars @ $10,258
Trucks @ $17,300

For Extra Practice Exercises, turn to page 174.

Solutions to Odd-Numbered Practice Problems

1. Let $x =$ the number of baseballs purchased
     $y =$ the number of bats purchased

Last week: $6x + 21y = 318$ ☐1
This week: $5x + 17y = 259$ ☐2

Multiply equation ☐1 by 5 and equation ☐2 by -6.

$30x + 105y = \ \ \ 1590$ ☐3
$\underline{-30x - 102y = -1554}$ ☐4
$\ \ \ \ \ \ \ \ \ \ \ 3y = \ \ \ \ \ \ \ 36$ Adding equations ☐3 and ☐4.
$\ \ \ \ \ \ \ \ \ \ \ \ y = 12$

Substitute $y = 12$ into equation $\boxed{2}$.

$$5x + 17(12) = 259$$
$$5x + 204 = 259$$
$$5x = 55$$
$$x = 11$$

Thus 11 baseballs and 12 bats were purchased. Can you verify these facts?

3. The rate of flight against the wind is

$$R = \frac{D}{T} = \frac{1950}{3} = 650 \text{ kilometers per hour}$$

The rate of flight with the wind is

$$R = \frac{D}{T} = \frac{1600}{2} = 800 \text{ kilometers per hour}$$

Let $\quad a =$ the speed of the airplane in still air
$\quad\quad w =$ the speed of the wind

$$
\begin{aligned}
\text{Against the wind:} \quad a - w &= 650 \qquad \boxed{1}\\
\text{With the wind:} \quad a + w &= 800 \qquad \boxed{2}\\
\hline
2a &= 1450 \qquad \text{Add } \boxed{1} \text{ and } \boxed{2}.\\
a &= 725
\end{aligned}
$$

Substituting $a = 725$ into $\boxed{2}$, we have

$$725 + w = 800$$
$$w = 75$$

Thus, the speed of the plane in still air is 725 kilometers per hour and the speed of the wind is 75 kilometers per hour.

5. Let $\quad x =$ the radius of wire A
$\quad\quad y =$ the radius of wire B
$\quad\quad z =$ the radius of wire C

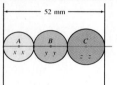

The distance from A to B is 13 millimeters. Thus, $x + y = 13$. The distance from B to C is 22 millimeters. Thus, $y + z = 22$. The distance between outside edges is 52 millimeters. Thus $2x + 2y + 2z = 52$. We can divide each term by 2 to obtain $x + y + z = 26$.

$$
\begin{aligned}
x + y \quad\;\; &= 13 \qquad \boxed{1}\\
y + z &= 22 \qquad \boxed{2}\\
x + y + z &= 26 \qquad \boxed{3}
\end{aligned}
$$

Multiply equation $\boxed{2}$ by -1 and add it to equation $\boxed{3}$.

$$
\begin{aligned}
-y - z &= -22 \qquad \boxed{4}\\
x + y + z &= \;\;\;26 \qquad \boxed{3}\\
\hline
x &= \;\;\;\;4
\end{aligned}
$$

Now substitute $x = 4$ into equation $\boxed{1}$.

$$4 + y = 13$$
$$y = 9$$

Now substitute $x = 4$ and $y = 9$ into equation $\boxed{3}$.

$$4 + 9 + z = 26$$
$$z = 13$$

Thus, the radius of wire A is 4 millimeters, of wire B is 9 millimeters, and of wire C is 13 millimeters. Can you verify this?

Answers to Even-Numbered Practice Problems

2. 20 small chairs and 24 large chairs could be made.
4. Machine A wraps 76 boxes per hour, machine B wraps 81 boxes per hour, and machine C wraps 103 boxes per hour.

3.4 DETERMINANTS

After studying this section, you will be able to:

1 *Evaluate a second-order determinant*

2 *Evaluate a third-order determinant*

1 The **value of a determinant** is a *number* that we obtain after operating on a square arrangement of numbers. We are particularly interested in determinants that have two rows and two columns,

$$\begin{vmatrix} 3 & 2 \\ 1 & 4 \end{vmatrix} \quad \text{and} \quad \begin{vmatrix} -6 & 0 \\ 1 & 3 \end{vmatrix}$$

which are called **second-order determinants**.

Mathematically, we define a determinant of second order as follows:

Definition

The value of the second-order determinant $\begin{vmatrix} a & b \\ d & c \end{vmatrix}$ is $ac - bd$.

Example 1 Find the value of each determinant. **(a)** $\begin{vmatrix} 2 & 3 \\ 1 & 5 \end{vmatrix}$ **(b)** $\begin{vmatrix} -4 & 2 \\ 3 & 6 \end{vmatrix}$

(a) $\begin{vmatrix} 2 & 3 \\ 1 & 5 \end{vmatrix} = (2)(5) - (1)(3) = 10 - 3 = 7$

(b) $\begin{vmatrix} -4 & 2 \\ 3 & 6 \end{vmatrix} = (-4)(6) - (3)(2) = -24 - 6 = -30$ ∎

Practice Problem 1 Evaluate the determinants.
(a) $\begin{vmatrix} 2 & -5 \\ 3 & 1 \end{vmatrix}$ **(b)** $\begin{vmatrix} -6 & -4 \\ -5 & 2 \end{vmatrix}$ ∎

When the determinant contains several negative numbers, be careful about signs.

Example 2 Find the value of each determinant.

(a) $\begin{vmatrix} -6 & 2 \\ -1 & 4 \end{vmatrix}$ **(b)** $\begin{vmatrix} 0 & -3 \\ -2 & 6 \end{vmatrix}$

(a) $\begin{vmatrix} -6 & 2 \\ -1 & 4 \end{vmatrix} = (-6)(4) - (-1)(2) = -24 - (-2) - 24 + 2 = -22$

(b) $\begin{vmatrix} 0 & -3 \\ -2 & 6 \end{vmatrix} = (0)(6) - (-2)(-3) = 0 - (+6) = -6$ ∎

Practice Problem 2 Find the value of the determinant.
(a) $\begin{vmatrix} -7 & 3 \\ -4 & -2 \end{vmatrix}$ **(b)** $\begin{vmatrix} 5 & 6 \\ 0 & -5 \end{vmatrix}$ ∎

2 *Third-order determinants* have three rows and three columns. Again, each determinant has exactly one value.

Definition

The value of the third-order determinant

$$\begin{vmatrix} a_1 & b_1 & c_1 \\ a_2 & b_2 & c_2 \\ a_3 & b_3 & c_3 \end{vmatrix}$$

is

$$a_1b_2c_3 + b_1c_2a_3 + c_1a_2b_3 - a_3b_2c_1 - b_3c_2a_1 - c_3a_2b_1$$

TEACHING TIP Students find it interesting that determinants have found their greatest use in the age of calculators and computers. Yet, determinants are quite old. Most mathematicians feel that Gottfried Leibniz discovered the concept of determinants in 1693, just 73 years after the Pilgrims came to America.

Because this definition is difficult to memorize and cumbersome to use, we evaluate third-order determinants by the simpler method called **expansion by minors**. The **minor** of an element (number or letter) of a third-order determinant is the second-order determinant that remains after you delete the row and column in which the element appears.

Example 3 Find **(a)** the minor of 6 and **(b)** the minor of -3 in the determinant

$$\begin{vmatrix} 6 & 1 & 2 \\ -3 & 4 & 5 \\ -2 & 7 & 8 \end{vmatrix}$$

(a) Since the element 6 appears in the first row and the first column we delete them.

$$\begin{vmatrix} 6 & 1 & 2 \\ -3 & 4 & 5 \\ -2 & 7 & 8 \end{vmatrix}$$

Therefore, the minor of 6 is

$$\begin{vmatrix} 4 & 5 \\ 7 & 8 \end{vmatrix}$$

(b) Since -3 appears in the first column and second row, we delete them.

$$\begin{vmatrix} 6 & 1 & 2 \\ -3 & 4 & 5 \\ -2 & 7 & 8 \end{vmatrix}$$

The minor of -3 is

$$\begin{vmatrix} 1 & 2 \\ 7 & 8 \end{vmatrix} \quad \blacksquare$$

Problem Practice 3 Find **(a)** the minor of 3 and **(b)** the minor of -6 in the determinant

$$\begin{vmatrix} 1 & 2 & 7 \\ -4 & -5 & -6 \\ 3 & 4 & -9 \end{vmatrix}$$

Thus, to evaluate a third-order determinant, we use expansion by minors of elements in the first column, for example, we have

$$\begin{vmatrix} a_1 & b_1 & c_1 \\ a_2 & b_2 & c_2 \\ a_3 & b_3 & c_3 \end{vmatrix} = a_1 \begin{vmatrix} b_2 & c_2 \\ b_3 & c_3 \end{vmatrix} - a_2 \begin{vmatrix} b_1 & c_1 \\ b_3 & c_3 \end{vmatrix} + a_3 \begin{vmatrix} b_1 & c_1 \\ b_2 & c_2 \end{vmatrix}$$

Note that the signs alternate. We then evaluate the second-order determinant according to our definition. $\blacksquare$

TEACHING TIP After discussing example 4 or a similar example, ask students to do the following problem at their seats: Evaluate

$$\begin{vmatrix} -1 & 3 & 5 \\ -7 & 4 & 2 \\ -6 & 2 & 0 \end{vmatrix}$$ by expanding it

by minors of elements in the first column. (Answer = 18.) Have students show the steps

$$(-1)\begin{vmatrix} 4 & 2 \\ 2 & 0 \end{vmatrix} + (+7)\begin{vmatrix} 3 & 5 \\ 2 & 0 \end{vmatrix}$$

$$+ (-6)\begin{vmatrix} 3 & 5 \\ 4 & 2 \end{vmatrix}$$

$$= (-1)(-4) + (+7)(-10)$$

$$+ (-6)(-14)$$

$$= 4 + (-70) + 84 = 18$$

Example 4 Evaluate the determinant $\begin{vmatrix} 2 & 3 & 6 \\ 4 & -2 & 0 \\ 1 & -5 & -3 \end{vmatrix}$ by expanding it by minors of elements in the first column.

$$\begin{vmatrix} 2 & 3 & 6 \\ 4 & -2 & 0 \\ 1 & -5 & -3 \end{vmatrix} = 2\begin{vmatrix} -2 & 0 \\ -5 & -3 \end{vmatrix} - 4\begin{vmatrix} 3 & 6 \\ -5 & -3 \end{vmatrix} + 1\begin{vmatrix} 3 & 6 \\ -2 & 0 \end{vmatrix}$$

$$= 2[(-2)(-3) - (-5)(0)] - 4[(3)(-3) - (-5)(6)] + 1[(3)(0) - (-2)(6)]$$

$$= 2[6 + 0] - 4[-9 - (-30)] + 1[0 - (-12)]$$

$$= 2(6) - 4(21) + 1(12)$$

$$= 12 - 84 + 12$$

$$= -60 \quad \blacksquare$$

Practice Problem 4 Evaluate the determinant $\begin{vmatrix} 1 & 2 & -3 \\ 2 & -1 & 2 \\ 3 & 1 & 4 \end{vmatrix}$. ■

We may expand by minors about *any* row or column. The sign that precedes any term of the three-term expansion is given by the array

$$\begin{array}{ccc} + & - & + \\ - & + & - \\ + & - & + \end{array}$$

Note that the signs *alternate* for each row and column.

Example 5 Use minors about the second row to evaluate:

$$\begin{vmatrix} 3 & -4 & 0 \\ -5 & 2 & 6 \\ -6 & 0 & -2 \end{vmatrix}$$

The products of the three elements in the second row with their minors are

$$-5\begin{vmatrix} -4 & 0 \\ 0 & -2 \end{vmatrix} \qquad 2\begin{vmatrix} 3 & 0 \\ -6 & -2 \end{vmatrix} \qquad 6\begin{vmatrix} 3 & -4 \\ -6 & 0 \end{vmatrix}$$

Connecting these products with the signs from the second row of the sign array, we have

$$-(-5)\begin{vmatrix} -4 & 0 \\ 0 & -2 \end{vmatrix} + 2\begin{vmatrix} 3 & 0 \\ -6 & -2 \end{vmatrix} - 6\begin{vmatrix} 3 & -4 \\ -6 & 0 \end{vmatrix}$$

Now we do the computations:

$$+5[(-4)(-2) - (0)(0)] + 2[(3)(-2) - (-6)(0)] - 6[(3)(0) - (-6)(-4)]$$
$$= +5(+8) + 2(-6) - 6(-24) = +40 - 12 + 144$$
$$= 172 \quad ■$$

Practice Problem 5 Evaluate the determinant by minors about the second row:

$$\begin{vmatrix} 5 & 2 & 1 \\ 3 & 0 & -2 \\ -4 & -1 & 2 \end{vmatrix}$$

Often a third-order determinant can be evaluated more quickly if we use a row or column that has at least one zero. ■

Example 6 Evaluate: $\begin{vmatrix} -7 & 8 & 2 \\ 3 & -4 & 0 \\ -2 & 9 & 0 \end{vmatrix}$.

If we evaluate by the third column, we will have two of the determinants multiplied by zero. The sign array of the third column is

$$\begin{array}{c} + \\ - \\ + \end{array}$$

Expanding by the third column gives

$$+2\begin{vmatrix} 3 & -4 \\ -2 & 9 \end{vmatrix} - 0\begin{vmatrix} -7 & 8 \\ -2 & 9 \end{vmatrix} + 0\begin{vmatrix} -7 & 8 \\ 3 & -4 \end{vmatrix}$$

Thus,

$$2\begin{vmatrix} 3 & -4 \\ -2 & 9 \end{vmatrix} = 2[(3)(9) - (-2)(-4)] = 2[27 - (+8)] = 2(19) = 38 \quad ■$$

TEACHING TIP After discussing example 6, ask students to evaluate the following determinant by selecting the most efficient row or column for evaluation.

$$\begin{vmatrix} 1 & 2 & -3 \\ 4 & -5 & 6 \\ 0 & 0 & -2 \end{vmatrix}$$

(Answer: Evaluate by the third row to obtain 26.)

Practice Problem 6 Evaluate the determinant $\begin{vmatrix} 3 & 6 & -2 \\ -4 & 0 & -1 \\ 5 & 0 & 8 \end{vmatrix}$. ∎

EXERCISES 3.4

Evaluate determinant.

1. $\begin{vmatrix} 5 & 6 \\ 2 & 1 \end{vmatrix}$
$5 - 12 = -7$

2. $\begin{vmatrix} 3 & 4 \\ 1 & 8 \end{vmatrix}$
$24 - 4 = 20$

3. $\begin{vmatrix} 2 & -1 \\ 3 & 6 \end{vmatrix}$
$12 + 3 = 15$

4. $\begin{vmatrix} -4 & 2 \\ 1 & 5 \end{vmatrix}$
$-20 - 2 = -22$

5. $\begin{vmatrix} -\dfrac{3}{2} & -\dfrac{1}{4} \\ 1 & 8 \end{vmatrix}$
$-12 + \dfrac{1}{4} = \dfrac{-47}{4}$

6. $\begin{vmatrix} 5 & 3 \\ -\dfrac{2}{5} & \dfrac{7}{10} \end{vmatrix}$
$-\dfrac{35}{10} + \dfrac{6}{5} = -\dfrac{23}{10}$

7. $\begin{vmatrix} -5 & 3 \\ -4 & -7 \end{vmatrix}$
$35 + 12 = 47$

8. $\begin{vmatrix} 2 & -3 \\ -4 & -6 \end{vmatrix}$
$-12 - 12 = -24$

9. $\begin{vmatrix} 0 & -6 \\ 3 & -4 \end{vmatrix}$
$0 + 18 = 18$

10. $\begin{vmatrix} -5 & 0 \\ 2 & -7 \end{vmatrix}$
$35 - 0 = 35$

11. $\begin{vmatrix} 2 & -5 \\ -4 & 10 \end{vmatrix}$
$20 - 20 = 0$

12. $\begin{vmatrix} -3 & 6 \\ 7 & -14 \end{vmatrix}$
$42 - 42 = 0$

13. $\begin{vmatrix} 0 & 0 \\ -2 & 6 \end{vmatrix}$
$0 - 0 = 0$

14. $\begin{vmatrix} -4 & 0 \\ -3 & 0 \end{vmatrix}$
$0 - 0 = 0$

15. $\begin{vmatrix} 0.3 & 0.6 \\ 1.2 & 0.4 \end{vmatrix}$
$0.12 - 0.72 = -0.6$

16. $\begin{vmatrix} 0.1 & 0.7 \\ 0.5 & 0.8 \end{vmatrix}$
$0.08 - 0.35 = -0.27$

17. $\begin{vmatrix} 2 & 3 & 1 \\ -3 & 1 & 0 \\ 2 & 1 & 4 \end{vmatrix}$
$2\begin{vmatrix} 1 & 0 \\ 1 & 4 \end{vmatrix} + 3\begin{vmatrix} 3 & 1 \\ 1 & 4 \end{vmatrix} + 2\begin{vmatrix} 3 & 1 \\ 1 & 0 \end{vmatrix}$
$2(4) + 3(11) + 2(-1) = 39$

18. $\begin{vmatrix} -4 & 0 & -1 \\ 2 & 1 & -1 \\ 0 & 3 & 2 \end{vmatrix}$
$-4\begin{vmatrix} 1 & -1 \\ 3 & 2 \end{vmatrix} - 2\begin{vmatrix} 0 & -1 \\ 3 & 2 \end{vmatrix} + 0\begin{vmatrix} 0 & -1 \\ 1 & -1 \end{vmatrix}$
$-4(5) - 2(3) = -26$

19. $\begin{vmatrix} 3 & -4 & -1 \\ -2 & 1 & 3 \\ 0 & 1 & 4 \end{vmatrix}$
$3\begin{vmatrix} 1 & 3 \\ 1 & 4 \end{vmatrix} + 2\begin{vmatrix} -4 & -1 \\ 1 & 4 \end{vmatrix} + 0\begin{vmatrix} -4 & -1 \\ 1 & 3 \end{vmatrix}$
$3(1) + 2(-15) = -27$

20. $\begin{vmatrix} 6 & 1 & -1 \\ 2 & -1 & 2 \\ 3 & 0 & -2 \end{vmatrix}$

$6 \begin{vmatrix} -1 & 2 \\ 0 & -2 \end{vmatrix} - 2 \begin{vmatrix} 1 & -1 \\ 0 & -2 \end{vmatrix} + 3 \begin{vmatrix} 1 & -1 \\ -1 & 2 \end{vmatrix}$

$6(2) - 2(-2) + 3(1) = 19$

21. $\begin{vmatrix} 1 & 2 & 3 \\ 4 & -2 & -1 \\ 5 & -3 & 2 \end{vmatrix}$

$1 \begin{vmatrix} -2 & -1 \\ -3 & 2 \end{vmatrix} - 4 \begin{vmatrix} 2 & 3 \\ -3 & 2 \end{vmatrix} + 5 \begin{vmatrix} 2 & 3 \\ -2 & -1 \end{vmatrix}$

$1(-7) - 4(13) + 5(4) = -39$

22. $\begin{vmatrix} 4 & 1 & 2 \\ -1 & -2 & -3 \\ 4 & -1 & 3 \end{vmatrix}$

$4 \begin{vmatrix} -2 & -3 \\ -1 & 3 \end{vmatrix} + 1 \begin{vmatrix} 1 & 2 \\ -1 & 3 \end{vmatrix} + 4 \begin{vmatrix} 1 & 2 \\ -2 & -3 \end{vmatrix}$

$4(-9) + 1(5) + 4(1) = -27$

23. $\begin{vmatrix} 1 & 2 & -1 \\ 0 & 0 & 6 \\ 3 & 4 & 1 \end{vmatrix}$

$0 \begin{vmatrix} 2 & -1 \\ 4 & 1 \end{vmatrix} + 0 \begin{vmatrix} 1 & -1 \\ 3 & 1 \end{vmatrix} + (-6) \begin{vmatrix} 1 & 2 \\ 3 & 4 \end{vmatrix}$

$= 0 + 0 + (-6)(-2) = 12$

24. $\begin{vmatrix} 2 & 0 & -2 \\ -1 & 0 & 2 \\ 3 & 4 & 3 \end{vmatrix}$

$0 \begin{vmatrix} -1 & 2 \\ 3 & 3 \end{vmatrix} + 0 \begin{vmatrix} 2 & -2 \\ 3 & 3 \end{vmatrix} + (-4) \begin{vmatrix} 2 & -2 \\ -1 & 2 \end{vmatrix}$

$= 0 + 0 + (-4)(2) = -8$

25. $\begin{vmatrix} 7 & 0 & 2 \\ 1 & 0 & -5 \\ 3 & 0 & 6 \end{vmatrix}$

$7 \begin{vmatrix} 0 & -5 \\ 0 & 6 \end{vmatrix} - 1 \begin{vmatrix} 0 & 2 \\ 0 & 6 \end{vmatrix} + 3 \begin{vmatrix} 0 & 2 \\ 0 & -5 \end{vmatrix}$

$7(0) - 1(0) + 3(0) = 0$

26. $\begin{vmatrix} 6 & -4 & 3 \\ 1 & 2 & 4 \\ 0 & 0 & 0 \end{vmatrix}$

$6 \begin{vmatrix} 2 & 4 \\ 0 & 0 \end{vmatrix} - 1 \begin{vmatrix} -4 & 3 \\ 0 & 0 \end{vmatrix} + 0 \begin{vmatrix} -4 & 3 \\ 2 & 4 \end{vmatrix}$

$6(0) - 1(0) + 0 = 0$

Solve for x in each equation, where x represents a real number. (Hint: Find the determinant and solve the resulting equation.)

27. $\begin{vmatrix} x & 3 \\ 2 & -4 \end{vmatrix} = 5$

$-4x - 6 = 5$

$x = -\dfrac{11}{4}$

28. $\begin{vmatrix} -2 & x \\ 1 & 3 \end{vmatrix} = 2$

$-6 - x = 2$

$-8 = x$

29. $\begin{vmatrix} 2x & 3x \\ 1 & 2 \end{vmatrix} = -7$

$4x - 3x = -7$

$x = -7$

30. $\begin{vmatrix} -3 & 1 \\ 4x & x \end{vmatrix} = -21$

$-3x - 4x = -21$

$x = 3$

31. $\begin{vmatrix} x+2 & 3x-1 \\ -2 & 4 \end{vmatrix} = 2$

$4(x+2) + 2(3x-1) = 2$

$10x + 6 = 2$

$x = -\dfrac{2}{5}$

32. $\begin{vmatrix} -3 & 4 \\ x-1 & 2x+1 \end{vmatrix} = -3$

$-3(2x+1) - 4(x-1) = -3$

$x = \dfrac{2}{5}$

? **To Think About**

The area A of a triangle whose vertices are in counterclockwise order (x_1, y_1), (x_2, y_2), and (x_3, y_3) can be found from the formula

$$A = \frac{1}{2} \begin{vmatrix} x_1 & y_1 & 1 \\ x_2 & y_2 & 1 \\ x_3 & y_3 & 1 \end{vmatrix}$$

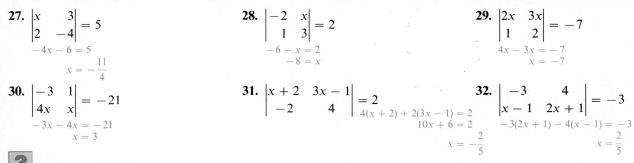

Find the area of each triangle, with the vertices as given (in counterclockwise order).

33. $(1, 1)$, $(3, 2)$, and $(1, 7)$

$A = \dfrac{1}{2} \begin{vmatrix} 1 & 1 & 1 \\ 3 & 2 & 1 \\ 1 & 7 & 1 \end{vmatrix}$

$A = \dfrac{1}{2} \left[1 \begin{vmatrix} 2 & 1 \\ 7 & 1 \end{vmatrix} - 3 \begin{vmatrix} 1 & 1 \\ 7 & 1 \end{vmatrix} + 1 \begin{vmatrix} 1 & 1 \\ 2 & 1 \end{vmatrix} \right]$

$A = \dfrac{1}{2} \left[1(-5) - 3(-6) + 1(-1) \right]$

$A = \dfrac{1}{2} [12] = 6$

34. $(2, 1)$, $(4, 3)$, and $(1, 6)$

$A = \dfrac{1}{2} \begin{vmatrix} 2 & 1 & 1 \\ 4 & 3 & 1 \\ 1 & 6 & 1 \end{vmatrix}$

$A = \dfrac{1}{2} \left[2 \begin{vmatrix} 3 & 1 \\ 6 & 1 \end{vmatrix} - 4 \begin{vmatrix} 1 & 1 \\ 6 & 1 \end{vmatrix} + 1 \begin{vmatrix} 1 & 1 \\ 3 & 1 \end{vmatrix} \right]$

$A = \dfrac{1}{2} \left[2(-3) - 4(-5) + 1(-2) \right]$

$A = \dfrac{1}{2} (12) = 6$

35. $(-4, -4), (2, -1),$ and $(-2, 3)$

$$A = \frac{1}{2} \begin{vmatrix} -4 & -4 & 1 \\ 2 & -1 & 1 \\ -2 & 3 & 1 \end{vmatrix}$$

$$A = \frac{1}{2} \left[-4 \begin{vmatrix} -1 & 1 \\ 3 & 1 \end{vmatrix} - 2 \begin{vmatrix} -4 & 1 \\ 3 & 1 \end{vmatrix} - 2 \begin{vmatrix} -4 & 1 \\ -1 & 1 \end{vmatrix} \right]$$

$$A = \frac{1}{2} \left[-4(-4) - 2(-7) - 2(-3) \right]$$

$$A = \frac{1}{2} (36) = 18$$

36. $(-1, -1), (3, -6),$ and $(5, 2)$

$$A = \frac{1}{2} \begin{vmatrix} -1 & -1 & 1 \\ 3 & -6 & 1 \\ 5 & 2 & 1 \end{vmatrix}$$

$$= \frac{1}{2} \left[-1 \begin{vmatrix} -6 & 1 \\ 2 & 1 \end{vmatrix} - 3 \begin{vmatrix} -1 & 1 \\ 2 & 1 \end{vmatrix} + 5 \begin{vmatrix} -1 & 1 \\ -6 & 1 \end{vmatrix} \right]$$

$$= \frac{1}{2} \left[-1(-8) - 3(-3) + 5(5) \right] = \frac{1}{2} (42) = 21$$

The sign array for a 4 × 4 determinant is

$$\begin{array}{cccc} + & - & + & - \\ - & + & - & + \\ + & - & + & - \\ - & + & - & + \end{array}$$

We can evaluate all determinants of order 4 by the method of expansion by minors, using this sign array. The expansion has four numbers (the elements of a row or column), each multiplied by a third-order determinant. The appropriate sign must be in front of the four numbers. Expand by a row or column with at least one zero when possible. Evaluate the determinant.

37.
$$\begin{vmatrix} 1 & 3 & 2 & 4 \\ -2 & 1 & 0 & 3 \\ 3 & 0 & 1 & 6 \\ 5 & 2 & 0 & 0 \end{vmatrix}$$

$$1 \begin{vmatrix} 1 & 0 & 3 \\ 0 & 1 & 6 \\ 2 & 0 & 0 \end{vmatrix} + 2 \begin{vmatrix} 3 & 2 & 4 \\ 0 & 1 & 6 \\ 2 & 0 & 0 \end{vmatrix} + 3 \begin{vmatrix} 3 & 2 & 4 \\ 1 & 0 & 3 \\ 2 & 0 & 0 \end{vmatrix} - 5 \begin{vmatrix} 3 & 2 & 4 \\ 1 & 0 & 3 \\ 0 & 1 & 6 \end{vmatrix}$$

$$= 1[0 - 0 - 6] + 2[0 - 0 + 16] + 3[0 - 0 + 12] - 5[-9 - 8 + 0]$$
$$= -6 + 32 + 36 + 85 = 147$$

38.
$$\begin{vmatrix} -3 & -2 & 1 & 0 \\ 2 & 1 & -1 & 0 \\ 3 & 4 & 2 & 1 \\ 2 & -1 & 1 & 2 \end{vmatrix}$$

$$-3 \begin{vmatrix} 1 & -1 & 0 \\ 4 & 2 & 1 \\ -1 & 1 & 2 \end{vmatrix} - 2 \begin{vmatrix} -2 & 1 & 0 \\ 4 & 2 & 1 \\ -1 & 1 & 2 \end{vmatrix} + 3 \begin{vmatrix} -2 & 1 & 0 \\ 1 & -1 & 0 \\ -1 & 1 & 2 \end{vmatrix} - 2 \begin{vmatrix} -2 & 1 & 0 \\ 1 & -1 & 0 \\ 4 & 2 & 1 \end{vmatrix}$$

$$= -3[3 + 8 + 1] - 2[-6 - 8 - 1] + 3[4 - 2 - 0] - 2[2 - 1 + 0]$$
$$= -3(12) - 2(-15) + 3(2) - 2(1) = -2$$

Cumulative Review Problems

Simplify.

39. $5x^2(2x - 3) - 5x(7x^2 - x)$

$10x^3 - 15x^2 - 35x^3 + 5x^2 = -25x^3 - 10x^2$

40. $\dfrac{1}{2}a - 3y + 5z - \dfrac{1}{3}a + 5y - 2z$

$\dfrac{1}{6}a + 2y + 3z$

41. $(3x^2y^3)(-2x^{-1}y^3)(4x^{-2}yz^2)$

$-24x^{-1}y^7z^2 = \dfrac{-24y^7z^2}{x}$

42. $\dfrac{(4x^{-3}y^2)^3}{(3x^2y)^4}$

$\dfrac{64x^{-9}y^6}{81x^8y^4} = \dfrac{64}{81}x^{-17}y^2$ or $\dfrac{64y^2}{81x^{17}}$

Calculator Problems

Evaluate. Round your answer to four decimal places.

43.
$$\begin{vmatrix} 92.6367 & 23.1273 \\ -15.1526 & 81.3052 \end{vmatrix}$$

7882.2841

44.
$$\begin{vmatrix} 2 & 3 & -2 \\ 1.926 & 3.841 & -1.762 \\ 7.079 & 5.924 & 5.251 \end{vmatrix}$$

25.0161

For Extra Practice Exercises, turn to page 175.

1. (a) $\begin{vmatrix} 2 & -5 \\ 3 & 1 \end{vmatrix} = (2)(1) - (3)(-5) = 2 - (-15) = 2 + 15 = 17$

(b) $\begin{vmatrix} -6 & -4 \\ -5 & 2 \end{vmatrix} = (-6)(2) - (-5)(-4) = -12 - (+20) = -12 - 20 = -32$

3. In the determinant $\begin{vmatrix} 1 & 2 & 7 \\ -4 & -5 & -6 \\ 3 & 4 & -9 \end{vmatrix}$ **(a)** The minor of 3 by deleting the 3 row and 3 column $\begin{vmatrix} 1 & 2 & 7 \\ -4 & -5 & -6 \\ 3 & 4 & -9 \end{vmatrix}$ is $\begin{vmatrix} 2 & 7 \\ -5 & -6 \end{vmatrix}$

(b) The minor of -6 by deleting the -6 row and -6 column $\begin{vmatrix} 1 & 2 & 7 \\ -4 & -5 & -6 \\ 3 & 4 & -9 \end{vmatrix}$ is $\begin{vmatrix} 1 & 2 \\ 3 & 4 \end{vmatrix}$

5. We expand by minors about the second row, noting that the signs from the array are

$$\begin{array}{ccc} + & - & + \\ - & + & - \\ + & - & + \end{array}$$

$$\begin{vmatrix} 5 & 2 & 1 \\ 3 & 0 & -2 \\ -4 & -1 & 2 \end{vmatrix} = -3 \begin{vmatrix} 2 & 1 \\ -1 & 2 \end{vmatrix} + 0 \begin{vmatrix} 5 & 1 \\ -4 & 2 \end{vmatrix} - (-2) \begin{vmatrix} 5 & 2 \\ -4 & -1 \end{vmatrix}$$

$$= -3[(2)(2) - (-1)(1)] + 0 + 2[(5)(-1) - (-4)(2)]$$
$$= -3[4 - (-1)] + 2[-5 - (-8)]$$
$$= -3(5) + 2(3) = -15 + 6 = -9$$

2. (a) 26 **(b)** -25 **4.** -25 **6.** 162

3.5 CRAMER'S RULE (OPTIONAL)

☐ After studying this section, you will be able to:

① Linear Systems with Two Equations

We can solve a linear system of two equations with two unknowns by Cramer's rule. The rule is named for Gabriel Cramer, a Swiss mathematician who lived from 1704 to 1752. Cramer's rule expresses the solution for each variable of a linear system as the quotient of two determinants. Computer programs are available to solve a system of equations by Cramer's Rule.

① *Solve a system of two linear equations with two unknowns by using Cramer's rule*

② *Solve a system of three linear equations with three unknowns by using Cramer's rule*

Cramer's Rule

The solution to

$$ax + by = c$$
$$dx + ey = f$$

is

$$x = \frac{D_x}{D} \quad \text{and} \quad y = \frac{D_y}{D} \quad (D \neq 0)$$

where

$$D_x = \begin{vmatrix} c & b \\ f & e \end{vmatrix} \qquad D_y = \begin{vmatrix} a & c \\ d & f \end{vmatrix} \qquad D = \begin{vmatrix} a & b \\ d & e \end{vmatrix}$$

Cramer's rule may look complicated, but it soon becomes easy. Notice that D is just the determinant of coefficients of the variables.

Example 1 Solve by Cramer's rule:

$$-x + 2y = 9$$
$$5x + 3y = 7$$

The determinant of coefficients is

$$D = \begin{vmatrix} -1 & 2 \\ 5 & 3 \end{vmatrix} \qquad \begin{aligned} -x + 2y &= 9 \\ 5x + 3y &= 7 \end{aligned}$$
$$= (-1)(3) - (5)(2)$$
$$= -3 - 10$$
$$= -13$$

For the determinant of the x variable, just replace the x coefficients by the values on the right side of the equals sign, and use the coefficients of y.

$$D_x = \begin{vmatrix} 9 & 2 \\ 7 & 3 \end{vmatrix} \qquad \begin{aligned} -x + 2y &= 9 \\ 5x + 3y &= 7 \end{aligned}$$

$$= (9)(3) - (7)(2)$$
$$= 27 - 14$$
$$= 13$$

Likewise, for D_y, replace the y coefficients by the right-side values.

$$D_y = \begin{vmatrix} -1 & 9 \\ 5 & 7 \end{vmatrix} \qquad \begin{aligned} -x + 2y &= 9 \\ 5x + 3y &= 7 \end{aligned}$$

$$= (-1)(7) - (5)(9)$$
$$= -7 - 45$$
$$= -52$$

According to Cramer's rule,

$$x = \frac{D_x}{D} = \frac{13}{-13} = -1$$

$$y = \frac{D_y}{D} = \frac{-52}{-13} = 4$$

Thus, the solution is $x = -1$ and $y = 4$. You should check the validity of this solution. ∎

Practice Problem 1 Find the solution to the system by Cramer's rule:

$$-2x + y = 8$$
$$3x + 4y = -1 \qquad ∎$$

Example 2 Solve by Cramer's rule:

$$-3x + y = 7$$
$$-4x - 3y = 5$$

$$D = \begin{vmatrix} -3 & 1 \\ -4 & -3 \end{vmatrix}$$

$$D_x = \begin{vmatrix} 7 & 1 \\ 5 & -3 \end{vmatrix}$$

$$D_y = \begin{vmatrix} -3 & 7 \\ -4 & 5 \end{vmatrix}$$

$$= (-3)(-3) - (-4)(1)$$
$$= (7)(-3) - (5)(1)$$
$$= (-3)(5) - (-4)(7)$$

$$= 9 - (-4)$$
$$= -21 - 5$$
$$= -15 - (-28)$$

$$= 9 + 4$$
$$= -26$$
$$= -15 + 28$$

$$= 13$$
$$= 13$$

Hence,

$$x = \frac{Dx}{D} = \frac{-26}{13} = -2$$

$$y = \frac{Dy}{D} = \frac{13}{13} = 1$$

The solution to the system is $x = -2$ and $y = 1$. Verify this. ■

Practice Problem 2 Solve by Cramer's rule:

$$5x + 3y = 17$$
$$2x - 5y = 13$$

If the system of equations is inconsistent or dependent, you cannot use Cramer's rule because the determinant of coefficients will be zero, and division by zero is not defined. ■

Linear Systems with Three Equations

It is quite easy to extend Cramer's rule to three linear equations.

2

Cramer's Rule

The solution to the system

$$a_1 x + b_1 y + c_1 z = d_1$$
$$a_2 x + b_2 y + c_2 z = d_2$$
$$a_3 x + b_3 y + c_3 z = d_3$$

is

$$x = \frac{D_x}{D} \qquad y = \frac{D_y}{D} \qquad z = \frac{D_z}{D} \qquad (D \neq 0)$$

where

$$D = \begin{vmatrix} a_1 & b_1 & c_1 \\ a_2 & b_2 & c_2 \\ a_3 & b_3 & c_3 \end{vmatrix} \qquad D_x = \begin{vmatrix} d_1 & b_1 & c_1 \\ d_2 & b_2 & c_2 \\ d_3 & b_3 & c_3 \end{vmatrix}$$

$$D_y = \begin{vmatrix} a_1 & d_1 & c_1 \\ a_2 & d_2 & c_2 \\ a_3 & d_3 & c_3 \end{vmatrix} \qquad D_z = \begin{vmatrix} a_1 & b_1 & d_1 \\ a_2 & b_2 & d_2 \\ a_3 & b_3 & d_3 \end{vmatrix}$$

TEACHING TIP After discussing example 2 or a similar example, have students solve the following system by Cramer's Rule:

$$3x + 4y = -6$$
$$2x - y = 7$$

The answer is $x = 2$, $y = -3$

$$D_x = \begin{vmatrix} -6 & 4 \\ 7 & -1 \end{vmatrix} = -22$$

$$D_y = \begin{vmatrix} 3 & -6 \\ 2 & 7 \end{vmatrix} = 33$$

$$D = \begin{vmatrix} 3 & 4 \\ 2 & -1 \end{vmatrix} = -11$$

TEACHING TIP You may want to point out to students that although you cannot find a solution by Cramer's Rule if $D = 0$, you can at least determine if the equations are dependent or if the system of equations is inconsistent. If $D = 0$ but D_x and D_y are not 0, then the system of equations is inconsistent. In such a case there is no solution to the system. If $D = 0$ and also $D_x = 0$ and $D_y = 0$, then the equations are dependent and there are an infinite number of solutions to the system.

Example 3 Use Cramer's rule to solve the system

$$2x - y + z = 6$$
$$3x + 2y - z = 5$$
$$2x + 3y - 2z = 1$$

For consistency we expand all determinants by the third row. (We could use any row or column.)

$$D = \begin{vmatrix} 2 & -1 & 1 \\ 3 & 2 & -1 \\ 2 & 3 & -2 \end{vmatrix} = 2\begin{vmatrix} -1 & 1 \\ 2 & -1 \end{vmatrix} - 3\begin{vmatrix} 2 & 1 \\ 3 & -1 \end{vmatrix} - 2\begin{vmatrix} 2 & -1 \\ 3 & 2 \end{vmatrix}$$

$$= -2 + 15 - 14 = -1$$

$$D_x = \begin{vmatrix} 6 & -1 & 1 \\ 5 & 2 & -1 \\ 1 & 3 & -2 \end{vmatrix} = 1\begin{vmatrix} -1 & 1 \\ 2 & -1 \end{vmatrix} - 3\begin{vmatrix} 6 & 1 \\ 5 & -1 \end{vmatrix} - 2\begin{vmatrix} 6 & -1 \\ 5 & 2 \end{vmatrix}$$

$$= -1 + 33 - 34 = -2$$

$$D_y = \begin{vmatrix} 2 & 6 & 1 \\ 3 & 5 & -1 \\ 2 & 1 & -2 \end{vmatrix} = 2\begin{vmatrix} 6 & 1 \\ 5 & -1 \end{vmatrix} - 1\begin{vmatrix} 2 & 1 \\ 3 & -1 \end{vmatrix} - 2\begin{vmatrix} 2 & 6 \\ 3 & 5 \end{vmatrix}$$

$$= -22 + 5 + 16 = -1$$

$$D_z = \begin{vmatrix} 2 & -1 & 6 \\ 3 & 2 & 5 \\ 2 & 3 & 1 \end{vmatrix} = 2\begin{vmatrix} -1 & 6 \\ 2 & 5 \end{vmatrix} - 3\begin{vmatrix} 2 & 6 \\ 3 & 5 \end{vmatrix} + 1\begin{vmatrix} 2 & -1 \\ 3 & 2 \end{vmatrix}$$

$$= -34 + 24 + 7 = -3$$

$$x = \frac{D_x}{D} = \frac{-2}{-1} = 2$$

$$y = \frac{D_y}{D} = \frac{-1}{-1} = 1$$

$$z = \frac{D_z}{D} = \frac{-3}{-1} = 3$$

Check: Verify this solution. ■

Practice Problem 3 Find the solution to the system by Cramer's rule:

$$2x + 3y - z = -1$$
$$3x + 5y - 2z = -3$$
$$x + 2y + 3z = 2$$

Cramer's rule is quite effective when we want the value of only one variable. ■

Example 4 Use Cramer's rule to find the value of y in the system

$$3x - y + 2z = 2$$
$$x + 4z = -1$$
$$3x - 2y = -1$$

First we write the system in the complete form, showing coefficients of 0.

$$3x - y + 2z = 2$$
$$x + 0y + 4z = -1$$
$$3x - 2y + 0z = -1$$

$$D = \begin{vmatrix} 3 & -1 & 2 \\ 1 & 0 & 4 \\ 3 & -2 & 0 \end{vmatrix} = 8$$

$$D_y = \begin{vmatrix} 3 & 2 & 2 \\ 1 & -1 & 4 \\ 3 & -1 & 0 \end{vmatrix} = 40$$

Thus,

$$y = \frac{D_y}{D} = \frac{40}{8} = 5 \quad \blacksquare$$

Practice Problem 4 Use Cramer's rule to find the value of x in the system

$$2x - 3y + 2z = -1$$
$$x + 2y \qquad = 14$$
$$-x \qquad + 3z = 5 \quad \blacksquare$$

TEACHING TIP Solving a system of equations for x, y, z by Cramer's Rule is usually a long and tedious job for most students. However, Cramer's Rule is the only method that allows you to find the value of one variable in a system without having to find the values of the other variables. Here is an additional example: Have the students find z only in the system

$$x + 2y - z = 4$$
$$2x - y + z = 0$$
$$x + y + z = 2$$

$\left(\text{Answer: } Dz = -2, D = 7,\right.$

$\left.\text{Therefore } z = \dfrac{-2}{7}.\right)$

Cases Where There Is No Unique Solution

If we try to solve a system of equations that is dependent or inconsistent, we will not obtain a unique solution, because $D = 0$. If the equations we are solving are dependent, then $D_x = 0$, $D_y = 0$, and $D_z = 0$ as well. If the system is inconsistent at least one of D_x, D_y, or D_z is nonzero.

EXERCISES 3.5

Solve each system by Cramer's rule, if possible. If there is no single solution, state the reason.

1. $x + 2y = 8$
$2x + y = 7$

$D = \begin{vmatrix} 1 & 2 \\ 2 & 1 \end{vmatrix} = 1 - 4 = -3$

$D_x = \begin{vmatrix} 8 & 2 \\ 7 & 1 \end{vmatrix} = 8 - 14 = -6$

$D_y = \begin{vmatrix} 1 & 8 \\ 2 & 7 \end{vmatrix} = 7 - 16 = -9$

$x = 2, y = 3$

2. $x + 3y = 6$
$2x + y = 7$

$D = \begin{vmatrix} 1 & 3 \\ 2 & 1 \end{vmatrix} = 1 - 6 = -5$

$D_x = \begin{vmatrix} 6 & 3 \\ 7 & 1 \end{vmatrix} = 6 - 21 = -15$

$D_y = \begin{vmatrix} 1 & 6 \\ 2 & 7 \end{vmatrix} = 7 - 12 = -5$

$x = 3, y = 1$

3. $3x + 5y = 11$
$2x + y = -2$

$D = \begin{vmatrix} 3 & 5 \\ 2 & 1 \end{vmatrix} = 3 - 10 = -7$

$D_x = \begin{vmatrix} 11 & 5 \\ -2 & 1 \end{vmatrix} = 11 + 10 = 21$

$D_y = \begin{vmatrix} 3 & 11 \\ 2 & -2 \end{vmatrix} = -6 - 22 = -28$

$x = -3, y = 4$

4. $5x + 4y = 10$
$-x + 2y = 12$

$D = \begin{vmatrix} 5 & 4 \\ -1 & 2 \end{vmatrix} = 10 + 4 = 14$

$D_x = \begin{vmatrix} 10 & 4 \\ 12 & 2 \end{vmatrix} = 20 - 48 = -28$

$D_y = \begin{vmatrix} 5 & 10 \\ -1 & 12 \end{vmatrix} = 60 + 10 = 70$

$x = -2, y = 5$

5. $x - 3y = 4$
$-3x + 4y = -12$

$D = \begin{vmatrix} 1 & -3 \\ -3 & 4 \end{vmatrix} = 4 - 9 = -5$

$D_x = \begin{vmatrix} 4 & -3 \\ -12 & 4 \end{vmatrix} = 16 - 36 = -20$

$D_y = \begin{vmatrix} 1 & 4 \\ -3 & -12 \end{vmatrix} = -12 + 12 = 0$

$x = 4, y = 0$

6. $x - 5y = 0$
$x + 6y = 22$

$D = \begin{vmatrix} 1 & -5 \\ 1 & 6 \end{vmatrix} = 6 + 5 = 11$

$D_x = \begin{vmatrix} 0 & -5 \\ 22 & 6 \end{vmatrix} = 0 + 110 = 110$

$D_y = \begin{vmatrix} 1 & 0 \\ 1 & 22 \end{vmatrix} = 22 - 0 = 22$

$x = 10, y = 2$

7. $4x + y = 0$
$9x + 2y = 4$

$D = \begin{vmatrix} 4 & 1 \\ 9 & 2 \end{vmatrix} = 8 - 9 = -1$

$D_x = \begin{vmatrix} 0 & 1 \\ 4 & 2 \end{vmatrix} = 0 - 4 = -4$

$D_y = \begin{vmatrix} 4 & 0 \\ 9 & 4 \end{vmatrix} = 16 - 0 = 16$

$x = 4, y = -16$

8. $-2x + 4y = 4$
$3x - 5y = -6$

$D = \begin{vmatrix} -2 & 4 \\ 3 & -5 \end{vmatrix} = 10 - 12 = -2$

$D_x = \begin{vmatrix} 4 & 4 \\ -6 & -5 \end{vmatrix} = -20 + 24 = 4$

$D_y = \begin{vmatrix} -2 & 4 \\ 3 & -6 \end{vmatrix} = 12 - 12 = 0$

$x = -2, y = 0$

9. $3x - 5y = 2$
$6x - 11y = 5$

$D = \begin{vmatrix} 3 & -5 \\ 6 & -11 \end{vmatrix} = -33 + 30 = -3$

$D_x = \begin{vmatrix} 2 & -5 \\ 5 & -11 \end{vmatrix} = -22 + 25 = 3$

$D_y = \begin{vmatrix} 3 & 2 \\ 6 & 5 \end{vmatrix} = 15 - 12 = 3$

$x = -1, y = -1$

10. $-x - 3y = -14$
$5x - 2y = 2$

$D = \begin{vmatrix} -1 & -3 \\ 5 & -2 \end{vmatrix} = 2 + 15 = 17$

$D_x = \begin{vmatrix} -14 & -3 \\ 2 & -2 \end{vmatrix} = 28 + 6 = 34$

$D_y = \begin{vmatrix} -1 & -14 \\ 5 & 2 \end{vmatrix} = -2 + 70 = 68$

$x = 2, y = 4$

11. $0.3x + 0.5y = 0.2$
$0.1x + 0.2y = 0.0$

$D = \begin{vmatrix} 0.3 & 0.5 \\ 0.1 & 0.2 \end{vmatrix} = 0.06 - 0.05 = 0.01$

$D_x = \begin{vmatrix} 0.2 & 0.5 \\ 0 & 0.2 \end{vmatrix} = 0.04 - 0 = 0.04$

$D_y = \begin{vmatrix} 0.3 & 0.2 \\ 0.1 & 0 \end{vmatrix} = 0 - 0.02 = -0.02$

$x = 4, y = -2$

12. $2x - 7y = 7$
$-4x + 14y = 3$

$D = \begin{vmatrix} 2 & -7 \\ -4 & 14 \end{vmatrix} = 28 - 28 = 0$

$D_x = \begin{vmatrix} 7 & -7 \\ 3 & 14 \end{vmatrix} = 98 + 21 = 119$

$D_y = \begin{vmatrix} 2 & 7 \\ -4 & 3 \end{vmatrix} = 6 + 28 = 34$

$x = \dfrac{119}{0}, y = \dfrac{34}{0}$

No sol.; inconsistent
system of eqs.

13. $-16x - 14y = 8$
$8x + 7y = -4$

$D = \begin{vmatrix} -16 & -14 \\ 8 & 7 \end{vmatrix} = -112 + 112 = 0$

$D_x = \begin{vmatrix} 8 & -14 \\ -4 & 7 \end{vmatrix} = 56 - 56 = 0$

$D_y = \begin{vmatrix} -16 & 8 \\ 8 & -4 \end{vmatrix} = 64 - 64 = 0$

$x = \dfrac{0}{0}, y = \dfrac{0}{0}$

Infinite number of solutions–dependent
eqs.

14. $0.3x - 0.1y = 0.2$
$0.6x - 0.2y = 0.4$

$D = \begin{vmatrix} 0.3 & -0.1 \\ 0.6 & -0.2 \end{vmatrix} = -0.06 + 0.06 = 0$

$D_x = \begin{vmatrix} 0.2 & -0.1 \\ 0.4 & -0.2 \end{vmatrix} = -0.04 + 0.04 = 0$

$D_y = \begin{vmatrix} 0.3 & 0.2 \\ 0.6 & 0.4 \end{vmatrix} = 0.12 - 0.12 = 0$

$x = \dfrac{0}{0}, y = \dfrac{0}{0}$

Infinite number of solutions–dependent
eqs.

Put each system of equations in the proper form and solve by Cramer's rule.

15. $3(x + 1) = 4 - y$
$5 + 2(y - 1) = 3 + x$

$3x + y = 1$
$x - 2y = 0$

$D = \begin{vmatrix} 3 & 1 \\ 1 & -2 \end{vmatrix} = -6 - 1 = -7$

$D_x = \begin{vmatrix} 1 & 1 \\ 0 & -2 \end{vmatrix} = -2 - 0 = -2$

$D_y = \begin{vmatrix} 3 & 1 \\ 1 & 0 \end{vmatrix} = 0 - 1 = -1$

$x = \dfrac{2}{7}, y = \dfrac{1}{7}$

16. $1 + 2(x + 3) + y = 13$
$x - y + 3(y + 1) = -6$

$2x + y = 6$
$x + 2y = -9$

$D = \begin{vmatrix} 2 & 1 \\ 1 & 2 \end{vmatrix} = 4 - 1 = 3$

$D_x = \begin{vmatrix} 6 & 1 \\ -9 & 2 \end{vmatrix} = 12 + 9 = 21$

$D_y = \begin{vmatrix} 2 & 6 \\ 1 & -9 \end{vmatrix} = -18 - 6 = -24$

$x = 7, y = -8$

17. $x - \dfrac{5}{4}y = \dfrac{17}{4}$

$\dfrac{3}{10}x - \dfrac{1}{10}y = 1$

$4x - 5y = 17$
$3x - y = 10$

$D = \begin{vmatrix} 4 & -5 \\ 3 & -1 \end{vmatrix} = -4 + 15 = 11$

$D_x = \begin{vmatrix} 17 & -5 \\ 10 & -1 \end{vmatrix} = -17 + 50 = 33$

$D_y = \begin{vmatrix} 4 & 17 \\ 3 & 10 \end{vmatrix} = 40 - 51 = -11$

$x = 3, y = -1$

18. $x = -\dfrac{5}{3}y - \dfrac{2}{3}$

$\dfrac{1}{5}y - \dfrac{2}{5}x = 2$

$3x + 5y = -2$
$-2x + y = 10$

$D = \begin{vmatrix} 3 & 5 \\ -2 & 1 \end{vmatrix} = 3 + 10 = 13$

$D_x = \begin{vmatrix} -2 & 5 \\ 10 & 1 \end{vmatrix} = -2 - 50 = -52$

$D_y = \begin{vmatrix} 3 & -2 \\ -2 & 10 \end{vmatrix} = 30 - 4 = 26$

$x = -4, y = 2$

19. $\dfrac{1}{2}x + \dfrac{1}{3}y = 3$

$\dfrac{1}{8}y + \dfrac{1}{2} = \dfrac{3(x + 1)}{8} + \dfrac{1}{8}$

$3x + 2y = 18$
$-3x + y = 0$

$D = \begin{vmatrix} 3 & 2 \\ -3 & 1 \end{vmatrix} = 3 + 6 = 9$

$D_x = \begin{vmatrix} 18 & 2 \\ 0 & 1 \end{vmatrix} = 18 - 0 = 18$

$D_y = \begin{vmatrix} 3 & 18 \\ -3 & 0 \end{vmatrix} = 0 + 54 = 54$

$x = 2, y = 6$

20. $\dfrac{1}{2}x - \dfrac{3}{8}y + \dfrac{1}{8} = 1$

$2(x + 1) - \dfrac{2}{3}y = x + 4$

$4x - 3y = 7$
$3x - 2y = 6$

$D = \begin{vmatrix} 4 & -3 \\ 3 & -2 \end{vmatrix} = -8 + 9 = 1$

$D_x = \begin{vmatrix} 7 & -3 \\ 6 & -2 \end{vmatrix} = -14 + 18 = 4$

$D_y = \begin{vmatrix} 4 & 7 \\ 3 & 6 \end{vmatrix} = 24 - 21 = 3$

$x = 4, y = 3$

Solve each system by Cramer's rule.

21. $2x + y + z = 4$
$x - y - 2z = -2$
$x + y - z = 1$

$D = \begin{vmatrix} 2 & 1 & 1 \\ 1 & -1 & -2 \\ 1 & 1 & -1 \end{vmatrix} = 2(3) - (-2) + 1(-1) = 7$

$D_x = \begin{vmatrix} 4 & 1 & 1 \\ -2 & -1 & -2 \\ 1 & 1 & -1 \end{vmatrix} = 4(3) + 2(-2) + 1(-1) = 7$

$D_y = \begin{vmatrix} 2 & 4 & 1 \\ 1 & -2 & -2 \\ 1 & 1 & -1 \end{vmatrix} = 2(4) - 1(-5) + 1(-6) = 7$

$D_z = \begin{vmatrix} 2 & 1 & 4 \\ 1 & -1 & -2 \\ 1 & 1 & 1 \end{vmatrix} = 2(1) - 1(-3) + 1(2) = 7$

$x = 1, y = 1, z = 1$

22. $x + 2y - z = -4$
$x + 4y - 2z = -6$
$2x + 3y + z = 3$

$D = \begin{vmatrix} 1 & 2 & -1 \\ 1 & 4 & -2 \\ 2 & 3 & 1 \end{vmatrix} = 1(10) - 1(5) + 2(0) = 5$

$D_x = \begin{vmatrix} -4 & 2 & -1 \\ -6 & 4 & -2 \\ 3 & 3 & 1 \end{vmatrix} = -4(10) + 6(5) + 3(0) = -10$

$D_y = \begin{vmatrix} 1 & -4 & -1 \\ 1 & -6 & -2 \\ 2 & 3 & 1 \end{vmatrix} = 1(0) - 1(-1) + 2(2) = 5$

$D_z = \begin{vmatrix} 1 & 2 & -4 \\ 1 & 4 & -6 \\ 2 & 3 & 3 \end{vmatrix} = 1(30) - 1(18) + 2(4) = 20$

$x = -2, y = 1, z = 4$

23. $-3x + 2y - 4z = -3$
$x - y + z = 0$
$2x + y - z = -3$

$D = \begin{vmatrix} -3 & 2 & -4 \\ 1 & -1 & 1 \\ 2 & 1 & -1 \end{vmatrix} = -3(0) - 1(2) + 2(-2) = -6$

$D_x = \begin{vmatrix} -3 & 2 & -4 \\ 0 & -1 & 1 \\ -3 & 1 & -1 \end{vmatrix} = -3(0) + 0(24) - 3(-2) = 6$

$D_y = \begin{vmatrix} -3 & -3 & -4 \\ 1 & 0 & 1 \\ 2 & -3 & -1 \end{vmatrix} = -3(3) - 1(-9) + 2(-3) = -6$

$D_z = \begin{vmatrix} -3 & 2 & -3 \\ 1 & -1 & 0 \\ 2 & 1 & -3 \end{vmatrix} = -3(3) - 1(-3) + 2(-3) = -12$

$x = -1, y = 1, z = 2$

24. $x + y - z = 4$
$3x - 2y - z = 3$
$2x + y + z = 1$

$D = \begin{vmatrix} 1 & 1 & -1 \\ 3 & -2 & -1 \\ 2 & 1 & 1 \end{vmatrix} = 1(-1) - 3(2) + 2(-3) = -13$

$D_x = \begin{vmatrix} 4 & 1 & -1 \\ 3 & -2 & -1 \\ 1 & 1 & 1 \end{vmatrix} = 4(-1) - 3(2) + 1(-3) = -13$

$D_y = \begin{vmatrix} 1 & 4 & -1 \\ 3 & 3 & -1 \\ 2 & 1 & 1 \end{vmatrix} = 1(4) - 3(5) + 2(-1) = -13$

$D_z = \begin{vmatrix} 1 & 1 & 4 \\ 3 & -2 & 3 \\ 2 & 1 & 1 \end{vmatrix} = 1(-5) - 3(-3) + 2(11) = 26$

$x = 1, y = 1, z = -2$

25. $x + 2y + z = 1$
$3x \qquad - 4z = 8$
$3y + 5z = -1$

$D = \begin{vmatrix} 1 & 2 & 1 \\ 3 & 0 & -4 \\ 0 & 3 & 5 \end{vmatrix} = 1(12) - 3(7) + 0(-8) = -9$

$D_x = \begin{vmatrix} 1 & 2 & 1 \\ 8 & 0 & -4 \\ -1 & 3 & 5 \end{vmatrix} = 1(12) - 8(7) - 1(-8) = -36$

$D_y = \begin{vmatrix} 1 & 1 & 1 \\ 3 & 8 & -4 \\ 0 & -1 & 5 \end{vmatrix} = 1(36) - 3(6) + 0(-12) = 18$

$D_z = \begin{vmatrix} 1 & 2 & 1 \\ 3 & 0 & 8 \\ 0 & 3 & -1 \end{vmatrix} = 1(-24) - 3(-5) + 0(16) = -9$

$x = 4, y = -2, z = 1$

26. $3x + y + z = 2$
$2y + 3z = -6$
$2x - y = -1$

$D = \begin{vmatrix} 3 & 1 & 1 \\ 0 & 2 & 3 \\ 2 & -1 & 0 \end{vmatrix} = 3(0 + 3) - 0 + 2(3 - 2) = 11$

$D_x = \begin{vmatrix} 2 & 1 & 1 \\ -6 & 2 & 3 \\ -1 & -1 & 0 \end{vmatrix} = 2(3) + 6(1) - 1(1) = 11$

$D_y = \begin{vmatrix} 3 & 2 & 1 \\ 0 & -6 & 3 \\ 2 & -1 & 0 \end{vmatrix} = 3(3) + 0(1) + 2(12) = 33$

$D_z = \begin{vmatrix} 3 & 1 & 2 \\ 0 & 2 & -6 \\ 2 & -1 & -1 \end{vmatrix} = 3(-8) + 0(1) + 2(-10) = -44$

$x = 1, y = 3, z = -4$

27. $2x - y + z = -2$
$4x \quad\quad + 5z = -2$
$\quad\quad 3y + 4z = \quad 2$

$D = \begin{vmatrix} 2 & -1 & 1 \\ 4 & 0 & 5 \\ 0 & 3 & 4 \end{vmatrix} = 2(-15) - 4(-7) + 0(-5) = -2$

$D_x = \begin{vmatrix} -2 & -1 & 1 \\ -2 & 0 & 5 \\ 2 & 3 & 4 \end{vmatrix} = -2(-15) + 2(-7) + 2(-5) = 6$

$D_y = \begin{vmatrix} 2 & -2 & 1 \\ 4 & -2 & 5 \\ 0 & 2 & 4 \end{vmatrix} = 2(-18) - 4(-10) + 0(-8) = 4$

$D_z = \begin{vmatrix} 2 & -1 & -2 \\ 4 & 0 & -2 \\ 0 & 3 & 2 \end{vmatrix} = 2(6) - 4(4) + 0(2) = -4$

$x = -3, y = -2, z = 2$

28. $2x + 5y + 3z = 1$
$x + 3y \quad\quad = 8$
$\quad\quad 4y - z = 5$

$D = \begin{vmatrix} 2 & 5 & 3 \\ 1 & 3 & 0 \\ 0 & 4 & -1 \end{vmatrix} = 2(-3) - 1(-17) + 0(-9) = 11$

$D_x = \begin{vmatrix} 1 & 5 & 3 \\ 8 & 3 & 0 \\ 5 & 4 & -1 \end{vmatrix} = 1(-3) - 8(-17) + 5(-9) = 88$

$D_y = \begin{vmatrix} 2 & 1 & 3 \\ 1 & 8 & 0 \\ 0 & 5 & -1 \end{vmatrix} = 2(-8) - 1(-16) + 0(-24) = 0$

$D_z = \begin{vmatrix} 2 & 5 & 1 \\ 1 & 3 & 8 \\ 0 & 4 & 5 \end{vmatrix} = 2(-17) - 1(21) + 0(37) = -55$

$x = 8, y = 0, z = -5$

Solve only for the variable specified, using Cramer's rule.

29. Solve for z:

$x + 2y - z = 2$
$x + \quad y + z = 6$
$2x - \quad y + z = 3$

$D = \begin{vmatrix} 1 & 2 & -1 \\ 1 & 1 & 1 \\ 2 & -1 & 1 \end{vmatrix} = 1(2) - 1(1) + 2(3) = 7$

$D_z = \begin{vmatrix} 1 & 2 & 2 \\ 1 & 1 & 6 \\ 2 & -1 & 3 \end{vmatrix} = 1(9) - 1(8) + 2(10) = 21$

$z = 3$

30. Solve for z:

$2x + \quad y + \quad z = \quad 0$
$x + 2y - \quad z = -3$
$4x + \quad y + 2z = \quad 3$

$D = \begin{vmatrix} 2 & 1 & 1 \\ 1 & 2 & -1 \\ 4 & 1 & 2 \end{vmatrix} = 2(5) - 1(1) + 4(-3) = -3$

$D_z = \begin{vmatrix} 2 & 1 & 0 \\ 1 & 2 & -3 \\ 4 & 1 & 3 \end{vmatrix} = 2(9) + (-1)(3) + 4(-3) = 3$

$z = -1$

31. Solve for y:

$2x + 3y + 5z = -1$
$2x + \quad y + \quad z = \quad 5$
$\quad\quad 2y + 5z = -4$

$D = \begin{vmatrix} 2 & 3 & 5 \\ 2 & 1 & 1 \\ 0 & 2 & 5 \end{vmatrix} = 2(3) - 2(5) + 0(-2) = -4$

$D_y = \begin{vmatrix} 2 & -1 & 5 \\ 2 & 5 & 1 \\ 0 & -4 & 5 \end{vmatrix} = 2(29) - 2(15) + 0(-26) = 28$

$y = -7$

32. Solve for x:

$x + 3y + 2z = \quad 3$
$2x - 5y + \quad z = \quad 7$
$\quad\quad y + \quad z = -3$

$D = \begin{vmatrix} 1 & 3 & 2 \\ 2 & -5 & 1 \\ 0 & 1 & 1 \end{vmatrix} = 1(-6) - 2(1) + 0(13) = -8$

$D_x = \begin{vmatrix} 3 & 3 & 2 \\ 7 & -5 & 1 \\ -3 & 1 & 1 \end{vmatrix} = 3(-6) - 7(1) - 3(13) = -64$

$x = 8$

2. $D = -31$, $D_x = -124$, $D_y = 31$; $x = 4$, $y = -1$ **4.** $D = 25$, $D_x = 100$; $x = 4$

EXTRA PRACTICE: EXERCISES

Section 3.1

Find the solution to each system by the substitution method.

1. $7x - y = 18$ $x = 2$
  $-5x + y = -14$ $y = -4$

2. $3x - 5y = 17$ $x = 4$
  $x + y = 3$ $y = -1$

3. $2x + 3y = -7$ $x = -2$
  $-3x + y = 5$ $y = -1$

4. $-x + 3y = -1$ $x = 1$
  $-6x + y = -6$ $y = 0$

5. $7x - y = 19$ $x = 3$
  $2x + y = 8$ $y = 2$

6. $a - 2b = 8$ $a = 2$
  $7a + 3b = 5$ $b = -3$

7. $5x + y = 7$ $x = 2, y = -3$
  $4x + 3y = -1$

Find the solution to each system by the addition (or elimination method).

8. $2x + 3y = -1$ $x = 1$
  $3x + 5y = -2$ $y = -1$

9. $3x + 4y = 24$ $x = 4$
  $2x - 3y = -1$ $y = 3$

10. $4x - 5y = -13$ $x = -2$
  $3x + 7y = 1$ $y = 1$

11. $4x - 5y = 2$ $x = -7$
  $-5x + 6y = -1$ $y = -6$

12. $7x - 2y = 31$ $x = 3$
  $4x - 3y = 27$ $y = -5$

13. $5x - 3y = 19$ $x = 5$
  $2x - 3y = 4$ $y = 2$

14. $5x - y = 25$ $x = 5, y = 0$
  $-4x + 19y = -20$

If possible, find one solution to each system of equations. Use any method. If there is not one solution to a system, state the reason.

15. $6x - 4y = 10$
  $9x + 10y = 7$

16. $-8x + 3y = 30$
  $6x + 2y = -14$

17. $y = 6 - 4x$
  $-8x = 20 + 2y$

18. $2x = y + 3$
  $-2y = 6 - 4x$

19. $-2x + y = 5(2 - x)$
  $5y + 3x = 2(8 + y) + 5y$

20. $y = 4(y - x)$
  $5(x - y) = 9 + y$

21. $\dfrac{5}{3}x + y = 10$

  $\dfrac{3}{7}x + \dfrac{3}{7}y = \dfrac{18}{7}$

22. $\dfrac{2}{3}x + \dfrac{2}{3}y = \dfrac{5}{3}$

  $\dfrac{1}{4}x = \dfrac{3}{4} - \dfrac{1}{4}y$

23. $\dfrac{1}{4}x + y = 2$

  $\dfrac{2}{3}x = \dfrac{16}{3} - \dfrac{8}{3}y$

24. $\dfrac{5}{3}x + \dfrac{2}{3}y = -3$

  $-\dfrac{3}{4}x + \dfrac{1}{4}y = \dfrac{1}{4}$

25. $0.3a + 0.1b = -1.0$ $a = -3, b = -1$
  $-0.1a + 0.2b = 0.1$

26. $0.6a + 0.4b = 0.0$ $a = 1, b = -\dfrac{3}{2}$
  $0.5a - 0.2b = 0.8$

27. $6s + 8t = -16$ $s = 2, t = -3.5$
  $2s - 3t = 14.5$

28. $3s - 4t = 14$ $s = -6, t = -8$
  $5s + 6t = -78$

29. $2x - y = 3$ $x = 6, y = 9$

  $\dfrac{7x - 15}{3} = y$

30. $\dfrac{5}{x + 2y} = \dfrac{7}{2x + y}$ $x = 3, y = 1$

  $\dfrac{7}{3x - 2} = \dfrac{5}{6 - y}$

31. $11a - 5b = 4$ $a = -1, b = -3$
  $8a - 6b = 10$

32. $-\dfrac{x}{2} + 12 = \dfrac{y + 32}{4}$ $x = 4, y = 8$

  $\dfrac{y}{8} + \dfrac{2x - 3y}{2} = -7$

33. $3x + y = 5$ No sol.; inconsistent eqs.
  $9x = 16 - 3y$

34. $3x - y = 6$ No sol.; inconsistent eqs.
  $6x - 2y = 3$

35. $\dfrac{x}{2} - 12 = \dfrac{y + 32}{4}$ No sol.; inconsistent eqs.

  $4x - 2y = 80$

36. $2.5x - 3.2y = -9.2$ $x = 4, y = 6$
  $7.5x + 2.3y = 43.8$

15. $x = \dfrac{4}{3}, y = -\dfrac{1}{2}$

16. $x = -3, y = 2$

17. No sol.; inconsistent system of eqs.
18. Infinite number of solutions–dependent eqs.
19. $x = 4, y = -2$

20. $x = -3, y = -4$
21. $x = 6, y = 0$

22. No sol.; inconsistent system of eqs.
23. Infinite number of solutions–dependent eqs.

24. $x = -1, y = -2$

Section 3.2

Find the solution for each system.

1. $x + 2y + z = 1$
  $2x + 3y - z = 0$
  $x - 2y + 3z = 7$

2. $2x - 3y + z = 7$
  $x + y + z = 2$
  $3x + 3y - z = -2$

5. $x - y + z = 8$
  $5x + 4y - z = 7$
  $2x + y - 3z = -7$

6. $4x - 2y + z = 3$
  $9x - 3y + z = 10$
  $x + y + z = 6$

3. $3x + 2y - z = 4$
  $2x - y + 2z = 6$
  $x + y + z = 6$

4. $2x - 3y + 5z = 8$
  $x - y + 2z = 3$
  $3x + y + z = -1$

7. $2x - y + z = 7$
  $x + y - 3z = 12$
  $x + 2y = -9$

8. $3x + 4y + z = -2$
  $2x - y - z = -5$
  $3y + z = 3$

1. $x = 2, y = -1, z = 1$
3. $x = 1, y = 2, z = 3$

2. $x = 1, y = -1, z = 2$
4. $x = -1, y = 0, z = 2$

5. $x = 3, y = -1, z = 4$
7. $x = 3, y = -6, z = -5$

6. $x = 2, y = 3, z = 1$
8. $x = -2, y = 1, z = 0$

9.
$$\begin{aligned} x + 2y \quad &= 8 \\ y - 2z &= -5 \\ 2x + \quad z &= 8 \end{aligned}$$
$x = 2, y = 3, z = 4$

10.
$$\begin{aligned} 2x + y \quad &= 7 \\ 3y - 3z &= 6 \\ 4x + \quad 4z &= 8 \end{aligned}$$
$x = 3, y = 1, z = -1$

11.
$$\begin{aligned} 3(x + y) - 2(x - z) &= 1 \\ 3(y + z) + 2(x + y) &= 4 \\ 3(x + y) - 23 &= -2x \end{aligned}$$
$x = 4, y = 1, z = -3$

12.
$$\begin{aligned} x + 2(x - z + 1) &= y \\ 3(y - z) - x - 2 &= z \\ 2(2 - z) &= 5(x - z) \end{aligned}$$
$x = 2, y = 4, z = 2$

13.
$$\begin{aligned} 3x + 4y - 3z &= 2 \\ x + 2y + 3z &= 14 \\ 2x + y + 2z &= 10 \end{aligned}$$
$x = 1, y = 2, z = 3$

14.
$$\begin{aligned} x + y + z &= 53 \\ x + 3y + 4z &= 134 \\ x + 2y + 3z &= 105 \end{aligned}$$
$x = 24, y = 6, z = 23$

15.
$$\begin{aligned} x - y + z &= 30 \\ 3y - x - z &= 12 \\ 7z - y + 2x &= 141 \end{aligned}$$
$x = 39, y = 21, z = 12$

16.
$$\begin{aligned} 8x - 5y + 2z &= 53 \\ x + y - z &= 9 \\ 13x - 9y + 3z &= 71 \end{aligned}$$
$x = 11, y = 13, z = 15$

17.
$$\begin{aligned} 2x + 3y + 4z &= 29 \\ 3x + 2y + 5z &= 32 \\ 4x + 3y + 2z &= 25 \end{aligned}$$
$x = 2, y = 3, z = 4$

18.
$$\begin{aligned} \tfrac{1}{6}x - \tfrac{1}{5}y + \tfrac{1}{4}z &= 3 \\ \tfrac{1}{5}x - \tfrac{1}{4}y + \tfrac{1}{5}z &= 1 \\ \tfrac{1}{4}x - \tfrac{1}{3}y + \tfrac{1}{2}z &= 5 \end{aligned}$$
$x = 60, y = 60, z = 20$

19.
$$\begin{aligned} x + y &= 9 \\ y + z &= 7 \\ z + x &= 5 \end{aligned}$$
$x = \tfrac{7}{2}, y = \tfrac{11}{2}, z = \tfrac{3}{2}$

20.
$$\begin{aligned} 2x - 3y + z &= -2 \\ 4x - 4y - 3z &= 2 \\ 6x + y - 4z &= 6 \end{aligned}$$
$x = \tfrac{1}{4}, y = \tfrac{1}{2}, z = -1$

21.
$$\begin{aligned} x - 2y + 3z &= 6 \\ 3x - 2y + 5z &= 26 \\ 2x + 3y - 4z &= 20 \end{aligned}$$
$x = 8, y = 4, z = 2$

22.
$$\begin{aligned} 5x - 2y - 2z &= 12 \\ 7x + 3y + 4z &= 42 \\ x + y + z &= 8 \end{aligned}$$
$x = 4, y = 2, z = 2$

23.
$$\begin{aligned} 2.5x - y - 2z &= 9 \\ 3x &= 4z \\ 0.25(3x - 2z) &= y + 6.5 \end{aligned}$$
$x = 4, y = -5, z = 3$

24.
$$\begin{aligned} 4x - 19y + 3z &= 1 \\ 5x - 21y - 6z &= 11 \\ 6x + 11y + 2z &= 4 \end{aligned}$$
$x = 1, y = 0, z = -1$

25.
$$\begin{aligned} \tfrac{x}{2} - \tfrac{y}{3} + \tfrac{z}{5} &= 4 \\[4pt] \tfrac{x}{3} - \tfrac{y}{2} - \tfrac{z}{7} &= 1 \\[4pt] \tfrac{x}{6} + \tfrac{y}{6} + \tfrac{z}{11} &= 3 \end{aligned}$$
$x = 12, y = 6, z = 0$

Attempt to find one unique solution to the systems in problems 13 and 14. Explain your results.

26.
$$\begin{aligned} 2x - y - z &= -4 \\ x + 4y - 2z &= 1 \\ -x - y + z &= 1 \end{aligned}$$
Infinite number of solutions–dependent eqs

27.
$$\begin{aligned} 2x - y - 2z &= 1 \\ -6x + 2y + 2z &= 2 \\ 2x + \quad 2z &= 5 \end{aligned}$$
No sol.; inconsistent system of eqs.

2. 22¢ stamps = 15, 37¢ stamps = 15   **3.** Subcompacts = $400, Compacts = $500
4. Width = 9 ft, Length = 12 ft   **5.** Without wind = 17.5 mph, Wind = 2.5 mph
7. A = 300 gals., B = 150 gals., C = 275 gals.

Section 3.3

1. Total ticket sales for a concert were $3190. A total of 530 students attended the concert. Reserved seats were $7, and general admission seats were $5. How many tickets of each kind were sold?   Reserved seats = 270, general admission = 260

2. Monica bought a combination of thirty 22¢ stamps and 37¢ stamps, and paid $8.85. How many 22¢ stamps did she buy? How many 37¢ stamps did she buy?

3. A large company rented compact cars and subcompact cars for their salespeople. Last month the company rented 16 subcompact cars and 20 compact cars and paid a rental fee of $16,400. This month the rental fee was $17,000 for 10 subcompact cars and 26 compact cars. What is the rental cost per month for each type of car?

4. A rectangular living room has a perimeter of 54 feet. A rectangular rug is 3 feet longer than it is wide. The perimeter of the rug is 12 feet less than the perimeter of the room. Determine the length and width of the rug.

5. Alfonse took a 5-mile bike trip along the beach. Going against the wind, the trip took 20 minutes. The return trip took only 15 minutes. Find the speed of the wind. How fast did Alphonse pedal without any wind?

6. A biologist is using a mixture of nutrient A and nutrient B. The nutrient A mixture contains 6 grams of vitamin C and 3 grams of vitamin B_{12}. The nutrient B mixture contains 2 grams of vitamin C and 4 grams of vitamin B_{12}. She needs 28 grams of vitamin C and 29 grams of vitamin B_{12}. How many bottles of nutrient A and nutrient B should she use?   Nutrient A = 3, Nutrient B = 5

7. Pumps A, B, and C can fill a 725-gallon tank in 1 hour. Pumps B and C working together can pump 425 gallons in 1 hour. When pump A works for 3 hours and pump B for 2 hours, 1200 gallons are pumped. How many gallons does each pump move in 1 hour?

8. Air Express ships three sizes of packages for a computer company. Large packages weigh 12 pounds, medium-sized packages weigh 7 pounds, and small packages weigh 4 pounds. A total of 29 packages of all sizes, weighing 253 pounds was shipped last week. The combined total of small and medium-sized packages was three less than the number of large packages. How many packages of each type were shipped?   Large pkgs. = 16, Med. pkgs. = 3, Small pkgs. = 10

9. Riverside Fruit Company packs three types of gift boxes of oranges, pink grapefruit, and white grapefruit. Box A contains 5 oranges, 2 pink grapefruit, and 1 white grapefruit. Box B contains 11 oranges, 3 pink grapefruit, and 2 white grapefruit. Box C contains 8 oranges, 2 pink grapefruit, and 2 white grapefruit. The shipping manager has available 114 oranges, 35 pink grapefruit, and 23 white grapefruit. If each fruit is used, how many of each type of gift box can he prepare? $A = 7, B = 5, C = 3$

10. The sprinklers located at points A, B, and C are connected by pipes and all send out a spray of water in a circular pattern. The circular patterns touch as shown in the diagram. The lengths are $AB = 50$ feet, $BC = 35$ feet, and $CA = 45$ feet. What is the radius of each circular sprinkling area?   Circle $A = 30$ ft, Circle $B = 20$ ft, Circle $C = 15$ ft.

16. Larger tank = 375 gals.

11. Al drives 300 miles in 11 hours, part of the time at 30 mph and part of the time at 25 mph. How many hours does he drive at each rate?   5 hrs @ 30 mph, 6 hrs @ 25 mph

12. The number of bridges on a certain railroad is 23 more than 15 times the number of tunnels. If the number of tunnels were 5 more, it would be $\frac{1}{14}$ of the number of bridges. Find the number of bridges.   728 bridges

13. If one cat weighs 1 pound more than twice a second cat, and the sum of their weights is 22 pounds, find the weight of the lighter cat.   Lighter cat = 7 lbs

14. If two large boxes weigh the same as five small boxes, and three large boxes weigh 2 pounds more than seven small boxes, find the weight of one small box.   Small box = 4 lbs

15. Kelly earns $100 more a week than John does. In one four-week period the sum of their wages was $4800. How much does Kelly earn in one week? $650

16. Two tanks hold 550 gallons of H_2O. If one held 75 gallons more and the other 125 gallons less, they would have held equal amounts. How many gallons did the larger tank hold?

17. A pier jutted into the water a distance that was 70 feet less than the length of the part on land, and $\frac{2}{3}$ of the total length was 190 feet more than that of the part over the water. Find the total length of the pier.   930 ft

18. If a sea captain earns $1100 a week while at sea and is paid $\frac{1}{2}$ of that while on shore, how many weeks was he at sea in the year 1989 if he earned $50,600?   40 weeks

19. Keith has half as many red balloons as green balloons. The sum of the numbers of red and blue balloons is 400. The number of blue balloons is $\frac{3}{2}$ the number of green balloons. How many red balloons does he have?   100 balloons

20. The sum of the weights of Keith, Kevin, and their dad is 400 pounds. Twice Keith's weight plus 3 times Kevin's weight is 610 pounds. Twice Dad's weight plus 4 times Keith's weight is 560 pounds. Find Keith's weight.   50 lbs

21. On "Woman's Day" at a certain theater, women are admitted free while men pay $4 and children pay $1. On one of these days 190 people showed up. There were twice as many men as children at the gate, and receipts were $450. How many women were admitted free?   40

22. A store sells only one type each of television sets, microwaves, and VCRs. On one day they sold 60 items. They sold 10 more television sets than VCR's. A television set costs $300, a microwave $200, and a VCR $400. If the total receipts were $17,500 on that day, how many of each of these items were sold?
25 television sets, 20 microwaves, and 15 VCR's.

Section 3.4

Compute each determinant.

1. $\begin{vmatrix} 6 & 1 \\ -3 & 4 \end{vmatrix}$ 27

2. $\begin{vmatrix} -2 & -5 \\ 1 & -3 \end{vmatrix}$ 11

3. $\begin{vmatrix} -7 & -2 \\ -8 & 1 \end{vmatrix}$ -23

4. $\begin{vmatrix} 1 & 1 \\ \frac{1}{3} & \frac{1}{2} \\ 2 & -4 \end{vmatrix}$ $-\frac{7}{3}$

5. $\begin{vmatrix} 0.1 & -0.6 \\ -0.5 & -0.3 \end{vmatrix}$ -0.33

6. $\begin{vmatrix} 0 & -5 \\ 2 & 0 \end{vmatrix}$ 10

7. $\begin{vmatrix} 0 & 1 \\ 0 & 7 \end{vmatrix}$ 0

8. $\begin{vmatrix} 3 & 7 \\ -8 & 0 \end{vmatrix}$ 56

9. $\begin{vmatrix} 2 & 5 \\ -6 & -15 \end{vmatrix}$ 0

10. $\begin{vmatrix} 2 & 1 \\ \frac{2}{3} & \frac{1}{2} \\ 4 & 6 \end{vmatrix}$ 2

11. $\begin{vmatrix} 0.2 & 0.6 \\ 0.4 & -0.1 \end{vmatrix}$ -0.26

12. $\begin{vmatrix} 8 & 11 \\ 4 & 10 \end{vmatrix}$ 36

13. $\begin{vmatrix} 40 & 60 \\ 50 & 20 \end{vmatrix}$ -2200

14. $\begin{vmatrix} 18 & 4 \\ -16 & 3 \end{vmatrix}$ 118

15. $\begin{vmatrix} 0 & 0 \\ 0 & \pi \end{vmatrix}$ 0

16. $\begin{vmatrix} 1 & 2 & -3 \\ 3 & 1 & 0 \\ -2 & 1 & 4 \end{vmatrix}$ -35

17. $\begin{vmatrix} 0 & -6 & 3 \\ 4 & 0 & 1 \\ 2 & 0 & -3 \end{vmatrix}$ -84

18. $\begin{vmatrix} 0 & 3 & 0 \\ 2 & -7 & 1 \\ 4 & 8 & -2 \end{vmatrix}$ 24

19. $\begin{vmatrix} 3 & 6 & -3 \\ 4 & -2 & 0 \\ 6 & 12 & -6 \end{vmatrix}$ 0

20. $\begin{vmatrix} 5 & 1 & -2 \\ 2 & -2 & 3 \\ 1 & 1 & 0 \end{vmatrix}$ -20

21. $\begin{vmatrix} 4 & 6 & -1 \\ -2 & 1 & -3 \\ 5 & -4 & 2 \end{vmatrix}$ -109

22. $\begin{vmatrix} 3 & -1 & 4 \\ 6 & 2 & 6 \\ 9 & -3 & -1 \end{vmatrix}$ -156

23. $\begin{vmatrix} 8 & 4 & 11 \\ 7 & 12 & 4 \\ -6 & -13 & -1 \end{vmatrix}$ 43

24. $\begin{vmatrix} 0.2 & 0.6 & 0.5 \\ 0.3 & -0.1 & 0 \\ 0.5 & -0.2 & 0.3 \end{vmatrix}$ -0.065

25. $\begin{vmatrix} \dfrac{1}{2} & 0 & \dfrac{3}{4} \\[2mm] 1 & \dfrac{1}{3} & 0 \\[2mm] \dfrac{1}{2} & 0 & \dfrac{1}{4} \end{vmatrix}$ $-\dfrac{1}{12}$

Solve for x.

26. $\begin{vmatrix} x-3 & 2 \\ -4 & -3 \end{vmatrix} = 2$ $x = 5$

27. $\begin{vmatrix} 5x+1 & -3 \\ 6x-1 & 2 \end{vmatrix} = -3$ $x = -\dfrac{1}{14}$

Solve for x and y.

28. $\begin{vmatrix} 5x & 6y \\ 3 & -2 \end{vmatrix} = 20$ and $\begin{vmatrix} -4x & -2 \\ 3y & \dfrac{1}{2} \end{vmatrix} = 4$ $x = -2,\ y = 0$

29. $\begin{vmatrix} \dfrac{x}{2} & \dfrac{y}{3} \\[2mm] 6 & 4 \end{vmatrix} = 0$ and $\begin{vmatrix} 3x & 2y \\ 7 & -4 \end{vmatrix} = -104$ $x = 4,\ y = 4$

30. Solve for x, y, and z. $x = 1,\ y = 2,\ z = 3$

$\begin{vmatrix} x & y \\ 2 & 4 \end{vmatrix} = 0$ $\begin{vmatrix} 3x & 2z \\ 5 & 4 \end{vmatrix} = -18$ $\begin{vmatrix} 2y & 4 \\ 3z & -1 \end{vmatrix} = -40$

31. Find the area of a triangle whose vertices are (in counterclockwise order) $(-2, -3)$, $(5, 1)$, and $(-4, 5)$.
Area = 32 sq. units

Section 3.5

If possible, solve by Cramer's rule. If there is not one solution to the system, state a reason.

1. $4x - y = 3$ $x = 1$
$3x - y = 2$ $y = 1$

2. $x - 2y = 3$ $x = 3$
$-2x + 3y = -6$ $y = 0$

3. $3x - 5y = 2$ $x = 9$
$3x + y = 32$ $y = 5$

4. $2x + 5y = -2$ $x = -6$
$-7x - 5y = 32$ $y = 2$

5. $2x + 3y = 6$ $x = -3$
$-3x + y = 13$ $y = 4$

6. $6x - 13y = 5$ $x = -10$
$x - 2y = 0$ $y = -5$

7. $4x - 8y = 40$ $x = 6$
$2x + 3y = 6$ $y = -2$

8. $2x - y = -6$ $x = -5$
$3x + 2y = -23$ $y = -4$

9. $5x - 2y = -3$ infinite number of solutions—dependent eqs.
$-10x + 4y = 6$

10. $-3x - 6y = 12$ No sol.; inconsistent system of eqs.
$2x + 4y = -6$

11. $4(x + 1) = 13 - 3y$ $x = 3,\ y = -1$
$2 + 3(y + 2) = x + 2$

12. $5(x + 2) = 11 - 2y$ $x = 3,\ y = -7$
$-2x = 3(y + 5)$

13. $x + 2y = -1$
$5x - 4y = 16$

14. $3x - 5y = 4$ $x = \dfrac{1}{2}$
$4x + 2y = 1$ $y = -\dfrac{1}{2}$

15. $x - 4y = 0$ $x = 0$
$5x + 7y = 0$ $y = 0$

16. $2x + y = 0$
$4x - 2y = 10$

17. $2x - 3y = 2$ $x = 4$
$x = 4$ $y = 2$

18. $6x + 3y = 4$
$10x - 6y = 3$

19. $4x + y = -4$ $x = -\dfrac{3}{2}$
$10x + 3y = -9$ $y = 2$

20. $2x + y = 1$
$3x - 2y = 3\dfrac{1}{4}$

21. $\dfrac{x}{2} + \dfrac{y}{7} = 9$ $x = 14,\ y = 14$
$\dfrac{x}{7} - \dfrac{y}{2} = -5$

22. $\dfrac{14x + 3}{5} - \dfrac{8(y + 4)}{17} = 0$ $x = \dfrac{1}{2},\ y = \dfrac{1}{4}$
$\dfrac{10x - 2}{3} - \dfrac{4y + 3}{4} = 0$

(Answers, right column)

13. $x = 2$
$y = -\dfrac{3}{2}$

16. $x = \dfrac{5}{4}$
$y = -\dfrac{5}{2}$

18. $x = \dfrac{1}{2}$
$y = \dfrac{1}{3}$

20. $x = \dfrac{3}{4}$
$y = -\dfrac{1}{2}$

Solve by Cramer's Rule.

23. $x + y + z = 2$ $x = 1,\ y = -1,\ z = 2$
$2x - 3y + z = 7$
$3x + 3y - z = -2$

24. $x - y + 3z = 13$ $x = 3,\ y = -7,\ z = 1$
$3x + 2y + z = -4$
$2x + y - z = -2$

25. $x - 2y + 3z = 4$ $x = 4,\ y = 3,\ z = 2$
$-3x + 4y - z = -2$
$y - 2z = -1$

26. $2x - y + 3z = 40$ $x = 3,\ y = 5,\ z = 13$
$x + 2y - z = 0$
$3x - 2y = -1$

27. $2x + y + z = 0$ $x = -3,\ y = 1,\ z = 5$
$3x = 2y - 3z + 4$
$7y + 2z = 2 - 5x$

28. $13 + 5z = 6x + 2y$ $x = 2,\ y = 3,\ z = 1$
$13 + 2z = 3x + 3y$
$5y - 26 = 3z - 7x$

Solve only for the variable specified, using Cramer's rule.

29. Solve for z:

$$3x + y - 2z = 12 \quad z = -2$$
$$2x + y - 3z = 11$$
$$x - 2y + 4z = -3$$

30. Solve for y:

$$4x - 5y = 11 \quad y = 1$$
$$2x + z = 7$$
$$2y + z = 1$$

31. Solve for z:

$$2x + 3y + 5z = 3 \quad z = \dfrac{1}{5}$$
$$12x - 18y + 3z = \dfrac{3}{5}$$
$$3x - 3y - 3z = -\dfrac{1}{10}$$

Topic	Procedure	Example
Solving a system of two linear equations by the substitution method, p. 130	The substitution method is most appropriate when *at least one variable has a coefficient of 1 or −1.* **1.** Solve for one variable in one of the equations. **2.** In the other equation replace that variable with the expression you obtained in step 1. **3.** Solve the resulting equation. **4.** Substitute the numerical value you obtain for a variable into the equation you found in step 1. **5.** Solve this equation to find the other variable.	Solve: $$2x + y = 11 \quad \boxed{1}$$ $$x + 3y = 18 \quad \boxed{2}$$ $y = 11 - 2x$ from equation $\boxed{1}$. Substitute this into equation $\boxed{2}$. $$x + 3(11 - 2x) = 18$$ $$x + 33 - 6x = 18$$ $$-5x + 33 = 18$$ $$-5x = -15$$ $$x = 3$$ Substitute $x = 3$ into $y = 11 - 2x$: $$y = 11 - 2(3) = 11 - 6$$ $$= 5$$ The solution is $x = 3$, $y = 5$.
Solving a system of two linear equations by the addition method, p. 133	The addition method is most appropriate when the variables *all have coefficients other than 1 or −1.* **1.** Multiply one or both equations by appropriate numerical values so that when the two resulting equations are added one variable is eliminated. **2.** Solve the resulting equation. **3.** Substitute the numerical value you obtain for the variable in one of the original equations. **4.** Solve this equation to find the other variable.	Solve: $$2x + 3y = 5 \quad \boxed{1}$$ $$-3x - 4y = -2 \quad \boxed{2}$$ Multiply equation $\boxed{1}$ by 3 and equation $\boxed{2}$ by 2. $$6x + 9y = 15$$ $$\underline{-6x - 8y = -4}$$ $$y = 11$$ Substitute $y = 11$ into equation $\boxed{1}$. $$2x + 3(11) = 5$$ $$2x + 33 = 5$$ $$2x = -28$$ $$x = -14$$ The solution is $x = -14$, $y = 11$.
Solving a system of three linear equations by algebraic methods, p. 141	If there is one solution to a system of three linear equations in three unknowns, it may be obtained in the following manner. **1.** Choose two equations from the system. **2.** Multiply one or both of the equations by the appropriate constants so that by adding the two equations together one variable can be eliminated. **3.** Choose a *different* pair of the three original equations and eliminate the *same* variable using the procedure of step 2. **4.** Solve the system formed by the two equations resulting from steps 2 and 3 for both variables. **5.** Substitute the two values obtained in step 4 above into one of the original three equations to find the third variable.	Solve: $$2x - y - 2z = -1 \quad \boxed{1}$$ $$x - 2y - z = 1 \quad \boxed{2}$$ $$x + y + z = 4 \quad \boxed{3}$$ Add equations $\boxed{2}$ and $\boxed{3}$ together to eliminate z. $$2x - y = 5 \quad \boxed{4}$$ Multiply equation $\boxed{3}$ by 2 and add to equation $\boxed{1}$. $$2x + 2y + 2z = 8$$ $$\underline{2x - y - 2z = -1}$$ $$4x + y = 7 \quad \boxed{5}$$ Add equations $\boxed{4}$ and $\boxed{5}$. $$2x - y = 5 \quad \boxed{4}$$ $$\underline{4x + y = 7} \quad \boxed{5}$$ $$6x = 12$$ $$x = 2$$

Topic	Procedure	Examples
Solving a system of three linear equations by algebraic methods (*continued*)		Substitute $x = 2$ into $\boxed{5}$. $$4(2) + y = 7$$ $$8 + y = 7$$ $$y = -1$$ Substitute $x = 2$, $y = -1$ into $\boxed{3}$. $$2 + (-1) + z = 4$$ $$1 + z = 4$$ $$z = 3$$ The solution is $x = 2$, $y = -1$, $z = 3$.
Inconsistent equations, p. 134	If there is *no solution* to a system of linear equations the system of equations is inconsistent. When you try to solve an inconsistent system you obtain an equation that is not true like $0 = 5$.	Attempt to solve the system $$4x + 3y = 10 \quad \boxed{1}$$ $$-8x - 6y = 5 \quad \boxed{2}$$ Multiply equation $\boxed{1}$ by 2 and add to equation $\boxed{2}$. $$\begin{aligned} 8x + 6y &= 20 \\ -8x - 6y &= 5 \\ \hline 0 &= 25 \end{aligned}$$ But $0 \neq 25$; there is no solution. The system of equations is inconsistent.
Dependent equations, p. 134	If there are an *infinite number of solutions* to a system of linear equations, at least one pair of equations is dependent. When you try to solve a system that contains dependent equations you will obtain a math equation that is always true (such as $0 = 0$ or $3 = 3$). These equations are called identities.	Attempt to solve the system: $$x - 2y = -5 \quad \boxed{1}$$ $$-3x + 6y = +15 \quad \boxed{2}$$ Multiply equation $\boxed{1}$ by 3 and add to equation $\boxed{2}$. $$\begin{aligned} 3x - 6y &= -15 \\ -3x + 6y &= 15 \\ \hline 0 &= 0 \end{aligned}$$ There are an infinite number of solutions. The equations are dependent.
Cramer's rule for a linear system containing two equations with two unknowns, p. 163	The solution to $$ax + by = c$$ $$dx + ey = f$$ is $$x = \frac{D_x}{D} \quad \text{and} \quad y = \frac{D_y}{D} \quad \text{if } D \neq 0$$ where $$D_x = \begin{vmatrix} c & b \\ f & e \end{vmatrix} \quad D_y = \begin{vmatrix} a & c \\ d & f \end{vmatrix} \quad D = \begin{vmatrix} a & b \\ d & e \end{vmatrix}$$	Solve by Cramer's rule: $$2x - y = 7$$ $$3x + 4y = 5$$ $$D = \begin{vmatrix} 2 & -1 \\ 3 & 4 \end{vmatrix}$$ $$= (2)(4) - (3)(-1)$$ $$= 8 - (-3) = 8 + 3 = 11$$ $$D_x = \begin{vmatrix} 7 & -1 \\ 5 & 4 \end{vmatrix}$$ $$= (7)(4) - (5)(-1)$$ $$= 28 - (-5) = 28 + 5 = 33$$ $$D_y = \begin{vmatrix} 2 & 7 \\ 3 & 5 \end{vmatrix}$$ $$= (2)(5) - (3)(7)$$ $$= 10 - 21 = -11$$ $$x = \frac{33}{11} = 3$$ $$y = \frac{-11}{11} = -1$$

Topic	Procedure	Examples
Cramer's rule for a linear system containing three equations with three unknowns, p. 165	The solution to the system $$a_1x + b_1y + c_1z = d_1$$ $$a_2x + b_2y + c_2z = d_2$$ $$a_3x + b_3y + c_3z = d_3$$ is given by $$x = \frac{D_x}{D} \qquad y = \frac{D_y}{D} \qquad z = \frac{D_z}{D} \qquad (D \neq 0)$$ $$D = \begin{vmatrix} a_1 & b_1 & c_1 \\ a_2 & b_2 & c_2 \\ a_3 & b_3 & c_3 \end{vmatrix} \qquad D_x = \begin{vmatrix} d_1 & b_1 & c_1 \\ d_2 & b_2 & c_2 \\ d_3 & b_3 & c_3 \end{vmatrix}$$ $$D_y = \begin{vmatrix} a_1 & d_1 & c_1 \\ a_2 & d_2 & c_2 \\ a_3 & d_3 & c_3 \end{vmatrix} \qquad D_z = \begin{vmatrix} a_1 & b_1 & d_1 \\ a_2 & b_2 & d_2 \\ a_3 & b_3 & d_3 \end{vmatrix}$$	Solve by Cramer's rule: $$3x - y - 2z = 1$$ $$2x - y + 2z = 8$$ $$x + 2y + 3z = 3$$ We will expand determinants by first column. $$D = \begin{vmatrix} 3 & -1 & -2 \\ 2 & -1 & 2 \\ 1 & 2 & 3 \end{vmatrix}$$ $$= (3)\begin{vmatrix} -1 & 2 \\ 2 & 3 \end{vmatrix} + (-2)\begin{vmatrix} -1 & -2 \\ 2 & 3 \end{vmatrix} + (1)\begin{vmatrix} -1 & -2 \\ -1 & 2 \end{vmatrix}$$ $$= (3)[-3 - 4] + (-2)[-3 + 4] + (1)[-2 - 2]$$ $$= -21 + (-2) + (-4) = -27$$ $$D_x = \begin{vmatrix} 1 & -1 & -2 \\ 8 & -1 & 2 \\ 3 & 2 & 3 \end{vmatrix}$$ $$= (1)\begin{vmatrix} -1 & 2 \\ 2 & 3 \end{vmatrix} + (-8)\begin{vmatrix} -1 & -2 \\ 2 & 3 \end{vmatrix} + (3)\begin{vmatrix} -1 & -2 \\ -1 & 2 \end{vmatrix}$$ $$= (1)[-3 - 4] + (-8)[-3 + 4] + (3)[-2 - 2]$$ $$= -7 + (-8) + (-12) = -27$$ In similar fashion, $$D_y = \begin{vmatrix} 3 & 1 & -2 \\ 2 & 8 & 2 \\ 1 & 3 & 3 \end{vmatrix} = 54$$ $$D_z = \begin{vmatrix} 3 & -1 & 1 \\ 2 & -1 & 8 \\ 1 & 2 & 3 \end{vmatrix} = -54$$ $$x = \frac{D_x}{D} = \frac{-27}{-27} = 1$$ $$y = \frac{D_y}{D} = \frac{54}{-27} = -2$$ $$z = \frac{D_z}{D} = \frac{-54}{-27} = +2$$
Cramer's rule with inconsistent systems, p. 167	If $D = 0$ and some of D_x, D_y, D_z are nonzero, the system of equations is inconsistent. There is no solution.	Attempt to solve $$3x + 4y = 6$$ $$-6x - 8y = 2$$ $$D = \begin{vmatrix} 3 & 4 \\ -6 & -8 \end{vmatrix} = -24 + 24 = 0$$ $$D_x = \begin{vmatrix} 6 & 4 \\ 2 & -8 \end{vmatrix} = -48 - 24 = -72$$ $$D_y = \begin{vmatrix} 3 & 6 \\ -6 & 2 \end{vmatrix} = 6 + 36 = 42$$ $$D = 0 \qquad D_x \neq 0 \qquad D_y \neq 0$$ The system is *inconsistent*—there is no solution.
Cramer's rule with dependent equations, p. 167	If $D = 0$ and $D_x = D_y = D_z = 0$, the system of equations contains dependent equations. There are an infinite number of solutions.	Attempt to solve $$x + 5y = -7$$ $$-2x - 10y = 14$$ $$D = \begin{vmatrix} 1 & 5 \\ -2 & -10 \end{vmatrix} = -10 + 10 = 0$$

Topic	Procedure	Examples
Cramer's rule with dependent equations (*continued*)		$D_x = \begin{vmatrix} -7 & 5 \\ 14 & -10 \end{vmatrix} = 70 - 70 = 0$ $D_y = \begin{vmatrix} 1 & -7 \\ -2 & 14 \end{vmatrix} = 14 - 14 = 0$ Since $D = D_x = D_y = 0$, we know that these equations are dependent. There are an infinite number of solutions.

REVIEW PROBLEMS CHAPTER 3

Solve by any appropriate method. If there is no unique solution, tell why.

1. $2x + 4y = 9$
$3x + 6y = 8$
No sol.; inconsistent system of eqs.

2. $x + 5y = 10$

$y = 2 - \dfrac{1}{5}x$

Infinite number of solutions–dependent eqs.

3. $7x + 6y = -10$
$2x + \ y = \ \ 0$
$x = 2, y = -4$

4. $3x + 4y = \ \ \ 1$
$9x - 2y = -4$
$x = -\dfrac{1}{3}, y = \dfrac{1}{2}$

5. $x + \dfrac{1}{3}y = \ \ \ 1$

$\dfrac{1}{4}x - \dfrac{3}{4}y = -\dfrac{9}{4}$

$x = 0, y = 3$

6. $\dfrac{2}{3}x + y = \ \ \dfrac{14}{3}$

$\dfrac{2}{3}x - y = -\dfrac{22}{3}$

$x = -2, y = 6$

7. $9a + 10b = \ \ 7$
$6a - \ \ 4b = 10$
$a = \dfrac{4}{3}, b = -\dfrac{1}{2}$

8. $3a + 5b = 8$
$2a + 4b = 3$
$a = \dfrac{17}{2}, b = -\dfrac{7}{2}$

9. $x + 3 = 3y + 1$
$1 - 2(x - 2) = 6y + 1$
$x = 0, y = \dfrac{2}{3}$

10. $10(x + 1) - 13 = -8y$
$4(2 - y) = 5(x + 1)$
No sol.; inconsistent system of eqs.

Solve by any appropriate method.

11. $3x - 2y - z = \ \ \ 3$
$2x + \ y + z = \ \ \ 1$
$-x - \ y + z = -4$
$x = 1, y = 1, z = -2$

12. $-2x + \ y - \ z = -7$
$x - 2y - \ z = \ \ 2$
$6x + 4y + 2z = \ \ 4$
$x = 1, y = -2, z = 3$

13. $2x + 5y + \ z = \ \ 3$
$x + \ y + 5z = 42$
$2x + \ y \ \ \ \ \ = \ \ 7$
$x = 5, y = -3, z = 8$

14. $x + 2y + z = \ \ \ 5$
$3x - 8y \ \ \ \ \ \ = \ \ 17$
$2y + z = -2$
$x = 7, y = \dfrac{1}{2}, z = -3$

Use a system of linear equations to solve each of the following problems.

15. A plane flies 720 miles against the wind in 3 hours. The return trip with the wind takes only $2\dfrac{1}{2}$ hours. Find the speed of the wind. Find the speed of the plane in still air.
Speed of plane in still air = 264 mph
Speed of wind = 24 mph

16. A local company has computerized its production line. Company officials have found that it takes 25 hours to train new employees to use the computerized equipment and 8 hours to review mathematics skills. Previously laid-off employees can be trained in 10 hours to use the computerized equipment and require only 3 hours to review mathematics skills. This month, the management team has 275 hours available to train people to use computerized equipment and 86 hours available to review necessary mathematics skills. How many new employees can be trained? This month, how many previously laid-off employees can be trained?
New employees = 7
Laid-off employees = 10

17. A baseball coach bought two hats, five shirts, and four pairs of pants for $129. His assistant purchased one hat, one shirt, and two pairs of pants for $42. Next week the coach returned to buy two hats, three shirts, and one pair of pants for $63. What is the cost for each item?

Hats = $3
Shirts = $15
Pants = $12

18. For an experiment a scientist needs three food packets. Packet A has 2 grams of carbohydrates, 4 grams of protein, and 3 grams of fat. Packet B has 3 grams of carbohydrates, 1 gram of protein, and 1 gram of fat. Packet C has 4 grams of carbohydrates, 3 grams of protein, and 2 grams of fat. The experiment requires 29 grams of carbohydrates, 23 grams of protein, and 17 grams of fat. How many packets should she use?

$A = 2$
$B = 3$
$C = 4$

Compute each determinant.

19. $\begin{vmatrix} 5 & -7 \\ 2 & -3 \end{vmatrix}$

-1

20. $\begin{vmatrix} 0 & -\dfrac{1}{4} \\ 2 & -\dfrac{3}{2} \end{vmatrix}$

$\dfrac{1}{2}$

21. $\begin{vmatrix} -6 & -8 \\ -2 & 3 \end{vmatrix}$

-34

22. $\begin{vmatrix} 2 & 1 & 6 \\ 3 & 4 & -2 \\ 1 & 2 & 3 \end{vmatrix}$

33

23. $\begin{vmatrix} 6 & 1 & 0 \\ 2 & 3 & 0 \\ 6 & -2 & 1 \end{vmatrix}$

16

Use Cramer's rule to solve each system.

24. $-x - 5z = -5$
$13x + 2z = 2$

$x = 0, z = 1$

25. $x + y = 10$
$6x + 9y = 70$

$x = \dfrac{20}{3}, y = \dfrac{10}{3}$

26. $x - 4y + 4z = -1$
$2x - y + 5z = -3$
$x - 3y + z = 4$

$x = 3, y = -1, z = -2$

27. Solve for y.

$x - 2y + z = -5$
$2x + z = -10$
$y - z = 15$

$y = -5$

28. Solve for x.

$\begin{vmatrix} -2 & 3 \\ x & 5x - 4 \end{vmatrix} = -2$

$x = \dfrac{10}{13}$

PUTTING YOUR SKILLS TO WORK

A system of linear equations can be used to solve for unknown values in electrical circuits. Here's an example of how to find currents in a direct current (dc) resistive circuit. Electric current (I), or the flow of electricity, is measured in amperes, voltage (V) in volts, and resistance in ohms (Ω). There are three fundamental important laws that all electrical circuits obey. The first two are called *Kirchhoff*'s laws; the third is *Ohm's law.*

> **Law 1:** The current entering a junction (a place where wires are connected) must be equal to the current leaving a junction. (In other words, the net current at the junction itself is zero.)
>
> **Law 2:** The *algebraic* sum of the voltage changes around a loop (closed path that the current flows through) must be zero.
>
> **Law 3:** The voltage is equal to the current multiplied by the resistance. (In symbols, $V = IR$.)

Now look at this sketch. The –ʍ– symbol means resistance. The circuit contains three resistors

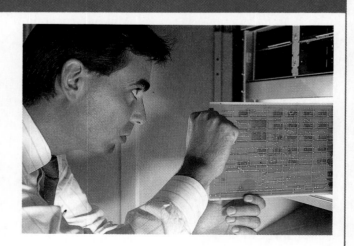

connected in parallel. In a parallel circuit the current is divided among the loops. The circuit also contains two batteries (the ⊥⊤ symbol).

According to Law 1, the currents entering and leaving junction B must equal zero. Thus (using + for currents entering the junction and − for currents leaving the junction),

$$I_1 + I_2 + I_3 = 0 \quad \boxed{1}$$

By Law 3 the voltage in the 8-Ω resistor is $8I$, that in the 15-Ω resistor is $15I_2$, and that in the 6-Ω resistor is $6I_3$.

Now by Law 2, the *algebraic* sum of the voltages between points A, B, E, and F is

$$8I_1 - 15I_2 = 4 \quad \boxed{2}$$

Applying this law to the loop $BCDE$, we have the equation

$$-15I_2 + 6I_3 = 6 \quad \boxed{3}$$

Therefore, our system is

$$I_1 + I_2 + I_3 = 0 \quad \boxed{1}$$
$$8I_1 - 15I_2 \quad\quad = 4 \quad \boxed{2}$$
$$-15I_2 + 6I_3 = 6 \quad \boxed{3}$$

Problem Find the currents I_1, I_2, and I_3 in the figure shown.

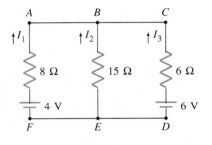

Let's use equation $\boxed{3}$. We therefore need to eliminate I_1 from equations $\boxed{1}$ and $\boxed{2}$. Multiply equation $\boxed{1}$ by -8 and add it to equation $\boxed{2}$:

$$\begin{array}{ll} -8I_1 - 8I_2 - 8I_3 = 0 & \boxed{4} \\ \underline{8I_1 - 15I_2 = 4} & \boxed{2} \\ -23I_2 - 8I_3 = 4 & \boxed{5} \end{array}$$

Now we solve the system containing equations $\boxed{3}$ and $\boxed{5}$:

$$-15I_2 + 6I_3 = 6 \quad \boxed{3}$$
$$-23I_2 - 8I_3 = 4 \quad \boxed{5}$$

Observe that every coefficient of equation $\boxed{3}$ is a multiple of 3. Thus, we divide equation $\boxed{3}$ by 3 and call the result equation $\boxed{6}$:

$$-5I_2 + 2I_3 = 2 \quad \boxed{6}$$
$$-23I_2 - 8I_3 = 4 \quad \boxed{5}$$

Now we solve this system by multiplying each term of equation $\boxed{6}$ by 4 to obtain the equivalent system

$$-20I_2 + 8I_3 = 8 \quad \boxed{7}$$
$$-23I_2 - 8I_3 = 4 \quad \boxed{5}$$

Adding the equations, we obtain

$$-43I_2 = 12$$

$$I_2 = -\frac{12}{43}$$

We can substitute this value into any equation with I_2 and I_3. Let's use equation $\boxed{6}$.

$$-5\left(-\frac{12}{43}\right) + 2I_3 = 2$$

$$\frac{60}{43} + 2I_3 = 2$$

$$2I_3 = \frac{86}{43} - \frac{60}{43}$$

$$2I_3 = \frac{23}{43}$$

$$I_3 = \frac{23}{86}$$

Finally, we substitute $I_3 = \frac{23}{86}$ and $I_2 = -\frac{12}{43}$ into equation $\boxed{1}$.

$$I_1 - \frac{12}{43} + \frac{23}{86} = 0$$

$$I_1 - \frac{24}{86} + \frac{23}{86} = 0$$

$$I_1 - \frac{1}{86} = 0$$

$$I_1 = \frac{1}{86}$$

Our final answer for each amount for current is

$$I_1 = \frac{1}{86} \text{ ampere} \quad I_2 = -\frac{12}{43} \text{ ampere} \quad I_3 = \frac{23}{86} \text{ ampere}$$

(The negative sign refers to the direction of current flow.) These answers are exact. Approximate decimal values rounded to the nearest thousand are $I_1 = 0.012$ ampere, $I_2 = -0.279$ ampere, and $I_3 = 0.267$ ampere.

A Challenge for You

Find the amount of current I_1, I_2, I_3 if the resistance from B to E is 18 Ω but the other values remain as in the original sketch.

Solve each system of equations. If there is no one solution to the system, explain why.

1. $3x + 2y = 7$
$\quad 2x - y = 14$

1. $x = 5, y = -4$

2. $2x + 3y = 12$
$\quad 3x - 5y = 18$

2. $x = 6, y = 0$

3. $5a + 8b = 14$
$\quad 2a + 7b = -2$

3. $a = 6, b = -2$

4. $\quad a - \dfrac{1}{2}b = -\dfrac{1}{2}$

$\quad -a + \dfrac{3}{5}b = \dfrac{6}{5}$

4. $a = 3, b = 7$

5. $3(2y - x) = 8$
$\quad 1 + 2(x - 2y + 10) = 15$

5. No sol.; inconsistent system of eqs.

6. $2(y + 1) = 5(1 - x)$
$\quad \dfrac{4}{5}y + 2x = \dfrac{6}{5}$

6. Infinite number of solutions–dependent eqs.

7. $x = 1, y = -1, z = 2$

7. $\begin{aligned} x - y + z &= 4 \\ x + 3y - z &= -4 \\ 2x + y + 2z &= 5 \end{aligned}$

8. $\begin{aligned} 2x + 3y - z &= 7 \\ x + 2y + 3z &= -1 \\ 4y - 5z &= -3 \end{aligned}$

8. $x = 6, y = -2, z = -1$

9. At a local concert advance tickets were \$4 and tickets at the door were \$6. The gross receipts of ticket sales were \$1780. The stage manager said that next year advance tickets would be \$5, and tickets at the door would be \$8. He would then expect (if the same crowd attended) gross ticket sales of \$2290. How many tickets of each type were sold this year?

9. 250 advance tickets
130 tickets at the door

10. In a factory three machines are used for sealing tin cans. When machines A, B, and C ran for 1 minute, 189 cans were sealed. When machines B and C ran for 1 minute, 133 cans were sealed. When machines A and B ran for 2 minutes and machine C ran for 3 minutes, 438 cans were sealed. How many cans are sealed in 1 minute by each machine?

10. Machine $A = 56$
Machine $B = 73$
Machine $C = 60$

Evaluate each determinant.

1. $\begin{vmatrix} 6 & -8 \\ 2 & -1 \end{vmatrix}$

2. $\begin{vmatrix} 3 & 4 \\ 0 & -12 \end{vmatrix}$

3. $\begin{vmatrix} -6 & \dfrac{1}{2} \\ -3 & -4 \end{vmatrix}$

4. $\begin{vmatrix} -6 & -9 \\ 1 & -3 \end{vmatrix}$

5. $\begin{vmatrix} 7 & 1 & 2 \\ 3 & 4 & 0 \\ -2 & -3 & 0 \end{vmatrix}$

6. $\begin{vmatrix} 1 & 2 & -3 \\ 2 & 1 & 0 \\ 3 & 4 & -1 \end{vmatrix}$

1. 10

2. -36

3. $\dfrac{51}{2}$ or 25.5

4. 27

5. -2

6. -12

7. $x = 3$, $y = 3$

Solve each system of equations by Cramer's rule.

7. $2x - y = 3$
$3x + y = 12$

8. $-3x + 5y = 2$
$2x - 3y = 1$

8. $x = 11$, $y = 7$

9. $2x - y + z = 9$
$x + y - 3z = -2$
$3x + y - z = 6$

9. $x = 3$, $y = -2$, $z = 1$

10. Solve for **x only** by Cramer's rule.

$$3x + 4y + 2z = -7$$
$$y + 2z = 2$$
$$2x + 3y = -4$$

10. $x = -5$

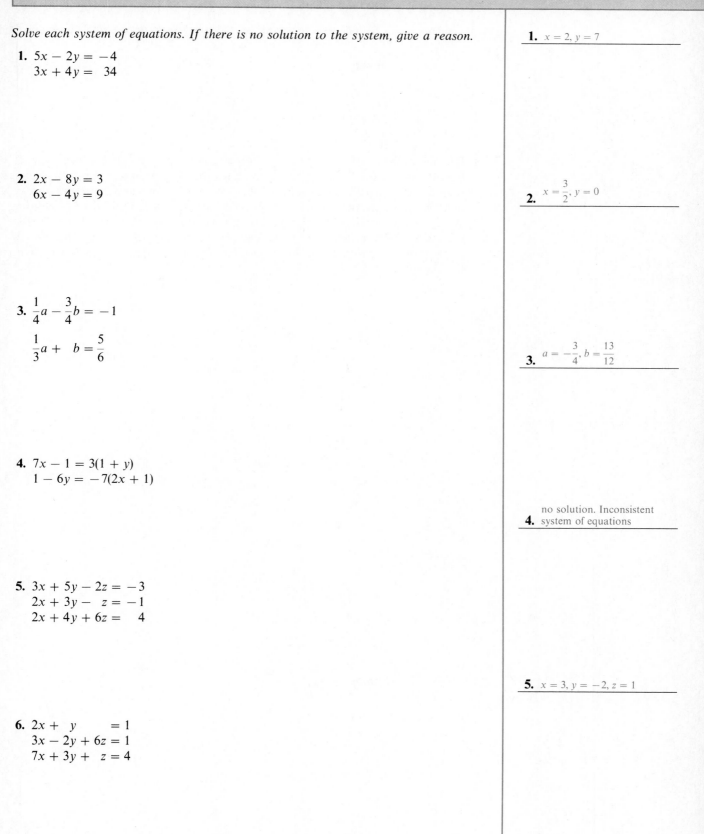

TEST CHAPTER 3

Solve each system of equations. If there is no solution to the system, give a reason.

1. $5x - 2y = -4$
$\quad 3x + 4y = 34$

2. $2x - 8y = 3$
$\quad 6x - 4y = 9$

3. $\dfrac{1}{4}a - \dfrac{3}{4}b = -1$

$\quad \dfrac{1}{3}a + b = \dfrac{5}{6}$

4. $7x - 1 = 3(1 + y)$
$\quad 1 - 6y = -7(2x + 1)$

5. $3x + 5y - 2z = -3$
$\quad 2x + 3y - z = -1$
$\quad 2x + 4y + 6z = 4$

6. $2x + y = 1$
$\quad 3x - 2y + 6z = 1$
$\quad 7x + 3y + z = 4$

1. $x = 2, y = 7$

2. $x = \dfrac{3}{2}, y = 0$

3. $a = -\dfrac{3}{4}, b = \dfrac{13}{12}$

4. no solution. Inconsistent system of equations

5. $x = 3, y = -2, z = 1$

6. $x = -3, y = 7, z = 4$

Speed of plane
in still air = 450 mph
7. Speed of wind = 50 mph

Use a system of linear equations to solve the following problems.

7. A plane flew 1000 miles with a tailwind in 2 hours. The return trip against the wind took $2\frac{1}{2}$ hours. Find the speed of the wind and the speed of the plane in still air.

Station wagons = 4,
2–door sedans = 6,
8. 4–door sedans = 6

8. On an automobile assembly line, station wagons require 5 minutes for rustproofing, 4 minutes for painting, and 3 minutes for heat drying. Four-door sedans require 4 minutes for rustproofing, 3 minutes for painting, and 2 minutes for drying. Two-door sedans require 3 minutes for rust-proofing, 3 minutes for painting, and 2 minutes for drying. The assembly-line supervisor wants to find an assembly plan to use 62 minutes of rustproofing time, 52 minutes of painting time, and 36 minutes of heat drying time. How many vehicles of each type should be sent down the assembly line?

Evaluate by Cramer's rule.

9. $x = 2, y = 2$

9. $4x - 5y = -2$
$7x + 3y = 20$

10. $\dfrac{1}{2}x + \dfrac{1}{4}y = 1$

$\dfrac{3}{7}x + y = \dfrac{17}{7}$

10. $x = 1, y = 2$

11. Solve for *z only* by Cramer's rule.

$$x + 5y + 4z = -3$$
$$x - y - 2z = -3$$
$$x + 2y + 3z = -5$$

11. $z = -1$

Approximately one-half of this test covers the content of Chapters 1 and 2. The remainder covers the content of Chapter 3.

1. State what property is illustrated: $7 + 0 = 7$.

2. Evaluate:
$\sqrt{25} + (2 - 3)^3 + 20 \div (-10)$.

3. Simplify: $(5x^{-2})(3x^{-4}y^2)$.

4. Simplify: $2x - 4[x - 3(2x + 1)]$.

5. Solve for P: $A = P(3 + 4rt)$.

6. Solve for x: $\dfrac{1}{4}x + 5 = \dfrac{1}{3}(x - 2)$.

7. Graph the line $4x - 8y = 10$. Plot at least three points.

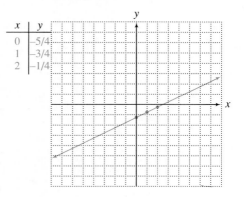

x	y
0	$-5/4$
1	$-3/4$
2	$-1/4$

8. Find the slope of a line passing through $(6, -1)$ and $(-4, -2)$.

1. Identity property for addition

2. 2

3. $15x^{-6}y^2$ or $\dfrac{15y^2}{x^6}$

4. $22x + 12$

5. $P = \dfrac{A}{3 + 4rt}$

6. $x = 68$

7. $4x - 8y = 10$

8. $m = \dfrac{1}{10}$

9. $6x - 5y = 27$

10. 1st side = 17 m,
2nd side = 24 m,
3rd side = 28 m

11. $1500 @ 7%, $4500 @ 9%

12. $x = 2, y = -4$

13. $x = 2, y = -1, z = -1$

14. Shirts = $21, Slacks = $30

15. $x = 5, y = 3$

16. $z = -2$

17. Infinite number of
solutions–dependent eqs.

9. Find the equation in standard form of a line passing through $(2, -3)$ and perpendicular to $5x + 6y = -2$.

10. A triangle has a perimeter of 69 meters. The second side is 7 meters longer than the first side. The third side is 6 meters shorter than double the length of the first side. Find the length of each side.

11. Victor invests $6000 in a bank. Part is invested at 7% interest and part at 9% interest. In one year Victor earns $510 in interest. How much did he invest at each amount?

12. Solve for (x, y):

$$5x + 2y = 2$$
$$4x + 3y = -4$$

13. Solve for (x, y, z):

$$2x + y - z = 4$$
$$x + 2y - 2z = 2$$
$$x - 3y + z = 4$$

14. Patricia bought five shirts and eight pairs of slacks for $345 at Super Discount Center. Joanna bought seven shirts and three pairs of the same slacks at the same store and her total was $237. How much did a shirt cost? How much did a pair of slacks cost?

15. Solve for (x, y) by Cramer's rule:

$$7x - 6y = 17$$
$$3x + y = 18$$

16. Solve for **z only**. Use Cramer's rule.

$$x + 3y + z = 5$$
$$2x - 3y - 2z = 0$$
$$x - 2y + 3z = -9$$

17. What happens when you attempt to solve

$$-5x + 6y = 2$$
$$10x - 12y = -4 \quad ?$$

Why is this?

Polynomials

Specialized equipment helps land surveyors make their measurements, but surveyors themselves must be able to apply mathematical formulas on their job.

4

PRETEST CHAPTER 4

If you are familiar with the topics in this chapter, take this test now. Check your answers with those in the back of the book. If an answer was wrong or you couldn't do a problem, study the appropriate section of the chapter.

If you are not familiar with the topics in this chapter, don't take this test now. Instead, study the examples, work the practice problems, and then take the test.

This test will help you identify those concepts that you have mastered and those that need more study.

Follow the directions. Simplify all answers.

Section 4.1

1. $(5x^2 - 3x + 2) + (-3x^2 - 5x - 8) - (x^2 + 3x - 10)$ $x^2 - 11x + 4$

2. $(5a - 8w)(6a - 7z)$ $30a^2 - 48aw - 35az + 56wz$

3. $(x^2 - 3xy - 4y^2)(2x^2 + xy - 2y^2)$ $2x^4 - 5x^3y - 13x^2y^2 + 2xy^3 + 8y^4$

Sections 4.2 and 4.3

4. $(25x^3y^2 - 30x^2y^3 - 50x^2y^2) \div 5x^2y^2$ $5x - 6y - 10$

5. $(3y^3 - 5y^2 + 2y - 1) \div (y - 2)$

6. $(2x^4 + 9x^3 + 8x^2 - 9x - 10) \div (2x + 5)$ $x^3 + 2x^2 - x - 2$

$3y^2 + y + 4 + \dfrac{7}{y-2}$

Section 4.4   Factor completely.

$12a^3b^2(2 + 3a - 5b)$

7. $24a^3b^2 + 36a^4b^2 - 60a^3b^3$

8. $3x(4x - 3y) - 2(4x - 3y)$

9. $10wx + 6xz - 15yz - 25wy$ $(5w + 3z)(2x - 5y)$

$(4x - 3y)(3x - 2)$

Section 4.5   Factor.

10. $x^2 - 7xy + 10y^2$ $(x - 5y)(x - 2y)$

11. $4y^2 - 4y - 15$ $(2y - 5)(2y + 3)$

12. $28x^2 - 19xy + 3y^2$ $(7x - 3y)(4x - y)$

Section 4.6   Factor.

13. $36x^2 - 60xy + 25y^2$ $(6x - 5y)^2$

14. $121x^2 - 1$ $(11x - 1)(11x + 1)$

15. $8x^3 - y^3$ $(2x - y)(4x^2 + 2xy + y^2)$

16. $64x^3 + 27$ $(4x + 3)(16x^2 - 12x + 9)$

Section 4.7   Factor if possible. Indicate the *prime* expressions.

17. $x^3y^3 - 27y^6$ $y^3(x - 3y)(x^2 + 3xy + 9y^2)$

18. $2x^3 - 2x^2 - 24x$ $2x(x - 4)(x + 3)$

19. $2x^2 + 8x - 3$ prime

20. $81a^3 + 126a^2y + 49ay^2$ $a(9a + 7y)^2$

☐ After studying this section, you will be able to:

1 *Identify types and degrees of polynomials*

2 *Add and subtract polynomials*

3 *Multiply polynomials*

4 *Multiply two binomials by FOIL*

5 *Multiply two binomials by $(a + b)(a - b) = a^2 - b^2$*

6 *Multiply two binomials by $(a + b)^2 = a^2 + 2ab + b^2$*

4.1 ADDITION, SUBTRACTION, AND MULTIPLICATION OF POLYNOMIALS

1 A **polynomial** is an algebraic expression of one or more terms. A **term** is a number, a variable, or a product of numbers and variables. All the exponents of the variables must be nonnegative integers and there must be no division by a variable. Three types of polynomials that you will see often are **monomials**, **binomials**, and **trinomials**.

> **1.** A **monomial** has *one* term.
>
> **2.** A **binomial** has *two* terms.
>
> **3.** A **trinomial** has *three* terms.

Polynomials are also classified by degree. The **degree of a term** is the sum of the exponents of its variables. The **degree of a polynomial** is the degree of the highest-degree term in the polynomial. If the polynomial has no variable; then it has degree zero.

Example 1 Name the type of polynomial and give its degree.

(a) $p = 5x^6 + 3x^2 + 2$ (b) $g = 7x + 6$
(c) $h = 5x^2y + 3xy^3 + 6xy$ (d) $f = 7x^4y^5$

(a) p is a trinomial of degree 6 .
(b) g is a binomial of degree 1 . (Remember, if no number appears as an exponent of a variable, the exponent is 1.)
(c) h is a trinomial of degree 4 .
(d) f is a monomial of degree 9 . ∎

Practice Problem 1 State the type of polynomial and give its degree.
(a) $p = 3x^5 - 6x^4 + x^2$ (b) $g = 5x^2 + 2$
(c) $h = 3ab + 5a^2b^2 - 6a^4b$ (d) $f = 16x^4y^6$ ∎

TEACHING TIP Remind students that determining the degree of a polynomial is very important in factoring, and later in solving, higher–degree equations. The highest–degree term is not always the first term, but student sometimes make a mistake because they do not remember this.

Many polynomials contain only one variable. A **polynomial in x** is an expression of the form

$$ax^n + bx^{n-1} + cx^{n-2} + \cdots + p$$

where n is a nonnegative integer and constants $a, b, c, \ldots, p$ are real numbers. We usually write polynomials in **descending order** of the variable. For example, $4x^5 - 2x^3 + 6x^2 + 5x - 8$ is written in descending order.

Here are some examples of polynomials.

	Monomial	Binomial	Trinomial	Polynomial
One variable	$8x^3$	$2y^2 + 3y$	$5x^2 + 2x - 6$	$x^4 + 2x^3 - x^2 + 9$
Two variables	$6x^2y$	$3x^2 - 5y^3$	$8x^2 + 5xy - 3y^2$	$x^3y + 5xy^2 + 3xy - 7y^5$
Three variables	$12uvw^3$	$11a^2b + 5c^2$	$4a^2b^4 + 7c^4 - 2a^5$	$3c^2 + 4c - 8d + 2e - e^2$

The following are *not* polynomials:

$$2x^{-3} + 5x^2 - 3 = 0$$

$$4ab^{1/2} = y$$

$$\frac{2}{x} + \frac{3}{y} = z$$

Can you give a reason why each expression is not a polynomial?

2 Adding and Subtracting Polynomials

We can add and subtract polynomials by combining like terms and using the methods of Section 1.5.

Example 2 Let $p = 4x^3 - 7x^2 + 2$ and $f = 7x^3 + 6x^2 - 8x - 5$. Find

(a) $p + f$ (b) $p - f$

(a) We simply combine like terms.

$$p + f = 4x^3 - 7x^2 + 2 + 7x^3 + 6x^2 - 8x - 5$$
$$= 11x^3 - x^2 - 8x - 3$$

(b) $p - f = 4x^3 - 7x^2 + 2 - (7x^3 + 6x^2 - 8x - 5)$
$$= 4x^3 - 7x^2 + 2 - 7x^3 - 6x^2 + 8x + 5$$
$$= -3x^3 - 13x^2 + 8x + 7 \quad \blacksquare$$

(Remember that the minus sign in front of the parentheses means -1 and must be distributed over the terms in parentheses.)

Practice Problem 2 Let $p = 2x^3 - 6x^2 + 5x - 2$ and $f = -7x^3 - 5x^2 + 3x + 4$. Find
(a) $p + f$ **(b)** $p - f$ $\blacksquare$

❸ Multiplying Polynomials

The distributive property is the basis for multiplying polynomials other than monomials.

$$a(b + c) = ab + ac$$
$$3xy(5x + 6) = 3xy(5x) + 3xy(6)$$
$$= 15x^2y + 18xy$$

A similar procedure can be used if we multiply two binomials

$$(3x + 5)(6x + 7) = (3x + 5)6x + (3x + 5)7$$

Now the distributive property also has the form

$$(b + c)a = ba + ca$$

So we use this to complete our problem

$$= (3x)(6x) + (5)(6x) + (3x)(7) + (5)(7)$$
$$= 18x^2 + 30x + 21x + 35$$
$$= 18x^2 + 51x + 35$$

The multiplication of a binomial and a trinomial is more involved. One way to multiply two polynomials is to write them vertically, as we do when multiplying two- and three-digit numbers. We then multiply them in the usual way.

Example 3 Multiply: $(4x^2 - 2x + 3)(-3x + 4)$.

$$
\begin{array}{r}
4x^2 - 2x + 3 \\
- 3x + 4 \\
\hline
16x^2 - 8x + 12 \\
-12x^3 + 6x^2 - 9x \\
\hline
-12x^3 + 22x^2 - 17x + 12
\end{array}
$$

Multiplying $(4x^2 - 2x + 3)(+4)$.
Multiplying $(4x^2 - 2x + 3)(-3x)$.
Add the two products. $\blacksquare$

Practice Problem 3 Multiply: $(2x^2 - 3x + 1)(x^2 - 5x)$ $\blacksquare$

Another way to multiply polynomials is to multiply horizontally: Let's redo Example 3.

Example 3 Revisited Multiply: $(4x^2 - 2x + 3)(-3x + 4)$.

Multiply $-3x$ by each term in the first parentheses to obtain

$$(4x^2 - 2x + 3)(-3x + 4) = -12x^3 + 6x^2 - 9x + 16x^2 - 8x + 12$$

Multiply 4 by each term in the second parentheses to obtain

Now combine like terms.

$$-12x^3 + 22x^2 - 17x + 12 \quad \blacksquare$$

TEACHING TIP Some students and faculty prefer to show multiplication by a trinomial in horizontal fashion. There is no absolute requirement to show multiplication of polynomials in columns. You may want to contrast for your students the method of example 3 and the method of example 3 revisited. However, students who perform at least some of the multiplication of trinomials in this column fashion seem to have less difficulty in performing the division of polynomials in section 4.2.

4 A similar method works especially well with binomials. To keep track of the order of multiplying these terms use the initials FOIL. The acronym FOIL means

F	First
O	Outer
I	Inner
L	Last

That is, we multiply the first terms, then the outer terms, then the inner terms, and finally, the last terms.

Example 4 Multiply: $(5x + 2)(7x - 3)$.

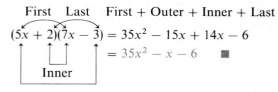

First   Last   First + Outer + Inner + Last

$$(5x + 2)(7x - 3) = 35x^2 - 15x + 14x - 6$$
$$= 35x^2 - x - 6 \quad \blacksquare$$

Inner

Outer

Practice Problem 4 Multiply: $(7x + 3)(2x - 5)$. ▦

Example 5 Multiply: $(7x^2 - 8)(2x - 3)$.

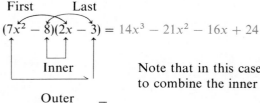

First   Last

$$(7x^2 - 8)(2x - 3) = 14x^3 - 21x^2 - 16x + 24$$

Inner

Note that in this case we were not able to combine the inner and outer product.

Outer ▦

Practice Problem 5 Multiply: $(5a - 2b)(3c - 4d)$. ▦

5 Special Products

Products of the form $(a + b)(a - b)$ occur often and deserve special attention.

$$(a + b)(a - b) = a^2 - ab + ab - b^2 = a^2 - b^2$$

Once you observe the pattern and understand it, you should memorize the formula:

$$(a + b)(a - b) = a^2 - b^2 \qquad (4.1)$$

Example 6 Multiply. **(a)** $(2a - 9b)(2a + 9b)$ **(b)** $(5x^2 + 7y^3)(5x^2 - 7y^3)$

(a) $(2a - 9b)(2a + 9b) = (2a)^2 - (9b)^2$
$$= 4a^2 - 81b^2$$

(b) $(5x^2 + 7y^3)(5x^2 - 7y^3) = (5x^2)^2 - (7y^3)^2$
$$= 25x^4 - 49y^6$$

Of course, we could have used the FOIL method, but recognizing the special product allowed us to save time. ▦

Practice Problem 6 Multiply.
(a) $(7x - 2y)(7x + 2y)$ **(b)** $(5a^2 + 8b^2)(5a^2 - 8b^2)$ ▦

6 A second special case is the square of a binomial:

$$(a - b)^2 = (a - b)(a - b) = a^2 - ab - ab + b^2 = a^2 - 2ab + b^2$$

Once you understand the pattern, you should memorize these two formulas:

$$(a - b)^2 = a^2 - 2ab + b^2 \qquad (4.2)$$
$$(a + b)^2 = a^2 + 2ab + b^2 \qquad (4.3)$$

This procedure is also called *expanding a binomial*. **Note:** $(a - b)^2 \neq a^2 - b^2$ and $(a + b)^2 \neq a^2 + b^2$. ∎

Example 7 Multiply (that is, expand the binomials).

(a) $(5a - 8b)^2$ **(b)** $(3u + 11v^2)^2$ **(c)** $(10x^2 - 3y^2)^2$ **(d)** $(12x^3 + 1)^2$

(a) $(5a - 8b)^2 = (5a)^2 - 2(5a)(8b) + (8b)^2$
$$= 25a^2 - 80ab + 64b^2$$

(b) Here $a = 3u$ and $b = 11v^2$.
$$(3u + 11v^2)^2 = (3u)^2 + 2(3u)(11v^2) + (11v^2)^2$$
$$= 9u^2 + 66uv^2 + 121v^4$$

(c) Here $a = 10x^2$ and $b = 3y^2$.
$$(10x^2 - 3y^2)^2 = (10x^2)^2 - 2(10x^2)(3y)^2 + (3y^2)^2$$
$$= 100x^4 - 60x^2y^2 + 9y^4$$

(d) Here $a = 12x^3$ and $b = 1^2$.
$$(12x^3 + 1)^2 = (12x^3)^2 + 2(12x^3)(1) + (1)^2$$
$$= 144x^6 + 24x^3 + 1 \quad ∎$$

Practice Problem 7 Multiply.
(a) $(3x - 7y)^2$ **(b)** $(4u + 5v)^2$ **(c)** $(9a + 2b)^2$ **(d)** $(7x^2 - 3y^2)$
∎

EXERCISES 4.1

Name the polynomial and give its degree.

1. $7x^3y + 8$
Binomial, 4th degree

2. $5a + ab + 6$
Trinomial, 2nd degree

3. $17x^3y^5z$
Monomial, 9th degree

4. $3xy^4 + 2x^2y^5$
Binomial, 7th degree

5. $\frac{3}{5}m^3n - \frac{2}{5}mn + \frac{1}{5}n^8$
Trinomial, 8th degree

6. $-27ab^3cd$
Monomial, 6th degree

In problems 7–20, write your answers in descending *order.*

7. $P = 5x^3 - 6x^2 + 8x - 12$
$Q = 3x^2 - 5x - 7$
$H = x^4 - x^3 + x^2 - 10$
(a) Find $P + Q$.
(b) Find $Q - H$.
(c) Find $H - P$.

(a) $5x^3 - 6x^2 + 8x - 12 + 3x^2 - 5x - 7 = 5x^3 - 3x^2 + 3x - 19$
(b) $3x^2 - 5x - 7 - (x^4 - x^3 + x^2 - 10) = -x^4 + x^3 + 2x^2 - 5x + 3$
(c) $x^4 - x^3 + x^2 - 10 - (5x^3 - 6x^2 + 8x - 12) = x^4 - 6x^3 + 7x^2 - 8x + 2$

8. $G = 2x^2 + 5x - 1$
$M = 4x^4 - 5x^3 - x^2 + 12$
$N = x^5 - 3x^3 + x^2 + 2x - 5$
(a) Find $G + N$. $x^5 - 3x^3 + 3x^2 + 7x - 6$
(b) Find $M - N$. $-x^5 + 4x^4 - 2x^3 - 2x^2 - 2x + 17$
(c) Find $N - G$. $x^5 - 3x^3 - x^2 - 3x - 4$

Perform each operation.

9. $(x^2 + 3x - 2) + (-2x^2 - 5x + 1) + (7x^2 - 6x - 3)$
$6x^2 - 8x - 4$

10. $(2x^2 - 5x - 1) + (3x^2 - 7x + 3) + (-7x^2 + 5x + 8)$
$-2x^2 - 7x + 10$

11. $(4x^3 - 6x^2 - 3x + 5) - (2x^3 + 3x^2 - 5x - 8)$
$2x^3 - 9x^2 + 2x + 13$

12. $(3x^3 + 2x^2 - 8x - 9) - (-5x^3 + x^2 - x - 12)$
$8x^3 + x^2 - 7x + 3$

13. $(5a^3 - 2a^2 - 6a + 8) + (5a + 6) - (2a^2 - 3a + 5)$
$5a^3 - 4a^2 + 2a + 9$

14. $(7a^2 - 2a + 6) + (-12a^3 - 6a + 5) - (3a^2 - a - 2)$
$-12a^3 + 4a^2 - 7a + 13$

Multiply.

15. $2x(3x^2 - 5x + 1)$
$6x^3 - 10x^2 + 2x$

16. $-5x(x^2 - 6x - 2)$
$-5x^3 + 30x^2 + 10x$

17. $-3xy(2x - 6y + 15)$
$-6x^2y + 18xy^2 - 45xy$

18. $4xy^2(x - y + 3)$
$4x^2y^2 - 4xy^3 + 12xy^2$

19. $(x + 5)(x - 6)$
$x^2 - x - 30$

20. $(x + 12)(x + 2)$
$x^2 + 14x + 24$

21. $(2x + 1)(3x + 2)$
$6x^2 + 7x + 2$

22. $(2x - 1)(x + 5)$
$2x^2 + 9x - 5$

23. $(7x - 6)(4x - 3)$
$28x^2 - 45x + 18$

24. $(2x - 4)(9x - 5)$
$18x^2 - 46x + 20$

25. $(5w + 2d)(3a - 4b)$
$15aw + 6ad - 20bw - 8bd$

26. $(7a + 8b)(5d - 8w)$
$35ad + 40bd - 56aw - 64bw$

27. $(3x - 2y)(-4x + y)$
$-12x^2 + 11xy - 2y^2$

28. $(-8x - 3y)(x + 2y)$
$-8x^2 - 19xy - 6y^2$

29. $(2r + 2s^2)(5r - 9s^2)$
$10r^2 - 8rs^2 - 18s^4$

30. $(-3r - 2s^2)(5r - 6s^2)$
$-15r^2 + 8rs^2 + 12s^4$

31. $(x + 2)(5x^2 - 6x + 1)$
$5x^3 + 4x^2 - 11x + 2$

32. $(x - 3)(2x^2 - 8x + 3)$
$2x^3 - 14x^2 + 27x - 9$

33. $(3x^2 - 2xy - 6y^2)(2x - y)$
$6x^3 - 7x^2y - 10xy^2 + 6y^3$

34. $(5x^2 + 3xy - 7y^2)(3x - 2y)$
$15x^3 - x^2y - 27xy^2 + 14y^3$

35. $(x^2 - 6x + 1)(2x^2 - 5x + 2)$
$2x^4 - 17x^3 + 34x^2 - 17x + 2$

36. $(3x^2 - 2x - 4)(x^2 + 2x + 3)$
$3x^4 + 4x^3 + x^2 - 14x - 12$

37. $(5a^3 - 3a^2 + 2a - 4)(a - 3)$
$5a^4 - 18a^3 + 11a^2 - 10a + 12$

38. $(2b^3 - 5b^2 - 4b + 1)(2b - 1)$
$4b^4 - 12b^3 - 3b^2 + 6b - 1$

39. $(r^2 + 3rs - 2s^2)(3r^2 - 4rs - 2s^2)$
$3r^4 + 5r^3s - 20r^2s^2 + 2rs^3 + 4s^4$

40. $(m^2 - 6mp + 2p^2)(2m^2 - 4mp + 3p^2)$
$2m^4 - 16m^3p + 31m^2p^2 - 26mp^3 + 6p^4$

Use equations (4-1), (4-2), and (4-3) to mentally multiply.

41. $(5x - 8y)(5x + 8y)$
$25x^2 - 64y^2$

42. $(2a - 7b)(2a + 7b)$
$4a^2 - 49b^2$

43. $(5a - 2b)^2$
$25a^2 - 20ab + 4b^2$

44. $(6a + 5b)^2$
$36a^2 + 60ab + 25b^2$

45. $(8x + 9)^2$
$64x^2 + 144x + 81$

46. $(7x - 8)^2$
$49x^2 - 112x + 64$

47. $(2x^2 + 1)(2x^2 - 1)$
$4x^4 - 1$

48. $(1 - 7x^3)(1 + 7x^3)$
$1 - 49x^6$

49. $(2a^2b^2 - 3)^2$
$4a^4b^4 - 12a^2b^2 + 9$

50. $(3x^2 - 5y^2)^2$
$9x^4 - 30x^2y^2 + 25y^4$

First multiply any two binomials in the problem, then multiply the result by the third binomial.

51. $(x + 2)(x - 3)(2x - 5)$
$2x^3 - 7x^2 - 7x + 30$

52. $(x - 6)(x + 2)(3x + 2)$
$3x^3 - 10x^2 - 44x - 24$

53. $(a + 3)(2 - a)(4 - 3a)$
$3a^3 - a^2 - 22a + 24$

54. $(6 - 5a)(a + 1)(2 - 3a)$
$15a^3 - 13a^2 - 16a + 12$

? **To Think About**

Assume that all variables used as components represent whole numbers. Multiply.

55. $(3x^{2n} + 4)(5x^{3n} - 2)$
$15x^{5n} + 20x^{3n} - 6x^{2n} - 8$

56. $(2x^{3n} - 1)(5x^{2n} + 4)$
$10x^{5n} + 8x^{3n} - 5x^{2n} - 4$

57. $(2a^{3 - 2n} + 4)(3a^n + 6)$
$6a^{3-n} + 12a^{3-2n} + 12a^n + 24$

58. $(4b^{2n+6} + 3)(2b^{n+1} + 5)$
$8b^{3n+7} + 20b^{2n+6} + 6b^{n+1} + 15$

59. The area of the base of a rectangular box measures $2x^2 + 5x + 8$ cm². The height of the box measures $3x + 5$ cm. Find the volume of the box.
$6x^3 + 25x^2 + 49x + 40$ cm³

60. A rectangular garden has $3n^2 + 4n + 7$ flowers planted in each row. The garden has $2n + 5$ rows. Find the number of flowers in the garden.
$6n^3 + 23n^2 + 34n + 35$ flowers

61. Collect like terms: $5x - 6y - 8x + 2y - 7x - 8y$.

$-10x - 12y$

62. Evaluate $2x^2 + 3x - 4$ when $x = -2$.

$2(4) - 6 - 4 = -2$

63. Simplify: $2\{3 - x[4 + x(2 - x)]\}$.

$2\{3 - 4x - 2x^2 + x^3\}$
$2x^3 - 4x^2 - 8x + 6$

64. Simplify: $(3x^3y^2)(4x^6y^{-3})$.

$12x^9y^{-1} = \dfrac{12x^9}{y}$

Calculator Problems

Simplify.

65. $(3.928x^2 - 5.617x) + (8.346x^2 - 9.098x) + (-1)(1.542x^2 - 3.986x)$

$10.732x^2 - 10.729x$

66. $(52.613x + 49.408y)(34.078x - 28.231y)$

$1792.945814x^2 + 198.408221xy - 1394.837248y^2$

For Extra Practice Exercises, turn to page 229.

Solutions to Odd-Numbered Practice Problems

1. (a) $p = 3x^5 - 6x^4 + x^2$
This is a trinomial of degree 6.
(b) $g = 5x^2 + 2$
This is binomial of degree 2.
(c) $h = 3ab + 5a^2b^2 - 6a^4b$
This is a trinomial of degree 5.
(d) $f = 16x^4y^6$
This is a monomial of degree 10.

3.
$$\begin{array}{r} 2x^2 - 3x + 1 \\ x^2 - 5x \\ \hline -10x^3 + 15x^2 - 5x \\ 2x^4 - 3x^3 + x^2 \\ \hline 2x^4 - 13x^3 + 16x^2 - 5x \end{array}$$

5. Using FOIL we have

$(5a - 2b)(3c - 4d) = 15ac - 20ad - 6bc + 8bd$

7. $(a + b)^2 = a^2 + 2ab + b^2 \qquad (a - b)^2 = a^2 - 2ab + b^2$
(a) $(3x - 7y)^2 = (3x)^2 - 2(3x)(7y) + (7y)^2 = 9x^2 - 42xy + 49y^2$
(b) $(4u + 5v)^2 = (4u)^2 + 2(4u)(5v) + (5v)^2 = 16u^2 + 40uv + 25v^2$
(c) $(9a + 2b)^2 = (9a)^2 + 2(9a)(2b) + (2b)^2 = 81a^2 + 36ab + 4b^2$
(d) $(7x^2 - 3y^2) = (7x^2)^2 - 2(7x^2)(3y^2) + (3y^2)^2 = 49x^4 - 42x^2y^2 + 9y^4$

Answers to Even-Numbered Practice Problems

2. (a) $p + f = -5x^3 - 11x^2 + 8x + 2$ **(b)** $p - f = 9x^3 - x^2 + 2x - 6$ **4.** $14x^2 - 29x - 15$
6. (a) $49x^2 - 4y^2$ **(b)** $25a^4 - 64b^4$

☐ **After studying the section, you will be able to:**

1 *Divide a polynomial by a monomial*

2 *Divide a polynomial by a polynomial*

4.2 DIVISION OF POLYNOMIALS

1 The easiest type of polynomial division occurs when the divisor is a monomial. We do this type of division just as if we were dividing numbers. First we write the indicated division as the sum of separate fractions, and then we reduce (if possible) each fraction.

Example 1 Divide: $(24x^2 - 18x + 2) \div 4$.

First write the division in fractional form:

$$(24x^2 - 18x + 2) \div 4 = \frac{24x^2 - 18x + 2}{4}$$

Now divide each member of the polynomial in the numerator by the monomial in the denominator.

$$\frac{24x^2 - 18x + 2}{4} = \frac{24x^2}{4} - \frac{18x}{4} + \frac{2}{4}$$

$$= 6x^2 - \frac{9}{2}x + \frac{1}{2} \quad \blacksquare$$

Practice Problem 1   Divide: $(16x^3 - 8x^2 + 3x) \div 2x$.   ∎

Example 2   Divide: $(15x^3 - 10x^2 + 40x) \div 5x$.

$$\frac{15x^3 - 10x^2 + 40x}{5x} = \frac{15x^3}{5x} - \frac{10x^2}{5x} + \frac{40x}{5x}$$
$$= 3x^2 - 2x + 8$$ ∎

Practice Problem 2   Divide: $(-16x^4 + 16x^3 + 8x^2 + 64x) \div 8x$.   ∎

2 When we divide polynomials by binomials or trinomials, we perform long division. This is much like dividing numbers. The polynomials must be in descending order.

Let's divide $6x^2 + 17x + 12$ by $2x + 3$. First we write the problem in the form of long division.

$$2x + 3 \overline{)\, 6x^2 + 17x + 12}$$

The divisor is $2x + 3$; the dividend is $6x^2 + 17x + 12$. Now we divide the first term of the dividend ($6x^2$) by the first term of the divisor ($2x$).

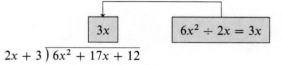

$$2x + 3 \overline{)\, 6x^2 + 17x + 12}$$

Now we multiply $3x$ (the first part of the quotient) by the divisor $2x + 3$.

$$\begin{array}{r} 3x \\ 2x + 3 \overline{)\, 6x^2 + 17x + 12} \\ 6x^2 + 9x \end{array}$$

The product of $3x(2x + 3)$.

Next, just as in arithmetic long division, we subtract this term from the dividend and bring down the next monomial.

$$\begin{array}{r} 3x \\ 2x + 3 \overline{)\, 6x^2 + 17x + 12} \\ 6x^2 + 9x \\ \hline 8x + 12 \end{array}$$

Subtract $6x^2 + 9x$ from $6x^2 + 17x$.

Bring down the next monomial.

Now we divide the first term of this binomial ($8x$) by the first term of the divisor ($2x$).

$$\begin{array}{r} 3x + 4 \\ 2x + 3 \overline{)\, 6x^2 + 17x + 12} \\ 6x^2 + 9x \\ \hline 8x + 12 \\ 8x + 12 \\ \hline 0 \end{array}$$

$8x \div 2x = 4$

The product $4(2x + 3)$

Note that we then multiplied $(2x + 3)(4)$ and subtracted, just as we did before. We continued this process until the remainder was zero.

Check: Multiply: $(2x + 3)(3x + 4) = 6x^2 + 17x + 12$.

For convenience, we summarize the steps involved.

TEACHING TIP   There are a few cases in higher–level courses where division by a negative monomial denominator is required. As an extended class example, you may want to show the following:

$$\frac{-21x^4y^3 + 15x^3y^2 - 30x^2y}{-3x^2y}$$
$$= \frac{-21x^4y^3}{-3x^2y} + \frac{15x^3y^2}{-3x^2y}$$
$$+ \frac{-30x^2y}{-3x^2y}$$
$$= 7x^2y^2 - 5xy + 10$$

TEACHING TIP There are often a few students who do not understand the checking step. It may help to show them that the division problem

$$\frac{21 \ R \ 22}{31 \overline{)\ 673}}$$

can be checked by doing the problem $31 \times 21 + 22$ $= 651 + 22 = 673$. Likewise, we check example 3 by multiplying $(3x - 1)(2x^2 + 3x + 1)$ and then adding the remainder of 4 to obtain $6x^3 + 7x^2 + 3$.

Example 3 Divide: $(6x^3 + 7x^2 + 3) \div (3x - 1)$.

There is no x term in the dividend, so we write $0x$.

$$
\begin{array}{r}
2x^2 + 3x + 1 \\
3x - 1 \overline{)\ 6x^3 + 7x^2 + 0x + 3} \\
\underline{6x^3 - 2x^2} \\
9x^2 + 0x \\
\underline{9x^2 - 3x} \\
3x + 3 \\
\underline{3x - 1} \\
4
\end{array}
$$

Note that we subtract $7x^2 - (-2x^2)$ to obtain $9x^2$.

Note that we subtract $0x - (-3x)$ to obtain $3x$.

The quotient is $2x^2 + 3x + 1$ with a remainder of 4. We may write this as

$$2x^2 + 3x + 1 + \frac{4}{3x - 1}$$

Check: $(3x - 1)(2x^2 + 3x + 1) + 4 \overset{?}{=} 6x^3 + 7x^2 + 3$
$6x^3 + 7x^2 - 0x - 1 + 4 \overset{?}{=} 6x^3 + 7x^2 + 3$
$6x^3 + 7x^2 + 3 \overset{?}{=} 6x^3 + 7x^2 + 3$ ✓ ∎

Practice Problem 3 Divide: $(14x + 8x^2 - 14) \div (-3 + 4x)$. ∎

TEACHING TIP If you find it helpful to do an additional sample example of about the same level of difficulty as example 3 before moving onto the problems with two variables, show students the following: $12x^3 + 2x^2 - 10x - 7$ divided by $4x + 2$ is $3x^2 - x - 2$ with a remainder of -3.

$$
\begin{array}{r}
3x^2 - \ \ x - 2 \\
4x + 2 \overline{)\ 12x^3 + 2x^2 - 10x - 7} \\
\underline{12x^3 + 6x^2} \\
-4x^2 - 10x \\
\underline{-4x^2 - \ 2x} \\
-8x - 7 \\
\underline{-8x - 4} \\
-3
\end{array}
$$

Example 4 Divide: $\dfrac{64x^3 - 125y^3}{4x - 5y}$.

This fraction is another way of writing the problem $(64x^3 - 125y^3) \div (4x - 5y)$.

Note that two terms are missing in the dividend. We write them with zero coefficients.

$$
\begin{array}{r}
16x^2 \ + \ 20xy \ + \ 25y^2 \\
4x - 5y \overline{)\ 64x^3 + \ 0x^2y + \ 0xy^2 - 125y^3} \\
\underline{64x^3 - 80x^2y} \\
80x^2y + \ 0xy^2 \\
\underline{80x^2y - 100xy^2} \\
100xy^2 - 125y^3 \\
\underline{100xy^2 - 125y^3} \\
0
\end{array}
$$

Note that $0x^2y - (-80x^2y) = 80x^2y$.

Note that $0xy^2 - (-100xy^2) = 100xy^2$.

The quotient is $16x^2 + 20xy + 25y^2$.
Check: Verify that $(4x - 5y)(16x^2 + 20xy + 25y^2) = 64x^3 - 125y^3$. ∎

Practice Problem 4 Divide: $(8x^3 + 27y^3) \div (2x + 3y)$. ∎

Example 5   Divide: $(7x^3 - 10x - 7x^2 + 2x^4 + 8) \div (2x^2 + x - 2)$.

Arrange the dividend in descending order before dividing.

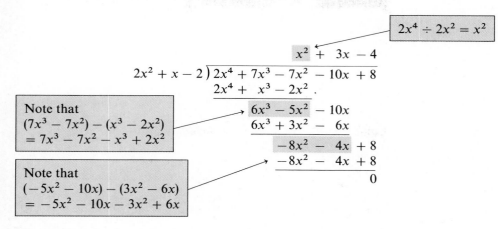

$2x^4 \div 2x^2 = x^2$

$$
\begin{array}{r}
x^2 + 3x - 4 \\
2x^2 + x - 2 \overline{\smash{)}\ 2x^4 + 7x^3 - 7x^2 - 10x + 8} \\
2x^4 + x^3 - 2x^2 \\
\hline
6x^3 - 5x^2 - 10x \\
6x^3 + 3x^2 - 6x \\
\hline
-8x^2 - 4x + 8 \\
-8x^2 - 4x + 8 \\
\hline
0
\end{array}
$$

Note that
$(7x^3 - 7x^2) - (x^3 - 2x^2)$
$= 7x^3 - 7x^2 - x^3 + 2x^2$

Note that
$(-5x^2 - 10x) - (3x^2 - 6x)$
$= -5x^2 - 10x - 3x^2 + 6x$

The quotient is $x^2 + 3x - 4$

Check: Verify that $(2x^2 + x - 2)(x^2 + 3x - 4) = 2x^4 + 7x^3 - 7x^2 - 10x + 8$. ■

Practice Problem 5 $(x^4 - 3x^3 + 3x + 4) \div (x^2 - 1)$. ■

EXERCISES 4.2

Divide.

1. $(15x^2 + 20x - 30) \div 5$
$3x^2 + 4x - 6$

2. $(14x^2 - 28x - 35) \div 7$
$2x^2 - 4x - 5$

3. $(36x^3 - 45x^2 - 36x) \div 9x$
$4x^2 - 5x - 4$

4. $(22x^4 + 33x^3 - 121x^2) \div 11x$
$2x^3 + 3x^2 - 11x$

5. $\dfrac{x^3 - 2x^2 + 5x}{x}$
$x^2 - 2x + 5$

6. $\dfrac{w^3 + 8w^2 - 4w}{w}$
$w^2 + 8w - 4$

7. $\dfrac{18a^3b^2 + 12a^2b^2 - 4ab^2}{2ab^2}$
$9a^2 + 6a - 2$

8. $\dfrac{25m^5n - 10m^4n + 15m^3n}{5m^3n}$
$5m^2 - 2m + 3$

Divide. Check your answers for problems 9–14.

9. $(12x^2 + 11x + 2) \div (4x + 1)$

$$\begin{array}{r} 3x + 2 \\ 4x + 1 \overline{\smash{)}12x^2 + 11x + 2} \\ \underline{12x^2 + 3x} \\ 8x + 2 \\ \underline{8x + 2} \end{array}$$

Ans. $3x + 2$

10. $(15x^2 + 23x + 4) \div (5x + 1)$

$$\begin{array}{r} 3x + 4 \\ 5x + 1 \overline{\smash{)}15x^2 + 23x + 4} \\ \underline{15x^2 + 3x} \\ 20x + 4 \\ \underline{20x + 4} \end{array}$$

Ans. $3x + 4$

11. $(30x^2 - 17x + 2) \div (5x - 2)$

$$\begin{array}{r} 6x - 1 \\ 5x - 2 \overline{\smash{)}30x^2 - 17x + 2} \\ \underline{30x^2 - 12x} \\ -5x + 2 \\ \underline{-5x + 2} \end{array}$$

Ans. $6x - 1$

12. $(28x^2 - 29x + 6) \div (4x - 3)$

$$\begin{array}{r} 7x - 2 \\ 4x - 3 \overline{\smash{)}28x^2 - 29x + 6} \\ \underline{28x^2 - 21x} \\ -8x + 6 \\ \underline{-8x + 6} \end{array}$$

Ans. $7x - 2$

13. $(6a^2 - 11a - 30) \div (3a + 5)$

$$\begin{array}{r} 2a - 7 \\ 3a + 5 \overline{\smash{)}6a^2 - 11a - 30} \\ \underline{6a^2 + 10a} \\ -21a - 30 \\ \underline{-21a - 35} \\ 5 \end{array}$$

Ans. $2a - 7 + \dfrac{5}{3a + 5}$

14. $(18a^2 + 9a - 17) \div (3a + 4)$

$$\begin{array}{r} 6a - 5 \\ 3a + 4 \overline{\smash{)}18a^2 + 9a - 17} \\ \underline{18a^2 + 24a} \\ -15a - 17 \\ \underline{-15a - 20} \\ 3 \end{array}$$

Ans. $6a - 5 + \dfrac{3}{3a + 4}$

15. $(x^3 - x^2 + 11x - 1) \div (x + 1)$

$$\begin{array}{r} x^2 - 2x + 13 \\ x + 1 \overline{\smash{)}x^3 - x^2 + 11x - 1} \\ \underline{x^3 + x^2} \\ -2x^2 + 11x \\ \underline{-2x^2 - 2x} \\ 13x - 1 \\ \underline{13x + 13} \\ -14 \end{array}$$

Ans. $x^2 - 2x + 13 - \dfrac{14}{x + 1}$

16. $(x^3 + 2x^2 - 3x + 2) \div (x + 1)$

$$\begin{array}{r} x^2 + x - 4 \\ x + 1 \overline{\smash{)}x^3 + 2x^2 - 3x + 2} \\ \underline{x^3 + x^2} \\ x^2 - 3x \\ \underline{x^2 + x} \\ -4x + 2 \\ \underline{-4x - 4} \\ 6 \end{array}$$

Ans. $x^2 + x - 4 + \dfrac{6}{x + 1}$

17. $(2x^3 - x^2 - 7) \div (x - 2)$

$$\begin{array}{r} 2x^2 + 3x + 6 \\ x - 2 \overline{\smash{)}2x^3 - x^2 + 0x - 7} \\ \underline{2x^3 - 4x^2} \\ 3x^2 + 0x \\ \underline{3x^2 - 6x} \\ 6x - 7 \\ \underline{6x - 12} \\ 5 \end{array}$$

Ans. $2x^2 + 3x + 6 + \dfrac{5}{x - 2}$

18. $(4x^3 - 6x - 11) \div (2x - 4)$

$$\begin{array}{r} 2x^2 + 4x + 5 \\ 2x - 4 \overline{\smash{)}4x^3 + 0x^2 - 6x - 11} \\ \underline{4x^3 - 8x^2} \\ 8x^2 - 6x \\ \underline{8x^2 - 16x} \\ 10x - 11 \\ \underline{10x - 20} \\ 9 \end{array}$$

Ans. $2x^2 + 4x + 5 + \dfrac{9}{x - 4}$

19. $\dfrac{x^3 - 7x^2 + 13x - 15}{x - 5}$

$$\begin{array}{r} x^2 - 2x + 3 \\ x - 5 \overline{\smash{)}x^3 - 7x^2 + 13x - 15} \\ \underline{x^3 - 5x^2} \\ -2x^2 + 13x \\ \underline{-2x^2 + 10x} \\ 3x - 15 \\ \underline{3x - 15} \end{array}$$

Ans. $x^2 - 2x + 3$

20. $\dfrac{2x^3 + 13x^2 + 9x - 6}{2x + 3}$

$$\begin{array}{r} x^2 + 5x - 3 \\ 2x + 3 \overline{\smash{)}2x^3 + 13x^2 + 9x - 6} \\ \underline{2x^3 + 3x^2} \\ 10x^2 + 9x \\ \underline{10x^2 + 15x} \\ -6x - 6 \\ \underline{-6x - 9} \\ 3 \end{array}$$

Ans. $x^2 + 5x - 3 + \dfrac{3}{2x + 3}$

21. $\dfrac{x^3 + 27}{x + 3}$

$$\begin{array}{r} x^2 - 3x + 9 \\ x + 3 \overline{\smash{)}x^3 + 0x^2 + 0x + 27} \\ \underline{x^3 + 3x^2} \\ -3x^2 + 0x \\ \underline{-3x^2 - 9x} \\ 9x + 27 \\ \underline{9x + 27} \end{array}$$

Ans. $x^2 - 3x + 9$

22. $\dfrac{x^3 - 64}{x - 4}$

$$\begin{array}{r} x^2 + 4x + 16 \\ x - 4 \overline{\smash{)}x^3 + 0x^2 + 0x - 64} \\ \underline{x^3 - 4x^2} \\ 4x^2 + 0x \\ \underline{4x^2 - 16x} \\ 16x - 64 \\ \underline{16x - 64} \end{array}$$

Ans. $x^2 + 4x + 16$

23. $\dfrac{x^4 - 2x^3 + 35x^2 - x + 1}{x + 5}$

$$\begin{array}{r} x^3 - 7x^2 + 70x - 351 \\ x + 5 \overline{\smash{)}x^4 - 2x^3 + 35x^2 - x + 1} \\ \underline{x^4 + 5x^3} \\ -7x^3 + 35x^2 \\ \underline{-7x^3 - 35x^2} \\ 70x^2 - x \\ \underline{70x^2 + 350x} \\ -351x + 1 \\ \underline{-351x - 1755} \\ 1756 \end{array}$$

Ans. $x^3 - 7x^2 + 70x - 351 + \dfrac{1756}{x + 5}$

24. $\dfrac{2x^4 - x^3 + 16x^2 - 4}{2x - 1}$

$$
\begin{array}{r}
x^3 \qquad\quad + 8x + 4 \\
2x - 1 \overline{)\, 2x^4 - x^3 + 16x^2 + 0x - 4} \\
\underline{2x^4 - x^3} \qquad\qquad\qquad \\
16x^2 + 0x \\
\underline{16x^2 - 8x} \\
8x - 4 \\
\underline{8x - 4}
\end{array}
$$

Ans. $x^3 + 8x + 4$

25. $\dfrac{15a^4 + 3a^3 + 4a^2 + 4}{3a^2 - 1}$

$$
\begin{array}{r}
5a^2 + \; a + 3 \\
3a^2 - 1 \overline{)\, 15a^4 + 3a^3 + 4a^2 + 0a + 4} \\
\underline{15a^4 \qquad\quad - 5a^2} \\
3a^3 + 9a^2 + 0a \\
\underline{3a^3 \qquad\quad - a} \\
9a^2 + \; a + 4 \\
\underline{9a^2 \qquad - 3} \\
a + 7
\end{array}
$$

Ans. $5a^2 + a + 3 + \dfrac{a + 7}{3a^2 - 1}$

26. $\dfrac{2a^4 + 3a^3 + 4a^2 + 9a - 6}{a^2 + 3}$

$$
\begin{array}{r}
2a^2 + 3a - 2 \\
a^2 + 3 \overline{)\, 2a^4 + 3a^3 + 4a^2 + 9a - 6} \\
\underline{2a^4 \qquad\quad + 6a^2} \\
3a^3 - 2a^2 + 9a \\
\underline{3a^3 \qquad\quad + 9a} \\
-2a^2 \qquad - 6 \\
\underline{-2a^2 \qquad - 6}
\end{array}
$$

Ans. $2a^2 + 3a - 2$

27. $\dfrac{6t^4 - 5t^3 - 8t^2 + 16t - 8}{3t^2 + 2t - 4}$

$$
\begin{array}{r}
2t^2 - \; 3t + 2 \\
3t^2 + 2t - 4 \overline{)\, 6t^4 - 5t^3 - 8t^2 + 16t - 8} \\
\underline{6t^4 + 4t^3 - 8t^2} \\
-9t^3 \qquad\quad + 16t \\
\underline{-9t^3 - 6t^2 + 12t} \\
6t^2 + \; 4t - 8 \\
\underline{6t^2 + \; 4t - 8}
\end{array}
$$

Ans. $2t^2 - 3t + 2$

28. $\dfrac{2t^4 + 5t^3 - 11t^2 - 20t + 12}{t^2 + t - 6}$

$$
\begin{array}{r}
2t^2 + \; 3t - \; 2 \\
t^2 + t - 6 \overline{)\, 2t^4 + 5t^3 - 11t^2 - 20t + 12} \\
\underline{2t^4 + 2t^3 - 12t^2} \\
3t^3 + \; t^2 - 20t \\
\underline{3t^3 + \; 3t^2 - 18t} \\
-2t^2 - \; 2t + 12 \\
\underline{-2t^2 - \; 2t + 12}
\end{array}
$$

Ans. $2t^2 + 3t - 2$

29. A rocket travels $6x^3 + 31x^2 + 31x - 14$ miles in $2x + 7$ hours. Find its rate of speed in miles per hour.

$3x^2 + 5x - 2$ miles per hour

30. A company makes a profit of $6x^3 + 13x^2 + 16x + 64$ dollars to be distributed to $3x + 8$ shares of stock. Find the profit per share.

$2x^2 - x + 8$ dollars per share

To Think About

Assume that m and n are positive integers.

31. Divide:
$(-36x^{2n}y^{m+5} - 60x^{n+8}y^{m+4} + 24x^{n+3}y^m) \div (-12x^n y^m)$.

$3x^{2n-n}y^{m+5-m} + 5x^{n+8-n}y^{m+4-m} - 2x^{n+3-n}$
$3x^n y^5 + 5x^8 y^4 - 2x^3$

32. Divide: $(x^{5n} + x^{3n} + 2x^{2n} + 2) \div (x^{3n} + 2)$.

$$
\begin{array}{r}
x^{2n} + 1 \\
x^{3n} + 2 \overline{)\, x^{5n} + x^{3n} + 2x^{2n} + 2} \\
\underline{x^{5n} \qquad\quad + 2x^{2n}} \\
x^{3n} \qquad\quad + 2 \\
\underline{x^{3n} \qquad\quad + 2}
\end{array}
$$

Cumulative Review Problems

Solve for x.

33. $3x + 4(3x - 5) = -x + 12$

$3x + 12x - 20 = -x + 12$
$16x = 32$
$x = 2$

34. $9x - 2x + 8 = 4x + 38$

$7x + 8 = 4x + 38$
$x = 10$

35. $2(x - 3) - 13 = 17 - 3(x + 2)$

$2x - 6 - 13 = 17 - 3x - 6$
$2x - 19 = 11 - 3x$
$x = 6$

36. $5 - \dfrac{x}{4} = x - 1$

$20 - x = 4x - 4$
$\dfrac{24}{5} = x$

Calculator Problems

Divide.

37. $(742.14x^2 - 124.362x + 3252.06) \div 12.6$

$58.9x^2 - 9.87x + 258.1$

38. $(13.1x^2 + 9.32x - 9.58) \div (2.62x + 3.50)$

$5x - 3.122137405 + \dfrac{1.34748092}{2.62x + 3.50}$

For Extra Practice Exercises, turn to page 229.

1. $\dfrac{16x^3 - 8x^2 + 3x}{2x} = \dfrac{16x^3}{2x} - \dfrac{8x^3}{2x} + \dfrac{3x}{2x}$

$\qquad\qquad\qquad = 8x^2 - 4x + \dfrac{3}{2}$

3. We write the divisor and dividend in descending order. The problem becomes $(8x^2 + 14x - 14) \div (4x - 3)$.

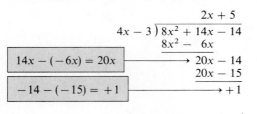

$$\begin{array}{r} 2x + 5 \\ 4x - 3\overline{\smash{\big)}\,8x^2 + 14x - 14} \\ \underline{8x^2 - 6x} \\ 20x - 14 \\ \underline{20x - 15} \\ +1 \end{array}$$

$14x - (-6x) = 20x$

$-14 - (-15) = +1$

The answer is $2x + 5$ remainder 1 or $2x + 5 + \dfrac{1}{4x - 3}$.

5. The x^2 term is missing in the dividend, so we write $0x^2$. It is *not* necessary for each term to be represented in the divisor, but it is more convenient to do so. So we write $x^2 - 1 = x^2 + 0x - 1$.

$$\begin{array}{r} x^2 - 3x + 1 \\ x^2 + 0x - 1\overline{\smash{\big)}\,x^4 - 3x^3 + 0x^2 + 3x + 4} \\ \underline{x^4 + 0x^3 - x^2} \\ -3x^3 + x^2 + 3x \\ \underline{-3x^3 + 0x^2 + 3x} \\ x^2 + 0x + 4 \\ \underline{x^2 + 0x - 1} \\ 5 \end{array}$$

The answer is $x^2 - 3x + 1 + \dfrac{5}{x^2 - 1}$.

2. $-2x^3 + 2x^2 + x + 8$ **4.** $4x^2 - 6xy + 9y^2$

☐ After studying this section, you will be able to:

1 *Use synthetic division to divide polynomials*

4.3 SYNTHETIC DIVISION

1 When dividing a polynomial by a binomial of the form $x + b$ or $x - b$, you may find a procedure known as **synthetic division** quite efficient. Notice the following division problems. The right-hand problem is the same as the left but without the variables.

$$\begin{array}{r} 3x^2 - 2x + 2 \\ x + 3\overline{\smash{\big)}\,3x^3 + 7x^2 - 4x + 3} \\ \underline{3x^3 + 9x^2} \\ -2x^2 - 4x \\ \underline{-2x^2 - 6x} \\ 2x + 3 \\ \underline{2x + 6} \\ -3 \end{array} \qquad \begin{array}{r} 3 \quad -2 \quad 2 \\ 1 + 3\overline{\smash{\big)}\,3 \quad7 \quad -4 \quad 3} \\ \underline{3 \quad9} \\ -2 \quad -4 \\ \underline{-2 \quad -6} \\ 2 \quad 3 \\ \underline{2 \quad 6} \\ -3 \end{array}$$

Eliminating the variables makes synthetic division efficient, and we can make the procedure simpler yet. Note that the colored numbers (3, -2, and 2) appear twice in the example above, once in the quotient and again in the subtraction. Synthetic division makes it possible to write each number only once. Also, in synthetic division we change the subtraction that division otherwise requires to addition. We do this by dropping the 1 which is the coefficient of x and taking the opposite of the second number in the divisor. In our first example, this means dropping the 1 and changing 3 to -3. The following steps detail synthetic division.

Step 1:

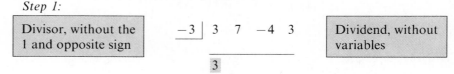

| Divisor, without the 1 and opposite sign | -3 | 3 | 7 | -4 | 3 | Dividend, without variables |

3

Step 2:

$$-3 \,\big|\, \begin{array}{rrrr} 3 & 7 & -4 & 3 \\ & -9 & & \\ \hline 3 & -2 & & \end{array}$$

Multiplying $(-3)(3) = -9$
and adding $7 + (-9) = -2$.

Step 3:

$$-3 \,\big|\, \begin{array}{rrrr} 3 & 7 & -4 & 3 \\ & -9 & 6 & \\ \hline 3 & -2 & 2 & \end{array}$$

Multiplying $(-3)(-2) = 6$
and adding $-4 + 6 = 2$.

Step 4:

$$-3 \,\big|\, \begin{array}{rrrr} 3 & 7 & -4 & 3 \\ & -9 & 6 & -6 \\ \hline 3 & -2 & 2 & -3 \\ \downarrow & \downarrow & \downarrow & \downarrow \end{array}$$

Multiplying $(-3)(2) = -6$
and adding $3 + (-6) = -3$.

$3x^2 - 2x + 2 +$ remainder of -3

Replace the variables, making sure their powers are correct.

The result is read from the bottom row. Our answer is $3x^2 - 2x + 2 + \dfrac{-3}{x + 3}$.

Example 1 Divide by synthetic division: $(3x^3 - x^2 + 4x + 8) \div (x + 2)$.

$$-2 \,\big|\, \begin{array}{rrrr} 3 & -1 & 4 & 8 \\ & -6 & +14 & -36 \\ \hline 3 & -7 & 18 & -28 \end{array}$$

The quotient is $3x^2 - 7x + 18 + \dfrac{-28}{x + 2}$. ∎

Practice Problem 1 Divide by synthetic division: $(x^3 - 3x^2 + 4x - 5) \div (x + 3)$. ∎

When a term is missing in the sequence of descending powers of x, we use a zero to indicate the coefficient of that term.

Example 2 Divide by synthetic division: $(3x^4 - 21x^3 + 31x^2 - 25) \div (x - 5)$.

$$5 \,\big|\, \begin{array}{rrrrr} 3 & -21 & 31 & 0 & -25 \\ & 15 & -30 & 5 & 25 \\ \hline 3 & -6 & 1 & 5 & 0 \end{array}$$ Note that the remainder is zero.

The quotient is $3x^3 - 6x^2 + x + 5$. ∎

Practice Problem 2 Divide by synthetic division: $(2x^4 - x^2 + 5x - 12) \div (x - 3)$. ∎

Example 3 Divide by synthetic division: $(3x^4 - 4x^3 + 8x^2 - 5x - 5) \div (x - 2)$.

$$2 \,\big|\, \begin{array}{rrrrr} 3 & -4 & 8 & -5 & -5 \\ & 6 & 4 & 24 & 38 \\ \hline 3 & 2 & 12 & 19 & 33 \end{array}$$

The quotient is $3x^3 + 2x^2 + 12x + 19 + \dfrac{33}{x - 2}$. ∎

Practice Problem 3 Divide by synthetic division: $(2x^4 - 9x^3 + 5x^2 + 13x - 3) \div (x - 3)$. ∎

TEACHING TIP Synthetic division is readily learned by students after they have seen several examples. If you wish to show them an additional example at the same level of difficulty as example 1 use the following: $2x^3 + 2x^2 - 44x + 7$ divided by $x + 4$ yields $2x^2 - 6x - 20$ with a remainder of 87.

$$-4 \,\big|\, \begin{array}{rrrr} 2 & 2 & -44 & 7 \\ & -8 & 24 & 80 \\ \hline 2 & -6 & -20 & 87 \end{array}$$

TEACHING TIP After discussing example 3 or a similar example, have students divide the following using synthetic division:
$3x^4 + 8x^3 - 7x^2 - 9x + 15$ divided by $x + 3$ yields $3x^3 - x^2 - 4x + 3$ Remainder 6.

$$-3 \,\big|\, \begin{array}{rrrrr} 3 & 8 & -7 & -9 & +15 \\ & -9 & 3 & 12 & -9 \\ \hline 3 & -1 & -4 & 3 & 6 \end{array}$$

Divide by synthetic division.

1. $(x^2 + 2x - 63) \div (x - 7)$

$$\begin{array}{r} 7 \underline{\smash{\big|}} \; 1 \quad +2 \quad -63 \\ \quad\quad\; 7 \quad +63 \quad\quad x+9 \\ \hline 1 \quad\; 9 \quad\; \boxed{0} \end{array}$$

2. $(x^2 + 2x - 80) \div (x - 8)$

$$\begin{array}{r} 8 \underline{\smash{\big|}} \; 1 \quad +2 \quad -80 \\ \quad\quad\; 8 \quad +80 \quad\quad x+10 \\ \hline 1 \quad 10 \quad\; \boxed{0} \end{array}$$

3. $(2x^2 - 11x - 8) \div (x - 6)$

$$\begin{array}{r} 6 \underline{\smash{\big|}} \; 2 \quad -11 \quad -8 \\ \quad\quad 12 \quad +6 \quad\quad 2x+1+\dfrac{-2}{x-6} \\ \hline 2 \quad\; 1 \quad \boxed{-2} \end{array}$$

4. $(2x^2 - 15x - 23) \div (x - 9)$

$$\begin{array}{r} 9 \underline{\smash{\big|}} \; 2 \quad -15 \quad -23 \\ \quad\quad 18 \quad +27 \quad\quad 2x+3+\dfrac{4}{x-9} \\ \hline 2 \quad\; 3 \quad \boxed{4} \end{array}$$

5. $(2x^3 + 4x^2 - 3x + 12) \div (x + 4)$

$$\begin{array}{r} -4 \underline{\smash{\big|}} \; 2 \quad +4 \quad -3 \quad +12 \\ \quad\quad -8 \quad +16 \quad -52 \quad\quad 2x^2-4x+13-\dfrac{40}{x+4} \\ \hline 2 \quad -4 \quad +13 \quad \boxed{-40} \end{array}$$

6. $(3x^3 + 10x^2 + 6x - 4) \div (x + 2)$

$$\begin{array}{r} -2 \underline{\smash{\big|}} \; 3 \quad +10 \quad +6 \quad -4 \\ \quad\quad -6 \quad -8 \quad +4 \quad\quad 3x^2+4x-2 \\ \hline 3 \quad +4 \quad -2 \quad \boxed{0} \end{array}$$

7. $(x^3 + 7x^2 + 17x + 15) \div (x + 3)$

$$\begin{array}{r} -3 \underline{\smash{\big|}} \; 1 \quad +7 \quad +17 \quad +15 \\ \quad\quad -3 \quad -12 \quad -15 \quad\quad x^2+4x+5 \\ \hline 1 \quad +4 \quad +5 \quad \boxed{0} \end{array}$$

8. $(3x^3 - x^2 + 4x + 8) \div (x + 2)$

$$\begin{array}{r} -2 \underline{\smash{\big|}} \; 3 \quad -1 \quad +4 \quad +8 \\ \quad\quad -6 \quad +14 \quad -36 \quad\quad 3x^2-7x+18-\dfrac{28}{x+2} \\ \hline 3 \quad -7 \quad +18 \quad \boxed{-28} \end{array}$$

9. $(x^3 + 4x^2 - x + 5) \div (x - 2)$

$$\begin{array}{r} 2 \underline{\smash{\big|}} \; 1 \quad +4 \quad -1 \quad +5 \\ \quad\quad 2 \quad +12 \quad +22 \quad\quad x^2+6x+11+\dfrac{27}{x-2} \\ \hline 1 \quad +6 \quad +11 \quad \boxed{+27} \end{array}$$

10. $(4x^3 + x^2 - 3x - 1) \div (x - 1)$

$$\begin{array}{r} 1 \underline{\smash{\big|}} \; 4 \quad +1 \quad -3 \quad -1 \\ \quad\quad 4 \quad\; 5 \quad\; 2 \quad\quad 4x^2+5x+2+\dfrac{1}{x-1} \\ \hline 4 \quad +5 \quad +2 \quad \boxed{+1} \end{array}$$

11. $(x^3 - 2x^2 + 8) \div (x + 2)$

$$\begin{array}{r} -2 \underline{\smash{\big|}} \; 1 \quad -2 \quad +0 \quad +8 \\ \quad\quad -2 \quad +8 \quad -16 \quad\quad x^2-4x+8-\dfrac{8}{x+2} \\ \hline 1 \quad -4 \quad +8 \quad \boxed{-8} \end{array}$$

12. $(2x^3 + 7x^2 - 5) \div (x + 3)$

$$\begin{array}{r} -3 \underline{\smash{\big|}} \; 2 \quad +7 \quad +0 \quad -5 \\ \quad\quad -6 \quad -3 \quad +9 \quad\quad 2x^2+x-3+\dfrac{4}{x+3} \\ \hline 2 \quad +1 \quad -3 \quad \boxed{+4} \end{array}$$

13. $(6x^4 + 15x^3 - 28x - 6) \div (x + 2)$

$$\begin{array}{r} -2 \underline{\smash{\big|}} \; 6 \quad +15 \quad +0 \quad -28 \quad -6 \\ \quad\quad -12 \quad -6 \quad +12 \quad +32 \quad\quad 6x^3+3x^2-6x-16+\dfrac{26}{x+2} \\ \hline 6 \quad +3 \quad -6 \quad -16 \quad \boxed{+26} \end{array}$$

14. $(3x^4 - 25x^2 - 18) \div (x - 3)$

$$\begin{array}{r} 3 \underline{\smash{\big|}} \; 3 \quad +0 \quad -25 \quad +0 \quad -18 \\ \quad\quad 9 \quad +27 \quad +6 \quad +18 \quad\quad 3x^3+9x^2+2x+6 \\ \hline 3 \quad +9 \quad +2 \quad +6 \quad \boxed{+0} \end{array}$$

15. $(x^4 - 6x^3 + x^2 - 9) \div (x + 1)$

$$\begin{array}{r} -1 \underline{\smash{\big|}} \; 1 \quad -6 \quad +1 \quad +0 \quad -9 \\ \quad\quad -1 \quad +7 \quad -8 \quad +8 \quad\quad x^3-7x^2+8x-8-\dfrac{1}{x+1} \\ \hline 1 \quad -7 \quad +8 \quad -8 \quad \boxed{-1} \end{array}$$

16. $(x^4 - 3x^3 - 11x^2 + 3x + 10) \div (x - 5)$

$$\begin{array}{r} 5 \underline{\smash{\big|}} \; 1 \quad -3 \quad -11 \quad +3 \quad +10 \\ \quad\quad 5 \quad +10 \quad -5 \quad -10 \quad\quad x^3+2x^2-x-2 \\ \hline 1 \quad\; 2 \quad -1 \quad -2 \quad \boxed{+0} \end{array}$$

17. $(3x^4 - x^3 + 2x^2 - 7x - 1) \div (x + 1)$

$$\begin{array}{r} -1 \underline{\smash{\big|}} \; 3 \quad -1 \quad +2 \quad -7 \quad -1 \\ \quad\quad -3 \quad +4 \quad -6 \quad +13 \quad\quad 3x^3-4x^2+6x-13+\dfrac{12}{x+1} \\ \hline 3 \quad -4 \quad +6 \quad -13 \quad \boxed{+12} \end{array}$$

18. $(2x^3 - 5x^2 - 4x + 6) \div (x - 2)$

$$\begin{array}{r} 2 \underline{\smash{\big|}} \; 2 \quad -5 \quad -4 \quad +6 \\ \quad\quad 4 \quad -2 \quad -12 \quad\quad 2x^2-x-6-\dfrac{6}{x-2} \\ \hline 2 \quad -1 \quad -6 \quad \boxed{-6} \end{array}$$

19. $(2x^5 + 5x^4 - 2x^3 + 2x^2 - 2x + 3) \div (x - 3)$

$$\begin{array}{r} 3 \underline{\smash{\big|}} \; 2 \quad +5 \quad -2 \quad +2 \quad -2 \quad +3 \\ \quad\quad +6 \quad +33 \quad +93 \quad +285 \quad +849 \\ \hline 2 \quad +11 \quad +31 \quad +95 \quad +283 \quad \boxed{+852} \end{array}$$

$$2x^4 + 11x^3 + 31x^2 + 95x + 283 + \dfrac{852}{x-3}$$

20. $(2x^5 - 3x^4 + x^3 - x^2 + 2x + 1) \div (x + 2)$

$$\begin{array}{r} -2 \underline{\smash{\big|}} \; 2 \quad -3 \quad +1 \quad -1 \quad +2 \quad +1 \\ \quad\quad -4 \quad +14 \quad -30 \quad +62 \quad -128 \\ \hline 2 \quad -7 \quad +15 \quad -31 \quad +64 \quad \boxed{-127} \end{array}$$

$$2x^4 - 7x^3 + 15x^2 - 31x + 64 - \dfrac{127}{x+2}$$

21. $(x^6 + x^4 - x) \div (x - 1)$

$$\begin{array}{r} 1 \underline{\smash{\big|}} \; 1 \quad +0 \quad +1 \quad +0 \quad +0 \quad -1 \quad +0 \\ \quad\quad 1 \quad\; 1 \quad\; 2 \quad\; 2 \quad\; 2 \quad\; 1 \\ \hline 1 \quad\; 1 \quad\; 2 \quad\; 2 \quad\; 2 \quad\; 1 \quad \boxed{1} \end{array}$$

$$x^5 + x^4 + 2x^3 + 2x^2 + 2x + 1 + \dfrac{1}{x-1}$$

22. $(x^6 + 2x^4 - 5x + 11) \div (x - 2)$

$$\begin{array}{r} 2 \underline{\smash{\big|}} \; 1 \quad +0 \quad +2 \quad +0 \quad +0 \quad -5 \quad +11 \\ \quad\quad 2 \quad\; 4 \quad 12 \quad 24 \quad 48 \quad 86 \\ \hline 1 \quad\; 2 \quad\; 6 \quad 12 \quad 24 \quad 43 \quad \boxed{97} \end{array}$$

$$x^5 + 2x^4 + 6x^3 + 12x^2 + 24x + 43 + \dfrac{97}{x-2}$$

? To Think About

How do we use synthetic division when the divisor is in the form $ax + b$? We divide the divisor by a to get $x + b/a$. After performing the division, we divide each term of the quotient by a. To divide

$$(2x^3 + 7x^2 - 5x - 4) \div (2x + 1)$$

we would use

$$-\frac{1}{2} \bigg|\; 2 \quad 7 \quad -5 \quad -4$$

and then divide each term of the quotient by 2.

In problems 23 and 24, divide by synthetic division.

23. $(2x^3 - 3x^2 + 6x + 4) \div (2x + 1)$

$$-\frac{1}{2} \bigg|\; \begin{array}{cccc} 2 & -3 & +6 & +4 \\ & -1 & +2 & -4 \\ \hline 2 & -4 & +8 & \boxed{0} \end{array}$$

$$\frac{2x^2 - 4x + 8}{2} = x^2 - 2x + 4$$

24. $(4x^3 - 6x^2 + 6) \div (2x + 3)$

$$-\frac{3}{2} \bigg|\; \begin{array}{cccc} 4 & -6 & +0 & +6 \\ & -6 & +18 & -27 \\ \hline 4 & -12 & +18 & \boxed{-21} \end{array}$$

$$\frac{4x^2 - 12x + 18}{2} - \frac{21}{2x + 3} = 2x^2 - 6x + 9 - \frac{21}{2x + 3}$$

25. $(x^4 + 3x^3 - 2x^2 + bx + 5) \div (x + 3)$ divides without any remainder. What is the value of b?

$$-3 \bigg|\; \begin{array}{ccccc} 1 & +3 & -2 & +b & +5 \\ & -3 & +0 & +6 & -3(6 + b) \\ \hline 1 & 0 & -2 & (b + 6) & \boxed{+5 - 18 - 3b} \end{array}$$

Since remainder $= 0 \Rightarrow (5 - 18 - 3b) = 0$

$$b = -\frac{13}{3}$$

26. $(2x^4 + 12x^3 + ax^2 - 5x + 75) \div (x + 5)$ divides without any remainder. What is the value of a?

$$-5 \bigg|\; \begin{array}{ccccc} 2 & +12 & +a & -5 & +75 \\ & -10 & -10 & -5(a - 10) & -5(-5a + 45) \\ \hline 2 & +2 & (a - 10) & +(-5a + 45) & \boxed{+(25a - 150)} \end{array}$$

Since remainder $= 0 \Rightarrow 25a - 150 = 0$

$$a = 6$$

Cumulative Review Problems

(a) *Divide the following problems by long division.* **(b)** *Then divide them by synthetic division.* **(c)** *How much more quickly can the problem be done by synthetic division.*

27. $(x^4 - 9x^3 + 23x^2 - 32x + 12) \div (x - 6)$

   (a) and **(b)** are the same $x^3 - 3x^2 + 5x - 2$

   (c) For most students in about $\frac{1}{2}$ the time.

28. $(x^4 - 9x^3 + 26x^2 - 32x + 32) \div (x - 4)$

   (a) and **(b)** are the same $x^3 - 5x^2 + 6x - 8$

   (c) For most students in about $\frac{1}{2}$ the time.

▦ Calculator Problems

Divide by synthetic division.

29. $(x^3 + 2.5x^2 - 3.6x + 5.4) \div (x - 1.2)$

   $x^2 + 3.7x + 0.84$ remainder 6.408

30. $(x^3 - 4.2x^2 - 8.8x + 3.7) \div (x + 1.8)$

   $x^2 - 6x + 2$ remainder 0.1

For Extra Practice Exercises, turn to page 229.

Solutions to Odd-Numbered Practice Problems

1. $$-3 \bigg|\; \begin{array}{cccc} 1 & -3 & 4 & -5 \\ & -3 & +18 & -66 \\ \hline 1 & -6 & 22 & -71 \end{array}$$

   The quotient is $x^2 - 6x + 22 + \dfrac{-71}{x + 3}$.

3. $$3 \bigg|\; \begin{array}{ccccc} 2 & -9 & 5 & 13 & -3 \\ & 6 & -9 & -12 & 3 \\ \hline 2 & -3 & -4 & 1 & 0 \end{array}$$

   The quotient is $2x^3 - 3x^2 - 4x + 1$.

Answer to Even-Numbered Practice Problem

2. The quotient is $2x^3 + 6x^2 + 17x + 56 + \dfrac{156}{x - 3}$.

1 Remove the greatest common factor from a polynomial

2 Factor a polynomial by the grouping method

4.4 REMOVING COMMON FACTORS; FACTORING BY GROUPING

We learned to multiply polynomials in Section 4.1. When two or more algebraic expressions (monomials, binomials, and so on) are multiplied, each expression is called a **factor**.

In the rest of this chapter, we will learn how to find the factors of a polynomial. Factoring is the opposite of multiplication and is an extremely important mathematical technique.

1 Removing the Greatest Common Factor

To remove a common factor, we make use of the distributive property.

$$ab + ac = a(b + c)$$

The greatest common factor simply means the largest factor in every term of the expression. It must contain

1. The largest possible numerical coefficient and
2. The largest possible exponent for each variable

Example 1 Remove the greatest common factor.

(a) $7x^2 - 14x$ **(b)** $40a^3 - 20a^2$

(a) $7x^2 - 14x = 7x(x - 2)$
Be careful. The greatest common factor is $7x$, not 7.

(b) $40a^3 - 20a^2 = 20a^2(2a - 1)$
The greatest common factor is $20a^2$. ■

Suppose we had written $10a(4a^2 - 2a)$ or $10a(2a)(2a - 1)$. Although we have factored the expression, we have not found the *greatest* common factor.

TEACHING TIP After discussing example 1 or a similar example, ask students to do the following classwork: Remove the greatest common factor:

A: $49x^3 - 21x^2$
B: $120abc - 40ab$
C: $36wy^2 + 42w^2y^2$

(The answers are
A: $7x^2(7x - 3)$ B: $40ab(3c - 1)$
C: $6wy^2(6 + 7w)$.)

Practice Problem 1 Remove the greatest common factor.
(a) $19x^3 - 38x^2$ **(b)** $100a^4 - 50a^2$ ■

Example 2 Remove the greatest common factor.

(a) $9x^2 - 18xy - 15y^2$ **(b)** $4a^3 - 12a^2b^2 - 8ab^3 + 6ab$

(a) $9x^2 - 18xy - 15y^2 = 3(3x^2 - 6xy - 5y^2)$
The greatest common factor is 3.

(b) $4a^3 - 12a^2b^2 - 8ab^3 + 6ab = 2a(2a^2 - 6ab^2 - 4b^3 + 3b)$
The greatest common factor is $2a$. ■

Practice Problem 2 Remove the greatest common factor.
(a) $21x^3 - 18x^2y + 24xy^2$
(b) $12xy^2 - 14x^2y + 20x^2y^2 + 36x^3y$ ■

Example 3 Remove the greatest common factor.

(a) $55x^3y^5z^6 - 121x^4y^3z^5 + 33x^2y^5z^7$ **(b)** $140a^3b^2 - 210a^2b^3 + 70a^2b^2$

(a) $55x^3y^5z^6 - 121x^4y^3z^5 + 33x^2y^5z^7$
$$= 11x^2y^3z^5 \, (5xy^2z - 11x^2 + 3y^2z^2)$$

Be careful. Do you see why $11x^2y^2z^5$ is the greatest common factor?

(b) $140a^3b^2 - 210a^2b^3 + 70a^2b^2$

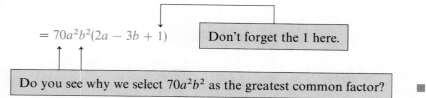

$= 70a^2b^2(2a - 3b + 1)$ | Don't forget the 1 here.

Do you see why we select $70a^2b^2$ as the greatest common factor? ■

Practice Problem 3 Remove the greatest common factor.
(a) $16a^5b^4 - 32a^3b^4 - 24a^6b^4$ **(b)** $50xyz^2 - 75x^2y^2z^2 + 100x^3y^2z^2$ ■

To Think About

How do you know if you have factored correctly? You can do two things to verify your answer.

1. Examine the polynomial in the parentheses. Its terms should not have any remaining common factors.
2. Multiply the polynomial by the common factor. You should obtain the original expression. ■

In the remaining examples you will be asked to **factor** several polynomials. This merely means to find the factors which when multiplied give that polynomial as a product. Our method when asked to factor is to remove the greatest common factor.

Example 4 Factor: $6x^3 - 9x^2y - 6x^2y^2$. Check your answer.

$$6x^3 - 9x^2y - 6x^2y^2 = 3x^2(2x - 3y - 2y^2)$$

Check:

1. $(2x - 3y - 2y^2)$ has no common factors. If it did, we would know that we had not removed the *greatest* common factor.
2. Multiply

$$3x^2(2x - 3y - 2y^2) = 6x^3 - 9x^2y - 6x^2y^2$$

Observe that we do obtain the original polynomial. ■

Practice Problem 4 Factor: $9a^3 - 12a^2b^2 - 15a^4$. Check your answer. ■

The greatest common factor need not always be a monomial. It may be a binomial, or even a trinomial. For example,

$$5a(x + 3) + 2(x + 3) = (x + 3)(5a + 2)$$
$$5a(x + 4y) + 2(x + 4y) = (x + 4y)(5a + 2)$$

The common factors are binomials.

Example 5 Factor.

(a) $2x(x + 5) - 3(x + 5)$ **(b)** $5a(a + b) - 2b(a + b) - 1(a + b)$

(a) $2x(x + 5) - 3(x + 5) = (x + 5)(2x - 3)$ | The common factor is $x + 5$.

TEACHING TIP Students need to be reminded of the importance of developing an ability to check factoring problems. After discussing example 4 or a similar example, have them do the following problem for classwork: Remove the greatest common factor:

$$12a^3 - 24a^2b - 36a^2b^2$$

Now check your answer by multiplication: (Answer: $12a^2(a - 2b - 3b^2)$.)
Check $12a^2(a - 2b - 3b^2)$
$= 12a^3 - 24a^2b - 36a^2b^2$.

(b) $5a(a+b) - 2b(a+b) - 1(a+b) = (a+b)(5a - 2b - 1)$ ■

The common factor is $a + b$.

Practice Problem 5 Factor: $7x(x + 2y) - 8y(x + 2y) - (x + 2y)$ ■

2 Factoring by Grouping

The common factors in our examples so far were already grouped inside parentheses, so it was easy to pick them out. However, this rarely happens, so we have to learn how to manipulate expressions to find the greatest common factor.

Polynomials of four terms can often be factored by the method of Example 5a. However, the parentheses are not always present in the original problem. When they are not present, we first group like terms. We then remove a common factor from the first two terms and a common factor from the second two terms. It should then be easy to find the greatest common factor.

Example 6 Factor: $ax + 2ay + 2bx + 4by$.

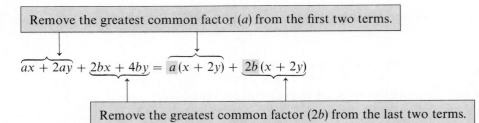

Remove the greatest common factor (a) from the first two terms.

$$ax + 2ay + 2bx + 4by = a(x + 2y) + 2b(x + 2y)$$

Remove the greatest common factor ($2b$) from the last two terms.

Now we can see that $(x + 2y)$ is a common factor.

$$a(x + 2y) + 2b(x + 2y) = (x + 2y)(a + 2b)$$ ■

Practice Problem 6 Factor: $bx + 5by + 2wx + 10wy$. ■

Example 7 Factor: $2x^2 - 18y - 12x + 3xy$.

First write the polynomial in this order: $2x^2 - 12x + 3xy - 18y$

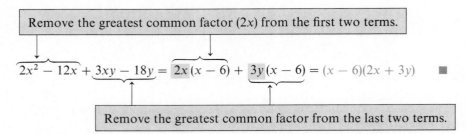

Remove the greatest common factor ($2x$) from the first two terms.

$$2x^2 - 12x + 3xy - 18y = 2x(x - 6) + 3y(x - 6) = (x - 6)(2x + 3y)$$ ■

Remove the greatest common factor from the last two terms.

Practice Problem 7 Factor: $5x^2 - 12y + 4xy - 15x$. ■

TEACHING TIP After discussing problem 8 or a similar problem, have them factor the following problem:

$2ab - 15 + 5a - 6b$

(Answer:
$2ab - 15 + 5a - 6b$
$= 2ab - 6b + 5a - 15$
$= 2b(a - 3) + 5(a - 3)$
$= (a - 3)(2b + 5)$.)

If a problem can be factored by this method, we must rearrange the order of the four terms whenever necessary so that the first two terms do have a common factor.

Example 8 Factor: $xy - 6 + 3x - 2y$.

$xy + 3x - 2y - 6$	Rearranging the terms so that the first two terms have a common factor.
$= x(y + 3) - 2(y + 3)$	Removing a common factor of x from the first two terms and a -2 from the second two terms.
$= (y + 3)(x - 2)$	Removing the common factor $y + 3$. ■

Practice Problem 8 Factor: $xy - 12 - 4x + 3y$. ■

Example 9 Factor: $2x^3 + 21 - 7x^2 - 6x$. Check your answer by multiplication.

$2x^3 - 7x^2 - 6x + 21$	Rearranging the terms.
$= x^2(2x - 7) - 3(2x - 7)$	Removing a common factor from each group of two terms.
$= (2x - 7)(x^2 - 3)$	Removing the common factor $2x - 7$.

  Check:

$$(2x - 7)(x^2 - 3) = 2x^3 - 6x - 7x^2 + 21 \qquad \text{Multiplying the two binomials.}$$
$$= 2x^3 + 21 - 7x^2 - 6x \qquad \text{Rearranging the terms.}$$

The product is identical to the original expression. ■

Practice Problem 9 Factor: $2x^3 - 15 - 10x + 3x^2$. ■

DEVELOPING YOUR STUDY SKILLS

HOW TO DO HOMEWORK

Set aside time each day for your homework assignments. Do not attempt to do a whole week's worth on the weekend. Two hours spent studying outside of class for each hour in class is usual for college courses. You may need more than that for mathematics.

Before beginning to solve your homework problems, read your textbook very carefully. Expect to spend much more time reading a few pages of a mathematics textbook than several pages of another text. Read for complete understanding, not just for the general idea.

As you begin your homework assignments, read the directions carefully. You need to understand what is being asked for. Concentrate on each exercise or problem, taking time to solve it accurately. Rushing through your work usually causes errors. Check your answers with those given in the back of the textbook. If your answer is incorrect, check to see that you are doing the right problem. Redo the problem, watching for little errors. If it is still wrong, check with a friend. Perhaps the two of you can figure it out.

Also, check the examples in the textbook or in your notes for a similar exercise or problem. Can this one be solved in the same way? Give it some thought. You may want to leave it for a while by taking a break or doing a different one. But come back later and try again. If you are still unable to figure it out, ask your instructor for help during office hours or in class.

Work on your assignments every day and do as many problems as it takes for you to know what you are doing. Begin by doing all the problems that have been assigned. If there are more available in the section in your text, then do more. When you think you have done enough problems to understand fully the type at hand, do a few more to be sure. This may mean that you do many more problems than the instructor assigns, but you can never practice too much. Practice improves your skills and increases your accuracy, speed, competence, and confidence.

EXERCISES 4.4

Factor. (Be sure to remove the greatest common factor.)

1. $20 - 5y$
  $5(4 - y)$

2. $16x - 16$
  $16(x - 1)$

3. $xy^2 - 3x^2y$
  $xy(y - 3x)$

4. $6a^2 - 18a$
  $6a(a - 3)$

5. $b^2x^2 + bx + b$

$b(bx^2 + x + 1)$

6. $a^3b^2 + a^2b^3 + a^2b^2$

$a^2b^2(a + b + 1)$

7. $2x^3 - 8x^2 + 12x$

$2x(x^2 - 4x + 6)$

8. $3x^4 - 6x^3 + 9x^2$

$3x^2(x^2 - 2x + 3)$

9. $9a^2b^2 - 36ab + 45ab^2$

$9ab(ab - 4 + 5b)$

10. $14x^2y - 35xy - 63x$

$7x(2xy - 5y - 9)$

11. $4a^3b^2c - 8a^2b^2c^2 + 6ab^2c^3$

$2ab^2c(2a^2 - 4ac + 3c^2)$

12. $20x^2y^2z^2 - 30x^3y^3z^2 + 25x^2yz^2$

$5x^2yz^2(4y - 6xy^2 + 5)$

13. $5x^3 - 10x^2 + 3$

There is no common factor.

14. $8x^3y - 4xy^2 + 5$

There is no common factor.

15. $12xy^3 - 24x^3y^2 + 36x^2y^4 - 60x^4y^3$

$12xy^2(y - 2x^2 + 3xy^2 - 5x^3y)$

16. $15a^3b^3 + 6a^4b^3 - 9a^2b^3 + 30a^5b^3$

$3a^2b^3(5a + 2a^2 - 3 + 10a^3)$

17. $3x(x + y) - 2(x + y)$

$(x + y)(3x - 2)$

18. $5a(a + 3b) + 4(a + 3b)$

$(a + 3b)(5a + 4)$

19. $5b(a - 3b) + 8(-3b + a)$

$5b(a - 3b) + 8(a - 3b)$
$(a - 3b)(5b + 8)$

20. $4y(x - 5y) - 3(-5y + x)$

$(x - 5y)(4y - 3)$

21. $8x(a + 3b) + (a + 3b)$

$(a + 3b)(8x + 1)$

22. $2w(s - 3t) - (s - 3t)$

$(s - 3t)(2w - 1)$

23. $2a^2(3x - y) - 5b^3(3x - y)$

$(3x - y)(2a^2 - 5b^3)$

24. $7a^3(5a + 4) - 2(5a + 4)$

$(5a + 4)(7a^3 - 2)$

25. $3x(5x + y) - 8y(5x + y) - (5x + y)$

$(5x + y)(3x - 8y - 1)$

26. $4w(y - 8x) + 5z(y - 8x) + (y - 8x)$

$(y - 8x)(4w + 5z + 1)$

27. $x^3 + 5x^2 + 3x + 15$

$x^2(x + 5) + 3(x + 5) = (x + 5)(x^2 + 3)$

28. $x^3 + 8x^2 + 2x + 16$

$x^2(x + 8) + 2(x + 8) = (x + 8)(x^2 + 2)$

29. $4x + 8y - 3wx - 6wy$

$4(x + 2y) - 3w(x + 2y)$
$(x + 2y)(4 - 3w)$

30. $ax + ay - 7bx - 7by$

$a(x + y) - 7b(x + y)$
$(x + y)(a - 7b)$

31. $a^2 - 3a + ay - 3y$

$a(a - 3) + y(a - 3) = (a - 3)(a + y)$

32. $6xy - 3x + 2py - p$

$3x(2y - 1) + p(2y - 1) = (2y - 1)(3x + p)$

33. $5ax - 15ay - 2bx + 6by$

$5a(x - 3y) - 2b(x - 3y) = (x - 3y)(5a - 2b)$

34. $4ax - 10ay - 2bx + 5by$

$2a(2x - 5y) - b(2x - 5y) = (2x - 5y)(2a - b)$

35. $t^2y - 25 - 5y + 5t^2$

$y(t^2 - 5) + 5(t^2 - 5) = (t^2 - 5)(y + 5)$

36. $5bc - a^3 - b + 5a^3c$

$b(5c - 1) + a^3(5c - 1) = (5c - 1)(b + a^3)$

37. $28x^2 + 6y^2w + 8xy^2 + 21xw$

$4x(7x + 2y^2) + 3w(7x + 2y^2) = (7x + 2y^2)(4x + 3w)$

38. $18ax - 6bx + 9ay^2 - 3by^2$

$3(6ax - 2bx + 3ay^2 - by^2)$
$3[2x(3a - b) + y^2(3a - b)]$
$3(3a - b)(2x + y^2)$

39. $12a^3 + c^3 - 3a^2c - 4ac^2$

$3a^2(4a - c) - c^2(4a - c)$
$(4a - c)(3a^2 - c^2)$

40. $6x^3 + 35wy - 14x^2y - 15xw$

$2x^2(3x - 7y) - 5w(3x - 7y)$
$(3x - 7y)(2x^2 - 5w)$

? **To Think About**

Let n, m be positive integers. Factor.

41. $147x^{m+2}y^{2n} - 105x^{m+1}y^n + 168x^my^{2n-1}$

$21x^my^n(7x^2y^n - 5x + 8y^{n-1})$

42. $5a^3x^n - 3b^ny^m + 5a^3y^m - 3b^nx^n$

$(5a^3x^n + 5a^3y^m) + (-3b^ny^m - 3b^nx^n)$
$= 5a^3(x^n + y^m) - 3b^n(x^n + y^m)$
$(x^n + y^m)(5a^3 - 3b^n)$

Graph.

43. $6x - 2y = -12$

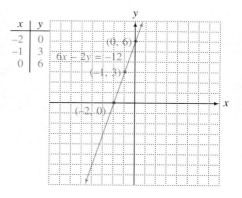

44. $y = \dfrac{2}{3}x - 2$

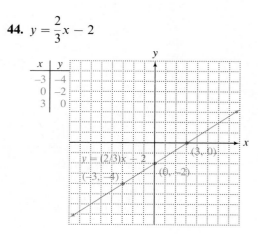

45. Find the slope of a line passing through $(6, -1)$ and $(2, 3)$.

$m = \dfrac{3 + 1}{2 - 6} = -1$

46. Find the slope and y-intercept of $2y + 6x = -3$.

$y = -3x - \dfrac{3}{2}$

$m = -3, \; b = -\dfrac{3}{2}$

Calculator Problems

47. Remove a common factor of 7.37:
$14.74x - 22.11y + 58.96$.

$7.37(2x - 3y + 8)$

48. Remove a common factor of 9.81:
$19.62x^2 - 29.43w + 147.15z^2$.

$9.81(2x^2 - 3w + 15z^2)$

For Extra Practice Exercises, turn to page 230.

Solutions to Odd-Numbered Practice Problems

1. (a) $19x^3 - 38x^2 = 19x^2(x - 2)$ **(b)** $100a^4 - 50a^2 = 50a^2(2a^2 - 1)$

3. (a) $16a^5b^4 - 32a^3b^4 - 24a^6b^4 = 8a^3b^4(2a^2 - 4 - 3a^3)$ **(b)** $50xyz^2 - 75x^2y^2z^2 + 100x^3y^2z^2 = 25xyz^2(2 - 3xy + 4x^2y)$

5. $7x(x + 2y) - 8y(x + 2y) - (x + 2y) = (x + 2y)(7x - 8y - 1)$ $\boxed{\text{Don't forget the } -1 \text{ for the last term.}}$

7. $5x^2 - 12y + 4xy - 15x = 5x^2 - 15x + 4xy - 12y$ Rearranging terms.
                  $= 5x(x - 3) + 4y(x - 3)$ Removing common factor for each group.
                  $= (x - 3)(5x + 4)$ Removing $x - 3$ as common factor.

9. $2x^3 + 3x^2 - 10x - 15 = x^2(2x + 3) - 5(2x + 3) = (2x + 3)(x^2 - 5)$

Answers to Even-Numbered Practice Problems

2. (a) $3x(7x^2 - 6xy + 8y^2)$ **(b)** $2xy(6y - 7x + 10xy + 18x^2)$ **4.** $3a^2(3a - 4b^2 - 5a^2)$

6. $(x + 5y)(b + 2w)$ or $(b + 2w)(x + 5y)$ **8.** $(y - 4)(x + 3)$ or $(x + 3)(y - 4)$

4.5   FACTORING TRINOMIALS

▮ Factoring Trinomials of the form $x^2 + bx + c$

If we multiply $(x + 4)(x + 5)$, we obtain $x^2 + 9x + 20$. But suppose that we already have the polynomial $x^2 + 9x + 20$ and need to factor it. In other words, we need to find the expressions that when multiplied give us the polynomial. Let's use this example to find a general procedure.

☐ After studying this section, you will be able to:

1 *Factor trinomials of the form $x^2 + bx + c$*

2 *Factor trinomials of the form $ax^2 + bx + c$*

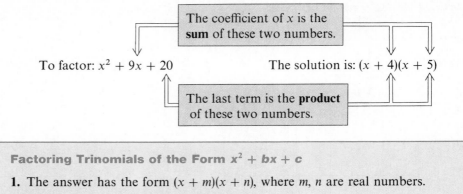

To factor: $x^2 + 9x + 20$ The solution is: $(x + 4)(x + 5)$

The coefficient of x is the **sum** of these two numbers.

The last term is the **product** of these two numbers.

> **Factoring Trinomials of the Form $x^2 + bx + c$**
>
> **1.** The answer has the form $(x + m)(x + n)$, where m, n are real numbers.
> **2.** The numbers m and n are chosen so that
>   **(a)** $m \cdot n = c$
>   **(b)** $m + n = b$

Example 1 Factor: $x^2 + 8x + 15$.

Because the trinomial has the form $x^2 + bx + c$, the answer has the form $(x + m)(x + n)$. Here $b = 8$ and $c = 15$. So we want to find the two numbers whose product is 15 but whose sum is 8. That is, $m \cdot n = 15$ and $m + n = 8$.

Factors of 15	Sum of the Factors
$(15)(1)$	$15 + 1 = 16$
$(3)(5)$	$3 + 5 = 8$ ✓

The factors whose sum is 8 are 3 and 5. Therefore, $m = 3$ and $n = 5$, and

$$x^2 + 8x + 15 = (x + 3)(x + 5) \qquad \blacksquare$$

Practice Problem 1 Factor: $x^2 + 14x + 48$. ■

If the last term of the trinomial is positive and the middle term is negative, the two factors we seek will be negative numbers.

Example 2 Factor: $x^2 - 14x + 24$. [Note that this is still of the form $x^2 + bx + c$ because we can write it as $x^2 + (-14)x + 24$.]

We want to find two numbers whose product is 24 but whose sum is -14. They will both be negative numbers.

Factors of 24	Sum of the factors
$(-24)(-1)$	$-24 - 1 = -25$
$(-12)(-2)$	$-12 - 2 = -14$ ✓
$(-6)(-4)$	$-6 - 4 = -10$
$(-8)(-3)$	$-8 - 3 = -11$

The factors whose sum is -14 are -12 and -2. Thus,

$$x^2 - 14x + 24 = (x - 12)(x - 2) \qquad \blacksquare$$

Practice Problem 2 Factor: $x^2 - 10x + 21$. ■

If the last term of the trinomial is negative, the two factors will be opposite in sign.

Example 3 Factor: $x^2 + 11x - 26$. [This is still in our general form if we write it as $x^2 + 11x + (-26)$.]

We want to find two numbers whose product is -26 but whose sum is $+11$. One number will be positive, the other negative.

Factors of -26	Sum of the Factors
$(-26)(1)$	$-26 + 1 = -25$
$(26)(-1)$	$26 - 1 = 25$
$(-13)(2)$	$-13 + 2 = -11$
$(13)(-2)$	$13 - 2 = 11$ ✓

The factors whose sum is $+11$ are -2 and 13. Thus,

$$x^2 + 11x - 26 = (x + 13)(x - 2) \quad \blacksquare$$

Practice Problem 3 Factor: $x^2 - 13x - 48$. ■

Example 4 Factor: $x^4 - 2x^2 - 24$.

You need to recognize that we can write this as $(x^2)^2 - 2(x^2) - 24$, or $y^2 + (-2)y + (-24)$, where $y = x^2$. So the factors will be $(y + m)(y + n)$. The two numbers whose product is -24 and whose sum is -2 are -6 and 4. Therefore, we have $(y - 6)(y + 4)$, but $y = x^2$, so our answer is

$$x^4 - 2x^2 - 24 = (x^2 - 6)(x^2 + 4) \quad \blacksquare$$

Practice Problem 4 Factor: $x^4 + 9x^2 + 8$. ■

Facts about Signs

To factor $x^2 + bx + c = (x + m)(x + n)$ we know certain facts about m and n.

1. m and n have the same sign if c is positive. (*Note:* We did *not* say they will have the same sign as c.)
   (a) They are positive if b is positive.
   (b) They are negative if b is negative.
2. m and n have opposite signs if c is negative. The larger number is positive if b is positive and negative if b is negative.

If you understand these sign facts, do Example 5. If not, review Examples 1–4.

Example 5 Factor.

(a) $x^2 + 17x + 30$
(c) $y^2 + 5y - 36$

(b) $x^2 - 11x + 28$
(d) $x^4 - 4x^2 - 12$

(a) $x^2 + 17x + 30 = (x + 15)(x + 2)$ Fact 1(a).
(b) $x^2 - 11x + 28 = (x - 4)(x - 7)$ Fact 1(b).
(c) $y^2 + 5y - 36 = (y + 9)(y - 4)$ The larger number (9) is positive because b is positive.

(d) $x^4 - 4x^2 - 12 = (x^2 - 6)(x^2 + 2)$ The larger number (6) is negative because b is negative. ■

Practice Problem 5 Factor.
(a) $x^2 + 15x + 50$
(c) $a^2 + 2a - 48$

(b) $x^2 - 12x + 35$
(d) $x^4 + 2x^2 - 15$ ■

Does the order in which we write the factors make any difference? In other words, is it true that $x^2 + bx + c = (x + n)(x + m)$? Since multiplication is commutative,

$$x^2 + bx + c = (x + n)(x + m) = (x + m)(x + n).$$

The order of the parentheses is not important.

We can also factor trinomials that have more than one variable.

TEACHING TIP After discussing material up to example 5, ask students to factor the following 4 problems as classwork. This will ensure that they are clear on their sign rules and that they use the proper exponent.

Factor A: $x^2 - 14x + 48$

B: $x^2 + 14x + 45$

C: $x^6 - 3x^3 - 4$

D: $x^4 + 3x^3 - 10$

(Answers A: $(x - 6)(x - 8)$
B: $(x + 5)(x + 9)$
C: $(x^3 + 1)(x^3 - 4)$
D: $(x^2 - 2)(x^2 + 5)$.)

Example 6   Factor.

(a) $x^2 - 21xy + 20y^2$ **(b)** $x^2 + 4xy - 21y^2$

(a) $x^2 - 21xy + 20y^2 = (x - 20y)(x - y)$

> The last terms in each factor contain the variable y.

(b) $x^2 + 4xy - 21y^2 = (x + 7y)(x - 3y)$ ■

Practice Problem 6   Factor.

(a) $x^2 - 16xy + 15y^2$ **(b)** $x^2 + xy - 42y^2$ ■

2 Factoring Trinomials of the Form $ax^2 + bx + c$

The Grouping Number Method

One way to factor a trinomial $ax^2 + bx + c$ is to write it as four terms and factor it by grouping as we did in Section 4.3. For example, the trinomial $2x^2 + 11x + 12$ can be written as $2x^2 + 3x + 8x + 12$.

$$2x^2 + 3x + 8x + 12 = x(2x + 3) + 4(2x + 3)$$
$$= (2x + 3)(x + 4)$$

We can factor all factorable trinomials of the form $ax^2 + bx + c$ in this way. Use the following procedure.

Grouping Number Method for Factoring Trinomials of the Form $ax^2 + bx + c = 0$

1. Obtain the grouping number ac.
2. Find the factors of the grouping number whose sum is b.
3. Use those two factors to write bx as the sum of the terms.
4. Factor by grouping.

TEACHING TIP Usually students at this course level divide into two distinct groups: Those students who can factor trinomials of the form $ax^2 + bx + c$ very quickly by the trial and error method, and those who find the trial and error method very frustrating. Explain that the Grouping Number Method was developed to help students factor more easily. If after trying it faithfully for about 20 minutes, they find it does not help them, they are welcome to use the trial and error method.

Example 7   Factor: $2x^2 + 19x + 24$.

1. The grouping number is $(2)(24) = 48$.
2. The factors of 48 are

$$48 \cdot 1 \qquad 12 \cdot 4$$
$$24 \cdot 2 \qquad 8 \cdot 6$$
$$\boxed{16 \cdot 3}$$

3. We use the numbers 16 and 3 to write $19x$ as the sum of $16x$ and $3x$.

$$2x^2 + 19x + 24 = 2x^2 + 16x + 3x + 24$$

4. Factor by grouping

$$2x^2 + 16x + 3x + 24 = 2x(x + 8) + 3(x + 8)$$
$$= (x + 8)(2x + 3)$$ ■

Practice Problem 7 $3x^2 + 2x - 8$. ■

Example 8   Factor: $6x^2 + 7x - 5$.

1. The grouping number is -30.

2. We want the factors of -30 whose sum is $+7$

$$-30 = (-30)(+1) \qquad -30 = (+5)(-6)$$
$$= (+30)(-1) \qquad = (-5)(+6)$$
$$= (+15)(-2) \qquad = (+3)(-10)$$
$$= (-15)(+2) \qquad = (-3)(+10)$$

3. Use -3 and 10 to write $6x^2 + 7x - 5$ with four terms.

$$6x^2 + 7x - 5 = 6x^2 - 3x + 10x - 5$$

4. Factor by grouping

$$6x^2 - 3x + 10x - 5 = 3x(2x - 1) + 5(2x - 1)$$
$$= (2x - 1)(3x + 5) \quad \blacksquare$$

Practice Problem 8   Factor: $10x^2 - 9x + 2$ $\blacksquare$

TEACHING TIP   After discussing example 8, have students factor by the Grouping Number Method.

$2x^2 - 5x - 25$

(Answer G.N. $= -50$ Two factors are $(-10)(+5)$
$2x^2 - 10x + 5x - 25$
$\quad = 2x(x - 5) + 5(x - 5)$
$\quad = (x - 5)(2x + 5)$.)

The Trial-and-Error Method

Another way to factor trinomials $ax^2 + bx + c$ is by trial and error. This method has some advantages if the grouping number is large and we would have to list many factors. In the trial-and-error method we try different values and see which can be multiplied out to obtain the original expression.

Example 9   Factor by trial and error: $2x^2 + 11x + 14$.

We know we will use the factors of $2x^2$: $(2x)(x)$. (If each factor is to contain a variable, there is no other way to factor $2x^2$.) Our answer will thus be in the form

$$(2x + ?)(x + ?)$$

The two unknown numbers must be factors of 14, but we have several choices. We list them all and multiply out the inner and outer products to obtain the middle term of the product.

Possible Factors	*Middle Term of Product*
$(2x + 14)(x + 1)$	$+16x$
$(2x + 1)(x + 14)$	$+29x$
$(2x + 2)(x + 7)$	$+16x$
$(2x + 7)(x + 2)$	$+11x$

Thus, $2x^2 + 11x + 14 = (2x + 7)(x + 2)$ $\blacksquare$

Practice Problem 9   Factor by trial and error: $3x^2 + 31x + 10$. $\blacksquare$

If the last term is negative, there can be many more sign possibilities.

Example 10   Factor by trial and error: $10x^2 - 49x - 5$.

The first terms could have factors of $(10x)$ and (x) or $(5x)$ and $(2x)$. The second terms could have factors of $(+1)$ and (-5) or (-1) and $(+5)$. We list all the possibilities and look for one that will yield a middle term of $-49x$.

Possible Factors	*Middle Term of Product*
$(2x - 1)(5x + 5)$	$+5x$
$(2x + 1)(5x - 5)$	$-5x$
$(2x + 5)(5x - 1)$	$+23x$
$(2x - 5)(5x + 1)$	$-23x$
$(10x - 5)(x + 1)$	$+5x$
$(10x + 5)(x - 1)$	$-5x$
$(10x - 1)(x + 5)$	$+49x$
$(10x + 1)(x - 5)$	$-49x$

Thus,

$$10x^2 - 49x - 5 = (10x + 1)(x - 5) \quad \blacksquare$$

Practice Problem 10   Factor by trial and error: $8x^2 - 6x - 5$.   ∎

As a check, it is always a good idea to multiply out the two binomials and see if you obtain the original expression.

Example 11   Factor by trial and error: $6x^4 + x^2 - 12$.

The first term of each factor must contain an x^2. Suppose that we try

Possible Factors	*Middle Term of Product*
$(2x^2 - 3)(3x^2 + 4)$	$-x^2$

We want a middle term that is opposite in sign since the original middle term was $+x^2$. In this case, we just need to reverse the signs of our possible factors. Do you see why? Therefore,

$$6x^4 + x^2 - 12 = (2x^2 + 3)(3x^2 - 4) \quad \blacksquare$$

Practice Problem 11   Factor by trial and error: $6x^4 + 13x^2 - 5$.   ∎

EXERCISES 4.5

Factor each polynomial. In each case the coefficient of the first variable is 1.

1. $x^2 + 4x + 3$
$(x + 3)(x + 1)$

2. $x^2 + 8x + 7$
$(x + 7)(x + 1)$

3. $x^2 + 7x - 18$
$(x + 9)(x - 2)$

4. $x^2 + 8x - 20$
$(x + 10)(x - 2)$

5. $x^2 + x - 30$
$(x + 6)(x - 5)$

6. $x^2 + 5x - 6$
$(x + 6)(x - 1)$

7. $x^2 + 8x + 12$
$(x + 6)(x + 2)$

8. $x^2 + 12x + 35$
$(x + 7)(x + 5)$

9. $a^2 - 2a - 15$
$(a - 5)(a + 3)$

10. $a^2 - 6a - 16$
$(a - 8)(a + 2)$

11. $a^2 + 4a - 45$
$(a + 9)(a - 5)$

12. $a^2 + 17a + 60$
$(a + 5)(a + 12)$

13. $x^2 - 9xy + 20y^2$
$(x - 4y)(x - 5y)$

14. $x^2 - 6xy - 27y^2$
$(x - 9y)(x + 3y)$

15. $x^2 + 5xy - 14y^2$
$(x + 7y)(x - 2y)$

16. $x^2 + 7xy + 10y^2$
$(x + 2y)(x + 5y)$

17. $x^4 - 3x^2 - 40$
$(x^2 - 8)(x^2 + 5)$

18. $x^4 + 6x^2 + 5$
$(x^2 + 5)(x^2 + 1)$

19. $x^4 - 16x^2 + 63$
$(x + 3)(x - 3)(x^2 - 7)$

20. $x^4 - 6x^2 - 55$
$(x^2 - 11)(x^2 + 5)$

Factor each polynomial. In each case the coefficient of the first variable is not 1. You may use either method we have studied.

21. $2x^2 - 7x + 3$
$(2x - 1)(x - 3)$

22. $3x^2 + 22x + 7$
$(3x + 1)(x + 7)$

23. $5x^2 + 14x + 8$
$(5x + 4)(x + 2)$

24. $18x^2 - 21x + 5$
$(3x - 1)(6x - 5)$

25. $6x^2 - 7x - 5$
$(3x - 5)(2x + 1)$

26. $5x^2 - 13x - 28$
$(5x + 7)(x - 4)$

27. $3a^2 - 8a + 5$
$(3a - 5)(a - 1)$

28. $6a^2 + 11a + 3$
$(3a + 1)(2a + 3)$

29. $8a^2 + 14a - 9$
$(4a + 9)(2a - 1)$

30. $3a^2 - 20a + 12$
$(3a - 2)(a - 6)$

31. $6x^2 - 13x + 6$
$(3x - 2)(2x - 3)$

32. $4x^2 + 4x - 15$
$(2x + 5)(2x - 3)$

33. $2x^2 + 13x + 15$
$(2x + 3)(x + 5)$

34. $5x^2 - 8x - 4$
$(5x + 2)(x - 2)$

35. $3x^4 - 8x^2 - 3$
$(3x^2 + 1)(x^2 - 3)$

36. $6x^4 + 7x^2 - 5$
$(3x^2 + 5)(2x^2 - 1)$

37. $6x^2 + 35xy + 11y^2$
$(3x + y)(2x + 11y)$

38. $5x^2 + 12xy + 7y^2$
$(5x + 7y)(x + y)$

Factor each polynomial.

39. $x^2 + 8x - 20$
$(x + 10)(x - 2)$

40. $2x^2 - 7x + 6$
$(2x - 3)(x - 2)$

41. $6x^2 + x - 2$
$(3x + 2)(2x - 1)$

42. $5x^2 + 17x + 6$
$(5x + 2)(x + 3)$

43. $3x^4 - 2x^2 - 5$
$(3x^2 - 5)(x^2 + 1)$

44. $x^2 - 20x + 99$
$(x - 9)(x - 11)$

45. $15x^2 + x - 2$
$(5x + 2)(3x - 1)$

46. $12x^2 - 5x - 3$
$(4x - 3)(3x + 1)$

47. $6x^2 + 25x + 25$
$(3x + 5)(2x + 5)$

48. $6x^4 - 13x^2 - 5$
$(3x^2 + 1)(2x^2 - 5)$

49. $7x^2 - 22xy + 3y^2$
$(7x - y)(x - 3y)$

50. $10x^2 - 17xy + 6y^2$
$(5x - 6y)(2x - y)$

51. $x^6 - 10x^3 - 39$
$(x^3 - 13)(x^3 + 3)$

52. $x^6 + 5x^3 - 84$
$(x^3 - 7)(x^3 + 12)$

? To Think About

Factor each polynomial. Assume that m and n are positive integers.

53. $x^{2n} + 38x^n + 217$
$(x^n + 7)(x^n + 31)$

54. $x^{2m} + 55x^m - 366$
$(x^m + 61)(x^m - 6)$

55. $21x^{2n} - 50x^n - 16$
$(7x^n + 2)(3x^n - 8)$

56. $15x^{2m} + 71x^m + 70$
$(3x^m + 10)(5x^m + 7)$

Cumulative Review Problems

57. Find the area of a circle of radius 3 inches.
$A = 3.14(9) = 28.26 \text{ in}^2$

58. Solve for b: $A = \dfrac{1}{2}(2a + 5b)$.

$2A = 2a + 5b$
$2A - 2a = 5b$
$\dfrac{2A - 2a}{5} = b$

59. Find the equation in standard form of a line parallel to $3y + x = 10$ that passes through $(6, -4)$.

$y = -\dfrac{1}{3}x + \dfrac{10}{3}$

Parallel line $m = -\dfrac{1}{3}$

$y + 4 = -\dfrac{1}{3}(x - 6)$
$x + 3y = -6$

60. Graph: $6x + 4y = -12$.

x	y
-2	0
0	-3
2	-6

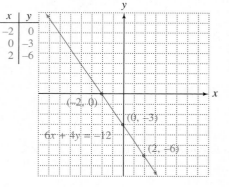

For Extra Practice Exercises, turn to page 230.

Solutions to Odd-Numbered Practice Problems

1. $x^2 + 14x + 48 = (x + 6)(x + 8)$ **3.** $x^2 - 13x - 48 = (x - 16)(x + 3)$
5. (a) $x^2 + 15x + 50 = (x + 5)(x + 10)$ **(b)** $x^2 - 12x + 35 = (x - 5)(x - 7)$ **(c)** $a^2 + 2a - 48 = (a + 8)(a - 6)$
(d) $x^4 + 2x^2 - 15 = (x^2 + 5)(x^2 - 3)$
7. $3x^2 + 2x - 8$ Grouping number $= -24$.
$3x^2 + 6x - 4x - 8$ Two numbers whose product is -24
$3x(x + 2) - 4(x + 2) = (x + 2)(3x - 4)$ and whose sum is $+2$ are $+6$ and -4.
9. $3x^2 + 31x + 10 = (3x + 1)(x + 10)$ **11.** $6x^4 + 13x^2 - 5 = (2x^2 + 5)(3x^2 - 1)$

Answers to Even-Numbered Practice Problems

2. $(x - 7)(x - 3)$ **4.** $(x^2 + 8)(x^2 + 1)$ **6. (a)** $(x - 15y)(x - y)$ **(b)** $(x + 7y)(x - 6y)$ **8.** $(2x - 1)(5x - 2)$
10. $(4x - 5)(2x + 1)$

4.6 SPECIAL CASES OF FACTORING

1 Difference of Two Squares

Recall the special product formula (4.1): $(a + b)(a - b) = a^2 - b^2$. We can use it now as a factoring formula.

> **Factoring the Difference of Two Squares**
> $$a^2 - b^2 = (a + b)(a - b)$$

Example 1 Factor. **(a)** $25x^2 - 36$ **(b)** $16x^2 - 81y^2$

In each case we will use the formula $a^2 - b^2 = (a + b)(a - b)$.
(a) $25x^2 - 36 = (5x)^2 - (6)^2 = (5x + 6)(5x - 6)$
(b) $16x^2 - 81y^2 = (4x)^2 - (9y)^2 = (4x + 9y)(4x - 9y)$ ∎

Practice Problem 1 Factor: $64x^2 - 121y^2$. ∎

Example 2 Factor. **(a)** $121x^6 - 1$ **(b)** $100w^4 - 9z^4$

(a) $121x^6 - 1 = (11x^3)^2 - (1)^2 = (11x^3 + 1)(11x^3 - 1)$
(b) $100w^4 - 9z^4 = (10w^2)^2 - (3z^2)^2 = (10w^2 + 3z^2)(10w^2 - 3z^2)$ ∎

Practice Problem 2 Factor.
(a) $49x^2 - 25y^4$ **(b)** $100x^6 - 1$ ∎

2 Perfect Square Trinomials

Recall our formulas for squaring a binomial:

$$(a - b)^2 = a^2 - 2ab + b^2 \qquad (4\text{-}2)$$

$$(a + b)^2 = a^2 + 2ab + b^2 \qquad (4\text{-}3)$$

We can use these formulas to factor a perfect square trinomial.

> **Perfect Square Factoring Formulas**
> $$a^2 - 2ab + b^2 = (a - b)^2$$
> $$a^2 + 2ab + b^2 = (a + b)^2$$

Recognizing these special cases will save you a lot of time when factoring. How can we recognize a perfect square trinomial?

1. The first and last terms are perfect squares. (The numerical values are 1, 4, 9, 16, 25, 36, . . . , and the variables have an exponent that is an even whole number.)
2. The middle term is twice the product of the values which when squared give the first and last terms.

Example 3 Factor: $25x^2 - 20x + 4$.

Is this trinomial a perfect square? Yes.

1. The first and last terms are perfect squares.

$$25x^2 - 20x + 4 = (5x)^2 - 20x + (2)^2$$

2. The middle term is twice the product of the value $5x$ and the value 2. In other words, $2(5x)(2) = 20x$.

$$(5x)^2 - 2(5x)(2) + (2)^2 = (5x - 2)^2$$

Therefore, we can use the formula $a^2 - 2ab + b^2 = (a - b)^2$. Thus,

$$25x^2 - 20x + 4 = (5x - 2)^2. \quad ∎$$

Practice Problem 3   Factor: $9x^2 - 6xy + y^2$.   ■

Example 4   Factor: $16x^2 - 24x + 9$.

1. The first and last terms are perfect squares because $(4x)^2 = 16x^2$ and $(3)^2 = 9$.
2. The middle term is twice the product of $(4x)(3)$.
   Therefore,

$$a^2 - 2ab + b^2 = (a - b)^2$$

$$16x^2 - 24x + 9 = (4x)^2 - 2(4x)(3) + (3)^2$$

$$16x^2 - 24x + 9 = (4x - 3)^2$$ ■

Practice Problem 4   Factor: $25x^2 - 70x + 49$.   ■

Example 5   Factor: $200x^2 + 360x + 162$.

First we remove the common factor of 2

$$200x^2 + 360x + 162 = 2(100x^2 + 180x + 81)$$

$$a^2 + 2ab + b^2 = (a + b)^2$$

$$2[100x^2 + 180x + 81] = 2[(10x)^2 + (2)(10x)(9) + (9)^2]$$

$$= 2(10x + 9)^2$$ ■

Practice Problem 5   Factor: $242x^2 + 88x + 8$.   ■

Example 6   Factor.

(a) $x^4 + 14x^2 + 49$ **(b)** $9x^4 + 30x^2y^2 + 25y^4$

(a) $x^4 + 14x^2 + 49 = (x^2)^2 + 2(x^2)(7) + (7)^2$
$$= (x^2 + 7)^2$$

(b) $9x^4 + 30x^2y^2 + 25y^4 = (3x^2)^2 + 2(3x^2)(5y^2) + (5y^2)^2$
$$= (3x^2 + 5y^2)^2$$ ■

Practice Problem 6   Factor: $49x^4 + 28x^2 + 4$.   ■

❸ Sum or Difference of Two Cubes

There are also special formulas for factoring cubic binomials. Review your solution to problems 21 and 22 of exercises 4.2. We see that the factors of $x^3 + 27$ are $(x + 3)(x^2 - 3x + 9)$ and that the factors of $x^3 - 64$ are $(x - 4)(x^2 + 4x + 16)$. Therefore, we can generalize this pattern and derive the following factoring formulas.

> **Sum and Difference of Cubes Factoring Formulas**
> $$a^3 + b^3 = (a + b)(a^2 - ab + b^2)$$
> $$a^3 - b^3 = (a - b)(a^2 + ab + b^2)$$

Example 7   Factor: $x^3 + 8$.

Here $a = x$ and $b = 2$.

$$a^3 + b^3 = (a + b)(a^2 - ab + b^2)$$

$$x^3 + 8 = (x)^3 + (2)^3 = (x + 2)(x^2 - 2x + 4)$$ ■

Practice Problem 7   Factor: $27x^3 + 64$.   ■

TEACHING TIP   After discussing examples 5 and 6, have students factor the following two problems as classwork:

Factor A: $81a^2 - 18ab + b^2$
         B: $25x^4 + 70x^2 + 49$

(Answers A: $(9a - b)^2$
B: $(5x^2 + 7)^2$)

Example 8 Factor: $125x^3 + y^3$.

Here $a = 5x$ and $b = y$.

$$a^3 + b^3 = (a + b) \quad (a^2 - ab + b^2)$$

$$125x^3 + y^3 = (5x)^3 + (y)^3 = (5x + y)(25x^2 - 5xy + y^2) \quad \blacksquare$$

Practice Problem 8 Factor: $8x^3 + 125y^3$. $\blacksquare$

Example 9 Factor: $64x^3 - 27$.

Here $a = 4x$ and $b = 3$.

$$a^3 - b^3 = (a - b) \quad (a^2 + ab + b^2)$$

$$64x^3 - 27 = (4x)^3 - (3)^3 = (4x - 3)(16x^2 + 12x + 9) \quad \blacksquare$$

Practice Problem 9 Factor: $64x^3 - 125y^3$. $\blacksquare$

Example 10 Factor: $125w^3 - 8z^6$.

Here $a = 5w$ and $b = 2z^2$.

$$a^3 - b^3 = (a - b) \quad (a^2 + ab + b^2)$$

$$125w^3 - 8z^6 = (5w)^3 - (2z^2)^3 = (5w - 2z^2)(25w^2 + 10wz^2 + 4z^4) \quad \blacksquare$$

Practice Problem 10 Factor: $27w^3 - 125z^6$. $\blacksquare$

Sometimes, polynomials are combinations of two forms. For example, what should you do if a problem is the difference of two cubes *and* the difference of two squares? Usually it's better to use the difference of two squares formula first. Then apply the difference of two cubes formula.

Example 11 Factor: $x^6 - y^6$.

We can write this binomial as $(x^2)^3 - (y^2)^3$ or as $(x^3)^2 - (y^3)^2$. Therefore, we can use either the difference of two cubes formula or the difference of two squares formula.

It's usually better to use the difference of two squares formula first, so we'll do that.

$$x^6 - y^6 = (x^3)^2 - (y^3)^2$$

Here $a = x^3$ and $b = y^3$. Therefore,

$$(x^3)^2 - (y^3)^2 = (x^3 + y^3)(x^3 - y^3)$$

now we use the sum of two cubes formula for the first factor, and the difference of two cubes formula for the second factor.

$$x^3 + y^3 = (x + y)(x^2 - xy + y^2)$$
$$x^3 - y^3 = (x - y)(x^2 + xy + y^2)$$

Hence,

$$x^6 - y^6 = (x + y)(x^2 - xy + y^2)(x - y)(x^2 + xy + y^2) \quad \blacksquare$$

Practice Problem 11 Factor: $64a^6 - 1$. $\blacksquare$

You'll see these special cases of factoring often. You should memorize the following formulas.

Special Cases of Factoring

Difference of Two Squares

$$a^2 - b^2 = (a + b)(a - b)$$

Perfect Square Trinomial

$$a^2 - 2ab + b^2 = (a - b)^2$$
$$a^2 + 2ab + b^2 = (a + b)^2$$

Sum and Difference of Cubes

$$a^3 + b^3 = (a + b)(a^2 - ab + b^2)$$
$$a^3 - b^3 = (a - b)(a^2 + ab + b^2)$$

DEVELOPING YOUR STUDY SKILLS

EXAM TIME: TAKING THE EXAM

Allow yourself plenty of time to get to your exam. You may even find it helpful to arrive a little early, in order to collect your thoughts and ready yourself. This will help you feel more relaxed.

After you get your exam, you will find it helpful to do the following:

1. Take two or three moderately deep breaths. Inhale, then exhale slowly. You will feel your entire body begin to relax.
2. Write down on the back of the exam any formulas or ideas that you need to remember.
3. Look over the entire test quickly in order to pace yourself and use your time wisely. Notice how many points each problem is worth. Spend more time on items of greater worth.
4. Read directions carefully, and be sure to answer all questions clearly. Keep your work neat and easy to read.
5. Ask your instructor about anything that is not clear to you.
6. Work the problems and answer the questions that are easiest for you first. Then come back to the more difficult ones.
7. Do not get bogged down on one problem too long, as it may jeopardize your chances of finishing other problems. Leave the tough problem and come back to it when you have time later.
8. Check your work. This will help you to catch minor errors.
9. Stay calm if others leave before you do. You are entitled to use the full amount of allotted time.

EXERCISES 4.6

Use the difference of two squares formula to factor. Be sure to remove any common factors.

1. $36x^2 - 25y^2$
$(6x - 5y)(6x + 5y)$

2. $100x^4 - 1$
$(10x^2 - 1)(10x^2 + 1)$

3. $1 - 81x^2y^2$
$(1 - 9xy)(1 + 9xy)$

4. $x^2 - 16$
$(x - 4)(x + 4)$

5. $w^4 - z^4$
$(w - z)(w + z)(w^2 + z^2)$

6. $81x^2 - 121$
$(9x - 11)(9x + 11)$

7. $49m^2 - 9n^2$
$(7m - 3n)(7m + 3n)$

8. $s^4t^4 - 1$
$(s^2t^2 + 1)(st - 1)(st + 1)$

9. $32x^2 - 18$
$2(16x^2 - 9)$
$2(4x + 3)(4x - 3)$

10. $50x^2 - 8$
$2(25x^2 - 4)$
$2(5x + 2)(5x - 2)$

11. $121x^3 - 4x$
$x(121x^2 - 4)$
$x(11x + 2)(11x - 2)$

12. $49x^3 - 36x$
$x(49x^2 - 36)$
$x(7x + 6)(7x - 6)$

Use the perfect square trinomial formula to factor. Be sure to remove any common factors.

13. $49x^2 - 14x + 1$
$(7x - 1)^2$

14. $9x^2 - 24x + 16$
$(3x - 4)^2$

15. $w^2 - 6w + 9$
$(w - 3)^2$

16. $36x^2 - 12x + 1$
$(6x - 1)^2$

17. $9x^4 + 6x^2y + y^2$
$(3x^2 + y)^2$

18. $4x^2 + 20x + 25$
$(2x + 5)^2$

19. $81w^2 + 36wt + 4t^2$
$(9w + 2t)^2$

20. $z^2 + 16z + 64$
$(z + 8)^2$

21. $25x^2 - 40xy + 16y^2$
$(5x - 4y)^2$

22. $49x^2 - 70xy + 25y^2$
$(7x - 5y)^2$

23. $8x^2 + 24x + 18$
$2(4x^2 + 12x + 9)$
$2(2x + 3)^2$

24. $128x^2 + 32x + 2$
$2(64x^2 + 16x + 1)$
$2(8x + 1)^2$

25. $36x^3 - 84x^2 + 49x$
$x(36x^2 - 84x + 49)$
$x(6x - 7)^2$

26. $100x^3 - 60x^2 + 9x$
$x(100x^2 - 60x + 9)$
$x(10x - 3)^2$

Use the sum and difference of cubes factoring formulas to factor. Be sure to remove any common factors.

27. $8x^3 + 27$
$(2x + 3)(4x^2 - 6x + 9)$

28. $x^3 + 125$
$(x + 5)(x^2 - 5x + 25)$

29. $64x^3 - 1$
$(4x - 1)(16x^2 + 4x + 1)$

30. $27x^3 - 64$
$(3x - 4)(9x^2 + 12x + 16)$

31. $125x^3 - 8$
$(5x - 2)(25x^2 + 10x + 4)$

32. $1 - 27x^3$
$(1 - 3x)(1 + 3x + 9x^2)$

33. $m^6 - 64n^6$
$(m^3 - 8n^3)(m^3 + 8n^3)$
$(m - 2n)(m^2 + 2mn + 4n^2)(m + 2n)(m^2 - 2mn + 4n^2)$

34. $64s^6 + t^6$
$(4s^2 + t^2)(16s^4 - 4s^2t^2 + t^4)$

35. $64x^3 + 125$
$(4x + 5)(16x^2 - 20x + 25)$

36. $8x^3 + 27$
$(2x + 3)(4x^2 - 6x + 9)$

37. $54y^3 - 16$
$2(27y^3 - 8)$
$2(3y - 2)(9y^2 + 6y + 4)$

38. $250y^3 - 2$
$2(125y^3 - 1)$
$2(5y - 1)(25y^2 + 5y + 1)$

39. $64x^4 + 27x$
$x(64x^3 + 27)$
$x(4x + 3)(16x^2 - 12x + 9)$

40. $64x^4 + 125x$
$x(64x^3 + 125)$
$x(4x + 5)(16x^2 - 20x + 25)$

41. $x^5 - 8x^2y^3$
$x^2(x^3 - 8y^3)$
$x^2(x - 2y)(x^2 + 2xy + 4y^2)$

42. $x^5 - 27x^2y^3$
$x^2(x^3 - 27y^3)$
$x^2(x - 3y)(x^2 + 3xy + 9y^2)$

Factor by the methods of this section.

43. $25w^6 - 1$
$(5w^3 - 1)(5w^3 + 1)$

44. $x^8 - 1$
$(x^4 + 1)(x^4 - 1)$
$(x^4 + 1)(x^2 - 1)(x^2 + 1)$
$(x^4 + 1)(x^2 + 1)(x - 1)(x + 1)$

45. $4w^6 + 4w^3 + 1$
$(2w^3 + 1)^2$

46. $9w^4 + 12w^2 + 4$
$(3w^2 + 2)^2$

47. $8a^3 - 27b^3$
$(2a - 3b)(4a^2 + 6ab + 9b^2)$

48. $27w^3 + 125$
$(3w + 5)(9w^2 - 15w + 25)$

49. $125m^3 + 8n^3$
$(5m + 2n)(25m^2 - 10mn + 4n^2)$

50. $64z^3 - 27w^3$
$(4z - 3w)(16z^2 + 12wz + 9w^2)$

51. $9x^2 - 100y^2$
$(3x - 10y)(3x + 10y)$

52. $49 - 64a^2b^2$
$(7 - 8ab)(7 + 8ab)$

53. $4w^2 - 20wz + 25z^2$
$(2w - 5z)^2$

54. $9x^2y^2 + 24xy + 16$
$(3xy + 4)^2$

55. $36a^2 - 81b^2$
$9(4a^2 - 9b^2)$
$9(2a - 3b)(2a + 3b)$

56. $121x^4 - 4y^2$
$(11x^2 + 2y)(11x^2 - 2y)$

57. $64x^3 + y^3z^3$
$(4x + yz)(16x^2 - 4xyz + y^2z^2)$

58. $w^3z^3 - 8y^3$
$(wz - 2y)(w^2z^2 + 2wyz + 4y^2)$

59. $81x^4 - 36x^2 + 4$
$(9x^2 - 2)^2$

60. $121 + 66y^2 + 9y^4$
$(11 + 3y^2)^2$

61. $16x^4 - 81y^4$
$(4x^2 + 9y^2)(4x^2 - 9y^2)$
$(4x^2 + 9y^2)(2x - 3y)(2x + 3y)$

62. $256x^4 - 1$
$(16x^2 - 1)(16x^2 + 1)$
$(4x - 1)(4x + 1)(16x^2 + 1)$

Try to factor the following four problems by using the formulas for the perfect square trinomial. Why can't the formulas be used? Then factor each problem correctly using an appropriate method.

63. $25x^2 + 25x + 4$
$(5x + 4)(5x + 1)$
$2[5(2)] = 20$, not 25

64. $16x^2 + 40x + 9$
$(4x + 1)(4x + 9)$
$2[4(3)] = 24$, not 40

65. $4x^2 - 15x + 9$
$(4x - 3)(x - 3)$
$2[2(3)] = 12$, not 15

66. $36x^2 - 65x + 25$
$(4x - 5)(9x - 5)$
$2[6(5)] = 60$, not 65

[?] **To Think About**

Factor completely.

67. $81x^{16} - 256$
$(9x^8 + 16)(9x^8 - 16) = (9x^8 + 16)(3x^4 - 4)(3x^4 + 4)$

68. $8x^{15} + 343y^{21}$
$(2x^5 + 7y^7)(4x^{10} - 14x^5y^7 + 49y^{14})$

69. $121x^{16} - 110x^8y^{10} + 25y^{20}$
$(11x^8 - 5y^{10})^2$

70. Belinda invested $4000 in mutual funds. In one year she earned $482. Part was invested at 14% and the remainder at 11%. How much did she invest at each rate?

$1400 @ 14%
$2600 @ 11%
$$x + y = 4000$$
$$0.14x + 0.11y = 482$$

71. A triangular circuit board has a perimeter of 66 centimeters. The first side is two-thirds as long as the second side. The third side is 14 centimeters shorter than the second side. Find the length of each side.

1st side $= \frac{2}{3}x = 20$ cm
2nd side $= x = 30$ cm
3rd side $= x - 14 = 16$ cm
$$\frac{2}{3}x + x + x - 14 = 66$$

72. Three friends each bought a portable compact disc player. The total for the three purchases was $858. Melinda paid $110 more that Hector. Alice paid $86 less than Hector. How much did each person pay?

$$x + 110 + x + x - 86 = 858$$
$$3x = 834$$
$$x = 278$$
Melinda $= x + 110 = 388
Hector $= x = 278
Alice $= x - 86 = 192

For Extra Practice Exercises, turn to page 230.

Solutions to Odd-Numbered Practice Problems

1.
$$a^2 - b^2 = (a + b)(a - b)$$
$$64x^2 - 121y^2 = (8x + 11y)(8x - 11y)$$

3.
$$a^2 - 2ab + b^2 = (a - b)^2$$
$$9x^2 - 6xy + y^2 = (3x - y)^2$$

5. $a^2 + 2ab + b^2 = (a + b)^2$
$$242x^2 + 88x + 8 = 2[121x^2 + 44x + 4]$$
$$= 2(11x + 2)^2$$

7. $a^3 + b^3 = (a + b)(a^2 - ab + b^2)$
$(3x)^3 = 27x^3$ $(4)^3 = 64$
Thus, $27x^3 + 64 = (3x)^3 + (4)^3 = (3x + 4)(9x^2 - 12x + 16)$

9. $a^3 - b^3 = (a - b)(a^2 + ab + b^2)$
$$64x^3 - 125y^3 = (4x)^3 - (5y)^3 = (4x - 5y)(16x^2 + 20xy + 25y^2)$$

11. We want to use the difference of two squares first.

$$(8a^3 + 1)(8a^3 - 1)$$ The formula for the sum and difference of two cubes.

$$(2a + 1)(4a^2 - 2a + 1)(2a - 1)(4a^2 + 2a + 1)$$

Answers to Even-Numbered Practice Problems

2. (a) $(7x + 5y^2)(7x - 5y^2)$ **(b)** $(10x^3 + 1)(10x^3 - 1)$ **4.** $(5x - 7)^2$ **6.** $(7x^2 + 2)^2$ **8.** $(2x + 5y)(4x^2 - 10xy + 25y^2)$
10. $(3w - 5z^2)(9w^2 + 15wz^2 + 25z^4)$

4.7 COMPLETELY FACTORING A POLYNOMIAL

☐ After studying this section, you will be able to:

1 Not all polynomials have the convenient form of one of the special formulas. Most do not. The following procedure will help you handle these common cases. You must practice this procedure until you can *recognize the various forms* and *determine which one to use*, which are the key steps in factoring.

1 *Factor a polynomial where several steps are needed*

2 *Identify prime polynomials*

Completely Factoring a Polynomial

1. *First*, check for a common factor. Remove the greatest common factor (if there is one) before doing anything else.

2. (a) If the remaining polynomial has two terms, try to factor as one of the following,
  (1) The difference of two squares: $a^2 - b^2 = (a + b)(a - b)$ or
  (2) The difference of two cubes: $a^3 - b^3 = (a - b)(a^2 + ab + b^2)$ or
  (3) The sum of two cubes: $a^3 + b^3 = (a + b)(a^2 - ab + b^2)$
(b) If the polynomial has three terms, try to factor it as one of the following,
  (1) A perfect square trinomial:
    $a^2 + 2ab + b^2 = (a + b)^2$ or $a^2 - 2ab + b^2 = (a - b)^2$ or
  (2) A general trinomial of the form $x^2 + bx + c$ or the form $ax^2 + bx + c$
(c) If the polynomial has four terms, try to factor by grouping.

TEACHING TIP As a way of emphasizing the need to factor in the first step, have students do the following problems in two distinct steps:

Factor A: $3x^3 - 12xy^2$

     B: $x^4y + 125xy^4$

     C: $2x^2 - 16x + 32$

     D: $3x^2 - 6x - 72$

(Answers: STEP 1 Remove the common factor.
A: $3x(x^2 - 4y^2)$
B: $xy(x^3 + 125y^3)$
C: $2(x^2 - 8x + 16)$
D: $3(x^2 - 2x - 24)$
STEP 2 Continue to factor.
A: $3x(x + 2y)(x - 2y)$
B: $xy(x + 5y)(x^2 - 5xy + 25y^2)$
C: $2(x - 4)^2$
D: $3(x - 6)(x + 4)$

We repeat that you must work many problems until all of these approaches are familiar to you.

Example 1 Factor: $2x^2 - 18$.

$$2x^2 - 18 = 2(x^2 - 9) \quad\quad \text{Removing the common factor.}$$
$$= 2(x + 3)(x - 3) \quad\quad \text{Use } a^2 - b^2 = (a + b)(a - b). \quad\blacksquare$$

Practice Problem 1 Factor: $12x^2 - 75$. ∎

Example 2 Factor: $27x^4 - 8x$.

$$27x^4 - 8x = x(27x^3 - 8) \quad\quad \text{Removing the common factor.}$$
$$= x(3x - 2)(9x^2 + 6x + 4) \quad \text{Use } a^3 - b^3 = (a - b)(a^2 + ab + b^2). \quad\blacksquare$$

Practice Problem 2 Factor: $7x^5 + 56x^2$. ∎

Example 3 Factor: $27x^2 + 36xy + 12y^2$.

$$27x^2 + 36xy + 12y^2 = 3(9x^2 + 12xy + 4y^2) \quad\quad \text{Removing the common factor.}$$
$$= 3(3x + 2y)^2 \quad\quad \text{Use } (a + b)^2 = a^2 + 2ab + b^2. \quad\blacksquare$$

Practice Problem 3 Factor: $125x^2 + 50xy + 5y^2$. ∎

Example 4 Factor: $2x^2 - 100x + 98$.

$$2x^2 - 100x + 98 = 2(x^2 - 50x + 49) \quad\quad \text{Removing the common factor.}$$
$$= 2(x - 49)(x - 1) \quad\quad \text{Trinomial has form } x^2 + bx + c. \quad\blacksquare$$

Practice Problem 4 Factor: $3x^2 - 39x + 126$. ∎

TEACHING TIP After discussing examples 5 and 6, have students do the two following factoring problems:
Factor *completely*:

A: $4a^3 + 2a^2 - 30a$
B: $4ax + 8bx - 12a - 24b$

(Answers A: $2a(a + 3)(2a - 5)$
B: $4(a + 2b)(x - 3)$)

Example 5 Factor: $6x^3 + 11x^2 - 10x$.

$$6x^3 + 11x^2 - 10x = x(6x^2 + 11x - 10) \quad\quad \text{Removing the common factor.}$$
$$= x(3x - 2)(2x + 5) \quad\quad \text{Trinomial has form } ax^2 + bx + c. \quad\blacksquare$$

Practice Problem 5 Factor: $6x^3 - x^2 - 12x$. ∎

Example 6 Factor: $5ax + 5ay - 20x - 20y$.

$$5ax + 5ay - 20x - 20y = 5[ax + ay - 4x - 4y] \quad\quad \text{Removing the common factor.}$$
$$= 5[a(x + y) - 4(x + y)] \quad\quad \text{Factoring by grouping.}$$
$$= 5(x + y)(a - 4) \quad\quad \text{Removing the common factor.} \quad\blacksquare$$

Practice Problem 6 Factor: $6ax + 6ay + 18bx + 18by$. ∎

To Think About

Can all polynomials be factored? No. Most polynomials cannot be factored. If a polynomial cannot be factored, it is said to be **prime**. ∎

Example 7 If possible, factor: $x^2 + 7x - 12$.

This trinomial has the form $x^2 + bx + c$. To factor it, must write it as $(x + ?)(x + ?)$ and try to find two numbers whose product is -12 and whose sum is $+7$. The chart shows there are none.

Factors of -12	Sum of the Factors
$(4)(-3)$	$+1$
$(-4)(3)$	-1
$(6)(-2)$	$+4$
$(2)(-6)$	-4
$(1)(-12)$	-11
$(-1)(12)$	$+11$

Therefore, the polynomial is prime—it cannot be factored. ∎

Practice Problem 7 If possible, factor: $x^2 - 3x - 20$. ∎

Example 8 If possible, factor: $6x^2 + 10x + 3$.

The trinomial has the form $ax^2 + bx + c$. The group number is 18. If it can be factored, we must find two numbers whose product is 18 and whose sum is 10.

Factors of 18	Sum of the Factors
$(18)(1)$	19
$(6)(3)$	9
$(9)(2)$	11

There are no factors meeting the necessary conditions. Thus, the polynomial is *prime*. (If you use the trial-and-error method, try all the possible factors and show that none of them have a middle term of $10x$.) ∎

Practice Problem 8 If possible, factor: $3x^2 - 10x + 4$. ∎

EXERCISES 4.7

1. In any factoring problem the first step is to $\underline{\text{Remove a common factor if possible}}$.

2. If $x^2 + bx + c = (x + e)(x + f)$ and c is positive and b is negative, what can you say about the sign of e and of f?
e and f must be negative

Factor, if possible. Be sure to factor completely.

3. $64x^2 - 1$
$(8x - 1)(8x + 1)$

4. $x^2 - x - 56$
$(x - 8)(x + 7)$

5. $2x^2 + 5x - 3$
$(2x - 1)(x + 3)$

6. $ax - 2xy + 3aw - 6wy$
$x(a - 2y) + 3w(a - 2y) = (a - 2y)(x + 3w)$

7. $8x^3 - 125y^3$
$(2x - 5y)(4x^2 + 10xy + 25y^2)$

8. $27x^3 + 64y^3$
$(3x + 4y)(9x^2 - 12xy + 16y^2)$

9. $x^2 + 2xy - xz$
$x(x + 2y - z)$

10. $x^2 + 16$
Prime

11. $2ab^2 - 50a$
$2a(b + 5)(b - 5)$

12. $2x^3 - 11x^2 + 12x$
$x(2x^2 - 11x + 12)$
$x(2x - 3)(x - 4)$

13. $18x^3 + 3x^2 - 6x$
$3x(6x^2 + x - 2)$
$3x(3x + 2)(2x - 1)$

14. $12y^3 - 36y^2 + 27y$
$3y(4y^2 - 12y + 9)$
$3y(2y - 3)^2$

15. $6x^2 - 23x - 4$
$(6x + 1)(x - 4)$

16. $25x^2 - 40x + 16$
$(5x - 4)^2$

17. $x^2 - x + y - xy$
$x(x - 1) - y(x - 1)$
$(x - 1)(x - y)$

18. $ac + bc - a - b$
$c(a + b) - 1(a + b)$
$(a + b)(c - 1)$

19. $16x^4 - 2x$
$2x(8x^3 - 1)$
$2x(2x - 1)(4x^2 + 2x + 1)$

20. $1 - 16x^4$
$(1 + 4x^2)(1 - 4x^2)$
$(1 + 4x^2)(1 - 2x)(1 + 2x)$

21. $2x^5 - 16x^3 - 18x$
$2x(x^4 - 8x^2 - 9)$
$2x(x^2 - 9)(x^2 + 1)$
$2x(x - 3)(x + 3)(x^2 + 1)$

22. $8a^3b - 50ab^3$
$2ab(4a^2 - 25b^2)$
$2ab(2a - 5b)(2a + 5b)$

23. $3x^4 + 27x^2$
$3x^2(x^2 + 9)$

24. $12x^3 - 3xy^2$
$3x(4x^2 - y^2)$
$3x(2x - y)(2x + y)$

25. $6x^3 - 9x^2 - 15x$

$3x(2x^2 - 3x - 5)$
$3x(2x - 5)(x + 1)$

26. $3x^2 + 2xy - 7y^2$

Prime

27. $4x^2 - 8x - 6$

$2(2x^2 - 4x - 3)$

28. $8x^2 + 10x - 12$

$2(4x^2 + 5x - 6)$
$2(4x - 3)(x + 2)$

29. $27y^3 - 36y^2 + 12y$

$3y(9y^2 - 12y + 4)$
$3y(3y - 2)^2$

30. $2a^6 + 20a^5b + 50a^4b^2$

$2a^4(a^2 + 10ab + 25b^2)$
$2a^4(a + 5b)^2$

31. $2a^2 - 24a + 70$

$2(a^2 - 12a + 35)$
$2(a - 7)(a - 5)$

32. $7a^2 + 14a - 168$

$7(a^2 + 2a - 24)$
$7(a + 6)(a - 4)$

33. $-3ax + 2a^2y - 6ay + a^2x$

$a[-3x + 2ay - 6y + ax]$
$a[2ay - 6y + ax - 3x]$
$a[2y(a - 3) + x(a - 3)]$
$a(a - 3)(2y + x)$

34. $8w^3 + awx + 4aw^2 + 2w^2x$

$w[8w^2 + ax + 4aw + 2wx]$
$w[8w^2 + 4aw + 2wx + ax]$
$w[4w(2w + a) + x(2w + a)]$
$w(2w + a)(4w + x)$

35. $64y - 49y^3$

$y(64 - 49y^2)$
$y(8 - 7y)(8 + 7y)$

36. $x^4 + 13x^3 + 36x^2$

$x^2(x^2 + 13x + 36)$
$x^2(x + 4)(x + 9)$

37. $2x^4 - 3x^2 - 5$

$(2x^2 - 5)(x^2 + 1)$

38. $150x^2y^2 - 96y^2$

$6y^2(25x^2 - 16)$
$6y^2(5x - 4)(5x + 4)$

39. $12x^2 + 11x - 2$

Prime

40. $2x^5 - 3x^4 + x^3$

$x^3(2x^2 - 3x + 1)$
$x^3(2x - 1)(x - 1)$

41. $54x^6y^6 - 2y^6$

$2y^6(27x^6 - 1)$
$2y^6(3x^2 - 1)(9x^4 + 3x^2 + 1)$

42. $3x^6 + 7x^3 + 2$

$(3x^3 + 1)(x^3 + 2)$

43. $4x^4 + 20x^2y^4 + 25y^8$

$(2x^2 + 5y^4)^2$

44. $81x^4z^6 - 25y^8$

$(9x^2z^3 - 5y^4)(9x^2z^3 + 5y^4)$

? To Think About

45. $2xy + 3y + 6 + 4x = (2x + 3)(y + b)$. What is the value of b?

$y(2x + 3) + 2(2x + 3)$
$(2x + 3)(y + 2) = (2x + 3)(y + b)$
Thus, $b = 2$

46. $25x^2 + ax + 169 = (5x - 13)^2$. What is the value of a?

$(5x - 13)^2 = 25x^2 + ax + 169$
$25x^2 - 130x + 169 = 25x^2 + ax + 169$
$a = -130$

Let n and m be positive integers. Factor.

47. $x^{4n} - a^{2n}x^{2n} - 132a^{4n}$

$(x^{2n} - 12a^{2n})(x^{2n} + 11a^{2n})$

48. $21x^{4m} - 32x^{2m} - 5$

$(3x^{2m} - 5)(7x^{2m} + 1)$

Cumulative Review Problems

Solve for (x, y).

49. $3x - 5y = 7$
  $x - 2y = 3$

$x = 3 + 2y$
$3(3 + 2y) - 5y = 7$
$x = -1, y = -2$

50. $2x + y = 10$
  $3x + 4y = 25$

$y = 10 - 2x$
$3x + 4(10 - 2x) = 25$
$x = 3, y = 4$

Solve for (x, y, z).

51. $3x - y - z = 12$
  $x - 2y + z = 6$
  $x + 3y + z = 16$

Eliminate z:
1 and 2 $4x - 3y = 18$ $\Rightarrow$ $4x - 3y = 18$
1 and 3 $4x + 2y = 28$ $-4x - 2y = -28$
_____
$x = 6, y = 2, z = 4$

52. $5x - 3y + z = 2$
  $2x + 2y + 3z = 13$
  $-3x + 4y - z = 5$

Eliminate z:
1 and 3 $2x + y = 7$
2 and 3 $-2x + 4y = 8$
_____
$x = 2, y = 3, z = 1$

For Extra Practice Exercises, turn to page 231.

Solutions to Odd-Numbered Practice Problems

1. $12x^2 - 75 = 3(4x^2 - 25)$ Removing the common factor of 3.
  $= 3(2x + 5)(2x - 5)$ Use $a^2 - b^2 = (a + b)(a - b)$.

3. $125x^2 + 50xy + 5y^2 = 5(25x^2 + 10xy + y^2)$ Removing the common factor of 5.
  $= 5(5x + y)^2$ Use $a^2 + 2ab + b^2 = (a + b)^2$.

5. $6x^3 - x^2 - 12x = x(6x^2 - x - 12)$ Removing the common factor of x.
  $= x(3x + 4)(2x - 3)$ Factoring as a trinomial of the form $ax^2 + bx + c$.

7. $x^2 - 3x - 20$ It has no common factor. It is of the form $x^2 + bx + c$. There are no factors of -20 whose sum is -3.
  Prime

2. $7x^2(x^3 + 8) = 7x^2(x + 2)(x^2 - 2x + 4)$ **4.** $3(x^2 - 13x + 42) = 3(x - 6)(x - 7)$
6. $6[ax + ay + 3bx + 3by] = 6(x + y)(a + 3b)$ **8.** Prime

EXTRA PRACTICE: EXERCISES

Section 4.1

1. (a) Is $7xy^3 + 3xy + 5$ a trinomial, binomial, or monomial?
   (b) What is the degree of this polynomial?   4th degree
2. $P(x) = 7x^2 - 2x + 5$ and $Q(x) = 5x^3 - x^2 + x - 8$.
   (a) Find $P(x) + Q(x)$. $5x^3 + 6x^2 - x - 3$
   (b) Find $Q(x) - P(x)$. $5x^3 - 8x^2 + 3x - 13$
   (c) Find $P(x) - Q(x)$. $-5x^3 + 8x^2 - 3x + 13$

Perform each operation.

3. $(a^3 - 3a^2 + 2a - 5) + (-5a^3 - 6a^2 - a + 6)$
4. $(3a + 2b) - (5a - 4b) + (a - 3b)$ $-a + 3b$
5. $(x^3 + 4x^2 - 7x - 3) - (-x^2 - 6x + 4)$ $x^3 + 5x^2 - x - 7$
6. $(4x^2 - 3x + 2) + (4x - 2x^2 + 3)$ $2x^2 + x + 5$
7. $(17x^3 - 4x + 1) - (3x^2 - 4x^3)$ $21x^3 - 3x^2 - 4x + 1$
8. $(4x^2 - 3x - 2) + (4 - 2x + 5x^2)$ $9x^2 - 5x + 2$
9. $(12x^5 - 4x^3 + 3x) - (4x^4 - 2x^2 + 6)$
   $12x^5 - 4x^4 - 4x^3 + 2x^2 + 3x - 6$

1(a) Trinomial
3. $-4a^3 - 9a^2 + a + 1$

Multiply.

10. $3a^3b(-2a + 3b^2 - 1)$ $-6a^4b + 9a^3b^3 - 3a^3b$
11. $(5x - 8)(2x - 7)$ $10x^2 - 51x + 56$
12. $(x^2 + 3x - 2)(2x^2 - x + 1)$ $2x^4 + 5x^3 - 6x^2 + 5x - 2$
13. $(2x - 3)(x + 4)(x - 1)$ $2x^3 + 3x^2 - 17x + 12$
14. $(5a^2 - b)(5a^2 + b)$ $25a^4 - b^2$
15. $(3y^2 + 2x^2)^2$ $9y^4 + 12x^2y^2 + 4x^4$
16. $5x^2y^3(4xy - 3x^2y^3 + 2)$ $20x^3y^4 - 15x^4y^6 + 10x^2y^3$
17. $(4x + 11y)(4x - 11y)$ $16x^2 - 121y^2$
18. $(2a + 5b)(4a^2 - 20ab + 25b^2)$ $8a^3 - 20a^2b - 50ab^2 + 125b^3$
19. $(x - 1)^3$ $x^3 - 3x^2 + 3x - 1$
20. $(2x + 3)(4x + 1)(2x - 3)$ $16x^3 + 4x^2 - 36x - 9$
21. $(x^2 - 4)(x^2 + 4)$ $x^4 - 16$
22. $(x + 3)(x - 2)(x - 3)(x + 2)$ $x^4 - 13x^2 + 36$
23. $(3x - 2)(4x^2 + 3x - 1)$ $12x^3 + x^2 - 9x + 2$
24. $(x^2 + x + 1)^2$ $x^4 + 2x^3 + 3x^2 + 2x + 1$

Sections 4.2 and 4.3

Divide.

1. $(12x^3 - 3x^2 + 6x) \div (3x)$ $4x^2 - x + 2$
2. $(2x^2 + 5x - 3) \div (x + 3)$ $2x - 1$
3. $(3x^2 + 29x + 28) \div (3x - 4)$
4. $(x^3 - 5x^2 - 3x + 15) \div (x - 5)$ $x^2 - 3$
5. $(2y^3 + y^2 - 8y + 11) \div (2y - 3)$
6. $(2y^3 - 3y^2 + 12) \div (y - 2)$ $2y^2 + y + 2 + \dfrac{16}{y - 2}$
7. $(x^5 + 3x^4 + x^2 + 18) \div (x + 3)$
8. $(24y^4 - 2y^3 - 9y^2 - 2y + 1) \div (4y - 1)$ $6y^3 + y^2 - 2y - 1$
9. $(8x^3 + 27) \div (2x + 3)$ $4x^2 - 6x + 9$
10. $(3a^4 - 12a^3 + 5a^2 - 8a + 2) \div (3a^2 + 2)$ $a^2 - 4a + 1$
11. $(2x^4 - 3x^3 - 9x^2 - x + 3) \div (x^2 - 2x - 3)$ $2x^2 + x - 1$
12. $(18x^3 - 12x^2 + 6x) \div 6x$ $3x^2 - 2x + 1$
13. $(x^2 - x - 6) \div (x - 3)$ $x + 2$
14. $(12x^2 - 13xy - 14y^2) \div (3x + 2y)$ $(4x - 7y)$
15. $[(x + y)a + (x + y)b] \div (x + y)$ $(a + b)$
16. $(4x^3 + 12x^2 - 19x + 6) \div (2x - 1)$ $2x^2 + 7x - 6$
17. $(x^4 - 1) \div (x^2 + 1)$ $x^2 - 1$
18. $(x^2 - 10xy + 25y^2) \div (x - 5y)$ $(x - 5y)$

19. $(4x^3 - 16x^2 + 23x - 13) \div (2x - 5)$
20. $(6x^4 + x^3 - 8x^2 + 4x - 3) \div (2x + 3)$ $3x^3 - 4x^2 + 2x - 1$
21. $(x^4 - 3x^3 + 3x + 4) \div (x^2 - 3x + 1)$
22. $(8x^4 - 16x^3 + 16x - 32) \div (x - 2)$ $8x^3 + 16$
23. $(6x^3 - 4x^2 + 12x - 8) \div (3x - 2)$ $2x^2 + 4$
24. $(16x^2 - 74x + 12) \div (8x - 1)$
25. $(x^3 - 1) \div (x^2 + x + 1)$ $(x - 1)$
26. $(x^2 + 6x + 13) \div (x + 3)$ $x + 3 + \dfrac{4}{x + 3}$
27. $(x^2 + 4x + 7) \div (x + 2)$ $x + 2 + \dfrac{3}{x + 2}$
28. $(x^3 - 3x^2 - 10x + 20) \div (x - 2)$ $x^2 - x - 12 - \dfrac{4}{x - 2}$
29. $(x^3 - 2x^2 - 6x - 8) \div (x - 4)$ $x^2 + 2x + 2$
30. $(x^3 + 4x^2 + x - 2) \div (x + 2)$
31. $(x^3 - 7x^2 - x + 3) \div (x + 3)$
32. $(3x^4 - 21x^3 + 31x^2 - 25) \div (x - 5)$ $3x^3 - 6x^2 + x + 5$
33. $(x^4 - 9x^3 + 20x^2 - 15x + 18) \div (x - 6)$ $x^3 - 3x^2 + 2x - 3$
34. $(2x^4 + 6x^3 - 4x^2 - 11x + 3) \div (x + 3)$ $2x^3 - 4x + 1$
35. $(x^5 - 3x^4 + 2x^2 - 5) \div (x + 2)$
36. $(x^5 + x^4 + 2x^2 - 1) \div (x - 1)$ $x^4 + 2x^3 + 2x^2 + 4x + 4 + \dfrac{3}{x - 1}$

3. $x + 11 + \dfrac{72}{3x - 4}$

5. $y^2 + 2y - 1 + \dfrac{8}{2y - 3}$

7. $x^4 + x - 3 + \dfrac{27}{x + 3}$

19. $2x^2 - 3x + 4 + \dfrac{7}{2x - 5}$

21. $x^2 - 1 + \dfrac{5}{x^2 - 3x + 1}$

24. $2x - 9 + \dfrac{3}{8x - 1}$

30. $x^2 + 2x - 3 + \dfrac{4}{x + 2}$

31. $x^2 - 10x + 29 - \dfrac{84}{x + 3}$

35. $x^4 - 5x^3 + 10x^2 - 18x + 36 - \dfrac{77}{x + 2}$

Section 4.4

Factor. Be sure to remove the greatest common factor.

1. $ay + a^2$ $a(y + a)$

2. $5x^3 - 10x^2 + 15x$ $5x(x^2 - 2x + 3)$

3. $9x^6y^4 - 15x^3y^5 - 6x^4y^4$ $3x^3y^4(3x^3 - 5y - 2x)$

4. $12x^5 - 30x^3 - 21x^2 + 15x$ $3x(4x^4 - 10x^2 - 7x + 5)$

5. $14x^3y^2 - 21x^6y^3 - 35x^3y^4$ $7x^3y^2(2 - 3x^3y - 5y^2)$

6. $100a^3b^4 - 50a^3b^3 - 25a^4$ $25a^3(4b^4 - 2b^3 - a)$

7. $3(x - 2y) + 5x(x - 2y)$ $(x - 2y)(3 + 5x)$

8. $8a(a - 4b) + 3b(a - 4b) - (a - 4b)$ $(a - 4b)(8a + 3b - 1)$

9. $xy + x - 2y^2 - 2y$ $(y + 1)(x - 2y)$

10. $6a^2 - 4ac - 15ab + 10bc$ $(3a - 2c)(2a - 5b)$

11. $a^2 - ab + a - b$ $(a - b)(a + 1)$

12. $8x^2y - 4x^2 - 3 + 6y$ $(2y - 1)(4x^2 + 3)$

13. $14x^2 - 7 - 4y^4 + 8x^2y^4$ $(2x^2 - 1)(7 + 4y^4)$

14. $5y - 8x^2 - 10 + 4x^2y$ $(5 + 4x^2)(y - 2)$

15. $a^3b^3 + 2a^3 + 10a^2 + 5a^2b^3$ $a^2(a + 5)(b^3 + 2)$

16. $2x^3y^3 - 12x^2y^2 + 10x^2y + 2x^2$ $2x^2(xy^3 - 6y^2 + 5y + 1)$

17. $c(a + b) - c(a - 2b)$ $3bc$

18. $\pi R^2 - \pi x + \pi r^2$ $\pi(R^2 - x + r^2)$

19. $8a^2bc - 12ab + 16bc$ $4b(2a^2c - 3a + 4c)$

20. $72x^3 - 54x$ $18x(4x^2 - 3)$

21. $x^4 + x^3 - x^2 + x$ $x(x^3 + x^2 - x + 1)$

22. $15m^3x - 30mx + 40x$ $5x(3m^3 - 6m + 8)$

23. $5x(a - b) + 4y(a - b) + 3z(a - b)$ $(a - b)(5x + 4y + 3z)$

24. $121x^2y^3 + 44x^3y^2 + 110xy^4 - 33x^3y^5$

25. $2x^2 - 8ax + 3nx - 12an$ $(x - 4a)(2x + 3n)$

26. $15rs^2 + 3r^2s - 45ns^2 - 9rns$ $3s(r - 3n)(5s + r)$

27. $16am - 6bn - 12bm + 8an$ $2(2m + n)(4a - 3b)$

28. $(x - 2)c + b(2 - x)$ $(x - 2)(c - b)$

29. $ax^2(b - c) + by^2(c - b)$ $(b - c)(ax^2 - by^2)$

24. $11xy^2(11xy + 4x^2 + 10y^2 - 3x^2y^3)$

Section 4.5

Factor.

1. $x^2 + 14x + 48$ $(x + 6)(x + 8)$

2. $x^2 - 14x + 45$ $(x - 9)(x - 5)$

3. $x^2 + 2x - 63$ $(x + 9)(x - 7)$

4. $x^2 - 3x - 40$ $(x - 8)(x + 5)$

5. $2x^2 + 7x + 6$ $(2x + 3)(x + 2)$

6. $2x^2 - 11x + 15$ $(2x - 5)(x - 3)$

7. $15x^2 - x - 2$ $(5x - 2)(3x + 1)$

8. $3x^2 - 10x + 8$ $(3x - 4)(x - 2)$

9. $x^4 + 5x^2 - 24$ $(x^2 - 3)(x^2 + 8)$

10. $x^6 - 3x^3 - 10$ $(x^3 - 5)(x^3 + 2)$

11. $2x^2 - xy - 21y^2$ $(2x - 7y)(x + 3y)$

12. $10x^2 - 17xy + 3y^2$ $(2x - 3y)(5x - y)$

13. $3a^2 - 19ab + 20b^2$ $(3a - 4b)(a - 5b)$

14. $5w^2 + 7wt - 6t^2$ $(5w - 3t)(w + 2t)$

15. $6x^4 - 13x^2 + 5$ $(3x^2 - 5)(2x^2 - 1)$

16. $4x^4 - 4x^2 - 15$ $(2x^2 + 3)(2x^2 - 5)$

17. $7x^2 + 3x - 10$ $(7x + 10)(x - 1)$

18. $32x^2 + 60x + 7$ $(4x + 7)(8x + 1)$

19. $12x^2 - 13xy - 14y^2$ $(3x + 2y)(4x - 7y)$

20. $c^2 - 3c - 54$ $(c - 9)(c + 6)$

21. $2x^2 + 13x + 18$ $(2x + 9)(x + 2)$

22. $4y^{2n} - 12y^n + 9$ $(2y^n - 3)^2$

23. $a^4 + 4a^2b^2 + 4b^4$ $(a^2 + 2b^2)^2$

24. $1 + 12a + 36a^2$ $(1 + 6a)^2$

25. $2a^2 - 5ab - 12b^2$ $(2a + 3b)(a - 4b)$

26. $12x^2 - 31x - 15$ $(12x + 5)(x - 3)$

27. $15a^2 - 26ab - 24b^2$ $(3a + 2b)(5a - 12b)$

28. $3x^2 - 7x - 6$ $(3x + 2)(x - 3)$

29. $6a^2 - 13ab - 6b^2$ Prime

30. $2a^2 + 23a - 12$ $(2a - 1)(a + 12)$

31. $2m^2 - 19m + 24$ $(2m - 3)(m - 8)$

Section 4.6

Factor.

1. $a^2 - 100$ $(a - 10)(a + 10)$

2. $81a^2 - 1$ $(9a - 1)(9a + 1)$

3. $121b^2 - 49d^2$ $(11b - 7d)(11b + 7d)$

4. $25x^2y^2 - 4$ $(5xy - 2)(5xy + 2)$

5. $4x^2 - 12xy + 9y^2$ $(2x - 3y)^2$

6. $25x^2 + 70x + 49$ $(5x + 7)^2$

7. $100x^2 + 60x + 9$ $(10x + 3)^2$

8. $144x^2 - 120x + 25$ $(12x - 5)^2$

9. $64x^3 - 27y^3$ $(4x - 3y)(16x^2 + 12xy + 9y^2)$

10. $125a^3 - 8b^3$ $(5a - 2b)(25a^2 + 10ab + 4b^2)$

11. $27a^3 + 125b^3$ $(3a + 5b)(9a^2 - 15ab + 25b^2)$

12. $8x^3y^3 + 64$ $8(xy + 2)(x^2y^2 - 2xy + 4)$

13. $64x^8 - 1$ $(8x^4 + 1)(8x^4 - 1)$

14. $x^4 + 6x^2 + 9$ $(x^2 + 3)^2$

15. $27w^6 - 64z^6$ $(3w^2 - 4z^2)(9w^4 + 12w^2z^2 + 16z^4)$

16. $81x^4 - 36y^4$ $9(3x^2 - 2y^2)(3x^2 + 2y^2)$

17. $49x^2 - 42xy + 9y^2$ $(7x - 3y)^2$

18. $121a^2 + 198ab + 81b^2$ $(11a + 9b)^2$

19. $16x^2 - 72xy^2 + 81y^4$ $(4x - 9y^2)^2$

20. $x^6 - 64$ $(x - 2)(x + 2)(x^2 + 2x + 4)(x^2 - 2x + 4)$

21. $4x^2 - 44x + 11$ Prime

22. $27b^6 + x^3$ $(3b^2 + x)(9b^4 - 3b^2x + x^2)$

23. $m^4n^4 - 81x^4$ $(m^2n^2 + 9x^2)(mn + 3x)(mn - 3x)$

24. $144 - 25x^2$ $(12 - 5x)(12 + 5x)$

25. $216x^3 - 125y^3$ $(6x - 5y)(36x^2 + 30xy + 25y^2)$

26. $121x^2 - 198x + 81$ $(11x - 9)^2$

27. $x^6 + 6x^3 + 9$ $(x^3 + 3)^2$

28. $4x^2 - 25y^6$ $(2x - 5y^3)(2x + 5y^3)$

29. $125x^3 - y^3$ $(5x - y)(25x^2 + 5xy + y^2)$

30. $9x^4 - 30x^2y + 25y^2$ $(3x^2 - 5y)^2$

31. $x^4 - 8x^2 + 16$ $(x + 2)^2(x - 2)^2$

32. $64x^{12} - 81z^6$ $(8x^6 - 9z^3)(8x^6 + 9z^3)$

Factor, if possible. Be sure to factor completely.

1. $21x^2y^3 - 7x^3y^5$ $7x^2y^3(3 - xy^2)$
2. $12x^3y^2 - 3xy^2$ $3xy^2(2x - 1)(2x + 1)$
3. $2a^4 - 16ab^3$ $2a(a - 2b)(a^2 + 2ab + 4b^2)$
4. $3a^6 + 81b^6$ $3(a^2 + 3b^2)(a^4 - 3a^2b^2 + 9b^4)$
5. $x^2 + 3x - 28$ $(x + 7)(x - 4)$
6. $4x^2 - 20x + 25$ $(2x - 5)^2$
7. $2x^2 - 28x + 98$ $2(x - 7)^2$
8. $3x^3 - 24x^2 + 45x$ $3x(x - 5)(x - 3)$
9. $54x^4 - 16x$ $2x(3x - 2)(9x^2 + 6x + 4)$
10. $dx + dy - 3ax - 3ay$ $(x + y)(d - 3a)$
11. $8y - 12 - 3x + 2xy$ $(2y - 3)(x + 4)$
12. $2x^4 + 8x^3 - 42x^2$ $2x^2(x + 7)(x - 3)$
13. $x^2 + 10x + 30$ Prime
14. $2x^2 + 7x - 3$ Prime
15. $3d - dx + 3cx - cx^2$ $(3 - x)(d + cx)$
16. $14x^2 + 17x - 6$ $(7x - 2)(2x + 3)$
17. $125a^4 - a^4x^3$ $a^4(5 - x)(25 + 5x + x^2)$
18. $2x^3 - 35w - 7x + 10wx^2$ $(2x^2 - 7)(x + 5w)$
19. $49x^2 - 112xy + 64y^2$ $(7x - 8y)^2$
20. $7x^2 - 55xy - 8y^2$ $(7x + y)(x - 8y)$
21. $2x^3 - 6x^2 + 30x$ $2x(x^2 - 3x + 15)$
22. $3x^6 + 6x^5 + 12x^4$ $3x^4(x^2 + 2x + 4)$
23. $675 - 27a^2$ $27(5 - a)(5 + a)$
24. $54x^6 - 250x^3$ $2x^3(3x - 5)(9x^2 + 15x + 25)$
25. $4x^{2n} + 14x^n - 30$ $2(2x^n - 3)(x^n + 5)$
26. $16t^2 - 32t - 128$ $16(t - 4)(t + 2)$
27. $4a^2x + 12ax^2$ $4ax(a + 3x)$
28. $169x^4 - 81$ $(13x^2 - 9)(13x^2 + 9)$
29. $16x^2 + 24x + 9$ $(4x + 3)^2$
30. $8x^4 - 14x^2 - 9$ $(2x + 3)(2x - 3)(2x^2 + 1)$
31. $8r^2 + 22rs - 6s^2$ $2(4r - s)(r + 3s)$
32. $12x^2 + 47xy - 4y^2$ $(12x - y)(x + 4y)$
33. $6y^2 - 33y - 18$ $3(2y + 1)(y - 6)$
34. $6x^4 - 96$ $6(x^2 + 4)(x + 2)(x - 2)$
35. $x^3 + 4x^2 + 5x + 20$ $(x + 4)(x^2 + 5)$

CHAPTER ORGANIZER

Topic	Procedure	Examples
Adding and subtracting polynomials, p. 193	Combine like terms following the rules of signs.	$(5x^2 - 6x - 8) + (-2x^2 - 5x + 3) = 3x^2 - 11x - 5$ $(3a^2 - 2ab - 5b^2) - (-7a^2 + 6ab - b^2)$ $\quad = (3a^2 - 2ab - 5b^2) + (7a^2 - 6ab + b^2)$ $\quad = 10a^2 - 8ab - 4b^2$
Multiplying polynomials, p. 194	1. Multiply each term of the first polynomial by each term of the second polynomial. 2. Combine like terms.	$2x^2(3x^2 - 5x - 6) = 6x^4 - 10x^3 - 12x^2$ $(3x + 4)(2x - 7) = 6x^2 - 21x + 8x - 28$ $\quad = 6x^2 - 13x - 28$ $(x - 3)(x^2 + 5x + 8)$ $\quad = x^3 + 5x^2 + 8x - 3x^2 - 15x - 24$ $\quad = x^3 + 2x^2 - 7x - 24$
Division of a polynomial by a monomial, p. 198	1. Write the division as the sum of separate fractions. 2. If possible, reduce the separate fractions.	$(16x^3 - 24x^2 + 56x) \div (-8x)$ $\quad = \dfrac{16x^3}{-8x} + \dfrac{-24x^2}{-8x} + \dfrac{56x}{-8x}$ $\quad = -2x^2 + 3x - 7$
Dividing a polynomial by a binomial or a trinomial, p. 200	1. Write the division as in arithmetic. Write both polynomials in descending order; write any missing terms with a coefficient of zero. 2. Divide the *first* term of the divisor into the first term of the dividend. The result is the first term of the quotient. 3. Multiply the first term of the quotient by *every* term in the divisor. 4. Write this product under the dividend (align like terms) and subtract. 5. Treat this difference as a new dividend. Repeat steps 2–4. Continue until the remainder is zero or is a polynomial of lower degree than the *first term* of the divisor.	Divide: $(6x^3 + 5x^2 - 2x + 1) \div (3x + 1)$. $$\begin{array}{r} 2x^2 + x - 1 \\ 3x + 1 \overline{)6x^3 + 5x^2 - 2x + 1} \\ \underline{6x^3 + 2x^2} \\ 3x^2 - 2x \\ \underline{3x^2 + x} \\ -3x + 1 \\ \underline{-3x - 1} \\ 2 \end{array}$$ The quotient is $2x^2 + x - 1 + \dfrac{2}{3x + 1}$.

Topic	Procedure	Examples
Synthetic division (optional topic), p. 204	Synthetic division can be used if the divisor is in the form $(x - b)$ or $(x + b)$. 1. Write the coefficients of the terms in descending order of the dividend. Write any missing terms with a coefficient of zero. 2. The division will be of the form $(x - b)$ or $(x + b)$. Write down the opposite of b to the left. 3. Bring down the first coefficient to the bottom row. 4. Multiply each coefficient on the bottom by the opposite of b and add it to the upper coefficient. 5. Continue until the bottom row is filled.	Divide: $(3x^5 - 2x^3 + x^2 - x + 7) \div (x + 2)$. $$\begin{array}{r\|rrrrrr} -2 & 3 & 0 & -2 & 1 & -1 & 7 \\ & & -6 & 12 & -20 & 38 & -74 \\ \hline & 3 & -6 & 10 & -19 & 37 & -67 \end{array}$$ The quotient is $3x^4 - 6x^3 + 10x^2 - 19x + 37 + \dfrac{-67}{x + 2}$.
Removing a common factor, p. 208	Remove greatest common factor from each term. Many factoring problems are two steps, of which this is the first.	$5x^3 - 25x^2 - 10x = 5x(x^2 - 5x - 2)$ $20a^3b^2 - 40a^4b^3 + 30a^3b^3 = 10a^3b^2(2 - 4ab + 3b)$
Factoring the difference of two squares, p. 220	$a^2 - b^2 = (a + b)(a - b)$	$9x^2 - 1 = (3x + 1)(3x - 1)$ $8x^2 - 50 = 2(4x^2 - 25) = 2(2x + 5)(2x - 5)$
Factoring the perfect square trinomial, p. 220	$a^2 + 2ab + b^2 = (a + b)^2$ $a^2 - 2ab + b^2 = (a - b)^2$	$16x^2 + 40x + 25 = (4x + 5)^2$ $18x^2 + 120xy + 200y^2 = 2(9x^2 + 60xy + 100y^2)$ $\qquad = (3x + 10y)^2$ $4x^2 - 36x + 81 = (2x - 9)^2$ $25a^3 - 10a^2b + ab^2 = a(25a^2 - 10ab + b^2)$ $\qquad = a(5a - b)^2$
Factoring the sum and difference of two cubes, p. 221	$a^3 + b^3 = (a + b)(a^2 - ab + b^2)$ $a^3 - b^3 = (a - b)(a^2 + ab + b^2)$	$8x^3 + 27 = (2x + 3)(4x^2 - 6x + 9)$ $250x^3 + 2y^3 = 2(125x^3 + y^3)$ $\qquad = 2(5x + y)(25x^2 - 5xy + y^2)$ $27x^3 - 64 = (3x - 4)(9x^2 + 12x + 16)$ $125y^4 - 8y = y(125y^3 - 8)$ $\qquad = y(5y - 2)(25y^2 + 10y + 4)$
Factoring the trinomials of the form $x^2 + bx + c$, p. 214	The factors will be of the form $(x + m)(x + n)$, where $m \cdot n = c$ and $m + n = b$.	$x^2 - 7x + 12 = (x - 4)(x - 3)$ $3x^2 - 36x + 30 = 3(x^2 - 12x + 20) = 3(x - 2)(x - 10)$ $x^2 + 2x - 15 = (x + 5)(x - 3)$ $2x^2 - 44x - 96 = 2(x^2 - 22x - 48)$ $\qquad = 2(x - 24)(x + 2)$
Factoring the trinomials of the form $ax^2 + bx + c$, p. 216	Use the trial-and-error method or the grouping number method.	$2x^2 + 7x + 3 = (2x + 1)(x + 3)$ $8x^2 - 26x + 6 = 2(4x^2 - 13x + 3) = 2(4x - 1)(x - 3)$ $7x^2 + 20x - 3 = (7x - 1)(x + 3)$ $5x^3 - 18x^2 - 8x = x(5x^2 - 18x - 8) = x(5x + 2)(x - 4)$
Factoring by grouping, p. 210	1. Make sure that the first two terms have a common factor; otherwise, rearrange the order. 2. Divide problem into two parts. Remove the common factor from each part. 3. Remove the common binomial in parentheses. 4. Place the remaining terms in other parentheses.	$6xy - 8y + 3xw - 4w$ $2y(3x - 4) + w(3x - 4) = (3x - 4)(2y + w)$

REVIEW PROBLEMS CHAPTER 4

1. $H(x) = 7x^3 + 5x^2 - 2x + 1$ and $P(x) = 5x^4 - x^3 + 3x - 2$.
   (a) Find $H(x) + P(x)$. $5x^4 + 6x^3 + 5x^2 + x - 1$
   (b) Find $P(x) - H(x)$. $5x^4 - 8x^3 - 5x^2 + 5x - 3$

Perform the operations indicated.

2. $(7x - 2) + (5 - 3x) + (2 - 2x)$
$2x + 5$

3. $(5x - 2x^2 - x^3) - (2x - 3 + 5x^2)$
$-x^3 - 7x^2 + 3x + 3$

Multiply.

4. $3xy(x^2 - xy + y^2)$
$3x^3y - 3x^2y^2 + 3xy^3$

5. $(3x^2 + 1)(2x - 1)$
$6x^3 - 3x^2 + 2x - 1$

6. $(5x^2 + 3)^2$
$25x^4 + 30x^2 + 9$

7. $(x - 3)(2x - 5)(x + 2)$
$2x^3 - 7x^2 - 7x + 30$

8. $(x^2 - 3x + 1)(-2x^2 + x - 2)$
$-2x^4 + 7x^3 - 7x^2 + 7x - 2$

Divide.

9. $(25x^3y - 15x^2y - 100xy) \div (-5xy)$
$-5x^2 + 3x + 20$

10. $(12x^2 - 16x - 4) \div (3x + 2)$
$4x - 8 + \dfrac{12}{3x + 2}$

11. $(2x^3 - 7x^2 + 2x + 8) \div (x - 2)$
$2x^2 - 3x - 4$

12. $(3y^3 - 2y + 5) \div (y - 3)$
$3y^2 + 9y + 25 + \dfrac{80}{y - 3}$

13. $(15a^4 - 3a^3 + 4a^2 + 4) \div (3a^2 - 1)$
$5a^2 - a + 3 + \dfrac{-a + 7}{3a^2 - 1}$

14. $(x^4 - x^3 - 7x^2 - 7x - 2) \div (x^2 - 3x - 2)$
$x^2 + 2x + 1$

15. $(2x^4 - 13x^3 + 16x^2 - 9x + 20) \div (x - 5)$
$2x^3 - 3x^2 + x - 4$

16. $(3x^4 + 5x^3 - x^2 + x - 2) \div (x + 2)$
$3x^3 - x^2 + x - 1$

17. $(4x^4 + 12x^3 - x^2 - x + 2) \div (x + 3)$
$4x^3 - x + 2 - \dfrac{4}{x + 3}$

18. $(2x^4 - 9x^3 + 5x^2 + 13x - 3) \div (x - 3)$
$2x^3 - 3x^2 - 4x + 1$

Factor, if possible. Be sure to factor completely.

19. $x^2 + 15x + 36$
$(x + 3)(x + 12)$

20. $5x^2 - 11x + 2$
$(5x - 1)(x - 2)$

21. $9x^2 - 121$
$(3x - 11)(3x + 11)$

22. $36x^2 + 25$
Prime

23. $x^2 - 8wy + 4xw - 2xy$
$(x + 4w)(x - 2y)$

24. $x^3 + 8x^2 + 12x$
$x(x + 6)(x + 2)$

25. $2x^2 - 7x - 3$
Prime

26. $x^2 + 6xy - 27y^2$
$(x + 9y)(x - 3y)$

27. $27x^4 - x$
$x(3x - 1)(9x^2 + 3x + 1)$

28. $21a^2 + 20ab + 4b^2$
$(7a + 2b)(3a + 2b)$

29. $-3a^3b^3 + 2a^2b^4 - a^2b^3$
$-a^2b^3(3a - 2b + 1)$

30. $a^4b^4 + a^3b^4 - 6a^2b^4$
$a^2b^4(a + 3)(a - 2)$

31. $3x^4 - 5x^2 - 2$
$(3x^2 + 1)(x^2 - 2)$

32. $2x^4 + 20x^2 - 48$
$2(x^2 + 12)(x^2 - 2)$

33. $9a^2b + 15ab - 14b$
$b(3a + 7)(3a - 2)$

34. $2x^4 + 7x^2 - 6$
Prime

35. $12x^2 + 12x + 3$
$3(2x + 1)^2$

36. $4y^4 - 13y^3 + 9y^2$
$y^2(4y - 9)(y - 1)$

37. $y^4 + 2y^3 - 35y^2$
$y^2(y + 7)(y - 5)$

38. $4x^2y^2 - 12x^2y - 8x^2$
$4x^2(y^2 - 3y - 2)$

39. $3x^4 - 7x^2 - 6$
$(3x^2 + 2)(x^2 - 3)$

40. $a^2 + 5ab^3 + 4b^6$
$(a + b^3)(a + 4b^3)$

41. $3x^2 - 12 - 8x + 2x^3$
$(2x + 3)(x + 2)(x - 2)$

42. $2x^4 - 12x^2 - 54$
$2(x - 3)(x + 3)(x^2 + 3)$

43. $8a + 8b - 4bx - 4ax$
$4(2 - x)(a + b)$

44. $8x^4 + 34x^2y^2 + 21y^4$
$(4x^2 + 3y^2)(2x^2 + 7y^2)$

45. $4x^3 + 10x^2 - 6x$
$2x(2x - 1)(x + 3)$

46. $2a^2x - 15ax + 7x$
$x(2a - 1)(a - 7)$

47. $16x^4y^2 - 56x^2y + 49$
$(4x^2y - 7)^2$

48. $128x^3y - 2xy$
$2xy(8x - 1)(8x + 1)$

49. $26x^3y - 13xy^3 + 52x^2y^4$
  $13xy(2x^2 - y^2 + 4xy^3)$

50. $5xb - 28y + 4by - 35x$
  $(5x + 4y)(b - 7)$

51. $27abc^2 - 12ab$
  $3ab(3c - 2)(3c + 2)$

52. $5a^6 + 40a^3b^3$
  $5a^3(a + 2b)(a^2 - 2ab + 4b^2)$

53. $50x^4 - 100x^3 + 64x^2$
  $2x^2(25x^2 - 50x + 32)$

54. $60x^2 - 100xy + 15y^2$
  $5(6x - y)(2x - 3y)$

PUTTING YOUR SKILLS TO WORK

The Use of Factoring to Minimize the Number of Calculations.

We can use factoring to rewrite a formula in order to simplify computations. For example, let's find the area of the doughnut-shaped object that follows, which is called a **torus** in mathematics.

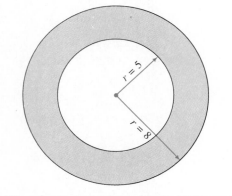

The inner radius is $r = 5.0000$ centimeters and the outer radius is $r = 8.0000$ centimeters, which are accurate to five significant digits. We can calculate this area as follows:

Shaded area = area of large circle − area of small circle
$$= \pi r_1{}^2 - \pi r_2{}^2 = \pi(8)^2 - \pi(5)^2$$

Since the radii are accurate to five significant digits, we must use five significant digits for π, so $\pi = 3.1416$.

$$\text{Shaded area} = (3.1416)(64) - (3.1416)(25)$$
$$= 201.0624 - 78.5400 = \boxed{122.5224}$$

Now let's use factoring to rewrite the formula:

$$\text{Shaded area} = \pi r_1^2 - \pi r_2^2 = \pi(r_1^2 - r_2^2)$$
$$= (3.1416)(8^2 - 5^2)$$
$$= (3.1416)(39) = \boxed{122.5224}$$

In this second calculation, we had to multiply by π only once. Since we have five significant digits in our work, we must round off to 122.52 square centimeters.

A Challenge for You

Find the total volume of eight cylinders. The radius of each cylinder (five significant digits) is 7.0000 inches. The heights of the cylinders are 5.50000 inches, 6.0000 inches, 7.5000 inches, 8.4000 inches, 8.8000 inches, 9.2000 inches, 9.6000 inches, and 9.7000 inches. Use the formula $V = \pi r^2 h$. (Use $\pi = 3.1416$, and round your answer to five significant digits.)
Answer: 9959.8 cubic inches

1. Let $P = 5x^3 - 6x^2 - 8$ and $H = 2x^2 - 6x - 7$.
  (a) Find $P + H$.
  (b) Find $P - H$.

2. Add: $(7x^2 + 3x - 2) + (4 - 2x) + (-3x^2 + x)$.

3. Subtract: $(2x^4 - 3x^3 + 7x - 1) - (5x^3 + 3x^2 - 8x - 2)$

Multiply.

4. $-2x^2(3x - 2y^2 + y)$

5. $(x + 7)(x - 7)$

6. $(7x^2 + 2)(x - 3)$

7. $(x + 6)(2x^2 - x - 4)$

8. $(x - 1)(2x + 1)(x - 2)$

9. $(2x^2 + 3y)^2$

1. $5x^3 - 4x^2 - 6x - 15$
   $5x^3 - 8x^2 + 6x - 1$

2. $4x^2 + 2x + 2$

3. $2x^4 - 8x^3 - 3x^2 + 15x + 1$

4. $-6x^3 + 4x^2y^2 - 2x^2y$

5. $x^2 - 49$

6. $7x^3 - 21x^2 + 2x - 6$

7. $2x^3 + 11x^2 - 10x - 24$

8. $2x^3 - 5x^2 + x + 2$

9. $4x^4 + 12x^2y + 9y^2$

10. $8xy - 4x + 2$ _____

11. $y^2 - 3y - 5$ _____

12. $x^3 - 4$ _____

13. $3(3a^3 - 6a^2b - 5b^2)$ _____

14. $10xy(6x^2 - 1)$ _____

15. $(a - 3b)(5x + 2y)$ _____

16. $(a - 3)(4b + 5a)$ _____

17. $(5a - 2x^2)(7y - 3x)$ _____

Divide.

10. $(16x^3y^2 - 8x^3y + 4x^2y) \div 2x^2y$

11. $(y^3 - 5y^2 + y + 10) \div (y - 2)$

12. $(2x^4 + 3x^3 - 8x - 12) \div (2x + 3)$

Factor by removing the greatest common factor.

13. $9a^3 - 18a^2b - 15b^2$

14. $60x^3y - 10xy$

15. $5x(a - 3b) + 2y(a - 3b)$

16. $4ab - 15a - 12b + 5a^2$

17. $35ay - 14x^2y - 15ax + 6x^3$

Factor.

1. $y^2 + 6y + 9$

2. $10y^2 + y - 2$

3. $x^2 - 17xy + 16y^2$

4. $49x^2 - 1$

5. $x^4 - 4x^2 - 12$

6. $4x^2 - 20xy + 25y^2$

7. $9x^4 + 24x^2 + 16$

8. $6x^2 - 11x - 10$

1. $(y + 3)^2$

2. $(5y - 2)(2y + 1)$

3. $(x - 16y)(x - y)$

4. $(7x + 1)(7x - 1)$

5. $(x^2 - 6)(x^2 + 2)$

6. $(2x - 5y)^2$

7. $(3x^2 + 4)^2$

8. $(3x + 2)(2x - 5)$

9. $(3y - 4)(1 - x)$

10. $2(3x + 5y)(2x - y)$

11. $2x(5x - 1)(5x + 1)$

12. $4a(2a^2 - 5)(a^2 + 3)$

13. $3(2x - 3y)^2$

14. $81(x^2 + 1)(x - 1)(x + 1)$

15. Prime

16. $2(w + 5)(x - 2)$

17. $2x(2x - 3)(4x^2 + 6x + 9)$

18. $(2x + 3)(x + 3)(x - 3)$

19. $2y(3y - 4)(y - 2)$

20. $(8y + 3)(2y + 3)$

Factor, if possible. Be sure to factor completely.

9. $3y - 4 - 3xy + 4x$

10. $12x^2 + 14xy - 10y^2$

11. $50x^3 - 2x$

12. $8a^5 + 4a^3 - 60a$

13. $12x^2 - 36xy + 27y^2$

14. $81x^4 - 81$

15. $7x^2 - 11x + 6$

16. $2wx - 4w + 10x - 20$

17. $16x^4 - 54x$

18. $2x^3 - 18x + 3x^2 - 27$

19. $6y^3 - 20y^2 + 16y$

20. $16y^2 + 30y + 9$

Combine.

1. $(3x^2y - 2xy^2 - 6) + (5 + 2xy^2 - 7x^2y)$

2. $(5a^2 - 3) - (2 + 5a) - (4a - 3)$

Multiply.

3. $2x^2(x - 3y)$

4. $(2x - 3y^2)^2$

5. $(x^2 + 6x - 2)(x^2 - 3x - 4)$

Divide.

6. $(-15x^3 - 12x^2 + 21x) \div (-3x)$

7. $(2x^4 - 7x^3 + 7x^2 - 9x + 10) \div (2x - 5)$

8. $(x^3 - x^2 - 5x + 2) \div (x + 2)$

9. $(x^4 + x^3 - x - 3) \div (x + 1)$

10. $(2x^5 - 7x^4 - 15x^2 - x + 5) \div (x - 4)$

1. $-4x^2y - 1$

2. $5a^2 - 9a - 2$

3. $2x^3 - 6x^2y$

4. $4x^2 - 12xy^2 + 9y^4$

5. $x^4 + 3x^3 - 24x^2 - 18x + 8$

6. $5x^2 + 4x - 7$

7. $x^3 - x^2 + x - 2$

8. $x^2 - 3x + 1$

9. $x^3 - 1 - \dfrac{2}{x + 1}$

10. $2x^4 + x^3 + 4x^2 + x + 3$ $+ \dfrac{17}{x - 4}$

11. $(11x - 5y)(11x + 5y)$

12. $(3x + 5y)^2$

13. $x(x - 2)(x - 24)$

14. $2(4x - 1)(3x + 2)$

15. $4x^2y(x + 2y + 1)$

16. $(x + 3y)(x - 2w)$

17. Prime

18. $3x^2(x + 2)(x + 10)$

19. $3(6x - 5)(x + 1)$

20. $y^4(5x - 4)(5x + 4)$

21. $2a(3a - 2)(9a^2 + 6a + 4)$

22. $x(3x^2 - y)^2$

23. $(3x^2 + 2)(x^2 + 5)$

24. $(x - 6y)(x - 2y)$

25. $(x + 2y)(3 - 5a)$

26. $(4x^2 + 1)(2x + 1)(2x - 1)$

Factor, if possible.

11. $121x^2 - 25y^2$

12. $9x^2 + 30xy + 25y^2$

13. $x^3 - 26x^2 + 48x$

14. $24x^2 + 10x - 4$

15. $4x^3y + 8x^2y^2 + 4x^2y$

16. $x^2 - 6wy + 3xy - 2wx$

17. $2x^2 - 3x + 2$

18. $3x^4 + 36x^3 + 60x^2$

19. $18x^2 + 3x - 15$

20. $25x^2y^4 - 16y^4$

21. $54a^4 - 16a$

22. $9x^5 - 6x^3y + xy^2$

23. $3x^4 + 17x^2 + 10$

24. $x^2 - 8xy + 12y^2$

25. $3x - 10ay + 6y - 5ax$

26. $16x^4 - 1$

Approximately one-half of this test covers the content of Chapters 1–3. The remainder covers the content of Chapter 4.

1. What property is illustrated by the equation $3(5 \cdot 2) = (3 \cdot 5)2$?

2. Evaluate: $\dfrac{2 + 6(-2)}{(2 - 4)^3 + 3}$.

3. Evaluate: $2\sqrt{16} + 3\sqrt{49}$.

4. Solve for x: $5x + 7y = 2$.

5. Solve for x:
$2(3x - 1) - 4 = 2x - (6 - x)$.

6. Find the slope of the line passing through $(-2, -3)$ and $(1, 5)$.

7. Graph: $y = -\dfrac{2}{3}x + 4$.

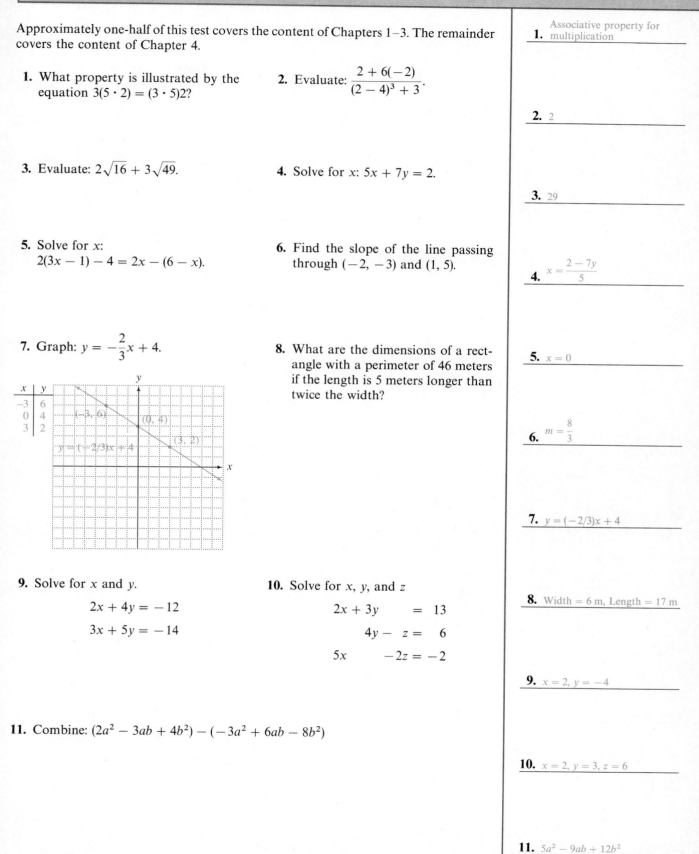

x	y
-3	6
0	4
3	2

8. What are the dimensions of a rectangle with a perimeter of 46 meters if the length is 5 meters longer than twice the width?

9. Solve for x and y.

$$2x + 4y = -12$$
$$3x + 5y = -14$$

10. Solve for x, y, and z

$$2x + 3y \quad = 13$$
$$4y - z = 6$$
$$5x \quad - 2z = -2$$

11. Combine: $(2a^2 - 3ab + 4b^2) - (-3a^2 + 6ab - 8b^2)$

---

1. Associative property for multiplication

2. 2

3. 29

4. $x = \dfrac{2 - 7y}{5}$

5. $x = 0$

6. $m = \dfrac{8}{3}$

7. $y = (-2/3)x + 4$

8. Width = 6 m, Length = 17 m

9. $x = 2$, $y = -4$

10. $x = 2$, $y = 3$, $z = 6$

11. $5a^2 - 9ab + 12b^2$

12. $-6x^2y^2 - 9xy^3 + 15x^2y^3$

13. $10x^3 - 19x^2 - 14x + 8$

14. $-3x^2 + 2x - 4$

15. $2x^2 + x + 5 + \dfrac{6}{x - 2}$

16. $2x^2(x - 5)$

17. $(8x + 7)(8x - 7)$

18. $x(3x - 4)^2$

19. $(5x + 6)^2$

20. $3(x - 7)(x + 2)$

21. $2(x + 2)(x + 10)$

22. Prime

23. $x(3x + 1)(2x + 3)$

24. $x(3x + 4)(9x^2 - 12x + 16)$

25. $(2m + 1)(7n + 5p)$

Multiply and simplify your answer.

12. $-3xy^2(2x + 3y - 5xy)$

13. $(5x - 2)(2x^2 - 3x - 4)$

Divide.

14. $(-21x^3 + 14x^2 - 28x) \div (7x)$

15. $(2x^3 - 3x^2 + 3x - 4) \div (x - 2)$

Factor, if possible.

16. $2x^3 - 10x^2$

17. $64x^2 - 49$

18. $9x^3 - 24x^2 + 16x$

19. $25x^2 + 60x + 36$

20. $3x^2 - 15x - 42$

21. $2x^2 + 24x + 40$

22. $16x^2 + 9$

23. $6x^3 + 11x^2 + 3x$

24. $27x^4 + 64x$

25. $14mn + 7n + 10mp + 5p$

Fractional Algebraic Expressions and Equations

A variety of mathematical calculations are made without technical equipment by professional photographers.

5

PRETEST CHAPTER 5

If you are familiar with the topics in this chapter, take this test now. Check your answers with those in the back of the book. If an answer was wrong or you couldn't do a problem, study the appropriate section of the chapter.

If you are not familiar with the topics in this chapter, don't take this test now. Instead, study the examples, work the practice problems, and then take the test.

This test will help you identify those concepts that you have mastered and those that need more study.

Section 5.1 Simplify.

1. $\dfrac{49x^2 - 9y^2}{7x^2 + 4xy - 3y^2}$ $\dfrac{7x + 3y}{x + y}$

2. $\dfrac{2x^3 + 3x^2 - x}{x - 5x^2 - 6x^3}$ $\dfrac{2x^2 + 3x - 1}{1 - 5x - 6x^2}$

Section 5.2 Simplify completely.

3. $\dfrac{2a^2 + 5a + 3}{a^2 + a + 1} \cdot \dfrac{a^3 - 1}{2a^2 + a - 3} \cdot \dfrac{6a - 30}{3a + 3}$ $2(a - 5)$

4. $\dfrac{5x^3y^2}{x^2y + 10xy^2 + 25y^3} \div \dfrac{2x^4y^5}{3x^3 - 75xy^2}$ $\dfrac{15(x - 5y)}{2y^4(x + 5y)}$

Section 5.3 Add or subtract these fractions. Simplify your answer.

5. $\dfrac{x}{3x - 6} - \dfrac{4}{3x}$ $\dfrac{x^2 - 4x + 8}{3x(x - 2)}$

6. $\dfrac{2}{x + 5} + \dfrac{3}{x - 5} + \dfrac{7x}{x^2 - 25}$ $\dfrac{12x + 5}{(x + 5)(x - 5)}$

7. $\dfrac{y + 1}{y^2 + y - 12} - \dfrac{y - 3}{y^2 + 7y + 12}$ $\dfrac{10y - 6}{(y + 3)(y - 3)(y + 4)}$

Section 5.4 Simplify each complex fraction.

8. $\dfrac{\dfrac{1}{12x} + \dfrac{5}{3x}}{\dfrac{2}{3x^2}}$ $\dfrac{21x}{8}$

9. $\dfrac{\dfrac{x}{4x^2 - 1}}{3 - \dfrac{2}{2x + 1}}$ $\dfrac{x}{(2x - 1)(6x + 1)}$

Section 5.5 Solve for the variable and check your solution. If there is no solution, say so.

10. $\dfrac{3}{y + 5} - \dfrac{1}{y - 5} = \dfrac{5}{y^2 - 25}$ $x = \dfrac{25}{2}$ or 12.5

11. $\dfrac{1}{6y} - \dfrac{4}{9} = \dfrac{4}{9y} - \dfrac{1}{2}$ $y = 5$

Section 5.6 Solve for the variable indicated.

12. $\dfrac{d_1}{d_2} = \dfrac{w_1}{w_2}$; for d_2 $d_2 = \dfrac{d_1 w_2}{w_1}$

13. $I = \dfrac{nE}{nr + R}$; for n $n = \dfrac{IR}{E - Ir}$

Set up a proportion and use it to find the desired quantity.

14. A house 49 feet tall casts a shadow 14 feet long. At the same time a nearby flagpole casts a 9-foot shadow. How tall is the flagpole? 31.5 ft

15. A drawing on a 3- by 5-inch card is projected on a wall. A $\dfrac{3}{4}$-inch line on the card is 2 feet long on the wall. What are the dimensions of the outline of the 3 by 5 card on the wall? $8'$ by $13\dfrac{1}{3}'$

5.1 REDUCING ALGEBRAIC FRACTIONS

After studying this section, you will be able to:

1 Reduce an algebraic fraction in which the numerator and denominator are factorable polynomials

1 An **algebraic fraction**, also called a **rational expression**, is an expression of the form P/Q, where P and Q are polynomials and Q *is not zero*. Remember that division by zero is not defined. (You may recall from Chapter 1 that a rational number is an exact quotient a/b of two numbers a and b, $b \neq 0$.) For example,

$$\frac{7}{x+2} \qquad \frac{x+5}{x-3} \qquad \text{and} \qquad \frac{x^2 + 2xy + 3y^2}{x^3 + y^3}$$

are algebraic fractions.

Now, since the denominator of the fraction cannot equal zero, the first expression is undefined if $x + 2 = 0$. Thus, $x = -2$ is not permitted as a value of x. In the second expression, if we let $x = 3$, the denominator becomes zero, so this value of x is not allowed. Note that the numerator *can* be zero, because any fraction $0/a$ ($a \neq 0$) is just 0.

What values of x make the third fraction undefined? By our definition, the fraction is undefined when the denominator is zero. So we need to find out what values of x make the denominator zero. You should be able to see that this means we must solve the equation

$$x^3 + y^3 = 0$$

Do you remember the special factoring formula from Chapter 4: $a^3 + b^3 = (a + b)(a^2 - ab + b^2)$? Using this formula, we write

$$x^3 + y^3 = 0$$
$$(x + y)(x^2 - xy + y^2) = 0$$

Now since an expression $ab = 0$ if $a = 0$ *or* if $b = 0$, we must have

$$x + y = 0 \qquad or \qquad x^2 - xy + y^2 = 0$$

$$x = -y \qquad \text{This expression cannot be factored further.}$$

Therefore, the algebraic fraction is undefined for $x = -y$. Sometimes we refer to this as the restricted list. The restricted list for these fractions is the list $x \neq -2$, $x \neq 3$, and $x \neq -y$. We have learned that fractions can be simplified (or reduced to lowest terms) by factoring the numerator and denominator into prime factors and dividing by the common factor. For example,

$$\frac{15}{25} = \frac{3 \cdot \cancel{5}}{5 \cdot \cancel{5}} = \frac{3}{5}$$

We can do the same thing with algebraic fractions by using the *basic rule* of *fractions*.

Basic Rule of Fractions

For any polynomials a, b, c

$$\frac{ac}{bc} = \frac{a}{b} \qquad \text{where } b, c \neq 0$$

Do you understand this rule? What we are doing is factoring out a common factor of 1 ($c/c = 1$). We have

$$\frac{ac}{bc} = \frac{a}{b} \cdot \frac{c}{c} = \frac{a}{b} \cdot 1 = \frac{a}{b}$$

Note that c must be a factor of the numerator *and* the denominator. Thus, the basic rule of fractions simply says that we may remove a *common* factor out of the numerator and denominator. This is the same as dividing the numerator and denominator of the fraction by the same nonzero value.

TEACHING TIP   Remind students that the nonzero value that is common to both numerator and denominator may be a number, a variable, or a polynomial. Show them that

$$\frac{24x + 15}{18x - 6} = \frac{3(8x + 5)}{3(6x - 2)} = \frac{8x + 5}{6x - 2}$$

where we have divided the numerator and denominator by 3. In the following problem:

$$\frac{3wx - 13xy}{3w^2 - 13wy} = \frac{x(3w - 13y)}{w(3w - 13y)}$$

$$= \frac{x}{w}$$

we have divided the numerator and denominator by $3w - 13y$.

Example 1   Simplify: $\dfrac{9x^2 + 7x}{18x + 14}$.

$$\frac{9x^2 + 7x}{18x + 14} = \frac{x(9x + 7)}{2(9x + 7)} \qquad \begin{array}{l}\text{Removing a common factor of } x \text{ from numerator.}\\ \text{Removing a common factor of 2 from denominator.}\end{array}$$

$$= \frac{x(9x + 7)}{2(9x + 7)} \qquad \text{Using the basic rule of fractions.}$$

$$= \frac{x}{2} \cdot 1 = \frac{x}{2} \quad \blacksquare$$

Practice Problem 1   Simplify: $\dfrac{4x^3 + 3x^2}{28x + 21}$. ◼

Example 2   Simplify: $\dfrac{2a^2 - ab - b^2}{a^2 - b^2}$.

$$\frac{(2a + b)(a - b)}{(a + b)(a - b)} = \frac{2a + b}{a + b} \cdot 1 = \frac{2a + b}{a + b}$$

As you become more familiar with this basic rule, you won't have to write out every step. We did so here to show the application of the rule. We cannot simplify this fraction any further. ◼

Practice Problem 2   Simplify: $\dfrac{x^2 - 36y^2}{x^2 - 3xy - 18y^2}$. ◼

Example 3   Simplify: $\dfrac{2x - 3y}{2x^2 - 7xy + 6y^2}$.

$$\frac{(2x - 3y)1}{(2x - 3y)(x - 2y)} = \frac{1}{x - 2y} \qquad \begin{array}{l}\text{Note: Do you see why it is necessary to have}\\ \text{a 1 in the numerator of the answer?} \quad ◼\end{array}$$

Practice Problem 3   Simplify: $\dfrac{9x^2y}{3xy^2 + 6x^2y}$. ◼

Example 4   Simplify: $\dfrac{2x^2 + 2x - 12}{x^3 + 7x^2 + 12x}$.

$$\frac{2x^2 + 2x - 12}{x^3 + 7x^2 + 12x} = \frac{2(x^2 + x - 6)}{x(x^2 + 7x + 12)} = \frac{2(x + 3)(x - 2)}{x(x + 3)(x + 4)} = \frac{2(x - 2)}{x(x + 4)}$$

We usually leave the answer in factored form. ◼

Practice Problem 4   Simplify: $\dfrac{2x^2 - 8x - 10}{2x^2 - 20x + 50}$. ◼

TEACHING TIP   In addition to example 5 you might want to show students the following example:

$$\frac{-5x^2 + 10x}{7x^2 - 11x - 6} = \frac{-5x(x - 2)}{(x - 2)(7x + 3)}$$

$$= \frac{-5x}{7x + 3}$$

Students usually need quite a bit of exposure to simplifying fractions where one factor in the numerator is opposite in sign to another factor in the denominator.

Be alert for situations where each term of one factor is opposite in sign from each term of another factor. In such cases you should factor -1 or another negative quantity from one polynomial.

Example 5   Simplify: $\dfrac{-2x + 14y}{x^2 - 5xy - 14y^2}$.

$$\frac{-2(x - 7y)}{(x + 2y)(x - 7y)} = \frac{-2}{x + 2y}$$

Notice that we had to factor -2 from each term in the numerator. ◼

Practice Problem 5   Simplify:

(a) $\dfrac{x^2 - 7x + 12}{6 - 2x}$

(b) $\dfrac{49 - x^2}{x^2 - 15x + 56}$ ◼

Example 6 Simplify: $\dfrac{25y^2 - 16x^2}{8x^2 - 14xy + 5y^2}$.

$$\frac{(5y + 4x)(5y - 4x)}{(4x - 5y)(2x - y)} = \frac{(5y + 4x)(5y - 4x)}{-1(-4x + 5y)(2x - y)} = \frac{5y + 4x}{-1(2x - y)} = \frac{5y + 4x}{y - 2x}$$

Observe that $4x - 5y = -1(-4x + 5y)$. ∎

Practice Problem 6 Simplify: $\dfrac{7a^2 - 23ab + 6b^2}{4b^2 - 49a^2}$. ∎

If a polynomial has four or more terms, try factoring by grouping.

Example 7 Simplify: $\dfrac{2y^3 - 7y^2 - 6y + 21}{a^2y^2 - 3a^2 + by^2 - 3b}$.

$$\frac{y^2(2y - 7) - 3(2y - 7)}{a^2(y^2 - 3) + b(y^2 - 3)} = \frac{(2y - 7)(y^2 - 3)}{(y^2 - 3)(a^2 + b)} = \frac{2y - 7}{a^2 + b}$$ ∎

Practice Problem 7 Simplify: $\dfrac{2ax + 2bx - ay - by}{6ax - 8bx - 3ay + 4by}$. ∎

TEACHING TIP   In addition to example 7, show students the following:

$$\frac{ax - 4a - 8b + 2bx}{x^2 - 7x + 12} = \frac{(x - 4)(a + 2b)}{(x - 3)(x - 4)}$$
$$= \frac{a + 2b}{x - 3}$$

EXERCISES 5.1

Simplify completely.

1. $\dfrac{2x + 10}{x^2 - 25}$

$\dfrac{2(x + 5)}{(x + 5)(x - 5)} = \dfrac{2}{x - 5}$

2. $\dfrac{x^2 - 16}{2x - 8}$

$\dfrac{(x + 4)(x - 4)}{2(x - 4)} = \dfrac{x + 4}{2}$

3. $\dfrac{y^3 - y^2}{y^3 + y^2 - 2y}$

$\dfrac{y^2(y - 1)}{y(y + 2)(y - 1)} = \dfrac{y}{y + 2}$

4. $\dfrac{9x - 9y}{11x - 11y}$

$\dfrac{9(x - y)}{11(x - y)} = \dfrac{9}{11}$

5. $\dfrac{2y^2 - 8}{2y + 4}$

$\dfrac{2(y + 2)(y - 2)}{2(y + 2)} = y - 2$

6. $\dfrac{x + 2}{7x^2 - 28}$

$\dfrac{x + 2}{7(x + 2)(x - 2)} = \dfrac{1}{7(x - 2)}$

7. $\dfrac{21x^3y}{14x^2y^2}$

$\dfrac{3x}{2y}$

8. $\dfrac{50ab^3}{25a^2b^2}$

$\dfrac{2b}{a}$

9. $\dfrac{3a^3b + 6a^2b}{3a^3b + 12a^2b}$

$\dfrac{3a^2b(a + 2)}{3a^2b(a + 4)} = \dfrac{a + 2}{a + 4}$

10. $\dfrac{x^2y^3 + 4xy^3}{x^2y^3 - 3xy^2}$

$\dfrac{xy^3(x + 4)}{xy^2(xy - 3)} = \dfrac{y(x + 4)}{xy - 3}$

11. $\dfrac{x^2 + xy - 2x - 2y}{x^2 + 2xy + y^2}$

$\dfrac{(x + y)(x - 2)}{(x + y)(x + y)} = \dfrac{x - 2}{x + y}$

12. $\dfrac{a^2 - ab + 2a - 2b}{a^2 - b^2}$

$\dfrac{(a - b)(a + 2)}{(a + b)(a - b)} = \dfrac{a + 2}{a + b}$

13. $\dfrac{2y^2 + 2y - 12}{y^2 + 2y - 8}$

$\dfrac{2(y + 3)(y - 2)}{(y + 4)(y - 2)} = \dfrac{2(y + 3)}{y + 4}$

14. $\dfrac{y^2 + 6y + 9}{2y^2 + y - 15}$

$\dfrac{(y + 3)(y + 3)}{(2y - 5)(y + 3)} = \dfrac{y + 3}{2y - 5}$

15. $\dfrac{x^3 + x^2 - 30x}{x^3 - x^2 - 20x}$

$\dfrac{x(x + 6)(x - 5)}{x(x - 5)(x + 4)} = \dfrac{x + 6}{x + 4}$

16. $\dfrac{x^4 + x^3 - 2x^2}{x^4 - x^3}$

$\dfrac{x^2(x + 2)(x - 1)}{x^3(x - 1)} = \dfrac{(x + 2)}{x}$

17. $\dfrac{2x - 6}{3x^2 - x^3}$

$\dfrac{-2(3 - x)}{x^2(3 - x)} = \dfrac{-2}{x^2}$

18. $\dfrac{4y - 2y^2}{5y - 10}$

$\dfrac{-2y(y - 2)}{5(y - 2)} = \dfrac{-2y}{5}$

19. $\dfrac{2y^2 - y - 15}{9 - y^2}$

$\dfrac{(2y + 5)(y - 3)}{(3 + y)(3 - y)} = -\dfrac{2y + 5}{3 + y}$

20. $\dfrac{25 - a^2}{3a^2 - 13a - 10}$

$-\dfrac{(a - 5)(a + 5)}{(3a + 2)(a - 5)} = \dfrac{-(a + 5)}{(3a + 2)}$

21. $\dfrac{a^2 - a - 12}{2a^2 + 5a - 12}$

$\dfrac{(a - 4)(a + 3)}{(2a - 3)(a + 4)}$

The fraction cannot be reduced.

22. $\dfrac{3y^2 - 2y - 1}{y^3 - y^2 + 2y - 2}$

$\dfrac{(3y + 1)(y - 1)}{(y - 1)(y^2 + 2)} = \dfrac{3y + 1}{y^2 + 2}$

23. $\dfrac{2x^3 - 3x^2 + 2x - 3}{2x^2 - x - 3}$

$\dfrac{(2x - 3)(x^2 + 1)}{(2x - 3)(x + 1)} = \dfrac{x^2 + 1}{x + 1}$

24. $\dfrac{b^2 + 4b - 12}{3b^2 + 7b + 2}$

$\dfrac{(b + 6)(b - 2)}{(3b + 1)(b + 2)}$

The fraction cannot be reduced.

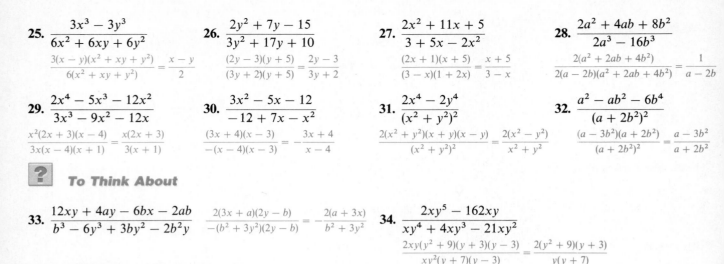

25. $\dfrac{3x^3 - 3y^3}{6x^2 + 6xy + 6y^2}$

$\dfrac{3(x-y)(x^2+xy+y^2)}{6(x^2+xy+y^2)} = \dfrac{x-y}{2}$

26. $\dfrac{2y^2 + 7y - 15}{3y^2 + 17y + 10}$

$\dfrac{(2y-3)(y+5)}{(3y+2)(y+5)} = \dfrac{2y-3}{3y+2}$

27. $\dfrac{2x^2 + 11x + 5}{3 + 5x - 2x^2}$

$\dfrac{(2x+1)(x+5)}{(3-x)(1+2x)} = \dfrac{x+5}{3-x}$

28. $\dfrac{2a^2 + 4ab + 8b^2}{2a^3 - 16b^3}$

$\dfrac{2(a^2+2ab+4b^2)}{2(a-2b)(a^2+2ab+4b^2)} = \dfrac{1}{a-2b}$

29. $\dfrac{2x^4 - 5x^3 - 12x^2}{3x^3 - 9x^2 - 12x}$

$\dfrac{x^2(2x+3)(x-4)}{3x(x-4)(x+1)} = \dfrac{x(2x+3)}{3(x+1)}$

30. $\dfrac{3x^2 - 5x - 12}{-12 + 7x - x^2}$

$\dfrac{(3x+4)(x-3)}{-(x-4)(x-3)} = -\dfrac{3x+4}{x-4}$

31. $\dfrac{2x^4 - 2y^4}{(x^2 + y^2)^2}$

$\dfrac{2(x^2+y^2)(x+y)(x-y)}{(x^2+y^2)^2} = \dfrac{2(x^2-y^2)}{x^2+y^2}$

32. $\dfrac{a^2 - ab^2 - 6b^4}{(a + 2b^2)^2}$

$\dfrac{(a-3b^2)(a+2b^2)}{(a+2b^2)^2} = \dfrac{a-3b^2}{a+2b^2}$

To Think About

33. $\dfrac{12xy + 4ay - 6bx - 2ab}{b^3 - 6y^3 + 3by^2 - 2b^2y}$

$\dfrac{2(3x+a)(2y-b)}{-(b^2+3y^2)(2y-b)} = -\dfrac{2(a+3x)}{b^2+3y^2}$

34. $\dfrac{2xy^5 - 162xy}{xy^4 + 4xy^3 - 21xy^2}$

$\dfrac{2xy(y^2+9)(y+3)(y-3)}{xy^2(y+7)(y-3)} = \dfrac{2(y^2+9)(y+3)}{y(y+7)}$

Cumulative Review Problems

Simplify each expression.

35. $\left(\dfrac{5x^2y^3}{2x^4y^2}\right)^3$

$\dfrac{125y^3}{8x^6}$

36. $(2x^{-3}y^4)^{-3}$

$\dfrac{x^9}{8y^{12}}$

Solve for w in each equation.

37. $5(2w - 3) + 4w = 2 - 6w - 7$

$14w - 15 = -6w - 5$

$w = \dfrac{1}{2}$

38. $\dfrac{1}{4}(w + 2) = 2(5 - w) + 4$

$w + 2 = -8w + 56$

$w = 6$

For Extra Practice Exercises, turn to page 275.

Solutions to Odd-Numbered Practice Problems

1. $\dfrac{4x^3 + 3x^2}{28x + 21} = \dfrac{x^2(4x+3)}{7(4x+3)} = \dfrac{x^2}{7}$

3. $\dfrac{9x^2y}{3xy^2 + 6x^2y} = \dfrac{3xy(3x)}{3xy(y+2x)} = \dfrac{3x}{y+2x}$

5. (a) $\dfrac{x^2 - 7x + 12}{6 - 2x} = \dfrac{(x-4)(x-3)}{-2(-3+x)} = \dfrac{(x-4)(x-3)}{-2(x-3)} = \dfrac{x-4}{-2}$ or $\dfrac{-x+4}{2}$

(b) $\dfrac{49 - x^2}{x^2 - 15x + 56} = \dfrac{-1(x^2-49)}{x^2-15x+56} = \dfrac{-1(x+7)(x-7)}{(x-7)(x-8)} = \dfrac{-x-7}{x-8}$ or $\dfrac{7+x}{8-x}$

7. $\dfrac{2ax + 2bx - ay - by}{6ax - 8bx - 3ay + 4by} = \dfrac{2x(a+b) - y(a+b)}{2x(3a-4b) - y(3a-4b)} = \dfrac{(a+b)(2x-y)}{(3a-4b)(2x-y)} = \dfrac{a+b}{3a-4b}$

Answers to Even-Numbered Practice Problems

2. $\dfrac{x + 6y}{x + 3y}$ **4.** $\dfrac{x + 1}{x - 5}$ **6.** $-\dfrac{a - 3b}{7a + 2b}$ or $\dfrac{-a + 3b}{7a + 2b}$

☐ After studying this section, you will be able to:

1 *Simplify the product of two or more algebraic fractions*

2 *Divide two algebraic fractions*

5.2 MULTIPLICATION AND DIVISION OF ALGEBRAIC FRACTIONS

1 Multiplication

Before you multiply algebraic fractions (rational expressions), always try to use the basic rule of fractions discussed in Section 5.1. Multiplication of algebraic fractions follows the same rules as multiplication of integer fractions. So we can write

Multiplying Algebraic Fractions

For any polynomials a, b, c, d,

$$\frac{a}{b} \cdot \frac{c}{d} = \frac{ac}{bd} \qquad \text{where } b, d \neq 0$$

Example 1   Multiply: $\dfrac{2x^2 - 4x}{x^2 - 5x + 6} \cdot \dfrac{x^2 - 9}{2x^4 + 14x^3 + 24x^2}$.

We first use the basic rule of fractions; that is, we factor (if possible) the numerator and denominator and remove common factors.

$$\frac{2x(x - 2)}{(x - 2)(x - 3)} \cdot \frac{(x + 3)(x - 3)}{2x^2(x^2 + 7x + 12)} = \frac{2x(x - 2)(x + 3)(x - 3)}{(2x)x(x - 2)(x - 3)(x + 3)(x + 4)}$$

$$= \frac{2x}{2x} \cdot \frac{1}{x} \cdot \frac{x - 2}{x - 2} \cdot \frac{x + 3}{x + 3} \cdot \frac{x - 3}{x - 3} \cdot \frac{1}{x + 4}$$

$$= 1 \cdot \frac{1}{x} \cdot 1 \cdot 1 \cdot 1 \cdot \frac{1}{x + 4}$$

$$= \frac{1}{x(x + 4)} \quad \text{or} \quad \frac{1}{x^2 + 4x}$$

Although either form of the answer is correct, we usually use the factored form. ∎

Practice Problem 1   Multiply: $\dfrac{2x^2 + 5xy + 2y^2}{4x^2 - y^2} \cdot \dfrac{2x^2 + xy - y^2}{x^2 + xy - 2y^2}$. ∎

Example 2   Multiply: $\dfrac{7x + 7y}{4ax + 4ay - 4bx - 4by} \cdot \dfrac{8a^2x^2 - 8b^2x^2}{35x^3}$.

$$\frac{7(x + y)}{4[ax + ay - bx - by]} \cdot \frac{8x^2(a^2 - b^2)}{35x^3} = \frac{7(x + y)}{4[a(x + y) - b(x + y)]} \cdot \frac{8x^2(a + b)(a - b)}{35x^3}$$

$$= \frac{\overset{1}{7(x + y)}}{\underset{}{4(x + y)(a - b)}} \cdot \frac{\overset{2}{8}x^2(a + b)(a - b)}{\underset{5x}{35x^3}}$$

$$= \frac{2(a + b)}{5x} \quad \text{or} \quad \frac{2a + 2b}{5x}$$

Note that we shortened our steps by not writing out every factor of 1 as we did in Example 1. Either way is correct. ∎

Practice Problem 2   Multiply: $\dfrac{2x^3 - 3x^2}{3x^2 + 3x} \cdot \dfrac{9x + 36}{10x^2 - 15x}$. ∎

TEACHING TIP   After discussing a couple of sample examples in this section, ask students to do the following problem at their seats.

$$\frac{x^2 - 5x - 24}{x^2 + x - 6} \cdot \frac{x^2 + 2x - 8}{x^2 - 7x - 8}.$$

$\left(\text{The answer is } \dfrac{x + 4}{x + 1}.\right)$

❷ Division

When we divide fractions, we take the **reciprocal** of the second fraction and then multiply the fractions. $\left(\text{Remember that the reciprocal of a fraction } \dfrac{m}{n} \text{ is } \dfrac{n}{m}. \text{ Thus the}\right.$ reciprocal of $\dfrac{2}{3}$ is $\dfrac{3}{2}$, and the reciprocal of $\dfrac{3x}{11y^2}$ is $\left.\dfrac{11y^2}{3x}.\right)$ We divide algebraic fractions in the same way.

Dividing Algebraic Fractions

For any polynomials a, b, c, d,

$$\frac{a}{b} \div \frac{c}{d} = \frac{a}{b} \cdot \frac{d}{c} \qquad \text{when } b, c, d \neq 0$$

TEACHING TIP After presenting example 3 or a similar example, you may want to do the following additional example.

$\dfrac{x^2 + 9xy + 8y^2}{x^2 + 7xy - 8y^2}$ divided by

$\dfrac{x^2 - y^2}{x^2 + 5xy - 6y^2}.$

$\left(\text{The answer is } \dfrac{x + 6y}{x - y}.\right)$

TEACHING TIP After presenting example 4 or a similar example, ask students to do the following example:

$\dfrac{2x^2 - 5x - 3}{2 - 5x - 3x^2}$ divided by

$\dfrac{2x^2 + 9x + 4}{3x^2 + 11x - 4}$

$\left(\text{The answer is } \dfrac{3 - x}{x + 2}.\right)$

Take the time to show the students two alternate ways of writing the answer. These are:

$-\dfrac{x - 3}{x + 2}$ as well as $\dfrac{x - 3}{-x - 2}.$

Students will thus see that correct answers may be written in several alternate ways.

Example 3 Divide: $\dfrac{4x^2 - y^2}{x^2 + 4xy + 4y^2} \div \dfrac{4x - 2y}{3x + 6y}.$

$$\dfrac{4x^2 - y^2}{x^2 + 4xy + 4y^2} \cdot \dfrac{3x + 6y}{4x - 2y} = \dfrac{(2x + y)(2x - y)}{(x + 2y)(x + 2y)} \cdot \dfrac{3(x + 2y)}{2(2x - y)}$$

$$= \dfrac{3(2x + y)}{2(x + 2y)} \quad \text{or} \quad \dfrac{6x + 3y}{2x + 4y} \quad \blacksquare$$

Practice Problem 3 Divide: $\dfrac{8x^3 + 27}{64x^3 - 1} \div \dfrac{4x^2 - 9}{16x^2 + 4x + 1}.$ $\blacksquare$

To Think About

Should you invert the fraction *before* you factor or after? Does it matter? Try it both ways. $\blacksquare$

Example 4 Divide: $\dfrac{24 + 10x - 4x^2}{2x^2 + 13x + 15} \div (2x - 8).$

$$\dfrac{-4x^2 + 10x + 24}{2x^2 + 13x + 15} \cdot \dfrac{1}{2x - 8} = \dfrac{-2(2x^2 - 5x - 12)}{(2x + 3)(x + 5)} \cdot \dfrac{1}{2(x - 4)}$$

$$= \dfrac{-2(x - 4)(2x + 3)}{(2x + 3)(x + 5)} \cdot \dfrac{1}{2(x - 4)} = \dfrac{-1}{x + 5} \quad \text{or} \quad -\dfrac{1}{x + 5}$$

$\blacksquare$

Practice Problem 4 Divide: $\dfrac{4x^2 - 9}{2x^2 + 11x + 12} \div (-6x + 9).$ $\blacksquare$

EXERCISES 5.2

Simplify.

1. $\dfrac{3a^2}{a + 2} \cdot \dfrac{a^2 - 4}{3a}$

$\dfrac{3a^2}{a + 2} \cdot \dfrac{(a + 2)(a - 2)}{3a} = a(a - 2)$

2. $\dfrac{5x^2}{x^2 - 4} \cdot \dfrac{x^2 + 4x + 4}{10x^3}$

$\dfrac{5x^2}{(x + 2)(x - 2)} \cdot \dfrac{(x + 2)(x + 2)}{10x^3} = \dfrac{x + 2}{2x(x - 2)}$

3. $\dfrac{x^2 + 3x + 8}{4x - 4} \cdot \dfrac{2x - 2}{x^2 + 3x + 8}$

$\dfrac{x^2 + 3x + 8}{4(x - 1)} \cdot \dfrac{2(x - 1)}{x^2 + 3x + 8} = \dfrac{1}{2}$

4. $\dfrac{x - 5}{10x - 2} \cdot \dfrac{25x^2 - 1}{x^2 - 10x + 25}$

$\dfrac{x - 5}{2(5x - 1)} \cdot \dfrac{(5x + 1)(5x - 1)}{(x - 5)(x - 5)} = \dfrac{5x + 1}{2(x - 5)}$

5. $\dfrac{12x^3y}{6xy^5} \cdot \dfrac{5xy^2}{25x^4y^4}$

$\dfrac{2}{5xy^6}$

6. $\dfrac{25ab^4}{125ab^3} \cdot \dfrac{10a^5b^4}{14a^3b}$

$\dfrac{a^2b^4}{7}$

7. $\dfrac{x^2 - 5x - 24}{x^2 - 9x + 8} \cdot \dfrac{x^2 + 6x - 7}{x^2 + 5x + 6}$

$\dfrac{(x + 3)(x - 8)}{(x - 8)(x - 1)} \cdot \dfrac{(x + 7)(x - 1)}{(x + 3)(x + 2)} = \dfrac{x + 7}{x + 2}$

8. $\dfrac{x^2 - 5x + 6}{x^2 + 3x - 18} \cdot \dfrac{x^2 + x - 30}{x^2 - 2x - 15}$

$\dfrac{(x - 2)(x - 3)}{(x + 6)(x - 3)} \cdot \dfrac{(x + 6)(x - 5)}{(x - 5)(x + 3)} = \dfrac{x - 2}{x + 3}$

9. $\dfrac{2y^2 - 5y - 12}{4y^2 + 8y + 3} \cdot \dfrac{2y^2 + 7y + 3}{y^2 - 16}$

$\dfrac{(2y + 3)(y - 4)}{(2y + 3)(2y + 1)} \cdot \dfrac{(2y + 1)(y + 3)}{(y - 4)(y + 4)} = \dfrac{y + 3}{y + 4}$

10. $\dfrac{6y^2 + y - 1}{6y^2 + 5y + 1} \cdot \dfrac{3y^2 + 4y + 1}{3y^2 + 2y - 1}$

$\dfrac{(3y - 1)(2y + 1)}{(3y + 1)(2y + 1)} \cdot \dfrac{(3y + 1)(y + 1)}{(3y - 1)(y + 1)} = 1$

11. $\dfrac{x^3 - 125}{x^5y} \cdot \dfrac{x^3y^2}{x^2 + 5x + 25}$

$\dfrac{(x - 5)(x^2 + 5x + 25)}{x^5y} \cdot \dfrac{x^3y^2}{x^2 + 5x + 25} = \dfrac{y(x - 5)}{x^2}$

12. $\dfrac{3a^3b^2}{8a^3 - b^3} \cdot \dfrac{4a^2 + 2ab + b^2}{12ab^4}$

$\dfrac{3a^3b^2}{(2a - b)(4a^2 + 2ab + b^2)} \cdot \dfrac{4a^2 + 2ab + b^2}{12ab^4} = \dfrac{a^2}{4b^2(2a - b)}$

13. $\dfrac{y^2 + 2y}{6y} \div \dfrac{y^2 - 4}{3y^2}$

$\dfrac{y(y + 2)}{6y} \cdot \dfrac{3y^2}{(y + 2)(y - 2)} = \dfrac{y^2}{2(y - 2)}$

14. $\dfrac{3y + 12}{8y^3} \div \dfrac{9y + 36}{16y^3}$

$\dfrac{3(y + 4)}{8y^3} \cdot \dfrac{16y^3}{9(y + 4)} = \dfrac{2}{3}$

15. $\dfrac{(4a + 5)^2}{3a^2 - 10a - 8} \div \dfrac{4a + 5}{(a - 4)^2}$

$\dfrac{(4a + 5)^2}{(3a + 2)(a - 4)} \cdot \dfrac{(a - 4)^2}{4a + 5} = \dfrac{(4a + 5)(a - 4)}{3a + 2}$

16. $\dfrac{2a^2 - 7a - 15}{(a + 4)^2} \div \dfrac{(a - 5)^2}{a + 4}$

$\dfrac{(2a + 3)(a - 5)}{(a + 4)(a + 4)} \cdot \dfrac{a + 4}{(a - 5)(a - 5)} = \dfrac{2a + 3}{(a + 4)(a - 5)}$

17. $\dfrac{x^2 - xy - 6y^2}{x^2 + 2} \div (x^2 + 2xy)$

$\dfrac{(x + 2y)(x - 3y)}{x^2 + 2} \cdot \dfrac{1}{x(x + 2y)} = \dfrac{x - 3y}{x(x^2 + 2)}$

18. $\dfrac{x^2 - 5x + 4}{2x - 8} \div (3x^2 - 3x)$

$\dfrac{(x - 4)(x - 1)}{2(x - 4)} \cdot \dfrac{1}{3x(x - 1)} = \dfrac{1}{6x}$

19. $\dfrac{9 - y^2}{y^2 + 5y + 6} \div \dfrac{2y - 6}{5y + 10}$

$\dfrac{-(y + 3)(y - 3)}{(y + 3)(y + 2)} \cdot \dfrac{5(y + 2)}{2(y - 3)} = \dfrac{-5}{2}$

20. $\dfrac{4 - 2y}{2y + y^2} \div \dfrac{3y^2 - 12}{2y^2 + 8y + 8}$

$\dfrac{-2(y - 2)}{y(y + 2)} \cdot \dfrac{2(y + 2)(y + 2)}{3(y + 2)(y - 2)} = \dfrac{-4}{3y}$

21. $\dfrac{3a^2 - 27b^2}{2a^2 - 5ab - 3b^2} \div \dfrac{6a^2 - 21ab + 9b^2}{4a^2 - b^2}$

$\dfrac{3(a + 3b)(a - 3b)}{(2a + b)(a - 3b)} \cdot \dfrac{(2a + b)(2a - b)}{3(2a - b)(a - 3b)} = \dfrac{a + 3b}{a - 3b}$

22. $\dfrac{4a^2 - 9b^2}{6a^2 - 5ab - 6b^2} \div \dfrac{4a^2 + 12ab + 9b^2}{2a^2 + ab - 3b^2}$

$\dfrac{(2a + 3b)(2a - 3b)}{(3a + 2b)(2a - 3b)} \cdot \dfrac{(2a + 3b)(a - b)}{(2a + 3b)(2a + 3b)} = \dfrac{a - b}{3a + 2b}$

23. $\dfrac{xy + x - 4y - 4}{xy - x + 3y - 3} \div \dfrac{xy + 2x - 4y - 8}{xy - 2x + 3y - 6}$

$\dfrac{(y + 1)(x - 4)}{(x + 3)(y - 1)} \cdot \dfrac{(x + 3)(y - 2)}{(x - 4)(y + 2)} = \dfrac{(y + 1)(y - 2)}{(y - 1)(y + 2)}$

24. $\dfrac{ax + bx - 3a - 3b}{ax + bx + 4a + 4b} \div \dfrac{2ax - 9 - 6a + 3x}{ax - 8 + 4a - 2x}$

$\dfrac{(x - 3)(a + b)}{(a + b)(x + 4)} \cdot \dfrac{(a - 2)(x + 4)}{(x - 3)(2a + 3)} = \dfrac{a - 2}{2a + 3}$

25. $\dfrac{x^2 + 5x + 6}{x^2 - 9} \cdot \dfrac{15x^2 - 7x - 2}{3x^2 + 4x - 4} \cdot \dfrac{5x^2 - 13x - 15}{10x^2 - 13x - 3}$

$\dfrac{(x + 3)(x + 2)}{(x + 3)(x - 3)} \cdot \dfrac{(3x - 2)(5x + 1)}{(3x - 2)(x + 2)} \cdot \dfrac{5x^2 - 13x - 15}{(5x + 1)(2x - 3)} = \dfrac{5x^2 - 13x - 15}{(x - 3)(2x - 3)}$

26. $\dfrac{3x^2 + 3x - 60}{2x - 8} \cdot \dfrac{25x^3}{x^3 + 3x^2 - 10x} \cdot \dfrac{x^2 - 7x + 10}{30x^2}$

$\dfrac{3(x + 5)(x - 4)}{2(x - 4)} \cdot \dfrac{25x^3}{x(x + 5)(x - 2)} \cdot \dfrac{(x - 5)(x - 2)}{30x^2} = \dfrac{5(x - 5)}{4}$

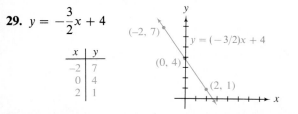 **To Think About**

Simplify.

27. $\dfrac{x^2 + 3x - 28}{3x^3 - 10x^2 - 8x} \cdot \left(\dfrac{2x^3 + 9x^2 - 5x}{x^2 + 10x + 21} \div \dfrac{2x^2y - 13xy + 6y}{3x^2y + 11xy + 6y} \right)$

$\dfrac{(x - 4)(x + 7)}{x(3x + 2)(x - 4)} \cdot \dfrac{x(2x - 1)(x + 5)}{(x + 7)(x + 3)} \cdot \dfrac{y(3x + 2)(x + 3)}{y(2x - 1)(x - 6)} = \dfrac{x + 5}{x - 6}$

28. $\dfrac{3x^2 - 3x - 6}{6x + 6} \div \left(\dfrac{x^3 - x^2 - 20x}{4x^2 + 8x - 32} \div \dfrac{x^3 - 25x}{4x^2 + 20x} \right)$

$\dfrac{3(x - 2)(x + 1)}{6(x + 1)} \div \left[\dfrac{x(x - 5)(x + 4)}{4(x + 4)(x - 2)} \cdot \dfrac{4x(x + 5)}{x(x + 5)(x - 5)} \right]$

$\dfrac{3(x - 2)(x + 1)}{6(x + 1)} \cdot \dfrac{x - 2}{x} = \dfrac{(x - 2)^2}{2x}$

Cumulative Review Problems

Graph the straight line. Plot at least three points.

29. $y = -\dfrac{3}{2}x + 4$

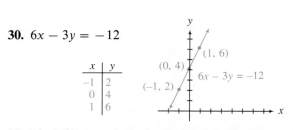

x	y
-2	7
0	4
2	1

$(-2, 7)$ $y = (-3/2)x + 4$

$(0, 4)$

$(2, 1)$

30. $6x - 3y = -12$

x	y
-1	2
0	4
1	6

$(0, 4)$ $(1, 6)$

$(-1, 2)$ $6x - 3y = -12$

31. Find the equation of a line in standard form that passes through $(0, 5)$ and $(-2, -3)$.

$m = \dfrac{5 + 3}{0 + 2} = 4$

$y - 5 = 4(x - 0)$

$4x - y = -5$

32. Find the equation of a line in standard form that is perpendicular to $3x + 4y = 12$ and passes through $(-4, 4)$.

$m = -\dfrac{3}{4}$

$m_\perp = \dfrac{4}{3}$

$y - 4 = \dfrac{4}{3}(x + 4)$

$4x - 3y = -28$

Calculator Problems

Simplify.

33. $\dfrac{x^2 + 5x + 6}{1.236x^2} \cdot \dfrac{8.652x^3}{2x^2 + x - 15}$

$\dfrac{7x(x + 2)}{(2x - 5)}$

34. $\dfrac{2x^2 - 32}{0.012xy} \div \dfrac{6x^2 - 20x - 8}{0.156x^2y^3}$

$\dfrac{13xy^2(x - 4)(x + 4)}{3x^2 - 10x - 4}$

For Extra Practice Exercises, turn to page 276.

Solutions to Odd Numbered Practice Problems

1. $\dfrac{2x^2 + 5xy + 2y^2}{4x^2 - y^2} \cdot \dfrac{2x^2 + xy - y^2}{x^2 + xy - 2y^2} = \dfrac{\cancel{(2x + y)}(x + 2y)}{\cancel{(2x + y)}(2x - y)} \cdot \dfrac{\cancel{(2x - y)}(x + y)}{(x + 2y)(x - y)} = \dfrac{x + y}{x - y}$

3. $\dfrac{8x^3 + 27}{64x^3 - 1} \div \dfrac{4x^2 - 9}{16x^2 + 4x + 1} = \dfrac{8x^3 + 27}{64x^3 - 1} \cdot \dfrac{16x^2 + 4x + 1}{4x^2 - 9} = \dfrac{(2x + 3)(4x^2 - 6x + 9)}{(4x - 1)\cancel{(16x^2 + 4x + 1)}} \cdot \dfrac{\cancel{16x^2 + 4x + 1}}{\cancel{(2x + 3)}(2x - 3)}$

$= \dfrac{4x^2 - 6x + 9}{(4x - 1)(2x - 3)}$ or $\dfrac{4x^2 - 6x + 9}{8x^2 - 14x + 3}$

Answers to Even-Numbered Practice Problems

2. $\dfrac{3(x + 4)}{5(x + 1)}$ **4.** $\dfrac{1}{-3(x + 4)}$ or $\dfrac{-1}{3(x + 4)}$

□ **After studying this section, you will be able to:**

1 *Add or subtract algebraic fractions with common denominators*

2 *Add or subtract algebraic fractions without common denominators*

5.3 ADDITION AND SUBTRACTION OF ALGEBRAIC FRACTIONS

1 We can add and subtract fractional algebraic expressions with the same denominator just as we do in arithmetic: We simply add or subtract the numerators.

> **Addition and Subtraction of Algebraic Fractions**
>
> For any polynomials a, b, c,
>
> $$\frac{a}{b} + \frac{c}{b} = \frac{a + c}{b} \qquad b \neq 0$$
>
> $$\frac{a}{b} - \frac{c}{b} = \frac{a - c}{b} \qquad b \neq 0$$

Example 1   Add: $\dfrac{3}{2x^2y} + \dfrac{8}{2x^2y}$.

$$\frac{3}{2x^2y} + \frac{8}{2x^2y} = \frac{11}{2x^2y} \quad \blacksquare$$

Practice Problem 1   Add: $\dfrac{7}{3a^2b} + \dfrac{-2 + a}{3a^2b}$.   ■

Example 2   Subtract: $\dfrac{5x + 2}{(x + 3)(x - 4)} - \dfrac{6x}{(x + 3)(x - 4)}$.

$$\frac{5x + 2}{(x + 3)(x - 4)} - \frac{6x}{(x + 3)(x - 4)} = \frac{-x + 2}{(x + 3)(x - 4)} \quad \blacksquare$$

Practice Problem 2   Subtract: $\dfrac{4x}{(x + 6)(2x - 1)} - \dfrac{3x + 1}{(x + 6)(2x - 1)}$.   ■

2 How do we add or subtract fractions when the denominators are not the same? We must find the least common denominator (LCD). The least common denominator of two or more fractions is the product of the **different prime factors** in each denominator. If factors are repeated, we use the *highest* power of each factor. Make sure that you understand this definition. After we find the LCD, we have to write each fraction as a new, equivalent, fraction with the LCD.

Here's how to find the LCD.

How to Find the LCD

1. Factor each denominator completely into prime factors.
2. The LCD is the product of all the **different prime factors**.
3. If a factor occurs more than once in the denominator, you must use the highest power of that factor. (In other words, take the factor that occurs the greatest number of times in the denominator.)

Now we'll do some sample problems.

Example 3 Find the LCD of these fractions and then add them:

$$\frac{7}{x^2 - 4} + \frac{2}{x - 2}$$

First we find the LCD. We use the three-step procedure.

Step 1. We factor each denominator completely (into prime factors).

$$(x^2 - 4) = (x + 2)(x - 2)$$

$x - 2$ cannot be factored.

Step 2. The LCD is the product of all the *different* factors. (Note that it is *not* the product of *all* the factors.) The different factors are $x + 2$ and $x - 2$. So the LCD is $(x + 2)(x - 2)$.

Now before we can add the fractions, we must rewrite our fractions as fractions with the LCD.

$$\frac{7}{(x + 2)(x - 2)} + \frac{2}{x - 2} \cdot \boxed{\frac{x + 2}{x + 2}}$$

Since $\dfrac{x + 2}{x + 2} = 1$, we have not changed the *value* of the fraction. We are simply writing it in another equivalent form. Thus, we now have

$$\frac{7}{(x + 2)(x - 2)} + \frac{2(x + 2)}{(x + 2)(x - 2)} = \frac{7 + 2(x + 2)}{(x + 2)(x - 2)}$$

$$= \frac{7 + 2x + 4}{(x + 2)(x - 2)}$$

$$= \frac{2x + 11}{(x + 2)(x - 2)} \quad \blacksquare$$

Practice Problem 3 Find the LCD and add: $\dfrac{8}{x^2 - x - 12} + \dfrac{3}{x - 4}$. $\blacksquare$

Example 4 Subtract: $\dfrac{2x + 1}{25x^2 + 10x + 1} - \dfrac{6x}{25x + 5}$.

TEACHING TIP After discussing the steps used to find the LCD show the students the following four examples: Find the LCD of each pair of fractions.

A: $\dfrac{1}{2xy}, \dfrac{1}{4y^2}$

B: $\dfrac{3}{x + 2y}, \dfrac{5}{x^2 - 4y^2}$

C: $\dfrac{x}{5a^2b^2}, \dfrac{y}{a^3b}$

D: $\dfrac{1}{2x^2 + 9x + 4}, \dfrac{1}{6x^2 + 13x + 5}$

(Answers: A: LCD $= 4xy^2$
B: LCD $= (x + 2y)(x - 2y)$
C: LCD $= 5a^3b^2$
D: LCD $= (2x + 1)(x + 4)(3x + 5)$.)

TEACHING TIP After discussing example 4 or a similar example have the students subtract the following:

$$\frac{5}{3x + 6} - \frac{4x}{x^2 + 6x + 8}$$

Make sure they understand how the LCD of $3(x + 2)(x + 4)$ was obtained.

$\left(\text{The answer is } \dfrac{-7x + 20}{3(x + 2)(x + 4)}.\right)$

Step 1. Factor each denominator into prime factors.

$$25x^2 + 10x + 1 = (5x + 1)^2$$

$$25x + 5 = 5(5x + 1)$$

Step 2. The different factors are 5 and $5x + 1$. However, $5x + 1$ appears to the first power *and* to the second power. So we need step 3.

Step 3. We must use the *highest* power of the common factor. In this example the highest power is 2, so we use $(5x + 1)^2$.

The LCD is the product of the *different* prime factors, and each factor has the highest power of all the factors. So our LCD is $5(5x + 1)^2$. Now we write

$$\frac{2x + 1}{(5x + 1)^2} - \frac{6x}{5(5x + 1)}$$

Notice that the first fraction does not have the factor 5 [the LCD is $5(5x + 1)^2$]. The second fraction does not have the factor $5x + 1$. (Of course, it has *one* factor $5x + 1$, but the LCD has two.) Therefore, we must multiply our fractions by the appropriate factor to change them to equivalent fractions with the LCD. We write

$$\frac{2x + 1}{(5x + 1)^2} \cdot \frac{5}{5} - \frac{6x}{5(5x + 1)} \cdot \frac{5x + 1}{5x + 1} = \frac{5(2x + 1) - 6x(5x + 1)}{5(5x + 1)^2}$$

$$= \frac{10x + 5 - 30x^2 - 6x}{5(5x + 1)^2}$$

$$= \frac{-30x^2 + 4x + 5}{5(5x + 1)^2} \quad ■$$

Practice Problem 4   Subtract: $\dfrac{7x - 3}{4x^2 + 20x + 25} - \dfrac{3x}{4x + 10}$. ■

Example 5   Add: $\dfrac{7}{2x^2y} + \dfrac{3}{xy^2}$.

As you become more familiar with the procedure for finding LCDs, you won't need to write down every step. You should be able to see that the LCD of these fractions is $2x^2y^2$. Hence,

$$\frac{7}{2x^2y} \cdot \frac{y}{y} + \frac{3}{xy^2} \cdot \frac{2x}{2x} = \frac{7y}{2x^2y^2} + \frac{6x}{2x^2y^2} = \frac{6x + 7y}{2x^2y^2} \quad ■$$

Practice Problem 5   Add: $\dfrac{7}{4ab^3} + \dfrac{1}{3a^3b^2}$. ■

Example 6   Add: $\dfrac{2}{x - 5} + \dfrac{3x}{x^2 - 2x - 15} + \dfrac{3}{x + 3}$.

After we factor the denominator of the second fraction, we see that the LCD is $(x - 5)(x + 3)$.

$$\frac{2}{x - 5} \cdot \frac{x + 3}{x + 3} + \frac{3x}{(x - 5)(x + 3)} + \frac{3}{x + 3} \cdot \frac{x - 5}{x - 5}$$

$$= \frac{2x + 6}{(x - 5)(x + 3)} + \frac{3x}{(x - 5)(x + 3)} + \frac{3x - 15}{(x - 5)(x + 3)}$$

$$= \frac{8x - 9}{(x - 5)(x + 3)} \quad ■$$

Practice Problem 6   Add: $\dfrac{7}{x + 4} + \dfrac{-5x}{x^2 - x - 20} + \dfrac{2}{x - 5}$. ■

Example 7 Subtract: $\dfrac{2}{x^2 + 3x + 2} - \dfrac{4}{x^2 + 4x + 3}$.

$$x^2 + 3x + 2 = (x + 1)(x + 2)$$
$$x^2 + 4x + 3 = (x + 1)(x + 3)$$

Therefore, the LCD is $(x + 1)(x + 2)(x + 3)$. We now have

$$\frac{2}{(x + 1)(x + 2)} \cdot \frac{x + 3}{x + 3} - \frac{4}{(x + 1)(x + 3)} \cdot \frac{x + 2}{x + 2}$$

$$= \frac{2x + 6}{(x + 1)(x + 2)(x + 3)} - \frac{4x + 8}{(x + 1)(x + 2)(x + 3)} = \frac{2x + 6 - 4x - 8}{(x + 1)(x + 2)(x + 3)}$$

$$= \frac{-2x - 2}{(x + 1)(x + 2)(x + 3)} = \frac{-2\cancel{(x + 1)}}{\cancel{(x + 1)}(x + 2)(x + 3)}$$

$$= \frac{-2}{(x + 2)(x + 3)} \quad \blacksquare$$

Study this problem carefully. Be sure you understand the reason for each step. You'll see this type of problem often.

Practice Problem 7 Subtract: $\dfrac{4x + 2}{x^2 + x - 12} - \dfrac{3x + 8}{x^2 + 6x + 8}$. ▪

Example 8 Add: $\dfrac{3}{2x} + \dfrac{4}{x + 2} + \dfrac{3x}{2x^2 + 4x}$.

The factors of the last denominator are $2x(x + 2)$. Therefore the LCD is $2x(x + 2)$. Our fractions can then be written as

$$\frac{3}{2x} \cdot \frac{x + 2}{x + 2} + \frac{4}{x + 2} \cdot \frac{2x}{2x} + \frac{3x}{2x(x + 2)} = \frac{3x + 6}{2x(x + 2)} + \frac{8x}{2x(x + 2)} + \frac{3x}{2x(x + 2)}$$

$$= \frac{14x + 6}{2x(x + 2)} = \frac{\cancel{2}(7x + 3)}{\cancel{2}x(x + 2)} = \frac{7x + 3}{x(x + 2)} \quad \blacksquare$$

Practice Problem 8 Add: $\dfrac{5a}{2a^2 + 3a} + \dfrac{7}{3a} + \dfrac{a}{2a + 3}$. ▪

TEACHING TIP   After discussing example 7 or a similar example, work out for students the following: Subtract

$$\frac{4x + 2}{x^2 + x - 12} - \frac{3x + 8}{x^2 + 6x + 8}$$

$\left(\text{Answer is } \dfrac{x + 7}{(x - 3)(x + 2)}.\right)$

DEVELOPING YOUR STUDY SKILLS

TAKING NOTES IN CLASS

An important part of mathematics studying is taking notes. In order to take meaningful notes, you must be an active listener. Keep your mind on what the instructor is saying, and be ready with questions whenever you do not understand something.

If you have previewed the lesson material, you will be prepared to take good notes. The important concepts will seem somewhat familiar. You will have a better idea of what needs to be written down. If you frantically try to write all that the instructor says or copy all the examples done in class, you may find your notes to be nearly worthless when you are home alone. You may find that you are unable to make sense of what you have written.

Write down *important* ideas and examples as the instructor lectures, making sure that you are listening and following the logic. Include any helpful hints or suggestions that your instructor gives you or refers to in your text. You will be amazed at how easily these are forgotten if they are not written down.

Successful notetaking requires active listening and processing. Stay alert in class. You will realize the advantages of taking your own notes over copying those of someone else.

Find the LCD.

1. $\dfrac{1}{6x}, \dfrac{3}{2xy^2}$

$6xy^2$

2. $\dfrac{3}{x^3y}, \dfrac{5}{2x}$

$2x^3y$

3. $\dfrac{5}{x+6y}, \dfrac{2}{x-2y}$

$(x+6y)(x-2y)$

4. $\dfrac{7}{2x+3y}, \dfrac{5}{x+3y}$

$(2x+3y)(x+3y)$

5. $\dfrac{1}{x^2+7xy+12y^2}, \dfrac{3}{x+4y}$

$(x+3y)(x+4y)$

6. $\dfrac{2}{4x^2-8x+3}, \dfrac{1}{2x-1}$

$(2x-1)(2x-3)$

7. $\dfrac{11x}{(2x+5)^3}, \dfrac{3x-1}{(x+6)(2x+5)^2}$

$(x+6)(2x+5)^3$

8. $\dfrac{12xy}{(x+5)(x-2)}, \dfrac{2xy}{(x+5)^4(x-2)}$

$(x-2)(x+5)^4$

9. $\dfrac{3x}{5x^2-7x}, \dfrac{5x}{5x^2-12x+7}$

$x(5x-7)(x-1)$

10. $\dfrac{5x}{3x^2+2x}, \dfrac{2x}{6x^2-5x-6}$

$x(3x+2)(2x-3)$

11. $\dfrac{5y}{9y^2-49}, \dfrac{2y+1}{9y^2-42y+49}$

$(3y+7)(3y-7)^2$

12. $\dfrac{2y+1}{16y^2-25}, \dfrac{3y-1}{16y^2+40y+25}$

$(4y-5)(4y+5)^2$

13. $\dfrac{3}{8x^2}, \dfrac{5x}{6x^2+18x}, \dfrac{x+2}{x^2-5x-24}$

$24x^2(x+3)(x-8)$

14. $\dfrac{5}{2x^2-50}, \dfrac{2x}{x^2-2x-35}, \dfrac{11x}{4x^2}$

$4x^2(x+5)(x-5)(x-7)$

Add or subtract the fractions and simplify your answer.

15. $\dfrac{2}{x+2}+\dfrac{3}{2x}$

$\dfrac{4x+3(x+2)}{2x(x+2)}=\dfrac{7x+6}{2x(x+2)}$

16. $\dfrac{5}{3x+y}+\dfrac{2}{3xy}$

$\dfrac{15xy+2(3x+y)}{3xy(3x+y)}=\dfrac{15xy+6x+2y}{3xy(3x+y)}$

17. $\dfrac{12}{5x^2}+\dfrac{2}{5xy}$

$\dfrac{12y+2x}{5x^2y}$

18. $\dfrac{7}{4ab}+\dfrac{3}{4b^2}$

$\dfrac{7b+3a}{4ab^2}$

19. $\dfrac{3}{x^2-7x+12}+\dfrac{5}{4-x}$

$\dfrac{3-5(x-3)}{(x-4)(x-3)}=\dfrac{-5x+18}{(x-4)(x-3)}$

20. $\dfrac{2}{x^2-9}+\dfrac{3}{3-x}$

$\dfrac{2-3(x+3)}{(x+3)(x-3)}=\dfrac{-3x-7}{(x+3)(x-3)}$

21. $\dfrac{7x}{49x^2-25y^2}+\dfrac{3}{7x-5y}$

$\dfrac{7x+3(7x+5y)}{(7x-5y)(7x+5y)}=\dfrac{28x+15y}{(7x-5y)(7x+5y)}$

22. $\dfrac{3}{x^2-3xy+2y^2}+\dfrac{5x}{x-2y}$

$\dfrac{3+5x(x-y)}{(x-2y)(x-y)}=\dfrac{3+5x^2-5xy}{(x-2y)(x-y)}$

23. $\dfrac{3y}{y^2+y-2}+\dfrac{2}{y^2-4y+3}$

$\dfrac{3y(y-3)+2(y+2)}{(y+2)(y-1)(y-3)}=\dfrac{3y^2-7y+4}{(y+2)(y-1)(y-3)}$

$=\dfrac{(3y-4)(y-1)}{(y+2)(y-1)(y-3)}=\dfrac{3y-4}{(y+2)(y-3)}$

24. $\dfrac{2y}{y^2-7y+10}+\dfrac{3y}{y^2-8y+15}$

$\dfrac{2y(y-3)+3y(y-2)}{(y-5)(y-2)(y-3)}=\dfrac{5y^2-12y}{(y-5)(y-2)(y-3)}$

25. $\dfrac{3a}{3a^2-12}+\dfrac{5}{2a^2+4a}$

$\dfrac{6a^2+15a-30}{6a(a+2)(a-2)}=\dfrac{2a^2+5a-10}{2a(a+2)(a-2)}$

26. $\dfrac{2b}{3b^2-48}+\dfrac{2}{4b+b^2}$

$\dfrac{2b^2+6(b-4)}{3b(b+4)(b-4)}=\dfrac{2b^2+6b-24}{3b(b+4)(b-4)}$

27. $\dfrac{y+2}{2y-3}-\dfrac{4}{y+3}$

$\dfrac{(y+2)(y+3)-4(2y-3)}{(2y-3)(y+3)}=\dfrac{y^2+5y+6-8y+12}{(2y-3)(y+3)}$

$=\dfrac{y^2-3y+18}{(2y-3)(y+3)}$

28. $\dfrac{y-5}{y+2}-\dfrac{2y}{4y-1}$

$\dfrac{(y-5)(4y-1)-2y(y+2)}{(y+2)(4y-1)}=\dfrac{4y^2-21y+5-2y^2-4y}{(y+2)(4y-1)}$

$=\dfrac{2y^2-25y+5}{(y+2)(4y-1)}$

29. $\dfrac{3x-2y}{x}-\dfrac{2x-3y}{y}$

$\dfrac{3xy-2y^2-2x^2+3xy}{xy}=\dfrac{-2x^2+6xy-2y^2}{xy}$

30. $\dfrac{x+4y}{4y}-\dfrac{x+2y}{2x}$

$\dfrac{x^2+4xy-2y(x+2y)}{4xy}=\dfrac{x^2+2xy-4y^2}{4xy}$

31. $\dfrac{3x}{x^2 + 3x - 10} - \dfrac{2x}{x^2 + x - 6}$

$$\dfrac{3x(x+3) - 2x(x+5)}{(x+5)(x-2)(x+3)} = \dfrac{3x^2 + 9x - 2x^2 - 10x}{(x+5)(x-2)(x+3)}$$

$$= \dfrac{x^2 - x}{(x+5)(x-2)(x+3)}$$

32. $\dfrac{1}{x^2 - x - 2} - \dfrac{3}{x^2 + 2x + 1}$

$$\dfrac{x + 1 - 3(x-2)}{(x+1)^2(x-2)} = \dfrac{-2x + 7}{(x+1)^2(x-2)}$$

33. $\dfrac{9}{9x^2 + 6xy - 8y^2} - \dfrac{6}{9x^2 - 4y^2}$.

$$\dfrac{9(3x+2y) - 6(3x+4y)}{(3x-2y)(3x+4y)(3x+2y)} = \dfrac{27x + 18y - 18x - 24y}{(3x-2y)(3x+4y)(3x+2y)}$$

$$= \dfrac{3(3x - 2y)}{(3x-2y)(3x+4y)(3x+2y)}$$

$$= \dfrac{3}{(3x+4y)(3x+2y)}$$

34. $\dfrac{4}{4x^2 - 9y^2} - \dfrac{6}{8x^2 - 6xy - 9y^2}$

$$\dfrac{4(4x+3y) - 6(2x+3y)}{(2x+3y)(2x-3y)(4x+3y)} = \dfrac{16x + 12y - 12x - 18y}{(2x+3y)(2x-3y)(4x+3y)}$$

$$= \dfrac{2(2x - 3y)}{(2x+3y)(2x-3y)(4x+3y)}$$

$$= \dfrac{2}{(2x+3y)(4x+3y)}$$

35. $\dfrac{8y^2}{y^3 - 16y} - \dfrac{4y}{y^2 - 4y}$

$$\dfrac{8y^2 - 4y(y+4)}{y(y+4)(y-4)} = \dfrac{4y^2 - 16y}{y(y+4)(y-4)} = \dfrac{4y(y-4)}{y(y+4)(y-4)} = \dfrac{4}{y+4}$$

36. $\dfrac{2y - 46}{2y^2 - 2y - 40} + \dfrac{4}{2y - 10}$

$$\dfrac{2y - 46 + 4(y+4)}{2(y-5)(y+4)} = \dfrac{6y - 30}{2(y-5)(y+4)} = \dfrac{6(y-5)}{2(y-5)(y+4)} = \dfrac{3}{y+4}$$

37. $a + 3 + \dfrac{2}{3a - 5}$

$$\dfrac{(a+3)(3a-5) + 2}{3a - 5} = \dfrac{3a^2 + 4a - 15 + 2}{3a - 5} = \dfrac{3a^2 + 4a - 13}{3a - 5}$$

38. $a - 2 + \dfrac{3}{2a + 1}$

$$\dfrac{(a-2)(2a+1) + 3}{2a + 1} = \dfrac{2a^2 - 3a - 2 + 3}{2a + 1} = \dfrac{2a^2 - 3a + 1}{2a + 1}$$

39. $\dfrac{2}{x^2 + 3xy + 2y^2} + \dfrac{4}{x^2 - xy - 2y^2} - \dfrac{3}{x^2 - 4y^2}$

$$\dfrac{2(x-2y) + 4(x+2y) - 3(x+y)}{(x+2y)(x+y)(x-2y)} = \dfrac{2x - 4y + 4x + 8y - 3x - 3y}{(x+2y)(x+y)(x-2y)} = \dfrac{3x + y}{(x+2y)(x+y)(x-2y)}$$

40. $\dfrac{2}{x^2 - 5xy + 6y^2} + \dfrac{1}{x^2 - 7xy + 12y^2} - \dfrac{3}{x^2 - 6xy + 8y^2}$

$$\dfrac{2(x-4y) + 1(x-2y) - 3(x-3y)}{(x-3y)(x-2y)(x-4y)} = \dfrac{2x - 8y + x - 2y - 3x + 9y}{(x-3y)(x-2y)(x-4y)} = \dfrac{-y}{(x-3y)(x-2y)(x-4y)}$$

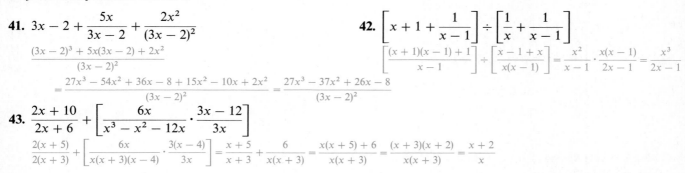

To Think About

Perform the operations indicated

41. $3x - 2 + \dfrac{5x}{3x - 2} + \dfrac{2x^2}{(3x - 2)^2}$

$$\dfrac{(3x-2)^3 + 5x(3x-2) + 2x^2}{(3x-2)^2}$$

$$= \dfrac{27x^3 - 54x^2 + 36x - 8 + 15x^2 - 10x + 2x^2}{(3x-2)^2} = \dfrac{27x^3 - 37x^2 + 26x - 8}{(3x-2)^2}$$

42. $\left[x + 1 + \dfrac{1}{x - 1} \right] \div \left[\dfrac{1}{x} + \dfrac{1}{x - 1} \right]$

$$\left[\dfrac{(x+1)(x-1) + 1}{x - 1} \right] \div \left[\dfrac{x - 1 + x}{x(x-1)} \right] = \dfrac{x^2}{x - 1} \cdot \dfrac{x(x-1)}{2x - 1} = \dfrac{x^3}{2x - 1}$$

43. $\dfrac{2x + 10}{2x + 6} + \left[\dfrac{6x}{x^3 - x^2 - 12x} \cdot \dfrac{3x - 12}{3x} \right]$

$$\dfrac{2(x+5)}{2(x+3)} + \left[\dfrac{6x}{x(x+3)(x-4)} \cdot \dfrac{3(x-4)}{3x} \right] = \dfrac{x + 5}{x + 3} + \dfrac{6}{x(x+3)} = \dfrac{x(x+5) + 6}{x(x+3)} = \dfrac{(x+3)(x+2)}{x(x+3)} = \dfrac{x + 2}{x}$$

Cumulative Review Problems

44. Alreda, Tony, and Melissa each purchased a car. The total cost of the cars was $26,500. Alreda purchased a used car that cost $1500 more than one purchased by Tony. Melissa purchased a car that cost $1000 more than double the cost of Tony's car. How much did each car cost?

Tony's car cost $6000, Melissa's car cost $13,000, Alreda's car cost $7500

45. A chemist must combine a mixture that is 15% acid with a mixture that is 30% acid to obtain 60 liters of a mixture that is 20% acid. How much of each kind should he use?

$$0.15x + 0.30(60 - x) = 0.20(60)$$
$$x = \text{number of liters @ 15\%} = 40 \text{ liters}$$
$$60 - x = \text{number of liters @ 30\%} = 20 \text{ liters}$$

46. A speedboat traveled up the river against the current a distance of 75 kilometers in 5 hours. The return trip with the current took only 3 hours. Find the speed of the current and the speed of the speedboat in still water. x = Boat in still water = 20 km/hr
y = Current = 5 km/hr
$5(x - y) = 75$
$3(x + y) = 75$

47. Hop Tyep invested $3,000 in bonds for one year. He earned $236 in interest. Part of the money was invested at 7% and part at 9%. How much was invested at each rate?
Amt. invested @ 7% = x = $1700
Amt. invested @ 9% = $3000 - x$ = $1300
$0.07x + 0.09(3000 - x) = $236

Calculator Problems

Simplify.

48. $\dfrac{1.2364}{x^2 - 7x + 12} + \dfrac{9.0521}{x - 3}$

$\dfrac{9.0521x - 34.972}{x^2 - 7x + 12}$

49. $\dfrac{0.0138}{2x + 5} - \dfrac{0.0273}{3x - 4}$

$\dfrac{-0.0132x - 0.1917}{6x^2 + 7x - 20}$

For Extra Practice Exercises, turn to page 276.

Solutions to Odd-Numbered Practice Problems

1. $\dfrac{7}{3a^2b} + \dfrac{-2 + a}{3a^2b} = \dfrac{5 + a}{3a^2b}$

3. $\dfrac{8}{x^2 - x - 12} + \dfrac{3}{x - 4} = \dfrac{8}{(x - 4)(x + 3)} + \dfrac{3}{x - 4}$

The LCD $= (x - 4)(x + 3)$.

$$\dfrac{8}{(x - 4)(x + 3)} + \dfrac{3}{x - 4} \cdot \dfrac{x + 3}{x + 3} = \dfrac{8}{(x - 4)(x + 3)} + \dfrac{3x + 9}{(x - 4)(x + 3)}$$

$$= \dfrac{3x + 17}{(x - 4)(x + 3)}$$

5. The LCD $= 12a^3b^3$.

$$\dfrac{7}{4ab^3} + \dfrac{1}{3a^3b^2} = \dfrac{7}{4ab^3} \cdot \dfrac{3a^2}{3a^2} + \dfrac{1}{3a^3b^2} \cdot \dfrac{4b}{4b}$$

$$= \dfrac{21a^2}{12a^3b^3} + \dfrac{4b}{12a^3b^3} = \dfrac{21a^2 + 4b}{12a^3b^3}$$

7. $\dfrac{4x + 2}{(x + 4)(x - 3)} - \dfrac{3x + 8}{(x + 4)(x + 2)}$

LCD $= (x + 4)(x - 3)(x + 2)$.

$$\dfrac{4x + 2}{(x + 4)(x - 3)} \cdot \dfrac{x + 2}{x + 2} - \dfrac{3x + 8}{(x + 4)(x + 2)} \cdot \dfrac{x - 3}{x - 3} = \dfrac{4x^2 + 10x + 4}{(x + 4)(x - 3)(x + 2)} - \dfrac{3x^2 - x - 24}{(x + 4)(x + 2)(x - 3)}$$

$$= \dfrac{x^2 + 11x + 28}{(x + 4)(x - 3)(x + 2)} = \dfrac{(x + 4)(x + 7)}{(x + 4)(x - 3)(x + 2)} = \dfrac{x + 7}{(x - 3)(x + 2)}$$

Answers to Even-Numbered Practice Problems

2. $\dfrac{x - 1}{(x + 6)(2x - 1)}$

4. LCD $= 2(2x + 5)^2$; $\dfrac{-6x^2 - x - 6}{2(2x + 5)^2}$

6. $\dfrac{4x - 27}{(x + 4)(x - 5)}$

8. $\dfrac{3a^2 + 29a + 21}{3a(2a + 3)}$

☐ After studying this section, you will be able to:

1 *Simplify complex fractions*

5.4 COMPLEX FRACTIONS

1 A *complex algebraic fraction* (or a *complex rational expression*) has a fraction in the numerator, or in the denominator, or in both the numerator and the denominator. For example,

$$\dfrac{7 + \dfrac{1}{x}}{x + 2} \qquad \dfrac{2}{\dfrac{x}{y} + 3} \qquad \dfrac{\dfrac{a + b}{7}}{\dfrac{1}{x} + \dfrac{1}{x + a}}$$

are complex fractional expressions.

There are two ways to simplify complex fractions. You can use whichever method you like.

> **Method 1: Combining Fractions in Both Numerator and Denominator**
>
> 1. Simplify the numerator and denominator, if possible, by combining quantities to obtain one fraction in the numerator and one fraction in the denominator.
> 2. Divide the numerator by the denominator (that is, multiply the numerator by the reciprocal of the denominator).
> 3. Simplify the expression.

> **Method 2: Multiplying Each Term by the LCD of All Individual Fractions**
>
> 1. Find the LCD of the algebraic fractions in the numerator and denominator.
> 2. Multiply the numerator and denominator of the complex fraction by the LCD.
> 3. Simplify the result.

Example 1   Simplify: $\dfrac{x + \dfrac{1}{x}}{\dfrac{1}{x} + \dfrac{3}{x^2}}$.

Method 1

1. Simplify numerator and denominator.

$$x + \frac{1}{x} = \frac{x^2 + 1}{x}$$

$$\frac{1}{x} + \frac{3}{x^2} = \frac{x + 3}{x^2}$$

2. Divide the numerator by the denominator.

$$\frac{\dfrac{x^2 + 1}{x}}{\dfrac{x + 3}{x^2}} = \frac{x^2 + 1}{x} \div \frac{x + 3}{x^2}$$

$$= \frac{x^2 + 1}{x} \cdot \frac{x^2}{x + 3}$$

$$= \frac{x^2 + 1}{\not{x}} \cdot \frac{\overset{x}{\not{x^2}}}{x + 3}$$

$$= \frac{x(x^2 + 1)}{x + 3}$$

3. Simplify. The result is already simplified. ■

Method 2

1. Find the LCD. The LCD is x^2.
2. Multiply the numerator and denominator by the LCD. Use the distributive property.

$$\frac{\left(x + \dfrac{1}{x}\right)}{\left(\dfrac{1}{x} + \dfrac{3}{x^2}\right)} \cdot \frac{x^2}{x^2} = \frac{x^3 + x}{x + 3}$$

3. Simplify.

$$\frac{x^3 + x}{x + 3} = \frac{x(x^2 + 1)}{x + 3}$$

TEACHING TIP   Most students will tend to use the method that the instructor prefers. If you have a personal preference for one method or the other it is perfectly acceptable to do most of the problems by that one method. However, it is best to use the other method at least once and mention that it is covered in the text.

Practice Problem 1   Simplify: $\dfrac{y + \dfrac{3}{y}}{\dfrac{2}{y^2} + \dfrac{5}{y}}$. ■

Example 2 Simplify: $\dfrac{\dfrac{1}{2x+6}+\dfrac{3}{2}}{\dfrac{3}{x^2-9}+\dfrac{x}{x-3}}$.

Method 1

1. Simplify the numerator.

$$\frac{1}{2x+6}+\frac{3}{2}=\frac{1}{2(x+3)}+\frac{3}{2}$$

$$=\frac{1}{2(x+3)}+\frac{3(x+3)}{2(x+3)}$$

$$=\frac{1+3x+9}{2(x+3)}$$

$$=\frac{3x+10}{2(x+3)}$$

Simplify the denominator.

$$\frac{3}{x^2-9}+\frac{x}{x-3}$$

$$=\frac{3}{(x+3)(x-3)}+\frac{x}{x-3}$$

$$=\frac{3}{(x+3)(x-3)}+\frac{x(x+3)}{(x+3)(x-3)}$$

$$=\frac{x^2+3x+3}{(x+3)(x-3)}$$

2. Divide the numerator by the denominator.

$$\frac{3x+10}{2(x+3)}\cdot\frac{(x+3)(x-3)}{x^2+3x+3}=\frac{(3x+10)(x-3)}{2(x^2+3x+3)}$$

3. Simplify. The answer is already simplified.

By either Method 1 or 2 we can leave the answer in factored form, or we can multiply it out to obtain

$$\frac{3x^2+x-30}{2x^2+6x+6}$$

Method 2

1. To find the LCD, we factor:

$$\frac{\dfrac{1}{2x+6}+\dfrac{3}{2}}{\dfrac{3}{x^2-9}+\dfrac{x}{x-3}}=\frac{\dfrac{1}{2(x+3)}+\dfrac{3}{2}}{\dfrac{3}{(x+3)(x-3)}+\dfrac{x}{x-3}}$$

The LCD of the two fractions in the numerator and the two in the denominator is

$$2(x+3)(x-3)$$

2. Multiply the numerator and denominator by the LCD.

$$\frac{\left(\dfrac{1}{2(x+3)}+\dfrac{3}{2}\right)}{\left(\dfrac{3}{(x+3)(x-3)}+\dfrac{x}{x-3}\right)}\cdot\frac{2(x+3)(x-3)}{2(x+3)(x-3)}$$

$$=\frac{\dfrac{1}{2(x+3)}\cdot 2(x+3)(x-3)+\dfrac{3}{2}\cdot 2(x+3)(x-3)}{\dfrac{3}{(x+3)(x-3)}\cdot 2(x+3)(x-3)+\dfrac{x}{x-3}\cdot 2(x+3)(x-3)}$$

$$=\frac{x-3+3(x+3)(x-3)}{6+2x(x+3)}$$

$$=\frac{3x^2+x-30}{2x^2+6x+6}=\frac{(3x+10)(x-3)}{2(x^2+3x+3)}$$

3. Simplify. The answer is already simplified. ■

Practice Problem 2 Simplify: $\dfrac{\dfrac{4}{16x^2-1}+\dfrac{3}{4x+1}}{\dfrac{x}{4x-1}+\dfrac{5}{4x+1}}$. ■

TEACHING TIP After discussing example 2, ask students to simplify the following complex fraction:

$$\frac{\dfrac{3}{x+4}-\dfrac{2}{x-4}}{\dfrac{5}{x^2-16}+\dfrac{1}{x+4}}$$

$$\left(\text{Answer }\frac{x-20}{x+1}.\right)$$

Example 3 Simplify by Method 1: $\dfrac{x+3}{\dfrac{9}{x}-x}$.

$$\frac{x+3}{\dfrac{9}{x}-\dfrac{x}{1}\cdot\dfrac{x}{x}}=\frac{x+3}{\dfrac{9}{x}-\dfrac{x^2}{x}}=\frac{\dfrac{x+3}{1}}{\dfrac{9-x^2}{x}}=\frac{x+3}{1}\div\frac{9-x^2}{x}=\frac{x+3}{1}\cdot\frac{x}{9-x^2}$$

$$=\frac{x+3}{1}\cdot\frac{x}{(3+x)(3-x)}=\frac{x}{3-x}$$ ■

Practice Problem 3 Simplify by Method 1: $\dfrac{4 + \dfrac{1}{x+3}}{\dfrac{2}{x^2 + 4x + 3}}$. ■

TEACHING TIP   After discussing example 3, you may want to do the following additional example:

$$\frac{\dfrac{x+5}{2}}{\dfrac{2}{x} - 3x}$$

$$\left(\text{Answer } \frac{x^2 + 5x}{2 - 3x^2}.\right)$$

Example 4   Simplify by Method 2: $\dfrac{\dfrac{3}{x+2} + \dfrac{1}{x}}{\dfrac{3}{y} - \dfrac{2}{x}}$.

The LCD of the numerator is $x(x+2)$. The LCD of the denominator is xy. Thus, the LCD of the complex fraction is $\boxed{xy(x+2)}$. Thus,

$$\frac{\dfrac{3}{x+2} + \dfrac{1}{x}}{\dfrac{3}{y} - \dfrac{2}{x}} \cdot \frac{xy(x+2)}{xy(x+2)} = \frac{3xy + xy + 2y}{3x(x+2) - 2y(x+2)}$$

$$= \frac{4xy + 2y}{(x+2)(3x-2y)}$$

$$= \frac{2y(2x+1)}{(x+2)(3x-2y)} \quad ■$$

Practice Problem 4   Simplify by Method 2: $\dfrac{\dfrac{7}{y+3} - \dfrac{3}{y}}{\dfrac{2}{y} + \dfrac{5}{y+3}}$. ■

EXERCISES 5.4

Simplify the complex fractions by any method.

1. $\dfrac{\dfrac{3}{x} + \dfrac{3}{y}}{\dfrac{6}{x^2 y^2}}$

$\dfrac{3(y+x)}{xy} \cdot \dfrac{x^2 y^2}{6} = \dfrac{xy(x+y)}{2}$

2. $\dfrac{\dfrac{2}{x^2}}{\dfrac{8}{x} + \dfrac{8}{y}}$

$\dfrac{2}{x^2} \cdot \dfrac{xy}{8(y+x)} = \dfrac{y}{4x(x+y)}$

3. $\dfrac{\dfrac{3x+2}{x-2y}}{\dfrac{5x-6}{x-2y}}$

$\dfrac{3x+2}{x-2y} \cdot \dfrac{x-2y}{5x-6} = \dfrac{3x+2}{5x-6}$

4. $\dfrac{\dfrac{x^2-4}{x+2}}{\dfrac{3x+6}{x+2}}$

$\dfrac{(x+2)(x-2)}{(x+2)} \cdot \dfrac{x+2}{3(x+2)} = \dfrac{x-2}{3}$

5. $\dfrac{1 - \dfrac{25}{y^2}}{\dfrac{5}{y} + 1}$

$\dfrac{y^2 - 25}{y^2} \cdot \dfrac{y}{y+5} = \dfrac{y-5}{y}$

6. $\dfrac{1 + \dfrac{3}{y}}{1 - \dfrac{9}{y^2}}$

$\dfrac{y+3}{y} \cdot \dfrac{y^2}{y^2 - 9} = \dfrac{y}{y-3}$

7. $\dfrac{\dfrac{y}{6} - \dfrac{1}{2y}}{\dfrac{3}{2y} - \dfrac{1}{y}}$

$\dfrac{y^2-3}{6y} \cdot \dfrac{2y}{1} = \dfrac{y^2-3}{3}$

8. $\dfrac{\dfrac{1}{3y} + \dfrac{1}{6y}}{\dfrac{1}{2y} + \dfrac{3}{4y}}$

$\dfrac{3}{6y} \cdot \dfrac{4y}{5} = \dfrac{2}{5}$

9. $\dfrac{\dfrac{2}{y-3}}{\dfrac{3}{y+3} + \dfrac{1}{y^2-9}}$

$\dfrac{2}{y-3} \cdot \dfrac{(y+3)(y-3)}{3y-8} = \dfrac{2(y+3)}{3y-8}$

10. $\dfrac{\dfrac{3}{y-4} - \dfrac{1}{y^2-16}}{\dfrac{2}{y+4}}$

$\dfrac{3y+12-1}{(y+4)(y-4)} \cdot \dfrac{y+4}{2} = \dfrac{3y+11}{2(y-4)}$

11. $\dfrac{\dfrac{7}{x} - 2}{\dfrac{x^2+1}{4}}$

$\dfrac{7-2x}{x} \cdot \dfrac{4}{x^2+1} = \dfrac{4(7-2x)}{x(x^2+1)}$

12. $\dfrac{\dfrac{x^2+2}{3}}{\dfrac{3}{x} + x}$

$\dfrac{x^2+2}{3} \cdot \dfrac{x}{3+x^2} = \dfrac{x(x^2+2)}{3(x^2+3)}$

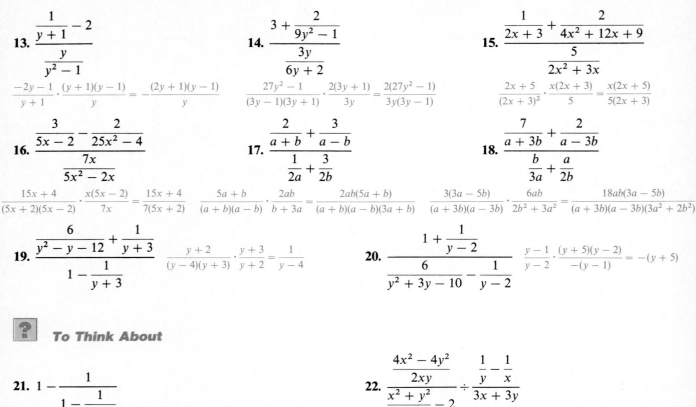

13. $\dfrac{\dfrac{1}{y+1}-2}{\dfrac{y}{y^2-1}}$

$\dfrac{-2y-1}{y+1}\cdot\dfrac{(y+1)(y-1)}{y}=-\dfrac{(2y+1)(y-1)}{y}$

14. $\dfrac{3+\dfrac{2}{9y^2-1}}{\dfrac{3y}{6y+2}}$

$\dfrac{27y^2-1}{(3y-1)(3y+1)}\cdot\dfrac{2(3y+1)}{3y}=\dfrac{2(27y^2-1)}{3y(3y-1)}$

15. $\dfrac{\dfrac{1}{2x+3}+\dfrac{2}{4x^2+12x+9}}{\dfrac{5}{2x^2+3x}}$

$\dfrac{2x+5}{(2x+3)^2}\cdot\dfrac{x(2x+3)}{5}=\dfrac{x(2x+5)}{5(2x+3)}$

16. $\dfrac{\dfrac{3}{5x-2}-\dfrac{2}{25x^2-4}}{\dfrac{7x}{5x^2-2x}}$

$\dfrac{15x+4}{(5x+2)(5x-2)}\cdot\dfrac{x(5x-2)}{7x}=\dfrac{15x+4}{7(5x+2)}$

17. $\dfrac{\dfrac{2}{a+b}+\dfrac{3}{a-b}}{\dfrac{1}{2a}+\dfrac{3}{2b}}$

$\dfrac{5a+b}{(a+b)(a-b)}\cdot\dfrac{2ab}{b+3a}=\dfrac{2ab(5a+b)}{(a+b)(a-b)(3a+b)}$

18. $\dfrac{\dfrac{7}{a+3b}+\dfrac{2}{a-3b}}{\dfrac{b}{3a}+\dfrac{a}{2b}}$

$\dfrac{3(3a-5b)}{(a+3b)(a-3b)}\cdot\dfrac{6ab}{2b^2+3a^2}=\dfrac{18ab(3a-5b)}{(a+3b)(a-3b)(3a^2+2b^2)}$

19. $\dfrac{\dfrac{6}{y^2-y-12}+\dfrac{1}{y+3}}{1-\dfrac{1}{y+3}}$ $\dfrac{y+2}{(y-4)(y+3)}\cdot\dfrac{y+3}{y+2}=\dfrac{1}{y-4}$

20. $\dfrac{1+\dfrac{1}{y-2}}{\dfrac{6}{y^2+3y-10}-\dfrac{1}{y-2}}$ $\dfrac{y-1}{y-2}\cdot\dfrac{(y+5)(y-2)}{-(y-1)}=-(y+5)$

To Think About

21. $1-\dfrac{1}{1-\dfrac{1}{y-2}}$

$1-\left[1\div\dfrac{y-3}{y-2}\right]=1-\dfrac{y-2}{y-3}=\dfrac{y-3-y+2}{y-3}=\dfrac{-1}{y-3}$

22. $\dfrac{\dfrac{4x^2-4y^2}{2xy}}{\dfrac{x^2+y^2}{xy}-2}\div\dfrac{\dfrac{1}{y}-\dfrac{1}{x}}{3x+3y}$

$\dfrac{4(x+y)(x-y)}{2xy}\cdot\dfrac{xy}{(x-y)(x-y)}\div\left[\dfrac{x-y}{xy}\cdot\dfrac{1}{3(x+y)}\right]$

$=\dfrac{2(x+y)}{x-y}\cdot\dfrac{3xy(x+y)}{x-y}=\dfrac{6xy(x+y)^2}{(x-y)^2}$

Cumulative Review Problems

Solve for x and y.

23. $5x+\;y=\;8$
$2x+3y=15$

$\underline{-15x-3y=-24}$
$\underline{\;\;2x+3y=\;\;\;15}$
$x=\dfrac{9}{13},\;y=\dfrac{59}{13}$

24. $3x+2y=2$
$7x+5y=3$

$\underline{15x+10y=\;\;10}$
$\underline{-14x-10y=-6}$
$x=4,\;y=-5$

Solve for x, y, and z.

25. $x+\;\;y+\;\;z=\;\;3$
$4x+3y\;\;\;\;\;=-2$
$-5y-2z=\;\;2$

Eliminate x:
$\boxed{1\text{ and }2}\quad\;\;-y-4z=-14$
$\underline{-2\times\text{Eq. }3\;\;10y+4z=\;\;-4}$
$x=1,\;y=-2,\;z=4$

26. $5x+\;\;y+\;\;z=\;\;-4$
$3x-4y+3z=-19$
$4x-\;\;y+2z=-11$

Eliminate y:
$\boxed{1\text{ and }2}\quad23x+7z=-35$
$\underline{\boxed{2\text{ and }3}\;-13x-5z=\;\;\;25}$
$\;\;\;\;115x+35z=-175$
$\underline{-91x-35z=\;\;\;175}$
$x=0,\;y=1,\;z=-5$

For Extra Practice Exercises, turn to page 277.

Solutions to Odd-Numbered Practice Problems

1. Simplify: $\dfrac{y+\dfrac{3}{y}}{\dfrac{2}{y^2}+\dfrac{5}{y}}$

Method 1

1. Simplify numerator.

$y+\dfrac{3}{y}=\dfrac{y^2}{y}+\dfrac{3}{y}=\dfrac{y^2+3}{y}$

$\dfrac{2}{y^2}+\dfrac{5}{y}=\dfrac{2}{y^2}+\dfrac{5y}{y^2}=\dfrac{2+5y}{y^2}$

Method 2

1. Find the LCD $=y^2$.

2. Multiply the numerator and denominator by the LCD.

$\dfrac{y+\dfrac{3}{y}}{\dfrac{2}{y^2}+\dfrac{5}{y}}\cdot\dfrac{y^2}{y^2}=\dfrac{y(y^2)+\dfrac{3}{y}(y^2)}{\dfrac{2}{y^2}(y^2)+\dfrac{5}{y}(y^2)}$

2. Divide the numerator by the denominator.

$$\frac{\dfrac{y^2 + 3}{y}}{\dfrac{2 + 5y}{y^2}} = \frac{y^2 + 3}{y} \cdot \frac{y^2}{2 + 5y}$$

$$= \frac{y(y^2 + 3)}{2 + 5y}$$

$$= \frac{y^3 + 3y}{2 + 5y} \quad \text{or} \quad \frac{y(y^2 + 3)}{2 + 5y}$$

No simplification needed.

No simplification needed.

3. The LCD in the numerator is $x + 3$.

$$\frac{\dfrac{4}{1} \cdot \dfrac{x + 3}{x + 3} + \dfrac{1}{x + 3}}{\dfrac{2}{(x + 1)(x + 3)}} = \frac{\dfrac{4x + 12}{x + 3} + \dfrac{1}{x + 3}}{\dfrac{2}{(x + 1)(x + 3)}}$$

$$= \frac{\dfrac{4x + 13}{x + 3}}{\dfrac{2}{(x + 1)(x + 3)}} = \frac{4x + 13}{x + 3} \cdot \frac{(x + 1)(x + 3)}{2}$$

$$= \frac{(4x + 13)(x + 1)}{2} \quad \text{or} \quad \frac{4x^2 + 17x + 13}{2}$$

Answers to Even-Numbered Practice Problems

2. $\dfrac{12x + 1}{4x^2 + 21x - 5}$ **4.** $\dfrac{4y - 9}{7y + 6}$

5.5 FRACTIONAL EQUATIONS

After studying this section, you will be able to:

1 A **fractional equation** (or a **rational equation**) is an equation that has a fractional (rational) expression and a variable in the denominator. To solve fractional equations, we find the LCD of all fractions in the equation, and multiply each term of the equation by the LCD. We then solve the resulting linear equation.

1 *Solve a rational equation that has a solution and be able to check the solution*

2 *Identify those rational equations that have no solution*

Example 1 Solve: $\dfrac{9}{4} - \dfrac{1}{2x} = \dfrac{4}{x}$. Check your solution.

$$4x\left(\frac{9}{4}\right) - 4x\left(\frac{1}{2x}\right) = 4x\left(\frac{4}{x}\right) \qquad \text{Multiplying each term by the LCD } 4x.$$

$$9x - 2 = 16 \qquad \text{Simplifying.}$$

$$9x = 18 \qquad \text{Collecting like terms.}$$

$$x = 2 \qquad \text{Dividing each side by coefficient of } x.$$

Check: $\dfrac{9}{4} - \dfrac{1}{2(2)} \stackrel{?}{=} \dfrac{4}{2}$

$$\frac{9}{4} - \frac{1}{4} \stackrel{?}{=} 2$$

$$\frac{8}{4} = 2 \checkmark \qquad \text{It checks.} \quad \blacksquare$$

Practice Problem 1 Solve and check: $\dfrac{4}{3x} + \dfrac{x + 1}{x} = \dfrac{1}{2}$. ∎

Remember, you must always check your solutions in the original equation because you might introduce an extraneous solution (see Example 4)—in other words, "roots" that don't satisfy the original equation—when you multiply an equation by an expression that has a variable.

TEACHING TIP After discussing example 2, you may want to do the following additional sample example:

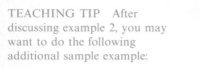

$$\frac{5}{4y} = 1 - \frac{3}{y}$$

$\bigg($ Students will usually have questions about why the LCD is $4y$. Emphasize the importance of multiplying each term by $4y$.

The answer is $y = \dfrac{17}{4}$. $\bigg)$

Example 2 Solve: $\dfrac{2}{3x + 6} = \dfrac{1}{6} - \dfrac{1}{2x + 4}$.

$$\frac{2}{3(x + 2)} = \frac{1}{6} - \frac{1}{2(x + 2)}$$ Factoring each denominator.

$$6(x+2)\left[\frac{2}{3(x+2)}\right] = 6(x + 2)\left[\frac{1}{6}\right] - 6(x+2)\left[\frac{1}{2(x+2)}\right]$$ Multiplying each term by the LCD $6(x + 2)$.

$$4 = x + 2 - 3$$ Simplifying.

$$4 = x - 1$$ Collecting like terms.

$$5 = x$$ Solving for x.

Check: Verify that $x = 5$ is the solution. ■

Practice Problem 2 Solve and check: $\dfrac{5x - 2}{x^2 - x} - \dfrac{2}{x - 1} = \dfrac{4}{x}$. ■

TEACHING TIP After discussing example 3, ask students to do the following problem:

$$\frac{4}{x - 2} + \frac{x}{x + 1} = \frac{x^2 - 2}{x^2 - x - 2}$$

(The answer is $x = -3$.)

Example 3 Solve: $\dfrac{y^2 - 10}{y^2 - y - 20} = 1 + \dfrac{7}{y - 5}$.

$$\frac{y^2 - 10}{(y - 5)(y + 4)} = 1 + \frac{7}{y - 5}$$ Factoring each denominator.

$$(y - 5)(y + 4)\left[\frac{y^2 - 10}{(y - 5)(y + 4)}\right]$$ Multiplying each term by the LCD $(y - 5)(y + 4)$.

$$= (y - 5)(y + 4)\,[1] + (y - 5)(y + 4)\left[\frac{7}{y - 5}\right]$$

$$y^2 - 10 = (y - 5)(y + 4)(1) + 7(y + 4)$$ Removing common factors.

$$y^2 - 10 = y^2 - y - 20 + 7y + 28$$ Simplifying.

$$y^2 - 10 = y^2 + 6y + 8$$ Collecting like terms.

$$-10 = 6y + 8$$ Subtracting y^2 from each side.

$$-18 = 6y$$ Adding -8 to each side.

$$-3 = y$$ Dividing each side by coefficient of y.

Check: $\dfrac{(-3)^2 - 10}{(-3)^2 - (-3) - 20} \overset{?}{=} 1 + \dfrac{7}{-3 - 5}$

$$\frac{9 - 10}{9 + 3 - 20} \overset{?}{=} 1 + \frac{7}{-8}$$

$$\frac{-1}{-8} \overset{?}{=} 1 - \frac{7}{8}$$

$$\frac{1}{8} = \frac{1}{8} \checkmark$$ ■

Practice Problem 3 Solve: $\dfrac{2y^2 - 15}{y^2 + y - 6} = \dfrac{y - 3}{y - 2} + \dfrac{y + 1}{y + 3}$. ∎

② Equations with No Solution

Some equations have no solution. This can happen in two distinct ways. In the first case, the variable adds to zero and no solution can be obtained. In the second case, we may solve an equation to get an *apparent* solution, but this "solution" may not satisfy the original equation. We call the apparent solution an **extraneous solution.** An equation that yields an extraneous solution has no solution.

Case 1: The Variable Drops Out

Example 4 Solve: $\dfrac{z + 1}{z^2 - 3z + 2} + \dfrac{3}{z - 1} = \dfrac{4}{z - 2}$.

$\dfrac{z + 1}{(z - 2)(z - 1)} + \dfrac{3}{z - 1} = \dfrac{4}{z - 2}$
  Factoring to find the LCD $(z - 2)(z - 1)$

$\cancel{(z-2)(z-1)}\left[\dfrac{z + 1}{\cancel{(z-2)(z-1)}}\right] + (z - 2)\cancel{(z-1)}\left[\dfrac{3}{\cancel{z-1}}\right]$

$\qquad = \cancel{(z-2)}(z - 1)\left[\dfrac{4}{\cancel{z-2}}\right]$
  Multiplying each term by LCD

$z + 1 + 3(z - 2) = 4(z - 1)$
  Cancelling common factors.

$z + 1 + 3z - 6 = 4z - 4$
  Simplifying.

$4z - 5 = 4z - 4$
  Collecting like terms.

$4z - 4z = -4 + 5$
  Obtaining variable terms on one side and constant values on the other.

$0z = 1$

$0 = 1$
  Simplifying.

Of course, $0 \neq 1$. Therefore, no value of z makes the original equation true. Hence, the equation has **no solution** ∎

Practice Problem 4 Solve: $\dfrac{2x - 1}{x^2 - 7x + 10} + \dfrac{3}{x - 5} = \dfrac{5}{x - 2}$. ∎

Case 2: The Obtained Value of the Variable Leads to a Denominator of Zero

Example 5 Solve: $\dfrac{4y}{y + 3} - \dfrac{12}{y - 3} = \dfrac{4y^2 + 36}{y^2 - 9}$.

$\dfrac{4y}{y + 3} - \dfrac{12}{y - 3} = \dfrac{4y^2 + 36}{(y + 3)(y - 3)}$
  Factoring each denominator to find the LCD $(y + 3)(y - 3)$

$\cancel{(y+3)}(y - 3)\left[\dfrac{4y}{\cancel{y+3}}\right] - (y + 3)\cancel{(y-3)}\left[\dfrac{12}{\cancel{y-3}}\right]$

$\qquad = \cancel{(y+3)(y-3)}\left[\dfrac{4y^2 + 36}{\cancel{(y+3)(y-3)}}\right]$
  Multiplying each term by LCD.

$4y(y - 3) - 12(y + 3) = 4y^2 + 36$
  Cancelling common factors.

$4y^2 - 12y - 12y - 36 = 4y^2 + 36$
  Removing parentheses.

$4y^2 - 24y - 36 = 4y^2 + 36$
  Collecting like terms.

$-24y - 36 = 36$
  Subtracting $4y^2$ from each side.

TEACHING TIP The most important case of equations that have no solutions are ones like the following: Ask students to solve it after you have discussed example 5.

$\dfrac{4}{y + 6} + \dfrac{1}{y - 3} = \dfrac{9}{y^2 + 3y - 18}$

The obtained value of $y = 3$ is invalid since that would involve division by zero. There is NO SOLUTION.

$$-24y = 72 \qquad \text{Adding 36 to each side.}$$

$$y = \frac{72}{-24} = -3 \qquad \text{Dividing each side by } -24$$

$$\text{Check: } \frac{4(-3)}{-3+3} - \frac{12}{-3-3} \overset{?}{=} \frac{4(-3)^2 + 36}{(-3)^2 - 9}$$

$$\frac{-12}{0} - \frac{12}{-6} \overset{?}{=} \frac{36 + 36}{0}$$

You cannot divide by zero. Division by zero is not defined. A value of a variable that makes a denominator in the original equation zero is not a solution to the equation. Thus this equation has no solution ∎

Practice Problem 5   Solve and check: $\dfrac{y}{y-2} - 3 = 1 + \dfrac{2}{y-2}$. ∎

DEVELOPING YOUR STUDY SKILLS

WHY IS REVIEW NECESSARY?

You master a course in mathematics by learning the concepts one step at a time. There are basic concepts like addition, subtraction, multiplication, and division of whole numbers that are considered the foundation upon which all of mathematics is built. These must be mastered first. Then the study of mathematics is built step by step upon this foundation, each step supporting the next. The process is a carefully designed procedure, and so no steps can be skipped. A student of mathematics needs to realize the importance of this building process to succeed.

Because learning new concepts depends on those previously learned, students often need to take time to review. The reviewing process will strengthen the understanding and application of concepts that are weak due to lack of mastery or passage of time. Review at the right time on the right concepts can strengthen previously learned skills and make progress possible.

Timely, periodic review of previously learned mathematical concepts is absolutely necessary in order to master new concepts. You may have forgotten a concept or grown a bit rusty in applying it. Reviewing is the answer. Make use of any review sections in your textbook, whether they are assigned or not. Look back to previous chapters whenever you have forgotten how to do something. Study the examples and practice some exercises to refresh your understanding.

Be sure that you understand and can perform the computations of each new concept. This will enable you to be able to move successfully on to the next ones.

Remember, mathematics is a step-by-step building process. Learn one concept at a time, skipping none, and reinforce and strengthen with review whenever necessary.

EXERCISES 5.5

Solve the equations and check your solution. If there is no solution, say so.

1. $\dfrac{3}{y} = \dfrac{9}{2y - 1}$

$3(2y - 1) = 9y$
$-1 = y$

2. $\dfrac{y + 1}{2y} = \dfrac{2}{3}$

$3y + 3 = 4y$
$3 = y$

3. $\dfrac{1}{x} - 3 = \dfrac{4}{x}$

$1 - 3x = 4$
$-3 = 3x$
$-1 = x$

4. $\dfrac{1}{y} + 2 = \dfrac{3}{y}$ $\begin{array}{c} 1 + 2y = 3 \\ 2y = 2 \\ y = 1 \end{array}$

5. $\dfrac{2}{x} - \dfrac{3}{5} = 1$ $\begin{array}{c} 10 - 3x = 5x \\ 10 = 8x \\ \frac{5}{4} = x \end{array}$

6. $\dfrac{x+2}{x-5} = 10$ $\begin{array}{c} x + 2 = 10x - 50 \\ \frac{52}{9} = x \end{array}$

7. $\dfrac{y+6}{y+3} - 2 = \dfrac{3}{y+3}$
$\begin{array}{c} y + 6 - 2(y + 3) = 3 \\ y + 6 - 2y - 6 = 3 \\ y = -3 \quad \text{No solution} \end{array}$

8. $4 - \dfrac{8x}{x+1} = \dfrac{8}{x+1}$
$\begin{array}{c} 4x + 4 - 8x = 8 \\ x = -1 \quad \text{No solution} \end{array}$

9. $\dfrac{3}{x} + \dfrac{4}{2x} = \dfrac{4}{x-1}$
$\begin{array}{c} 6(x - 1) + 4(x - 1) = 8x \\ x = 5 \end{array}$

10. $\dfrac{1}{2x} + \dfrac{5}{x} = \dfrac{3}{x-1}$
$\begin{array}{c} x - 1 + 10(x - 1) = 6x \\ x = \frac{11}{5} \end{array}$

11. $\dfrac{1}{x-1} + \dfrac{x+1}{x^2 + 2x - 3} = \dfrac{1}{x+3}$
$\begin{array}{c} x + 3 + x + 1 = x - 1 \\ x = -5 \end{array}$

12. $\dfrac{3}{2x-1} + \dfrac{3}{2x+1} = \dfrac{8x}{4x^2 - 1}$
$\begin{array}{c} 6x + 3 + 6x - 3 = 8x \\ x = 0 \end{array}$

13. $\dfrac{6}{x} - \dfrac{3}{x^2 - x} = \dfrac{7}{x-1}$
$\begin{array}{c} 6x - 6 - 3 = 7x \\ x = -9 \end{array}$

14. $\dfrac{5-x}{x^2 - 1} + \dfrac{7}{x+1} = \dfrac{6}{x}$
$\begin{array}{c} 5x - x^2 + 7x^2 - 7x = 6x^2 - 6 \\ x = 3 \end{array}$

15. $\dfrac{4}{y+2} - \dfrac{11}{9} = \dfrac{1}{3y+6}$
$\begin{array}{c} 36 - 11(y + 2) = 3 \\ y = 1 \end{array}$

16. $\dfrac{3}{y+3} - \dfrac{1}{y-2} = \dfrac{5}{2y+6}$
$y = -8$

17. $1 - \dfrac{10}{z-3} = \dfrac{-5}{3z-9}$
$z = \dfrac{34}{3}$

18. $\dfrac{3}{2} + \dfrac{2}{2z-8} = \dfrac{1}{z-4}$
$\begin{array}{c} 3z - 12 + 2 = 2 \\ z = 4 \quad \text{No solution} \end{array}$

19. $\dfrac{4}{y+5} - \dfrac{32}{y^2 - 25} = \dfrac{-2}{y-5}$
$\begin{array}{c} 4y - 20 - 32 = -2y - 10 \\ y = 7 \end{array}$

20. $\dfrac{8y+5}{10y^2 - y - 2} + \dfrac{3}{5y+2} = \dfrac{2}{2y-1}$ $\begin{array}{c} 8y + 5 + 6y - 3 = 10y + 4 \\ y = \frac{1}{2} \quad \text{No solution} \end{array}$

21. $\dfrac{4}{z^2 - 9} = \dfrac{2}{z^2 - 3z}$
$\begin{array}{c} 4z = 2z + 6 \\ z = 3 \quad \text{No solution} \end{array}$

22. $\dfrac{z^2 + 16}{z^2 - 16} = \dfrac{z}{z+4} - \dfrac{4}{z-4}$
$\begin{array}{c} z^2 + 16 = z^2 - 4z - 4z - 16 \\ z = -4 \quad \text{No solution} \end{array}$

23. $\dfrac{1}{2x-1} + \dfrac{2}{x-5} = \dfrac{-22}{2x^2 - 11x + 5}$
$\begin{array}{c} x - 5 + 4x - 2 = -22 \\ x = -3 \end{array}$

24. $\dfrac{5}{2x+3} + \dfrac{-4}{3x-4} = \dfrac{3x}{6x^2 + x - 12}$
$\begin{array}{c} 15x - 20 - 8x - 12 = 3x \\ x = 8 \end{array}$

25. $\dfrac{6}{x+1} = \dfrac{6}{x-1} + \dfrac{-9}{x^2 - 1}$ $\begin{array}{c} 6x - 6 = 6x - 3 \\ 0 \neq 3 \quad \text{No solution} \end{array}$

26. $\dfrac{2}{2x+3} + \dfrac{12}{4x^2 - 4x - 15} = \dfrac{2}{2x-5}$
$\begin{array}{c} 4x - 10 + 12 = 4x + 6 \\ 2 \neq 6 \quad \text{No solution} \end{array}$

? To Think About

27. In what situations will a fractional equation have no solution?

When the solved value of the variable causes the denominator of any fraction to = 0, or when the variable drops out.

28. What does "extraneous solution" mean? What must we do to determine if a solution is an extraneous solution?

An extraneous solution is an apparent solution which, when substituted into the original equation, does not make the equation a true statement.

Solve the equations and check your solutions.

29. $\dfrac{1}{3}\left[\dfrac{13x+7}{x+3} \div \dfrac{5x-1}{3} \right] = \dfrac{5x+7}{5x^2 + 14x - 3}$
Multiply both sides by $3(x + 3)(5x - 1)$
$\begin{array}{c} 39x + 21 = 15x + 21 \\ x = 0 \end{array}$

30. $\dfrac{y^2 + 2y - 15}{y^2 - 4y + 3} \cdot \dfrac{3y^2 - 3}{y^2 + y - 20} = -3$
$\dfrac{(y+5)(y-3)}{(y-3)(y-1)} \cdot \dfrac{3(y+1)(y-1)}{(y+5)(y-4)} = -3$
$\dfrac{3(y+1)}{y-4} = -3$
$y = \dfrac{3}{2}$

Cumulative Review Problems

Factor completely.

31. $7x^2 - 63$
$7(x + 3)(x - 3)$

32. $2x^2 + 20x + 50$
$2(x + 5)^2$

33. $64x^3 - 27y^3$
$(4x - 3y)(16x^2 + 12xy + 9y^2)$

34. $3x^2 - 13x + 14$
$(3x - 7)(x - 2)$

Solve for x.

35. $\dfrac{28.9236}{x + 5} = \dfrac{17.8328}{2x - 1}$

$x = 2.951127594$

36. $\dfrac{1.9861}{3x} + \dfrac{2.4631}{x + 2} = \dfrac{8.8276}{3x^2 + 6x}$

$x = 0.517887237$

For Extra Practice Exercises, turn to page 278.

Solutions to Odd-Numbered Practice Problems

1. $LCD = 6x$.

$$6x\left[\dfrac{4}{3x}\right] + 6x\left[\dfrac{x + 1}{x}\right] = 6x\left[\dfrac{1}{2}\right]$$

$$8 + 6(x + 1) = 3x$$
$$8 + 6x + 6 = 3x$$
$$14 + 6x = 3x$$
$$14 = -3x$$
$$-\dfrac{14}{3} = x$$

Check: $\dfrac{4}{3\left(-\dfrac{14}{3}\right)} + \dfrac{-\dfrac{14}{3} + 1}{-\dfrac{14}{3}} \overset{?}{=} \dfrac{1}{2}$

$$\dfrac{4}{-14} + \dfrac{-\dfrac{11}{3}}{-\dfrac{14}{3}} \overset{?}{=} \dfrac{1}{2}$$

$$-\dfrac{2}{7} + \dfrac{11}{14} \overset{?}{=} \dfrac{7}{14} \qquad -\dfrac{4}{14} + \dfrac{11}{14} = \dfrac{7}{14} \checkmark$$

3. $LCD = (y + 3)(y - 2)$.

$$\dfrac{2y^2 - 15}{(y + 3)(y - 2)} = \dfrac{y - 3}{y - 2} + \dfrac{y + 1}{y + 3}$$

$$(y + 3)(y - 2)\left[\dfrac{2y^2 - 15}{(y + 3)(y - 2)}\right] = (y + 3)(y - 2)\left[\dfrac{y - 3}{y - 2}\right] + (y + 3)(y - 2)\left[\dfrac{y + 1}{y + 3}\right]$$

$$2y^2 - 15 = (y + 3)(y - 3) + (y - 2)(y + 1)$$
$$2y^2 - 15 = y^2 - 9 + y^2 - y - 2$$
$$2y^2 - 15 = 2y^2 - y - 11$$

$-15 = -y - 11$ Adding $-2y^2$ to each side.

$-15 + 11 = -y$ Adding 11 to each side.

$$-4 = -1y$$

$\dfrac{-4}{-1} = \dfrac{-1y}{-1}$ Dividing each side by -1.

$$4 = y$$

5. $(y - 2)\left[\dfrac{y}{y - 2}\right] - (y - 2)[3] = (y - 2)[1] + (y - 2)\left[\dfrac{2}{y - 2}\right]$

$$y - 3(y - 2) = 1(y - 2) + 2$$
$$y - 3y + 6 = y - 2 + 2$$
$$-2y + 6 = y$$
$$6 = 3y$$
$$2 = y$$

Check: $\dfrac{2}{2 - 2} - 3 \overset{?}{=} 1 + \dfrac{2}{2 - 2}$

$$\dfrac{2}{0} - 3 \overset{?}{=} 1 + 1 + \dfrac{2}{0}$$

Division by zero is not defined.

The value $y = 2$ is therefore not a solution to the original equation. **There is no solution.**

Answers to Even-Numbered Practice Problems

2. $x = 2$ **4.** No solution.

5.6 APPLICATIONS: FORMULAS AND RATIO PROBLEMS

After studying this section, you will be able to:

1 Solve a formula containing a fraction for a particular variable

2 Solve ratio problems

1 Formulas

In science, economics, business, and mathematics, we use formulas that contain algebraic fractions. We often have to solve these formulas for a specific variable in terms of the other variables.

Example 1   Solve for r: $S = \dfrac{a}{1 - r}$.

$S(1 - r) = \left[\dfrac{a}{1 - r}\right](1 - r)$ Multiplying both sides by the LCD $(1 - r)$.

$S - Sr = a$ Simplifying.

$-Sr = a - S$ Isolating the term containing r.

$r = \dfrac{a - S}{-S}$ Dividing each side by $-S$.

To avoid a negative sign in the denominator, the answer may be expressed as

$$r = \frac{a - S}{S} \quad \text{or} \quad r = \frac{-a + S}{S}$$

(Do you see why?)   ■

Practice Problem 1   Solve for a: $B = \dfrac{2x}{5 - 3a}$.   ■

Example 2   Solve for a: $\dfrac{1}{f} = \dfrac{1}{a} + \dfrac{1}{b}$.

$abf\left[\dfrac{1}{f}\right] = abf\left[\dfrac{1}{a}\right] + abf\left[\dfrac{1}{b}\right]$ Multiplying each term by the LCD abf.

$ab = bf + af$ Simplifying.

$ab - af = bf$ Obtaining all the terms containing a on one side of the equation.

$a(b - f) = bf$ Factoring.

$a = \dfrac{bf}{b - f}$ Dividing each side by $b - f$.   ■

TEACHING TIP   After the students have seen you work out example 2, see if they can do the following similar problem with four variables: Solve for b.

$$\frac{1}{g} = \frac{1}{a} + \frac{1}{b} + \frac{1}{c}$$

$\left(\text{Answer is } b = \dfrac{gac}{ac - gc - ag}.\right)$

Practice Problem 2   Solve for R: $\dfrac{1}{R} = \dfrac{1}{R_1} + \dfrac{1}{R_2}$.   ■

Example 3   The gravitational force F between two masses m_1 and m_2 a distance d apart is

$$F = \frac{Gm_1m_2}{d^2}.$$

Solve for m_2.

   The subscripts on the variable m mean that m_1 and m_2 are *different*. (The m just stands for "mass.")

$d^2[F] = d^2\left[\dfrac{Gm_1m_2}{d^2}\right]$ Multiplying each side by the LCD d^2.

$d^2F = Gm_1m_2$ Simplifying.

$$\frac{d^2F}{Gm_1} = \frac{Gm_1m_2}{Gm_1}$$ Dividing each side by the coefficient of m_2, which is Gm_1.

$$\frac{d^2F}{Gm_1} = m_2 \quad \blacksquare$$

Practice Problem 3 Solve for q: $H = \dfrac{2bqx}{y^2}$. ■

◻ Ratio and Proportion

The **ratio** of two values is the first value divided by the second value.

> The **ratio** of a to b $(b \neq 0)$ is written as $\dfrac{a}{b}$ or $a \div b$ or $a{:}b$.

Example 4 Smithville College has 88 faculty, 24 administrators, and 2056 students. What is the student-to-faculty ratio?

There are 2056 students to 88 faculty. So the ratio of students to faculty is $\dfrac{2056}{88} = \dfrac{257}{11}$ or $257{:}11$ ■

Practice Problem 4 Last month the Smithville plant produced 414 perfect parts and 36 defective parts. What is the ratio of perfect parts to defective parts? ■

A **proportion** is an equation that says that two ratios are equal. If a has the same ratio to b as c has to d we can write the proportion equation $\dfrac{a}{b} = \dfrac{c}{d}$. We will use proportions to solve Examples 5 and 6.

Example 5 On a long trip, Susan's car needed 7 gallons of gas to go 180 miles. If her car continues to consume gas at this rate, how many miles can she travel on 11 gallons of gas? Round your answer to the nearest whole mile.

Let $x =$ number of miles she can travel. Our first ratio is $\dfrac{7}{180}$ because it took 7 gallons of gas to drive 180 miles. Our second ratio is $\dfrac{11}{x}$ because we want to know how far the car will travel on 11 gallons of gas. Our proportion is

$$\frac{11}{x} = \frac{7}{180}$$

because a proportion equates two ratios. Now we solve for x.

$$\frac{7}{180} = \frac{11}{x}$$

$$180x\left[\frac{7}{180}\right] = 180x\left[\frac{11}{x}\right]$$ Multiplying each side of the equation by the LCD $180x$.

$$7x = 1980$$

$$x = \frac{1980}{7}$$

$$x \approx 282.86 \approx 283 \text{ miles}$$

TEACHING TIP After explaining example 5 or a similar example, ask students to do the following problem: The insurance company has rated 4 out of every 15 drivers in the LA Gear factory as extremely safe drivers. If the factory employs 120 people, how many extemely safe drivers would you expect to find?

$\left(\text{Students should be able to set up the ratio } \dfrac{4}{15} = \dfrac{x}{120}.\right)$

(The answer is 32 people.)

She can travel approximately 283 miles more. ■

Note: The proportion must be set up logically. We set up our proportion by taking the ratios of the number of gallons of gas needed to drive a certain distance. It would make no sense to set up the proportion relating the initial amount of gas (7 gallons) to the unknown number of miles to be driven.

However, there are other ways to set up the proportion. For example, we could set up one ratio between amounts of gas, and one ratio between miles driven.

Initial amount of gas ⟶ $\dfrac{7}{11} = \dfrac{180}{x}$ ⟵ Initial number of miles driven
New amount of gas ⟶ ⟵ New number of miles driven

We then get

$$7x = 11 \cdot 180$$

$$x = \frac{1980}{7}$$

$$x \approx 283 \text{ miles}$$

Practice Problem 5   If there are 13 milliliters of acid in 37 milliliters of solution, how much acid will be contained in 296 milliliters of solution?   ■

Example 6   A company plans to employ 910 people with a ratio of two managers for every 11 workers. How many managers should be hired? How many workers?

If we let x = the number of managers, then $910 - x$ = the number of workers. We are given the ratio of managers to workers, so let's set up our proportion in that way.

Proposed number of managers ⟶ $\dfrac{2}{11} = \dfrac{x}{910 - x}$ ⟵ actual number of managers needed
Proposed number of workers ⟶ ⟵ actual number of workers needed

The LCD is $11(910 - x)$. Multiplying by the LCD, we get

$$11(910 - x)\left[\frac{2}{11}\right] = 11(910 - x)\left[\frac{x}{910 - x}\right]$$

$$2(910 - x) = 11x$$

$$1820 - 2x = 11x$$

$$1820 = 13x$$

$$140 = x$$

$$910 - x = 910 - 140 = 770$$

The number of managers needed is 140. The number of workers needed is 770.   ■

Practice Problem 6   Western University has 168 faculty. The university always maintains a student-to-faculty ratio of 21:2. How many students should they enroll to maintain that ratio?   ■

The next example concerns *similar triangles*. These triangles have corresponding angles equal and corresponding sides that are *proportional* (not equal). Similar triangles are frequently used to determine distances that cannot be conveniently measured. For example, in this sketch, x and X are corresponding angles, y and Y are corresponding angles, and s and S are corresponding sides. Hence angle x = angle X, angle y = angle Y, and side s is proportional to side S (again, note that we did not say that side s is equal to side S). So, really, one triangle is just a magnification of the other triangle.

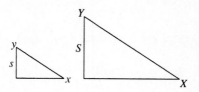

Example 7   A helicopter is hovering to an unknown distance above an 850-foot building. A man watching the helicopter is 500 feet from the base of the building and 11 feet from a flagpole that is 29 feet tall. The man's line of sight to the helicopter is directly above the flagpole as you can see on this sketch. How far above the building is the helicopter? Round your answer to the nearest foot.

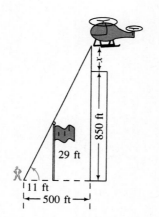

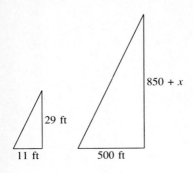

29 ft
11 ft
850 + x
500 ft

Can you see the two triangles in the diagram? For convenience, let's separate them in our next sketch. We want to find the distance x. Again for convenience, let's assume that the flagpole is perfectly vertical (not leaning or bending) and that the building's side is also perfectly vertical. Can you see that we have two similar triangles? The angles at the bases of the triangles are equal. (Why?) It follows, then, the top angles must also be equal. (Remember, the angles of *any* triangle add up to 180°.) The sides of each triangle are proportional, so we can set up our proportion like this:

$$\frac{11}{29} = \frac{500}{850 + x}$$

or like this:

$$\frac{11}{500} = \frac{29}{850 + x}$$

We'll work with the first equation.
The LCD is $29(850 + x)$:

$$29(850 + x)\left[\frac{11}{29}\right] = 29(850 + x)\left[\frac{500}{850 + x}\right]$$

$$11(850 + x) = 29(500)$$

$$9350 + 11x = 14{,}500$$

$$11x = 5150$$

$$x = \frac{5150}{11} = 468.\overline{18}$$

So the helicopter is about 468 feet above the building. ■

Practice Problem 7   Solve the problem in the same way as Example 7 for a man watching 450 feet from the base of a 900-foot building as shown in this figure. This flagpole is 35 feet tall and the man is 10 feet from the flagpole. ■

We will encounter some challenging problems involving similar triangles in Exercises 39 and 40.

EXERCISES 5.6

Solve for the variable indicated.

1. $I = \dfrac{E}{R}$; for R

$IR = E$
$R = \dfrac{E}{I}$

2. $t = \dfrac{d}{r}$; for d

$tr = d$

3. $P = \dfrac{A}{1 + rt}$; for t

$P + Prt = A$
$t = \dfrac{A - P}{Pr}$

4. $\dfrac{1}{f} = \dfrac{1}{a} + \dfrac{1}{b}$; for b

$ab = bf + af$
$b(a - f) = af$
$b = \dfrac{af}{a - f}$

5. $W = \dfrac{ab}{x}$; for x

$Wx = ab$
$x = \dfrac{ab}{W}$

6. $I^2 = \dfrac{P}{R}$; for R

$RI^2 = P$
$R = \dfrac{P}{I^2}$

7. $S = \dfrac{V_1 t + V_2 t}{2}$; for t

$2s = V_1 t + V_2 t$
$t = \dfrac{2S}{V_1 + V_2}$

8. $A = \dfrac{ha + hb}{2}$; for h

$2A = ha + hb$
$\dfrac{2A}{a + b} = h$

9. $\dfrac{P_1 V_1}{T_1} = \dfrac{P_2 V_2}{T_2}$; for T_1

$P_1 V_1 T_2 = P_2 V_2 T_1$
$T_1 = \dfrac{P_1 V_1 T_2}{P_2 V_2}$

10. $F = \dfrac{Gm_1 m_2}{d^2}$; for d^2

$Fd^2 = Gm_1 m_2$
$d^2 = \dfrac{Gm_1 m_2}{F}$

11. $I = \dfrac{nE}{R + nr}$; for n

$IR + Inr = nE$
$n = \dfrac{IR}{E - Ir}$

12. $T = \dfrac{24I}{B + Bn}$; for B

$TB + TBN = 24I$
$B = \dfrac{24I}{T + Tn}$

13. $m = \dfrac{y_2 - y_1}{x_2 - x_1}$; for x_1

$mx_2 - mx_1 = y_2 - y_1$

$x_1 = \dfrac{mx_2 - y_2 + y_1}{m}$

14. $\dfrac{A}{2\pi r} = b + h$; for r

$\dfrac{A}{2\pi(b + h)} = r$

15. $\dfrac{3V}{\pi h} = r^2$; for h

$3V = \pi h r^2$

$\dfrac{3V}{\pi r^2} = h$

16. $E = 1 - \dfrac{T_1}{T_2}$; for T_2

$ET_2 = T_2 - T_1$

$ET_2 - T_2 = -T_1$

$T_2 = \dfrac{-T_1}{E - 1}$

17. $Q = \dfrac{kA(t_1 - t_2)}{L}$; for t_2

$QL = kAt_1 - kAt_2$

$t_2 = \dfrac{kAt_1 - QL}{kA}$

18. $Q = \dfrac{kA(t_1 - t_2)}{L}$; for A

$QL = kAt_1 - kAt_2$

$\dfrac{QL}{kt_1 - kt_2} = A$

19. $\dfrac{V}{V_0} = 1 + b(T - T_0)$; for T

$V = V_0 + bV_0T - bV_0T_0$

$\dfrac{V - V_0 + bV_0T_0}{bV_0} = T$

20. $\dfrac{T_2W}{T_2 - T_1} = q$; for T_2

$T_2W = qT_2 - qT_1$

$T_2 = \dfrac{-qT_1}{W - q}$

21. $d = \dfrac{LR_2}{R_2 + R_1}$; for R_1

$dR_2 + dR_1 = LR_2$

$R_1 = \dfrac{LR_2 - dR_2}{d}$

22. $V = \dfrac{mv}{m + M}$; for m

$Vm + VM = mv$

$VM = mv - Vm$

$\dfrac{VM}{v - V} = m$

In problems 23–40, round your answer to the nearest hundredth.

23. A map scale reads 2 inches = 5 miles. The distance between two cities on the map is 5.5 inches. How many miles apart are the cities?

$\dfrac{2}{5} = \dfrac{5.5}{x}$, $x = 13.75$ miles

24. A blueprint of an engine was drawn with a scale of 3:5. The drawing of an engine part on the blueprint is 15.6 centimeters long. How long is the part?

$\dfrac{3}{5} = \dfrac{15.6}{x}$, $x = 26$ cm

25. A speed of 60 miles per hour (mph) is equivalent to a speed of 88 kilometers per hour (km/h). In parts of Canada the speed limit is 100 km/h. Convert this speed limit to mph.

$\dfrac{60}{88} = \dfrac{x}{100}$, $x \approx 68.18$ mph

26. In Smith Valley a meteorologist found that 140 centimeters of snow melted to 17 centimeters of water. How much water is in 200 centimeters of snow?

$\dfrac{140}{17} = \dfrac{200}{x}$, $x = 24.29$ cm

27. Quality control engineers were checking a sample of 37 new car engines. They found defects in three of the engines. If they sampled 259 engines, how many defective engines would they find? (Assume that the ratio is the same.)

$\dfrac{3}{37} = \dfrac{x}{259}$, $x = 21$ defectives

28. Mr. and Mrs. McDonald used 12 pounds of hamburger to feed seven people with their hot barbecue recipe. The barbecue was such a success that the McDonalds scheduled another one and told their seven guests to each bring five friends. How many pounds of hamburger will they need?

$\dfrac{12}{7} = \dfrac{x}{35}$, $x = 60$ lbs

29. Fifty deer were captured and tagged by wildlife officials. The deer were then released to roam with the general deer population of the wildlife refuge. Several months later, 80 deer were captured and 16 had tags. Estimate the number of deer in the wildlife refuge.

$\dfrac{50}{x} = \dfrac{16}{80}$, $x = 250$ deer

30. Forty small-mouth bass were caught from a lake and marked by department of fisheries personnel. They were then put back in the lake. Several months later, 70 fish were caught from the same lake and 8 were marked. Estimate the number of small-mouth bass in the lake.

$\dfrac{40}{x} = \dfrac{8}{70}$, $x = 350$ bass

31. A boat can travel 108 kilometers on 12 liters of gas. How far can it go on 20 liters of gas?

$\dfrac{108}{12} = \dfrac{x}{20}$, $x = 180$ km

32. A metal beam 5.5 meters long weighs 30.6 kilograms. How much will a similar beam weigh if it were 10.0 meters long?

$\dfrac{5.5}{30.6} = \dfrac{10}{x}$, $x \approx 55.64$ kg

33. A photographer is making prints from negatives that are 3 inches by 4 inches. The largest side of the print is 14 inches. How long is the shortest side?

$\frac{3}{4} = \frac{x}{14}$, $x = 10.5$ in.

34. A farmer needed a larger pasture, so he cut down trees around his old pasture, which measured 500 yards by 800 yards. The larger pasture has the *same ratio* of width to length. The new width is 1200 yards. What is the new length?

$\frac{500}{800} = \frac{1200}{x}$, $x = 1920$ yds

35. A radio receiver weighing 40 kilograms on earth weighs only 6.4 kilograms on the moon. How much does a receiver weigh on earth if it weighs 20 kilograms on the moon?

$\frac{40}{6.4} = \frac{x}{20}$, $x = 125$ kg

36. At a depth of 120 feet, the water pressure on a submarine is 52 pounds per square inch. What is the pressure at 300 feet below the surface?

$\frac{52}{120} = \frac{x}{300}$, $x = 130$ lbs

37. The ratio of detectives to patrol officers at Center City is 2:9. The police force has 187 detectives and patrolmen. How many are detectives? How many are patrol officers?

$\frac{2}{9} = \frac{x}{187 - x}$
$x = 34$ detectives, $187 - x = 153$ officers

38. A city auto dealer took a poll to find out how many people preferred station wagons. The ratio of those preferring station wagons to those preferring sedans was 3:11. If the dealer wanted to order 224 sedans and station wagons, how many of each should he order?

$\frac{3}{11} = \frac{x}{224 - x}$
$x = 48$ station wagons, $224 - x = 176$ sedans

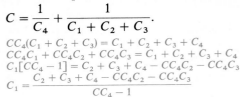

To Think About

To find the width of a river, a hiking club laid out a triangular pattern of measurements. See the figure. Use your knowledge of similar triangles to solve problems 39 and 40.

39. If the observer stands at point O, then $a = 2$ feet, $b = 5$ feet, and $c = 116$ feet. What is the width of the river?

$\frac{2}{5} = \frac{116}{8 + x}$, $x = 282'$

40. What is the width of the river if $a = 3$ feet, $b = 8$ feet, and $c = 297$ feet?

$\frac{3}{8} = \frac{297}{8 + x}$, $x = 784'$

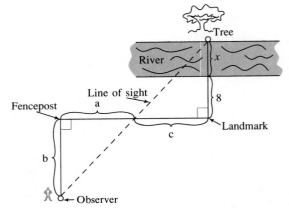

41. A carpenter has to make a frame for a picture that is 22.5 feet by 34.5 feet. The frame must maintain the same ratio and have an *outside* perimeter of 120 feet. What must be the dimensions of the frame?

$\frac{22.5}{34.5} = \frac{x}{60 - x}$
$x \approx 23.68'$
$60 - x \approx 36.32'$

42. Solve for C_1 in terms of the other variables:

$$C = \frac{1}{C_4} + \frac{1}{C_1 + C_2 + C_3}.$$

$CC_4(C_1 + C_2 + C_3) = C_1 + C_2 + C_3 + C_4$
$CC_4C_1 + CC_4C_2 + CC_4C_3 = C_1 + C_2 + C_3 + C_4$
$C_1[CC_4 - 1] = C_2 + C_3 + C_4 - CC_4C_2 - CC_4C_3$
$C_1 = \dfrac{C_2 + C_3 + C_4 - CC_4C_2 - CC_4C_3}{CC_4 - 1}$

Cumulative Review Problems

Factor completely.

43. $8x^2 + 6x - 3$
   Prime

44. $x^2 - 2x - 120$
   $(x - 12)(x + 10)$

45. $25x^2 - 90xy + 81y^2$
   $(5x - 9y)^2$

46. $5yx^2 - 20y$
   $5y(x + 2)(x - 2)$

Calculator Problems

Round your answer to four decimal places.

47. Solve for T: $\dfrac{1.98V}{1.96V_0} = 0.983 + 5.936(T - T_0)$

$T = T_0 + 0.1702\left(\dfrac{V}{V_0}\right) - 0.1656$

48. The scale on a maritime map is 2 centimeters = 13.62 nautical miles. The ship's captain lays a course that measures 13.65 centimeters. How many nautical miles does he plan to travel?

92.9565 nautical miles

For Extra Practice Exercises, turn to page 278.

Solutions to Odd-Numbered Practice Problems

1. Solve for a: $B = \dfrac{2x}{5 - 3a}$.

$(5 - 3a)B = (5 - 3a)\left[\dfrac{2x}{5 - 3a}\right]$ Multiplying each side by $(5 - 3a)$.

$5B - 3aB = 2x$ Simplifying.

$-3aB = 2x - 5B$ Adding $-5B$ to each side.

$\dfrac{-3aB}{-3B} = \dfrac{2x - 5B}{-3B}$ Dividing each side by $-3B$.

$a = -\dfrac{2x - 5B}{3B}$ or $\dfrac{-2x + 5B}{3B}$

3. Solve for q: $H = \dfrac{2bqx}{y^2}$.

$y^2(H) = y^2\left[\dfrac{2bqx}{y^2}\right]$ Multiplying each side by y^2

$y^2H = 2bqx$ Simplifying.

$\dfrac{y^2H}{2bx} = q$ Dividing each side by $2bx$.

5. Let $x =$ the number of milliliters of acid in the larger solution.

$$\dfrac{13}{37} = \dfrac{x}{296}$$

The LCD is $37 \cdot 296$, which we leave in factored form.

$$37 \cdot 296\left[\dfrac{13}{37}\right] = 37 \cdot 296\left[\dfrac{x}{296}\right]$$

$$13 \cdot 296 = 37x$$

$$3848 = 37x$$

$$104 = x$$

The larger solution has 104 milliliters of acid.

7. The two similiar triangles are shown in the figure.

$$\dfrac{10}{35} = \dfrac{450}{900 + x}$$

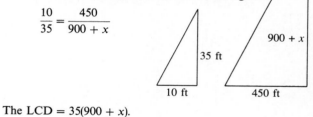

The LCD = $35(900 + x)$.

$$35(900 + x)\left[\dfrac{10}{35}\right] = 35(900 + x)\left[\dfrac{450}{900 + x}\right]$$

$$10(900 + x) = 35(450)$$

$$9000 + 10x = 15{,}750$$

$$10x = 6750$$

$$x = 675$$

The helicopter is about 675 feet over the building.

Answers to Even-Numbered Practice Problems

2. $R = \dfrac{R_1R_2}{R_2 + R_1}$ **4.** The ratio of perfect parts to defective parts is $\dfrac{23}{2}$ or $23:2$.   **6.** They should enroll 1764 students.

EXTRA PRACTICE: EXERCISES

Section 5.1

Simplify completely.

1. $\dfrac{30y + 10}{10y + 15}$ $\dfrac{2(3y + 1)}{2y + 3}$

2. $\dfrac{5x + 25}{40x - 15}$ $\dfrac{x + 5}{8x - 3}$

5. $\dfrac{18a^3b}{75ab^4}$ $\dfrac{6a^2}{25b^3}$

6. $\dfrac{-12ab^4}{18a^5b^5}$ $\dfrac{-2}{3a^4b}$

3. $\dfrac{2x^2 + x - 3}{x^2 + 7x - 8}$ $\dfrac{2x + 3}{x + 8}$

4. $\dfrac{3x^2 + 23x - 8}{x^2 + 3x - 40}$ $\dfrac{3x - 1}{x - 5}$

7. $\dfrac{6y^2 - 11y + 3}{4y^2 - 12y + 9}$ $\dfrac{3y - 1}{2y - 3}$

8. $\dfrac{y^2 - 3y}{10y - 30}$ $\dfrac{y}{10}$

9. $\dfrac{2x^2-32}{8x-32}$ $\dfrac{x+4}{4}$

10. $\dfrac{3x^2-5x+2}{3x^2+4x-4}$ $\dfrac{x-1}{x+2}$

21. $\dfrac{x^2-4}{x^2-x-6}$ $\dfrac{x-2}{x-3}$

22. $\dfrac{2x^2-13x+15}{4x^2-9}$ $\dfrac{x-5}{2x+3}$

11. $\dfrac{x^3-x^2+2x-2}{3x^2-2x-1}$ $\dfrac{x^2+2}{3x+1}$

12. $\dfrac{2x^3-3x^2+2x-3}{4x^2-2x-6}$

23. $\dfrac{2x^2-5x-3}{10x^2+5x}$ $\dfrac{x-3}{5x}$

24. $\dfrac{12x^3+5x^2-2x}{3x^4-4x^3-4x^2}$ $\dfrac{4x-1}{x(x-2)}$

13. $\dfrac{a^4-a^2b^2}{a^3-2a^2b+ab^2}$ $\dfrac{a(a+b)}{a-b}$

14. $\dfrac{9x^2y^2-6xy^2+y^2}{12x^2y^2-4xy^2}$ $\dfrac{3x-1}{4x}$

25. $\dfrac{a^2-ac+ab-bc}{a^2+ac+ab+bc}$ $\dfrac{a-c}{a+c}$

26. $\dfrac{(a+b)^2-1}{a^2c+abc+ac}$ $\dfrac{a+b-1}{ac}$

15. $\dfrac{18+3x-3x^2}{2x^4-8x^2}$ $\dfrac{3(3-x)}{2x^2(x-2)}$

16. $\dfrac{4x^2-22x+24}{9x^2-6x^3}$ $\dfrac{-2(x-4)}{3x^2}$

27. $\dfrac{2a^2b^2-8b^4}{4a^3b-32b^4}$

28. $\dfrac{a^3+ax^2}{4a^3x+4ax^3}$ $\dfrac{1}{4x}$

17. $\dfrac{15x^2}{8x-4(3+2x)}$ $-\dfrac{5x^2}{4}$

18. $\dfrac{(16x^2-9)(4x^2+x-3)}{(4x-3)^2(16x^2+24x+9)}$

29. $\dfrac{x^3+8y^3}{x^2+2xy}$ $\dfrac{x^2-2xy+4y^2}{x}$

30. $\dfrac{x^3+3x^2y-xy^2+xy}{x^2+x}$

19. $\dfrac{ax}{ax+ay}$ $\dfrac{x}{x+y}$

20. $\dfrac{x^2-4x+3}{3-x}$ $-(x-1)$

31. $\dfrac{8x^3-125y^3}{4x^3-25xy^2}$ $\dfrac{4x^2+10xy+25y^2}{x(2x+5y)}$

12. $\dfrac{x^2+1}{2(x+1)}$ 18. $\dfrac{x+1}{4x+3}$

27. $\dfrac{b(a+2b)}{2(a^2+2ab+4b^2)}$

30. $\dfrac{x^2+3xy-y^2+y}{x+1}$

Section 5.2

Simplify.

1. $\dfrac{x^2-9}{2x+6}\cdot\dfrac{4x^2}{xy-3y}$ $\dfrac{2x^2}{y}$

2. $\dfrac{5x^2+5x}{4x-4}\cdot\dfrac{12x-12}{x^4}$ $\dfrac{15(x+1)}{x^3}$

3. $\dfrac{y^2+y-20}{-y-5}\cdot\dfrac{3y+12}{y^2-16}$ -3

4. $\dfrac{8x^2y}{15xy^3}\cdot\dfrac{25y}{16x^2}$ $\dfrac{5}{6xy}$

5. $\dfrac{x^2-y^2}{4x^2+4xy+y^2}\cdot\dfrac{2x^2-xy-y^2}{x^2+2xy+y^2}$ $\dfrac{(x-y)^2}{(2x+y)(x+y)}$

6. $\dfrac{3x^2-4x-4}{x^2-4}\cdot\dfrac{27-x^3}{6+7x-3x^2}$ $\dfrac{9+3x+x^2}{x+2}$

7. $\dfrac{y^2+y-12}{3y^2+12y}\div\dfrac{4xy^2-12xy}{6y^2}$ $\dfrac{1}{2x}$

8. $\dfrac{2y^2+4y}{12xy^2}\div\dfrac{2y^2+12y+16}{18y}$ $\dfrac{3}{2x(y+4)}$

9. $\dfrac{3x^2+27x+42}{x^2+2x-35}\div(2x+4)$ $\dfrac{3}{2(x-5)}$

10. $\dfrac{2a^4+a^3b-a^2b^2}{4a^2-b^2}\div(3a^2b+3ab^2)$ $\dfrac{a}{3b(2a+b)}$

11. $\dfrac{4x+6}{2x^2+2}\cdot\dfrac{2x^4+2x^2}{5x+10}\cdot\dfrac{3x^2-3}{18x+27}$ $\dfrac{2x^2(x+1)(x-1)}{15(x+2)}$

12. $\dfrac{x^2-25}{3x^2+11x+6}\cdot\dfrac{5x^2+16x+3}{5x^2-24x-5}\cdot\dfrac{3x^2+17x+10}{x^2+10x+25}$ 1

13. $\dfrac{3x^2-5xy-2y^2}{3x-12y}\div\dfrac{3x^2+13xy+4y^2}{16y^2-x^2}$ $-\dfrac{x-2y}{3}$

14. $\dfrac{15+7x-2x^2}{(2x+8)^2}\div\dfrac{4xy+16y}{(2x-10)^2}$ $-\dfrac{(x-5)^3(2x+3)}{4y(x+4)^3}$

15. $\dfrac{10x^2y}{x^2-7xy+10y^2}\cdot\dfrac{2x^2+6xy-20y^2}{25x^2y^2}\cdot\dfrac{6xy-24y^2}{x^2y+xy^2-20y^3}$ $\dfrac{24}{5y(x-5y)}$

16. $\dfrac{5x+5}{2x-8}\cdot\dfrac{8+6x-2x^2}{x^2-x-2}\cdot\dfrac{2x^4-10x^3+12x^2}{6+4x-2x^2}$ $5x^2$

17. $\dfrac{x^2+3x-4}{x^2-1}\div\dfrac{x^2-16}{x^2+x}$ $\dfrac{x}{x-4}$

18. $\dfrac{2y+1}{3x}\div(8y+4)$ $\dfrac{1}{12x}$

19. $\dfrac{8a^3-1}{9a^2-12a+4}\cdot\dfrac{9a^2-4}{2a-1}\cdot\left(1-\dfrac{4}{3a+2}\right)$ $4a^2+2a+1$

20. $\dfrac{a-5}{a^2+2a+4}\cdot\dfrac{a^4-8a}{a^2-4a+5}\div\dfrac{a^3-a^2-2a}{a^2+2a+1}$ 1

21. $\dfrac{x^2+2x}{x^2-3x}\cdot\dfrac{x^2-x-6}{x^2+4x+4}$ 1

22. $\dfrac{2x^2+x-15}{3x^2-x-2}\cdot\dfrac{3x^2-7x-6}{2x^2-3x-5}$ $\dfrac{(x+3)(x-3)}{(x+1)(x-1)}$

23. $\dfrac{x^3+y^3}{x^2-y^2}\cdot\dfrac{x^2-xy}{x^2-xy+y^2}$ x

24. $\dfrac{x^6-y^6}{x^3+x^2y+xy^2}\cdot\dfrac{3x^2}{x^4+xy^3}$ $3(x-y)$

25. $\dfrac{3x-12}{2x^2-7x+6}\cdot\dfrac{6x^2-5x-6}{3x^2-10x-8}$ $\dfrac{3}{x-2}$

26. $\left(R^2+\dfrac{1}{R^2}+2\right)\div\left(R+\dfrac{1}{R}\right)$ $\dfrac{R^2+1}{R}$

27. $\dfrac{1}{2ab}\cdot\dfrac{4a}{1}\cdot\dfrac{a^4-b^4}{2a+2b}\cdot\dfrac{a-b}{a^2+b^2}$ $\dfrac{(a-b)^2}{b}$

Section 5.3

List the LCD only for the fractions given.

1. $\dfrac{1}{a^3b},\dfrac{3}{2ab^2}$ $2a^3b^2$

2. $\dfrac{1}{2x},\dfrac{1}{4x^2+2xy}$ $2x(2x+y)$

3. $\dfrac{5}{x^2+7x+12},\dfrac{7}{2x^2-18}$ $2(x+4)(x+3)(x-3)$

4. $\dfrac{4}{2x^2-3x-2},\dfrac{3}{6x^2+x-1}$ $(2x+1)(x-2)(3x-1)$

5. $\dfrac{1}{(2x+3)^3(5x+1)},\dfrac{2}{10x^2+17x+3}$ $(5x+1)(2x+3)^3$

6. $\dfrac{1}{x^2+12x+20},\dfrac{3}{25-x^2}$ $(x+10)(x+2)(5-x)(5+x)$

Add or subtract. Be sure to simplify your answer.

7. $\dfrac{5}{3x+2} + \dfrac{2}{3x}$ $\dfrac{21x+4}{3x(3x+2)}$

8. $\dfrac{7}{x+2y} + \dfrac{3}{2y}$ $\dfrac{20y+3x}{2y(x+2y)}$

9. $\dfrac{8x}{x^2-25} + \dfrac{3}{5x+10}$ $\dfrac{43x^2+80x-75}{5(x+2)(x-5)(x+5)}$

10. $\dfrac{8}{5x-5} + \dfrac{2}{1-x}$ $\dfrac{-2}{5(x-1)}$

11. $\dfrac{y}{y^2-5y+6} + \dfrac{7}{y-2}$ $\dfrac{8y-21}{(y-2)(y-3)}$

12. $\dfrac{3y+1}{y-2} + \dfrac{2y+1}{y+1}$ $\dfrac{5y^2+y-1}{(y-2)(y+1)}$

13. $\dfrac{4x+12}{x^2+7x+12} - \dfrac{x+3}{x^2+4x+3}$ $\dfrac{3x}{(x+4)(x+1)}$

14. $\dfrac{3}{y^2-4} - \dfrac{1}{y^2+4y+4}$ $\dfrac{2y+8}{(y-2)(y+2)^2}$

15. $\dfrac{3}{x} + \dfrac{2}{x+2} - \dfrac{1}{x^2+7x+10}$ $\dfrac{5(x^2+6x+6)}{x(x+2)(x+5)}$

16. $\dfrac{5}{x-3} + \dfrac{1}{x} - \dfrac{2}{x^2-9}$ $\dfrac{6x^2+13x-9}{x(x+3)(x-3)}$

17. $x+3 - \dfrac{2x-3}{2x+1}$ $\dfrac{2x^2+5x+6}{2x+1}$

18. $3y-4 + \dfrac{2-5y}{y-3}$ $\dfrac{3y^2-18y+14}{y-3}$

19. $\dfrac{a-1}{2a^2+3a-2} + \dfrac{a}{2a^2-?a+1}$ $\dfrac{2a^2+1}{(2a-1)(a+2)(a-1)}$

20. $\dfrac{2a-5}{2a^2-9a+4} + \dfrac{a-2}{2a^2+5a-3}$ $\dfrac{3a^2-5a-7}{(2a-1)(a-4)(a+3)}$

21. $\dfrac{a}{a-b} + \dfrac{b}{a-b} + \dfrac{a^2+b^2}{b^2-a^2}$ $\dfrac{2ab}{a^2-b^2}$

22. $\dfrac{b-c}{bc} - \dfrac{a-c}{ac}$ $\dfrac{b-a}{ab}$

23. $\dfrac{3a}{5} + \dfrac{b}{2} - 3 + \dfrac{1}{b}$ $\dfrac{6ab+5b^2-30b+10}{10b}$

24. $\dfrac{a-b}{2(a+b)} + \dfrac{a^2+b^2}{a^2-b^2} + \dfrac{a}{b-a}$ $\dfrac{a-3b}{2(a+b)}$

25. $\dfrac{a+33}{a^2-9} - \dfrac{6}{a-3} + \dfrac{10}{a+3}$ $\dfrac{5}{a+3}$

26. $\dfrac{5(x-3)}{x^2-x-2} - \dfrac{2(x+2)}{x^2+4x+3} - \dfrac{x-1}{6-x-x^2}$ $\dfrac{4x^2-38}{(x-2)(x+1)(x+3)}$

27. $\dfrac{2a-3b}{1} - \dfrac{4a^2+9b^2}{2a+3b}$ $\dfrac{-18b^2}{2a+3b}$

28. $\dfrac{x+y}{x-y} - \dfrac{x-y}{x+y}$ $\dfrac{4xy}{(x+y)(x+y)}$

29. $\dfrac{4}{a+b} - \dfrac{3}{a-b} + \dfrac{2a}{a^2-b^2}$ $\dfrac{3a-7b}{(a+b)(a-b)}$

30. $\dfrac{1}{a+3} + \dfrac{7}{a^2-a-12} + \dfrac{a-3}{a-4}$ $\dfrac{a-2}{a-4}$

31. $\dfrac{a}{x} + \dfrac{c}{xy} - \dfrac{b}{y}$ $\dfrac{ay+c-bx}{xy}$

32. $\dfrac{4}{5-x} + \dfrac{3}{x+5} - \dfrac{7x+2}{x^2-25}$ $\dfrac{-8x-37}{(x+5)(x-5)}$

33. $\dfrac{x+1}{x+5} + \dfrac{x-2}{x-3} - \dfrac{2x^2+x-13}{x^2+2x-15}$ 0

Section 5.4

Simplify each complex fraction.

1. $\dfrac{\dfrac{5}{ab^2}}{\dfrac{3}{a}+\dfrac{2}{b}}$ $\dfrac{5}{b(2a+3b)}$

2. $\dfrac{\dfrac{7}{xy}+\dfrac{2}{y}}{\dfrac{3}{x^2y^2}}$ $\dfrac{xy(7+2x)}{3}$

3. $\dfrac{\dfrac{y-3}{2y^2-18}}{y}$ $\dfrac{1}{2y(y+3)}$

4. $\dfrac{\dfrac{x^2-7x+12}{x+5}}{x-3}$ $\dfrac{x-4}{x+5}$

5. $\dfrac{4-\dfrac{1}{y+2}}{2+\dfrac{3}{y+2}}$ $\dfrac{4y+7}{2y+7}$

6. $\dfrac{5+\dfrac{5}{x}}{3-\dfrac{3}{x}}$ $\dfrac{5(x+1)}{3(x-1)}$

7. $\dfrac{\dfrac{2}{3x}+\dfrac{1}{10x}}{\dfrac{3}{2}+\dfrac{7}{4x}}$ $\dfrac{46}{90x+105}$

8. $\dfrac{\dfrac{2}{x-3}+\dfrac{1}{x^2-9}}{\dfrac{5}{x+3}}$ $\dfrac{2x+7}{5(x-3)}$

9. $\dfrac{\dfrac{a}{a+3}-\dfrac{1}{a}}{a-\dfrac{1}{a+3}}$ $\dfrac{a^2-a-3}{a^3+3a^2-a}$

10. $\dfrac{\dfrac{1}{b+1}+1}{\dfrac{2}{b+1}+\dfrac{1}{b}}$ $\dfrac{b(b+2)}{3b+1}$

11. $\dfrac{1+\dfrac{4}{y^2-4}}{\dfrac{1}{y+2}-\dfrac{1}{y-2}}$ $-\dfrac{y^2}{4}$

12. $\dfrac{\dfrac{x}{x^3+y^3}}{\dfrac{1}{x+y}+\dfrac{x-y}{x^2-xy+y^2}}$ $\dfrac{1}{2x-y}$

13. $\dfrac{\dfrac{2}{2x-3}+\dfrac{1}{4x^2-12x+9}}{\dfrac{5}{4x-6}+2}$ $\dfrac{2(4x-5)}{(8x-7)(2x-3)}$

14. $2+\dfrac{3}{4+\dfrac{1}{x}}$ $\dfrac{11x+2}{4x+1}$

15. $\dfrac{m-\dfrac{3m}{x}}{x-\dfrac{x}{m}}$ $\dfrac{m^2(x-3)}{x^2(m-1)}$

16. $\dfrac{\dfrac{x+y}{y}-\dfrac{x+y}{x}}{\dfrac{1}{y}-\dfrac{1}{x}}$ $x+y$

17. $\dfrac{1+\dfrac{3}{x}}{1-\dfrac{9}{x^2}}$ $\dfrac{x}{x-3}$

18. $\dfrac{\dfrac{15}{x}-2+x}{1-\dfrac{5}{x}}$ $\dfrac{x^2-2x+15}{x-5}$

19. $\dfrac{\dfrac{1}{x}+\dfrac{4}{x^2}+\dfrac{4}{x^3}}{1+\dfrac{5}{x}+\dfrac{6}{x^2}}$ $\dfrac{x+2}{x(x+3)}$

20. $\dfrac{\dfrac{x-5}{2}-7+\dfrac{24}{x}}{\dfrac{9-3x}{x}}$ $\dfrac{16-x}{6}$

21. $\dfrac{\dfrac{a}{1+a}+\dfrac{1-a}{a}}{\dfrac{a}{a+1}-\dfrac{1-a}{a}}$ $\dfrac{1}{2a^2-1}$

24. $\dfrac{2x-3}{4x-9+\dfrac{12}{2x+1}}$ $\dfrac{2x+1}{4x-1}$

22. $\dfrac{1-\dfrac{x-7}{x^2-9}}{x+\dfrac{4x-6}{x-3}}$ $\dfrac{x+1}{(x+3)^2}$

23. $\dfrac{\dfrac{x+y}{y}-\dfrac{x+y}{x}}{\dfrac{1}{y}-\dfrac{1}{x}}$ $x+y$

25. $\dfrac{\dfrac{1}{x+3y}+\dfrac{2}{x-3y}+\dfrac{9}{3y-x}}{\dfrac{1}{9y^2-x^2}}$ $6x+24y$

Section 5.5

Solve for the variable and check your solution. If there is no solution, say so.

1. $\dfrac{9}{x}=\dfrac{3}{x-2}$ $x=3$

2. $\dfrac{3}{2x}+\dfrac{7}{6}=\dfrac{5}{x}$ $x=3$

3. $\dfrac{3}{y}-\dfrac{2}{y-1}=\dfrac{1}{2y}$ $y=5$

4. $\dfrac{y+2}{y-1}=\dfrac{y+1}{y+2}$ $y=-\dfrac{5}{4}$

5. $4-\dfrac{2}{x-2}=\dfrac{2x-6}{x-2}$ No sol.

6. $\dfrac{2}{3x-3}+\dfrac{5}{12}=\dfrac{-1}{x-1}$ $x=-3$

7. $\dfrac{3}{x^2-9}-\dfrac{2}{x+3}=\dfrac{1}{x-3}$ $x=2$

8. $\dfrac{y^2-3}{y^2+y-12}+\dfrac{5}{y+4}=\dfrac{y}{y-3}$ $y=18$

9. $\dfrac{2x-14}{x^2+3x-28}+\dfrac{x-2}{x-4}=\dfrac{x+3}{x+7}$ $x=2$

10. $\dfrac{4-y}{2y+10}=\dfrac{3}{y+5}-1$ $y=-8$

11. $\dfrac{5}{2}-\dfrac{2y+7}{y+6}=3$ $y=-4$

12. $\dfrac{2y-1}{3y}-\dfrac{1}{9y}=\dfrac{y+2}{y}-\dfrac{1}{9}$ $y=-11$

13. $\dfrac{4z^2+36}{z^2-9}+\dfrac{12}{z-3}=\dfrac{4z}{z+3}$ No solution

14. $2-\dfrac{1}{3z-2}=\dfrac{2z}{z+1}$ $z=1$

15. $\dfrac{2x}{x+3}+\dfrac{x}{x-5}-3=\dfrac{1}{2x-10}$ $x=29$

16. $\dfrac{6r-7}{9r+6}-\dfrac{5r+5}{12r+8}=\dfrac{1}{12}$ $r=\dfrac{15}{2}$

17. $\dfrac{10x+17}{18}-\dfrac{5x-2}{9}=\dfrac{12x-9}{11x-8}$ $x=\dfrac{2}{5}$

18. $\dfrac{x^3+2}{x+1}-\dfrac{x^3-2}{x-1}=\dfrac{10}{x^2-1}-2x$ $x=5$

19. $\dfrac{\dfrac{21}{x}-1}{9}+\dfrac{\dfrac{100}{x}+\dfrac{5}{3}}{15}=\dfrac{1+\dfrac{18}{x}}{5}+\dfrac{17+\dfrac{3}{x}}{3}$ $x=\dfrac{3}{4}$

20. $\dfrac{3}{x+1}=\dfrac{2}{x+2}+\dfrac{1}{x-2}$ $x=-10$

21. $\dfrac{4s}{s^2-9}+\dfrac{1}{3-s}=\dfrac{5}{s+3}$ $s=6$

22. $\dfrac{x+4}{2x+4}-\dfrac{x+3}{3x+6}=\dfrac{5}{6}$ $x=-1$

23. $\dfrac{2y^2+7}{(y+3)(y-2)}=\dfrac{2y^2-8y-1}{(y+3)(y-2)}$ $y=-1$

24. $\dfrac{6x+8}{2x+1}-\dfrac{2x+38}{x+12}=1$ $x=2$

25. $\dfrac{5x+3}{2x-3}=\dfrac{5x+7}{2x}$ $x=-3$

26. $\dfrac{7x-11}{x-11}-\dfrac{4x-2}{x+1}=3$ $x=0$

27. $\dfrac{20x^2}{4x-3}=5x+3$ $x=-3$

Section 5.6

Solve for the variable indicated.

1. $C=\dfrac{E}{R+r}$; for r $r=\dfrac{E-CR}{C}$

2. $\dfrac{N}{V}=\dfrac{m}{M+m}$; for m $m=\dfrac{NM}{V-N}$

3. $\dfrac{1}{A}+\dfrac{1}{B}=\dfrac{1}{C}$; for B $B=\dfrac{AC}{A-C}$

4. $F=\dfrac{mV^2}{gr}$; for r $r=\dfrac{mV^2}{Fg}$

5. $\dfrac{S-P}{Pr}=t$; for P $P=\dfrac{S}{rt+1}$

6. $\dfrac{E-Ir}{I}=R$; for E $E=RI+Ir$

7. $m=\dfrac{y-y_0}{x-x_0}$; for y $y=mx-mx_0+y_0$

8. $\dfrac{P_1V_1}{T_1}=\dfrac{P_2V_2}{T_2}$; for V_1 $V_1=\dfrac{T_1P_2V_2}{P_1T_2}$

9. $V=C\left(1-\dfrac{N}{T}\right)$; for T $T=\dfrac{CN}{C-V}$

10. $K=\dfrac{1}{1-m-mt}$; for t $t=\dfrac{K-Km-1}{Km}$

11. $Q=\dfrac{kA(t_1-t_2)}{L}$; for A $A=\dfrac{QL}{kt_1-kt_2}$

12. $\dfrac{T_2w}{T_2-T_1}=q$; for T_1 $T_1=\dfrac{qT_2-T_2w}{q}$

13. $\dfrac{V}{V_0}=1+b(T-T_0)$; for b $b=\dfrac{V-V_0}{V_0T-V_0T_0}$

14. $I=\dfrac{nE}{R+nr}$; for n $n=\dfrac{IR}{E-Ir}$

15. $S=\dfrac{H}{mt_1-mt_2}$; for t_1 $t_1=\dfrac{H+Smt_2}{Sm}$

16. $r=\dfrac{(x-x_1)(y-y_1)}{(n-1)S_1S_2}$; for x $x=\dfrac{(rn-r)S_1S_2+x_1y-x_1y_1}{y-y_1}$

17. $S = \dfrac{rl - a}{r - 1}$; for r $r = \dfrac{S - a}{S - l}$

18. $\dfrac{w_1}{w_2} = \dfrac{l_2}{l_1}$; for l_1 $l_1 = \dfrac{w_2 l_2}{w_1}$

19. $C = \dfrac{em}{R + nr}$; for R $R = \dfrac{em - Cnr}{C}$

20. $\dfrac{c^2 - x^2}{nx} + \dfrac{n^2}{cx} = \dfrac{a}{c}$; for a $a = \dfrac{c^3 - cx^2 + n^3}{nx}$

21. $\dfrac{5}{x - a} = 2$; for x $x = \dfrac{2a + 5}{2}$

22. $\dfrac{3 - x}{5 - x} = \dfrac{h}{k}$; for x $x = \dfrac{5h - 3k}{h - k}$

23. $\dfrac{6}{x - h} = \dfrac{5}{h - k}$; for x $x = \dfrac{11h - 6k}{5}$

24. $k(hy + 2h + k) = h^2(y - 1)$; for y $y = \dfrac{2hk + k^2 + h^2}{h^2 - kh}$

Set up a proportion and use it to find the desired quantity. If necessary, round your answer to the nearest hundredth.

25. A car travels 150 miles on 4 gallons of gas. How far would it travel on 6 gallons of gas?   225 miles

26. A support timber that is 4 feet long weighs 25 pounds. How much would the same type of support timber weigh that was 7 feet long?   43.75 lbs

27. There are 39.37 inches in 1 meter. How many inches are in 20 meters? How many meters are in 100 inches?

28. There is 0.62 mile in 1 kilometer. How many miles are in 15 kilometers? How many kilometers are in 12 miles?

29. If 210 cups of coffee can be made from 6 pounds of coffee, how many cups can be made from 10 pounds of coffee?
350 cups

27. 787.4 in., 2.54 meters   **28.** 9.3 miles, 19.35 km

30. A small engine uses an oil to gas mixture of 4 pints of oil for every 11 gallons of gas. How many gallons of gas should be mixed with 23 pints of oil?   63.25 gal.

31. $\dfrac{3}{4}$ inch on a map represents a distance of 20 miles. How long a distance is represented by $7\dfrac{1}{2}$ inches on the same map?   200 miles

32. An enlargement is made whose longest side is 21 inches. The colored slide from which it is made measures 35 millimeters by 23 millimeters. What is the length of the shortest side of the enlargement?   13.8 in.

33. The ratio of defective parts to nondefective parts at an appliance factory is 2:33. How many defective parts should be expected in a shipment of 385 parts?   22

34. A steel transmission tower needs a ratio of above-ground distance to below-ground distance of 29:2. How many feet above ground should the tower be if its total length (including the below-ground structure) is 372 feet?   348 ft

35. The three angles of a triangle have a ratio of 1:2:3. Find the angles.   30°, 60°, 90°

36. Find two numbers in the ratio of 1:3 whose sum is 360.

37. If 14 fish feed 42 people, how many fish would feed 210 people?   70

38. If an 80-foot tree casts a shadow of 60 feet, how long a shadow would the 50-foot tree beside it cast at the same time?   37.5 ft

39. If P oranges cost C cents, how many oranges (in terms of P, C, and D) can I buy for D dollars? $\dfrac{100PD}{C}$

36. 90, 270

CHAPTER ORGANIZER

Topic	Procedure	Examples
Simplifying fractions where numerator and denominator are polynomials, p. 245	1. Factor the numerator and denominator, if possible. 2. Any *factor* that is common to both numerator and denominator can be divided out. This is an application of the basic rule of fractions. *Basic rule of fractions:* For any polynomials a, b, c (where $b \neq 0$ and $c \neq 0$), $$\dfrac{ac}{bc} = \dfrac{a}{b}$$	Simplify: $\dfrac{6x^2 - 14x + 4}{6x^2 - 20x + 6}$. $\dfrac{2(3x^2 - 7x + 2)}{2(3x^2 - 10x + 3)} = \dfrac{2(3x - 1)(x - 2)}{2(3x - 1)(x - 3)} = \dfrac{x - 2}{x - 3}$
Multiplying fractional algebraic expressions, p. 249	1. Factor all numerators and denominators, if possible. 2. Any *factor* that is common to a numerator of one factor and the denominator of the same fraction or any fraction that is multiplied by it can be divided out. 3. Write the indicated product of the remaining factors in the numerator. Write the indicated product of the remaining factors in the denominator. $$\dfrac{a}{b} \cdot \dfrac{c}{d} = \dfrac{ac}{bd}$$	Multiply: $\dfrac{x^2 - 4x}{6x - 12} \cdot \dfrac{3x^2 - 6x}{x^3 + 3x^2}$. $\dfrac{x(x - 4)}{6(x - 2)} \cdot \dfrac{3x(x - 2)}{x^2(x + 3)} = \dfrac{x - 4}{2(x + 3)}$ or $\dfrac{x - 4}{2x + 6}$

Topic	Procedure	Examples
Dividing fractional algebraic expressions, p. 250	**1.** Invert the second fraction and multiply it by the first fraction. $$\frac{a}{b} \div \frac{c}{d} = \frac{a}{b} \cdot \frac{d}{c}$$ **2.** Apply the steps for multiplying fractional algebraic expressions.	Divide: $\dfrac{6x^2 - 5x - 6}{24x^2 + 13x - 2} \div \dfrac{4x^2 + x - 3}{8x^2 + 7x - 1}$. $$\frac{6x^2 - 5x - 6}{24x^2 + 13x - 2} \cdot \frac{8x^2 + 7x - 1}{4x^2 + x - 3}$$ $$= \frac{(3x+2)(2x-3)}{(3x+2)(8x-1)} \cdot \frac{(8x-1)(x+1)}{(x+1)(4x-3)} = \frac{2x-3}{4x-3}$$
Adding fractional algebraic expressions, p. 252	**1.** If all fractions have a common denominator, add the numerators and place the result over the common denominator. $$\frac{a}{c} + \frac{b}{c} = \frac{a+b}{c}$$ **2.** If the fractions do not have a common denominator, factor the denominators (if necessary) and determine the least common denominator (LCD). **3.** Multiply each fraction by the necessary value so that each fraction becomes an equivalent fraction with the LCD as the denominator. **4.** Add the numerators and place the result over the common denominator. **5.** Simplify, if possible.	Add: $\dfrac{7x}{x^2 - 9} + \dfrac{x+2}{x+3}$. $$\frac{7x}{(x+3)(x-3)} + \frac{x+2}{x+3}$$ The LCD = $(x+3)(x-3)$. $$\frac{7x}{(x+3)(x-3)} + \frac{x+2}{x+3} \cdot \frac{x-3}{x-3}$$ $$= \frac{7x}{(x+3)(x-3)} + \frac{x^2 - x - 6}{(x+3)(x-3)}$$ $$= \frac{x^2 + 6x - 6}{(x+3)(x-3)}$$
Subtracting fractional algebraic expressions, p. 252	Follow the procedures of adding fractional algebraic expressions except that you subtract the second numerator from the first after each fraction has the LCD as the denominator. $$\frac{a}{c} - \frac{b}{c} = \frac{a-b}{c}$$	Subtract: $\dfrac{4x}{3x-2} - \dfrac{5x}{x+4}$. The LCD = $(3x-2)(x+4)$. $$\frac{4x}{3x-2} \cdot \frac{x+4}{x+4} - \frac{5x}{x+4} \cdot \frac{3x-2}{3x-2}$$ $$= \frac{4x^2 + 16x}{(3x-2)(x+4)} - \frac{15x^2 - 10x}{(x+4)(3x-2)}$$ $$= \frac{-11x^2 + 26x}{(3x-2)(x+4)}$$
Simplifying a complex fraction by Method 1, p. 259	**1.** Simplify the numerator and denominator, if possible, by combining quantities to obtain one fraction in the numerator and one fraction in the denominator. **2.** Divide the numerator by the denominator. (That is, multiply the numerator by the reciprocal of the denominator.) **3.** Simplify the result.	Simplify by Method 1: $\dfrac{4 - \dfrac{1}{x^2}}{\dfrac{2}{x} + \dfrac{1}{x^2}}$ *Step 1:* $\dfrac{\dfrac{4x^2}{x^2} - \dfrac{1}{x^2}}{\dfrac{2x}{x^2} + \dfrac{1}{x^2}} = \dfrac{\dfrac{4x^2 - 1}{x^2}}{\dfrac{2x + 1}{x^2}}$ *Step 2:* $\dfrac{4x^2 - 1}{x^2} \cdot \dfrac{x^2}{2x + 1}$ *Step 3:* $\dfrac{(2x+1)(2x-1)}{x^2} \cdot \dfrac{x^2}{2x+1} = 2x - 1$
Simplifying a complex fraction by Method 2, p. 259	**1.** Find the LCD of the algebraic fractions in the numerator and the denominator. **2.** Multiply the numerator and the denominator of the complex fraction by the LCD. **3.** Simplify the results.	Simplify by Method 2: $\dfrac{4 - \dfrac{1}{x^2}}{\dfrac{2}{x} + \dfrac{1}{x^2}}$

Topic	Procedure	Examples
		Step 1: The LCD of the fractions is x^2.
		Step 2: $\dfrac{\left[4 - \dfrac{1}{x^2}\right]x^2}{\left[\dfrac{2}{x} - \dfrac{1}{x^2}\right]x^2} = \dfrac{4(x^2) - \left(\dfrac{1}{x^2}\right)(x^2)}{\left(\dfrac{2}{x}\right)(x^2) - \left(\dfrac{1}{x^2}\right)(x^2)}$
		$= \dfrac{4x^2 - 1}{2x - 1}$
		Step 3: $\dfrac{(2x + 1)(2x - 1)}{(2x - 1)} = 2x + 1$
Solving equations involving algebraic fractions, p. 263	1. Determine the LCD of all denominators in the equation. 2. Multiply each term in the equation by the LCD. 3. Simplify and remove parentheses. 4. Collect any like terms. 5. Solve for the variable. 6. Check your answer. Be sure that the value you obtained does not make any fraction in the original equation have a value of 0 in the denominator. If so, there is no solution.	Solve: $\dfrac{4}{y - 1} + \dfrac{-y + 5}{3y^2 - 4y + 1} = \dfrac{9}{3y - 1}$. The LCD $= (y - 1)(3y - 1)$. $(y - 1)(3y - 1)\left[\dfrac{4}{y - 1}\right]$ $\quad + (y - 1)(3y - 1)\left[\dfrac{-y + 5}{(y - 1)(3y - 1)}\right]$ $\qquad = (y - 1)(3y - 1)\left[\dfrac{9}{3y - 1}\right]$ $4(3y - 1) + (-y) + 5 = 9(y - 1)$ $12y - 4 - y + 5 = 9y - 9$ $11y + 1 = 9y - 9$ $11y - 9y = -9 - 1$ $2y = -10$ $y = -5$ *Check:* $\dfrac{4}{-5 - 1} + \dfrac{-(-5) + 5}{3(-5)^2 - 4(-5) + 1} \overset{?}{=} \dfrac{9}{3(-5) - 1}$ $\dfrac{4}{-6} + \dfrac{10}{96} \overset{?}{=} \dfrac{9}{-16}$ $-\dfrac{2}{3} + \dfrac{5}{48} \overset{?}{=} -\dfrac{9}{16}$ $-\dfrac{32}{48} + \dfrac{5}{48} \overset{?}{=} -\dfrac{27}{48}$ $-\dfrac{27}{48} = -\dfrac{27}{48}$ ✓
Solving formulas containing fractions for a specified variable, p. 269	1. Remove any parentheses. 2. Multiply each term of the equation by the LCD. 3. Add or subtract a quantity to each side of the equation so that only terms containing the desired variable are on one side of the equation while all other terms are on the other side. 4. If there are two or more unlike terms containing the desired variable, remove that variable as a common factor. 5. Divide each side of the equation by the coefficient of the desired variable. 6. Simplify, if possible.	Solve for n: $v = c\left(1 - \dfrac{t}{n}\right)$. $v = c - \dfrac{ct}{n}$ $n(v) = n(c) - n\left(\dfrac{ct}{n}\right)$ $nv = nc - ct$ $nv - nc = -ct$ $n(v - c) = -ct$ $n = \dfrac{-ct}{v - c}$ or $\dfrac{ct}{-v + c}$

Topic	Procedure	Examples
Solving proportions in applied problems, p. 270	1. Determine a given ratio in the problem for which both values are known. 2. Determine a similar ratio where only one value is known. Describe the other value by a variable. 3. Determine how the ratios may be made into one equation. 4. Solve the resulting equation.	The student to faculty ratio at Central University is 25:2. If there are 3700 students at the university, how many faculty are there? The ratio of students to faculty: $\dfrac{25}{2}$ Let $f =$ the number of faculty. $$\frac{25}{2} = \frac{3700}{f}$$ $$25f = 7400$$ $$f = 296$$ There are 296 faculty.

REVIEW PROBLEMS CHAPTER 5

Simplify.

1. $\dfrac{6x^3 - 9x^2}{12x^2 - 18x}$

$\dfrac{x}{2}$

2. $\dfrac{12x^4}{3x^5 - 15x^2}$

$\dfrac{4x^2}{x^3 - 5}$

3. $\dfrac{28a^3b^3}{35a^6b^2}$

$\dfrac{4b}{5a^3}$

4. $\dfrac{a^2 - a - 20}{a^2 - 2a - 15}$

$\dfrac{a + 4}{a + 3}$

5. $\dfrac{14 - 19y - 3y^2}{3y^2 - 23y + 14}$

$-\dfrac{y + 7}{y - 7}$

6. $\dfrac{ax + 2a - bx - 2b}{3x^2 - 12}$

$\dfrac{a - b}{3(x - 2)}$

7. $\dfrac{a^4 - 1}{a^4 + 3a^2 + 2}$

$\dfrac{(a + 1)(a - 1)}{a^2 + 2}$

8. $\dfrac{6x^2y + 6xy - 36y}{3x^2y - 15xy + 18y}$

$\dfrac{2(x + 3)}{x - 3}$

9. $\dfrac{4x^2 - 1}{x^2 - 4} \cdot \dfrac{2x^2 + 4x}{4x + 2}$

$\dfrac{x(2x - 1)}{x - 2}$

10. $\dfrac{3y}{4xy - 6y^2} \cdot \dfrac{2x - 3y}{12xy}$

$\dfrac{1}{8xy}$

11. $\dfrac{y^2 + 8y - 20}{y^2 + 6y - 16} \cdot \dfrac{y^2 + 3y - 40}{y^2 + 6y - 40}$

$\dfrac{y - 5}{y - 4}$

12. $\dfrac{3x^3y}{x^2 + 7x + 12} \cdot \dfrac{x^2 + 8x + 15}{6xy^2}$

$\dfrac{x^2(x + 5)}{2y(x + 4)}$

13. $\dfrac{2x + 12}{3x - 15} \div \dfrac{2x^2 - 6x - 20}{x^2 - 10x + 25}$

$\dfrac{x + 6}{3(x + 2)}$

14. $\dfrac{6x^2 - 6a^2}{3x^2 + 3} \div \dfrac{x^4 - a^4}{a^2x^2 + a^2}$

$\dfrac{2a^2}{x^2 + a^2}$

15. $\dfrac{y^4 - 1}{1 + y^2} \cdot \dfrac{y^2 + 8y + 15}{y^2 - 2y + 1} \cdot \dfrac{1 - y^2}{y^2 + 10y + 25}$

$-\dfrac{(y + 1)^2(y + 3)}{y + 5}$

16. $\dfrac{y^2 + y - 20}{y^2 - 4y + 4} \cdot \dfrac{y^2 + y - 6}{12 + y - y^2} \cdot \dfrac{10 - 5y}{2y + 10}$

$\dfrac{5}{2}$

17. $\dfrac{9y^2 - 3y - 2}{6y^2 - 13y - 5} \div \dfrac{3y^2 + 10y - 8}{2y^2 + 13y + 20}$

$\dfrac{2y + 5}{2y - 5}$

18. $\dfrac{4a^2 + 12a + 5}{2a^2 - 7a - 13} \div (4a^2 + 2a)$

$\dfrac{2a + 5}{2a(2a^2 - 7a - 13)}$

Add or subtract the fractions and simplify your answers.

19. $\dfrac{4}{xy^2} + \dfrac{3}{x^2y} - \dfrac{2}{x^2y^2}$

$\dfrac{4x + 3y - 2}{x^2y^2}$

20. $\dfrac{5}{x - 3} + \dfrac{2}{3x + 1}$

$\dfrac{17x - 1}{(x - 3)(3x + 1)}$

21. $\dfrac{5}{4x} + \dfrac{-3}{x + 4}$

$\dfrac{-7x + 20}{4x(x + 4)}$

22. $\dfrac{x - 5}{2x + 1} - \dfrac{x + 1}{x - 2}$

$-\dfrac{x^2 + 10x - 9}{(2x + 1)(x - 2)}$

23. $\dfrac{4}{y + 5} + \dfrac{3y + 2}{y^2 - 25}$

$\dfrac{7y - 18}{(y + 5)(y - 5)}$

24. $\dfrac{2y - 1}{12y} - \dfrac{3y + 2}{9y}$

$\dfrac{-6y - 11}{36y}$

25. $\dfrac{y^2 - 4y - 19}{y^2 + 8y + 15} - \dfrac{2y - 3}{y + 5}$

$-\dfrac{y + 2}{y + 3}$

26. $\dfrac{4y}{y^2 + 2y + 1} + \dfrac{3}{y^2 - 1}$

$\dfrac{4y^2 - y + 3}{(y + 1)^2(y - 1)}$

27. $\dfrac{a}{5 - a} - \dfrac{2}{a + 3} + \dfrac{2a^2 - 2a}{a^2 - 2a - 15}$

$\dfrac{a - 2}{a + 3}$

28. $\dfrac{5}{a^2 + 3a + 2} + \dfrac{6}{a^2 + 4a + 3} - \dfrac{7}{a^2 + 5a + 6}$

$\dfrac{4a + 20}{(a + 1)(a + 2)(a + 3)}$

29. $4a + 3 - \dfrac{2a + 1}{a + 4}$

$\dfrac{4a^2 + 17a + 11}{a + 4}$

30. $\dfrac{1}{a} + \dfrac{1}{3a} + 3a + 2$

$\dfrac{9a^2 + 6a + 4}{3a}$

Simplify the complex fractions.

31. $\dfrac{\dfrac{2}{x} + \dfrac{3}{y}}{\dfrac{7}{xy}}$

$\dfrac{2y + 3x}{7}$

32. $\dfrac{\dfrac{1}{x} + \dfrac{3}{2y}}{\dfrac{1}{4y} + \dfrac{7}{2y}}$

$\dfrac{2(2y + 3x)}{15x}$

33. $\dfrac{\dfrac{5}{x} + 1}{1 - \dfrac{25}{x^2}}$

$\dfrac{x}{x - 5}$

34. $\dfrac{\dfrac{4}{x + 3}}{\dfrac{2}{x - 2} - \dfrac{1}{x^2 + x - 6}}$

$\dfrac{4(x - 2)}{2x + 5}$

35. $\dfrac{\dfrac{y}{y + 1} + \dfrac{1}{y}}{\dfrac{y}{y + 1} - \dfrac{1}{y}}$

$\dfrac{y^2 + y + 1}{y^2 - y - 1}$

36. $\dfrac{\dfrac{10}{a + 2} - 5}{\dfrac{4}{a + 2} - 2}$

$\dfrac{5}{2}$

37. $\dfrac{\dfrac{2}{x + 4} - \dfrac{1}{x^2 + 4x}}{\dfrac{3}{2x + 8}}$

$\dfrac{2(2x - 1)}{3x}$

38. $\dfrac{\dfrac{y^2}{y^2 - x^2} - 1}{x + \dfrac{xy}{x - y}}$

$\dfrac{-1}{x + y}$

39. $y - \dfrac{y}{1 + \dfrac{1}{1 - \dfrac{1}{y}}}$

$\dfrac{y^2}{2y - 1}$

40. $\dfrac{\dfrac{3}{x} - \dfrac{2}{x + 1}}{\dfrac{5}{x^2 + 5x + 4} - \dfrac{1}{x + 4}}$

$\dfrac{-(x + 3)(x + 4)}{x(x - 4)}$

Solve for the variable and check your solution. If there is no solution, say so.

41. $\dfrac{3}{7} + \dfrac{4}{x + 1} = 1$

$x = 6$

42. $\dfrac{3}{2} = 1 - \dfrac{1}{x - 1}$

$x = -1$

43. $\dfrac{1}{x + 2} - \dfrac{1}{x} = \dfrac{-2}{x}$

$x = -1$

44. $\dfrac{3}{x - 2} + \dfrac{8}{x + 3} = \dfrac{6}{x - 2}$

$x = 5$

45. $\dfrac{5}{2a} = \dfrac{2}{a} - \dfrac{1}{12}$

$a = -6$

46. $\dfrac{1}{2a} = \dfrac{2}{a} - \dfrac{3}{8}$

$a = 4$

47. $\dfrac{1}{y} + \dfrac{1}{2y} = 2$

$y = \dfrac{3}{4}$

48. $\dfrac{5}{y^2} + \dfrac{7}{y} = \dfrac{6}{y^2}$

$y = \dfrac{1}{7}$

49. $\dfrac{a + 2}{2a + 6} = \dfrac{3}{2} - \dfrac{3}{a + 3}$

$a = -\dfrac{1}{2}$

50. $\dfrac{5}{a + 5} + \dfrac{a + 4}{2a + 10} = \dfrac{3}{2}$

$a = -\dfrac{1}{2}$

51. $\dfrac{1}{x + 2} - \dfrac{5}{x - 2} = \dfrac{-15}{x^2 - 4}$

$x = \dfrac{3}{4}$

52. $\dfrac{y + 1}{y^2 + 2y - 3} - \dfrac{1}{y + 3} = \dfrac{1}{y - 1}$

$y = -1$

Solve for the variable indicated.

53. $\dfrac{N}{V} = \dfrac{m}{M + N}$; for M $\quad M = \dfrac{mV}{N} - N$ **54.** $m = \dfrac{y - y_0}{x - x_0}$; for x $\quad x = \dfrac{y - y_0 + mx_0}{m}$ **55.** $\dfrac{P_1 V_1}{T_1} = \dfrac{P_2 V_2}{T_2}$; for T_1 $\quad T_1 = \dfrac{P_1 V_1 T_2}{P_2 V_2}$

56. $\dfrac{1}{f} = \dfrac{1}{a} + \dfrac{1}{b}$; for a $\quad a = \dfrac{bf}{b - f}$ **57.** $S = \dfrac{V_1 t + V_2 t}{2}$; for t $\quad t = \dfrac{2S}{V_1 + V_2}$ **58.** $A = \dfrac{12I}{p + 3pr}$; for p

$$p = \dfrac{12I}{A(1 + 3r)}$$

59. $d = \dfrac{LR_2}{R_2 + R_1}$; for R_2 **60.** $\dfrac{S - P}{Pr} = t$; for r

$$R_2 = \dfrac{dR_1}{L - d}$$ $$r = \dfrac{S - P}{Pt}$$

Solve the following problems. If necessary, round your answer to the nearest hundredth.

61. A company tested a random sample of 50 calculators and found 3 defective ones. In a batch of 950 calculators, how many were probably defective?
57

62. The ratio of kilograms to pounds is 5:11. How much does a 143-pound man weigh in kilograms?
65 kilograms

63. How long will it take a pump to empty a 4900-gallon pool if the same pump can empty a 3500-gallon pool in 4 hours?
5.6 hrs

64. In a sanctuary a sample of 100 wild rabbits are tagged and released by the wildlife management team. In a few weeks, after they have mixed with the general rabbit population, a sample of 40 rabbits are caught and 8 have a tag. Estimate the population of rabbits in the sanctuary.
500 rabbits

65. The ratio of a picture's width to length is 5:7. If the length of the picture is 21 centimeters, what is the width?
15 cm

66. The ratio of officers to state troopers is 2:9. If there are 154 men and women on the force, how many are officers?
28 officers

PUTTING YOUR SKILLS TO WORK

A Statistical Formula

An advertising company claims that 45% of all shoppers can recognize a certain toothpaste by the color of the stripe on the tube. To determine if that proportion is correct, a statistician might use the formula

$$Q^2 = \dfrac{x - np}{np(1 - p)}$$

where x is some assigned value for a particular shopper, (how this value is determined cannot be explained here), n is the number of shoppers, and p is the proportion of shoppers recognizing the toothpaste by the stripe color. Q is a measure of validity.

A Challenge for You

Can you find the number of shoppers when $x = 2459.7$, $p = 0.45$, and $Q = 9$?

Simplify.

1. $\dfrac{3xy - 2y^2}{-12x^2 + 8xy}$

2. $\dfrac{3x^2 - x - 2}{4x^2 - 7x + 3}$

3. $\dfrac{2y^2 + 12y + 18}{3y^2 + 12y + 9} \cdot \dfrac{3y^2 + 3y}{2y^2 - 18}$

4. $\dfrac{3x^2y}{x^2 + 10x + 25} \cdot \dfrac{2x^2 - 50}{18xy^3} \cdot \dfrac{3x + 15}{2x - 10}$

5. $\dfrac{2x^2 + 20x + 42}{8x^2 - 8x} \div \dfrac{2x^2 - 18}{x^2 + 7x - 8}$

6. $\dfrac{x^2 - 3xy - 10y^2}{x^2 + 8xy + 12y^2} \div \dfrac{3x^2 - 19xy + 20y^2}{x^2 + 12xy + 36y^2}$

1. $-\dfrac{y}{4x}$

2. $\dfrac{3x + 2}{4x - 3}$

3. $\dfrac{y}{y - 3}$

4. $\dfrac{x}{2y^2}$

5. $\dfrac{(x + 7)(x + 8)}{8x(x - 3)}$

6. $\dfrac{x + 6y}{3x - 4y}$

7. $\dfrac{10x + 5y - 6xy}{2xy(2x + y)}$

Add or subtract.

7. $\dfrac{5}{2xy} - \dfrac{3}{2x + y}$

8. $\dfrac{3x + 15}{(x + 3)(x + 2)}$

8. $\dfrac{6}{x^2 + 5x + 6} + \dfrac{3}{x + 2}$

9. $-\dfrac{3x + 4}{x(x - 4)(x - 2)}$

9. $\dfrac{2}{x^2 - 4x} - \dfrac{5}{x^2 - 6x + 8}$

10. $\dfrac{5}{2y + 1} + \dfrac{3}{2y^2 - 5y - 3} + \dfrac{3}{y - 3}$

10. $\dfrac{11y - 9}{(2y + 1)(y - 3)}$

11. $4 + \dfrac{2x}{x - 1}$

11. $\dfrac{6x - 4}{x - 1}$

12. $\dfrac{2x}{8x^3 + 27} - \dfrac{3}{4x^2 - 6x + 9}$

12. $\dfrac{-4x - 9}{(2x + 3)(4x^2 - 6x + 9)}$

Simplify.

1. $\dfrac{\dfrac{2}{y+1}+\dfrac{1}{y^2-1}}{\dfrac{4y-2}{2y+2}}$

2. $\dfrac{1-\dfrac{25}{y^2}}{\dfrac{5}{y}+1}$

3. $\dfrac{\dfrac{1}{2x}-\dfrac{1}{x}}{\dfrac{3}{2}+\dfrac{5}{2x}}$

Solve if possible. If there is no solution, so state.

4. $\dfrac{4y+5}{6y-1}=\dfrac{3}{3y-4}+\dfrac{2y}{3y-4}$

5. $\dfrac{1}{9}+\dfrac{2y-1}{3y}=\dfrac{y+2}{y}+\dfrac{1}{9y}$

6. $\dfrac{5}{2}-\dfrac{2x+7}{x+6}=3$

7. $\dfrac{3}{y+3}=\dfrac{-y}{y-3}+\dfrac{y^2+9}{y^2-9}$

---

1. $\dfrac{1}{y-1}$

2. $\dfrac{y-5}{y}$

3. $\dfrac{-1}{3x+5}$

4. $y=-1$

5. $y=-11$

6. $x=-4$

7. No solution

8. $C_1 = \dfrac{CC_2}{C_2 - C}$

9. $t_1 = \dfrac{QL + kAt_2}{kA}$

10. $A = \pi r S + \pi r^2$

11. 22.5 in.

12. 2280 students

13. 12.1 meters

Solve for the variable indicated.

8. $\dfrac{1}{C} = \dfrac{1}{C_1} + \dfrac{1}{C_2}$; for C_1

9. $Q = \dfrac{kA(t_1 - t_2)}{L}$; for t_1

10. $\dfrac{A - \pi r^2}{\pi r} = S$; for A

11. The legend of a large wall map gives a scale of 3 inches for every 5 miles. Two cities are actually 37.5 miles apart. How far apart are they on the map?

12. A sample of students at Central University revealed that 12 students smoked and 19 students did not smoke. Assume the same ratio for the general student population. If the university has 3720 students, how many of them do *not* smoke?

13. A metal beam weighs 20.4 kilograms and is 2.2 meters long. How long would a similar beam be if it weighed 112.2 kilograms?

Simplify.

1. $\dfrac{x^3 + 3x^2 + 2x}{x^3 - 2x^2 - 3x}$

2. $\dfrac{y^2 - 4}{y^3 + 8}$

3. $\dfrac{2y^2 + 7y - 4}{y^2 + 2y - 8} \cdot \dfrac{2y^2 - 8}{3y^2 + 11y + 10}$

4. $\dfrac{4 - 2x}{3x^2 - 2x - 8} \div \dfrac{2x^2 + x - 1}{9x + 12}$

5. $\dfrac{3x + 8}{x^2 - 25} - \dfrac{5}{x - 5}$

6. $\dfrac{2}{x^2 + 5x + 6} + \dfrac{3x}{x^2 + 6x + 9}$

7. $\dfrac{\dfrac{4}{y + 2} - 2}{5 - \dfrac{10}{y + 2}}$

8. $\dfrac{\dfrac{1}{x} - \dfrac{3}{x + 2}}{\dfrac{2}{x^2 + 2x}}$

---

1. $\dfrac{x + 2}{x - 3}$

2. $\dfrac{y - 2}{y^2 - 2y + 4}$

3. $\dfrac{2(2y - 1)}{3y + 5}$

4. $\dfrac{-6}{(2x - 1)(x + 1)}$

5. $\dfrac{-2x - 17}{(x + 5)(x - 5)}$

6. $\dfrac{3x^2 + 8x + 6}{(x + 3)^2(x + 2)}$

7. $-\dfrac{2}{5}$

8. $-x + 1$

Solve for the variable and check your answer. If no solution exists, so state.

9. $\dfrac{3}{2x + 3} - \dfrac{1}{2x - 3} = \dfrac{2}{4x^2 - 9}$

10. $\dfrac{1}{2y + 4} - \dfrac{1}{6} = \dfrac{-2}{3y + 6}$

11. Solve for W: $h = \dfrac{S - 2WL}{2W + 2L}$.

12. A successful business has 1400 employees. A high-speed printer requires 30 minutes to print the payroll. If the company expands to 2450 employees, how long will it take to print the payroll?

Approximately one-half of this test covers the content of Chapters 1–4. The remainder covers the content of Chapter 5.

1. Simplify: $\left(\dfrac{3x^{-2}y^3}{z^4}\right)^{-2}$.

2. Solve for x: $\dfrac{2}{3}(3x - 1) = \dfrac{2}{5}x + 3$.

3. Graph the straight line:
$-6x + 2y = -12$.

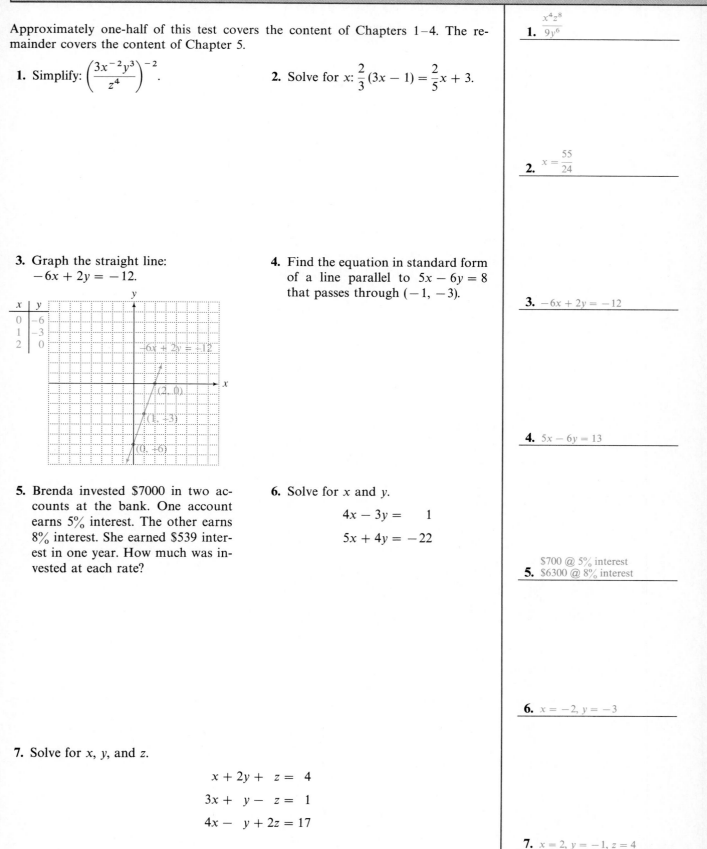

x	y
0	-6
1	-3
2	0

4. Find the equation in standard form of a line parallel to $5x - 6y = 8$ that passes through $(-1, -3)$.

5. Brenda invested $7000 in two accounts at the bank. One account earns 5% interest. The other earns 8% interest. She earned $539 interest in one year. How much was invested at each rate?

6. Solve for x and y.

$$4x - 3y = 1$$
$$5x + 4y = -22$$

7. Solve for x, y, and z.

$$x + 2y + z = 4$$
$$3x + y - z = 1$$
$$4x - y + 2z = 17$$

1. $\dfrac{x^4 z^8}{9y^6}$

2. $x = \dfrac{55}{24}$

3. $-6x + 2y = -12$

4. $5x - 6y = 13$

5. $700 @ 5% interest
$6300 @ 8% interest

6. $x = -2$, $y = -3$

7. $x = 2$, $y = -1$, $z = 4$

8. $(3x + 5y)(9x^2 - 15xy + 25y^2)$

Factor.

8. $27x^3 + 125y^3$ **9.** $81x^3 - 90x^2y + 25xy^2$

9. $x(9x - 5y)^2$

Simplify.

10. $\dfrac{7(x - 2)}{x + 4}$

10. $\dfrac{7x^2 - 28}{x^2 + 6x + 8}$ **11.** $\dfrac{2x^2 + x - 1}{2x^2 - 9x + 4} \cdot \dfrac{3x^2 - 12x}{6x + 15}$

11. $\dfrac{x(x + 1)}{2x + 5}$

12. $\dfrac{x^3 + 27}{x^2 + 7x + 12} \div \dfrac{x^2 - 6x + 9}{2x^2 + 13x + 20}$ **13.** $\dfrac{5}{2x - 8} - \dfrac{3x}{x^2 - 9x + 20}$

12. $\dfrac{(x^2 - 3x + 9)(2x + 5)}{(x - 3)^2}$

13. $-\dfrac{x + 25}{2(x - 4)(x - 5)}$

14. $\dfrac{\dfrac{1}{2x + 1} + 1}{4 - \dfrac{3}{4x^2 - 1}}$

14. $\dfrac{2(x + 1)(2x - 1)}{16x^2 - 7}$

Solve for the variable and check your answer.

15. $\dfrac{1}{2x + 3} - \dfrac{4}{4x^2 - 9} = \dfrac{3}{2x - 3}$ **16.** $\dfrac{1}{4x} - \dfrac{3}{2x} = \dfrac{5}{8}$

15. $x = -4$

16. $x = -2$

17. Solve for b: $H = \dfrac{3b + 2x}{5 - 4b}$. **18.** At this time of day the Bay Bridge handles 1650 cars in 12 minutes. How many cars will it handle in 1 hour?

17. $b = \dfrac{5H - 2x}{3 + 4H}$

18. 8250 cars

Rational Exponents and Radicals

The health and safety factors and dangers in a workplace can be measured by using mathematical equations. The Occupational Safety and Health Administration (OSHA) is concerned with all aspects of on-the-job safety.

6

PRETEST CHAPTER 6

If you are familiar with the topics in this chapter, take this test now. Check your answers with those in the back of the book. If an answer was wrong or you couldn't do a problem, study the appropriate section of the chapter.

If you are not familiar with the topics in this chapter, don't take this test now. Instead, study the examples, work the practice problems, and then take the test.

This test will help you identify those concepts that you have mastered and those that had need more study.

Section 6.1

1. Multiply and simplify your answer: $(-2x^{1/4}y^{1/3})(-5x^{-1/3}y^{1/6})$. $\dfrac{10y^{1/2}}{x^{1/12}}$

Simplify.

2. $\left(\dfrac{32x^3y^{-4}}{x^{-7}y}\right)^{3/5}$ $\quad \dfrac{8x^6}{y^3}$

3. $\dfrac{20x^2y^{-3}}{-4x^{1/2}y^{-4}}$ $\quad -5x^{3/2}y$

4. $(-3x^{1/4}y^{-1/3})^3$ $\quad \dfrac{-27x^{3/4}}{y}$

Section 6.2 Evaluate.

5. $16^{-3/4}$ $\quad \dfrac{1}{8}$

6. $\sqrt[3]{-27}+\sqrt{121}$ $\quad 8$

7. $\sqrt[3]{125a^6b^{21}c^9}$ $\quad 5a^2b^7c^3$

Section 6.3

8. Simplify: $\sqrt[4]{48x^7y^{12}}$. $\quad 2xy^3\sqrt[4]{3x^3}$

9. Combine like terms where possible: $2\sqrt{75x^3}+3\sqrt[3]{81}-5\sqrt[3]{24}-3x\sqrt{27x}$. $\quad x\sqrt{3x}-\sqrt[3]{3}$

Section 6.4

10. Multiply and simplify: $(2\sqrt{3}-4\sqrt{6})(\sqrt{12}-5\sqrt{6})$. $\quad 132-54\sqrt{2}$

11. Rationalize the denominator; simplify your answer: $\dfrac{2x}{\sqrt[3]{4x^5}}$. $\quad \dfrac{\sqrt[3]{2x}}{x}$

12. Rationalize the denominator; simplify your answer: $\dfrac{\sqrt{2}+\sqrt{3}}{\sqrt{6}-\sqrt{2}}$. $\quad \dfrac{2\sqrt{3}+3\sqrt{2}+2+\sqrt{6}}{4}$

Section 6.5 Perform the operations indicated.

13. $(7-3i)-(-2+4i)$ $\quad 9-7i$

14. $i^{19}+\sqrt{-49}$ $\quad 6i$

15. $(5-2i)^2$ $\quad 21-20i$

16. $\dfrac{4+3i}{1+2i}$ $\quad 2-i$

□ After studying this section, you will be able to apply the laws of exponents to:

1 *Simplify expressions with rational number exponents*

2 *State expressions containing two or more fractions with rational number exponents as one fraction*

3 *Remove a variable common factor from an expression with rational number exponents*

4 *Simplify expressions with rational number exponents so that they may be combined with other expressions*

6.1 RATIONAL EXPONENTS

Before studying this section, you should review Section 1.4. For convenience, we list the rules of exponents that we learned there.

$$x^m x^n = x^{m+n}$$

$$x^0 = 1$$

$$\frac{x^m}{x^n} = x^{m-n}$$

$$(x^m)^n = x^{mn}$$

$$x^{-n} = \frac{1}{x^n}$$

$$(xy)^n = x^n y^n$$

$$\frac{x^{-n}}{y^{-m}} = \frac{y^m}{x^n}$$

$$\left(\frac{x}{y}\right)^n = \frac{x^n}{y^n}$$

To ensure that you understand these rules, study carefully example 1 and work practice problem 1.

Example 1 Simplify: $\left(\dfrac{5xy^{-3}}{2x^{-4}y}\right)^{-2}$.

$$\left(\frac{5xy^{-3}}{2x^{-4}y}\right)^{-2} = \frac{(5xy^{-3})^{-2}}{(2x^{-4}y)^{-2}} \qquad\qquad \left(\frac{x}{y}\right)^n = \frac{x^n}{y^n}.$$

$$= \frac{5^{-2}x^{-2}(y^{-3})^{-2}}{2^{-2}(x^{-4})^{-2}y^{-2}} \qquad (xy)^n = x^ny^n.$$

$$= \frac{5^{-2}x^{-2}y^6}{2^{-2}x^8y^{-2}} \qquad\qquad (x^m)^n = x^{mn}.$$

$$= \frac{5^{-2}}{2^{-2}} \cdot \frac{x^{-2}}{x^8} \cdot \frac{y^6}{y^{-2}}$$

$$= \frac{2^2}{5^2} \cdot x^{-2-8} \cdot y^{6+2} \qquad \frac{x^{-n}}{y^{-m}} = \frac{y^m}{x^n}; \quad \frac{x^m}{x^n} = x^{m-n}.$$

$$= \frac{4}{25}x^{-10}y^8$$

The answer can also be written as $\dfrac{4y^8}{25x^{10}}$ Do you see why? ∎

Practice Problem 1 Simplify: $\left(\dfrac{3x^{-2}y^4}{2x^{-5}y^2}\right)^{-3}$. ∎

We will now write most fractional exponents using diagonal lines. This is usually done in the more advanced mathematics courses. Thus, we will write $\dfrac{5}{6}$ as 5/6 and $\dfrac{a}{b}$ as a/b throughout this chapter when writing exponents.

1 These rules for exponents can also be extended to include rational exponents—that is, exponents that are fractions. (As you recall, rational numbers are of the form a/b, where a and b are integers and b does not equal zero.) For now we restrict the base to *positive* real numbers. Later we will talk about negative bases.

Example 2 Simplify.

(a) $(x^{2/3})^4$ **(b)** $\dfrac{x^{5/6}}{x^{1/6}}$ **(c)** $x^{2/3} \cdot x^{-1/3}$ **(d)** $5^{3/7} \cdot 5^{2/7}$

We will not write out every step or every rule of exponents that we use. You should be able to follow the solutions.

(a) $(x^{2/3})^4 = x^{2/3 \cdot 4/1} = x^{8/3}$ **(b)** $\dfrac{x^{5/6}}{x^{1/6}} = x^{5/6 - 1/6} = x^{4/6} = x^{2/3}$

(c) $x^{2/3} \cdot x^{-1/3} = x^{2/3 - 1/3} = x^{1/3}$ **(d)** $5^{3/7} \cdot 5^{2/7} = 5^{3/7 + 2/7} = 5^{5/7}$ ∎

Practice Problem 2 Simplify.

(a) $(x^4)^{3/8}$ **(b)** $\dfrac{x^{3/7}}{x^{2/7}}$ **(c)** $x^{-7/5} \cdot x^{4/5}$ ∎

Example 3 Simplify. Express your answer with positive exponents only.

(a) $\dfrac{3x^{1/4}}{x^{1/3}}$ **(b)** $(2x^{1/2})(3x^{1/3})$ **(c)** $\dfrac{18x^{1/4}y^{-1/3}}{-6x^{-1/2}y^{1/6}}$

(a) $\dfrac{3x^{1/4}}{x^{1/3}} = 3x^{1/4 - 1/3} = 3x^{3/12 - 4/12} = 3x^{-1/12} = \dfrac{3}{x^{1/12}}$

(b) $(2x^{1/2})(3x^{1/3}) = 6x^{1/2 + 1/3} = 6x^{3/6 + 2/6} = 6x^{5/6}$

TEACHING TIP Students sometimes feel that negative exponents are handled differently from positive exponents. It is good sometimes to list some examples side by side so that they see how the exact same rule is applied to positive and negative exponents.

PRODUCT RULE:
$x^5 \cdot x^3 = x^8$, $x^{-6} \cdot x^{-4} = x^{-10}$

QUOTIENT RULE:
$\dfrac{x^9}{x^3} = x^{9-3} = x^6$

$\dfrac{x^{-12}}{x^{-5}} = x^{-12-(-5)} = x^{-12+5}$

$= x^{-7}$

POWER RULE:
$(x^3)^4 = x^{12}$ $(x^{-7})^{-3} = x^{21}$

TEACHING TIP Emphasize to students that sometimes it is necessary to express the answer with only positive exponents. After discussing example 3 or a similar example, ask them to do the following and express the answer WITH POSITIVE EXPONENTS.

Simplify A: $\dfrac{-12x^{-4}}{6x^3}$

Simplify B: $(-4x^{1/5})(-2x^{-3/5})$

Ans. A: $\dfrac{-2}{x^7}$ Ans. B: $\dfrac{8}{x^{2/5}}$

(c) $-3x^{1/4-(-1/2)}y^{-1/3-1/6} = \boxed{-3x^{1/4+2/4}y^{-2/6-1/6}} = -3x^{3/4}y^{-1/2} = \dfrac{-3x^{3/4}}{y^{1/2}}$ ∎

Practice Problem 3 Simplify. Express your answer with positive exponents only.

(a) $\dfrac{x^4}{4x^{1/2}}$ (b) $(-3x^{1/4})(2x^{1/2})$ (c) $\dfrac{13x^{1/12}y^{-1/4}}{26x^{-1/3}y^{1/2}}$ ∎

Example 4 Multiply and simplify: $-2x^{5/6}(3x^{1/2} - 4x^{-1/3})$.

$-2x^{5/6}(3x^{1/2} - 4x^{-1/3}) = \boxed{-6x^{5/6+1/2} + 8x^{5/6-1/3}} = -6x^{5/6+3/6} + 8x^{5/6-2/6}$

$\qquad\qquad\qquad\qquad\qquad = -6x^{8/6} + 8x^{3/6} = -6x^{4/3} + 8x^{1/2}$ ∎

Practice Problem 4 Multiply and simplify: $-3x^{1/2}(2x^{1/4} + 3x^{-1/2})$. ∎

2 **Example 5** Write as one fraction with positive exponents: $2x^{-1/2} + x^{1/2}$.

$2x^{-1/2} + x^{1/2} = \boxed{\dfrac{2}{x^{1/2}}} + \dfrac{x^{1/2} \cdot x^{1/2}}{x^{1/2}} = \dfrac{2}{x^{1/2}} + \dfrac{x^1}{x^{1/2}} = \dfrac{2+x}{x^{1/2}}$ ∎

Practice Problem 5 Write as one fraction with only positive exponents: $3x^{1/3} + x^{-1/3}$. ∎

3 **Example 6** Remove a common factor of 2x: $2x^{3/2} + 4x^{5/2}$

$2x^{3/2} + 4x^{5/2} = 2x^{2/2+1/2} + 4x^{2/2+3/2} = 2x^{2/2}(x^{1/2} + 2x^{3/2}) = 2x(x^{1/2} + 2x^{3/2})$ ∎

Practice Problem 6 Remove a common factor of 4y: $4y^{3/2} - 8y^{5/2}$. ∎

Example 7 Remove a common factor of $x^{-1/2}$: $x^{3/2} - 5x^{-1/2}$

$x^{3/2} - 5x^{-1/2} = x^{-1/2+4/2} - 5x^{-1/2} = x^{-1/2}(x^2 - 5)$ ∎

Practice Problem 7 Remove a common factor of $x^{-3/2}$: $x^{5/2} - 2x^{-3/2}$. ∎

4 **Example 8** Simplify: $(2^3x^3)^{2/3} + (x^{-12})^{-1/6}$.

$(2^3x^3)^{2/3} + (x^{-12})^{-1/6} = 2^{3 \cdot 2/3}x^{3 \cdot 2/3} + x^{(-12)(-1/6)}$

$\qquad\qquad\qquad\qquad\qquad = 2^2x^2 + x^2 = 4x^2 + x^2 = 5x^2$ ∎

Practice Problem 8 Simplify: $(4^{1/4}x^{3/4})^4 + (2^{-10}x^{-5})^{-3/5}$. ∎

Numerical values raised to a rational power can sometimes be simplified if they are placed in exponent form.

Example 9 Evaluate. (a) $(25)^{3/2}$ (b) $(27)^{2/3}$

(a) $(25)^{3/2} = (\boxed{5^2})^{3/2} = 5^{2/1 \cdot 3/2} = 5^3 = 125$

(b) $(27)^{2/3} = (\boxed{3^3})^{2/3} = 3^{3/1 \cdot 2/3} = 3^2 = 9$ ∎

Practice Problem 9 Evaluate. (a) $4^{5/2}$ (b) $27^{4/3}$ ∎

It is best first to simplify the expression within the parentheses before using the power rule of exponents.

Example 10 Simplify: $\left(\dfrac{36y^{3n}}{y^{n-2}}\right)^{1/2}$.

$\left(\dfrac{36y^{3n}}{y^{n-2}}\right)^{1/2} = (6^2y^{3n}y^{-(n-2)})^{1/2} = (6^2y^{3n-n+2})^{1/2} = (6^2y^{2n+2})^{1/2} = 6^{2 \cdot 1/2}y^{(2n+2)/(1/2)}$

$\qquad\qquad\qquad = 6y^{n+1}$ ∎

Practice Problem 10 Simplify: $\left(\dfrac{27x^{5n}}{x^{2n-6}}\right)^{1/3}$. ∎

In the next section, we'll see what rational exponents stand for.

Simplify and express your answer with positive exponents.

1. $(x^{1/2}y^{1/3})(x^{1/3}y^{2/3})$
$x^{3/6+2/6}y^{1/3+2/3} = x^{5/6}y$

2. $(x^{-1/3}y^{2/3})(x^{1/3}y^{1/4})$
$x^0 y^{8/12+3/12} = y^{11/12}$

3. $(7x^{1/3}y^{1/4})(-2x^{1/4}y^{-1/6})$
$-14x^{7/12}y^{1/12}$

4. $(8x^{-1/5}y^{1/3})(-3x^{-1/4}y^{1/6})$
$-24x^{-9/20}y^{1/2} = -\dfrac{-24y^{1/2}}{x^{9/20}}$

5. $5^{-2/3} \cdot 5^{1/6}$ $5^{-1/2} = \dfrac{1}{5^{1/2}}$

6. $7^{3/4} \cdot 7^{-1/4}$
$7^{1/2}$

7. $\dfrac{2x^{1/5}}{x^{-1/2}}$
$2x^{7/10}$

8. $\dfrac{3y^{2/3}}{y^{-1/4}}$
$3y^{11/12}$

9. $\dfrac{24x^{-2/3}y^{1/4}}{-6x^{-1/2}y^{-3/4}}$ $\dfrac{-4y}{x^{1/6}}$

10. $\dfrac{-25x^{1/3}y^{-1/5}}{5x^{-1/12}y^{-1/3}}$
$-5x^{5/12}y^{2/15}$

11. $\left(\dfrac{8a^2b^6}{a^{-1}b^3}\right)^{1/3}$
$2ab$

12. $\left(\dfrac{16a^5b^{-2}}{a^{-1}b^{-6}}\right)^{1/2}$
$4a^3b^2$

13. $\left(\dfrac{a^5b^{-5}}{81ab^3}\right)^{3/4}$ $\dfrac{a^3}{3^3b^6} = \dfrac{a^3}{27b^6}$

14. $\left(\dfrac{a^7b^3}{32a^2b^{-7}}\right)^{2/5}$ $\dfrac{a^2b^4}{2^2} = \dfrac{a^2b^4}{4}$

15. $(7x^{2/3}y^{1/4}z^{3/2})^2$
$7^2x^{4/3}y^{1/2}z^3 = 49x^{4/3}y^{1/2}z^3$

16. $(5x^{-1/2}y^{1/3}z^{4/5})^3$ $\dfrac{125yz^{12/5}}{x^{3/2}}$

17. $(5^4x^4y^2z^6)^{1/2}$
$25x^2yz^3$

18. $(3^3x^6y^3z^{12})^{1/3}$
$3x^2yz^4$

19. $x^{2/3}(x^{4/3} - x^{1/5})$
$x^2 - y^{13/15}$

20. $x^{-1/4}(x^{2/3} + x^{3/4})$
$x^{-3/12+8/12} + x^{-1/4+3/4} = x^{5/12} + x^{1/2}$

21. $a^{5/6}(a^{-1/2} + 3a^{1/5})$
$a^{5/6-3/6} + 3a^{25/30+6/30} = a^{1/3} + 3a^{31/30}$

22. $a^{2/3}(a^{1/2} + 4a^{-1/4})$
$a^{4/6+3/6} + 4a^{8/12-3/12} = a^{7/6} + 4a^{5/12}$

23. $(a^{1/5}b^{2/3})^{1/4}$
$a^{1/20}b^{1/6}$

24. $(a^{2/5}b^{1/8})^{4/5}$
$a^{8/25}b^{1/10}$

25. $\dfrac{(x^{-5/6}x^4)^{3/4}}{x^{2/3}}$
$\dfrac{(x^{19/6})^{3/4}}{x^{2/3}} = \dfrac{x^{19/8}}{x^{2/3}} = x^{57/24-16/24}$
$= x^{41/24}$

26. $\dfrac{(x^{1/3}x^3)^{3/2}}{x^{-1/4}}$
$\dfrac{(x^{10/3})^{3/2}}{x^{-1/4}} = \dfrac{x^5}{x^{-1/4}} = x^{21/4}$

27. $81^{3/4} + 25^{1/2}$
$(3^4)^{3/4} + (5^2)^{1/2} = 32$

28. $27^{2/3} + 16^{3/2}$
$(3^3)^{2/3} + (4^2)^{3/2} = 73$

? **To Think About**

29. What is the value of a if $x^a \cdot x^{1/4} = x^{-1/8}$?
$a + \dfrac{1}{4} = -\dfrac{1}{8}, \quad a = -\dfrac{3}{8}$

30. What is the value of b if $x^b \div x^{1/3} = x^{-1/12}$?
$b - \dfrac{1}{3} = -\dfrac{1}{12}, \quad b = \dfrac{1}{4}$

Remove a common factor of $3x^{1/2}$.

31. $-12x^{3/2} + 6x^{5/2}$
$3x^{1/2}(-4x + 2x^2)$

32. $27x^{5/2} - 3x^{3/2}$
$3x^{1/2}(9x^2 - x)$

Remove a common factor of $2a$.

33. $6a^{4/3} - 8a^{3/2}$
$2a(3a^{1/3} - 4a^{1/2})$

34. $10a^{5/4} - 4a^{8/5}$
$2a(5a^{1/4} - 2a^{3/5})$

Write each expression as one fraction with positive exponents.

35. $3y^{1/2} + y^{-1/2}$
$\dfrac{3y + 1}{y^{1/2}}$

36. $2y^{1/3} + y^{-2/3}$
$\dfrac{2y + 1}{y^{2/3}}$

37. $y^{-2/3} + 4^{1/3}$
$\dfrac{1}{y^{2/3}} + 4^{1/3} = \dfrac{1 + 4^{1/3}y^{2/3}}{y^{2/3}}$

38. $3^{-1/2} + y^{-1/2}$
$\dfrac{1}{3^{1/2}} + \dfrac{1}{y^{1/2}} = \dfrac{y^{1/2} + 3^{1/2}}{3^{1/2}y^{1/2}}$

Simplify using only positive exponents. Assume that n is a positive integer.

39. $(x^{1/3}y^{-2/3})^n$

$\dfrac{x^{n/3}}{y^{2n/3}}$

40. $(x^{1/4}y^{-3/4})^n$

$\dfrac{x^{n/4}}{y^{3n/4}}$

41. $\left(\dfrac{x^{7n}}{x^{n-2}}\right)^{1/2}$

$(x^{7n-n+2})^{1/2} = x^{3n+1}$

42. $\left(\dfrac{x^{4n+3}}{x^n}\right)^{1/3}$

$(x^{4n+3-n})^{1/3} = x^{n+1}$

43. $\left(\dfrac{8a^{3n}b^{2n}}{a^{-6n}b^{-n}}\right)^{1/3}$

$(2^3a^{9n}b^{3n})^{1/3} = 2a^{3n}b^n$

44. $\left(\dfrac{a^{5n}b^{-7n}}{100a^nb^n}\right)^{1/2}$

$\left(\dfrac{a^{4n}}{10^2b^{8n}}\right)^{1/2} = \dfrac{a^{2n}}{10b^{4n}}$

Simplify.

45. $(x^{1/3} + y^{1/3})(x^{2/3} + y^{-1/3})$

$x^{1/3+2/3} + x^{2/3}y^{1/3} + x^{1/3}y^{-1/3} + y^0$
$= x + x^{2/3}y^{1/3} + x^{1/3}y^{-1/3} + 1$

46. $(x^{1/2} + y^{1/2})(x^{1/2} - 2y^{1/2})$

$x - 2x^{1/2}y^{1/2} + x^{1/2}y^{1/2} - 2y$
$x - x^{1/2}y^{1/2} - 2y$

47. $(3x^{1/4} - 2y^{1/3})(x^{1/2} - y^{2/3})$

$3x^{1/4+2/4} - 2x^{1/2}y^{1/3} - 3x^{1/4}y^{2/3} + 2y^{1/3+2/3}$
$3x^{3/4} - 2x^{1/2}y^{1/3} - 3x^{1/4}y^{2/3} + 2y$

48. $(x^{1/5} - y^{1/2})(x^{4/5} + 5y^{1/3})$

$x - x^{4/5}y^{1/2} + 5x^{1/5}y^{1/3} - 5y^{5/6}$

? To Think About

Simplify. Assume that n is a positive integer.

49. $(5x^{3n/2} + y^{4/3})(2x^{5n/2} - y^{1/2})$

$10x^{4n} + 2x^{5n/2}y^{4/3} - 5x^{3n/2}y^{1/2} - y^{11/6}$

50. $(3x^{2n-8}y^{16-n^2})^{1/(n-4)}$

$3^{1/(n-4)}x^{2(n-4)/(n-4)}y^{-(n+4)(n-4)/(n-4)} = 3^{1/(n-4)}x^2y^{-(n+4)}$

Cumulative Review Problems

Solve for x.

51. $-4(x+1) = \dfrac{1}{3}(3-2x)$

$-12x - 12 = 3 - 2x$
$-15 = 10x$
$-\dfrac{3}{2} = x$

52. $2 + 5(x+1) = x - 3(2x+1)$

$2 + 5x + 5 = x - 6x - 3$
$x = -1$

Solve for b.

53. $A = \dfrac{h}{2}(a+b)$

$2A = ah + hb$
$\dfrac{2A - ah}{h} = b$

54. $3by - 4 = 2x + 5by$

$-4 - 2x = 5by - 3by$
$\dfrac{2+x}{y} = b$

or

$-\dfrac{(2+x)}{y} = b$

▦ Calculator Problems

Simplify.

55. $(5.8276x^{1/4}y^{-2/3})(-3.0761x^{5/4}y^{-4/3})$

$-17.92628036x^{3/2}y^{-2}$

56. $\dfrac{-82.32206x^8y^{1/2}}{-17.89610x^{-6}y^{1/4}}$

$4.6x^{14}y^{1/4}$

For Extra Practice Exercises, turn to page 322.

Solutions to Odd-Numbered Practice Problems

1. $\left(\dfrac{3x^{-2}y^4}{2x^{-5}y^2}\right)^{-3} = \dfrac{3^{-3}x^6y^{-12}}{2^{-3}x^{15}y^{-6}} = \dfrac{2^3x^{6-15}y^{-12-(-6)}}{3^3} = \boxed{\dfrac{8x^{-9}y^{-6}}{27}}$ or $\boxed{\dfrac{8}{27x^9y^6}}$

Both of these answers are considered simplified.

3. (a) $\dfrac{x^4}{4x^{1/2}} = \dfrac{x^{8/2-1/2}}{4} = \boxed{\dfrac{x^{7/2}}{4}}$ or $\boxed{\dfrac{1}{4}x^{7/2}}$ **(b)** $(-3x^{1/4})(2x^{1/2}) = -6x^{1/4+1/2} = -6x^{1/4+2/4} = \boxed{-6x^{3/4}}$

(c) $\dfrac{13x^{1/12}y^{-1/4}}{26x^{-1/3}y^{1/2}} = \dfrac{x^{1/12-(-1/3)}y^{-1/4-1/2}}{2} = \dfrac{x^{1/12+4/12}y^{-1/4-2/4}}{2} = \boxed{\dfrac{x^{5/12}y^{-3/4}}{2}}$ or $\boxed{\dfrac{x^{5/12}}{2y^{3/4}}}$

5. $3x^{1/3} + x^{-1/3} = 3x^{1/3} + \dfrac{1}{x^{1/3}} = \dfrac{3x^{1/3}(x^{1/3})}{x^{1/3}} + \dfrac{1}{x^{1/3}}$ **7.** $x^{5/2} - 2x^{-3/2} = x^{-3/2}(x^{8/2} - 2)$
$$= \dfrac{3x^{2/3}}{x^{1/3}} + \dfrac{1}{x^{1/3}} = \boxed{\dfrac{3x^{2/3} + 1}{x^{1/3}}} \qquad = \boxed{x^{-3/2}(x^4 - 2)}$$

9. (a) $4^{5/2} = (2^2)^{5/2} = 2^5 = \boxed{32}$ **(b)** $27^{4/3} = (3^3)^{4/3} = 3^4 = \boxed{81}$

Answers to Even-Numbered Practice Problems

2. (a) $x^{3/2}$ **(b)** $x^{1/7}$ **(c)** $x^{-3/5}$ or $\dfrac{1}{x^{3/5}}$ **4.** $-6x^{3/4} - 9$ **6.** $4y(y^{1/2} - 2y^{3/2})$ **8.** $4x^3 + 64x^3 = 68x^3$ **10.** $3x^{n+2}$

6.2 RADICAL EXPRESSIONS

☐ After studying this section, you will be able to:

1 *Understand the concept of a radical and be able to evaluate radical expressions*

2 *Transform radical expressions into expressions with rational exponents*

3 *Transform expressions with rational exponents into radical expressions*

4 *Evaluate higher-order radicals whenever possible when the radicand is negative*

1 In Section 1.3 we studied simple radical expressions called square roots. The **square root** of a number is *one* of that number's two equal factors. That is, since $3 \cdot 3 = 9$, 3 is a square root of 9. But $(-3) \cdot (-3) = 9$, so -3 is also a square root. We call the positive square root the **principal** square root.

The symbol $\sqrt{\ }$ is called a **radical sign**. We use it to denote positive square roots (and higher-order roots also). A negative square root is written $-\sqrt{\ }$. Thus, we write

$$\sqrt{9} = 3 \qquad -\sqrt{9} = -3$$
$$\sqrt{64} = 8 \qquad (\text{because } 8 \cdot 8 = 64)$$
$$\sqrt{121} = 11 \qquad (\text{because } 11 \cdot 11 = 121)$$

Now because $\sqrt{9} = \sqrt{3 \cdot 3} = \sqrt{3^2} = 3$, we can say that

> **Definition of Square Root**
>
> If x is a positive real number, then $\sqrt{x}$ is the *positive* (or principal) *square root* of x; in other words, $(\sqrt{x})^2 = x$.

Note that x must be *positive*. Why? Suppose we want to find $\sqrt{-36}$. We must find two equal factors that when multiplied together give -36. Are there any? No, because

$$6 \cdot 6 = 36$$
$$(-6)(-6) = 36$$

So there is no real number that we can square to get -36.

We call $\sqrt[n]{x}$ a **radical expression**. The $\sqrt{\ }$ symbol is the **radical sign**, the x is the **radicand**, and the n is the **index** of the radical. When no number for n appears in the radical expression, it is understood that 2 is the index, which means we are looking for the square root. For example, in the radical expression $\sqrt{25}$, with no number given for the index, n, we take the index to be 2. Thus $\sqrt{25}$ is the principal square root of 25.

We can extend the notion of square root to higher-order roots, such as cube roots, fourth roots, and so on. A cube root of a number is one of that number's three equal factors. The index of the radical, n, is 3, and the radical sign is $\sqrt[3]{\ }$. Similarly, a fourth root of a number is one of that number's four equal factors. The index of the radical, n, is 4, and the radical sign is $\sqrt[4]{}$. For example,

$$\sqrt[3]{27} = 3 \qquad \text{because } 3 \cdot 3 \cdot 3 = 3^3 = 27$$
$$\sqrt[3]{8} = 2 \qquad \text{because } 2 \cdot 2 \cdot 2 = 2^3 = 8$$
$$\sqrt[4]{81} = 3 \qquad \text{because } 3 \cdot 3 \cdot 3 \cdot 3 = 3^4 = 81$$
$$\sqrt[5]{32} = 2 \qquad \text{because } 2 \cdot 2 \cdot 2 \cdot 2 \cdot 2 = 2^5 = 32$$
$$\sqrt[3]{-64} = -4 \qquad \text{because } (-4)(-4)(-4) = (-4)^3 = -64$$

You should be able to see the pattern here.

$$\sqrt[3]{27} = \sqrt[3]{3^3} = 3$$
$$\sqrt[4]{81} = \sqrt[4]{3^4} = 3$$
$$\sqrt[5]{32} = \sqrt[5]{2^5} = 2$$
$$\sqrt[6]{729} = \sqrt[6]{3^6} = 3$$
$$\sqrt[3]{-64} = \sqrt[3]{(-4)^3} = -4$$

In these cases, we see that $\sqrt[n]{x^n} = x$. We now give the following definition:

Definition of Higher-Order Roots

1. If x is a *nonnegative* real number, then $\sqrt[n]{x}$ is a positive nth root and has the property that

$$\left(\sqrt[n]{x}\right)^n = x$$

2. If x is a *negative* real number, then

   a. $\left(\sqrt[n]{x}\right)^n = x$ when n is an *odd integer*

   b. $\left(\sqrt[n]{x}\right)^n$ is *not* a real number   when n is an *even integer*.

TEACHING TIP Students who find square roots quite readily are often not comfortable with higher order roots. If after doing example 1 some students seem confused, show them the following additional examples.

CUBE ROOTS: $\sqrt[3]{27} = 3$, $\sqrt[3]{-27} = -3$, $\sqrt[3]{7^3} = 7$, $\sqrt[3]{(-8)^3} = -8$

FOURTH ROOTS: $\sqrt[4]{16} = 2$, $\sqrt[4]{81} = 3$, $-\sqrt[4]{16} = -2$, $\sqrt[4]{-81}$ is not a real number

FIFTH ROOTS: $\sqrt[5]{243} = 3$, $\sqrt[5]{-243} = -3$, $\sqrt[5]{(12)^5} = 12$, $\sqrt[5]{(-6)^5} = -6$

Example 1 If possible, find the root of each negative number. If there is no real number answer, say so.

(a) $\sqrt[3]{-216}$ **(b)** $\sqrt[5]{-32}$ **(c)** $\sqrt[4]{-16}$ **(d)** $\sqrt[6]{-64}$

(a) $\sqrt[3]{-216} = \sqrt[3]{(-6)^3} = -6$ **(b)** $\sqrt[5]{-32} = \sqrt[5]{(-2)^5} = -2$

(c) $\sqrt[4]{-16}$ is not a real number because n is even and x is negative.

(d) $\sqrt[6]{-64}$ is not a real number because n is even and x is negative. ∎

Practice Problem 1 If possible, find the roots. If there is no real number answer, say so.

(a) $\sqrt[3]{216}$ **(b)** $\sqrt[5]{32}$ **(c)** $\sqrt[3]{-8}$ **(d)** $\sqrt[4]{-81}$ ∎

Now we want to extend our definition of roots to rational exponents. By the laws of exponents we know that

$$x^{1/2} \cdot x^{1/2} = x^{1/2 + 1/2} = x^1 = x$$

This equation tells us that $x^{1/2}$ must be a square root of x, since it is one of x's two equal factors. We could write it like this:

$$x^{2/2} = (x^2)^{1/2} = x$$

Therefore, $x^{1/2} = \sqrt{x}$.

In the same way we can write

$$x^{1/3} \cdot x^{1/3} \cdot x^{1/3} = x$$

$$x^{1/4} \cdot x^{1/4} \cdot x^{1/4} \cdot x^{1/4} = x$$

$$\vdots$$

$$\underbrace{x^{1/n} \cdot x^{1/n} \cdots x^{1/n}}_{n \text{ factors}} = x$$

Therefore, we are ready to define fractional exponents in general.

Definition

If n is a positive integer and x is a positive real number, then

$$x^{1/n} = \sqrt[n]{x}$$

Example 2 Change to rational exponents and simplify.

(a) $\sqrt[4]{x^4}$ **(b)** $\sqrt[5]{(32)^5}$ **(c)** $\sqrt[6]{2^6}$ **(d)** $\sqrt[7]{x^{14}}$

(a) $\sqrt[4]{x^4} = (x^4)^{1/4} = x^{4/4} = x^1 = x$
(b) $\sqrt[5]{(32)^5} = (32^5)^{1/5} = 32^{5/5} = 32^1 = 32$
(c) $\sqrt[6]{2^6} = (2^6)^{1/6} = 2^{6/6} = 2^1 = 2$
(d) $\sqrt[7]{x^{14}} = (x^{14})^{1/7} = x^{14/7} = x^2$ ■

Practice Problem 2 Change to rational exponents and simplify.

(a) $\sqrt[3]{x^3}$ **(b)** $\sqrt[4]{y^4}$ **(c)** $\sqrt[5]{(8)^5}$ **(d)** $\sqrt[6]{x^{12}}$ ■

Again using the laws of exponents, we know that

$$x^{m/n} = (x^m)^{1/n} = (x^{1/n})^m$$

So we can make the following general definition:

Definition

For positive integers m and n and any real number x for which $x^{1/n}$ is defined,

$$x^{m/n} = (\sqrt[n]{x})^m = \sqrt[n]{x^m}$$

If one of m or n is negative, then

$$x^{-m/n} = \frac{1}{x^{m/n}} = \frac{1}{(\sqrt[n]{x})^m} = \frac{1}{\sqrt[n]{x^m}}$$

Example 3 Change to radical form and evaluate.

(a) $16^{3/2}$ **(b)** $125^{2/3}$ **(c)** $(-27)^{2/3}$
(d) $(-16)^{5/2}$ **(e)** $144^{-1/2}$ **(f)** $32^{-4/5}$

(a) $16^{3/2} = (\sqrt{16})^3 = (4)^3 = 64$
(b) $125^{2/3} = (\sqrt[3]{125})^2 = (5)^2 = 25$
(c) $(-27)^{2/3} = (\sqrt[3]{-27})^2 = (-3)^2 = 9$
(d) $(-16)^{5/2} = (\sqrt{-16})^5$; however, $\sqrt{-16}$ is not a real number.

(e) $144^{-1/2} = \dfrac{1}{144^{1/2}} = \dfrac{1}{\sqrt{144}} = \dfrac{1}{12}$

(f) $32^{-4/5} = \dfrac{1}{32^{4/5}} = \dfrac{1}{(\sqrt[5]{32})^4} = \dfrac{1}{(2)^4} = \dfrac{1}{16}$ ■

Practice Problem 3 Evaluate.

(a) $8^{2/3}$ **(b)** $4^{3/2}$ **(c)** $(-8)^{4/3}$

(d) $(-25)^{3/2}$ **(e)** $100^{-3/2}$ **(f)** $32^{-3/5}$ ■

2 **Example 4** Replace all radicals with rational exponents.

(a) $\sqrt[3]{x^2}$ **(b)** $\left(\sqrt[5]{w}\right)^7$ **(c)** $\sqrt[4]{(ab)^3}$ **(d)** $\sqrt[4]{\sqrt[3]{x}}$

(a) $\sqrt[3]{x^2} = x^{2/3}$ **(b)** $\left(\sqrt[5]{w}\right)^7 = w^{7/5}$

(c) $\sqrt[4]{(ab)^3} = (ab)^{3/4}$ or $a^{3/4}b^{3/4}$ **(d)** $\sqrt[4]{\sqrt[3]{x}} = \sqrt[4]{x^{1/3}} = (x^{1/3})^{1/4} = x^{1/12}$ ■

Practice Problem 4 Replace all radicals with rational exponents.

(a) $\sqrt[4]{x^3}$ **(b)** $\sqrt[5]{(xy)^7}$ **(c)** $\left(\sqrt[5]{z}\right)^4$ ■

3 **Example 5** Write each rational exponent as a radical.

(a) $(xy)^{5/7}$ **(b)** $w^{-2/3}$ **(c)** $3x^{3/4}$ **(d)** $(3x)^{3/4}$

(a) $(xy)^{5/7} = \left(\sqrt[7]{xy}\right)^5$ **(b)** $w^{-2/3} = \dfrac{1}{w^{2/3}} = \dfrac{1}{\sqrt[3]{w^2}}$

(c) $3x^{3/4} = 3\sqrt[4]{x^3}$ **(d)** $(3x)^{3/4} = \sqrt[4]{(3x)^3} = \sqrt[4]{27x^3}$

                                                      or $(3x)^{3/4} = \left(\sqrt[4]{3x}\right)^3$ ■

Practice Problem 5 Write each rational exponent as a radical.

(a) $x^{3/4}$ **(b)** $y^{-1/3}$ **(c)** $(2x)^{4/5}$ **(d)** $2x^{4/5}$ ■

       We now consider the case where the radicand is negative. Refer to the definition for higher-order roots on page 300.

4

> **Definition**
>
> When x is a **negative real number**, or if we cannot determine if x is positive or negative, then
> $$\sqrt[n]{x^n} = |x| \qquad \text{when } n \text{ is an } \textit{even} \text{ positive integer}$$
> $$\sqrt[n]{x^n} = x \qquad \text{when } n \text{ is an } \textit{odd} \text{ positive integer}$$

TEACHING TIP After discussing example 6 or a similar example, ask students to simplify the following two problems as a class exercise.

A: $\sqrt[3]{(-7)^3}$ Ans. -7

B: $\sqrt[4]{(-8)^4}$ Ans. $|-8| = 8$

Remind them of the need for the absolute value.

TEACHING TIP After discussing example 7 or a similar exercise, show students the following additional example. Discuss the difference in simplifying a square root, a cube root, and a fourth root. Assume all variables are positive.

$\sqrt{36x^4y^6} = 6x^2y^3$,

$\sqrt[4]{81x^{12}y^{20}} = 3x^3y^5$

$\sqrt[3]{8x^3y^{12}} = 2xy^4$

Example 6 Evaluate; x may be a positive or negative real number.

(a) $\sqrt[3]{(-2)^3}$ **(b)** $\sqrt[4]{(-2)^4}$ **(c)** $\sqrt[5]{x^5}$ **(d)** $\sqrt[6]{x^6}$

(a) $\sqrt[3]{(-2)^3} = -2$ because the index is odd.

(b) $\sqrt[4]{(-2)^4} = |-2| = 2$ because the index is even.

(c) $\sqrt[5]{x^5} = x$ because the index is odd.

(d) $\sqrt[6]{x^6} = |x|$ because the index is even. ■

Practice Problem 6 Evaluate; x may be a positive or negative real number.

(a) $\sqrt[5]{(-3)^5}$ **(b)** $\sqrt[4]{(-5)^4}$ **(c)** $\sqrt[4]{w^4}$ **(d)** $\sqrt[7]{y^7}$ ■

Example 7 Evaluate or simplify. Assume all variables are positive.

(a) $\sqrt[5]{32x^{10}}$ **(b)** $\sqrt[3]{-125x^9}$ **(c)** $(16x^4)^{3/4}$ **(d)** $25(x^8y^4)^{5/2}$

(a) $\sqrt[5]{32x^{10}} = (2^5x^{10})^{1/5} = 2x^2$ **(b)** $\sqrt[3]{-125x^9} = [(-5)^3x^9]^{1/3} = -5x^3$

(c) $(16x^4)^{3/4} = (2^4x^4)^{3/4} = 2^3x^3 = 8x^3$

(d) $25(x^8y^4)^{5/2} = 25x^{8/1 \cdot 5/2}y^{4/1 \cdot 5/2} = 25x^{20}y^{10}$ ■

Practice Problem 7 Evaluate or simplify. Assume all variables are positive.

(a) $\sqrt[4]{81x^{12}}$ **(b)** $\sqrt[3]{-27x^6}$ **(c)** $(32x^5)^{3/5}$ **(d)** $16(x^6y^8)^{7/2}$ ■

1. In a simple sentence, explain what a square root is.

A sq. root of a number is one of that number's two equal factors.

2. In a simple sentence, explain what a cube root is.

A cube root of a number is one of that number's three equal factors.

For all problems 3–58, assume that variables represent positive real numbers.

Write each radical in exponential form.

3. $\sqrt[3]{9}$

$9^{1/3}$

4. $\sqrt{5}$

$5^{1/2}$

5. $\sqrt[5]{2x}$

$(2x)^{1/5}$

6. $\sqrt[4]{3y}$

$(3y)^{1/4}$

7. $\sqrt[7]{(a+b)^3}$

$(a+b)^{3/7}$

8. $\sqrt[9]{(a-b)^5}$

$(a-b)^{5/9}$

9. $\sqrt{\sqrt[3]{x}}$

$[(x)^{1/3}]^{1/2} = x^{1/6}$

10. $\sqrt[5]{\sqrt{y}}$

$(y^{1/2})^{1/5} = y^{1/10}$

11. $\left(\sqrt[6]{3x}\right)^5$

$[(3x)^{1/6}]^5 = (3x)^{5/6}$

12. $\left(\sqrt[5]{2x}\right)^3$

$[(2x)^{1/5}]^3 = (2x)^{3/5}$

Write each rational exponent in radical form.

13. $x^{3/4}$

$(\sqrt[4]{x})^3$

14. $y^{2/3}$

$(\sqrt[3]{y})^2$

15. $7^{-2/3}$

$\dfrac{1}{(\sqrt[3]{7})^2}$

16. $5^{-3/5}$

$\dfrac{1}{(\sqrt[5]{5})^3}$

17. $(2a+b)^{5/7}$

$(\sqrt[7]{2a+b})^5$

18. $(x+3y)^{4/7}$

$(\sqrt[7]{x+3y})^4$

19. $(-x)^{3/5}$

$(\sqrt[5]{-x})^3$

20. $(-y)^{5/7}$

$(\sqrt[7]{-y})^5$

Evaluate if possible.

21. $\sqrt{144}$

$\sqrt{12^2} = 12$

22. $\sqrt{100}$

10

23. $\sqrt{25} + \sqrt{49}$

$5 + 7 = 12$

24. $\sqrt{16} + \sqrt{81}$

13

25. $-\sqrt{\dfrac{1}{9}}$

$-\dfrac{1}{3}$

26. $-\sqrt{\dfrac{4}{25}}$

$-\dfrac{2}{5}$

27. $\sqrt[3]{27}$

3

28. $\sqrt[3]{64}$

4

29. $\sqrt[3]{-125}$

-5

30. $\sqrt[3]{-8}$

-2

31. $\sqrt[4]{625}$

5

32. $\sqrt[4]{81}$

3

33. $-\sqrt[6]{64}$

-2

34. $\sqrt[5]{-32}$

-2

35. $\sqrt[7]{-128}$

-2

36. $-\sqrt[8]{1}$

-1

37. $\sqrt[4]{-81}$

Not a real number

38. $\sqrt[6]{-64}$

Not a real number

39. $\sqrt[5]{(8)^5}$

8

40. $\sqrt[6]{(9)^6}$

9

41. $\sqrt[8]{(5)^8}$

5

42. $\sqrt[7]{(11)^7}$

11

Evaluate or simplify.

43. $4^{-3/2}$

$(\sqrt{4})^{-3} = \dfrac{1}{8}$

44. $27^{-2/3}$

$(\sqrt[3]{27})^{-2} = \dfrac{1}{9}$

45. $(-8)^{1/3}$

-2

46. $\left(\dfrac{1}{49}\right)^{1/2}$

$\dfrac{1}{7}$

47. $\left(\dfrac{16}{81}\right)^{3/4}$

$\left(\sqrt[4]{\dfrac{16}{81}}\right)^3 = \dfrac{8}{27}$

48. $(-125)^{2/3}$

$(\sqrt[3]{-125})^2 = (-5)^2 = 25$

49. $(25x^4)^{1/2}$

$5x^2$

50. $(36y^8)^{1/2}$

$6y^4$

51. $(-27x^3y^6)^{2/3}$

$(\sqrt[3]{-27x^3y^6})^2 = (-3xy^2)^2 = 9x^2y^4$

52. $(-64a^6b^9)^{2/3}$

$(\sqrt[3]{-64a^6b^9})^2 = (-4a^2b^3)^2 = 16a^4b^6$

53. $\sqrt{36x^6y^8z^{10}}$

$6x^3y^4z^5$

54. $\sqrt{100x^{10}y^{12}z^2}$

$10x^5y^6z$

55. $\sqrt[3]{216a^3b^9c^{12}}$

$6ab^3c^4$

56. $\sqrt[3]{-125a^6b^{15}c^{21}}$

$-5a^2b^5c^7$

57. $\sqrt[4]{16x^8y^{12}} + \sqrt[4]{81x^8y^{12}}$

$2x^2y^3 + 3x^2y^3 = 5x^2y^3$

58. $\sqrt[5]{32a^5b^{15}} + \sqrt[5]{a^5b^{15}}$

$2ab^3 + ab^3 = 3ab^3$

Simplify. Assume that the variables represent any positive or negative real number.

59. $\sqrt[6]{64x^6y^{18}z^{12}}$

$2z^2|xy^3|$

60. $\sqrt[4]{625x^8y^{20}z^4}$

$5x^2|y^5z|$

A company finds that the daily cost of producing appliances at one of its factories is $C = 120\sqrt[3]{n} + 375$ where n is the number of parts produced in a day and C is the cost in dollars.

61. Find the cost if 343 parts are produced per day.

Cost = $1215 per day

62. Find the cost if 216 parts are produced per day.

Cost = $1095 per day

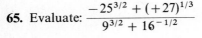

To Think About

63. Are $\sqrt[4]{(-16)^2}$ and $\left(\sqrt[4]{-16}\right)^2$ equivalent? Explain.

No, $\sqrt[4]{256} = 4$ but $\left(\sqrt[4]{-16}\right)^2$ is not a real number.

64. Is the equation $(x^{1/n})^m = (x^m)^{1/n}$ *always* true?

No, $n \neq 0$

65. Evaluate: $\dfrac{-25^{3/2} + (+27)^{1/3}}{9^{3/2} + 16^{-1/2}}$

$-\dfrac{488}{109}$

66. Assume that $x > 0$, $y > 0$, $z > 0$ and simplify:

$\dfrac{\sqrt[12]{3^{12}x^{36}y^{12}z^0}}{\sqrt[18]{2^{18}x^{72}y^{36}z^{54}}}$

$\dfrac{3x^3y}{2x^4y^2z^3} = \dfrac{3}{2xyz^3}$

Cumulative Review Problems

Collect like terms.

67. $\dfrac{1}{2}xy + \dfrac{1}{4}x^2 - 3xy - \dfrac{1}{2}x^2$

$-\dfrac{1}{4}x^2 - \dfrac{5}{2}xy$

68. $\dfrac{1}{5}ab - 2a^2 - 2ab + \dfrac{1}{3}a^2$

$-\dfrac{5}{3}a^2 - \dfrac{9}{5}ab$

Evaluate.

69. $2 + (-3)^2 + \sqrt{25} \div (-5)$

10

70. $\dfrac{5 + 6(-2)}{(-3)(-5) + 1(6 - 8) - 8 \div (-8)}$

$-\dfrac{1}{2}$

Calculator Problems

Evaluate.

71. $\sqrt[3]{12,167}$

23

72. $\sqrt[4]{456,976}$

26

73. $(-16,807)^{1/5}$

-7

74. $(117,649)^{1/6}$

7

For Extra Practice Exercises, turn to page 323.

Solutions to Odd-Numbered Practice Problems

1. (a) $\sqrt[3]{216} = \sqrt[3]{6^3} = 6$ **(b)** $\sqrt[5]{32} = \sqrt[5]{2^5} = 2$ **(c)** $\sqrt[3]{-8} = \sqrt[3]{(-2)^3} = -2$ **(d)** $\sqrt[6]{-64}$ is not a real number. We will *not* find a real number answer for $\sqrt[n]{x}$ when the index n is even and x is a negative real number.

3. (a) $8^{2/3} = \left(\sqrt[3]{8}\right)^2 = 2^2 = 4$ **(b)** $4^{3/2} = \left(\sqrt{4}\right)^3 = 2^3 = 8$ **(c)** $(-8)^{4/3} = \left(\sqrt[3]{-8}\right)^4 = (-2)^4 = 16$

(d) $(-25)^{3/2} = \left(\sqrt{-25}\right)^3$ *This is not a real number.*   **(e)** $100^{-3/2} = \dfrac{1}{100^{3/2}} = \dfrac{1}{\left(\sqrt{100}\right)^3} = \dfrac{1}{10^3} = \dfrac{1}{1000}$

(f) $32^{-3/5} = \dfrac{1}{32^{3/5}} = \dfrac{1}{\left(\sqrt[5]{32}\right)^3} = \dfrac{1}{2^3} = \dfrac{1}{8}$

5. (a) $x^{3/4} = \left(\sqrt[4]{x}\right)^3$ or $\sqrt[4]{x^3}$ **(b)** $y^{-1/3} = \dfrac{1}{y^{1/3}} = \dfrac{1}{\sqrt[3]{y}}$ **(c)** $(2x)^{4/5} = \left(\sqrt[5]{2x}\right)^4$ or $\sqrt[5]{16x^4}$ **(d)** $2x^{4/5} = 2\sqrt[5]{x^4}$ or $2\left(\sqrt[5]{x}\right)^4$

7. (a) $\sqrt[4]{81x^{12}} = (3^4 x^{12})^{1/4} = 3x^3$ **(b)** $\sqrt[3]{-27x^6} = [(-3)^3 x^6]^{1/3} = -3x^2$ **(c)** $(32x^5)^{3/5} = (2^5 x^5)^{3/5} = 2^3 x^3 = 8x^3$
(d) $16(x^6 y^8)^{7/2} = 16(x^{6\cdot 7/2} y^{8\cdot 7/2}) = 16x^{21} y^{28}$

Answers to Even-Numbered Practice Problems

2. (a) x **(b)** y **(c)** 8 **(d)** x^2 **4. (a)** $x^{3/4}$ **(b)** $(xy)^{7/5}$ or $x^{7/5} y^{7/5}$ **(c)** $z^{4/5}$ **6. (a)** -3 **(b)** 5 **(c)** $|w|$ **(d)** y

---

6.3 SIMPLIFYING, ADDING, AND SUBTRACTING RADICALS

☐ After studying this section, you will be able to:

1 *Simplify a radical by using the product rule*

2 *Combine like radical terms*

1 Simplifying

When we simplify a radical, we want to get an equivalent expression with the smallest possible quantity in the radicand. We can use the product rule for radicals to simplify radicals.

> **Product Rule for Radicals**
>
> For all positive real numbers a, b and positive integers n,
> $$\sqrt[n]{a}\sqrt[n]{b} = \sqrt[n]{ab}$$

You should be able to derive the product rule from your knowledge of the laws of exponents. We have

$$\sqrt[n]{ab} = (ab)^{1/n} = a^{1/n} b^{1/n} = \sqrt[n]{a}\,\sqrt[n]{b}$$

Throughout the remainder of this chapter assume that all variables in any radicand represent positive numbers, unless a specific statement is made to the contrary.

Example 1 Simplify: $\sqrt{32}$.

Solution 1: $\sqrt{32} = \sqrt{16 \cdot 2} = \sqrt{16}\sqrt{2} = 4\sqrt{2}$

Solution 2: $\sqrt{32} = \sqrt{8 \cdot 4} = \sqrt{8}\sqrt{4} = 2\sqrt{8} = 2\sqrt{4 \cdot 2} = 2\sqrt{4}\sqrt{2} = 4\sqrt{2}$

Although we obtained the same answer both times, the first solution is much shorter. You should try to use the largest factor that is a perfect square when you use the product rule. ∎

Practice Problem 1 Simplify: $\sqrt{20}$. ∎

Example 2 Simplify: **(a)** $\sqrt{125}$ **(b)** $\sqrt{48}$

(a) $\sqrt{125} = \sqrt{25}\sqrt{5} = 5\sqrt{5}$ **(b)** $\sqrt{48} = \sqrt{16}\sqrt{3} = 4\sqrt{3}$ ∎

Practice Problem 2 Simplify.
(a) $\sqrt{75}$ **(b)** $\sqrt{27}$ ∎

Example 3 Simplify: **(a)** $\sqrt[3]{16}$ **(b)** $\sqrt[3]{-81}$

(a) $\sqrt[3]{16} = \sqrt[3]{8}\sqrt[3]{2} = 2\sqrt[3]{2}$ **(b)** $\sqrt[3]{-81} = \sqrt[3]{-27}\sqrt[3]{3} = -3\sqrt[3]{3}$ ∎

Practice Problem 3 Simplify.
(a) $\sqrt[3]{24}$ **(b)** $\sqrt[3]{-108}$ ∎

Example 4 Simplify: $\sqrt[4]{48}$.

$$\sqrt[4]{48} = \sqrt[4]{16}\sqrt[4]{3} = 2\sqrt[4]{3}$$ ∎

Practice Problem 4 Simplify: $\sqrt[4]{64}$. ∎

TEACHING TIP After discussing example 2 or a similar example, ask students to simplify the following radicals.

A: $\sqrt{250}$ Ans. $5\sqrt{10}$

B: $\sqrt{98}$ Ans. $7\sqrt{2}$

TEACHING TIP Students often make errors in simplifying radicals by confusing whether they are working with a square root, a cube root, or a fourth root. After presenting example 4, discuss the differences in these three problems:

A: Simplify $\sqrt{63} = \sqrt{9}\sqrt{7} = 3\sqrt{7}$

B: Simplify $\sqrt[3]{135} = \sqrt[3]{27}\sqrt[3]{5} = 3\sqrt[3]{5}$

C: Simplify $\sqrt[4]{80} = \sqrt[4]{16}\sqrt[4]{5} = 2\sqrt[4]{5}$

Example 5   Simplify: $\sqrt{27x^3y^4}$; $x > 0$, $y > 0$.

$$\sqrt{27x^3y^4} = \sqrt{9x^2y^4}\sqrt{3x} = 3xy^2\sqrt{3x}$$ ■

Practice Problem 5   Simplify: $\sqrt{45x^6y^7}$; $x > 0$, $y > 0$. ■

Example 6   Simplify: $\sqrt{100a^4b^7c^0}$; $a > 0$, $b > 0$, $c > 0$.

$$\sqrt{100a^4b^7c^0} = \sqrt{100a^4b^6}\sqrt{b} = 10a^2b^3\sqrt{b}$$ ■

Practice Problem 6   Simplify: $\sqrt{81a^4b^0c^7}$; $a > 0$, $b > 0$, $c > 0$. ■

Example 7   Simplify: $\sqrt[3]{16x^4y^3z^6}$.

$$\sqrt[3]{16x^4y^3z^6} = \sqrt[3]{8x^3y^3z^6}\sqrt[3]{2x} = 2xyz^2\sqrt[3]{2x}$$ ■

Practice Problem 7   Simplify: $\sqrt[3]{27a^7b^8c^9}$. ■

Example 8   Simplify: $\sqrt[4]{10,000x^9y^8w^5}$.

$$\sqrt[4]{10,000x^9y^8w^5} = \sqrt[4]{10,000x^8y^8w^4}\sqrt[4]{xw} = 10x^2y^2w\sqrt[4]{xw}$$ ■

Practice Problem 8   Simplify: $\sqrt[4]{256a^8b^{11}c^{17}}$. ■

2   Adding and Subtracting Radicals

Only like **radicals** can be added or subtracted. Two radicals are like if they have the same radicand and the same index. When we combine radicals, we combine like terms by using the distributive property.

Example 9   Combine.   **(a)** $2\sqrt{5} + 3\sqrt{5} - 4\sqrt{5}$ **(b)** $5\sqrt[3]{x} - 8\sqrt[3]{x} - 12\sqrt[3]{x}$

(a) $2\sqrt{5} + 3\sqrt{5} - 4\sqrt{5} = (2 + 3 - 4)\sqrt{5} = 1\sqrt{5} = \sqrt{5}$

(b) $5\sqrt[3]{x} - 8\sqrt[3]{x} - 12\sqrt[3]{x} = (5 - 8 - 12)\sqrt[3]{x} = -15\sqrt[3]{x}$ ■

Practice Problem 9   Combine.

(a) $5\sqrt[3]{7} - 12\sqrt[3]{7} - 6\sqrt[3]{7}$ **(b)** $19\sqrt{xy} + 5\sqrt{xy} - 10\sqrt{xy}$ ■

Example 10   Combine: $5\sqrt{3} - \sqrt{27} + 2\sqrt{48}$.

$$5\sqrt{3} - \sqrt{27} + 2\sqrt{48} = 5\sqrt{3} - \sqrt{9}\sqrt{3} + 2\sqrt{16}\sqrt{3}$$
$$= 5\sqrt{3} - 3\sqrt{3} + 2(4)\sqrt{3}$$
$$= 5\sqrt{3} - 3\sqrt{3} + 8\sqrt{3}$$
$$= 10\sqrt{3}$$ ■

Practice Problem 10   Combine: $4\sqrt{2} - 5\sqrt{50} - 3\sqrt{98}$. ■

Example 11   Combine: $6\sqrt{x} + 4\sqrt{12x} - \sqrt{75x} + 3\sqrt{x}$.

$$6\sqrt{x} + 4\sqrt{12x} - \sqrt{75x} + 3\sqrt{x} = 6\sqrt{x} + 4\sqrt{4}\sqrt{3x} - \sqrt{25}\sqrt{3x} + 3\sqrt{x}$$
$$= 6\sqrt{x} + 8\sqrt{3x} - 5\sqrt{3x} + 3\sqrt{x}$$
$$= 6\sqrt{x} + 3\sqrt{x} + 8\sqrt{3x} - 5\sqrt{3x}$$
$$= 9\sqrt{x} + 3\sqrt{3x}$$ ■

Practice Problem 11   Combine: $4\sqrt{2x} + \sqrt{18x} - 2\sqrt{125x} - 6\sqrt{20x}$. ■

Example 12   Combine: $2\sqrt[3]{81x^3y^4} + 3xy\sqrt[3]{24y}$.

$$2\sqrt[3]{81x^3y^4} + 3xy\sqrt[3]{24y} = 2\sqrt[3]{27x^3y^3}\sqrt[3]{3y} + 3xy\sqrt[3]{8}\sqrt[3]{3y}$$
$$= 2(3xy)\sqrt[3]{3y} + 3xy(2)\sqrt[3]{3y}$$
$$= 6xy\sqrt[3]{3y} + 6xy\sqrt[3]{3y}$$
$$= 12xy\sqrt[3]{3y}$$ ■

Practice Problem 12   Combine: $3x\sqrt[3]{54x^4} - 3\sqrt[3]{16x^7}$. ■

Simplify. Assume that all variables are positive real numbers. If no real value is possible, so state.

1. $\sqrt{50}$
$\sqrt{25}\sqrt{2} = 5\sqrt{2}$

2. $\sqrt{32}$
$\sqrt{16}\sqrt{2} = 4\sqrt{2}$

3. $\sqrt{48}$
$\sqrt{16}\sqrt{3} = 4\sqrt{3}$

4. $\sqrt{75}$
$\sqrt{25}\sqrt{3} = 5\sqrt{3}$

5. $\sqrt{120}$
$\sqrt{4}\sqrt{30} = 2\sqrt{30}$

6. $\sqrt{80}$
$\sqrt{16 \cdot 5} = 4\sqrt{5}$

7. $\sqrt{81}$
9

8. $\sqrt{108}$
$\sqrt{36 \cdot 3} = 6\sqrt{3}$

9. $\sqrt{9x^3}$
$\sqrt{9x^2}\sqrt{x} = 3x\sqrt{x}$

10. $\sqrt{16x^5}$
$\sqrt{16x^4}\sqrt{x} = 4x^2\sqrt{x}$

11. $\sqrt{60a^4b^5}$
$\sqrt{4a^4b^4}\sqrt{15b} = 2a^2b^2\sqrt{15b}$

12. $\sqrt{45a^3b^8}$
$\sqrt{9a^2b^8}\sqrt{5a} = 3ab^4\sqrt{5a}$

13. $\sqrt{24xy^8z^3}$
$\sqrt{4y^8z^2}\sqrt{6xz} = 2y^4z\sqrt{6xz}$

14. $\sqrt{98x^5y^6z}$
$\sqrt{49x^4y^6 \cdot 2xz} = 7x^2y^3\sqrt{2xz}$

15. $\sqrt[3]{8}$
2

16. $\sqrt[3]{27}$
3

17. $\sqrt[3]{108}$
$\sqrt[3]{27 \cdot 4} = 3\sqrt[3]{4}$

18. $\sqrt[3]{128}$
$\sqrt[3]{64 \cdot 2} = 4\sqrt[3]{2}$

19. $\sqrt[3]{56}$
$\sqrt[3]{8 \cdot 7} = 2\sqrt[3]{7}$

20. $\sqrt[3]{104}$
$\sqrt[3]{8 \cdot 13} = 2\sqrt[3]{13}$

21. $\sqrt[3]{8a^3b^8}$
$\sqrt[3]{8a^3b^6} \cdot \sqrt[3]{b^2} = 2ab^2\sqrt[3]{b^2}$

22. $\sqrt[3]{125a^6b^2}$
$\sqrt[3]{125a^6}\sqrt[3]{b^2} = 5a^2\sqrt[3]{b^2}$

23. $\sqrt[3]{56x^{10}y^{12}}$
$\sqrt[3]{8x^9y^{12}}\sqrt[3]{7x} = 2x^3y^4\sqrt[3]{7x}$

24. $\sqrt[3]{72x^5y^{20}}$
$\sqrt[3]{8x^3y^{18}}\sqrt[3]{9x^2y^2} = 2xy^6\sqrt[3]{9x^2y^2}$

25. $\sqrt[3]{-16a^6b^3c^{12}}$
$\sqrt[3]{-8a^6b^3c^{12}}\sqrt[3]{2} = -2a^2bc^4\sqrt[3]{2}$

26. $\sqrt[3]{-40a^3b^7c^{14}}$
$\sqrt[3]{-8a^3b^6c^{12}}\sqrt[3]{5bc^2} = -2ab^2c^4\sqrt[3]{5bc^2}$

27. $\sqrt[4]{48x^8y^{13}}$
$\sqrt[4]{16x^8y^{12}}\sqrt[4]{3y} = 2x^2y^3\sqrt[4]{3y}$

28. $\sqrt[4]{32x^5y^{10}}$
$\sqrt[4]{16x^4y^8}\sqrt[4]{2xy^2} = 2xy^2\sqrt[4]{2xy^2}$

29. $\sqrt[4]{81kp^{23}}$
$\sqrt[4]{81p^{20}}\sqrt[4]{kp^3} = 3p^5\sqrt[4]{kp^3}$

30. $\sqrt[4]{16k^{12}p^{18}}$
$\sqrt[4]{16k^{12}p^{16}}\sqrt[4]{p^2} = 2k^3p^4\sqrt[4]{p^2}$ or $2k^3p^4\sqrt{p}$

31. $\sqrt[5]{-32x^5y^6}$
$\sqrt[5]{-32x^5y^5}\sqrt[5]{y} = -2xy\sqrt[5]{y}$

32. $\sqrt[5]{-243x^4y^{10}}$
$\sqrt[5]{-243y^{10}}\sqrt[5]{x^4} = -3y^2\sqrt[5]{x^4}$

33. $\sqrt[6]{8x^6y^{12}}$
$\sqrt[6]{x^6y^{12}} \cdot \sqrt[6]{8} = xy^2\sqrt[6]{8}$ or $xy^2\sqrt{2}$

34. $\sqrt[6]{64x^6y^8}$
$\sqrt[6]{64x^6y^6}\sqrt[6]{y^2} = 2xy\sqrt[6]{y^2}$ or $2xy\sqrt[3]{y}$

To Think About

35. $\sqrt[4]{1792} = a\sqrt[4]{7}$. What is the value of a?
$\sqrt[4]{256 \cdot 7} = \sqrt[4]{4^4 \cdot 7}$ $a = 4$

36. $\sqrt[3]{3072} = b\sqrt[3]{6}$. What is the value of b?
$\sqrt[3]{3072} = \sqrt[3]{6 \cdot 512} = \sqrt[3]{8^3 \cdot 6}$ $b = 8$

Combine. Assume that all variables represent positive real numbers.

37. $\sqrt{49} + \sqrt{100}$
17

38. $\sqrt{25} + \sqrt{81}$
14

39. $\sqrt{3} + 7\sqrt{3} - 2\sqrt{3}$
$6\sqrt{3}$

40. $\sqrt{11} - 5\sqrt{11} + 3\sqrt{11}$
$-\sqrt{11}$

41. $2\sqrt{12} - \sqrt{3}$
$4\sqrt{3} - \sqrt{3} = 3\sqrt{3}$

42. $3\sqrt{50} - \sqrt{2}$
$15\sqrt{2} - \sqrt{2} = 14\sqrt{2}$

43. $2\sqrt{8} - 3\sqrt{32} - \sqrt{18}$
$4\sqrt{2} - 12\sqrt{2} - 3\sqrt{2} = -11\sqrt{2}$

44. $\sqrt{75} - 2\sqrt{27} + 3\sqrt{12}$
$5\sqrt{3} - 6\sqrt{3} + 6\sqrt{3} = 5\sqrt{3}$

45. $-5\sqrt{45} + 6\sqrt{20} + 3\sqrt{5}$
$-15\sqrt{5} + 12\sqrt{5} + 3\sqrt{5} = 0$

46. $-7\sqrt{10} + 4\sqrt{40} - 8\sqrt{90}$
$-7\sqrt{10} + 8\sqrt{10} - 24\sqrt{10} = -23\sqrt{10}$

47. $2\sqrt{7x} - 3\sqrt{63x} + 4\sqrt{28x}$
$2\sqrt{7x} - 9\sqrt{7x} + 8\sqrt{7x} = \sqrt{7x}$

48. $\sqrt{75x} + 2\sqrt{108x} - 6\sqrt{3x}$
$5\sqrt{3x} + 12\sqrt{3x} - 6\sqrt{3x} = 11\sqrt{3x}$

49. $x\sqrt{20} - 3\sqrt{125x^2}$

$2x\sqrt{5} - 15x\sqrt{5} = -13x\sqrt{5}$

50. $-3\sqrt{45a^6} + a\sqrt{80a^4}$

$-9a^3\sqrt{5} + 4a^3\sqrt{5} = -5a^3\sqrt{5}$

51. $\sqrt[3]{16} + 3\sqrt[3]{54}$

$2\sqrt[3]{2} + 9\sqrt[3]{2} = 11\sqrt[3]{2}$

52. $\sqrt[3]{128} - 4\sqrt[3]{16}$

$4\sqrt[3]{2} - 8\sqrt[3]{2} = -4\sqrt[3]{2}$

53. $-2\sqrt[3]{125x^3y^4} + 3y^2\sqrt[3]{8x^3}$

$-10xy\sqrt[3]{y} + 6xy^2$

54. $2x\sqrt[3]{40xy} - 3\sqrt[3]{5x^4y}$

$4x\sqrt[3]{5xy} - 3x\sqrt[3]{5xy} = x\sqrt[3]{5xy}$

55. $-2\sqrt{72x^3y} + \sqrt[3]{3x^4y} - 3x\sqrt{50xy} + 4x\sqrt[3]{81xy}$

$-12x\sqrt{2xy} + x\sqrt[3]{3xy} - 15x\sqrt{2xy} + 12x\sqrt[3]{3xy}$
$= -27x\sqrt{2xy} + 13x\sqrt[3]{3xy}$

56. $5\sqrt[3]{16a^4b} + \sqrt{45a} - 3a\sqrt[3]{54ab} - 2\sqrt{80a}$

$10a\sqrt[3]{2ab} + 3\sqrt{5a} - 9a\sqrt[3]{2ab} - 8\sqrt{5a} = a\sqrt[3]{2ab} - 5\sqrt{5a}$

? To Think About

Combine. Assume that all variables represent positive real numbers.

57. $3\sqrt[6]{2x^{-3}y^{10}z^3x^4} + 2\sqrt[6]{(2xyz)^4(8x^{-3}y^6z^{-1})}$

$3\sqrt[6]{2xy^{10}z^3} + 2\sqrt[6]{(16x^4y^4z^4)(8x^{-3}y^6z^{-1})}$
$3\sqrt[6]{2xy^{10}z^3} + 2\sqrt[6]{128xy^{10}z^3}$
$3y\sqrt[6]{2xy^4z^3} + 4y\sqrt[6]{2xy^4z^3} = 7y\sqrt[6]{2xy^4z^3}$

58. $\sqrt[5]{(\sqrt{36x^6y^4})(3x)^3} + 2x\sqrt[5]{(81x^{-2})(2x^3y^2)}$

$\sqrt[5]{6x^3y^2 \cdot 27x^3} + 2x\sqrt[5]{162xy^2}$
$\sqrt[5]{162x^6y^2} + 2x\sqrt[5]{162xy^2}$
$x\sqrt[5]{162xy^2} + 2x\sqrt[5]{162xy^2} = 3x\sqrt[5]{162xy^2}$

Cumulative Review Problems

Solve for x.

59. $\dfrac{5}{7}(x-4) = \dfrac{5}{7}(4-x)$

$5x - 20 = 20 - 5x$
$10x = 40$
$x = 4$

60. $-4x + 12 - 2x = 2 - 6x + 4x$

$-6x + 12 = -2x + 2$
$\dfrac{5}{2} = x$

Factor completely.

61. $81x^2y - 25y$

$y(9x + 5)(9x - 5)$

62. $16x^3 - 56x^2y + 49xy^2$

$x(4x - 7y)^2$

Calculator Problems

63. Simplify: $\sqrt{0.066564x^3y^6}$.

$0.258x^{3/2}y^3$

64. Show that $\sqrt{98} + \sqrt{50} + \sqrt{128} = 20\sqrt{2}$ by evaluating the expression on the left-hand side, evaluating the expression on the right-hand side, and showing that the two decimal approximations are equal.

$20\sqrt{2} \overset{?}{=} 7\sqrt{2} + 5\sqrt{2} + 8\sqrt{2}$
$20\sqrt{2} \overset{?}{=} 20\sqrt{2}$
$20(1.414213567) \overset{?}{=} 9.899494937 + 7.071067812 + 11.31370850$
$28.28427125 = 28.28427124 \checkmark$

For Extra Practice Exercises, turn to page 323.

Solutions to Odd-Numbered Practice Problems

1. $\sqrt{20} = \sqrt{4 \cdot 5} = \sqrt{4}\sqrt{5} = 2\sqrt{5}$ **3. (a)** $\sqrt[3]{24} = \sqrt[3]{8}\sqrt[3]{3} = 2\sqrt[3]{3}$ **(b)** $\sqrt[3]{-108} = \sqrt[3]{-27}\sqrt[3]{4} = -3\sqrt[3]{4}$
5. $\sqrt{45x^6y^7} = \sqrt{9x^6y^6}\sqrt{5y} = 3x^3y^3\sqrt{5y}$ **7.** $\sqrt[3]{27a^7b^8c^9} = \sqrt[3]{27a^6b^6c^9}\sqrt[3]{ab^2} = 3a^2b^2c^3\sqrt[3]{ab^2}$
9. (a) $5\sqrt[3]{7} - 12\sqrt[3]{7} - 6\sqrt[3]{7} = (5 - 12 - 6)\sqrt[3]{7} = -13\sqrt[3]{7}$ **(b)** $19\sqrt{xy} + 5\sqrt{xy} - 10\sqrt{xy} = (19 + 5 - 10)\sqrt{xy} = 14\sqrt{xy}$
11. $4\sqrt{2x} + \sqrt{18x} - 2\sqrt{125x} - 6\sqrt{20x}$
$= 4\sqrt{2x} + \sqrt{9}\sqrt{2x} - 2\sqrt{25}\sqrt{5x} - 6\sqrt{4}\sqrt{5x}$
$= 4\sqrt{2x} + 3\sqrt{2x} - 10\sqrt{5x} - 12\sqrt{5x}$
$= 7\sqrt{2x} - 22\sqrt{5x}$

Answers to Even-Numbered Practice Problems

2. (a) $5\sqrt{3}$ **(b)** $3\sqrt{3}$ **4.** $2\sqrt[4]{4}$ **6.** $9a^2c^3\sqrt{c}$ **8.** $4a^2b^2c^4\sqrt[4]{b^3c}$ **10.** $-42\sqrt{2}$ **12.** $3x^2\sqrt[3]{2x}$

6.4 MULTIPLICATION AND DIVISION OF RADICALS

☐ After studying this section, you will be able to:

1 *Multiply radical expressions*

2 *Divide radical expressions by rationalizing the denominator*

1 Multiplication

We again use the product rule for radicals to multiply radical expressions.

Example 1 Multiply.   (a) $(\sqrt{3})(\sqrt{5})$ (b) $(3\sqrt{2})(5\sqrt{11x})$

(a) $(\sqrt{3})(\sqrt{5}) = \sqrt{15}$

(b) $(3\sqrt{2})(5\sqrt{11x}) = (3)(5)(\sqrt{2})(\sqrt{11x}) = 15\sqrt{22x}$ ∎

Practice Problem 1 Multiply.   (a) $\sqrt{7}\sqrt{5}$ (b) $(-4\sqrt{2})(-3\sqrt{13x})$ ∎

Example 2 Multiply.   (a) $\sqrt{5}(\sqrt{2} + 5\sqrt{5})$ (b) $\sqrt{6x}(\sqrt{3} + \sqrt{2x} + \sqrt{5})$

(a) $\sqrt{5}(\sqrt{2} + 5\sqrt{5}) = \sqrt{5}\sqrt{2} + \sqrt{5}(5\sqrt{5}) = \sqrt{10} + 5\sqrt{25} = \sqrt{10} + 5(5) = \sqrt{10} + 25$

(b) $\sqrt{6x}(\sqrt{3} + \sqrt{2x} + \sqrt{5}) = (\sqrt{6x})(\sqrt{3}) + (\sqrt{6x})(\sqrt{2x}) + (\sqrt{6x})(\sqrt{5})$
$$= \sqrt{18x} + \sqrt{12x^2} + \sqrt{30x}$$
$$= \sqrt{9}\sqrt{2x} + \sqrt{4x^2}\sqrt{3} + \sqrt{30x}$$
$$= 3\sqrt{2x} + 2x\sqrt{3} + \sqrt{30x}$$ ∎

Practice Problem 2 Multiply.

(a) $\sqrt{3}(\sqrt{6} - 5\sqrt{7})$ (b) $\sqrt{2x}(\sqrt{5} + 2\sqrt{3x} + \sqrt{8})$ ∎

To multiply two binomials containing radicals, we can use the distributive property. Most students find that the FOIL approach is helpful in remembering how to quickly find the four products.

Example 3 Multiply: $(\sqrt{2} + 3\sqrt{5})(2\sqrt{2} - \sqrt{5})$.

By FOIL:
$$(\sqrt{2} + 3\sqrt{5})(2\sqrt{2} - \sqrt{5}) = 2\sqrt{4} - \sqrt{10} + 6\sqrt{10} - 3\sqrt{25}$$
$$= 4 + 5\sqrt{10} - 15$$
$$= -11 + 5\sqrt{10}$$

By the distributive property:
$$(\sqrt{2} + 3\sqrt{5})(2\sqrt{2} - \sqrt{5}) = (\sqrt{2} + 3\sqrt{5})(2\sqrt{2}) - (\sqrt{2} + 3\sqrt{5})\sqrt{5}$$
$$= (2\sqrt{2})\sqrt{2} + (3\sqrt{5})(2\sqrt{2}) - \sqrt{5}\sqrt{2} - (3\sqrt{5})\sqrt{5}$$
$$= 2\sqrt{4} + 6\sqrt{10} - \sqrt{10} - 3\sqrt{25}$$
$$= 4 + 5\sqrt{10} - 15 = -11 + 5\sqrt{10}$$ ∎

Practice Problem 3 Multiply: $(\sqrt{7} + 4\sqrt{2})(2\sqrt{7} - 3\sqrt{2})$. ∎

Example 4 Multiply: $(7 - 3\sqrt{2})(4 - \sqrt{3})$.
$$(7 - 3\sqrt{2})(4 - \sqrt{3}) = 28 - 7\sqrt{3} - 12\sqrt{2} + 3\sqrt{6}$$ ∎

Practice Problem 4 Multiply: $(2 - 5\sqrt{5})(3 - 2\sqrt{2})$. ∎

Example 5 Multiply: $(\sqrt{7} + \sqrt{3x})^2$.

Solution 1: We can use the FOIL method or the distributive property.
$$(\sqrt{7} + \sqrt{3x})(\sqrt{7} + \sqrt{3x}) = \sqrt{49} + \sqrt{21x} + \sqrt{21x} + \sqrt{9x^2}$$
$$= 7 + \sqrt{21x} + \sqrt{21x} + 3x$$
$$= 7 + 2\sqrt{21x} + 3x$$

TEACHING TIP   Students have more difficulty multiplying two binomials similar to the binomials in example 4 than some of the other types. After discussing example 4, you may want to show them the following additional example:

$(4 + 5\sqrt{7})(3 + 2\sqrt{7})$
$= 12 + 8\sqrt{7} + 15\sqrt{7}$
$\quad + 10\sqrt{49}$
$= 12 + 23\sqrt{7} + 70$
$= 82 + 23\sqrt{7}$

Solution 2: We could also use this formula from Chapter 4:

$$(a + b)^2 = a^2 + 2ab + b^2$$

where $a = \sqrt{7}$ and $b = \sqrt{3x}$. Then

$$(\sqrt{7} + \sqrt{3x})^2 = (\sqrt{7})^2 + 2\sqrt{7}\sqrt{3x} + (\sqrt{3x})^2$$
$$= 7 + 2\sqrt{21x} + 3x \quad \blacksquare$$

Practice Problem 5 Multiply: $(\sqrt{5x} + \sqrt{10})^2$ $\blacksquare$

Use the approach that seems easiest to you.

TEACHING TIP The type of multiplication encountered in example 6 is needed in solving radical equations. After discussing example 6, ask students to do the following problem as classwork. Multiply and simplify your answer.

$$(\sqrt{2x - 1} - 3)^2$$

Ans. $2x + 8 - 6\sqrt{2x - 1}$

Example 6 Multiply: $(\sqrt{3x + 1} + 2)^2$.

Solution 1:

$$(\sqrt{3x + 1} + 2)(\sqrt{3x + 1} + 2) = (\sqrt{3x + 1})^2 + 2\sqrt{3x + 1} + 2\sqrt{3x + 1} + 4$$
$$= 3x + 1 + 4\sqrt{3x + 1} + 4$$
$$= 3x + 5 + 4\sqrt{3x + 1}$$

Solution 2: In the formula $(a + b)^2 = a^2 + 2ab + b^2$, $a = \sqrt{3x + 1}$ and $b = 2$.

$$(\sqrt{3x + 1} + 2)^2 = (\sqrt{3x + 1})^2 + 2(\sqrt{3x + 1})(2) + (2)^2$$
$$= 3x + 1 + 4\sqrt{3x + 1} + 4$$
$$= 3x + 5 + 4\sqrt{3x + 1} \quad \blacksquare$$

Practice Problem 6 Multiply: $(\sqrt{4x - 1} + 3)^2$. $\blacksquare$

Example 7 Multiply. **(a)** $\sqrt[3]{3x}(\sqrt[3]{x^2} + 3\sqrt[3]{4y})$ **(b)** $(\sqrt[3]{2y} + \sqrt[3]{4})(2\sqrt[3]{4y^2} - 3\sqrt[3]{2})$

(a) $\sqrt[3]{3x}(\sqrt[3]{x^2} + 3\sqrt[3]{4y}) = (\sqrt[3]{3x})(\sqrt[3]{x^2}) + 3(\sqrt[3]{3x})(\sqrt[3]{4y})$
$$= \sqrt[3]{3x^3} + 3\sqrt[3]{12xy}$$
$$= x\sqrt[3]{3} + 3\sqrt[3]{12xy}$$

(b) $(\sqrt[3]{2y} + \sqrt[3]{4})(2\sqrt[3]{4y^2} - 3\sqrt[3]{2}) = 2\sqrt[3]{8y^3} - 3\sqrt[3]{4y} + 2\sqrt[3]{16y^2} - 3\sqrt[3]{8}$
$$= 2(2y) - 3\sqrt[3]{4y} + 2\sqrt[3]{8}\sqrt[3]{2y^2} - 3(2)$$
$$= 4y - 3\sqrt[3]{4y} + 4\sqrt[3]{2y^2} - 6 \quad \blacksquare$$

Practice Problem 7 Multiply.
(a) $\sqrt[3]{2x}(\sqrt[3]{4x^2} + 3\sqrt[3]{y})$ **(b)** $(\sqrt[3]{7} + \sqrt[3]{x^2})(2\sqrt[3]{49} - \sqrt[3]{x})$ $\blacksquare$

2 Division

When we multiply radicals, we want to simplify the answer so that the smallest possible quantity is in the radicand. In order to achieve a similar goal for division of radicals we will need the following quotient rule:

Quotient Rule for Radicals

For all positive real numbers a, b and positive integers n,

$$\frac{\sqrt[n]{a}}{\sqrt[n]{b}} = \sqrt[n]{\frac{a}{b}}$$

By the laws of exponents once again, $\sqrt[n]{\dfrac{a}{b}} = \left(\dfrac{a}{b}\right)^{1/n}$
$$= \frac{a^{1/n}}{b^{1/n}}$$
$$= \frac{\sqrt[n]{a}}{\sqrt[n]{b}}$$

Thus to simplify $\sqrt{\dfrac{7}{16}}$ we have

$$\sqrt{\frac{7}{16}} = \frac{\sqrt{7}}{\sqrt{16}} = \frac{\sqrt{7}}{4}$$

If the expression contains a square root in the denominator, it is not simplified. To simplify the expression we may then multiply the numerator and denominator by the radical in the denominator. This is nothing more than applying the simple rules that for $x > 0$:

$$\sqrt{x}\sqrt{x} = \sqrt{x^2} = x \qquad \text{and} \qquad \frac{\sqrt{x}}{\sqrt{x}} = 1$$

This procedure is called **rationalizing the denominator**.

Example 8   Simplify by rationalizing the denominator: $\dfrac{3}{\sqrt{2}}$.

$$\frac{3}{\sqrt{2}} = \frac{3}{\sqrt{2}} \cdot \frac{\sqrt{2}}{\sqrt{2}} \qquad \text{Since } \frac{\sqrt{2}}{\sqrt{2}} = 1.$$

$$= \frac{3\sqrt{2}}{\sqrt{4}} \qquad \text{Product rule of radicals.}$$

$$= \frac{3\sqrt{2}}{2} \qquad \text{Simplifying.} \quad \blacksquare$$

Practice Problem 8   Simplify by rationalizing the denominator: $\dfrac{7}{\sqrt{3}}$. $\blacksquare$

We can rationalize the denominator either before or after we multiply the numerator and the denominator by a radical.

Example 9   Simplify: $\dfrac{3}{\sqrt{12x}}$.

Solution 1: First we simplify the radical in the denominator and then we multiply.

$$\frac{3}{\sqrt{12x}} = \frac{3}{\sqrt{4}\sqrt{3x}} = \frac{3}{2\sqrt{3x}} \cdot \frac{\sqrt{3x}}{\sqrt{3x}} = \frac{\cancel{3}\sqrt{3x}}{2(\cancel{3}x)} = \frac{\sqrt{3x}}{2x}$$

Solution 2: We can multiply numerator and denominator by a value that will make the denominator a perfect square.

$$\frac{3}{\sqrt{12x}} = \frac{3}{\sqrt{12x}} \cdot \frac{\sqrt{3x}}{\sqrt{3x}} = \frac{3\sqrt{3x}}{\sqrt{36x^2}}$$

$$= \frac{3\sqrt{3x}}{6x} = \frac{\sqrt{3x}}{2x} \quad \blacksquare$$

Practice Problem 9   Simplify $\dfrac{8}{\sqrt{20x}}$. $\blacksquare$

If the radical expression has a fraction, it is not considered to be simplified. We can use the quotient rule of radicals and then rationalize the denominator to simplify the radical. We have already rationalized denominators when they contain square roots. Now we will also need to rationalize the denominator if the denominator contains radical expressions that are cube roots or higher order roots.

TEACHING TIP Students find simplifying cube roots more difficult than square roots. You may want to do the following additional example. Simplify:

$$\frac{3}{\sqrt[3]{2a^2b}} = \frac{3}{\sqrt[3]{2a^2b}} \cdot \frac{\sqrt[3]{4ab^2}}{\sqrt[3]{4ab^2}}$$

$$= \frac{3\sqrt[3]{4ab^2}}{\sqrt[3]{8a^3b^3}} = \frac{3\sqrt[3]{4ab^2}}{2ab} \text{ Ans.}$$

Example 10   Simplify: $\sqrt[3]{\dfrac{2}{3x^2}}$.

Solution 1: $\sqrt[3]{\dfrac{2}{3x^2}} = \dfrac{\sqrt[3]{2}}{\sqrt[3]{3x^2}}$ Quotient rule of radicals.

$$= \frac{\sqrt[3]{2}}{\sqrt[3]{3x^2}} \cdot \boxed{\frac{\sqrt[3]{9x}}{\sqrt[3]{9x}}}$$ Multiplying by appropriate value so that denominator will be a perfect cube.

$$= \frac{\sqrt[3]{18x}}{\sqrt[3]{27x^3}}$$ Observe that we can evaluate the cube root.

$$= \frac{\sqrt[3]{18x}}{3x}$$ Simplifying.

Solution 2: $\sqrt[3]{\dfrac{2}{3x^2}} = \sqrt[3]{\dfrac{2}{3x^2} \cdot \boxed{\dfrac{9x}{9x}}}$ $\dfrac{9x}{9x} = 1.$

$$= \sqrt[3]{\frac{18x}{27x^3}}$$ Multiplying.

$$= \frac{\sqrt[3]{18x}}{\sqrt[3]{27x^3}}$$ Quotient rule.

$$= \frac{\sqrt[3]{18x}}{3x}$$ Simplifying. ■

Practice Problem 10   Simplify: $\sqrt[3]{\dfrac{6}{5x}}$. ■

If the radical expression contains a sum or difference with radicals, we multiply the numerator and denominator by the **conjugate** of the denominator. For example, the conjugate of $x + \sqrt{y}$ is $x - \sqrt{y}$; similarly, the conjugate of $x - \sqrt{y}$ is $x + \sqrt{y}$. What is the conjugate of $3 + \sqrt{2}$? It is $3 - \sqrt{2}$. How about $\sqrt{11} + \sqrt{xyz}$? It is $\sqrt{11} - \sqrt{xyz}$.

> **Conjugates**
>
> The expressions $\sqrt{x} + \sqrt{y}$ and $\sqrt{x} - \sqrt{y}$ are called *conjugates*. Each expression is the conjugate of the other expression.

Multiplying by conjugates is simply an application of the formula $(a+b)(a-b) = a^2 - b^2$. For example,

$$(\sqrt{x} + \sqrt{y})(\sqrt{x} - \sqrt{y}) = (\sqrt{x})^2 - (\sqrt{y})^2 = x - y$$

Example 11   Simplify: $\dfrac{5}{3 + \sqrt{2}}$.

$$\frac{5}{3 + \sqrt{2}} = \frac{5}{3 + \sqrt{2}} \cdot \boxed{\frac{3 - \sqrt{2}}{3 - \sqrt{2}}}$$ Multiplying numerator and denominator by the conjugate of $3 + \sqrt{2}$.

$$= \frac{15 - 5\sqrt{2}}{(3)^2 - (\sqrt{2})^2}$$

$$= \frac{15 - 5\sqrt{2}}{9 - 2} = \frac{15 - 5\sqrt{2}}{7}$$ ■

Practice Problem 11   Simplify $\dfrac{4}{2 + \sqrt{5}}$. ■

Example 12   Simplify: $\dfrac{\sqrt{7}+\sqrt{3}}{\sqrt{7}-\sqrt{3}}$.

The conjugate of $\sqrt{7}-\sqrt{3}$ is $\sqrt{7}+\sqrt{3}$.

$$\frac{\sqrt{7}+\sqrt{3}}{\sqrt{7}-\sqrt{3}}\cdot\frac{\sqrt{7}+\sqrt{3}}{\sqrt{7}+\sqrt{3}}=\frac{\sqrt{49}+2\sqrt{21}+\sqrt{9}}{(\sqrt{7})^2-(\sqrt{3})^2}$$

$$=\frac{7+2\sqrt{21}+3}{7-3}$$

$$=\frac{10+2\sqrt{21}}{4}$$

$$=\frac{2(5+\sqrt{21})}{2\cdot2}$$

$$=\frac{\cancel{2}(5+\sqrt{21})}{\cancel{2}\cdot2}$$

$$=\frac{5+\sqrt{21}}{2}\quad\blacksquare$$

Practice Problem 12   Simplify: $\dfrac{\sqrt{11}+\sqrt{2}}{\sqrt{11}-\sqrt{2}}$. ▪

TEACHING TIP After discussing example 12 you may want to present a slightly more difficult example for students to consider. Simplify:

$$\frac{2\sqrt{3}+\sqrt{6}}{\sqrt{3}-2\sqrt{6}}\cdot\frac{\sqrt{3}+2\sqrt{6}}{\sqrt{3}+2\sqrt{6}}$$

$$=\frac{2\sqrt{9}+4\sqrt{18}+\sqrt{18}+\sqrt{36}}{\sqrt{9}-4\sqrt{36}}$$

$$=\frac{6+5\sqrt{18}+6}{3-24}$$

$$=\frac{12+15\sqrt{2}}{-21}$$

$$=\frac{3(4+5\sqrt{2})}{3(-7)}$$

$$=\frac{4+5\sqrt{2}}{-7}\ \text{or}\ \frac{-4-5\sqrt{2}}{7}$$

EXERCISES 6.4

Multiply and simplify. Assume that all variables represent positive numbers.

1. $(\sqrt{3})(\sqrt{5})$
$\sqrt{15}$

2. $(\sqrt{6})(\sqrt{11})$
$\sqrt{66}$

3. $(2\sqrt{6})(-3\sqrt{2})$
$-6\sqrt{12}=-12\sqrt{3}$

4. $(-4\sqrt{5})(2\sqrt{10})$
$-8\sqrt{50}$
$-8(5\sqrt{2})=-40\sqrt{2}$

5. $(3\sqrt{2xy^2})(5\sqrt{6x^3y^2})$
$15\sqrt{12x^4y^4}=15\sqrt{4x^4y^4}\sqrt{3}$
$30x^2y^2\sqrt{3}$

6. $(8\sqrt{5x^4y})(2\sqrt{3xy^3})$
$16\sqrt{15x^5y^4}$
$16\sqrt{x^4y^4}\sqrt{15x}$
$16x^2y^2\sqrt{15x}$

7. $\sqrt{10}(\sqrt{5}+3\sqrt{10})$
$\sqrt{50}+3(10)$
$5\sqrt{2}+30$

8. $\sqrt{6}(2\sqrt{6}-5\sqrt{2})$
$2(6)-5\sqrt{12}$
$12-5\sqrt{4}\sqrt{3}$
$12-10\sqrt{3}$

9. $2\sqrt{x}(3\sqrt{x}-4\sqrt{5})$
$6x-8\sqrt{5x}$

10. $5\sqrt{y}(\sqrt{2y}+3\sqrt{5})$
$5\sqrt{2y^2}+15\sqrt{5y}$
$5y\sqrt{2}+15\sqrt{5y}$

11. $(2\sqrt{3}+\sqrt{6})(\sqrt{3}-\sqrt{6})$
$2(3)+\sqrt{18}-2\sqrt{18}-6$
$-\sqrt{18}$
$-3\sqrt{2}$

12. $(5\sqrt{2}+\sqrt{10})(\sqrt{2}-\sqrt{10})$
$5(2)+\sqrt{20}-5\sqrt{20}-10$
$-4\sqrt{20}=-8\sqrt{5}$

13. $(2\sqrt{3}+\sqrt{2})(2\sqrt{3}-4\sqrt{2})$
$4(3)+2\sqrt{6}-8\sqrt{6}-4(2)$
$4-6\sqrt{6}$

14. $(3\sqrt{3}+\sqrt{5})(\sqrt{3}-2\sqrt{5})$
$3(3)+\sqrt{15}-6\sqrt{15}-2(5)$
$-1-5\sqrt{15}$

15. $(\sqrt{7}+4\sqrt{5})(2\sqrt{7}+3\sqrt{5})$
$2(7)+8\sqrt{35}+3\sqrt{35}+12(5)$
$74+11\sqrt{35}$

16. $(\sqrt{6}+3\sqrt{3})(5\sqrt{6}+2\sqrt{3})$
$5(6)+15\sqrt{18}+2\sqrt{18}+6(3)$
$48+17\sqrt{18}$
$48+17(3)\sqrt{2}$
$48+51\sqrt{2}$

17. $(\sqrt{x}-4)(\sqrt{x}-2)$ $x-6\sqrt{x}+8$

18. $(3-\sqrt{x})(2-\sqrt{x})$
$6-5\sqrt{x}+x$

19. $(\sqrt{3}+2\sqrt{2})(\sqrt{5}+\sqrt{3})$
$\sqrt{15}+2\sqrt{10}+3+2\sqrt{6}$

20. $(3\sqrt{5}+\sqrt{8})(\sqrt{2}+2\sqrt{5})$
$3\sqrt{10}+6(5)+\sqrt{16}+2\sqrt{40}$
$3\sqrt{10}+34+4\sqrt{10}$
$7\sqrt{10}+34$

21. $(\sqrt{x}-2\sqrt{3x})(\sqrt{x}+2\sqrt{3x})$
$x-2\sqrt{3x^2}+2\sqrt{3x^2}-4(3x)$
$-11x$

22. $(2\sqrt{x}+\sqrt{5x})(2\sqrt{x}-\sqrt{5x})$
$4x+2\sqrt{5x^2}-2\sqrt{5x^2}-5x$
$-x$

23. $(\sqrt{5}-2\sqrt{6})^2$
$5-4\sqrt{30}+4(6)$
$29-4\sqrt{30}$

24. $(\sqrt{3} + 4\sqrt{7})^2$
$3 + 8\sqrt{21} + 16(7)$
$115 + 8\sqrt{21}$

25. $(\sqrt{3x + 4} + 3)^2$
$3x + 4 + 6\sqrt{3x + 4} + 9$
$3x + 13 + 6\sqrt{3x + 4}$

26. $(\sqrt{2x + 1} - 2)^2$
$2x + 1 - 4\sqrt{2x + 1} + 4$
$2x + 5 - 4\sqrt{2x + 1}$

27. $(2\sqrt{a} - 5\sqrt{b})^2$
$4a - 20\sqrt{ab} + 25b$

28. $(5\sqrt{a} + 4\sqrt{b})^2$
$25a + 40\sqrt{ab} + 16b$

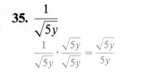

To Think About

29. What answer do you obtain when you multiply $(\sqrt[3]{6} + \sqrt[3]{5})(\sqrt[3]{36} - \sqrt[3]{30} + \sqrt[3]{25})$? Why?
In the form of
$(a + b)(a^2 - ab + b^2), (\sqrt[3]{6})^3 + (\sqrt[3]{5})^3 = 6 + 5 = 11,$
which equals $a^3 + b^3$

30. What answer do you obtain when you multiply $(\sqrt[3]{9} - \sqrt[3]{4})(3\sqrt[3]{3} + \sqrt[3]{36} + 2\sqrt[3]{2})$? Why?
In the form of
$(a - b)(a^2 + ab + b^2), (\sqrt[3]{9})^3 - (\sqrt[3]{4})^3 = 9 - 4 = 5,$
which equals $a^3 - b^3$

Simplify by rationalizing the denominator.

31. $\dfrac{3}{\sqrt{2}}$
$\dfrac{3}{\sqrt{2}} \cdot \dfrac{\sqrt{2}}{\sqrt{2}} = \dfrac{3\sqrt{2}}{2}$

32. $\dfrac{5}{\sqrt{7}}$
$\dfrac{5}{\sqrt{7}} \cdot \dfrac{\sqrt{7}}{\sqrt{7}} = \dfrac{5\sqrt{7}}{7}$

33. $\sqrt{\dfrac{x}{8}}$
$\dfrac{\sqrt{x}}{\sqrt{8}} \cdot \dfrac{\sqrt{2}}{\sqrt{2}} = \dfrac{\sqrt{2x}}{4}$

34. $\sqrt{\dfrac{y}{12}}$
$\dfrac{\sqrt{y}}{2\sqrt{3}} \cdot \dfrac{\sqrt{3}}{\sqrt{3}} = \dfrac{\sqrt{3y}}{6}$

35. $\dfrac{1}{\sqrt{5y}}$
$\dfrac{1}{\sqrt{5y}} \cdot \dfrac{\sqrt{5y}}{\sqrt{5y}} = \dfrac{\sqrt{5y}}{5y}$

36. $\dfrac{1}{\sqrt{3x}}$
$\dfrac{1}{\sqrt{3x}} \cdot \dfrac{\sqrt{3x}}{\sqrt{3x}} = \dfrac{\sqrt{3x}}{3x}$

37. $\dfrac{3\sqrt{3}}{\sqrt{6x}}$
$\dfrac{3\sqrt{3}}{\sqrt{6x}} \cdot \dfrac{\sqrt{6x}}{\sqrt{6x}} = \dfrac{3\sqrt{18x}}{6x} = \dfrac{3\sqrt{2x}}{2x}$

38. $\dfrac{4\sqrt{2}}{\sqrt{20y}}$
$\dfrac{4\sqrt{2}}{2\sqrt{5y}} \cdot \dfrac{\sqrt{5y}}{\sqrt{5y}} = \dfrac{2\sqrt{10y}}{5y}$

39. $\sqrt{\dfrac{5y}{7x^2}}$
$\dfrac{\sqrt{5y}}{x\sqrt{7}} \cdot \dfrac{\sqrt{7}}{\sqrt{7}} = \dfrac{\sqrt{35y}}{7x}$

40. $\sqrt{\dfrac{8x}{3y^2}}$
$\dfrac{2\sqrt{2x}}{y\sqrt{3}} \cdot \dfrac{\sqrt{3}}{\sqrt{3}} = \dfrac{2\sqrt{6x}}{3y}$

41. $\dfrac{2}{\sqrt{6} + \sqrt{3}}$
$\dfrac{2}{\sqrt{6} + \sqrt{3}} \cdot \dfrac{\sqrt{6} - \sqrt{3}}{\sqrt{6} - \sqrt{3}} = \dfrac{2(\sqrt{6} - \sqrt{3})}{6 - 3} = \dfrac{2(\sqrt{6} - \sqrt{3})}{3}$

42. $\dfrac{5}{\sqrt{2} + \sqrt{7}}$
$\dfrac{5}{\sqrt{2} + \sqrt{7}} \cdot \dfrac{\sqrt{2} - \sqrt{7}}{\sqrt{2} - \sqrt{7}} = \dfrac{5(\sqrt{2} - \sqrt{7})}{2 - 7} = -(\sqrt{2} - \sqrt{7})$

43. $\dfrac{\sqrt{7}}{\sqrt{7} - 1}$
$\dfrac{\sqrt{7}}{\sqrt{7} - 1} \cdot \dfrac{\sqrt{7} + 1}{\sqrt{7} + 1} = \dfrac{7 + \sqrt{7}}{7 - 1} = \dfrac{7 + \sqrt{7}}{6}$

44. $\dfrac{\sqrt{3}}{\sqrt{5} - 2}$
$\dfrac{\sqrt{3}}{\sqrt{5} - 2} \cdot \dfrac{\sqrt{5} + 2}{\sqrt{5} + 2} = \dfrac{\sqrt{15} + 2\sqrt{3}}{5 - 4} = \sqrt{15} + 2\sqrt{3}$

45. $\dfrac{\sqrt{x}}{\sqrt{3x} + \sqrt{2}}$
$\dfrac{\sqrt{x}}{\sqrt{3x} + \sqrt{2}} \cdot \dfrac{\sqrt{3x} - \sqrt{2}}{\sqrt{3x} - \sqrt{2}} = \dfrac{x\sqrt{3} - \sqrt{2x}}{3x - 2}$

46. $\dfrac{\sqrt{x}}{\sqrt{5} + \sqrt{2x}}$
$\dfrac{\sqrt{x}}{\sqrt{5} + \sqrt{2x}} \cdot \dfrac{\sqrt{5} - \sqrt{2x}}{\sqrt{5} - \sqrt{2x}} = \dfrac{\sqrt{5x} - x\sqrt{2}}{5 - 2x}$

47. $\dfrac{\sqrt{5} + \sqrt{3}}{\sqrt{5} - \sqrt{3}}$
$\dfrac{\sqrt{5} + \sqrt{3}}{\sqrt{5} - \sqrt{3}} \cdot \dfrac{\sqrt{5} + \sqrt{3}}{\sqrt{5} + \sqrt{3}} = \dfrac{5 + 2\sqrt{15} + 3}{5 - 3} = 4 + \sqrt{15}$

48. $\dfrac{\sqrt{11} - \sqrt{5}}{\sqrt{11} + \sqrt{5}}$
$\dfrac{\sqrt{11} - \sqrt{5}}{\sqrt{11} + \sqrt{5}} \cdot \dfrac{\sqrt{11} - \sqrt{5}}{\sqrt{11} - \sqrt{5}} = \dfrac{11 - 2\sqrt{55} + 5}{11 - 5} = \dfrac{8 - \sqrt{55}}{3}$

49. $\dfrac{\sqrt{3x} - \sqrt{y}}{\sqrt{3x} + \sqrt{y}}$
$\dfrac{\sqrt{3x} - \sqrt{y}}{\sqrt{3x} + \sqrt{y}} \cdot \dfrac{\sqrt{3x} - \sqrt{y}}{\sqrt{3x} - \sqrt{y}} = \dfrac{3x - 2\sqrt{3xy} + y}{3x - y}$

50. $\dfrac{\sqrt{x} + 2\sqrt{y}}{\sqrt{x} - 2\sqrt{y}}$
$\dfrac{\sqrt{x} + 2\sqrt{y}}{\sqrt{x} - 2\sqrt{y}} \cdot \dfrac{\sqrt{x} + 2\sqrt{y}}{\sqrt{x} + 2\sqrt{y}} = \dfrac{x + 4\sqrt{xy} + 4y}{x - 4y}$

51. $\dfrac{5\sqrt{3} - 3\sqrt{2}}{3\sqrt{2} - 2\sqrt{3}}$
$\dfrac{5\sqrt{3} - 3\sqrt{2}}{3\sqrt{2} - 2\sqrt{3}} \cdot \dfrac{3\sqrt{2} + 2\sqrt{3}}{3\sqrt{2} + 2\sqrt{3}} = \dfrac{15\sqrt{6} - 18 + 30 - 6\sqrt{6}}{9(2) - 4(3)} = \dfrac{3\sqrt{6} + 4}{2}$

52. $\dfrac{2\sqrt{6} + \sqrt{5}}{3\sqrt{6} - \sqrt{5}}$
$\dfrac{2\sqrt{6} + \sqrt{5}}{3\sqrt{6} - \sqrt{5}} \cdot \dfrac{3\sqrt{6} + \sqrt{5}}{3\sqrt{6} + \sqrt{5}} = \dfrac{36 + 5\sqrt{30} + 5}{9(6) - 5} = \dfrac{41 + 5\sqrt{30}}{49}$

53. $\dfrac{2\sqrt{5} + 1}{\sqrt{5} + 2}$
$\dfrac{2\sqrt{5} + 1}{\sqrt{5} + 2} \cdot \dfrac{\sqrt{5} - 2}{\sqrt{5} - 2} = \dfrac{10 - 3\sqrt{5} - 2}{5 - 4} = 8 - 3\sqrt{5}$

54. $\dfrac{2\sqrt{2} - 1}{2\sqrt{2} + 1}$
$\dfrac{2\sqrt{2} - 1}{2\sqrt{2} + 1} \cdot \dfrac{2\sqrt{2} - 1}{2\sqrt{2} - 1} = \dfrac{8 - 4\sqrt{2} + 1}{8 - 1} = \dfrac{9 - 4\sqrt{2}}{7}$

Multiply and simplify your answer.

55. $\left(\sqrt[4]{6x}\right)\left(3\sqrt[4]{8x^7}\right)$

$3\sqrt[4]{48x^8} = 3\sqrt[4]{16x^8}\sqrt[4]{3} = 6x^2\sqrt[4]{3}$

56. $\left(\sqrt[4]{9y^3}\right)\left(2\sqrt[4]{27y^3}\right)$

$2\sqrt[4]{243y^6} = 2\sqrt[4]{81y^4}\sqrt[4]{3y^2} = 6y\sqrt[4]{3y^2}$

57. $\left(\sqrt[3]{x^2}\right)\left(3\sqrt[3]{4x} - 4\sqrt[3]{x^5}\right)$

$3\sqrt[3]{4x^3} - 4\sqrt[3]{x^7} = 3x\sqrt[3]{4} - 4x^2\sqrt[3]{x}$

58. $\left(2\sqrt[3]{x}\right)\left(\sqrt[3]{4x^2} - \sqrt[3]{14x}\right)$

$2\sqrt[3]{4x^3} - 2\sqrt[3]{14x^2} = 2x\sqrt[3]{4} - 2\sqrt[3]{14x^2}$

59. $\left(\sqrt[3]{x} + \sqrt[3]{2x^2}\right)\left(3\sqrt[3]{x} - \sqrt[3]{4x}\right)$

$3\sqrt[3]{x^2} + 3\sqrt[3]{2x^3} - \sqrt[3]{4x^2} - \sqrt[3]{8x^3}$
$= 3\sqrt[3]{x^2} + 3x\sqrt[3]{2} - \sqrt[3]{4x^2} - 2x$

60. $\left(4\sqrt[3]{4x} - \sqrt[3]{2x^2}\right)\left(\sqrt[3]{x} + 2\sqrt[3]{2x}\right)$

$4\sqrt[3]{4x^2} - \sqrt[3]{2x^3} + 8\sqrt[3]{8x^2} - 2\sqrt[3]{4x^3}$
$= 4\sqrt[3]{4x^2} - x\sqrt[3]{2} + 16\sqrt[3]{x^2} - 2x\sqrt[3]{4}$

Simplify by rationalizing the denominator.

61. $\dfrac{3}{\sqrt[4]{2x^3}}$

$\dfrac{3}{\sqrt[4]{2x^3}} \cdot \dfrac{\sqrt[4]{2^3x}}{\sqrt[4]{2^3x}} = \dfrac{3\sqrt[4]{8x}}{2x}$

62. $\dfrac{6}{\sqrt[4]{8x}}$

$\dfrac{6}{\sqrt[4]{2^3x}} \cdot \dfrac{\sqrt[4]{2x^3}}{\sqrt[4]{2x^3}} = \dfrac{6\sqrt[4]{2x^3}}{2x} = \dfrac{3\sqrt[4]{2x^3}}{x}$

63. $\dfrac{\sqrt[3]{3x^5}}{\sqrt[3]{7x^2}}$

$\dfrac{x\sqrt[3]{3x^2}}{x} \cdot \dfrac{\sqrt[3]{7^2x}}{\sqrt[3]{7^2x}} = \dfrac{x\sqrt[3]{147x^3}}{7x} = \dfrac{x\sqrt[3]{147}}{7}$

64. $\dfrac{\sqrt[3]{6y^4}}{\sqrt[3]{4x^5}}$

$\dfrac{y\sqrt[3]{6y}}{x\sqrt[3]{2^2x^2}} \cdot \dfrac{\sqrt[3]{2x}}{\sqrt[3]{2x}} = \dfrac{y\sqrt[3]{12xy}}{2x^2}$

65. $\dfrac{2x^2y}{\sqrt[5]{4x^2y^4}}$

$\dfrac{2x^2y}{\sqrt[5]{2^2x^2y^4}} \cdot \dfrac{\sqrt[5]{2^3x^3y}}{\sqrt[5]{2^3x^3y}} = \dfrac{2x^2y\sqrt[5]{8x^3y}}{2xy} = x\sqrt[5]{8x^3y}$

66. $\dfrac{3xy^2}{\sqrt[5]{8xy^3}}$

$\dfrac{3xy^2}{\sqrt[5]{2^3xy^3}} \cdot \dfrac{\sqrt[5]{2^2x^4y^2}}{\sqrt[5]{2^2x^4y^2}} = \dfrac{3xy^2\sqrt[5]{4x^4y^2}}{2xy} = \dfrac{3y\sqrt[5]{4x^4y^2}}{2}$

? To Think About

In calculus, students are sometimes required to rationalize the numerator of an expression. In this case the numerator will not have a radical in the answer. Rationalize the numerator in each of the following.

67. $\dfrac{\sqrt{5}}{7}$

$\dfrac{\sqrt{5}}{7} \cdot \dfrac{\sqrt{5}}{\sqrt{5}} = \dfrac{5}{7\sqrt{5}}$

68. $\dfrac{\sqrt{6}}{10}$

$\dfrac{\sqrt{6}}{10} \cdot \dfrac{\sqrt{6}}{\sqrt{6}} = \dfrac{6}{10\sqrt{6}} = \dfrac{3}{5\sqrt{6}}$

69. $\dfrac{\sqrt{3} + 2\sqrt{7}}{8}$

$\dfrac{\sqrt{3} + 2\sqrt{7}}{8} \cdot \dfrac{\sqrt{3} - 2\sqrt{7}}{\sqrt{3} - 2\sqrt{7}} = \dfrac{3 - 28}{8\left(\sqrt{3} - 2\sqrt{7}\right)} = \dfrac{-25}{8\left(\sqrt{3} - 2\sqrt{7}\right)}$

70. $\dfrac{\sqrt{5} - 4\sqrt{3}}{6}$

$\dfrac{\sqrt{5} - 4\sqrt{3}}{6} \cdot \dfrac{\sqrt{5} + 4\sqrt{3}}{\sqrt{5} + 4\sqrt{3}} = \dfrac{5 - 16(3)}{6\left(\sqrt{5} + 4\sqrt{3}\right)} = \dfrac{-43}{6\left(\sqrt{5} + 4\sqrt{3}\right)}$

A triangular piece of lawn is fertilized. The cost is \$0.18 per square foot. Find the cost to fertilize the lawn if:

71. The base of the triangle is $\sqrt{21}$ feet and the altitude is $\sqrt{50}$ feet. Round answer to nearest cent.

Cost = \$2.92

72. The base of the triangle is $\sqrt{17}$ feet and the altitude is $\sqrt{40}$ feet. Round answer to nearest cent.

Cost = \$2.35

Rationalize each fraction and then add the radical expressions.

73. $\dfrac{2}{\sqrt{2a}} + \dfrac{3}{\sqrt{3a}} + \dfrac{4}{\sqrt{5a}}$

$\dfrac{2\sqrt{2a}}{2a} + \dfrac{3\sqrt{3a}}{3a} + \dfrac{4\sqrt{5a}}{5a} = \dfrac{\sqrt{2a}}{a} + \dfrac{\sqrt{3a}}{a} + \dfrac{4\sqrt{5a}}{5a} = \dfrac{5\sqrt{2a} + 5\sqrt{3a} + 4\sqrt{5a}}{5a}$

74. $\dfrac{3}{\sqrt{6x}} - \dfrac{4}{\sqrt{2x}} + \dfrac{1}{\sqrt{12x}}$

$\dfrac{3\sqrt{6x}}{6x} - \dfrac{4\sqrt{2x}}{2x} + \dfrac{\sqrt{3x}}{6x} = \dfrac{\sqrt{6x}}{2x} - \dfrac{2\sqrt{2x}}{x} + \dfrac{\sqrt{3x}}{6x} = \dfrac{3\sqrt{6x} - 12\sqrt{2x} + \sqrt{3x}}{6x}$

Cumulative Review Problems

Solve for x and y.

75. $2x + 3y = 13$
$5x - 2y = 4$

$\begin{array}{r} 4x + 6y = 26 \\ 15x - 6y = 12 \\ \hline 19x = 38 \end{array}$
$x = 2,\ y = 3$

76. $4x - 3y = 7$
$x - \dfrac{2}{3}y = 2$

$\begin{array}{r} 8x - 6y = 14 \\ -9x + 6y = -18 \\ \hline x = 4,\ y = 3 \end{array}$

Solve for x, y, and z.

77. $3x - y - z = 5$
$\ 2x + 3y - z = -16$
$\ \ \ x + 2y + 2z = -3$

Eliminate z:

$\boxed{\text{1 and 3}}\ 7x = 7 \Rightarrow x = 1$
$\boxed{\text{1 and 2}}\ x - 4y = 21$
$y = -5,\ z = 3$

78. $2x + z = -10$
$\ 4x - 2y = -8$
$\ \ \ \ \ \ \ \ \ 3y - 5z = 14$

Eliminate z:

$\boxed{\text{1 and 3}}\ 10x + 3y = -36$
$\boxed{2}\ \ \ \ \ \ \ 4x - 2y = -8$
$20x + 6y = -72$
$\underline{12x - 6y = -24}$
$x = -3,\ y = -2,\ z = -4$

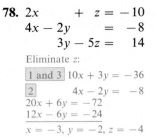

Calculator Problems

79. Multiply and simplify:

$(1.263\sqrt{x} - 1.425\sqrt{y})(2.815\sqrt{x} + 1.804\sqrt{y}).$

$3.555345x - 1.732923\sqrt{xy} - 2.5707y$

80. A student rationalized the denominator of $\dfrac{\sqrt{5}}{\sqrt{5}+\sqrt{3}}$

and obtained $\dfrac{5 - \sqrt{15}}{2}$. Find a decimal approxima-

tion of each expression. Are the decimals equal? Did
the student do the work correctly?

$\dfrac{\sqrt{5}}{\sqrt{5}+\sqrt{3}} = 0.563508327$

$\dfrac{5 - \sqrt{15}}{2} = 0.563508327$ Yes

For Extra Practice Exercises, turn to page 324.

Solutions to Odd-Numbered Practice Problems

1. (a) $\sqrt{7}\sqrt{5} = \sqrt{35}$
(b) $(-4\sqrt{2})(-3\sqrt{13x}) = (-4)(-3)\sqrt{2}\sqrt{3x} = 12\sqrt{26x}$

3. By FOIL

$(\sqrt{7} + 4\sqrt{2})(2\sqrt{7} - 3\sqrt{2}) = 2\sqrt{49} - 3\sqrt{14} + 8\sqrt{14} - 12\sqrt{4}$
$= 14 + 5\sqrt{14} - 24$
$= -10 + 5\sqrt{14}$

5. *Solution 1:*

$(\sqrt{5x} + \sqrt{10})(\sqrt{5x} + \sqrt{10}) = \sqrt{25x^2} + \sqrt{50x} + \sqrt{50x} + \sqrt{100}$
$= 5x + 2\sqrt{50x} + 10$
$= 5x + 10\sqrt{2x} + 10$

Solution 2: Use $(a + b)^2 = a^2 + 2ab + b^2$ where $a = \sqrt{5x}$ and $b = \sqrt{10}$

$(\sqrt{5x} + \sqrt{10})^2 = (\sqrt{5x})^2 + 2(\sqrt{5x})(\sqrt{10}) + (\sqrt{10})^2$
$= 5x + 2\sqrt{50x} + 10$
$= 5x + 10\sqrt{2x} + 10$

7. (a) $\sqrt[3]{2x}(\sqrt[3]{4x^2} + 3\sqrt[3]{y}) = \sqrt[3]{8x^3} + 3\sqrt[3]{2xy}$
$= 2x + 3\sqrt[3]{2xy}$

(b) $(\sqrt[3]{7} + \sqrt[3]{x^2})(2\sqrt[3]{7^2} - \sqrt[3]{x}) = 2\sqrt[3]{7^3} - \sqrt[3]{7x} + 2\sqrt[3]{7^2 x^2} - \sqrt[3]{x^3}$
$= 14 - \sqrt[3]{7x} + 2\sqrt[3]{49x^2} - x$

9. *Solution 1:* $\dfrac{8}{\sqrt{20x}} = \dfrac{8}{\sqrt{4}\sqrt{5x}} = \dfrac{8}{2\sqrt{5x}} = \dfrac{4}{\sqrt{5x}} \cdot \dfrac{\sqrt{5x}}{\sqrt{5x}} = \dfrac{4\sqrt{5x}}{5x}$

Solution 2: $\dfrac{8}{\sqrt{20x}} \cdot \dfrac{\sqrt{5x}}{\sqrt{5x}} = \dfrac{8\sqrt{5x}}{\sqrt{100x^2}} = \dfrac{8\sqrt{5x}}{10x} = \dfrac{4\sqrt{5x}}{5x}$

11. $\dfrac{4}{2 + \sqrt{5}} \cdot \dfrac{2 - \sqrt{5}}{2 - \sqrt{5}} = \dfrac{8 - 4\sqrt{5}}{(2)^2 - (\sqrt{5})^2}$
$= \dfrac{8 - 4\sqrt{5}}{4 - 5} = \dfrac{8 - 4\sqrt{5}}{-1}$
$= \dfrac{-1(8 - 4\sqrt{5})}{1}$
$= -8 + 4\sqrt{5}$

Answers to Even-Numbered Practice Problems

2. (a) $3\sqrt{2} - 5\sqrt{21}$ **(b)** $\sqrt{10x} + 2x\sqrt{6} + 4\sqrt{x}$ **4.** $6 - 4\sqrt{2} - 15\sqrt{5} + 10\sqrt{10}$ **6.** $4x + 8 + 6\sqrt{4x - 1}$ **8.** $\dfrac{7\sqrt{3}}{3}$

10. $\dfrac{\sqrt[3]{150x^2}}{5x}$ **12.** $\dfrac{13 + 2\sqrt{22}}{9}$

6.5 COMPLEX NUMBERS

After studying this section, you will be able to:

1 *Simplify square roots that contain negative radicands using the i notation*

2 *Add or subtract two or more complex numbers*

3 *Multiply two complex numbers*

4 *Evaluate the i^n power for any integer n*

5 *Divide two complex numbers by multiplying the fraction by the conjugate of the denominator*

1 Until now we have not been able to evaluate expressions such as $x^2 = -4$ because there is no *real* number that satisfies this equation. However, this equation *does* have a solution, but the solution is not a real number. It is an **imaginary** number.

We define a new number

$$i = \sqrt{-1} \quad \text{or} \quad i^2 = -1$$

Then

$$\sqrt{-4} = \sqrt{4(-1)} = \sqrt{4}\sqrt{-1} = \sqrt{4}\,i = 2i$$

Thus one solution to the equation $x^2 + 4 = 0$ is $x = 2i$. Let's check it.

$$x^2 + 4 = 0$$
$$(2i)^2 + 4 = 0$$
$$4i^2 + 4 = 0$$
$$4(-1) + 4 = 0$$
$$0 = 0$$

The conjugate $-2i$ is also a solution. You should verify this. A **complex number** is a combination of a real number and an imaginary number.

If you have difficulty grasping this concept, don't despair—the concept of a complex number is quite sophisticated. Many great mathematicians could not understand how the expression $\sqrt{-1}$ had any meaning at all, and they refused to use it. An understanding of complex numbers is essential to understanding electricity, physics, and many advanced mathematical topics. An entire branch of mathematics is devoted to complex analysis.

Now we formalize our definitions and give some examples.

> **Definition of Imaginary Number**
>
> The imaginary number i is defined as
> $$i = \sqrt{-1} \quad \text{and} \quad i^2 = -1$$

> **Definition**
>
> For all positive real numbers a,
> $$\sqrt{-a} = \sqrt{-1}\sqrt{a} = i\sqrt{a}$$

Example 1 Simplify. **(a)** $\sqrt{-36}$ **(b)** $\sqrt{-17}$

(a) $\sqrt{-36} = \sqrt{-1}\sqrt{36} = (i)(6) = 6i$
(b) $\sqrt{-17} = \sqrt{-1}\sqrt{17} = i\sqrt{17}$ ■

Practice Problem 1 Simplify. **(a)** $\sqrt{-49}$ **(b)** $\sqrt{-31}$ ■

To avoid confusing $\sqrt{17}i$ with $\sqrt{17i}$, we write the i before the radical.

Example 2 Simplify. **(a)** $\sqrt{-12}$ **(b)** $\sqrt{-45}$

(a) $\sqrt{-12} = \sqrt{-1}\sqrt{12} = i\sqrt{12} = i\sqrt{4}\sqrt{3} = 2i\sqrt{3}$
(b) $\sqrt{-45} = \sqrt{-1}\sqrt{45} = i\sqrt{45} = i\sqrt{9}\sqrt{5} = 3i\sqrt{5}$ ■

Practice Problem 2 Simplify.
(a) $\sqrt{-98}$ **(b)** $\sqrt{-150}$ ■

TEACHING TIP Students sometimes get confused with the three types of radical expressions that they may need to simplify. After discussing example 2, show them the following example. Simplify:

A: $\sqrt{-49} = \sqrt{-1}\sqrt{49} = (i)(7)$
   $= 7i$

B: $\sqrt{-80} = \sqrt{-1}\sqrt{80}$
   $= i\sqrt{16}\sqrt{5} = 4i\sqrt{5}$

C: $\sqrt{-43} = \sqrt{-1}\sqrt{43}$
   $= i\sqrt{43}$

The rule $\sqrt{a}\sqrt{b} = \sqrt{ab}$ requires that $a \geq 0$ and $b \geq 0$. Therefore, we cannot use our product rule when the radicands are negative unless we first use the definition of $\sqrt{-1}$. For example,

$$\sqrt{-1} \cdot \sqrt{-1} = i \cdot i = i^2 = -1$$

which is correct.

Example 3 Multiply: $\sqrt{-16} \cdot \sqrt{-25}$.

First we must use the definition $\sqrt{-1} = i$. Thus

$$(\sqrt{-16})(\sqrt{-25}) = (i\sqrt{16})(i\sqrt{25})$$
$$= i^2(4)(5)$$
$$= -1(20)$$
$$= -20 \quad \blacksquare$$

Practice Problem 3 Change to the i notation and multiply: $\sqrt{-8} \cdot \sqrt{-2}$ ▪

Now we formally define a complex number.

Definition

A number that can be placed in the form $a + bi$, where a and b are real numbers, is a **complex number**.

Under this definition every real number is also a complex number. For example, the real number 5 can be written as $5 + 0i$. Therefore, 5 is a complex number. In similar fashion, the imaginary number $2i$ can be written as $0 + 2i$. Thus, $2i$ is a complex number. Thus, the set of complex numbers includes the set of real numbers.

Definition

Two complex numbers $a + bi$ and $c + di$ are equal if and only if $a = c$ and $b = d$.

This definition means that two complex numbers are equal only if their real parts are equal *and* their imaginary parts are equal.

Example 4 Find real numbers x and y if $x + 3i\sqrt{7} = -2 + yi$.

By our definition, the real parts must be equal, so x must be -2; the imaginary parts must also be equal, so y must be $3\sqrt{7}$. ▪

Practice Problem 4 Find real numbers x and y if $-7 + 2yi\sqrt{3} = x + 6i\sqrt{3}$. ▪

2

Adding and Subtracting Complex Numbers

For all real numbers, a, b, c, and d,

$$(a + bi) + (c + di) = (a + c) + (b + d)i$$
$$(a + bi) - (c + di) = (a - c) + (b - d)i$$

In other words, we add (or subtract) the real parts, and we add (or subtract) the imaginary parts.

Example 5 **(a)** Add: $(7 - 3i) + (-4 - 2i)$. **(b)** Subtract: $(6 - 2i) - (3 - 5i)$.

(a) $(7 - 3i) + (-4 - 2i) = (7 - 4) + (-3 - 2)i$
$$= 3 - 5i$$

(b) $(6 - 2i) - (3 - 5i) = (6 - 2i) + (-3 + 5i) = (6 - 3) + (-2 + 5)i$
$$= 3 + 3i \quad \blacksquare$$

Practice Problem 5
(a) Add: $(-6 - 2i) + (5 - 8i)$.   **(b)** Subtract: $(3 - 4i) - (-2 - 18i)$.   ■

3 We can multiply numbers just as we did binomials.

Example 6   Multiply: $(7 - 6i)(2 + 3i)$.

$$(7 - 6i)(2 + 3i) = (7)(2) + (7)(3i) + (-6i)(2) + (-6i)(3i)$$
$$= 14 + 21i - 12i - 18i^2$$
$$= 14 + 21i - 12i - 18(-1)$$
$$= 14 + 21i - 12i + 18$$
$$= 32 + 9i \quad \blacksquare$$

TEACHING TIP   After explaining example 6, ask the class to do the following problem as a class exercise. Multiply and simplify:

$$(8 + 5i)(7 + 4i)$$

Ans. $36 + 67i$

Practice Problem 6   Multiply: $(4 - 2i)(3 - 7i)$.   ■

Example 7   Multiply: $3i(4 - 5i)$.

Use the distributive property.

$$3i(4 - 5i) = (3)(4)i + (3)(-5)i^2$$
$$= 12i - 15i^2$$
$$= 12i - 15(-1)$$
$$= 15 - 12i \quad \blacksquare$$

Practice Problem 7   Multiply: $-2i(5 + 6i)$.   ■

4 Another principle of multiplication is important. How would you evaluate i^n where n is any positive integer? We have defined

$$i^2 = -1$$

We could write

$$i^3 = i^2 \cdot i = (-1)i = -i$$

and similarly,

$$i^4 = i^2 \cdot i^2 = (-1)(-1) = +1$$
$$i^5 = i \cdot i^4 = (+1)i = +i$$

Using the same technique, we can obtain the following interesting pattern:

$i = i$	$i^2 = -1$	$i^3 = -i$	$i^4 = 1$
$i^5 = i$	$i^6 = -1$	$i^7 = -i$	$i^8 = 1$
$i^9 = i$	$i^{10} = -1$	$i^{11} = -i$	$i^{12} = 1$

and so on.

Example 8   Evaluate.

(a) i^{36} **(b)** i^{27}

(a) $i^{36} = (i^4)^9 = (1)^9 = 1$
(b) $i^{27} = (i^{24+3}) = (i^{24})(i^3) = (i^8)^3(i^3) = (1)^3(-i) = -i$ ■

The solutions to Example 8 can be obtained by using other approaches as well. Can you think of another way to obtain the answers?

Practice Problem 8   Evaluate.
(a) i^{42} **(b)** i^{53} ■

5 The complex numbers $a + bi$ and $a - bi$ are called **conjugates**. The product of two complex conjugates is always a real number.

$$(a + bi)(a - bi) = a^2 - abi + abi + b^2i^2$$
$$= a^2 - b^2(-1)$$
$$= a^2 + b^2$$

To divide two complex numbers, we want to remove any expression involving i from the denominator. So when dividing two complex numbers, we multiply the numerator and denominator by the conjugate of the denominator. This is just what we did when we rationalized the denominator in a radical expression.

TEACHING TIP Students tend to make sign errors with this type of problem. After discussing example 9, you may want to do the following additional sample example. Divide and simplify your answer.

$(2 - 7i) \div (8 - 3i)$

$= \dfrac{2 - 7i}{8 - 3i} \cdot \dfrac{8 + 3i}{8 + 3i}$

$= \dfrac{16 + 6i - 56i - 21i^2}{64 - 9i^2}$

$= \dfrac{16 - 50i + 21}{64 + 9}$

$= \dfrac{37 - 50i}{73}$

Example 9 Divide: $\dfrac{7 + i}{3 - 2i}$.

$$\dfrac{(7 + i)}{(3 - 2i)} \cdot \dfrac{(3 + 2i)}{(3 + 2i)} = \dfrac{21 + 14i + 3i + 2i^2}{9 - 4i^2} = \dfrac{21 + 17i + 2(-1)}{9 - 4(-1)} = \dfrac{21 + 17i - 2}{9 + 4}$$

$$= \dfrac{19 + 17i}{13} \quad \text{or} \quad \dfrac{19}{13} + \dfrac{17}{13}i \quad ■$$

Practice Problem 9 Divide: $\dfrac{4 + 2i}{3 + 4i}$. ■

Example 10 Divide: $\dfrac{3 - 2i}{4i}$.

The conjugate of $0 + 4i$ is $0 - 4i$ or simply $-4i$.

$$\dfrac{(3 - 2i)}{(4i)} \cdot \dfrac{(-4i)}{(-4i)} = \dfrac{-12i + 8i^2}{-16i^2} = \dfrac{-12i + 8(-1)}{-16(-1)}$$

$$= \dfrac{-8 - 12i}{16} = \dfrac{\cancel{4}(-2 - 3i)}{\cancel{4} \cdot 4}$$

$$= \dfrac{-2 - 3i}{4} \quad \text{or} \quad -\dfrac{1}{2} - \dfrac{3}{4}i \quad ■$$

Practice Problem 10 Divide: $\dfrac{5 - 6i}{-2i}$. ■

EXERCISES 6.5

Simplify.

1. $\sqrt{-49}$
  $7i$

2. $\sqrt{-100}$
  $10i$

3. $\sqrt{-19}$
  $i\sqrt{19}$

4. $\sqrt{-30}$
  $i\sqrt{30}$

5. $\sqrt{-50}$
  $5i\sqrt{2}$

6. $\sqrt{-48}$
  $4i\sqrt{3}$

7. $\sqrt{-63}$
  $3i\sqrt{7}$

8. $\sqrt{-52}$
  $2i\sqrt{13}$

Find the real numbers x and y.

9. $x - 5i\sqrt{2} = 3 + yi$
  $x = 3, y = -5\sqrt{2}$

10. $7 + yi = x - 5i$
  $x = 7, y = -5$

11. $23 + yi = 17 - x + 3i$
  $x = -6, y = 3$

12. $2 + x - 11i = 19 + yi$
  $x = 17, y = -11$

13. $5 + 3i - x + 2yi = 8 - 4i$
  $x = -3, y = -\dfrac{7}{2}$

14. $7 - 4i + x + 4yi = -3 + 7i$
  $x = -10, y = \dfrac{11}{4}$

Perform the addition or subtraction.

15. $(7 - 8i) + (-12 - 4i)$

$7 - 8i - 12 - 4i = -5 - 12i$

16. $(-3 + 5i) + (23 - 7i)$

$-3 + 5i + 23 - 7i = 20 - 2i$

17. $(-13 + i) + (-13 - 5i)$

$-13 - 13 + i - 5i = -26 - 4i$

18. $(7 + 15i) + (-10 - 15i)$

$7 + 15i - 10 - 15i = -3$

19. $(12 - 3i) - (5 + 3i)$

$12 - 3i - 5 - 3i = 7 - 6i$

20. $(20 + 5i) - (6 - 3i)$

$20 + 5i - 6 + 3i = 14 + 8i$

21. $(-18 - 2i) - (3 - 2i)$

$-18 - 2i - 3 + 2i = -21$

22. $(3 - 7i) - (-2 - 6i)$

$3 - 7i + 2 + 6i = 5 - i$

Multiply and simplify your answer.

23. $(2 + 3i)(2 - i)$

$4 + 4i - 3i^2 = 7 + 4i$

24. $(4 - 6i)(2 + i)$

$8 - 8i - 6i^2 = 14 - 8i$

25. $(-7 + 2i)(-3 - 4i)$

$21 + 22i - 8i^2 = 29 + 22i$

26. $(-5 - 2i)(6 - 3i)$

$-30 + 3i + 6i^2 = -36 + 3i$

27. $4 - 3(-10 + 2i)$

$4 + 30 - 6i = 34 - 6i$

28. $6 - 5(7 - 6i)$

$6 - 35 + 30i = -29 + 30i$

29. $2i(5i - 6)$

$10i^2 - 12i = -10 - 12i$

30. $4i(7 - 2i)$

$28i - 8i^2 = 28i + 8$

31. $(6 - 3i)^2$

$36 - 36i + 9i^2 = 27 - 36i$

32. $(5 - 4i)^2$

$25 - 40i + 16i^2 = 9 - 40i$

Evaluate.

33. i^{17}

$(i^4)^4 \cdot i = i$

34. i^{21}

$(i^4)^5 \cdot i = i$

35. i^{24}

$(i^4)^6 = 1$

36. i^{16}

$(i^4)^4 = 1$

37. $i^{30} + i^{28}$

$i^{28} \cdot i^2 + i^{28} = -1 + 1 = 0$

38. $i^{26} + i^{24}$

$(i^{24})(i^2) + i^{24} = -1 + 1 = 0$

Divide.

39. $\dfrac{2 + i}{3 - i}$

$\dfrac{2 + i}{3 - i} \cdot \dfrac{3 + i}{3 + i} = \dfrac{6 + 5i + i^2}{9 - i^2}$

$= \dfrac{1 + i}{2}$

40. $\dfrac{4 + 2i}{2 - i}$

$\dfrac{4 + 2i}{2 - i} \cdot \dfrac{2 + i}{2 + i} = \dfrac{8 + 8i + 2i^2}{4 - i^2}$

$= \dfrac{6 + 8i}{5}$

41. $\dfrac{5 + 3i}{4 + 2i}$

$\dfrac{5 + 3i}{4 + 2i} \cdot \dfrac{4 - 2i}{4 - 2i} = \dfrac{20 + 2i - 6i^2}{16 - 4i^2}$

$= \dfrac{13 + i}{10}$

42. $\dfrac{7 - 2i}{3 + 5i}$

$\dfrac{7 - 2i}{3 + 5i} \cdot \dfrac{3 - 5i}{3 - 5i} = \dfrac{21 - 41i + 10i^2}{9 - 25i^2}$

$= \dfrac{11 - 41i}{34}$

43. $\dfrac{8 - 6i}{3i}$

$\dfrac{8 - 6i}{3i} \cdot \dfrac{i}{i} = \dfrac{8i - 6i^2}{3i^2}$

$= -\dfrac{8i + 6}{3}$

44. $\dfrac{5 + 2i}{4i}$

$\dfrac{5 + 2i}{4i} \cdot \dfrac{i}{i} = \dfrac{5i + 2i^2}{4i^2}$

$= -\dfrac{5i - 2}{4}$

45. $\dfrac{7}{5 - 6i}$

$\dfrac{7}{5 - 6i} \cdot \dfrac{5 + 6i}{5 + 6i} = \dfrac{7(5 + 6i)}{61}$

$= \dfrac{35 + 42i}{61}$

46. $\dfrac{3}{4 + 2i}$

$\dfrac{3}{4 + 2i} \cdot \dfrac{4 - 2i}{4 - 2i}$

$\dfrac{3(4 - 2i)}{20} = \dfrac{3(2 - i)}{10} = \dfrac{6 - 3i}{10}$

? **To Think About**

47. What is *wrong* with this "solution"?

$$(2\sqrt{-3})(3\sqrt{-27}) = 6\sqrt{81} = 6(9) = 54$$

What is the correct answer?

$\sqrt{-3}$ and $\sqrt{-27}$ are not real nos.

$(2i\sqrt{3})(3i\sqrt{27}) = 6i^2\sqrt{81} = 54i^2 = -54$

48. (a) Why are these two expressions not equal?

$$\sqrt{-2}(\sqrt{-2} + \sqrt{-8}) \neq \sqrt{4} + \sqrt{16} = 2 + 4 = 6$$

(b) Now correctly evaluate $\sqrt{-2}(\sqrt{-2} + \sqrt{-8})$

(a) $\sqrt{-2}$ and $\sqrt{-8}$ are not real nos. They must be written in i notation first.

(b) $i\sqrt{2}(i\sqrt{2} + i\sqrt{8}) =$

$i^2\sqrt{4} + i^2\sqrt{16} = -2 + (-4) = -6$

49. Evaluate: $(4 - 3i)^3$.

$(4 - 3i)(4 - 3i)(4 - 3i)$

$(16 - 24i + 9i^2)(4 - 3i) = (7 - 24i)(4 - 3i)$

$= 28 - 117i + 72i^2 = -44 - 117i$

50. Simplify the expression and add the two quantities. Express your answer in the form $a + bi$.

$$\dfrac{2 + 3i}{1 - i} + 2i$$

$\dfrac{2 + 3i}{1 - i} \cdot \dfrac{1 + i}{1 + i} + 2i = \dfrac{-1 + 5i}{2} + \dfrac{4i}{2} = \dfrac{-1 + 9i}{2}$

$= -\dfrac{1}{2} + \dfrac{9}{2}i$

Cumulative Review Problems

Combine.

51. $\dfrac{2x+4}{x^2+4x+3}-\dfrac{3}{x+3}$

$\dfrac{2x+4}{(x+3)(x+1)}-\dfrac{3}{x+3}=\dfrac{2x+4-3(x+1)}{(x+3)(x+1)}$

$=-\dfrac{-x+1}{(x+3)(x+1)}$

52. $\dfrac{6}{x^2+x-2}+\dfrac{3x+4}{x^2+3x+2}$

$\dfrac{6}{(x+2)(x-1)}+\dfrac{3x+4}{(x+2)(x+1)}=\dfrac{6(x+1)+(3x+4)(x-1)}{(x+2)(x+1)(x-1)}$

$=\dfrac{3x+1}{(x-1)(x+1)}$

53. Solve for x: $\dfrac{3}{4x}-\dfrac{2}{x}=\dfrac{5}{12}$.

$9-24=5x$
$-3=x$

54. Simplify: $\dfrac{\dfrac{9x^2-4y^2}{xy}}{\dfrac{3}{y}-\dfrac{2}{x}}$.

$\dfrac{(3x-2y)(3x+2y)}{xy}\cdot\dfrac{xy}{3x-2y}=3x+2y$

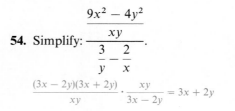

Calculator Problems

55. Find the value of x and y:
$6.3285+19.213yi=5.2304x-38.426i$.

$x=1.209945702$
$y=-2$

56. Multiply and simplify:
$(3.246-5.998i)(1.913-2.440i)$.

$-8.425522-19.394414i$

For Extra Practice Exercises, turn to page 325

Solutions to Odd-Numbered Practice Problems

1. (a) $\sqrt{-49}=\sqrt{-1}\sqrt{49}=(i)(7)=7i$ **(b)** $\sqrt{-31}=\sqrt{-1}\sqrt{31}=i\sqrt{31}$ **3.** $\sqrt{-8}\cdot\sqrt{-2}=(i\sqrt{8})(i\sqrt{2})=i^2\sqrt{16}=-1\sqrt{16}$
$=-1(4)=-4$

5. (a) $(-6-2i)+(5-8i)=-1-10i$ **(b)** $(3-4i)-(-2-18i)=3-4i+(2+18i)$
$=(3+2)+(-4+18)i$
$=5+14i$

7. $-2i(5+6i)=(-2)(5)i+(-2)(6)i^2$ **9.** $\dfrac{(4+2i)}{(3+4i)}\cdot\dfrac{(3-4i)}{(3-4i)}=\dfrac{12-16i+6i-8i^2}{9-16i^2}=\dfrac{12-10i-8(-1)}{9-16(-1)}=\dfrac{12-10i+8}{9+16}$
$\quad\quad=-10i-12i^2$
$\quad\quad=-10i-12(-1)$ $\quad\quad\quad\quad=\dfrac{20-10i}{25}=\dfrac{\cancel{5}(4-2i)}{\cancel{5}(5)}=\dfrac{4-2i}{5}$ or $\dfrac{4}{5}-\dfrac{2}{5}i$
$\quad\quad=12-10i$

Answers to Even-Numbered Practice Problems

2. (a) $7i\sqrt{2}$ **(b)** $5i\sqrt{6}$ **4.** $x=-7,\ y=3$ **6.** $-2-34i$ **8. (a)** -1 **(b)** i **10.** $\dfrac{6+5i}{2}$ or $3+\dfrac{5}{2}i$

EXTRA PRACTICE: EXERCISES

Section 6.1

Simplify and express your answer using only positive exponents.

1. $(2x^{1/4}y^{1/2})(-3x^{1/2}y^{1/4})$ $\quad -6x^{3/4}y^{3/4}$

2. $(5x^{1/6}y^{1/5})(-2x^{1/3}y^{1/10})$ $\quad -10x^{1/2}y^{3/10}$

3. $\dfrac{3^{1/5}}{3^{1/10}}$ $\quad 3^{1/10}$

4. $\dfrac{2^{3/7}}{2^{1/14}}$ $\quad 2^{5/14}$

5. $\dfrac{-30x^{-1/3}y^{1/4}}{-5x^{1/2}y^{-1/2}}$ $\quad \dfrac{6y^{3/4}}{x^{5/6}}$

6. $\dfrac{-3x^{1/5}y^{-1/10}}{-36x^{-1/2}y^{1/2}}$ $\quad \dfrac{x^{7/10}}{12y^{3/5}}$

7. $\left(\dfrac{a^3b^{-2}}{16a^5b^2}\right)^{3/2}$ $\quad \dfrac{1}{64a^3b^6}$

8. $\left(\dfrac{27a^{-4}b^2}{a^8b^4}\right)^{2/3}$ $\quad \dfrac{9}{a^8b^{4/3}}$

9. $(2^4x^3y^5z)^{1/2}$ $\quad 2^2x^{3/2}y^{5/2}z^{1/2}$

10. $(5^6x^8y^6z^3)^{1/3}$ $\quad 5^2x^{8/3}y^2z$

11. $a^{-2/3}(a^{1/4} + 2a^{1/3})$ $\quad \frac{1}{a^{5/12}} + \frac{2}{a^{1/3}}$ 12. $a^{1/4}(a^{-3/4} - 3a^{1/2})$

13. $27^{4/3} + 100^{1/2}$ 91   14. $49^{3/2} + 64^{2/3}$ 359

15. $\left(\frac{x^{2/3}x^4}{x^{-3/4}}\right)^{1/2}$ $x^{65/24}$ 16. $\left(\frac{x^{1/6}x^3}{x^{-2/3}}\right)^{2/3}$ $x^{23/9}$

17. $(-32)^{1/5}$ -2 18. $\frac{16^{3/4} \cdot 8^{2/3}}{64^{2/3}}$ 2

19. $\left(\frac{m^{-2}n^{-2/3}}{x^{1/6}}\right)^{-3}$ $m^6n^2x^{1/2}$ 20. $\left(\frac{27^{-1/3}}{a^{-1}}\right)^{-1/2}$ $\frac{27^{1/6}}{a^{1/2}}$

21. $\frac{-8^{2/3} + (-27)^{-2/3} + 8^0}{(-8)^{-2/3} - 27^{2/3}}$ $\frac{104}{315}$ 22. $\frac{x^2 - y^2}{(x^{1/2} + y^{1/2})(x^{1/2} - y^{1/2})}$ $x + y$

23. $\left(\frac{x^{-3} \div x^{-5}}{4x^{-4}}\right)^{-1/2}$ $\frac{2}{x^3}$ 24. $32^{3/5} + 125^{2/3} - 216^{1/3}$ 27

25. $(n^{-2})(an^{5/2})$ $an^{1/2}$

26. $(a^{1/5}b^{-1/2} + 1 + a^{-1/5}b^{1/2})(a^{1/5}b^{-1/2} - 1 + a^{-1/5}b^{1/2})$

27. Remove a common factor of $3x^{1/3}$ from $3x^{7/3} - 6x^{4/3}$.

28. Remove a common factor of $2a$ from $6a^{5/4} - 2a^{5/3}$.

29. Remove a common factor of $6a^{1/2}$ from $12a^3 - 18a^{5/2}$.

12. $\frac{1}{a^{1/2}} - 3a^{3/4}$

In problems 30 and 32, combine and express as a fraction with only positive exponents.

30. $2x^{1/4} + x^{-3/4}$ $\frac{2x+1}{x^{3/4}}$ 31. $2^{-1/2} + x^{-3/2}$ $\frac{x^{3/2} + 2^{1/2}}{2^{1/2}x^{3/2}}$

32. $4a^{-1/3} + 6a^{2/3}$ $\frac{4 + 6a}{a^{1/3}}$

Simplify. Use only positive exponents in your answer. Assume that n is a positive integer.

33. $(3x^{1/4}y^{-2/3})^n$ $\frac{3^n x^{n/4}}{y^{2n/3}}$ 34. $\left(\frac{x^{5n+2}}{x^n}\right)^{1/2}$ x^{2n+1}

35. $\left(\frac{27x^{5n}y^{7n}}{x^{8n}y^{-2n}}\right)^{1/3}$ $\frac{3y^{3n}}{x^n}$ 36. $\left(\frac{x^{4n}y^{19n}}{32x^{-n}y^{-n}}\right)^{1/5}$ $\frac{x^n y^{4n}}{2}$

37. $(8^{-2n/3})^{-2}$ 2^{4n}

Simplify.

38. $(a^{2/3} + b^{1/4})(a^{1/3} + 2b^{7/4})$ $a + 2a^{2/3}b^{7/4} + a^{1/3}b^{1/4} + 2b^2$

39. $(3a^{1/4} - 2b^{1/3})(2a^{1/8} + b^{2/3})$
$6a^{3/8} + 3a^{1/4}b^{2/3} - 4a^{1/8}b^{1/3} - 2b$

26. $a^{2/5}b^{-1} + 1 + a^{-2/5}b$ 28. $2a(3a^{1/4} - a^{2/3})$

27. $3x^{1/3}(x^2 - 2x)$ or $3x^{1/3}(x^{6/3} - 2x^{3/3})$ 29. $6a^{1/2}(2a^{5/2} - 3a^2)$

Section 6.2

Write each radical in exponential form.

1. $\sqrt[7]{3x}$ $(3x)^{1/7}$ 2. $\sqrt[6]{5y}$ $(5y)^{1/6}$

3. $(\sqrt[8]{2y})^5$ $(2y)^{5/8}$ 4. $(\sqrt[9]{4x})^4$ $(4x)^{4/9}$

5. $\sqrt{\sqrt[4]{x}}$ $x^{1/8}$ 6. $\sqrt[5]{\sqrt{y}}$ $y^{1/10}$

7. $\sqrt{\sqrt[3]{8x^6}}$ $(2x^2)^{1/2}$ 8. $(\sqrt[3]{6x^2})^6$ $(6x^2)^2$

9. $\sqrt[4]{x^3y^0z}$ $(x^3z)^{1/4}$

Write in radical form.

10. $6^{-3/4}$ $\frac{1}{\sqrt[4]{6^3}}$ 11. $x^{7/8}$ $\sqrt[8]{x^7}$

12. $(-x)^{5/3}$ $\sqrt[3]{(-x)^5}$ 13. $(x + 2)^{3/4}$ $\sqrt[4]{(x + 2)^3}$

14. $8x^{1/3}$ $8\sqrt[3]{x}$ 15. $(16x^4)^{1/8}$ $\sqrt[8]{16x^4}$ or $\sqrt{2x}$

16. $12x^{-2/3}$ $\frac{12}{\sqrt[3]{x^2}}$

Evaluate if possible.

17. $\sqrt{121} + \sqrt{49}$ 18   18. $\sqrt{144} + \sqrt{64}$ 20

19. $-\sqrt{\frac{25}{36}}$ $-\frac{5}{6}$ 20. $-\sqrt{\frac{9}{49}}$ $-\frac{3}{7}$

21. $\sqrt[3]{125}$ 5   22. $\sqrt[3]{-27}$ -3

23. $\sqrt[3]{-\frac{1}{8}}$ $-\frac{1}{2}$ 24. $\sqrt[3]{\frac{1}{64}}$ $\frac{1}{4}$

25. $\sqrt[4]{16}$ 2   26. $\sqrt[4]{625}$ 5

27. $\sqrt[5]{32} + \sqrt[5]{-32}$ 0   28. $\sqrt[6]{64} + \sqrt[4]{1}$ 3

29. $\sqrt[6]{-1}$ Not a real no.   30. $\sqrt[4]{-16}$ Not a real no.

31. $\sqrt[3]{8} - \sqrt[4]{256} + \sqrt[5]{32}$ 0   32. $\sqrt[4]{\frac{81}{256}}$ $\frac{3}{4}$

33. $\sqrt[3]{-27} + \sqrt{64}$ 5   34. $\sqrt[4]{(-2)^8}$ 4

Evaluate. Assume that all variables represent positive real numbers.

35. $125^{-1/3}$ $\frac{1}{5}$ 36. $16^{-3/2}$ $\frac{1}{64}$

37. $81^{3/4}$ 27   38. $(-8)^{4/3}$ 16

39. $(100x^6)^{1/2}$ $10x^3$ 40. $(64y^{10})^{1/2}$ $8y^5$

41. $(-125a^3b^{12})^{2/3}$ $25a^2b^8$ 42. $(-8a^{21}b^{15})^{2/3}$ $4a^{14}b^{10}$

43. $\sqrt{144x^8y^2z^{10}}$ $12x^4yz^5$ 44. $\sqrt{81x^4y^0z^6}$ $9x^2z^3$

45. $\sqrt[3]{-8a^{12}b^0c^9}$ $-2a^4c^3$

46. $\sqrt[3]{-64a^3b^{15}c^{99}}$ $-4ab^5c^{33}$

47. $\sqrt[4]{2^8 \cdot 3^4 \cdot a^4x^{12}}$ $12ax^3$ 48. $(81x^4y^8)^{-1/4}$ $\frac{1}{3xy^2}$

Simplify and collect like terms, if possible.

49. $\sqrt[5]{32x^{10}y^{20}} + \sqrt[4]{625x^8y^{16}}$ $7x^2y^4$

50. $\sqrt[4]{81x^{12}y^{20}} + \sqrt[6]{64x^{18}y^{30}}$ $5x^3y^5$

51. $\sqrt[3]{27x^3y^6z^9} - \sqrt[4]{256x^4y^8z^{12}}$ $-xy^2z^3$

In problems 52 and 53, simplify. Assume that the variables in the radicand represent any real number.

52. $\sqrt{169x^4y^{12}z^6}$ $13x^2y^6z^3$ 53. $\sqrt[4]{81x^{12}y^{20}z^8}$ $3x^3y^5z^2$

54. Explain the difference between $\sqrt[8]{(-2)^4}$ and $(\sqrt[8]{-2})^4$. Why is this difference important?

$(\sqrt[8]{-2})^4$ is not a real no., whereas $(\sqrt[8]{(-2)^4}) = \sqrt[8]{16}$ is a real no.

Section 6.3

Simplify. Assume that all variables represent positive real numbers. If no real value is possible, say so.

1. $\sqrt{75x^5y^6}$ $5x^2y^3\sqrt{3x}$ 2. $\sqrt{27x^8y^3}$ $3x^4y\sqrt{3y}$

3. $\sqrt{68a^8b^4c^0}$ $2a^4b^2\sqrt{17}$ 4. $\sqrt{52a^{10}b^0c^{12}}$ $2a^5c^6\sqrt{13}$

5. $\sqrt[3]{-81x^3y^{12}z^{14}}$ $-3xy^4z^4\sqrt[3]{3z^2}$ 6. $\sqrt[3]{-125x^6y^0z^8}$ $-5x^2z^2\sqrt[3]{z^2}$

7. $\sqrt[3]{40x^{15}y^{13}z^{17}}$ $2x^5y^4z^5\sqrt[3]{5yz^2}$ 8. $\sqrt[3]{88x^7y^{14}z^3}$ $2x^2y^4z\sqrt[3]{11xy^2}$

9. $\sqrt[4]{-81x^4y^8}$ Not a real no.   10. $\sqrt[4]{-16x^8y^{12}}$ Not a real no.

11. $\sqrt[4]{80x^{20}y^{13}}$ $2x^5y^3\sqrt[4]{5y}$ 12. $\sqrt[4]{48x^{16}y^7}$ $2x^4y\sqrt[4]{3y^3}$

13. $\sqrt[5]{-64x^{15}y^{18}}$ $-2x^3y^3\sqrt[5]{2y^3}$ 14. $\sqrt[5]{-96x^{30}y^{36}}$ $-2x^6y^7\sqrt[5]{3y}$

15. $\sqrt[6]{5x^{20}y^6z^{15}}$ $x^3yz^2\sqrt[6]{5x^2z^3}$ 16. $\sqrt[6]{64x^3y^7z^{14}}$ $2yz^2\sqrt[6]{x^3yz^2}$

17. $\sqrt[4]{81x^4y^5z^6}$ $3xyz\sqrt[4]{yz^2}$ 18. $\sqrt[3]{56x^4y^0}$ $2x\sqrt[3]{7x}$

19. $\sqrt[5]{-32xy^{10}z^6}$ $-2y^2z\sqrt[5]{xz}$ 20. $\sqrt[4]{243x^4(a - b)^5}$

21. $\sqrt{288xy^2z^3}$ $12yz\sqrt{2xz}$ 22. $\sqrt[3]{-192x^4}$ $-4x\sqrt[3]{3x}$

23. $\sqrt[5]{3105x^{21}}$ $x^4\sqrt[5]{3105x}$

20. $3x(a - b)\sqrt[4]{3(a - b)}$

Combine. Assume that all variables represent positive real numbers.

24. $\sqrt{8} + 3\sqrt{2}$ $5\sqrt{2}$
25. $\sqrt{75} + 2\sqrt{3}$ $7\sqrt{3}$
26. $2\sqrt{27} - 3\sqrt{12}$ 0
27. $5\sqrt{8} - 2\sqrt{50}$ 0
28. $\sqrt{128} + 3\sqrt{98}$ $29\sqrt{2}$
29. $\sqrt{48} + 4\sqrt{147}$ $32\sqrt{3}$
30. $-3x\sqrt{8x} + 2x\sqrt{2x}$ $-4x\sqrt{2x}$
31. $-5y\sqrt{7y} + 3y\sqrt{28y}$ $y\sqrt{7y}$
32. $3y\sqrt{x^3y} - 5\sqrt{x^3y^3}$ $-2xy\sqrt{xy}$
33. $5\sqrt{x^5y^5} - 6xy\sqrt{x^3y^3}$ $-x^2y^2\sqrt{xy}$
34. $\sqrt[3]{128} + 3\sqrt[3]{16}$ $10\sqrt[3]{2}$
35. $\sqrt[3]{54} + 4\sqrt[3]{128}$ $19\sqrt[3]{2}$

36. $\sqrt[3]{4x^4} + 2x\sqrt[3]{32x}$ $5x\sqrt[3]{4x}$
37. $4x\sqrt[3]{8x} + x\sqrt[3]{27x}$ $11x\sqrt[3]{x}$
38. $\sqrt{9x^3} + \sqrt[3]{9x^3} + 2\sqrt{36x^3} - 4x\sqrt[3]{7x}$ $15x\sqrt{x} + x\sqrt[3]{9} - 4x\sqrt[3]{7x}$
39. $2\sqrt{8ab} + 3\sqrt[3]{5a^4} - 15\sqrt{2ab} - 3a\sqrt[3]{5a}$ $-11\sqrt{2ab}$
40. $5\sqrt{32} - 4\sqrt[3]{16} - 3\sqrt{8}$ $14\sqrt{2} - 8\sqrt[3]{2}$
41. $\sqrt{28} - 3\sqrt{63}$ $-7\sqrt{7}$
42. $2x\sqrt{8x^3} - x^2\sqrt{18} + 5\sqrt{2x^4}$ $2x^2\sqrt{2} + 4x^2\sqrt{2x}$
43. $\sqrt[3]{7x} - 2\sqrt[3]{56x} + 4\sqrt[3]{128x}$ $-3\sqrt[3]{7x} + 16\sqrt[3]{2x}$
44. $2x\sqrt{2x} - \sqrt[3]{4x^4} + \sqrt{18x}$ $(2x + 3)\sqrt{2x} - x\sqrt[3]{4x}$
45. $3\sqrt[5]{32x} - 4\sqrt[5]{243x}$ $-6\sqrt[5]{x}$

Section 6.4

Multiply and simplify. Assume that all variables represent positive numbers.

1. $(3\sqrt{5})(-2\sqrt{10})$ $-30\sqrt{2}$
2. $(5\sqrt{8})(-3\sqrt{6})$ $-60\sqrt{3}$
3. $(2\sqrt{3x^3y})(2\sqrt{4xy^5})$ $8x^2y^3\sqrt{3}$
4. $(7\sqrt{xy^4})(3\sqrt{4x^3y^3})$ $42x^2y^3\sqrt{y}$
5. $-3\sqrt{2}(\sqrt{5} + 2\sqrt{8})$ $-3\sqrt{10} - 24$
6. $-4\sqrt{3}(\sqrt{3} - \sqrt{30})$ $-12 + 12\sqrt{10}$
7. $2\sqrt{x}(3\sqrt{x^3} - 5x\sqrt{x})$ $-4x^2$
8. $7\sqrt{y}(2\sqrt{y} - 3\sqrt{y^6})$ $14y - 21y^3\sqrt{y}$
9. $(2\sqrt{5} - \sqrt{6})(\sqrt{5} + 2\sqrt{6})$ $3\sqrt{30} - 2$
10. $(2\sqrt{3} + 3\sqrt{6})(\sqrt{3} - \sqrt{6})$ $3\sqrt{2} - 12$
11. $(\sqrt{2x} - 3\sqrt{y})(2\sqrt{2x} - 4\sqrt{y})$ $4x - 10\sqrt{2xy} + 12y$
12. $(2\sqrt{x} - 5\sqrt{3y})(\sqrt{x} - 2\sqrt{3y})$ $2x - 9\sqrt{3xy} + 30y$
13. $(\sqrt{40} + 6\sqrt{2})(\sqrt{40} - \sqrt{2})$ $28 + 20\sqrt{5}$
14. $(\sqrt{45} - 3\sqrt{2})(\sqrt{45} + 2\sqrt{2})$ $33 - 3\sqrt{10}$
15. $(5 - \sqrt{2x + 1})^2$ $26 + 2x - 10\sqrt{2x + 1}$
16. $(3 - \sqrt{4x - 1})^2$ $8 + 4x - 6\sqrt{4x - 1}$
17. $(\sqrt{3} + 5\sqrt{2})^2$ $53 + 10\sqrt{6}$
18. $(3\sqrt{5} - \sqrt{2})^2$ $47 - 6\sqrt{10}$
19. $(7 - \sqrt{x})(8 - \sqrt{x})$ $56 - 15\sqrt{x} + x$
20. $(2 - \sqrt{x})(13 - \sqrt{x})$ $26 - 15\sqrt{x} + x$
21. $(3\sqrt{a} + 2\sqrt{b})(3\sqrt{a} - 2\sqrt{b})$ $9a - 4b$
22. $(5\sqrt{a} - 6\sqrt{b})(5\sqrt{a} + 6\sqrt{b})$ $25a - 36b$
23. $(4\sqrt{2} - 7\sqrt{3})(4\sqrt{2} + 7\sqrt{3})$ -115
24. $(\sqrt{20})(\sqrt{6})(\sqrt{20})(\sqrt{6})$ 120
25. $(5\sqrt{3})(2\sqrt{3} - 3\sqrt{27})$ -105
26. $(5\sqrt{2xy^3})(3\sqrt{2xy^5})$ $30xy^4$
27. $(\sqrt{a} + \sqrt{b})(\sqrt{a} - \sqrt{b})$ $a - b$
28. $(2\sqrt{x} - \sqrt{yz})(\sqrt{yz} + 2\sqrt{x})$ $4x - yz$
29. $(\sqrt{28} + 3\sqrt{3})(2\sqrt{7} - \sqrt{27})$ 1

Simplify by rationalizing the denominator.

30. $\dfrac{7}{\sqrt{3}}$ $\dfrac{7\sqrt{3}}{3}$
31. $\dfrac{3}{\sqrt{11}}$ $\dfrac{3\sqrt{11}}{11}$
32. $\sqrt{\dfrac{z}{5}}$ $\dfrac{\sqrt{5z}}{5}$
33. $\sqrt{\dfrac{x}{3}}$ $\dfrac{\sqrt{3x}}{3}$
34. $\dfrac{3}{\sqrt{7x}}$ $\dfrac{3\sqrt{7x}}{7x}$
35. $\dfrac{8}{\sqrt{11x}}$ $\dfrac{8\sqrt{11x}}{11x}$
36. $\dfrac{2\sqrt{5}}{3\sqrt{10x}}$ $\dfrac{\sqrt{2x}}{3x}$
37. $\dfrac{3\sqrt{7}}{4\sqrt{21x}}$ $\dfrac{\sqrt{3x}}{4x}$

38. $\sqrt{\dfrac{3x}{5y^2}}$ $\dfrac{\sqrt{15x}}{5y}$
39. $\sqrt{\dfrac{5w^2}{16x}}$ $\dfrac{w\sqrt{5x}}{4x}$
40. $\dfrac{x}{\sqrt{2} - \sqrt{3}}$ $-x(\sqrt{2} + \sqrt{3})$
41. $\dfrac{x}{\sqrt{5} + \sqrt{6}}$ $-x(\sqrt{5} - \sqrt{6})$
42. $\dfrac{\sqrt{2}}{\sqrt{2} + 3}$ $\dfrac{3\sqrt{2} - 2}{7}$
43. $\dfrac{\sqrt{5}}{\sqrt{5} - 2}$ $5 + 2\sqrt{5}$
44. $\dfrac{\sqrt{x}}{\sqrt{3x} + \sqrt{2}}$ $\dfrac{x\sqrt{3} - \sqrt{2x}}{3x - 2}$
45. $\dfrac{\sqrt{y}}{\sqrt{2y} - \sqrt{5}}$ $\dfrac{y\sqrt{2} + \sqrt{5y}}{2y - 5}$
46. $\dfrac{\sqrt{3} + \sqrt{13}}{\sqrt{5} - \sqrt{2}}$
47. $\dfrac{\sqrt{3} - \sqrt{2}}{\sqrt{5} + \sqrt{6}}$
48. $\dfrac{\sqrt{3} + 3\sqrt{2}}{\sqrt{2} - 2\sqrt{3}}$ $-\dfrac{12 + 7\sqrt{6}}{10}$
49. $\dfrac{\sqrt{5} + 2\sqrt{2}}{2\sqrt{5} - \sqrt{2}}$ $\dfrac{14 + 5\sqrt{10}}{18}$
50. $\sqrt{\dfrac{8x^2}{27}}$ $\dfrac{2x\sqrt{6}}{9}$
51. $\dfrac{\sqrt{5} + \sqrt{2}}{\sqrt{5} - \sqrt{2}}$ $\dfrac{7 + 2\sqrt{10}}{3}$
52. $\dfrac{\sqrt{12} + \sqrt{75}}{\sqrt{48}}$ $\dfrac{7}{4}$
53. $\dfrac{2}{3\sqrt{x} - \sqrt{2}}$ $\dfrac{6\sqrt{x} + 2\sqrt{2}}{9x - 2}$
54. $\sqrt{\dfrac{a + b}{x + y}}$ $\dfrac{\sqrt{(a + b)(x + y)}}{x + y}$

Multiply and simplify your answer.

55. $(2\sqrt[4]{3x})(4\sqrt[4]{27x^6})$ $24x\sqrt[4]{x^3}$
56. $(4\sqrt[5]{5x^3})(3\sqrt[4]{3x^7y^{12}})$ $12x^2y^3\sqrt[4]{15x^2}$
57. $3\sqrt[3]{2x^2}(\sqrt[3]{8x} - 3\sqrt[3]{2x^2})$ $6x\sqrt[3]{2} - 9x\sqrt[3]{4x}$
58. $(\sqrt[3]{9x} + \sqrt[3]{2})(3\sqrt[3]{3x^2} - 4\sqrt[3]{2})$ $9x + 3\sqrt[3]{6x^2} - 4\sqrt[3]{18x} - 4\sqrt[3]{4}$
59. $(\sqrt[3]{4})(\sqrt[3]{2})(\sqrt[3]{9})(\sqrt[3]{3})$ 6
60. $(\sqrt[3]{2x} - \sqrt[3]{3y})(\sqrt[3]{4x^2} + \sqrt[3]{6xy} + \sqrt[3]{9y^2})$ $2x - 3y$

Simplify by rationalizing the denominator.

61. $\dfrac{7}{\sqrt[4]{27x^3}}$ $\dfrac{7\sqrt[4]{3x}}{3x}$
62. $\dfrac{3x}{\sqrt[4]{4x^7y^2}}$ $\dfrac{3\sqrt[4]{4xy^2}}{2xy}$
63. $\dfrac{\sqrt[3]{3x^2}}{\sqrt[3]{5x^5}}$ $\dfrac{\sqrt[3]{75}}{5x}$
64. $\dfrac{3x^2y^4}{\sqrt[5]{2x^3y^4}}$ $\dfrac{3xy^3\sqrt[5]{16x^2y}}{2}$
65. $\dfrac{\sqrt[3]{243x^3y^2}}{\sqrt[3]{81xy^4}}$ $\dfrac{\sqrt[3]{3x^2y}}{y}$
66. $\dfrac{2}{\sqrt[3]{x} + \sqrt[3]{y}}$ $\dfrac{2\sqrt[3]{x^2} - 2\sqrt[3]{xy} + 2\sqrt[3]{y^2}}{x + y}$

46. $\dfrac{\sqrt{15} + \sqrt{65} + \sqrt{6} + \sqrt{26}}{3}$
47. $-\sqrt{15} + \sqrt{10} + 3\sqrt{2} - 2\sqrt{3}$

Simplify.

1. $\sqrt{-121}$ $11i$ **2.** $\sqrt{-144}$ $12i$

3. $\sqrt{-99}$ $3i\sqrt{11}$ **4.** $\sqrt{-108}$ $6i\sqrt{3}$

5. $\sqrt{-243}$ $9i\sqrt{3}$ **6.** $\sqrt[3]{-8}$ -2

7. $\sqrt{-4x^2 y}$ $2ix\sqrt{y}$

Find the real numbers x and y.

8. $2x + 3 + 0i = 7 + 6yi$ $x = 2, y = 0$

9. $11i - 2x + 4 = 10 - 3i + 2yi$ $x = -3, y = 7$

10. $x - 3i = 2 + 5x + 12yi$

11. $x - 17 + 3i = 2x + 4 - 15yi$

12. $3x - 3 + 4i - yi = 0$ $x = 1, y = 4$

13. $6x - 2 - 2i = 4yi$

10. $x = -\dfrac{1}{2}, y = -\dfrac{1}{4}$

11. $x = -21, y = -\dfrac{1}{5}$

13. $x = \dfrac{1}{3}, y = -\dfrac{1}{2}$

Add or subtract to simplify.

14. $(-16 - 3i) + (12 - 4i)$ $-4 - 7i$

15. $(7 - 8i) + (-2 + 3i)$ $5 - 5i$

16. $(13 + 4i) - (2 - 3i)$ $11 + 7i$

17. $(-8 - 5i) - (3 + 5i)$ $-11 - 10i$

18. $(-28 + 3i) + (-16 - 4i)$ $-44 - i$

19. $(-56 - 28) + (3i - 11i)$ $-84 - 8i$

20. $(21 - 4i) - (6i - 3)$ $24 - 10i$

Multiply and simplify your answer.

21. $(-2 + 7i)(3 - 4i)$ $22 + 29i$

22. $(5 - 9i)(2 - 8i)$ $-62 - 58i$

23. $-3i(6i - 7)$ $18 + 21i$ **24.** $(5 - 4i)^2$ $9 - 40i$

25. $(6 + 7i)(6 - 7i)$ 85 **26.** $(4 - 8i)(8i + 4)$ 80

Evaluate.

27. i^{23} $-i$ **28.** i^{42} -1 **29.** i^{123} $-i$

Divide.

30. $\dfrac{2 - i}{3 + 2i}$ $\dfrac{4 - 7i}{13}$ **31.** $\dfrac{-3 + i}{7 - 2i}$ $\dfrac{-23 + i}{53}$

32. $\dfrac{11 + 2i}{3 - 2i}$ $\dfrac{29 + 28i}{13}$ **33.** $\dfrac{5 - 3i}{4 - 2i}$ $\dfrac{13 - i}{10}$

34. $\dfrac{6 - 3i}{4i - 1}$ $-\dfrac{18 + 21i}{17}$ **35.** $\dfrac{6 + i}{3 + 2i}$ $\dfrac{20 - 9i}{13}$

36. $\dfrac{4 - 2i}{3i}$ $\dfrac{-2 - 4i}{3}$ **37.** $\dfrac{-5 + 4i}{-2i}$ $\dfrac{-4 - 5i}{2}$

38. $\dfrac{5}{4 - 2i}$ $\dfrac{2 + i}{2}$ **39.** $\dfrac{2i}{3 + 4i}$ $\dfrac{8 + 6i}{25}$

40. $\dfrac{8 - 12i}{4i}$ $-3 - 2i$ **41.** $\dfrac{8 - 7i}{8 + 7i}$ $\dfrac{15 - 112i}{113}$

42. $\dfrac{(6 - 3i)^2}{(6 + 3i)^2}$ $\dfrac{-7 - 24i}{25}$

CHAPTER ORGANIZER

Topic	Procedure	Examples
Multiplication of variables with rational exponents, p. 295	$x^m x^n = x^{m+n}$	$(3x^{1/5})(-2x^{3/5}) = -6x^{4/5}$
Division of variables with rational exponents, p. 295	$\dfrac{x^m}{x^n} = x^{m-n}$	$\dfrac{-16x^{3/20}}{24x^{5/20}} = \dfrac{-2x^{-1/10}}{3}$
Removing negative exponents, p. 295	$x^{-n} = \dfrac{1}{x^n}$ $\dfrac{x^{-n}}{y^{-m}} = \dfrac{y^m}{x^n}$	Write with positive exponents: $3x^{-4} = \dfrac{3}{x^4}$ $\dfrac{2x^{-6}}{5y^{-8}} = \dfrac{2y^8}{5x^6}$ $4^{-2} = \dfrac{1}{4^2} = \dfrac{1}{16}$
Zero exponent, p. 294	$x^0 = 1$ (if $x \neq 0$)	$(3x^{1/2})^0 = 1$
Raising a variable with an exponent to a power, p. 295	$(x^m)^n = x^{mn}$ $(xy)^n = x^n y^n$ $\left(\dfrac{x}{y}\right)^n = \dfrac{x^n}{y^n}$	$(x^{-1/2})^{-2/3} = x^{1/3}$ $(3x^{-2}y^{-1/2})^{2/3} = 3^{2/3}x^{-4/3}y^{-1/3}$ $\left(\dfrac{4x^{-2}}{3^{-1}y^{-1/2}}\right)^{1/4} = \dfrac{4^{1/4}x^{-1/2}}{3^{-1/4}y^{-1/8}}$
Multiplication of expressions with rational exponents, p. 296	Add exponents whenever variables with same base are multiplied.	$x^{2/3}(x^{1/3} - x^{1/4}) = x^{3/3} - x^{2/3 + 1/4} = x - x^{11/12}$

Topic	Procedure	Examples
Higher-order roots, p. 300	If x is a nonnegative real number, $\sqrt[n]{x}$ is a positive nth root and has the property that $$\left(\sqrt[n]{x}\right)^n = x$$ If x is a negative real number, $\left(\sqrt[n]{x}\right)^n = x$ when n is an odd integer. If x is a negative real number, $\left(\sqrt[n]{x}\right)^n$ is not a real number when n is an even integer.	$\sqrt[3]{27} = 3$ because $3^3 = 27$. $\sqrt[5]{-32} = -2$ because $(-2)^5 = -32$. $\sqrt[4]{-16}$ is *not* a real number.
Rational exponents and radicals, p. 301	For positive integers m and n and x being any real number for which $x^{1/n}$ is defined, $$x^{m/n} = \left(\sqrt[n]{x}\right)^m = \sqrt[n]{x^m}$$ $$x^{1/n} = \sqrt[n]{x}$$	Write as a radical: $x^{3/7} = \sqrt[7]{x^3}$ $\quad 3^{1/5} = \sqrt[5]{3}$ Write as an expression with a fractional exponent: $\sqrt[4]{w^3} = w^{3/4}$ Evaluate: $$25^{3/2} = \left(\sqrt{25}\right)^3 = (5)^3 = 125$$
Higher-order roots and absolute value, p. 302	$\sqrt[n]{x^n} = |x|$ when n is an even positive integer. $\sqrt[n]{x^n} = x$ when n is an odd positive integer.	$\sqrt[6]{x^6} = |x|$ $\sqrt[5]{x^5} = x$
Evaluation of higher-order roots, p. 301	Use exponent notation.	$\sqrt[5]{-32x^{15}} = \sqrt[5]{(-2)^5 x^{15}}$ $\quad = [(-2)^5 x^{15}]^{1/5} = (-2)^1 x^3 = -2x^3$
Simplification of radicals, p. 305	Use product rule: $$\sqrt[n]{a}\,\sqrt[n]{b} = \sqrt[n]{ab}$$	Simplify when $x > 0$, $y > 0$: $\sqrt{75x^3} = \sqrt{25x^2}\sqrt{3x}$ $\quad = 5x\sqrt{3x}$ $\sqrt[3]{16x^5 y^6} = \sqrt[3]{8x^3 y^6}\sqrt[3]{2x^2}$ $\quad = 2xy^2 \sqrt[3]{2x^2}$
Combining radicals, p. 306	Simplify radicals and combine them if they have the same index and same radicand.	Combine: $2\sqrt{50} - 3\sqrt{98} = 2\sqrt{25}\sqrt{2} - 3\sqrt{49}\sqrt{2}$ $\quad = 2(5)\sqrt{2} - 3(7)\sqrt{2}$ $\quad = 10\sqrt{2} - 21\sqrt{2} = -11\sqrt{2}$
Multiplying radicals, p. 309	1. Multiply coefficients outside radical and then multiply radicands. 2. Simplify answer.	$(2\sqrt{3})(4\sqrt{5}) = 8\sqrt{15}$ $2\sqrt{6}(\sqrt{2} - 3\sqrt{12}) = 2\sqrt{12} - 6\sqrt{72}$ $\quad = 2\sqrt{4}\sqrt{3} - 6\sqrt{36}\sqrt{2}$ $\quad = 4\sqrt{3} - 36\sqrt{2}$ $(\sqrt{2} + \sqrt{3})(2\sqrt{2} - \sqrt{3})$ Use FOIL $\quad = 2\sqrt{4} - \sqrt{6} + 2\sqrt{6} - \sqrt{9}$ $\quad = 4 + \sqrt{6} - 3$ $\quad = 1 + \sqrt{6}$
Simplifying quotients of radicals, p. 311	$$\sqrt[n]{\dfrac{a}{b}} = \dfrac{\sqrt[n]{a}}{\sqrt[n]{b}}$$	$\sqrt[3]{\dfrac{5}{27}} = \dfrac{\sqrt[3]{5}}{\sqrt[3]{27}} = \dfrac{\sqrt[3]{5}}{3}$
Rationalizing denominators, p. 311	Multiply numerator and denominator by a value that eliminates the radical in the denominator.	$\dfrac{2}{\sqrt{7}} \cdot \dfrac{\sqrt{7}}{\sqrt{7}} = \dfrac{2\sqrt{7}}{7}$ $\dfrac{3}{\sqrt{5} + \sqrt{2}} \cdot \dfrac{\sqrt{5} - \sqrt{2}}{\sqrt{5} - \sqrt{2}} = \dfrac{3\sqrt{5} - 3\sqrt{2}}{(\sqrt{5})^2 - (\sqrt{2})^2}$ $\quad = \dfrac{3\sqrt{5} - 3\sqrt{2}}{5 - 2}$ $\quad = \dfrac{3\sqrt{5} - 3\sqrt{2}}{3}$ $\quad = \sqrt{5} - \sqrt{2}$

Topic	Procedure	Examples
Simplifying imaginary numbers, p. 317	Use $i = \sqrt{-1}$ and $i^2 = -1$.	$\sqrt{-16} = \sqrt{-1}\sqrt{16} = 4i$ $\sqrt{-18} = \sqrt{-1}\sqrt{18} = i\sqrt{9}\sqrt{2} = 3i\sqrt{2}$
Combining complex numbers, p. 318	Combine real coefficients and imaginary coefficients separately.	$(5 + 6i) + (2 - 4i) = 7 + 2i$ $(-8 + 3i) - (4 - 2i) = -8 + 3i - 4 + 2i$ $\qquad = -12 + 5i$
Multiplying complex numbers, p. 319	Use the FOIL method and $i^2 = -1$.	$(5 - 6i)(2 - 4i) = 10 - 20i - 12i + 24i^2$ $\qquad = 10 - 32i + 24(-1)$ $\qquad = 10 - 32i - 24$ $\qquad = -14 - 32i$
Dividing complex numbers, p. 320	Multiply numerator and denominator by conjugate of denominator.	$\dfrac{5 + 2i}{4 - i} = \dfrac{5 + 2i}{4 - i} \cdot \dfrac{4 + i}{4 + i} = \dfrac{20 + 5i + 8i + 2i^2}{16 - i^2}$ $\qquad = \dfrac{20 + 13i + 2(-1)}{16 - (-1)}$ $\qquad = \dfrac{20 + 13i - 2}{16 + 1}$ $\qquad = \dfrac{18 + 13i}{17}$ or $\dfrac{18}{17} + \dfrac{13}{17}i$
Raising i to a power, p. 319	$i^1 = i$ $i^2 = -1$ $i^3 = -i$ $i^4 = 1$	Evaluate: $i^{27} = i^{24} \cdot i^3$ $\qquad = (i^4)^6 \cdot i^3$ $\qquad = (1)^6(-i)$ $\qquad = -i$

REVIEW PROBLEMS CHAPTER 6

In all problems assume that the variables represent positive real numbers.

Simplify using only positive exponents in your answer. Assume that n is a positive integer.

1. $(2a^{1/3}b^{1/4})(-3a^{1/2}b^{1/2})$
$-6a^{5/6}b^{3/4}$

2. $\dfrac{6x^{2/3}y^{1/10}}{12x^{1/6}y^{-1/5}}$
$\dfrac{x^{1/2}y^{3/10}}{2}$

3. $(2x^{-1/5}y^{1/10}z^{4/5})^{-5}$
$\dfrac{x}{32y^{1/2}z^4}$

4. $\left(\dfrac{49a^3b^6}{a^{-7}b^4}\right)^{1/2}$
$7a^5b$

5. $a^{1/5}(2a^{3/4} - 3a^{1/10})$
$2a^{19/20} - 3a^{3/10}$

6. $\dfrac{(x^{3/4}y^{2/5})^{1/2}}{x^{-1/8}}$
$x^{1/2}y^{1/5}$

7. $\left(\dfrac{27x^{5n}}{x^{2n-3}}\right)^{1/3}$
$3x^{n+1}$

8. Remove a common factor of $3x$ from $6x^{3/2} - 9x^{1/2}$.
$3x(2x^{1/2} - 3x^{-1/2})$

9. Combine as one fraction containing only positive exponents: $2x^{1/3} + x^{-2/3}$.
$\dfrac{2x + 1}{x^{2/3}}$

10. Multiply and simplify: $(2x^{1/4} - 3y^{3/4})(6x^{3/4} - y^{1/4})$.
$12x - 18x^{3/4}y^{3/4} - 2x^{1/4}y^{1/4} + 3y$

In problems 11–22, assume that all variables are positive real numbers.

11. Write in exponential form: $\sqrt{\sqrt[5]{2x}}$.
$(2x)^{1/10}$

12. Write in radical form: $(2x + 3y)^{4/9}$.
$\left(\sqrt[9]{2x + 3y}\right)^4$

13. Evaluate: $\sqrt[3]{125} + \sqrt[4]{81}$.
8

14. Explain the difference between $-\sqrt[6]{64}$ and $\sqrt[6]{-64}$.
$\sqrt[6]{-64}$ is not a real no.
$-\sqrt[6]{64} = -2$

Evaluate or simplify each expression.

15. $27^{-4/3}$ $\dfrac{1}{81}$

16. $\left(\dfrac{4}{9}\right)^{3/2}$ $\dfrac{8}{27}$

17. $\sqrt{99x^3y^6z^{10}}$
$3xy^3z^5\sqrt{11x}$

18. $\sqrt[3]{-56a^8b^{10}c^{12}}$
$-2a^2b^3c^4\sqrt[3]{7a^2b}$

19. $\sqrt[4]{16x^8y^3z^{11}}$
$2x^2z^2\sqrt[4]{y^3z^3}$

20. $\sqrt[5]{x^7y^{10}z^{23}}$
$xy^2z^4\sqrt[5]{x^2z^3}$

21. $\sqrt{144x^{10}y^{12}z^0}$
$12x^5y^6$

22. $\sqrt[3]{125a^9b^6c^{300}}$
$5a^3b^2c^{100}$

Combine where possible.

23. $\sqrt{50} + 2\sqrt{32} - \sqrt{8}$
$11\sqrt{2}$

24. $\sqrt{28} - 4\sqrt{7} + 5\sqrt{63}$
$13\sqrt{7}$

25. $\sqrt[3]{8} + 3\sqrt[3]{16} - 4\sqrt[3]{54}$
$2 - 6\sqrt[3]{2}$

26. $\sqrt[3]{2y^4} + 3y\sqrt[3]{16y}$
$7y\sqrt[3]{2y}$

27. $2\sqrt{32x} - 5x\sqrt{2} + \sqrt{18x} + 2\sqrt{8x^2}$
$11\sqrt{2x} - x\sqrt{2}$

28. $2\sqrt[3]{5x^3y} + 6x\sqrt{3y} - 5x\sqrt[3]{40y} - \sqrt{75x^2y}$
$-8x\sqrt[3]{5y} + x\sqrt{3y}$

Multiply and simplify.

29. $(5\sqrt{12})(3\sqrt{6})$
$90\sqrt{2}$

30. $3\sqrt{x}(2\sqrt{8x} - 3\sqrt{48})$
$12x\sqrt{2} - 36\sqrt{3x}$

31. $(5\sqrt{2} + \sqrt{3})(\sqrt{2} - 2\sqrt{3})$
$4 - 9\sqrt{6}$

32. $(5\sqrt{6} - 2\sqrt{2})(\sqrt{6} - \sqrt{2})$
$34 - 14\sqrt{3}$

33. $(2\sqrt{5} - 3\sqrt{6})^2$
$74 - 12\sqrt{30}$

34. $(\sqrt[3]{2x} + \sqrt[3]{6})(\sqrt[3]{4x^2} - \sqrt[3]{y})$
$2x + 2\sqrt[3]{3x^2} - \sqrt[3]{2xy} - \sqrt[3]{6y}$

Rationalize the denominator and simplify the expression.

35. $\sqrt{\dfrac{3x^2}{y}}$ $\dfrac{x\sqrt{3y}}{y}$

36. $\dfrac{2}{\sqrt{3y}}$ $\dfrac{2\sqrt{3y}}{3y}$

37. $\dfrac{3\sqrt{7x}}{\sqrt{21x}}$ $\sqrt{3}$

38. $\dfrac{2}{\sqrt{6} - \sqrt{5}}$ $2\sqrt{6} + 2\sqrt{5}$

39. $\dfrac{\sqrt{x}}{3\sqrt{x} + \sqrt{y}}$ $\dfrac{3x - \sqrt{xy}}{9x - y}$

40. $\dfrac{\sqrt{5}}{\sqrt{7} - 3}$ $\dfrac{-(\sqrt{35} + 3\sqrt{5})}{2}$

41. $\dfrac{2\sqrt{3} + \sqrt{6}}{\sqrt{3} + 2\sqrt{6}}$ $\dfrac{2 + 3\sqrt{2}}{7}$

42. $\dfrac{5\sqrt{2} - \sqrt{3}}{\sqrt{6} - \sqrt{3}}$ $\dfrac{10\sqrt{3} - 3\sqrt{2} + 5\sqrt{6} - 3}{3}$

43. $\dfrac{3\sqrt{x} + \sqrt{y}}{\sqrt{x} - \sqrt{y}}$ $\dfrac{3x + 4\sqrt{xy} + y}{x - y}$

44. $\dfrac{2xy}{\sqrt[3]{16xy^5}}$ $\dfrac{\sqrt[3]{4x^2y}}{2y}$

45. Simplify: $\sqrt{-16} + \sqrt{-45}$.
$4i + 3i\sqrt{5}$

46. Find x and y: $2x - 3i + 5 = yi - 2 + \sqrt{6}$.
$x = \dfrac{-7 + \sqrt{6}}{2}$
$y = -3$

Simplify by performing the operation indicated.

47. $(-12 - 6i) + (3 - 5i)$
$-9 - 11i$

48. $(2 - i) - (12 - 3i)$
$-10 + 2i$

49. $(7 + 3i)(2 - 5i)$
$29 - 29i$

50. $(8 - 4i)^2$
$48 - 64i$

51. $2i(3 + 4i)$
$6i - 8$

52. $3 - 4(2 + i)$
$-5 - 4i$

53. Evaluate: i^{34}.
-1

Divide.

54. $\dfrac{7 - 2i}{3 + 4i}$
$\dfrac{13 - 34i}{25}$

55. $\dfrac{5 - 2i}{1 - 3i}$
$\dfrac{11 + 13i}{10}$

56. $\dfrac{4 - 3i}{5i}$
$\dfrac{-(4i + 3)}{5}$

57. $\dfrac{12}{3 - 5i}$
$\dfrac{18 + 30i}{17}$

58. $\dfrac{10 - 4i}{2 + 5i}$
$-2i$

Simplify and express your answer using only positive exponents in problems 1–4.

1. $(3x^{-1/4}y^{1/3})(-2x^{1/5}y^{1/6})$

2. $\dfrac{12x^{2/3}y^{1/2}}{-6x^{1/4}y^{1/4}}$

3. $\left(\dfrac{a^{-5}b^{-2}}{16a^7b^{-4}}\right)^{1/2}$

4. $(2^4x^8y^{12}z^0)^{3/4}$

5. Remove a common factor of $4x$ from $4x^{3/2} - 12x^{1/2}$.

6. Combine as a single fraction with only positive exponents for the variable x: $4x^{1/2} + x^{-1/2}$.

1. $\dfrac{-6y^{1/2}}{x^{1/20}}$

2. $-2x^{5/12}y^{1/4}$

3. $\dfrac{b}{4a^6}$

4. $8x^6y^9$

5. $4x(x^{1/2} - 3x^{-1/2})$

6. $\dfrac{4x + 1}{x^{1/2}}$

7. 5 _____

8. -2 _____

9. $\dfrac{3}{2}$ _____

10. $\dfrac{1}{81}$ _____

11. $10x^3z^4$ _____

12. $-3x^2y^4$ _____

13. $2a^5b^8c$ _____

14. 9 _____

Evaluate or simplify, if possible. Assume that all variables in the radicand represent positive real numbers.

7. $\sqrt[3]{125}$

8. $\sqrt[5]{-32}$

9. $\left(\dfrac{81}{16}\right)^{1/4}$

10. $27^{-4/3}$

11. $\sqrt{100x^6y^0z^8}$

12. $\sqrt[3]{-27x^6y^{12}}$

13. $\sqrt[4]{16a^{20}b^{32}c^4}$

14. $\sqrt{16} + \sqrt[3]{27} + \sqrt[4]{16}$

Assume that all variables represent positive real numbers.

Simplify.

1. $\sqrt{75x^3y^4z^0}$

2. $\sqrt[3]{-40a^3b^{10}c^{12}}$

3. $\sqrt[4]{32a^8b^3c^{11}}$

4. $\sqrt[5]{-32x^6}$

Combine when possible.

5. $2\sqrt{18} + 3\sqrt{50} - \sqrt{8}$

6. $-2\sqrt{32} + \sqrt[3]{16} + \sqrt[3]{54} + \sqrt{98}$

7. $3x\sqrt{2x} + 5\sqrt{50x^3} - 4\sqrt{8x^3}$

8. $\sqrt[3]{16a^4b} + 3a\sqrt[3]{54ab}$

---

1. $5xy^2\sqrt{3x}$

2. $-2ab^3c^4\sqrt[3]{5b}$

3. $2a^2c^2\sqrt[4]{2b^3c^3}$

4. $-2x\sqrt[5]{x}$

5. $19\sqrt{2}$

6. $-\sqrt{2} + 5\sqrt[3]{2}$

7. $20x\sqrt{2x}$

8. $11a\sqrt[3]{2ab}$

9. $36x\sqrt{6}$ _____

10. $4\sqrt{3} - 4\sqrt{15}$ _____

11. 12 _____

12. $187 - 20\sqrt{21}$ _____

13. $\dfrac{3\sqrt{5}}{5}$ _____

14. $\dfrac{2\sqrt[3]{9x}}{3x}$ _____

15. $\dfrac{\sqrt{5} - 1}{2}$ _____

16. $\dfrac{27 + 7\sqrt{6}}{29}$ _____

17. $8 + 3i$ _____

18. $5i$ _____

19. $7 - 26i$ _____

20. $\dfrac{6i - 4}{3}$ _____

21. $\dfrac{1 + 7i}{10}$ _____

22. $13 - 84i$ _____

Multiply and simplify.

9. $(3\sqrt{12x})(2\sqrt{18x})$

10. $2\sqrt{6}(\sqrt{2} - \sqrt{10})$

11. $(\sqrt{6} + \sqrt{2})(3\sqrt{6} - 3\sqrt{2})$

12. $(2\sqrt{3} - 5\sqrt{7})^2$

Simplify by rationalizing the denominator.

13. $\dfrac{6}{\sqrt{20}}$

14. $\dfrac{2}{\sqrt[3]{3x^2}}$

15. $\dfrac{2}{\sqrt{5} + 1}$

16. $\dfrac{3\sqrt{2} + \sqrt{3}}{4\sqrt{2} - \sqrt{3}}$

Simplify by using the properties of complex numbers.

17. $(12 - 3i) - (4 - 6i)$

18. $i^{33} + \sqrt{-16}$

19. $(5 - 2i)(3 - 4i)$

20. $\dfrac{6 + 4i}{-3i}$

21. $\dfrac{1 + 2i}{3 - i}$

22. $(7 - 6i)^2$

TEST CHAPTER 6

Simplify.

1. $(2x^{1/3}y^{1/4})(-3x^{1/5}y^{1/2})$

2. $\dfrac{5x^2}{3x^{1/2}}$

3. $(2x^{1/4})^{2/3}$

Evaluate.

4. $64^{-2/3}$

5. $81^{3/2}$

Simplify. Assume all variables are positive.

6. $\sqrt[3]{81x^5y^9}$

7. $\sqrt{100x^4y^7}$

8. $\sqrt{48a^5b^{10}}$

Combine like terms where possible.

9. $-2\sqrt{50} + \sqrt[3]{16x^4} - 5\sqrt{8} + 2x\sqrt[3]{54x}$

10. $\sqrt{18} - 2\sqrt{50} + 3\sqrt{98}$

1. $-6x^{8/15}y^{3/4}$

2. $\dfrac{5x^{3/2}}{3}$

3. $2^{2/3}x^{1/6}$

4. $\dfrac{1}{16}$

5. 729

6. $3xy^3\sqrt[3]{3x^2}$

7. $10x^2y^3\sqrt{y}$

8. $4a^2b^5\sqrt{3a}$

9. $-20\sqrt{2} + 8x\sqrt[3]{2x}$

10. $14\sqrt{2}$

11. $30\sqrt{6} - 54\sqrt{2}$

12. $60 - 55\sqrt{2}$

13. $\dfrac{\sqrt[3]{4x}}{x}$

14. $\dfrac{\sqrt{5x}}{x}$

15. $2 + \sqrt{3}$

16. $5 + 11i$

17. $6i$

18. $-1 - 18i$

19. $\dfrac{11 + 10i}{17}$

20. $27 + 36i$

Multiply and simplify.

11. $3\sqrt{12}\left(5\sqrt{2} - 3\sqrt{6}\right)$

12. $\left(3\sqrt{5} - \sqrt{10}\right)\left(2\sqrt{5} - 3\sqrt{10}\right)$

Rationalize the denominator.

13. $\dfrac{2}{\sqrt[3]{2x^2}}$

14. $\sqrt{\dfrac{5}{x}}$

15. $\dfrac{5 + 2\sqrt{3}}{4 - \sqrt{3}}$

Simplify by using the properties of complex numbers.

16. $(7 + 3i) - 2(1 - 4i)$

17. $i^{17} + \sqrt{-25}$

18. $(4 - 3i)(2 - 3i)$

19. $\dfrac{3 - 2i}{1 - 4i}$

20. $(6 + 3i)^2$

Approximately one-half of this test covers the content of Chapters 1–5. The remainder covers the content of Chapter 6.

1. Identify what property of real numbers is illustrated by the equation $7 + (2 + 3) = (7 + 2) + 3$.

2. Remove parentheses and collect like terms: $2a(3a^3 - 4) - 3a^2(a - 5)$.

3. Perform in the proper order: $7(12 - 14)^3 - 7 + 3 \div (-3)$.

4. Solve for x: $y = \frac{2}{3}x - 8$.

5. Graph: $3x - 5y = 15$.

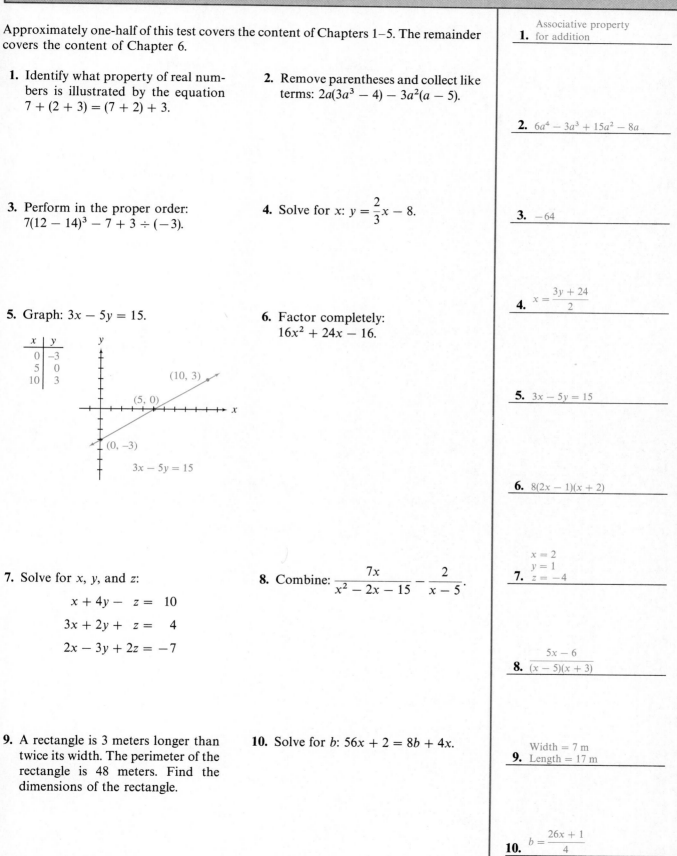

6. Factor completely: $16x^2 + 24x - 16$.

7. Solve for x, y, and z:

$$x + 4y - z = 10$$
$$3x + 2y + z = 4$$
$$2x - 3y + 2z = -7$$

8. Combine: $\dfrac{7x}{x^2 - 2x - 15} - \dfrac{2}{x - 5}$.

9. A rectangle is 3 meters longer than twice its width. The perimeter of the rectangle is 48 meters. Find the dimensions of the rectangle.

10. Solve for b: $56x + 2 = 8b + 4x$.

1. Associative property for addition

2. $6a^4 - 3a^3 + 15a^2 - 8a$

3. -64

4. $x = \dfrac{3y + 24}{2}$

5. $3x - 5y = 15$

6. $8(2x - 1)(x + 2)$

7. $x = 2$
$y = 1$
$z = -4$

8. $\dfrac{5x - 6}{(x - 5)(x + 3)}$

9. Width = 7 m
Length = 17 m

10. $b = \dfrac{26x + 1}{4}$

11. $\dfrac{1}{2x^{1/2}y^{15/2}}$

12. $\dfrac{x^{1/6}}{3^{1/3}y^{2/3}}$

13. $\dfrac{1}{4}$

14. $2xy^3\sqrt[3]{5x^2}$

15. $4\sqrt{5x}$

16. $-34 + 3\sqrt{6}$

17. $\dfrac{16 + 9\sqrt{3}}{-13}$

18. $12i$

19. $-5 + 12i$

20. $\dfrac{13 + i}{10}$

Simplify.

11. $\dfrac{2x^{-3}y^{-4}}{4x^{-5/2}y^{7/2}}$

12. $(3x^{-1/2}y^2)^{-1/3}$

13. Evaluate: $64^{-1/3}$.

14. Simplify: $\sqrt[3]{40x^5y^9}$.

15. Combine like terms:
$\sqrt{80x} + 2\sqrt{45x} - 3\sqrt{20x}$

16. Multiply and simplify:
$(2\sqrt{3} - 5\sqrt{2})(\sqrt{3} + 4\sqrt{2})$.

17. Rationalize the denominator:
$\dfrac{\sqrt{3} + 2}{2\sqrt{3} - 5}$.

18. Simplify: $i^{21} + \sqrt{-16} + \sqrt{-49}$.

19. Simplify: $(2 + 3i)^2$

20. Simplify: $\dfrac{1 + 4i}{1 + 3i}$.

Quadratic Equations

A forest technologist uses mathematics to measure the growth rates of trees and animals to gauge the impact of acid rain and other pollutants on the environment.

7

PRETEST CHAPTER 7

If you are familiar with the topics in this chapter, take this test now. Check your answers with those in the back of the book. If an answer was wrong or you couldn't do a problem, study the appropriate section of the chapter.

If you are not familiar with the topics in this chapter, don't take this test now. Instead, study the examples, work the practice problems, and then take the test.

This test will help you identify those concepts that you have mastered and those that need more study.

Section 7.1 Solve by *factoring*.

1. $12x^2 + x - 6 = 0$ $\quad \frac{2}{3}, -\frac{3}{4}$

2. $3x^2 + 5x = 7x^2 - 2x$ $\quad 0, \frac{7}{4}$

3. $\frac{18}{x} + \frac{12}{x+1} = 9$ $\quad -\frac{2}{3}, 3$

Section 7.2

4. Solve by taking the square root of each side of the equation: $3x^2 + 5 = 41$.

5. Solve by completing the square: $2x^2 - 4x - 3 = 0$. $\quad \frac{2 \pm \sqrt{10}}{2}$ $\qquad \pm 2\sqrt{3}$

Section 7.3 Solve by the quadratic formula.

6. $4x^2 - 4x - 7 = 0$

7. $5x(x+1) = 1 + 6x$ $\quad \frac{1 \pm \sqrt{21}}{10}$

8. Solve for the complex roots of the equation: $4x^2 = -12x - 17$.

$\qquad$ 6. $\frac{1 \pm 2\sqrt{2}}{2}$ $\quad$ 8. $\frac{-3 \pm 2i\sqrt{2}}{2}$

Section 7.4 Solve and check your solution(s).

9. $\sqrt{2x+7} - 4 = x$ $\quad -3$

10. $\sqrt{2x-1} - \sqrt{x-4} = 2$ $\quad 5, 13$

Section 7.5 Solve for any real roots and check your answers.

11. $x^6 - 7x^3 - 8 = 0$ $\quad 2, -1$

12. $w^{4/3} - 6w^{2/3} + 8 = 0$ $\quad \pm 8, \pm 2\sqrt{2}$

13. $x = \frac{-2w - 5b \pm \sqrt{4w^2 + 20wb + 25b^2 + 96w}}{6}$

Section 7.6

13. Solve for x. Assume that b and w are positive constants.

$$3x^2 + 2wx + 5bx - 8w = 0$$

14. The area of a rectangle is 52 square meters. The length of the rectangle is 1 meter longer than three times its width. Find the length and width of the rectangle.
$W = 4$ m
$L = 13$ m

After studying this section, you will be able to:

1 Solve to find the roots of a quadratic equation

2 Solve fractional equations that may be written as quadratic equations

7.1 SOLVING QUADRATIC EQUATIONS BY FACTORING

Up to now, we have solved only linear, or first-degree, equations. In this chapter we solve quadratic, or second-degree, equations.

> **Definition**
>
> A second-degree equation of the form $ax^2 + bx + c = 0$, where a, b, c are real numbers and $a \neq 0$, is a **quadratic equation**. $ax^2 + bx + c = 0$ is the **standard form** of a quadratic equation.

Quadratic equations are extremely important and frequently encountered. They are used to describe the motion of falling bodies, trajectories of missiles, the motion of a spring, and many, many other physical phenomena.

We will learn four methods for solving quadratic equations.

1. Factoring
2. Taking square roots of each side of the equation (the Square Root Method.)
3. Completing the square
4. Quadratic formula

Before solving a quadratic equation, we will first write the equation in standard form. Although it is not necessary that a, b, and c be integers, the equation is usually written this way. So we'll write our quadratic equations so that a, b, and c are integers.

1 The key to solving quadratic equations by factoring is the zero factor property.

Zero Factor Property

If $a \cdot b = 0$, then $a = 0$ or $b = 0$ or both $= 0$.

For example, we already know from Chapter 4 that the equation $a^2 - b^2 = 0$ can be factored as

$$(a + b)(a - b) = 0$$

By the zero factor property, we must have

$$a + b = 0$$

or

$$a - b = 0$$

or

$$a + b = 0 \quad \text{and} \quad a - b = 0$$

Thus, to use the zero factor property, we

---

1. Put the quadratic equation in standard form and if possible, *factor* the quadratic expression.
2. Set each factor equal to zero.
3. Solve the resulting equations to find each root. (A quadratic equation has two roots.)
4. Check our solutions.

Example 1 Solve the equation $x^2 + 15x = 100$.

When we say "solve the equation" or "find the roots," we mean find the values of x that satisfy the equation.

$x^2 + 15x - 100 = 0$	Puting the equation in standard form.
$(x + 20)(x - 5) = 0$	Factoring the trinomial.
$x + 20 = 0 \quad or \quad x - 5 = 0$	Setting each factor equal to 0.
$x = -20 \qquad x = 5$	Solving each equation.

Check: $x^2 + 15x = 100$ Use the *original* equation.

$$x = -20: \quad (-20)^2 + 15(-20) \stackrel{?}{=} 100$$

$$400 - 300 \stackrel{?}{=} 100$$

$$100 = 100 \checkmark \quad \text{It checks.}$$

TEACHING TIP   Students are often hesitant to check solutions. After explaining example 1, have them solve and check the solutions for the equation:

$$x^2 - 9x + 14 = 0$$

Ans. $x = 2$
    $x = 7$

Check: $(2)^2 - 9(2) + 14 \stackrel{?}{=} 0$
    $4 - 18 + 14 = 0 \checkmark$
    $(7)^2 - 9(7) + 14 \stackrel{?}{=} 0$
    $49 - 63 + 14 = 0 \checkmark$

$$x = 5: \quad (5)^2 + 15(5) \overset{?}{=} 100$$

$$25 + 75 \overset{?}{=} 100$$

$$\boxed{100 = 100} \quad \checkmark \quad \text{It checks.}$$

Thus $x = 5$ and $x = -20$ are both roots of the quadratic equation $x^2 + 15x = 100$. ■

Practice Problem 1   Find the roots of $x^2 + x = 56$. ■

Example 2   Find the roots of $6x^2 + 4 = 7(x + 1)$.

$6x^2 + 4 = 7x + 7$	Applying the distributive property.
$6x^2 - 7x - 3 = 0$	Putting equation in standard form.
$(2x - 3)(3x + 1) = 0$	Factoring the trinomial.
$\boxed{2x - 3 = 0} \quad or \quad \boxed{3x + 1 = 0}$	Setting each factor equal to 0.
$2x = 3 \qquad\qquad 3x = -1$	Solving the equations.
$x = \dfrac{3}{2} \qquad\qquad x = -\dfrac{1}{3}$	

Check: $6x^2 + 4 = 7(x + 1)$ Use the original equation.

$$x = \frac{3}{2}: \quad 6\left(\frac{3}{2}\right)^2 + 4 \overset{?}{=} 7\left(\frac{3}{2} + 1\right)$$

$$6\left(\frac{9}{4}\right) + 4 \overset{?}{=} 7\left(\frac{5}{2}\right)$$

$$\frac{27}{2} + 4 \overset{?}{=} \frac{35}{2}$$

$$\frac{27}{2} + \frac{8}{2} \overset{?}{=} \frac{35}{2}$$

$$\boxed{\frac{35}{2} = \frac{35}{2}} \quad \checkmark$$

It checks, so $x = \dfrac{3}{2}$ is a root.

Verify that $x = -\dfrac{1}{3}$ is also a root. ■

Practice Problem 2   Find the roots of $12x^2 - 11x + 2 = 0$. ■

Example 3   Find the roots of $3x^2 - 5x = 0$.

$3x^2 - 5x = 0$	The equation is already in standard form.
$x(3x - 5) = 0$	Factoring.
$\boxed{x = 0} \quad or \quad \boxed{3x - 5 = 0}$	Setting each factor equal to zero.
$\qquad\qquad 3x = 5$	
$\qquad\qquad x = \dfrac{5}{3}$	

Check: Verify that $x = 0$ and $x = \dfrac{5}{3}$ are roots of $3x^2 - 5x = 0$. ■

Practice Problem 3   Find the roots of $7x^2 - 14x = 0$. ■

Example 4   Solve: $7x^2 + 2x = 3x(x - 4)$.

$$7x^2 + 2x = 3x^2 - 12x \qquad \text{Distributive property.}$$

$$7x^2 - 3x^2 + 2x + 12x = 0 \qquad \text{Combining the terms on the left side.}$$

$$4x^2 + 14x = 0 \qquad \text{Puting equation in standard form.}$$

$$2x(2x + 7) = 0 \qquad \text{Factoring.}$$

$$2x = 0 \quad \text{or} \quad 2x + 7 = 0 \qquad \text{Setting each factor equal to 0.}$$

$$\frac{2x}{2} = \frac{0}{2} \qquad\qquad 2x = -7 \qquad \text{Solving each equation.}$$

$$x = 0 \qquad\qquad x = -\frac{7}{2}$$

Check: Verify that $x = 0$ and $x = -\dfrac{7}{2}$ are roots of $7x^2 + 2x = 3x(x - 4)$.   ∎

Practice Problem 4   Solve: $5x^2 - 7x = 2x(x - 3)$.   ∎

Example 5   Solve: $9x(x - 1) = 3x - 4$.

$$9x^2 - 9x = 3x - 4 \qquad \text{Removing parentheses.}$$

$$9x^2 - 9x - 3x + 4 = 0 \qquad \text{Getting all terms on the left side.}$$

$$9x^2 - 12x + 4 = 0 \qquad \text{Placing in standard form.}$$

$$(3x - 2)^2 = 0 \qquad \text{Factoring.}$$

$$3x - 2 = 0 \quad \text{or} \quad 3x - 2 = 0$$

$$3x = 2 \qquad\qquad 3x = 2$$

$$x = \frac{2}{3} \qquad\qquad x = \frac{2}{3}$$

We obtain the same answer twice. This value is called a **double root**.   ∎

Practice Problem 5   Solve: $16x(x - 2) = 8x - 25$.   ∎

2   If the quadratic equation contains a variable in the denominator, we must check to ensure that one or more roots are not extraneous.

Example 6   Find any roots of $\dfrac{2}{a^2} - \dfrac{3}{a} + 1 = 0$.

First we must multiply each term by the LCD a^2.

$$a^2\left(\frac{2}{a^2}\right) - a^2\left(\frac{3}{a}\right) + a^2(1) = a^2(0)$$

$$2 - 3a + a^2 = 0 \qquad \text{Simplifying.}$$

$$a^2 - 3a + 2 = 0 \qquad \text{Putting in standard form.}$$

$$(a - 2)(a - 1) = 0$$

$$a - 2 = 0 \quad \text{or} \quad a - 1 = 0$$

$$a = 2 \qquad\qquad a = 1$$

Check:

$$a = 2: \quad \frac{2}{2^2} - \frac{3}{2} + 1 \stackrel{?}{=} 0 \qquad a = 1: \quad \frac{2}{1^2} - \frac{3}{1} + 1 \stackrel{?}{=} 0$$

$$\frac{1}{2} - \frac{3}{2} + \frac{2}{2} = 0 \checkmark \qquad\qquad 2 - 3 + 1 = 0 \checkmark \qquad ∎$$

TEACHING TIP   Some students will forget that the equation must be set equal to zero in order to use the zero factor property. After discussing example 4, stress that concept. Then ask the students to do the following problem as a class exercise. Solve:

$$12x^2 - 2x + 7 = 7(x + 1)$$

Ans. $x = 0$, $x = \dfrac{3}{4}$

Practice Problem 6   Find any roots of $6 - \dfrac{1}{a} = \dfrac{12}{a^2}$.   ■

TEACHING TIP   Students have more difficulty with this type of problem than with any other concept in section 7.1. After discussing example 7, you may want to show them the following additional example. Solve:

$$\frac{2}{x+1} + \frac{1}{x-1} = 1$$

Sol. $(x+1)(x-1)\left[\dfrac{2}{x+1}\right]$

$\qquad + (x+1)(x-1)\left[\dfrac{1}{x-1}\right]$

$\qquad\qquad = (x+1)(x-1)$

$2x - 2 + x + 1 = x^2 - 1$

$3x - 1 = x^2 - 1$

$0 = x^2 - 3x$

$x = 0, \; x = 3$

Example 7   Find any roots of $\dfrac{5}{y-3} = 2 + \dfrac{30}{y^2 - 9}$.

First we factor.

$$\frac{5}{y-3} = 2 + \frac{30}{(y+3)(y-3)}$$

The LCD is $(y+3)(y-3)$. Next we multiply each term of the equation by the LCD.

$$(y+3)(y-3)\,\frac{5}{y-3} = 2(y+3)(y-3) + (y+3)(y-3)\,\frac{30}{(y+3)(y-3)}$$

$$5(y+3) = 2(y^2 - 9) + 30$$

$$5y + 15 = 2y^2 - 18 + 30$$

$$0 = 2y^2 - 5y - 3$$

$$0 = (2y+1)(y-3)$$

$2y + 1 = 0$ or $y - 3 = 0$

$\qquad y = -\dfrac{1}{2} \qquad\qquad y = 3$

Note that we may write the equation with the zero on the left-hand side if this is more convenient.

Check: $\dfrac{5}{y-3} = 2 + \dfrac{30}{y^2 - 9}$

$y = -\dfrac{1}{2}:$ $\dfrac{5}{-\dfrac{1}{2} - 3} \stackrel{?}{=} 2 + \dfrac{30}{\left(-\dfrac{1}{2}\right)^2 - 9}$

$\qquad\qquad \dfrac{5}{-\dfrac{7}{2}} \stackrel{?}{=} 2 + \dfrac{30}{-\dfrac{35}{4}}$

$\qquad\qquad -\dfrac{10}{7} \stackrel{?}{=} 2 + \dfrac{-24}{7}$

$\qquad\qquad -\dfrac{10}{7} \stackrel{?}{=} \dfrac{14}{7} - \dfrac{24}{7}$

$\qquad\qquad -\dfrac{10}{7} = -\dfrac{10}{7}$ ✓

It checks, so $y = -\dfrac{1}{2}$ is a root.

$y = 3:$ $\dfrac{5}{3-3} \stackrel{?}{=} 2 + \dfrac{30}{3^2 - 9}$

$\qquad\qquad \dfrac{5}{0} \stackrel{?}{=} 2 + \dfrac{30}{0}$

Division by 0 is not defined. Thus, $y = 3$ is an extraneous root and cannot be used. The only valid root of the equation is $y = -\dfrac{1}{2}$ ■

Practice Problem 7   Find the roots and check your answer: $\dfrac{1}{x-4} + \dfrac{1}{4} = \dfrac{-1}{x+2}$.

■

EXERCISES 7.1

Find all the roots and check your answer.

1. $x^2 + 11x + 10 = 0$
$(x + 10)(x + 1) = 0$
$x = -10, \; x = -1$

2. $x^2 - 8x + 15 = 0$
$(x - 5)(x - 3) = 0$
$x = 5, \; x = 3$

3. $x^2 - 13x = -36$
$(x - 9)(x - 4) = 0$
$x = 9, \; x = 4$

4. $x^2 - 3x = 10$
$(x - 5)(x + 2) = 0$
$x = 5, \; x = -2$

342   Chap. 7   Quadratic Equations

5. $5x^2 - 6x = 0$
$x(5x - 6) = 0$
$x = 0, x = \dfrac{6}{5}$

6. $3x^2 + 5x = 0$
$x(3x + 5) = 0$
$x = 0, x = -\dfrac{5}{3}$

7. $2x^2 - 7x + 5 = 0$
$(2x - 5)(x - 1) = 0$
$x = \dfrac{5}{2}, x = 1$

8. $2x^2 + 3x - 5 = 0$
$(2x + 5)(x - 1) = 0$
$x = -\dfrac{5}{2}, x = 1$

9. $3x^2 - 2x - 8 = 0$
$(3x + 4)(x - 2) = 0$
$x = -\dfrac{4}{3}, x = 2$

10. $4x^2 - 13x + 3 = 0$
$(4x - 1)(x - 3) = 0$
$x = \dfrac{1}{4}, x = 3$

11. $6x^2 + 11x = 10$
$(3x - 2)(2x + 5) = 0$
$x = \dfrac{2}{3}, x = -\dfrac{5}{2}$

12. $9x^2 + 9x = -2$
$(3x + 2)(3x + 1) = 0$
$x = -\dfrac{2}{3}, x = -\dfrac{1}{3}$

13. $8x^2 = 11x - 3$
$(8x - 3)(x - 1) = 0$
$x = \dfrac{3}{8}, x = 1$

14. $5x^2 = 11x - 2$
$(5x - 1)(x - 2) = 0,$
$x = \dfrac{1}{5}, x = 2$

15. $x(x - 6) = 27$
$(x - 9)(x + 3) = 0,$
$x = 9, x = -3$

16. $x(x - 21) = 22$
$(x - 22)(x + 1) = 0$
$x = 22, x = -1$

17. $4(x - 5) = (1 + x)(1 - x)$
$(x + 7)(x - 3) = 0, x = -7, x = 3$

18. $8(1 - x) = -1(4 + x^2)$
$(x - 6)(x - 2) = 0, x = 6, x = 2$

19. $3x^2 + 5x = 2x$
$3x(x + 1) = 0, x = 0, x = -1$

20. $2x^2 - 5x = x$
$2x(x - 3) = 0, x = 0, x = 3$

21. $2x^2 + 3x = -14x^2 + 5x$
$2x(8x - 1) = 0, x = 0, x = \dfrac{1}{8}$

22. $5x^2 - 2x = x^2 - 8x$
$2x(2x + 3) = 0, x = 0, x = -\dfrac{3}{2}$

Clear each equation of fractions, then solve the resulting quadratic equation and check your answer.

23. $x + \dfrac{12}{x} = 8$
$(x - 6)(x - 2) = 0$
$x = 6, x = 2$

24. $x + \dfrac{15}{x} - 8 = 0$
$(x - 5)(x - 3) = 0$
$x = 5, x = 3$

25. $1 - \dfrac{3}{x} - \dfrac{10}{x^2} = 0$
$(x - 5)(x + 2) = 0$
$x = 5, x = -2$

26. $1 + \dfrac{2}{x} - \dfrac{24}{x^2} = 0$
$(x + 6)(x - 4) = 0$
$x = -6, x = 4$

27. $\dfrac{1}{4} - \dfrac{1}{x} = \dfrac{21}{4x^2}$
$(x - 7)(x + 3) = 0$
$x = 7, x = -3$

28. $\dfrac{1}{x^2} + \dfrac{1}{10} = \dfrac{7}{10x}$
$(x - 5)(x - 2) = 0$
$x = 5, x = 2$

29. $\dfrac{12}{x} - \dfrac{12}{x - 1} = -1$
$(x - 4)(x + 3)$
$x = 4, x = -3$

30. $\dfrac{5}{x + 1} + \dfrac{4}{2x - 1} = 3$
$(6x + 1)(x - 2) = 0$
$x = 2, x = -\dfrac{1}{6}$

31. $\dfrac{5}{2x + 1} + \dfrac{1}{x + 2} = -2$
$(x + 3)(4x + 5) = 0, x = -3, x = -\dfrac{5}{4}$

32. $\dfrac{x + 16}{4x + 1} = x + 1$
$(2x + 5)(2x - 3) = 0, x = -\dfrac{5}{2}, x = \dfrac{3}{2}$

33. $\dfrac{3x - 1}{x + 3} - \dfrac{4x}{x - 3} + 3 = 0$
$x^2 - 11x - 12 = 0, x = 12, x = -1$

34. $\dfrac{x^2 + 2}{x - 2} = 4 + \dfrac{3x}{x - 2}$
$(x - 5)(x - 2) = 0, x = 5$ only

35. $\dfrac{2x}{3x - 1} + 3 = \dfrac{3}{2x + 1}$
$22x^2 - 4x = 0, x = 0, x = \dfrac{2}{11}$

36. $\dfrac{4}{x + 2} + \dfrac{1}{2x - 5} = 1$
$(2x - 2)(x - 4) = 0, x = 1, x = 4$

A manufacturer finds that the profit in dollars for manufacturing n units is $P = 2n^2 - 19n - 10$

37. How many units are produced when the profit is $0?
10 units

38. How many units are produced when the profit is $410? 20 units

39. The equation $x^2 + bx - 12 = 0$ has a solution of $x = -4$. What is the value of b? What is the other solution of the equation?
$x = -4$ so $x + 4$ is a factor
$(x + 4)(x - 3) = 0 = x^2 + x - 12 = 0, b = 1$

40. The equation $2x^2 - 3x + c = 0$ has a solution of $x = -\dfrac{1}{2}$. What is the value of c? What is the other solution of the equation?
$x + \dfrac{1}{2}$ is a factor so $(2x + 1)(x + c) = 0$ $x + 2xc = -3x, x(1 + 2c) = -3x,$ $1 + 2c = -3, c = -2$

Find the roots.

41. $40x^2 - 23x - 44 = 0$
$(8x - 11)(5x + 4) = 0, x = \dfrac{11}{8}, x = -\dfrac{4}{5}$

42. $2 + 3(1 - x) + 8(2x - 1) = -2x(1 + x) + 5$
$(2x - 1)(x + 8) = 0, x = \dfrac{1}{2}, x = -8$

Cumulative Review Problems

Simplify.

43. $(2x^3y^2)^3(5xy^2)^2$

$200x^{11}y^{10}$

44. $\dfrac{(2a^3b^2)^3}{16a^5b^8}$

$\dfrac{a^4}{2b^2}$

45. $(-3x^{-2}y^4z)^{-2}$

$(-3)^{-2}x^4y^{-8}z^{-2} = \dfrac{x^4}{9y^8z^2}$

46. $\left(\dfrac{5xy^{-2}}{2x^{-3}y}\right)^3$

$\left(\dfrac{5x^4}{2y^3}\right)^3 = \dfrac{125x^{12}}{8y^9}$

Calculator Problems

47. Remove a common factor of 2.193 from each term, then factor the resulting trinomial to find the roots:

$$2.193x^2 + 13.158x + 17.544 = 0$$

$2.193(x + 4)(x + 2) = 0$
$x = -2, -4$

48. Remove a common factor of 3.587 from each term, then factor the resulting trinomial to find the roots:

$$7.174x^2 - 17.935x - 10.761 = 0$$

$3.587(2x + 1)(x - 3) = 0$

$x = -\dfrac{1}{2}, 3$

For Extra Practice Exercises, turn to page 376.

Solutions to Odd-Numbered Practice Problems

1.
$x^2 + x = 56$
$x^2 + x - 56 = 0$
$(x + 8)(x - 7) = 0$
$x + 8 = 0 \quad$ or $\quad x - 7 = 0$
$x = -8 \qquad\qquad x = 7$

3.
$7x^2 - 14x = 0$
$7x(x - 2) = 0$
$7x = 0 \quad$ or $\quad x - 2 = 0$
$\qquad\qquad\qquad x = 2$
$\dfrac{7x}{7} = \dfrac{0}{7}$
$x = 0$

5.
$16x(x - 2) = 8x - 25$
$16x^2 - 32x = 8x - 25$
$16x^2 - 32x - 8x + 25 = 0$
$16x^2 - 40x + 25 = 0$
$(4x - 5)^2 = 0$
$4x - 5 = 0 \qquad 4x - 5 = 0$
$4x = 5$
$x = \dfrac{5}{4} \qquad$ Is a double root

7. $\dfrac{1}{x - 4} + \dfrac{1}{4} = \dfrac{-1}{x + 2}$; LCD $= 4(x - 4)(x + 2)$

$$4(x - 4)(x + 2)\dfrac{1}{x - 4} + 4(x - 4)(x + 2)\dfrac{1}{4} = 4(x - 4)(x + 2)\dfrac{-1}{x + 2}$$

$$4(x + 2) + (x - 4)(x + 2) = -4(x - 4)$$
$$4x + 8 + x^2 - 2x - 8 = -4x + 16$$
$$x^2 + 2x = -4x + 16$$
$$x^2 + 6x - 16 = 0$$
$$(x + 8)(x - 2) = 0$$
$$x = -8 \quad \text{or} \quad x = 2$$

Check:

$x = -8:$
$\dfrac{1}{-8 - 4} + \dfrac{1}{4} \overset{?}{=} \dfrac{-1}{-8 + 2}$

$\dfrac{1}{-12} + \dfrac{1}{4} \overset{?}{=} \dfrac{-1}{-6}$

$-\dfrac{1}{12} + \dfrac{3}{12} \overset{?}{=} \dfrac{2}{12}$

$\dfrac{2}{12} \overset{?}{=} \dfrac{2}{12} \checkmark$

$x = 2:$
$\dfrac{1}{2 - 4} + \dfrac{1}{4} \overset{?}{=} \dfrac{-1}{2 + 2}$

$\dfrac{1}{-2} + \dfrac{1}{4} \overset{?}{=} \dfrac{-1}{4}$

$\dfrac{-2}{4} + \dfrac{1}{4} \overset{?}{=} \dfrac{-1}{4}$

$\dfrac{-1}{4} = \dfrac{-1}{4} \checkmark$

Answers to Even-Numbered Practice Problems

2. $x = \dfrac{1}{4}, x = \dfrac{2}{3}$ **4.** $x = 0, x = \dfrac{1}{3}$ **6.** $a = -\dfrac{4}{3}, a = \dfrac{3}{2}$

7.2 SOLVING QUADRATIC EQUATIONS BY TAKING SQUARE ROOTS OR BY COMPLETING THE SQUARE

After studying this section, you will be able to:

1 Solve quadratic equations by taking the square root of each side

2 Solve quadratic equations by completing the square

1 Taking Square Roots

If $b = 0$ in the quadratic equation $ax^2 + bx + c = 0$, we would have $ax^2 + c = 0$. We can next add $-c$ to each side. Finally we can take the square root of each side of the equation to solve for x. This is sometimes called the *square root method* of solving a quadratic equation.

Definition

If $x^2 = a$, then $x = \pm\sqrt{a}$ for all nonnegative real numbers a.

The notation $\pm\sqrt{a}$ is a shorthand way of writing "$+\sqrt{a}$ or $-\sqrt{a}$." The symbol $\pm$ is read "plus or minus."

Example 1 Solve and check: $x^2 - 36 = 0$.

If we add 36 to each side we have $x^2 = 36$.

$$x = \pm\sqrt{36}$$
$$x = \pm 6$$

Thus the two roots are 6 and -6.

Check: $6^2 = 36$ and $(-6)^2 = 36$. ∎

Practice Problem 1 Solve: $x^2 = 121$. ∎

Example 2 Solve: $x^2 = 15$.

If $x^2 = 15$, then $x = \pm\sqrt{15}$. The roots are $\sqrt{15}$ and $-\sqrt{15}$. ∎

Practice Problem 2 Solve: $x^2 = 29$. ∎

Example 3 Solve: $x^2 = 48$.

If $x^2 = 48$, then

$$x = \pm\sqrt{48} = \pm\sqrt{16 \cdot 3}$$
$$x = \pm 4\sqrt{3}$$

The roots are $4\sqrt{3}$ and $-4\sqrt{3}$. ∎

Practice Problem 3 Solve: $x^2 = 18$. ∎

Example 4 Solve and check: $3x^2 + 2 = 77$.

$$3x^2 = 75$$
$$x^2 = 25$$
$$x = \pm\sqrt{25}$$
$$x = \pm 5$$

The roots are 5 and -5.

Check:

$3(5)^2 + 2 \overset{?}{=} 77$	$3(-5)^2 + 2 \overset{?}{=} 77$
$3(25) + 2 \overset{?}{=} 77$	$3(25) + 2 \overset{?}{=} 77$
$75 + 2 \overset{?}{=} 77$	$75 + 2 \overset{?}{=} 77$
$77 = 77$ ✓	$77 = 77$ ✓ ∎

TEACHING TIP Students often confuse $\sqrt{a}$ with $\pm\sqrt{a}$. You will probably find it helpful to emphasize that the radical sign alone indicates the principal (positive) square root. When you take the square root of each side of the equation you must consider BOTH the positive and negative value.

TEACHING TIP Example 4 is very important. Students often think they understand it when in fact they really do not. You may want to do the following additional example after discussing example 4. Solve:

$$2x^2 - 7 = 91 \quad \text{Sol. } 2x^2 = 98$$
$$x^2 = 49$$
$$x = \pm 7$$

Practice Problem 4   Solve: $5x^2 + 1 = 46$.   ■

Example 5   Solve and check: $4x^2 = -16$.

$$x^2 = -4$$
$$x = \boxed{\pm\sqrt{-4}}$$
$$x = \pm 2i \qquad \text{Simplify using } \sqrt{-1} = i.$$

The roots are $2i$ and $-2i$.

$$\text{Check: } 4(2i)^2 \overset{?}{=} -16 \qquad 4(-2i)^2 \overset{?}{=} -16$$
$$4(4i^2) \overset{?}{=} -16 \qquad 4(4i^2) \overset{?}{=} -16$$
$$4(-4) \overset{?}{=} -16 \qquad 4(-4) \overset{?}{=} -16$$
$$-16 \overset{?}{=} -16 \checkmark \qquad -16 \overset{?}{=} -16 \checkmark \qquad ■$$

Practice Problem 5   Solve: $3x^2 = -27$.   ■

Example 6   Solve: $(4x - 1)^2 = 5$.

$$\sqrt{(4x-1)^2} = \pm\sqrt{5} \quad\Longleftarrow Note: \text{ we really have } \pm\sqrt{(4x-1)^2} = \pm\sqrt{5}.$$
$$4x - 1 = \pm\sqrt{5} \qquad \text{Thus we have "four" solutions. However,}$$
$$\qquad\qquad\qquad\qquad \text{these four simplify to two. (A quadratic}$$
$$4x = 1 \pm \sqrt{5} \qquad \text{equation cannot have more than two}$$
$$\qquad\qquad\qquad\qquad \text{solutions.)}$$
$$x = \frac{1 \pm \sqrt{5}}{4}$$

The roots are $x = \dfrac{1 + \sqrt{5}}{4}$ and $x = \dfrac{1 - \sqrt{5}}{4}$.

Check: Verify this answer.   ■

Practice Problem 6   Solve: $(2x + 3)^2 = 7$.   ■

❷ Completing the Square

Often, a quadratic equation cannot be factored (or it may be difficult to factor). So we use another method of solving the equation, called **completing the square**. When we complete the square, we are changing the polynomial to a perfect square trinomial (see Section 4.4). The form of the equation then becomes $(x + d)^2 = e$.

Now we already know that

$$\boxed{(x + d)^2 = x^2 + 2dx + d^2}$$

Notice three things about the quadratic equation on the right-hand side.

1. The coefficient of the quadratic term (x^2) is 1.
2. The coefficient of the linear (x) terms is $2d$.
3. The constant term (d^2) is the square of *half* the coefficient of the linear term.

For example, in the trinomial $x^2 + 6x + 9$, the coefficient of the linear term is 6 and the constant term is $\left(\dfrac{6}{2}\right)^2 = (3)^2 = 9$.

For the trinomial $x^2 - 10x + 25$, the coefficient of the linear term is -10 and the constant term is $\left(\dfrac{-10}{2}\right)^2 = (-5)^2 = 25$.

What number n makes the trinomial $x^2 + 12x + n$ a perfect square?

$$n = \left(\frac{12}{2}\right)^2 = 6^2 = 36$$

Hence, the trinomial $x^2 + 12x + 36$ is a perfect square trinomial and can be written as $(x + 6)^2$.

Now let's solve some equations.

Example 7   Solve and check: $x^2 + 6x + 1 = 0$.

This equation cannot be factored. Since $b \neq 0$, we cannot use the square root method. Hence, we'll solve it by completing the square.

Step 1. First put the equation in proper form:

$$x^2 + 6x = -1$$

Step 2. We want to complete the square of $x^2 + 6x$. That is, we want to add a constant term to $x^2 + 6x$ so that we get a perfect square trinomial. We do this by taking half the coefficient of x and squaring it.

$$\left(\frac{6}{2}\right)^2 = 3^2 = 9$$

Adding 9 to $x^2 + 6x$ gives the perfect square trinomial $x^2 + 6x + 9$, which we factor to $(x + 3)^2$. *But* we cannot just add 9 to the left side of our equation unless we also add 9 to the right side. (Why?) Thus, we now have

$$x^2 + 6x \boxed{+9} = -1 \boxed{+9}$$

Step 3. Now we factor.

$$(x + 3)^2 = 8$$

Step 4. We now can take square roots as we did before.

$$(x + 3) = \pm\sqrt{8}$$
$$x + 3 = \pm\sqrt{8}$$

Step 5. Next we simplify and solve for x.

$$x + 3 = \pm\sqrt{4 \cdot 2} = \pm 2\sqrt{2}$$
$$x = -3 \pm 2\sqrt{2}$$

The roots are $x = -3 + 2\sqrt{2}$ and $-3 - 2\sqrt{2}$.

Step 6. We *must* check our solution in the *original* equation (not the perfect square trinomial we constructed).

$$x^2 + 6x + 1 = 0 \qquad\qquad x^2 + 6x + 1 = 0$$
$$\left(-3 + 2\sqrt{2}\right)^2 + 6\left(-3 + 2\sqrt{2}\right) + 1 \overset{?}{=} 0 \quad \left(-3 - 2\sqrt{2}\right)^2 + 6\left(-3 - 2\sqrt{2}\right) + 1 \overset{?}{=} 0$$
$$9 - 12\sqrt{2} + 8 - 18 + 12\sqrt{2} + 1 \overset{?}{=} 0 \qquad 9 + 12\sqrt{2} + 8 - 18 - 12\sqrt{2} + 1 \overset{?}{=} 0$$
$$18 - 18 - 12\sqrt{2} + 12\sqrt{2} \overset{?}{=} 0 \qquad\qquad 18 - 18 + 12\sqrt{2} - 12\sqrt{2} \overset{?}{=} 0$$
$$\boxed{0 = 0} \checkmark \qquad\qquad\qquad\qquad \boxed{0 = 0} \checkmark$$

Therefore, both answers are valid roots of the quadratic equation. As you become more skilled at completing the square, you won't need to write every step. We will not supply such details for every solution. ◼

Practice Problem 7   Solve by completing the square: $x^2 + 8x + 3 = 0$. ◼

Example 8   Complete the square to solve: $x^2 - 5x - 24 = 0$.

$$x^2 - 5x + \underline{\quad\quad} = 24 + \underline{\quad\quad} \qquad\qquad \text{One-half of } -5 \text{ squared is}$$

$$\left[\frac{1}{2}(-5)\right]^2 = \left[-\frac{5}{2}\right]^2 = \frac{25}{4}$$

TEACHING TIP After explaining example 8 or a similar example, ask students to do the following problem as a class exercise. Complete the square to solve:

$$x^2 + 7x - 30 = 0$$

Ans. $x = -10$,
      $x = 3$

$$x^2 - 5x + \boxed{\frac{25}{4}} = 24 + \boxed{\frac{25}{4}}$$ Adding $\frac{25}{4}$ to each side.

$$\left(x - \frac{5}{2}\right)^2 = \frac{96}{4} + \frac{25}{4}$$ Factoring left side.

$$\left(x - \frac{5}{2}\right)^2 = \frac{121}{4}$$ Simplifying.

$$\left(x - \frac{5}{2}\right) = \pm\sqrt{\frac{121}{4}}$$ Taking square root of each side.

$$x - \frac{5}{2} = \pm\frac{11}{2}$$ Simplifying.

$$x = \frac{5}{2} \pm \frac{11}{2} = \frac{5 \pm 11}{2}$$

So $x = \dfrac{5 + 11}{2} = 8$ and $x = \dfrac{5 - 11}{2} = -3$. Can you verify that these are roots of the given equation? ■

Practice Problem 8 Solve by completing the square: $x^2 + 3x - 18 = 0$. ■

TEACHING TIP Quadratic equations with the x term having a coefficient that is not 1 are the most difficult for students to solve by completing the square. After presenting example 9, you may want to do the following additional example. Solve:

$$9x^2 - 6x - 4 = 0$$

Sol. $x^2 - \dfrac{2}{3}x = \dfrac{4}{9}$

$$x^2 - \frac{2}{3}x + \frac{1}{9} = \frac{4}{9} + \frac{1}{9}$$

$$\left(x - \frac{1}{3}\right)^2 = \frac{5}{9}$$

$$x - \frac{1}{3} = \frac{\pm\sqrt{5}}{3}$$

$$x = \frac{1 \pm \sqrt{5}}{3}$$

Example 9 Solve: $3x^2 - 8x + 1 = 0$.

$$3x^2 - 8x = -1$$ Adding -1 to each side.

$$\frac{3x^2}{3} - \frac{8x}{3} = -\frac{1}{3}$$ Dividing each term by 3. (Remember that the coefficient of the quadratic term must be 1.)

$$x^2 - \frac{8}{3}x + \boxed{\frac{16}{9}} = -\frac{1}{3} + \boxed{\frac{16}{9}}$$

$$\left(x - \frac{4}{3}\right)^2 = \frac{13}{9}$$

$$x - \frac{4}{3} = \pm\sqrt{\frac{13}{9}}$$

$$x - \frac{4}{3} = \pm\frac{\sqrt{13}}{3}$$

$$x = \frac{4}{3} \pm \frac{\sqrt{13}}{3}$$

$$x = \frac{4 \pm \sqrt{13}}{3}$$ ■

Practice Problem 9 Solve by completing the square: $2x^2 + 4x + 1 = 0$. ■

Let's summarize the steps involved in completing the square.

> **Completing the Square**
> 1. Put the equation in the form $ax^2 + bx = c$. If $a \neq 1$, divide each term by a.
> 2. Square $\dfrac{b}{2}$ and add $\left(\dfrac{b}{2}\right)^2$ to both sides of the equation.
> 3. Factor the left side (a perfect square trinomial).
> 4. Take square roots of both sides.
> 5. Solve the equations.
> 6. Check solutions in the *original* equation.

Solve for the roots by taking the square root of each side. Simplify your answer.

1. $x^2 = 121$
$x = \pm 11$

2. $x^2 = 144$
$x = \pm 12$

3. $x^2 - 20 = 0$
$x = \pm 2\sqrt{5}$

4. $x^2 - 50 = 0$
$x = \pm 5\sqrt{2}$

5. $2x^2 - 26 = 0$
$x = \pm\sqrt{13}$

6. $2x^2 - 10 = 0$
$x = \pm\sqrt{5}$

7. $3x^2 + 1 = 28$
$x = \pm 3$

8. $4x^2 + 3 = 43$
$x = \pm\sqrt{10}$

9. $4x^2 - 20 = 124$
$x = \pm 6$

10. $10x^2 + 2 = 92$
$x = \pm 3$

11. $(x - 3)^2 = 12$
$x = 3 \pm 2\sqrt{3}$

12. $(x + 2)^2 = 18$
$x + 2 = \pm\sqrt{18}$
$x = -2 \pm 3\sqrt{2}$

13. $(2x + 1)^2 = 7$
$2x + 1 = \pm\sqrt{7}$
$x = \dfrac{-1 \pm \sqrt{7}}{2}$

14. $(3x + 2)^2 = 5$
$3x + 2 = \pm\sqrt{5}$
$x = \dfrac{-2 \pm \sqrt{5}}{3}$

15. $(4x - 3)^2 = 36$
$4x - 3 = \pm 6$
$x = \dfrac{9}{4}, \ -\dfrac{3}{4}$

16. $(5x - 2)^2 = 25$
$5x - 2 = \pm 5$
$x = \dfrac{7}{5}, \ -\dfrac{3}{5}$

17. $(3x - 4)^2 = 8$
$3x - 4 = \pm 2\sqrt{2}$
$x = \dfrac{4 \pm 2\sqrt{2}}{3}$

18. $(2x + 7)^2 = 27$
$2x + 7 = \pm 3\sqrt{3}$
$x = \dfrac{-7 \pm 3\sqrt{3}}{2}$

Solve for the roots by completing the square. Simplify your answer. Express imaginary numbers in i notation.

19. $x^2 - 2x = 5$
$x^2 - 2x + 1 = 5 + 1$
$(x - 1)^2 = 6$
$x = 1 \pm \sqrt{6}$

20. $x^2 - 4x = 11$
$x^2 - 4x + 4 = 11 + 4$
$(x - 2)^2 = 15$
$x - 2 = \pm\sqrt{15}$
$x = 2 \pm \sqrt{15}$

21. $x^2 + 10x + 5 = 0$
$x^2 + 10x + 25 = -5 + 25$
$(x + 5)^2 = 20$
$x = -5 \pm 2\sqrt{5}$

22. $x^2 + 6x + 2 = 0$
$x^2 + 6x + 9 = -2 + 9$
$(x + 3)^2 = 7$
$x = -3 \pm \sqrt{7}$

23. $x^2 - 8x = 17$
$x^2 - 8x + 16 = 17 + 16$
$(x - 4)^2 = 33$
$x = 4 \pm \sqrt{33}$

24. $x^2 - 12x = 4$
$x^2 - 12x + 36 = 4 + 36$
$(x - 6)^2 = 40$
$x = 6 \pm 2\sqrt{10}$

25. $x^2 - 6x + 4 = 0$
$x^2 - 6x + 9 = -4 + 9$
$(x - 3)^2 = 5$
$x = 3 \pm \sqrt{5}$

26. $x^2 + 20x + 10 = 0$
$x^2 + 20x + 100 = -10 + 100$
$(x + 10)^2 = 90$
$x = -10 \pm 3\sqrt{10}$

27. $2y^2 + 10y = -11$
$y^2 + 5y + \dfrac{25}{4} = -\dfrac{22}{4} + \dfrac{25}{4}$
$\left(x + \dfrac{5}{2}\right)^2 = \dfrac{3}{4}$
$x = \dfrac{-5 \pm \sqrt{3}}{2}$

28. $6y^2 - 6y = 3$
$y^2 - y + \dfrac{1}{4} = \dfrac{2}{4} + \dfrac{1}{4}$
$\left(y - \dfrac{1}{2}\right)^2 = \dfrac{3}{4}$
$y = \dfrac{1 \pm \sqrt{3}}{2}$

29. $4x^2 - 4x - 3 = 0$
$x^2 - x + \dfrac{1}{4} = \dfrac{3}{4} + \dfrac{1}{4}$
$\left(x - \dfrac{1}{2}\right)^2 = 1$
$x = \dfrac{1}{2} \pm 1$
$x = \dfrac{3}{2}, \ x = -\dfrac{1}{2}$

30. $2x^2 - 7x + 4 = 0$
$x^2 - \dfrac{7}{2}x + \dfrac{49}{16} = -2 + \dfrac{49}{16}$
$\left(x - \dfrac{7}{4}\right)^2 = \dfrac{17}{16}$
$x = \dfrac{7 \pm \sqrt{17}}{4}$

31. $2y^2 - y = 15$
$y^2 - \dfrac{1}{2}y + \dfrac{1}{16} = \dfrac{15}{2} + \dfrac{1}{16}$
$\left(y - \dfrac{1}{4}\right)^2 = \dfrac{121}{16}$
$y = \dfrac{1 \pm 11}{4}$
$y = 3, \ y = -\dfrac{5}{2}$

32. $2y^2 - y = 6$
$y^2 - \dfrac{1}{2}y + \dfrac{1}{16} = 3 + \dfrac{1}{16}$
$\left(y - \dfrac{1}{4}\right)^2 = \dfrac{49}{16}$
$y = \dfrac{1 \pm 7}{4}$
$y = 2, \ y = -\dfrac{3}{2}$

33. $6x^2 + 3x = 1$
$x^2 + \dfrac{1}{2}x + \dfrac{1}{16} = \dfrac{1}{6} + \dfrac{1}{16}$
$\left(x + \dfrac{1}{4}\right)^2 = \dfrac{11}{48}$
$x + \dfrac{1}{4} = \pm\sqrt{\dfrac{11}{48}} = \pm\dfrac{\sqrt{33}}{12}$
$x = \dfrac{-3 \pm \sqrt{33}}{12}$

34. $3x^2 - 6x = 2$
$x^2 - 2x + 1 = \dfrac{2}{3} + 1$
$(x - 1)^2 = \dfrac{5}{3}$
$x - 1 = \pm\sqrt{\dfrac{5}{3}} = \pm\dfrac{\sqrt{15}}{3}$
$x = \dfrac{3 \pm \sqrt{15}}{3}$

35. $4x^2 + 7x + 2 = 3$ $\quad x^2 + \dfrac{7}{4}x + \dfrac{49}{64} = \dfrac{1}{4} + \dfrac{49}{64}$

$$\left(x + \dfrac{7}{8}\right)^2 = \dfrac{65}{64}$$

$$x + \dfrac{7}{8} = \dfrac{\pm\sqrt{65}}{8}$$

$$x = \dfrac{-7 \pm \sqrt{65}}{8}$$

36. $3x^2 + 8x + 3 = 2$ $\quad x^2 + \dfrac{8}{3}x + \dfrac{16}{9} = -\dfrac{1}{3} + \dfrac{16}{9}$

$$\left(x + \dfrac{4}{3}\right)^2 = \dfrac{13}{9}$$

$$x + \dfrac{4}{3} = \dfrac{\pm\sqrt{13}}{3}$$

$$x = \dfrac{-4 \pm \sqrt{13}}{3}$$

? **To Think About**

Solve by completing the square.

37. $y^2 + \sqrt{2}y - 2 = 0$ $\quad y^2 + \sqrt{2}y + \dfrac{1}{2} = 2 + \dfrac{1}{2}$

$$\left(y + \dfrac{1}{\sqrt{2}}\right)^2 = \dfrac{5}{2}$$

$$y + \dfrac{1}{\sqrt{2}} = \dfrac{\pm\sqrt{5}}{\sqrt{2}}$$

$$y = \dfrac{\pm\sqrt{5} - 1}{\sqrt{2}} = \dfrac{\pm\sqrt{10} - \sqrt{2}}{2}$$

38. $y^2 + \sqrt{3}y - 1 = 0$ $\quad y^2 + \sqrt{3}y + \dfrac{3}{4} = 1 + \dfrac{3}{4}$

$$\left(y + \dfrac{\sqrt{3}}{2}\right)^2 = \dfrac{7}{4}$$

$$y + \dfrac{\sqrt{3}}{2} = \dfrac{\pm\sqrt{7}}{2}$$

$$y = \dfrac{-\sqrt{3} \pm \sqrt{7}}{2}$$

39. Solve for x by completing the square.

$$(2x + 5)(2x - 5) + 4 + 13x = -12$$

$4x^2 + 13x = 9$

$x^2 + \dfrac{13}{4} + \dfrac{169}{64} = \dfrac{9}{4} + \dfrac{169}{64}$

$\left(x + \dfrac{13}{8}\right)^2 = \dfrac{313}{64}$

$x = \dfrac{-13 \pm \sqrt{313}}{8}$

40. Solve for x by completing the square. w is a constant value.

$x^2 + \dfrac{w}{2}x + \dfrac{w^2}{16} = \dfrac{9}{2} + \dfrac{w^2}{16}$ $2x^2 + wx - 9 = 0$

$\left(x + \dfrac{w}{4}\right)^2 = \dfrac{72 + w^2}{16}$

$x + \dfrac{w}{4} = \dfrac{\pm\sqrt{w^2 + 72}}{4}$

$x = \dfrac{-w \pm \sqrt{w^2 + 72}}{4}$

The Formula $D = 16t^2$ is used to approximate the distance in feet that an object falls in t seconds.

41. A parachutist jumps from an airplane, falls for 3600 feet, then opens her parachute. For how many seconds was the parachutist falling before opening the parachute?

15 seconds

42. How long would it take an object to fall to the ground from a helicopter hovering at 1936 feet above the ground?

11 seconds

Cumulative Review Problems

Evaluate.

43. $\sqrt{b^2 - 4ac}$; $b = 4$, $a = 3$, $c = -4$

$\sqrt{4^2 - 4(3)(-4)} = \sqrt{64} = 8$

44. $\sqrt{b^2 - 4ac}$; $b = -5$, $a = 2$, $c = -3$

$\sqrt{(-5)^2 - 4(2)(-3)} = \sqrt{49} = 7$

45. $5x^2 - 6x + 8$; $x = -2$

$20 + 12 + 8 = 40$

46. $2x^2 + 3x - 5$; $x = -3$

$18 - 9 - 5 = 4$

Find the square roots by isolating the variable and then taking the square root of each side of the equation. Approximate your answers to four decimal places.

47. $3x^2 - 55 = 0$

$x = \pm 4.2817$

48. $5x^2 + 2 = 80$

$x = \pm 3.9497$

For Extra Practice Exercises, turn to page 376.

Solutions to Odd-Numbered Practice Problems

1. If $x^2 = a$, then $x = \pm\sqrt{a}$; if $x^2 = 121$, then $x = \pm\sqrt{121}$. $x = \pm 11$. **3.** $x^2 = 18$

$$x = \pm\sqrt{18} = \pm 3\sqrt{2}$$

5. $3x^2 = -27$

$$\frac{3x^2}{3} = \frac{-27}{3}$$

$$x^2 = -9$$

$$x = \pm\sqrt{-9}$$

$$= \pm i\sqrt{9}$$

$$= \pm 3i$$

7. $x^2 + 8x + 3 = 0$

$$x^2 + 8x = -3$$

$$x^2 + 8x + \boxed{16} = -3 + \boxed{16}$$

$$(x + 4)^2 = 13$$

$$x + 4 = \pm\sqrt{13}$$

$$x = -4 \pm \sqrt{13}$$

9. $2x^2 + 4x = -1$

$$x^2 + 2x = -\frac{1}{2}$$

$$x^2 + 2x + 1 = -\frac{1}{2} + 1$$

$$(x + 1)^2 = -\frac{1}{2} + \frac{2}{2}$$

$$(x + 1)^2 = \frac{1}{2}$$

$$\sqrt{(x + 1)^2} = \pm\sqrt{\frac{1}{2}}$$

$$x + 1 = \pm\frac{1}{\sqrt{2}}$$

$$x + 1 = \pm\frac{\sqrt{2}}{2}$$

$$x = -1 \pm \frac{\sqrt{2}}{2} \quad \text{Answer}$$

or

$$x = -\frac{2}{2} \pm \frac{\sqrt{2}}{2}$$

$$= \frac{-2 \pm \sqrt{2}}{2} \quad \text{Alternative answer}$$

Answers to Even-Numbered Practice Problems

2. $x = \pm\sqrt{29}$ **4.** $x = \pm 3$ **6.** $x = \dfrac{-3 \pm \sqrt{7}}{2}$ **8.** $x = -6, x = 3$

7.3 THE QUADRATIC FORMULA

1 The last method we'll study for solving quadratic equations is the **quadratic formula**. This method works for *any* quadratic equation.

The quadratic formula is developed from completing the square. We begin with the standard form of the equation

$$ax^2 + bx + c = 0$$

To complete the square, we want the equation to be in the *form* $x^2 + dx = e$. Thus we divide by a.

$$\frac{ax^2}{a} + \frac{b}{a}x + \frac{c}{a} = 0$$

$$x^2 + \frac{b}{a}x = -\frac{c}{a}$$

Now we complete the square and add $\left(\dfrac{b}{2a}\right)^2$ to each side.

$$x^2 + \frac{b}{a}x + \boxed{\left(\frac{b}{2a}\right)^2} = -\frac{c}{a} + \boxed{\left(\frac{b}{2a}\right)^2}$$

Factor the left side and write the right hand side as one fraction.

$$\left(x + \frac{b}{2a}\right)^2 = \frac{b^2 - 4ac}{4a^2}$$

☐ After studying this section, you will be able to:

1 *Solve a quadratic equation that has real roots using the quadratic formula*

2 *Use the discriminant to determine the nature of the roots of a quadratic equation*

3 *Solve a quadratic equation that has complex roots using the quadratic formula*

Now take the square root of each side.

$$x + \frac{b}{2a} = \pm\sqrt{\frac{b^2 - 4ac}{4a^2}}$$

Now we solve for x and simplify.

$$x = -\frac{b}{2a} \pm \sqrt{\frac{b^2 - 4ac}{4a^2}}$$

$$x = \frac{-b \pm \sqrt{b^2 - 4ac}}{2a}$$

This is the quadratic formula.

Quadratic Formula

For all equations $ax^2 + bx + c = 0$,

$$x = \frac{-b \pm \sqrt{b^2 - 4ac}}{2a} \qquad \text{where } a \neq 0$$

TEACHING TIP   Students must memorize thoroughly the quadratic formula. Many think they have it memorized only to discover they did not memorize it correctly. Stress the importance of memorizing the formula first, and then doing all the homework problems based on memory of the formula.

Example 1   Solve by using the quadratic formula: $2x^2 + 3x - 7 = 0$.

Substituting $a = 2$, $b = 3$, and $c = -7$ into the quadratic formula

$$x = \frac{-b \pm \sqrt{b^2 - 4ac}}{2a}$$

gives

$$x = \frac{-3 \pm \sqrt{(3)^2 - 4(2)(-7)}}{2(2)}$$

$$x = \frac{-3 \pm \sqrt{9 + 56}}{4}$$

$$x = \frac{-3 \pm \sqrt{65}}{4}$$

Note: Although we haven't taken the time to do so, you may want to check your solutions in the original equation to verify that they are valid roots. ■

Practice Problem 1   Solve by the quadratic formula: $3x^2 + 4x - 5 = 0$. ■

Example 2   Solve by using the quadratic formula: $x^2 + 8x = -3$.

The standard form is $x^2 + 8x + 3 = 0$, $a = 1$, $b = 8$, and $c = 3$. Then

$$x = \frac{-b \pm \sqrt{b^2 - 4ac}}{2a}$$

$$x = \frac{-8 \pm \sqrt{8^2 - 4(1)(3)}}{2(1)}$$

$$x = \frac{-8 \pm \sqrt{64 - 12}}{2} = \frac{-8 \pm \sqrt{52}}{2} = \frac{-8 \pm \sqrt{4}\sqrt{13}}{2}$$

$$x = \frac{-8 \pm 2\sqrt{13}}{2} = \frac{2(-4 \pm \sqrt{13})}{2}$$

$$x = -4 \pm \sqrt{13} \quad ■$$

TEACHING TIP   Students often find simplifying the answer to be a difficult step. After presenting example 2, you may want to do the following additional example. Solve by the quadratic formula:

$$x^2 - 12x = -24$$

$$x^2 - 12x + 24 = 0$$

$$x = \frac{-(-12) \pm \sqrt{(-12)^2 - 4(1)(24)}}{2(1)}$$

$$= \frac{12 \pm \sqrt{48}}{2}$$

$$= \frac{12 \pm 4\sqrt{3}}{2}$$

$$= 6 \pm 2\sqrt{3}$$

Practice Problem 2   Solve by the quadratic formula: $x^2 + 5x = -1 + 2x$ ■

Example 3   Solve by using the quadratic formula: $3x^2 - x - 2 = 0$.

Here $a = 3$, $b = -1$, and $c = -2$.

$$x = \frac{-b \pm \sqrt{b^2 - 4ac}}{2a}$$

$$x = \frac{-(-1) \pm \sqrt{(-1)^2 - 4(3)(-2)}}{2(3)}$$

$$x = \frac{1 \pm \sqrt{1 + 24}}{6} = \frac{1 \pm \sqrt{25}}{6}$$

$$x = \frac{1 + 5}{6} = \frac{6}{6} \quad or \quad x = \frac{1 - 5}{6} = -\frac{4}{6}$$

$$x = 1 \qquad\qquad\qquad x = -\frac{2}{3} \quad \blacksquare$$

Practice Problem 3   Solve by the quadratic formula: $2x^2 + 7x + 6 = 0$.   ∎

Example 4   Solve by using the quadratic formula: $2x^2 - 48 = 0$.

$a = 2$, $b = 0$, and $c = -48$.

$$x = \frac{-b \pm \sqrt{b^2 - 4ac}}{2a}$$

$$x = \frac{-0 \pm \sqrt{(0)^2 - 4(2)(-48)}}{2(2)}$$

$$x = \frac{\pm\sqrt{384}}{4}$$

$$x = \frac{\pm\sqrt{64}\sqrt{6}}{4} = \frac{\pm 8\sqrt{6}}{4}$$

$$x = \pm 2\sqrt{6} \quad \blacksquare$$

Practice Problem 4   Solve by the quadratic formula: $2x^2 - 26 = 0$.   ∎

When the quadratic equation contains fractions, eliminate them by multiplying each term by the LCD. Then put the equation into standard form.

Example 5   Solve by using the quadratic formula: $\dfrac{2x}{x + 2} = 1 - \dfrac{3}{x + 4}$.

You may think that this equation isn't quadratic because it doesn't look like one. That's why we clear fractions first. The LCD is $(x + 2)(x + 4)$.

$$\frac{2x}{x+2}(x+2)(x+4) = 1(x+2)(x+4) - \frac{3}{x+4}(x+2)(x+4)$$

$$2x(x + 4) = (x + 2)(x + 4) - 3(x + 2)$$

$$2x^2 + 8x = x^2 + 6x + 8 - 3x - 6 \qquad \text{Now you can see that the}$$
$$\text{equation really is quadratic.}$$
$$2x^2 + 8x = x^2 + 3x + 2$$

$$x^2 + 5x - 2 = 0$$

Now the equation is in standard form, so we use the quadratic formula to solve it, where $a = 1$, $b = 5$, and $c = -2$.

$$x = \frac{-5 \pm \sqrt{5^2 - 4(1)(-2)}}{2(1)} = \frac{-5 \pm \sqrt{25 + 8}}{2}.$$

$$x = \frac{-5 \pm \sqrt{33}}{2} \quad \blacksquare$$

Practice Problem 5   Solve by the quadratic formula: $\dfrac{1}{x} + \dfrac{1}{x - 1} = \dfrac{5}{6}$.   ∎

Quadratic Equations with Complex Roots

2 The Discriminant

In using the quadratic formula so far, we have solved quadratic equations that had two real roots (sometimes the roots were rational; and sometimes they were irrational). It is possible to have complex roots also. This occurs when the expression $b^2 - 4ac$ is negative. Recall that $b^2 - 4ac$ is the radicand in the quadratic equation

$$x = \frac{-b \pm \sqrt{b^2 - 4ac}}{2a}$$

The expression $b^2 - 4ac$ is called the **discriminant**. Depending on whether the discriminant is positive, zero, or negative, the roots of the quadratic equation will be rational, irrational, or complex. We summarize the type of solutions in the following table.

If the discriminant $b^2 - 4ac$ is:	The number of solutions is:	And the solutions are:
positive	2	rational or irrational
zero	1	rational
negative	2	complex

If the discriminant is positive and the square of an integer, there will be two different rational solutions. If the discriminant is positive but not the square of an integer, there will be two different irrational solutions.

Example 6 What type of solutions does the equation $2x^2 - 9x - 35 = 0$ have? Do not solve the equation.

$a = 2$, $b = -9$, and $c = -35$. Thus,

$$b^2 - 4ac = (-9)^2 - 4(2)(-35) = 361$$

Since the discriminant is positive, the equation has two real (rational or irrational) roots ■

Practice Problem 6 Use the discriminant to find what type of solutions the equation $9x^2 + 12x + 4 = 0$ has. Do not solve the equation. ■

Example 7 Discuss the solutions of the equation $x^2 = 6x - 13$. Solve for the roots.

First we place in standard form $ax^2 + bx + c = 0$. Thus we have $x^2 - 6x + 13 = 0$.

Now $a = 1$, $b = -6$, $c = 13$. Thus, $b^2 - 4ac = (-6)^2 - 4(1)(13) = -16$

Hence, the equation has two complex roots.

$$x = \frac{-b \pm \sqrt{b^2 - 4ac}}{2a} \qquad x = \frac{6 + \sqrt{-16}}{2}$$

$$x = \frac{6 \pm 4i}{2} \qquad x = 3 \pm 2i \quad ■$$

Practice Problem 7 Discuss the solutions to the equation $x^2 - 4x + 13 = 0$. Solve for the roots. ■

3 **Example 8** Solve: $8x^2 - 4x + 1 = 0$. Simplify your answer.

$a = 8, b = -4, c = 1.$

$$x = \frac{-(-4) \pm \sqrt{(-4)^2 - 4(8)(1)}}{2(8)}$$

$$x = \frac{4 \pm \sqrt{16 - 32}}{16} = \frac{4 \pm \sqrt{-16}}{16}$$

$$x = \frac{4 \pm 4i}{16} = \boxed{\frac{4(1 \pm i)}{16}} = \frac{1 \pm i}{4} \quad \blacksquare$$

Practice Problem 8   Solve by the quadratic formula: $2x^2 - 4x + 5 = 0$. $\blacksquare$

You may have noticed that complex roots come in pairs. In other words, if $a + bi$ is a solution of a quadratic equation, its conjugate $a - bi$ is also a solution.

EXERCISES 7.3

Solve by the quadratic formula. Simplify your answer.

1. $x^2 + 3x - 20 = 0$

$a = 1, b = 3, c = -20$

$x = \dfrac{-3 \pm \sqrt{9 - 4(1)(-20)}}{2(1)}$

$x = \dfrac{-3 \pm \sqrt{89}}{2}$

2. $x^2 + 5x - 10 = 0$

$a = 1, b = 5, c = -10$

$x = \dfrac{-5 \pm \sqrt{25 - 4(1)(-10)}}{2(1)}$

$x = \dfrac{-5 \pm \sqrt{65}}{2}$

3. $5x^2 - x - 1 = 0$

$a = 5, b = -1, c = -1$

$x = \dfrac{1 \pm \sqrt{1 - 4(5)(-1)}}{2(5)}$

$x = \dfrac{1 \pm \sqrt{21}}{10}$

4. $2x^2 + x - 4 = 0$

$a = 2, b = 1, c = -4$

$x = \dfrac{-1 \pm \sqrt{1 - 4(2)(-4)}}{2(2)}$

$x = \dfrac{-1 \pm \sqrt{33}}{4}$

5. $x^2 + 5x - 3 = 0$

$a = 1, b = 5, c = -3$

$x = \dfrac{-5 \pm \sqrt{25 - 4(1)(-3)}}{2(1)}$

$x = \dfrac{-5 \pm \sqrt{37}}{2}$

6. $2x^2 - 3x - 1 = 0$

$a = 2, b = -3, c = -1$

$x = \dfrac{3 \pm \sqrt{9 - 4(2)(-1)}}{2(2)}$

$x = \dfrac{3 \pm \sqrt{17}}{4}$

7. $x^2 + 8x + 13 = 0$

$a = 1, b = 8, c = 13$

$x = \dfrac{-8 \pm \sqrt{64 - 4(1)(13)}}{2(1)}$

$x = \dfrac{-8 \pm \sqrt{12}}{2} = -4 \pm \sqrt{3}$

8. $x^2 - 2x - 17 = 0$

$a = 1, b = -2, c = -17$

$x = \dfrac{2 \pm \sqrt{4 - 4(1)(-17)}}{2(1)}$

$x = \dfrac{2 \pm \sqrt{72}}{2} = 1 \pm 3\sqrt{2}$

9. $6x^2 - x - 1 = 0$

$a = 6, b = -1, c = -1$

$x = \dfrac{1 \pm \sqrt{1 - 4(6)(-1)}}{2(6)}$

$x = \dfrac{1 \pm \sqrt{25}}{12}$

$x = \dfrac{1}{2}, x = -\dfrac{1}{3}$

10. $4x^2 + 11x - 3 = 0$

$a = 4, b = 11, c = -3$

$x = \dfrac{-11 \pm \sqrt{121 - 4(4)(-3)}}{2(4)}$

$x = \dfrac{-11 \pm 13}{8}$

$x = \dfrac{1}{4}, x = -3$

11. $4x^2 + 3x - 2 = 0$

$a = 4, b = 3, c = -2$

$x = \dfrac{-3 \pm \sqrt{9 - 4(4)(-2)}}{2(4)}$

$x = \dfrac{-3 \pm \sqrt{41}}{8}$

12. $6x^2 - 2x - 1 = 0$

$a = 6, b = -2, c = -1$

$x = \dfrac{2 \pm \sqrt{4 - 4(6)(-1)}}{2(6)}$

$x = \dfrac{2 \pm \sqrt{28}}{12} = \dfrac{1 \pm \sqrt{7}}{6}$

13. $3x^2 + 1 = 4x + 4$

$a = 3, b = -4, c = -3$

$x = \dfrac{4 \pm \sqrt{16 - 4(3)(-3)}}{2(3)}$

$x = \dfrac{4 \pm \sqrt{52}}{6}$

$x = \dfrac{2 \pm \sqrt{13}}{3}$

14. $2x^2 - 5x + 4 = x + 1$

$a = 2, b = -6, c = 3$

$x = \dfrac{6 \pm \sqrt{36 - 4(2)(3)}}{2(2)}$

$x = \dfrac{6 \pm \sqrt{12}}{4} = \dfrac{3 \pm \sqrt{3}}{2}$

15. $2x^2 - 7x + 4 = x - 1$

$a = 2, b = -8, c = 5$

$x = \dfrac{8 \pm \sqrt{64 - 4(2)(5)}}{2(2)}$

$x = \dfrac{8 \pm 2\sqrt{6}}{4} = \dfrac{4 \pm \sqrt{6}}{2}$

16. $2x^2 - 2x + 2 = 7$

$a = 2, b = -2, c = -5$

$x = \dfrac{2 \pm \sqrt{4 - 4(2)(-5)}}{2(2)}$

$x = \dfrac{2 \pm \sqrt{44}}{4} = \dfrac{1 \pm \sqrt{11}}{2}$

17. $3x^2 + 5x + 1 = 5x + 4$

$x^2 - 1 = 0$

$a = 1, b = 0, c = -1$

$x = \dfrac{0 \pm \sqrt{0 - 4(1)(-1)}}{2(1)}$

$x = \dfrac{\pm \sqrt{4}}{2} = \pm 1$

18. $2x^2 - 7x - 3 = 9 - 7x$

$x^2 - 6 = 0$

$a = 1, b = 0, c = -6$

$x = \dfrac{0 \pm \sqrt{0 - 4(1)(-6)}}{2(1)}$

$x = \dfrac{\pm \sqrt{24}}{2} = \pm \sqrt{6}$

19. $(x - 3)(x + 2) = 1$

$x^2 - x - 7 = 0$

$x = \dfrac{1 \pm \sqrt{1 - 4(1)(-7)}}{2(1)}$

$x = \dfrac{1 \pm \sqrt{29}}{2}$

20. $(x + 4)(x - 2) = 3x$

$x^2 - x - 8 = 0$

$x = \dfrac{1 \pm \sqrt{1 - 4(1)(-8)}}{2(1)}$

$x = \dfrac{1 \pm \sqrt{33}}{2}$

21. $3x^2 + 7x - 4 = x^2 - 8$

$2x^2 + 7x + 4 = 0$

$x = \dfrac{-7 \pm \sqrt{49 - 4(2)(4)}}{2(2)}$

$x = \dfrac{-7 \pm \sqrt{17}}{4}$

22. $2x^2 - 5x + 1 = -3x^2 - 12x$

$5x^2 + 7x + 1 = 0$

$x = \dfrac{-7 \pm \sqrt{49 - 4(5)(1)}}{2(5)}$

$x = \dfrac{-7 \pm \sqrt{29}}{10}$

23. $\dfrac{1}{x + 3} + \dfrac{1}{x} = \dfrac{1}{4}$

$x^2 - 5x - 12 = 0$

$x = \dfrac{5 \pm \sqrt{25 - 4(1)(-12)}}{2(1)}$

$x = \dfrac{5 \pm \sqrt{73}}{2}$

24. $\dfrac{1}{x + 2} + \dfrac{1}{x} = \dfrac{1}{3}$

$x^2 - 4x - 6 = 0$

$x = \dfrac{4 \pm \sqrt{16 - 4(1)(-6)}}{2(1)}$

$x = \dfrac{4 \pm \sqrt{40}}{2} = 2 \pm \sqrt{10}$

25. $\dfrac{1}{y} + \dfrac{2}{y + 3} = \dfrac{1}{4}$

$y^2 - 9y - 12 = 0$

$y = \dfrac{9 \pm \sqrt{81 - 4(1)(-12)}}{2(1)}$

$y = \dfrac{9 \pm \sqrt{129}}{2}$

26. $\dfrac{1}{y} + \dfrac{1}{y - 4} = \dfrac{5}{6}$

$5y^2 - 32y + 24 = 0$

$y = \dfrac{32 \pm \sqrt{1024 - 4(5)(24)}}{2(5)}$

$y = \dfrac{32 \pm \sqrt{544}}{10} = \dfrac{16 \pm 2\sqrt{34}}{5}$

27. $\dfrac{1}{15} + \dfrac{3}{y} = \dfrac{4}{y + 1}$

$y^2 - 14y + 45 = 0$

$y = \dfrac{14 \pm \sqrt{196 - 4(1)(45)}}{2(1)}$

$y = \dfrac{14 \pm \sqrt{16}}{2}$

$y = 9, \; y = 5$

28. $\dfrac{1}{4} + \dfrac{6}{y + 2} = \dfrac{6}{y}$

$y^2 + 2y - 48 = 0$

$y = \dfrac{-2 \pm \sqrt{4 - 4(1)(-48)}}{2(1)}$

$y = \dfrac{-2 \pm \sqrt{196}}{2}$

$y = 6, \; y = -8$

Use the discriminant to find what type of solutions (two rational, two irrational, one rational, or two complex) each of the following equations has. Do not solve the equation.

29. $x^2 - 6x + 17 = 0$

$b^2 - 4ac = 36 - 4(1)(17) = -32$
(2 complex roots)

30. $2x^2 + 4x + 3 = 0$

$b^2 - 4ac = 16 - 4(2)(3) = -8$
(2 complex roots)

31. $6x^2 - 1x + 6 = 0$

$b^2 - 4ac = 1 - 4(6)(6) = -143$
(2 complex roots)

32. $4x^2 - 20x + 25 = 0$

$b^2 - 4ac = 400 - 4(4)(25) = 0$
(1 rational root)

33. $2x^2 + 10x + 8 = 0$

$b^2 - 4ac = 100 - 4(2)(8) = 36$
(2 rational roots)

34. $2x^2 - 7x - 4 = 0$

$b^2 - 4ac = 49 - 4(2)(-4) = 81$
(2 rational roots)

Use the quadratic formula to find the complex roots and simplify.

35. $x^2 - 4x + 8 = 0$

$x = \dfrac{4 \pm \sqrt{16 - 4(1)(8)}}{2(1)}$

$x = \dfrac{4 \pm \sqrt{-16}}{2} = 2 \pm 2i$

36. $x^2 - 2x + 4 = 0$

$x = \dfrac{2 \pm \sqrt{4 - 4(1)(4)}}{2(1)}$

$x = \dfrac{2 \pm \sqrt{-12}}{2} = 1 \pm i\sqrt{3}$

37. $2x^2 + 2x + 1 = 0$

$x = \dfrac{-2 \pm \sqrt{4 - 4(2)(1)}}{2(2)}$

$x = \dfrac{-2 \pm \sqrt{-4}}{4} = \dfrac{-1 \pm i}{2}$

38. $5x^2 + 5x + 2 = 0$

$x = \dfrac{-5 \pm \sqrt{25 - 4(5)(2)}}{2(5)}$

$x = \dfrac{-5 \pm \sqrt{25 - 40}}{10}$

$x = \dfrac{-5 \pm i\sqrt{15}}{10}$

39. $3x^2 - 8x + 7 = 0$

$x = \dfrac{8 \pm \sqrt{64 - 4(3)(7)}}{2(3)}$

$x = \dfrac{8 \pm \sqrt{-20}}{6} = \dfrac{4 \pm i\sqrt{5}}{3}$

40. $3x^2 - 4x + 6 = 0$

$x = \dfrac{4 \pm \sqrt{16 - 4(3)(6)}}{2(3)}$

$x = \dfrac{4 \pm \sqrt{-56}}{6} = \dfrac{2 \pm i\sqrt{14}}{3}$

41. $x^2 = \dfrac{1}{3}x - \dfrac{4}{3}$

$3x^2 - x + 4 = 0$

$x = \dfrac{1 \pm \sqrt{1 - 4(3)(4)}}{2(3)}$

$x = \dfrac{1 \pm \sqrt{-47}}{6} = \dfrac{1 \pm i\sqrt{47}}{6}$

42. $\dfrac{1}{2}x + \dfrac{3}{4} = -\dfrac{1}{2}x^2$

$2x^2 + 2x + 3 = 0$

$x = \dfrac{-2 \pm \sqrt{4 - 4(2)(3)}}{2(2)}$

$x = \dfrac{-2 \pm \sqrt{-20}}{4} = \dfrac{-1 \pm i\sqrt{5}}{2}$

43. The solutions to the equation $ax^2 + 3x - 6 = 0$ are $x = \dfrac{-3 \pm \sqrt{57}}{4}$. What is the value of a?

$x = \dfrac{-3 \pm \sqrt{9 + 24a}}{2a}$

Thus, $9 + 24a = 57$,   or $2a = 4$

$24a = 48$ $a = 2$

$a = 2$

44. The solutions to the equation $2x^2 + 7x + c = 0$ are $x = \dfrac{-7 \pm \sqrt{65}}{4}$. What is the value of c?

$x = \dfrac{-7 \pm \sqrt{49 - 4(2)c}}{4}$

so $49 - 8c = 65$

$-8c = 16$

$c = -2$

Use the quadratic formula to solve.

45. Solve for x: $5x^2 + dx + 3f = 0$.

$a = 5, b = d, c = 3f$

$x = \dfrac{-d \pm \sqrt{d^2 - 4(5)(3f)}}{2(5)}$

$x = \dfrac{-d \pm \sqrt{d^2 - 60f}}{10}$

46. Solve for r: $S = 2\pi rh + 2\pi r^2$.

$a = 2\pi, b = 2\pi h, c = -S$

$r = \dfrac{-2\pi h \pm \sqrt{4\pi^2 h^2 - 4(2\pi)(-S)}}{2(2\pi)}$

$r = \dfrac{-2\pi h \pm 2\sqrt{\pi^2 h^2 + 2\pi S}}{4\pi}$

$r = \dfrac{-\pi h \pm \sqrt{\pi^2 h^2 + 2\pi S}}{2\pi}$

47. Verify that $y = \dfrac{2 + \sqrt{3}}{2}$ is a solution of the equation $4y^2 = 8y - 1$.

$4\left(\dfrac{2 + \sqrt{3}}{2}\right)^2 \overset{?}{=} 8\left(\dfrac{2 + \sqrt{3}}{2}\right) - 1$

$4\left[\dfrac{4 + 4\sqrt{3} + 3}{4}\right] \overset{?}{=} 8 + 4\sqrt{3} - 1$

$7 + 4\sqrt{3} = 7 + 4\sqrt{3}$

48. Verify that $\dfrac{3 + \sqrt{2}}{2}$ is a solution of the equation $4y^2 = 12y - 7$.

$4\left(\dfrac{3 + \sqrt{2}}{2}\right)^2 \overset{?}{=} 12\left(\dfrac{3 + \sqrt{2}}{2}\right) - 7$

$11 + 6\sqrt{2} \overset{?}{=} 18 + 6\sqrt{2} - 7$

$11 + 6\sqrt{2} = 11 + 6\sqrt{2}$

Cumulative Review Problems

Simplify.

49. $9x^2 - 6x + 3 - 4x - 12x^2 + 8$

$-3x^2 - 10x + 11$

50. $2a^2 - 3a^3 + 4a - 7a^3 + 5a^2 - 6a$

$-10a^3 + 7a^2 - 2a$

51. $\dfrac{1}{2}(8x^2 - 6x) + 2x(x - 4)$

$4x^2 - 3x + 2x^2 - 8x = 6x^2 - 11x$

52. $3y(2 - y) + \dfrac{1}{5}(10y^2 - 15y)$

$6y - 3y^2 + 2y^2 - 3y = -y^2 + 3y$

Calculator Problems

Solve for x by using the quadratic formula. Approximate your answers to four decimal places.

53. $3x^2 + 5x - 9 = 0$

$x = -2.7554, 1.0888$

54. $1.2x^2 - 12.3x - 4.2 = 0$

$x = -0.3308$

$x = 10.5808$

For Extra Practice Exercises, turn to page 377.

Solutions to Odd-Numbered Practice Problems

1. $3x^2 + 4x - 5 = 0$; $a = 3$, $b = 4$; $c = -5$.

$$x = \frac{-4 \pm \sqrt{4^2 - 4(3)(-5)}}{2(3)}$$

$$= \frac{-4 \pm \sqrt{16 + 60}}{6}$$

$$= \frac{-4 \pm \sqrt{76}}{6} = \frac{-4 \pm 2\sqrt{19}}{6}$$

$$= \frac{\cancel{2}(-2 \pm \sqrt{19})}{\underset{3}{\cancel{6}}} = \frac{-2 \pm \sqrt{19}}{3}$$

3. $2x^2 + 7x + 6 = 0$; $a = 2$, $b = 7$, $c = 6$.

$$x = \frac{-7 \pm \sqrt{7^2 - 4(2)(6)}}{2(2)} = \frac{-7 \pm \sqrt{49 - 48}}{4}$$

$$= \frac{-7 \pm \sqrt{1}}{4} = \frac{-7 \pm 1}{4}$$

$$x = \frac{-7 + 1}{4} = \frac{-6}{4} = \frac{-3}{2} \quad or \quad x = \frac{-7 - 1}{4} = \frac{-8}{4} = -2$$

5. $\dfrac{1}{x} + \dfrac{1}{x - 1} = \dfrac{5}{6}$; $LCD = 6x(x - 1)$

$$6x(x - 1)\frac{1}{x} + 6x(x - 1)\frac{1}{x - 1} = 6x(x - 1)\frac{5}{6}$$

$$6(x - 1) + 6x = 5x(x - 1)$$

$$6x - 6 + 6x = 5x^2 - 5x$$

$$12x - 6 = 5x^2 - 5x$$

$$0 = 5x^2 - 17x + 6$$

Now $a = 5$, $b = -17$, $c = 6$.

$$x = \frac{-(-17) \pm \sqrt{(-17)^2 - 4(5)(6)}}{2(5)}$$

$$= \frac{17 \pm \sqrt{289 - 120}}{10}$$

$$= \frac{17 \pm \sqrt{169}}{10}$$

$$x = \frac{17 + 13}{10} = \frac{30}{10} = 3 \qquad x = \frac{17 - 13}{10} = \frac{4}{10} = \frac{2}{5}$$

7. $x^2 - 4x + 13 = 0$; $a = 1$, $b = -4$, $c = 13$.

$$b^2 - 4ac = (-4)^2 - 4(1)(13)$$

$$= 16 - 52 = -36$$

Since $b^2 - 4ac < 0$, there are two complex roots to the equation.

$$x = \frac{-b \pm \sqrt{b^2 - 4ac}}{2a} = \frac{-(-4) \pm \sqrt{-36}}{2(1)} = \frac{4 \pm 6i}{2} = \frac{2(2 \pm 3i)}{2}$$

$$= 2 \pm 3i$$

Answers to Even-Numbered Practice Problems

2. $x = \dfrac{-3 \pm \sqrt{5}}{2}$ **4.** $x = \pm\dfrac{\sqrt{208}}{4} = \pm\sqrt{13}$ **6.** It has one rational root.   **8.** $x = \dfrac{2 \pm i\sqrt{6}}{2}$

☐ After studying this section, you will be able to:

1 Solve a radical equation by squaring each side once

2 Solve a radical equation by squaring each side twice

7.4 RADICAL EQUATIONS

A **radical equation** is an equation with a variable in one or more of the radicands. We solve radical equations by raising each side of the equation to the appropriate power. (In other words, we square both sides if the radicals are square roots; we cube both sides if the radicals are cube roots, and so on.) Always isolate one radical before raising each side to a power. After solving the equation, *always* check your answers to see if extraneous solutions have been introduced.

1 **Example 1**   Solve $\sqrt{2x + 9} = x + 3$.

$$\left(\sqrt{2x + 9}\right)^2 = (x + 3)^2 \qquad \text{Squaring each side.}$$

$$2x + 9 = x^2 + 6x + 9 \qquad \text{Simplifying.}$$

$$0 = x^2 + 4x \qquad \text{Collecting all terms on one side.}$$

$$0 = x(x + 4) \qquad \text{Factoring.}$$

$$x = 0 \quad or \quad x = -4 \qquad \text{Solving for } x.$$

Check: $\sqrt{2x + 9} = x + 3$

$x = 0$: $\sqrt{2(0) + 9} \stackrel{?}{=} 0 + 3$ $\qquad$ $x = -4$: $\sqrt{2(-4) + 9} \stackrel{?}{=} -4 + 3$

$\qquad\qquad\quad \sqrt{9} \stackrel{?}{=} 3$ $\qquad\qquad\qquad\qquad\qquad \sqrt{1} \stackrel{?}{=} -1$

$\qquad\qquad\quad 3 = 3 \checkmark$ $\qquad\qquad\qquad\qquad\qquad 1 \neq -1$

Therefore, $x = 0$ is the only solution to this equation. ∎

Practice Problem 1 Solve and check your solution(s): $\sqrt{3x - 8} + 2 = x$. ∎

Example 2 Solve: $\sqrt{10x + 5} - 1 = 2x$.

$\sqrt{10x + 5} = 2x + 1$ $\qquad\qquad$ Isolating the radical term.

$(\sqrt{10x + 5})^2 = (2x + 1)^2$ $\qquad$ Squaring each side.

$10x + 5 = 4x^2 + 4x + 1$ $\qquad$ Simplifying.

$0 = 4x^2 - 6x - 4$ $\qquad$ Setting equation equal to zero.

$0 = 2(2x^2 - 3x - 2)$ $\qquad$ Removing the common factor.

$0 = 2(2x + 1)(x - 2)$

$2x + 1 = 0 \qquad or \quad x - 2 = 0$

$2x = -1 \qquad\qquad\quad x = 2$

$x = -\dfrac{1}{2}$

Check: $\sqrt{10x + 5} - 1 = 2x$

$x = -\dfrac{1}{2}$: $\sqrt{10\left(-\dfrac{1}{2}\right) + 5} - 1 \stackrel{?}{=} 2\left(-\dfrac{1}{2}\right)$ $\qquad$ $x = 2$: $\sqrt{10(2) + 5} - 1 \stackrel{?}{=} 2(2)$

$\qquad\qquad\quad \sqrt{-5 + 5} - 1 \stackrel{?}{=} -1$ $\qquad\qquad\qquad\qquad \sqrt{25} - 1 \stackrel{?}{=} 4$

$\qquad\qquad\qquad \sqrt{0} - 1 \stackrel{?}{=} -1$ $\qquad\qquad\qquad\qquad\qquad 5 - 1 \stackrel{?}{=} 4$

$\qquad\qquad\qquad\qquad -1 = -1 \checkmark$ $\qquad\qquad\qquad\qquad\qquad 4 = 4 \checkmark$

Both answers check, so $x = -\dfrac{1}{2}$ and $x = 2$ are roots of the equation. ∎

Practice Problem 2 Solve and check your solutions: $\sqrt{x + 4} = x + 4$. ∎

2 In some problems, we must square each side twice in order to remove all the radicals. It is important to isolate at least one radical before squaring each side.

Example 3 Solve: $\sqrt{5x + 1} - \sqrt{3x} = 1$.

$\sqrt{5x + 1} = 1 + \sqrt{3x}$ $\qquad\qquad$ Isolating one of the radicals.

$(\sqrt{5x + 1})^2 = (1 + \sqrt{3x})^2$ $\qquad$ Squaring each side.

$5x + 1 = (1 + \sqrt{3x})(1 + \sqrt{3x})$

$5x + 1 = 1 + 2\sqrt{3x} + 3x$

$2x = 2\sqrt{3x}$ $\qquad\qquad$ Isolating the radical.

$x = \sqrt{3x}$ $\qquad\qquad$ Dividing each side by 2.

$(x)^2 = (\sqrt{3x})^2$ $\qquad\qquad$ Squaring each side.

$x^2 = 3x$

$x^2 - 3x = 0$

$x(x - 3) = 0$

TEACHING TIP   After discussing examples 1 and 2, ask students to solve the following problem as a class exercise. Solve and check:

$$2x = 3 + \sqrt{3x + 13}$$

Ans. $x = 4$ only

$$\left[x = -\dfrac{1}{4} \text{ does not check}\right]$$

TEACHING TIP   Students find that solving radical equations where both sides must be squared twice to be fairly difficult. After presenting example 3, you may want to show the following additional sample example: Solve and check:

$$\sqrt{3x + 1} = 1 + \sqrt{x + 4}$$

Sol. $(\sqrt{3x + 1})^2 = (1 + \sqrt{x + 4})^2$

$\qquad 3x + 1 = x + 5 + 2\sqrt{x + 4}$

$\qquad 2x - 4 = 2\sqrt{x + 4}$

$\qquad (x - 2)^2 = (\sqrt{x + 4})^2$

$\qquad x^2 - 4x + 4 = x + 4$

$\qquad x(x - 5) = 0$

$\qquad x = 0 \quad x = 5$

Check $x = 0$

$\sqrt{3(0) + 1} \stackrel{?}{=} 1 + \sqrt{0 + 4}$

$\qquad\quad 1 \neq 1 + 2$

Check $x = 5$

$\sqrt{3(5) + 1} \stackrel{?}{=} 1 + \sqrt{5 + 4}$

$\qquad\qquad 4 = 1 + 3 \checkmark$

$x = 5$ is only answer

$$x = 0 \quad or \quad x - 3 = 0$$
$$x = 3$$

$Check:$ $\sqrt{5x + 1} - \sqrt{3x} = 1$

$x = 0:$ $\sqrt{5(0) + 1} - \sqrt{3(0)} \stackrel{?}{=} 1$ $x = 3:$ $\sqrt{5(3) + 1} - \sqrt{3(3)} \stackrel{?}{=} 1$

$\sqrt{1} - \sqrt{0} \stackrel{?}{=} 1$ $\sqrt{16} - \sqrt{9} \stackrel{?}{=} 1$

$1 = 1$ ✓ $1 = 1$ ✓

Both answers check. The solutions are $x = 0$ and $x = 3$. ■

Practice Problem 3   Solve and check your solution(s): $\sqrt{2x + 5} - 2\sqrt{2x} = 1$. ■

Example 4   Solve: $\sqrt{2y + 5} - \sqrt{y - 1} = \sqrt{y + 2}$.

$$(\sqrt{2y + 5} - \sqrt{y - 1})^2 = (\sqrt{y + 2})^2$$
$$(\sqrt{2y + 5} - \sqrt{y - 1})(\sqrt{2y + 5} - \sqrt{y - 1}) = y + 2$$
$$2y + 5 - 2\sqrt{(y - 1)(2y + 5)} + y - 1 = y + 2$$
$$-2\sqrt{(y - 1)(2y + 5)} = -2y - 2$$

$$\sqrt{(y - 1)(2y + 5)} = y + 1 \qquad \text{Dividing each term by } -2.$$

$$(\sqrt{2y^2 + 3y - 5})^2 = (y + 1)^2 \qquad \text{Squaring each side.}$$
$$2y^2 + 3y - 5 = y^2 + 2y + 1$$
$$y^2 + y - 6 = 0 \qquad \text{Setting equation equal to zero.}$$

$$(y + 3)(y - 2) = 0$$
$$y = -3 \quad or \quad y = 2$$

$Check:$ Verify that $y = 2$ is a valid solution but $y = -3$ is not a valid solution. ■

Practice Problem 4   Solve and check your solutions:
$$\sqrt{y - 1} + \sqrt{y - 4} = \sqrt{4y - 11}. \quad ■$$

EXERCISES 7.4

1. Before squaring each side of a radical equation what step should be taken first?

Isolate one of the radicals on one side of the equation.

2. Why do we have have to check the solutions when we solve radical equations?

There is a possibility of extraneous roots; that is, a solution to the equation which when substituted into the original problem does not make the original statement true.

3. $x = \sqrt{6x + 7}$
$x^2 - 6x - 7 = 0$
$(x - 7)(x + 1) = 0$
$x = 7$
$x = -1$ (Extraneous)

4. $\sqrt{7x + 8} = x$
$x^2 - 7x - 8 = 0$
$(x - 8)(x + 1) = 0$
$x = 8$
$x = -1$ (Extraneous)

5. $\sqrt{2x + 1} = x - 7$
$x^2 - 16x + 48 = 0$
$(x - 12)(x - 4) = 0$
$x = 12$
$x = 4$ (Extraneous)

6. $\sqrt{5x + 1} = x + 1$
$x^2 - 3x = 0$
$x(x - 3) = 0$
$x = 0$
$x = 3$

7. $y - \sqrt{y - 3} = 5$
$y^2 - 11y + 28 = 0$
$(y - 7)(y - 4) = 0$
$y = 7$
$y = 4$ (Extraneous)

8. $\sqrt{2y - 4} + 2 = y$
$y^2 - 6y + 8 = 0$
$(y - 4)(y - 2) = 0$
$y = 4$
$y = 2$

9. $\sqrt{y + 3} = y + 1$
$y^2 + y - 2 = 0$
$y = 1$
(Extraneous)
$y = -2$

10. $5 + \sqrt{2y + 5} = y$
$y^2 - 12y + 20 = 0$
$(y - 10)(y - 2) = 0$
$y = 10$
$y = 2$ (Extraneous)

11. $3\sqrt{x+5} = x+5$
$x^2 + x - 20 = 0$
$(x+5)(x-4) = 0$
$x = -5$
$x = 4$

12. $2\sqrt{2x-9} = x-3$
$x^2 - 14x + 45 = 0$
$(x-9)(x-5) = 0$
$x = 9$
$x = 5$

13. $\sqrt{x^2 - 8x} = 3$
$x^2 - 8x - 9 = 0$
$(x+1)(x-9) = 0$
$x = 9$
$x = -1$

14. $\sqrt{x^2 + 36} = 10$
$x^2 = 64$
$x = \pm 8$

15. $\sqrt[3]{2x+3} = 2$
$2x + 3 = 8$
$x = \dfrac{5}{2}$

16. $\sqrt[3]{3x-6} = 3$
$3x - 6 = 27$
$x = 11$

17. $\sqrt[3]{x+10} = \sqrt[3]{x^2 + 4x}$
$x^2 + 3x - 10 = 0$
$(x+5)(x-2) = 0$
$x = -5$
$x = 2$

18. $\sqrt[3]{x^2 - 4x + 8} = \sqrt[3]{3x-4}$
$x^2 - 7x + 12 = 0$
$(x-4)(x-3) = 0$
$x = 4$
$x = 3$

19. $\sqrt[3]{1-7x} - 4 = 0$
$1 - 7x = 64$
$x = -9$

20. $\sqrt[3]{4x-3} - 5 = 0$
$4x - 3 = 125$
$x = 32$

21. $\sqrt{x-1} = 4\sqrt{x+1}$
$15x = -17$
$x = -\dfrac{17}{15}$
(No sol.)

22. $\sqrt{x-5} = 2 + \sqrt{x+3}$
$144 = 16x + 48$
$x = 6$
(No. sol.)

23. $\sqrt{3x+1} - \sqrt{x-4} = 3$
$x^2 - 13x + 40 = 0$
$(x-5)(x-8) = 0$
$x = 5$
$x = 8$

24. $\sqrt{3x+3} + \sqrt{x-1} = 4$
$x^2 - 28x + 52 = 0$
$x = 26$ (Extraneous)
$x = 2$

25. $\sqrt{2x-1} + 2 = \sqrt{3x+10}$
$x^2 - 18x + 65 = 0$
$x = 5$
$x = 13$

26. $\sqrt{2y+1} - \sqrt{5-y} = 2$
$9y^2 - 32y - 16 = 0$
$(9y+4)(y-4) = 0$
$y = 4$
$y = -\dfrac{4}{9}$ (Extraneous)

27. $\sqrt{4x+1} = \sqrt{x+3} + \sqrt{x-2}$
$x^2 = x^2 + x - 6$
$x = 6$

28. $\sqrt{3x+4} + \sqrt{x+5} = \sqrt{7-2x}$
$6x^2 - 13x - 19 = 0$
$(6x-19)(x+1) = 0$
$x = -1$
$x = \dfrac{19}{6}$ (Extraneous)

29. $\sqrt{2x+6} = \sqrt{7-2x} + 1$
$4x^2 - 2x - 6 = 0$
$(2x-3)(x+1) = 0$
$x = \dfrac{3}{2}$
$x = -1$ (Extraneous)

30. $2\sqrt{x} - \sqrt{x-5} = \sqrt{2x-2}$
$7x^2 - 62x - 9 = 0$
$(7x+1)(x-9) = 0$
$x = 9$
$x = -\dfrac{1}{7}$ (Extraneous)

31. $\sqrt{x + \sqrt{x+2}} = 2$
$x^2 - 9x + 14 = 0$
$(x-7)(x-2) = 0$
$x = 2$
$x = 7$ (Extraneous)

32. $\sqrt{3 - 2\sqrt{x}} = \sqrt{x}$
$x^2 - 10x + 9 = 0$
$(x-9)(x-1) = 0$
$x = 1$
$x = 9$ (Extraneous)

33. $\sqrt{1 + 4\sqrt{y}} = 1 + \sqrt{y}$
$y^2 - 4y = 0$
$y(y-4) = 0$
$y = 0$
$y = 4$

34. $\sqrt{3y-5} = \sqrt{2\sqrt{y+1}}$
$9y^2 - 34y + 21 = 0$
$(9y-7)(y-3) = 0$
$y = 3$
$y = \dfrac{7}{9}$ (Extraneous)

To Think About

35. The solution to the equation $\sqrt{x^2 - 4x + c} = x - 1$ is $x = 4$. What is the value of c?

$\sqrt{16 - 16 + c} = 4 - 1$
$\sqrt{c} = 3$
$c = 9$

36. The solution to the equation $\sqrt{x+b} - \sqrt{x} = -2$ is $x = 16$. What is the value of b?

$\sqrt{16+b} - \sqrt{16} = -2$
$\sqrt{16+b} = 2$
$b = -12$

Solve and check your solution.

37. $13 + 4x + \sqrt{x+3} = \sqrt{11x + 58} + 4x + 8$

$\sqrt{11x+58} = x + 8$
$x^2 + 5x + 6 = 0$
$(x+3)(x+2) = 0$
$x = -3$
$x = -2$

38. $\dfrac{3y - 2\sqrt{2y+1}}{2y + 3\sqrt{2y+1}} = \dfrac{6}{17}$

$3y = 4\sqrt{2y+1}$
$9y^2 - 32y - 16 = 0$
$(y-4)(9y+4) = 0$
$y = 4$
$y = -\dfrac{4}{9}$ (Extraneous)

Simplify.

39. $(4^3x^6)^{2/3}$
$4^2x^4 = 16x^4$

40. $(2^{-3}x^{-6})^{1/3}$
$2^{-1}x^{-2} = \dfrac{1}{2x^2}$

41. $\sqrt[3]{-216x^6y^9}$
$-6x^2y^3$

42. $\sqrt[4]{64x^{12}y^{16}}$
$2x^3y^4\sqrt[4]{4}$

Calculator Problems

Solve for x. Round your answer to four decimal places.

43. $x = \sqrt{5.326x - 1.983}$
$x = 4.9232, 0.4028$

44. $\sqrt[3]{5.62x + 9.93} = 1.47$
$x = -1.2017$

For Extra Practice Exercises, turn to page 377.

Solutions to Odd-Numbered Practice Problems

1. $\sqrt{3x - 8} + 2 = x$
$\sqrt{3x - 8} = x - 2$
$(\sqrt{3x - 8})^2 = (x - 2)^2$
$3x - 8 = x^2 - 4x + 4$
$0 = x^2 - 7x + 12$
$0 = (x - 3)(x - 4)$
$x = 3 \ or \ x = 4$

   Check:

$x = 3$: $\sqrt{3(3) - 8} + 2 \overset{?}{=} 3$
$3 = 3 \checkmark$

$x = 4$: $\sqrt{3(4) - 8} + 2 \overset{?}{=} 4$
$4 = 4 \checkmark$

Both solutions check. $x = 3$, $x = 4$.

3. $\sqrt{2x + 5} - 2\sqrt{2x} = 1$
$\sqrt{2x + 5} = 1 + 2\sqrt{2x}$
$(\sqrt{2x + 5})^2 = (1 + 2\sqrt{2x})^2$
$2x + 5 = 1 + 4\sqrt{2x} + 4(2x)$
$2x + 5 = 4\sqrt{2x} + 8x + 1$
$-6x + 4 = 4\sqrt{2x}$
$-3x + 2 = 2\sqrt{2x}$
$(-3x + 2)^2 = (2\sqrt{2x})^2$
$9x^2 - 12x + 4 = 8x$
$9x^2 - 20x + 4 = 0$
$(9x - 2)(x - 2) = 0$
$x = \dfrac{2}{9} \ \ or \ \ x = 2$

Check: Show that only $x = \dfrac{2}{9}$ checks, thus the only valid solution is $x = \dfrac{2}{9}$.

Answers to Even-Numbered Practice Problems

2. $x = -4$, $x = -3$ **4.** $y = 5$

☐ After studying this section, you will be able to:

1 *Solve equations of higher degree that can be transformed to quadratic form*

2 *Solve equations with fractional exponents that can be transformed to quadratic form*

7.5 EQUATIONS THAT CAN BE TRANSFORMED TO QUADRATIC FORM

1 Some higher-order equations can be solved by writing them in the form of a quadratic equation. An equation is **quadratic in form** if we can substitute a linear term for the lowest-degree variable and get an equation of the form $ay^2 + by + c = 0$.

Example 1 Solve: $x^4 - 13x^2 + 36 = 0$.

Let $y = x^2$. Then $y^2 = x^4$. Thus, our new equation is

$y^2 - 13y + 36 = 0$	Replacing x^2 by y, x^4 by y^2.
$(y - 4)(y - 9) = 0$	Factoring.
$y - 4 = 0 \quad or \quad y - 9 = 0$	Solving for y.
$y = 4 \qquad\qquad y = 9$	These are *not* the roots to the original
$x^2 = 4 \qquad\qquad x^2 = 9$	equation. We must replace y by x^2.
$x = \pm\sqrt{4} \qquad\ x^2 = \pm\sqrt{9}$	
$x = \pm 2 \qquad\quad x = \pm 3$	

Thus there are *four* solutions to the original equation: $x = +2$, $x = -2$, $x = +3$, $x = -3$. This is clearly possible, since the degree of the equation is 4. ■

Practice Problem 1 $x^4 - 5x^2 - 36 = 0$. ■

Example 2   Solve for all real roots: $2x^6 - x^3 - 6 = 0$.

Let $y = x^3$. Then $y^2 = x^6$. Thus, we have

$$2y^2 - y - 6 = 0 \qquad \text{Replacing } x^3 \text{ by } y \text{ and } x^6 \text{ by } y^2.$$

$$(2y + 3)(y - 2) = 0 \qquad \text{Factoring.}$$

$$2y + 3 = 0 \quad \text{or} \quad y - 2 = 0$$

$$y = -\frac{3}{2} \qquad\qquad y = 2 \qquad \text{Solving for } y.$$

$$x^3 = -\frac{3}{2} \quad \text{or} \quad x^3 = 2 \qquad \boxed{\text{Replacing } y \text{ by } x^3.}$$

$$x = \sqrt[3]{-\frac{3}{2}} \qquad\qquad x = \sqrt[3]{2} \qquad \text{Taking cube root of each side of the equation.}$$

$$x = \frac{\sqrt[3]{-12}}{2} \qquad\qquad \text{Simplifying } \sqrt[3]{-\frac{3}{2}} \text{ by rationalizing.}$$

Check these solutions. ■

Practice Problem 2   Solve for all real roots: $x^6 - 5x^3 + 4 = 0$. ■

2 Equations with Fractional Exponents

Example 3   Solve: $x^{2/3} - 3x^{1/3} + 2 = 0$.

Let $y = x^{1/3}$ and $y^2 = x^{2/3}$.

$$y^2 - 3y + 2 = 0 \qquad \text{Replacing } x^{1/3} \text{ by } y.$$

$$(y - 2)(y - 1) = 0 \qquad \text{Factoring.}$$

$$y - 2 = 0 \quad \text{or} \quad y - 1 = 0$$

$$y = 2 \qquad\qquad y = 1 \qquad \text{Solving for } y.$$

$$\boxed{x^{1/3} = 2} \quad \text{or} \quad \boxed{x^{1/3} = 1} \qquad \boxed{\text{Replacing } y \text{ by } x^{1/3}.}$$

$$(x^{1/3})^3 = (2)^3 \qquad (x^{1/3})^3 = (1)^3 \qquad \text{Cubing each side of the equation.}$$

$$x = 8 \qquad\qquad x = 1$$

Check: $x^{2/3} - 3x^{1/3} + 2 = 0$

$x = 8$: $(8)^{2/3} - 3(8)^{1/3} + 2 \overset{?}{=} 0$ $\qquad$ $x = 1$: $(1)^{2/3} - 3(1)^{1/3} + 2 \overset{?}{=} 0$

$\qquad (\sqrt[3]{8})^2 - 3(\sqrt[3]{8}) + 2 \overset{?}{=} 0$ $\qquad\qquad\qquad (\sqrt[3]{1})^2 - 3\sqrt[3]{1} + 2 \overset{?}{=} 0$

$\qquad\qquad (2)^2 - 3(2) + 2 \overset{?}{=} 0$ $\qquad\qquad\qquad\qquad 1 - 3 + 2 = 0$

$\qquad\qquad\qquad 4 - 6 + 2 \overset{?}{=} 0$ $\qquad\qquad\qquad\qquad\qquad \boxed{0 = 0} \checkmark$ ■

$\qquad\qquad\qquad\qquad \boxed{0 = 0} \checkmark$

Practice Problem 3   Solve and check: $3x^{4/3} - 5x^{2/3} + 2 = 0$. ■

Example 4   Solve: $2x^{1/2} = 5x^{1/4} + 12$. Check your solutions.

$$2x^{1/2} - 5x^{1/4} - 12 = 0 \qquad \text{Placing in standard form.}$$

$$2y^2 - 5y - 12 = 0 \qquad \text{Replacing } x^{1/4} \text{ by } y, x^{1/2} \text{ by } y^2.$$

$$(2y + 3)(y - 4) = 0 \qquad \text{Factoring.}$$

TEACHING TIP Some students will ask why they cannot factor $x^4 - 13x^2 + 36 = 0$ directly as $(x^2 - 4)(x^2 - 9) = 0$. Tell them they are welcome to solve the problem that way. However, certain other types of problems that are quadratic in form cannot be handled as easily. Therefore, they are encouraged to see if they can solve all the problems in this section by the substitution method.

TEACHING TIP After presenting examples 1 and 2, ask students to do the following problem as classwork. Solve:

$$x^{-4} - 7x^{-2} + 10 = 0$$
(Hint: Let $y = -x^{-2}$)

Ans. $x = \pm\dfrac{\sqrt{2}}{2}$

$\qquad x = \pm\dfrac{\sqrt{5}}{5}$

TEACHING TIP   After
presenting examples 3 and 4,
ask students to do the
following problem as
classwork. Solve:

$x^{2/3} + 5x^{1/3} - 14 = 0$

Ans. $x = -343$

$x = 8$

$$2y = -3 \quad or \quad y = 4$$

$$y = -\frac{3}{2} \qquad\qquad \text{Solving for } y.$$

$$x^{1/4} = -\frac{3}{2} \quad or \quad x^{1/4} = 4 \qquad \text{Replacing } y \text{ by } x^{1/4}.$$

$$(x^{1/4})^4 = \left(-\frac{3}{2}\right)^4 \qquad (x^{1/4})^4 = (4)^4 \qquad \text{Solving for } x.$$

$$x = \frac{81}{16} \qquad\qquad x = 256$$

Check: $2x^{1/2} - 5x^{1/4} - 12 = 0$

$x = \frac{81}{16}$: $2\left(\frac{81}{16}\right)^{1/2} - 5\left(\frac{81}{16}\right)^{1/4} - 12 \overset{?}{=} 0$ $x = 256$: $2(256)^{1/2} - 5(256)^{1/4} - 12 \overset{?}{=} 0$

$$2\left(\frac{9}{4}\right) - 5\left(\frac{3}{2}\right) - 12 \overset{?}{=} 0 \qquad\qquad 2(16) - 5(4) - 12 \overset{?}{=} 0$$

$$\frac{9}{2} - \frac{15}{2} - 12 \overset{?}{=} 0 \qquad\qquad\qquad 32 - 20 - 12 \overset{?}{=} 0$$

$$0 = 0 \checkmark$$

$$-15 \neq 0 \qquad\qquad \text{Thus, } x = 256 \text{ is the only valid solution.}$$

Thus, $x = \frac{81}{16}$ is extraneous and not a valid solution.   ■

Practice Problem 4   Solve: $3x^{1/2} = 8x^{1/4} - 4$. Check your solutions.   ■

EXERCISES 7.5

Solve. Express any imaginary numbers in i notation.

1. $x^4 - 9x^2 + 20 = 0$

$y = x^2$
$y^2 - 9y + 20 = 0$
$y = 5, y = 4$ Thus,
$x^2 = 5, x^2 = 4$
$x = \pm\sqrt{5}, x = \pm 2$

2. $x^4 - 11x^2 + 18 = 0$

$y = x^2$
$y^2 - 11y + 18 = 0$
$y = 9, y = 2,$ so
$x^2 = 9, x^2 = 2$
$x = \pm 3, x = \pm\sqrt{2}$

3. $2x^4 - x^2 - 3 = 0$

$y = x^2$
$2y^2 - y - 3 = 0$
$y = \frac{3}{2}, y = -1,$ so
$x^2 = \frac{3}{2}, x^2 = -1$
$x = \frac{\pm\sqrt{6}}{2}, x = \pm i$

4. $2x^4 + 5x^2 - 12 = 0$

$y = x^2$
$2y^2 + 5y - 12 = 0$
$y = \frac{3}{2}, y = -4$ Thus,
$x^2 = \frac{3}{2}, x^2 = -4$
$x = \pm\frac{\sqrt{6}}{2}, x = \pm 2i$

5. $3x^4 = 10x^2 + 8$

$y = x^2$
$3y^2 - 10y - 8 = 0$
$y = -\frac{2}{3}, y = 4,$ so
$x^2 = -\frac{2}{3}, x^2 = 4$
$x = \pm\frac{i\sqrt{6}}{3}, x = \pm 2$

6. $5x^4 = 4x^2 + 1$

$y = x^2$
$5y^2 - 4y - 1 = 0$
$(5y + 1)(y - 1) = 0$
$y = -\frac{1}{5}, y = 1,$ so
$x^2 = -\frac{1}{5}, x^2 = 1$
$x = \frac{\pm i\sqrt{5}}{5}, x = \pm 1$

In problems 7–10, find all valid real roots for each equation.

7. $x^6 - 7x^3 + 12 = 0$

$y = x^3$
$y^2 - 7y + 12 - 0$
$(y - 4)(y - 3) = 0$
$y = 4, y = 3,$ so
$x^3 = 4, x^3 = 3$
$x = \sqrt[3]{4}, x = \sqrt[3]{3}$

8. $x^6 - 8x^3 + 15 = 0$

$y = x^3$
$y^2 - 8y + 15 = 0$
$(y - 5)(y - 3) = 0$
$y = 5, y = 3$ Thus,
$x^3 = 5, x^3 = 3$
$x = \sqrt[3]{5}, x = \sqrt[3]{3}$

9. $2x^6 - 7x^3 - 4 = 0$

$y = x^3$
$2y^2 - 7y - 4 = 0$
$(2y + 1)(y - 4) = 0$
$y = -\frac{1}{2}, y = 4$ Thus,
$x^3 = -\frac{1}{2}, x^3 = 4$
$x = -\frac{\sqrt[3]{4}}{2}, x = \sqrt[3]{4}$

10. $12x^6 + 5x^3 - 2 = 0$

$y = x^3$
$12y^2 + 5y - 2 = 0$
$(4y - 1)(3y + 2) = 0$
$y = \frac{1}{4}, y = -\frac{2}{3},$ so
$x^3 = \frac{1}{4}, x^3 = \frac{-2}{3}$
$x = \frac{\sqrt[3]{2}}{2}, x = \frac{-\sqrt[3]{18}}{3}$

11. $x^8 = 3x^4 - 2$

$y = x^4$

$y^2 - 3y + 2 = 0$

$y = 2, y = 1$, so

$x^4 = 2, x^4 = 1$

$x = \pm\sqrt[4]{2}, x = \pm 1$

12. $x^8 = 7x^4 - 12$

$y = x^4$

$y^2 - 7y + 12 = 0$

$y = 3, y = 4$, so

$x^4 = 3, x^4 = 4$

$x = \pm\sqrt[4]{3}, x = \pm\sqrt[4]{4}$

13. $3x^8 + 13x^4 = 10$

$y = x^4$

$3y^2 + 13y - 10 = 0$

$y = \dfrac{2}{3}, y = -5$

$x^4 = \dfrac{2}{3}, x^4 = -5$

$x = \pm\dfrac{\sqrt[4]{54}}{3}$ These are the only real roots

14. $3x^8 - 10x^4 = 8$

$y = x^4$

$3y^2 - 10y - 8 = 0$

$(3y + 2)(y - 4) = 0$

$y = \dfrac{-2}{3}, y = 4$

$x^4 = -\dfrac{2}{3}, x^4 = 4$

$x = \pm\sqrt[4]{4} = \pm\sqrt{2}$

These are the only real roots

15. $x^{2/3} + 2x^{1/3} - 8 = 0$

$y = x^{1/3}$

$y^2 + 2y - 8 = 0$

$(y + 4)(y - 2) = 0$

$y = -4, y = 2$

$x^{1/3} = -4, x^{1/3} = 2$

$x = (-4)^3 = -64$

$x = 2^3 = 8$

16. $x^{2/3} + x^{1/3} - 12 = 0$

$y = x^{1/3}$

$y^2 + y - 12 = 0$

$(y + 4)(y - 3) = 0$

$y = -4, y = 3$

$x^{1/3} = -4, x^{1/3} = 3$

$x = (-4)^3 = -64$

$x = 3^3 = 27$

17. $x^{2/3} - 10x^{1/3} = -21$

$y = x^{1/3}$

$y^2 - 10y + 21 = 0$

$y = 7, y = 3$

$x^{1/3} = 7, x^{1/3} = 3$

$x = 7^3 = 343$

$x = 3^3 = 27$

18. $x^{2/3} + 9x^{1/3} = -18$

$y = x^{1/3}$

$y^2 + 9y + 18 = 0$

$y = -6, y = -3$

$x^{1/3} = -6, x^{1/3} = -3$

$x = (-3)^3 = -27$

$x = (-6)^3 = -216$

19. $2x^{1/2} - 5x^{1/4} - 3 = 0$

$y = x^{1/4}$

$2y^2 - 5y - 3 = 0$

$y = -\dfrac{1}{2}, y = 3$

$x^{1/4} = -\dfrac{1}{2}, x^{1/4} = 3$

$x = \left(-\dfrac{1}{2}\right)^4 = \dfrac{1}{16}$ (Extraneous)

$x = 3^4 = 81$

20. $3x^{1/2} - 14x^{1/4} - 5 = 0$

$y = x^{1/4}$

$3y^2 - 14y - 5 = 0$

$(3y + 1)(y - 5) = 0$

$y = -\dfrac{1}{3}, y = 5$

$x^{1/4} = -\dfrac{1}{3}, x^{1/4} = 5$

$x = \left(-\dfrac{1}{3}\right)^4 = \dfrac{1}{81}$ (Extraneous)

$x = 5^4 = 625$

21. $8x^{1/2} + 7x^{1/4} = 1$

$y = x^{1/4}$

$8y^2 + 7y - 1 = 0$

$(8y - 1)(y + 1) = 0$

$y = \dfrac{1}{8}, y = -1$

$x^{1/4} = \dfrac{1}{8}, x^{1/4} = -1$

$x = \left(\dfrac{1}{8}\right)^4 = \dfrac{1}{4096}$

$x = (-1)^4 = 1$ (Extraneous)

22. $x^{1/2} + 13x^{1/4} + 36 = 0$

$y = x^{1/4}$

$y^2 + 13y + 36 = 0$

$(y + 9)(y + 4) = 0$

$y = -9, y = -4$

$x^{1/4} = -9, x^{1/4} = -4$

$x = (-9)^4 = 6561$ (Extraneous)

$x = (-4)^4 = 256$ (Extraneous)

No sol.

23. $x^{2/5} + x^{1/5} - 2 = 0$

$y = x^{1/5}$

$y^2 + y - 2 = 0$

$y = -2, y = 1$

$x^{1/5} = -2, x^{1/5} = 1$

$x = (-2)^5 = -32$

$x = 1^5 = 1$

24. $2x^{2/5} + 7x^{1/5} + 3 = 0$

$y = x^{1/5}$

$2y^2 + 7y + 3 = 0$

$y = -\dfrac{1}{2}, y = -3$

$x^{1/5} = -\dfrac{1}{2}, x^{1/5} = -3$

$x = \left(-\dfrac{1}{2}\right)^5 = \dfrac{-1}{32}$

$x = (-3)^5 = -243$

In each problem make an appropriate substitution to make the equation quadratic in form. Find all real or complex values for x.

25. $(x^2 + x)^2 - 5(x^2 + x) = -6$

$y = x^2 + x$

$y^2 - 5y + 6 = 0$

$y = 2, y = 3$

$x^2 + x = 2, x^2 + x = 3$

$x^2 + x - 2 = 0, x^2 + x - 3 = 0$

$x = -2, x = 1, x = \dfrac{-1 \pm \sqrt{13}}{2}$

26. $(x^2 - 2x)^2 + 2(x^2 - 2x) = 3$

$y = x^2 - 2x$

$y^2 + 2y - 3 = 0$

$y = -3, y = 1$

$x^2 - 2x = -3, x^2 - 2x = 1$

$x^2 - 2x + 3 = 0, x^2 - 2x - 1 = 0$

$x = 1 \pm i\sqrt{2}, x = 1 \pm \sqrt{2}$

27. $x - 4x^{1/2} - 21 = 0$

$y = x^{1/2}$

$y^2 - 4y - 21 = 0$

$y = 7, y = -3$

$x^{1/2} = 7, x^{1/2} = -3$

$x = 7^2 = 49$

$x = (-3)^2 = 9$ (Extraneous)

28. $x - 6x^{1/2} + 8 = 0$

$y = x^{1/2}$

$y^2 - 6y + 8 = 0$

$y = 4, y = 2$

$x^{1/2} = 4, x^{1/2} = 2$

$x = 4^2 = 16$

$x = 2^2 = 4$

29. $10x^{-2} + 7x^{-1} + 1 = 0$

$y = x^{-1}$

$10y^2 + 7y + 1 = 0$

$y = -\dfrac{1}{5}, y = -\dfrac{1}{2}$

$x^{-1} = -\dfrac{1}{5}, x^{-1} = -\dfrac{1}{2}$

$x = \left(-\dfrac{1}{5}\right)^{-1} = -5$

$x = \left(-\dfrac{1}{2}\right)^{-1} = -2$

30. $20x^{-2} + 9x^{-1} + 1 = 0$

$y = x^{-1}$

$20y^2 + 9y + 1 = 0$

$(4y + 1)(5y + 1) = 0$

$y = -\dfrac{1}{4}, y = -\dfrac{1}{5}$

$x^{-1} = -\dfrac{1}{4}, x^{-1} = \dfrac{-1}{5}$

$x = \left(-\dfrac{1}{4}\right)^{-1}, x = \left(\dfrac{-1}{5}\right)^{-1}$

$x = -4, x = -5$

31. $\dfrac{2}{(x-1)^2} + \dfrac{3}{x-1} = 2$

$y = x - 1$
$2y^2 - 3y - 2 = 0$
$y = -\dfrac{1}{2},\ y = 2$
$x - 1 = -\dfrac{1}{2},\ x - 1 = 2$
$x = \dfrac{1}{2},\ x = 3$

32. $\dfrac{3}{(x-2)^2} - \dfrac{4}{(x-2)} + 1 = 0$

$y = x - 2$
$y^2 - 4y + 3 = 0$
$y = 1,\ y = 3$
$x - 2 = 1,\ x - 2 = 3$
$x = 3,\ x = 5$

? To Think About

Solve. Find all valid real roots for each equation.

33. $15 - \dfrac{2x}{x-1} = \dfrac{x^2}{x^2 - 2x + 1}$

$15(x-1)^2 - 2x(x-1) = x^2$
$12x^2 - 28x + 15 = 0$
$x = \dfrac{5}{6},\ x = \dfrac{3}{2}$

34. $4 - \dfrac{x^3 + 1}{x^3 + 6} = \dfrac{x^3 - 3}{x^3 + 2}$

$\dfrac{3x^3 + 23}{x^3 + 6} = \dfrac{x^3 - 3}{x^3 + 2}$
$2x^6 + 26x^3 + 64 = 0$
$x^6 + 13x^3 + 32 = 0$
$x^3 = \dfrac{-13 \pm \sqrt{41}}{2}$
$x = \sqrt[3]{\dfrac{-13 \pm \sqrt{41}}{2}}$

Cumulative Review Problems

Simplify.

35. $\sqrt{8x} + 3\sqrt{2x} - 4\sqrt{50x}$

$2\sqrt{2x} + 3\sqrt{2x} - 20\sqrt{2x} = -15\sqrt{2x}$

36. $\sqrt{27x} + 5\sqrt{3x} - 2\sqrt{48x}$

$3\sqrt{3x} + 5\sqrt{3x} - 8\sqrt{3x} = 0$

Multiply and simplify.

37. $3\sqrt{2}(\sqrt{5} - 2\sqrt{6})$

$3\sqrt{10} - 6\sqrt{12} = 3\sqrt{10} - 12\sqrt{3}$

38. $(\sqrt{2} + \sqrt{6})(3\sqrt{2} - 2\sqrt{5})$

$3\sqrt{4} + 3\sqrt{12} - 2\sqrt{10} - 2\sqrt{30} = 6 + 6\sqrt{3} - 2\sqrt{10} - 2\sqrt{30}$

For Extra Practice Exercises, turn to page 378.

Solutions to Odd-Numbered Practice Problems

1. $x^4 - 5x^2 - 36 = 0$; let $x^2 = y$, $x^4 = y^2$.

$y^2 - 5y - 36 = 0$
$(y - 9)(y + 4) = 0$
$y = 9 \quad or \quad y = -4$
$x^2 = 9 \quad or \quad x^2 = -4$
$x = \pm\sqrt{9} \qquad x = \pm\sqrt{-4}$
$x = \pm 3 \qquad x = \pm 2i$

3. $3x^{4/3} - 5x^{2/3} + 2 = 0$; let $x^{2/3} = y$, $x^{4/3} = y^2$.

$3y^2 - 5y + 2 = 0$
$(3y - 2)(y - 1) = 0$
$y = \dfrac{2}{3} \quad or \quad y = 1$
$x^{2/3} = \dfrac{2}{3} \quad or \quad x^{2/3} = 1$
$(x^{2/3})^3 = \left(\dfrac{2}{3}\right)^3 \qquad (x^{2/3})^3 = 1^3$
$x^2 = \dfrac{8}{27} \qquad x^2 = 1$
$x = \pm\sqrt{\dfrac{8}{27}} \qquad x = \pm\sqrt{1}$
$x = \pm\dfrac{2\sqrt{6}}{9} \qquad x = \pm 1$

Verify that all four answers check.

Answers to Even-Numbered Practice Problems

2. $x = \sqrt[3]{4},\ x = 1$ **4.** $x = \dfrac{16}{81},\ x = 16$

7.6 FORMULAS AND APPLICATIONS

After studying this section, you will be able to:

1 Solve a quadratic equation containing several variables

2 Solve applied problems requiring the use of a quadratic equation

3 Solve applied problems requiring the use of the Pythagorean theorem

In mathematics, physics, and engineering we must often solve an equation for a variable in terms of other variables. You recall we solved linear equations in several variables in Section 1.8. We will now examine several cases where the variable that we are solving for is squared. If the variable we are solving for is squared, and there is no other term containing that variable, then the quadratic equation can be solved by taking the square root of each side.

1 **Example 1**   Solve for x: $3x^2 + 5 = 2b^2$.

$$3x^2 = 2b^2 - 5 \qquad \text{Adding } -5 \text{ to each side.}$$

$$x^2 = \frac{2b^2 - 5}{3} \qquad \text{Dividing each side by 3.}$$

$$x = \pm\sqrt{\frac{2b^2 - 5}{3}} \qquad \text{Taking square root of each side.} \quad \blacksquare$$

Practice Problem 1   Solve: for x: $5x^2 - 8 = 3x^2 + 2w$. $\blacksquare$

Some quadratic equations containing many variables can be solved for one variable by factoring.

Example 2   Solve for y: $y^2 - 2yz - 15z^2 = 0$.

$$(y + 3z)(y - 5z) = 0 \qquad \text{Factoring.}$$

$$y + 3z = 0 \qquad y - 5z = 0 \qquad \text{Setting each factor equal to 0.}$$

$$y = -3z \qquad y = 5z \qquad \text{Solving for } y. \quad \blacksquare$$

Practice Problem 2   Solve for y: $2y^2 + 9wy + 7w^2 = 0$. $\blacksquare$

Sometimes the quadratic formula is required in order to solve the equation.

Example 3   Solve for x: $2x^2 + 3xw - 4z = 0$.

We use the quadratic formula where the variable is considered to be x and the letters w and z are considered constants. Thus, $a = 2$, $b = 3w$, $c = -4z$.

$$x = \frac{-b \pm \sqrt{b^2 - 4ac}}{2a}$$

$$x = \frac{-3w \pm \sqrt{(3w)^2 - 4(2)(-4z)}}{2(2)} = \frac{-3w \pm \sqrt{9w^2 + 32z}}{4}$$

Note that this answer cannot be simplified. $\blacksquare$

Practice Problem 3   Solve for y: $3y^2 + 2yf - 7g = 0$. $\blacksquare$

2 **Example 4**   The radius of an old circular pipe under a roadbed is 10 inches. Designers wanted to replace it with a smaller pipe and decided they could use a pipe with an area 36π square inches smaller. How much smaller should the radius of the new pipe be?

First we need the formula for the area of a circle.

$$A = \pi r^2$$

where A is the area and r is the radius. The area of the old pipe is

$$A_{\text{old}} = \pi(10)^2$$

$$= 100\pi$$

TEACHING TIP   After explaining example 3, ask students to do the following problem as classwork. Solve for x and simplify:

$$3dx^2 - 4fx + 12 = 0$$

Ans. $x = \dfrac{4f \pm \sqrt{16f^2 - 144d}}{6d}$

$= \dfrac{2f \pm 2\sqrt{f^2 - 9d}}{3d}$

We could use 3.14 for π, but for convenience, we will leave it as is. The area of the new pipe is 36π smaller, so it must be

$$A_{new} = 100\pi - 36\pi = 64\pi$$

The radius of the new pipe is also smaller than the radius of the old pipe (10 inches) by some unknown amount x. So the new radius is $10 - x$. Since $A_{new} = \pi r^2$ we have

$$64\pi = \pi(10 - x)^2$$

$$64 = (10 - x)^2$$

$$\pm\sqrt{64} = 10 - x$$

$$x = \pm 8 + 10$$

$$x = 18 \quad or \quad x = 2$$

Which answer is correct? Well we cannot decrease a radius only *10* inches long by *18* inches, because we would have a circle with a negative radius—an impossibility. Therefore, our answer is $x = 2$. The radius of the new pipe should be 2 inches smaller. Note that the new radius is *not* 2 inches. It is $10 - 2 = 8$ inches. ∎

Practice Problem 4   Redo Example 4 if the radius under the roadbed is 6 inches and the designers wanted to replace it with a pipe with an area that is 45π square inches larger. How much larger should the radius of the new pipe be? ∎

Example 5   The McSwiggins were moving to a new home 50 miles away from their present home. Ms. McSwiggin drove the family car, and Mr. McSwiggin drove the rental moving van. Ms. McSwiggin drove 5 mph faster tnan her husband and arrived at their new home $\frac{1}{2}$ hour sooner than he did. Find the speed of each vehicle.

We need the formula

$$d = rt$$

where d = distance, r = speed, and t = time. We need to use this equation twice. (Why?). Let's set up the following table:

Driver	Distance	Rate	Time
Ms. McSwiggin	50	$r + 5$	$t - \dfrac{1}{2}$
Mr. McSwiggin	50	r	t

So Mr. McSwiggin traveled

$$50 = rt \tag{1}$$

Ms. McSwiggin traveled

$$50 = (r + 5)\left(t - \frac{1}{2}\right) \tag{2}$$

To get just one equation, we need to solve for one variable in terms of another. It doesn't matter which one we pick, so let's solve (1) for t:

$$t = \frac{50}{r}$$

Now we can substitute this value for t into (2):

$$50 = (r + 5)\left(\frac{50}{r} - \frac{1}{2}\right)$$

$$50 = (r + 5)\left(\frac{100 - r}{2r}\right) \qquad \text{Multiplying by the LCD } 2r.$$

$$100r = (r + 5)(100 - r) \qquad \text{Clearing fractions.}$$

$$100r = 100r - r^2 + 500 - 5r$$

$$r^2 + 5r - 500 = 0 \qquad \text{Simplifying.}$$

In a problem like this, try to factor to obtain $(r + 25)(r - 20)$. If you are not able to obtain the factors in a reasonable time, then the quadratic formula,

$$r = \frac{-5 \pm \sqrt{5^2 - (4)(1)(-500)}}{2(1)} = \frac{-5 \pm \sqrt{2025}}{2} = \frac{-5 \pm 45}{2}$$

$$r = \frac{-5 + 45}{2} = 20 \qquad \text{or} \qquad r = \frac{-5 - 45}{2} = -25$$

Since the McSwiggins were not driving backward, we disregard the negative answer. So Mr. McSwiggin drove at the quite safe speed of 20 mph, and Ms. McSwiggin drove at 25 mph. ∎

Practice Problem 5   Redo Example 5 if the new house is 100 miles away, and the family car is driven 25 miles per hour faster than the rental moving van. Find the speed of each vehicle if the car takes 2 hours less than the rental van. ∎

Example 6   The formula for the curved surface area S of a right circular cone of altitude h and base radius r is $S = \pi r \sqrt{r^2 + h^2}$. Solve for r^2.

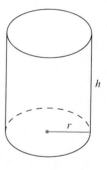

$$S = \pi r \sqrt{r^2 + h^2}$$

$$\frac{S}{\pi r} = \sqrt{r^2 + h^2} \qquad \text{Isolating the radical.}$$

$$\frac{S^2}{\pi^2 r^2} = r^2 + h^2 \qquad \text{Squaring both sides.}$$

$$\frac{S^2}{\pi^2} = r^4 + h^2 r^2 \qquad \text{Multiplying by } r^2.$$

$$0 = r^4 + h^2 r^2 - \frac{S^2}{\pi^2} \qquad \text{Subtracting } S^2/\pi^2.$$

We can make this equation quadratic in form by letting $y = r^2$. Then

$$0 = y^2 + h^2 y - \frac{S^2}{\pi^2}$$

By the quadratic formula,

$$y = \frac{-h^2 \pm \sqrt{(h^2)^2 - 4(1)\left(-\dfrac{S^2}{\pi^2}\right)}}{2}$$

$$y = \frac{-h^2 \pm \sqrt{\dfrac{\pi^2 h^4}{\pi^2} + \dfrac{4S^2}{\pi^2}}}{2}$$

$$y = \frac{-h^2 \pm \dfrac{1}{\pi}\sqrt{\pi^2 h^4 + 4S^2}}{2}$$

$$y = \frac{-\pi h^2 \pm \sqrt{\pi^2 h^4 + 4S^2}}{2\pi}$$

Since $y = r^2$, we have

$$r^2 = \frac{-\pi h^2 \pm \sqrt{\pi^2 h^4 + 4S^2}}{2\pi} \qquad \blacksquare$$

Practice Problem 6   The formula for the number of diagonals d in a polygon of n sides is $d = \dfrac{n^2 + 2n}{2}$. Solve for n.   ■

3 A most useful formula is the Pythagorean theorem for right triangles.

Pythagorean Theorem

If c is the longest side of a right triangle, then $a^2 + b^2 = c^2$.

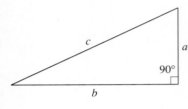

The longest side of a right triangle is called the **hypotenuse**. The two other sides are called the **legs** of the triangle.

Example 7

(a) In the Pythagorean formula $a^2 + b^2 = c^2$, solve for a.
(b) Find the value of a if $c = 13$ and $b = 5$.

(a) $a^2 = c^2 - b^2$ Subtract b^2 from each side.
     $a = \pm\sqrt{c^2 - b^2}$ Take square root of each side.

Since a, b, and c are positive numbers representing the lengths of the sides of a triangle, we use only the positive root, $a = \sqrt{c^2 - b^2}$

(b) $a = \sqrt{c^2 - b^2}$
       $= \sqrt{(13)^2 - (5)^2} = \sqrt{169 - 25} = \sqrt{144} = 12$
Thus $a = 12$ ■

Practice Problem 7
(a) In the Pythagorean formula, solve for b.
(b) Find the value of b if $c = 26$ and $a = 24$.   ■

Example 8   The perimeter of a triangular piece of land is 12 miles. One leg of the triangle is 1 mile longer than the other leg. Find the length of each boundary of the land if the triangle is a right triangle.

We can use the Pythagorean theorem. First, we want only one variable in our equation (right now, both c and x are not known).

We are given that the perimeter is 12 miles, so

$$x + (x + 1) + c = 12$$

Thus,

$$c = -2x + 11$$

By the Pythagorean theorem,

$$x^2 + (x + 1)^2 = (-2x + 11)^2$$

$$x^2 + x^2 + 2x + 1 = 4x^2 - 44x + 121$$

$$0 = 2x^2 - 46x + 120$$

$$0 = x^2 - 23x + 60$$

By the quadratic formula,

$$x = \frac{-(-23) \pm \sqrt{(-23)^2 - 4(1)(60)}}{2(1)}$$

$$= \frac{23 \pm \sqrt{289}}{2}$$

$$= \frac{23 \pm 17}{2}$$

$$x = \frac{40}{2} = 20 \quad or \quad \frac{6}{2} = 3$$

TEACHING TIP   After explaining example 8, ask students to do the following problem as classwork:
The area of a rectangle is 102 square meters. The perimeter of a rectangle is 46 meters. Find the length and width of the rectangle.
Ans. Length = 17 meters
         Width = 6 meters

The only answer that makes sense is $x = 3$. Thus, the sides of the triangle are $x = 3$, $x + 1 = 3 + 1 = 4$, and $-2x + 11 = -2(3) + 11 = 5$. The answer $x = 20$ cannot be right because the perimeter (the sum of *all* the sides) was only 12. The triangle thus has sides of 3 miles, 4 miles, and 5 miles.   ■

Practice Problem 8   The perimeter of a triangular piece of land is 30 miles. One leg of the triangle is 7 miles shorter than the other leg. Find the length of each boundary of the land if the triangle is a right triangle.   ■

Example 9   Find the base and altitude of a triangle that has an area of 35 square meters if the base is 3 meters shorter than the altitude.

The area of a triangle is given by

$$A = \frac{1}{2}ab$$

Let a = the length in meters of the altitude. Then $a - 3$ = the length in meters of the base.

$35 = \dfrac{1}{2}a(a - 3)$	Replacing A (area) by 35. Replacing b (base) by $a - 3$.
$70 = a(a - 3)$	Multiplying each side by 2.
$70 = a^2 - 3a$	Removing parentheses.
$0 = a^2 - 3a - 70$	Subtracting 70 from each side.
$0 = (a - 10)(a + 7)$	
$a = 10 \quad or \quad a = -7$	

The side of a triangle must be a positive number, so we disregard -7. Thus,

$$\text{altitude} = a = 10 \text{ meters}$$

$$\text{base} = a - 3 = 7 \text{ meters} \quad ■$$

Practice Problem 9   The length of a rectangle is 3 feet less than twice the width. The area of the rectangle is 54 square feet. Find the dimensions of the rectangle.   ■

Example 10   When Bob was training for a bicycle race, he rode a total of 135 miles on Monday and Tuesday. On Monday he rode for 75 miles in the rain. On Tuesday he rode 5 miles per hour faster because the weather was better. His total cycling time for the two days was 8 hours. Find his speed for each day.

Let x = the cycling rate in miles per hour on Monday. Then $x + 5$ = the cycling rate in miles per hour on Tuesday. Using the formula $D = RT$, we can solve for T to obtain

$$\frac{D}{R} = T$$

Therefore, the time he cycled on Monday was $\frac{75}{x}$, and the time he cycled on Tuesday was $\frac{60}{x + 5}$. Since the total cycling time was 8 hours, we have

Time cycling Monday + time cycling Tuesday = 8 hours

$$\frac{75}{x} + \frac{60}{x + 5} = 8$$

The LCD of this equation is $x(x + 5)$. Multiply each term by the LCD.

$$x(x + 5)\left(\frac{75}{x}\right) + x(x + 5)\left(\frac{60}{x + 5}\right) = x(x + 5)(8)$$

$$75(x + 5) + 60x = 8x(x + 5)$$

$$75x + 375 + 60x = 8x^2 + 40x$$

$$0 = 8x^2 - 95x - 375$$

$$0 = (x - 15)(8x + 25)$$

$$x - 15 = 0 \quad or \quad 8x + 25 = 0$$

$$x = 15 \qquad\qquad x = \frac{-25}{8}$$

We disregard the negative answer. The cyclist does not have a negative rate of speed— unless he was pedaling backward! Thus, $x = 15$, so Bob's rate of speed on Monday was 15 mph; and $x + 5 = 20$, so Bob's rate of speed on Tuesday was 20 mph ∎

Practice Problem 10 Carlos traveled in his car at a constant speed for 150 miles on a secondary road. Then he traveled 10 mph faster on a better road for 240 miles. If Carlos drove for 7 hours, find the car's speed for each part of the trip. ∎

EXERCISES 7.6

Solve for the variable specified.

1. $3H = x^2$; for x
$x = \pm\sqrt{3H}$

2. $5B = y^2$; for y
$y = \pm\sqrt{5B}$

3. $4y^2 + 5 = 2A$; for y
$y^2 = \dfrac{2A - 5}{4}$
$y = \dfrac{\pm\sqrt{2A - 5}}{2}$

4. $9x^2 - 2 = 3B$; for x
$x^2 = \dfrac{3B + 2}{9}$
$x = \dfrac{\pm\sqrt{3B + 2}}{3}$

5. $F = \dfrac{kbV^2}{r}$; for V
$kbV^2 = Fr$
$V^2 = \dfrac{Fr}{kb}$
$V = \pm\sqrt{\dfrac{Fr}{kb}}$

6. $P = \dfrac{gtw^2}{x}$; for w
$gtw^2 = Px$
$w^2 = \dfrac{Px}{gt}$
$w = \pm\sqrt{\dfrac{Px}{gt}}$

7. $V = \pi(r^2 + R^2)h$; for r
$\pi r^2 h + \pi R^2 h - V = 0$
$\pi r^2 h = V - \pi R^2 h$
$r = \pm\sqrt{\dfrac{V - \pi R^2 h}{\pi h}}$

8. $S = 2\pi rh + \pi r^2$; for r
$\pi r^2 + 2\pi rh - S = 0$
$a = \pi, \ b = 2\pi h, \ c = -S$
$x = \dfrac{-2\pi h \pm \sqrt{4\pi^2 h^2 - 4(\pi)(-S)}}{2\pi}$
$x = \dfrac{-\pi h \pm \sqrt{\pi^2 h^2 + S\pi}}{\pi}$

9. $B = 3abx^2 - 5x$; for x

$3abx^2 - 5x - B = 0$
$a = 3ab, b = -5, c = -B$

$$x = \frac{5 \pm \sqrt{25 - 4(3ab)(-B)}}{2(3ab)}$$

$$x = \frac{5 \pm \sqrt{25 + 12abB}}{6ab}$$

10. $H = b(a^2 + w^2)$; for w

$bw^2 = H - ba^2$

$$w = \pm \sqrt{\frac{H - ba^2}{b}}$$

11. $(a + 1)x^2 + 5x + 2w = 0$; for x

$a = a + 1, b = 5, c = 2w$

$$x = \frac{-5 \pm \sqrt{25 - 4(a + 1)(2w)}}{2(a + 1)}$$

$$x = \frac{-5 \pm \sqrt{25 - 8aw - 8w}}{2a + 2}$$

12. $(b - 2)x^2 - 3x + 5y = 0$; for x

$a = b - 2, b = -3, c = 5y$

$$x = \frac{3 \pm \sqrt{9 - 4(b - 2)(5y)}}{2(b - 2)}$$

$$x = \frac{3 \pm \sqrt{9 - 20by + 40y}}{2b - 4}$$

13. $5w^2 + 2bw - 8 = 0$; for w

$a = 5, b = 2b, c = -8$

$$w = \frac{-2b \pm \sqrt{4b^2 - 4(5)(-8)}}{2(5)}$$

$$w = \frac{-2b \pm 2\sqrt{b^2 + 40}}{10}$$

$$w = \frac{-b \pm \sqrt{b^2 + 40}}{5}$$

14. $7w^2 - 5bw + 3 = 0$; for w

$a = 7, b = -5b, c = 3$

$$w = \frac{5b \pm \sqrt{25b^2 - 4(7)(3)}}{2(7)}$$

$$w = \frac{5b \pm \sqrt{25b^2 - 84}}{14}$$

15. $L = \dfrac{kd^4}{h^2}$; for h

$Lh^2 = Kd^4$

$$h = \pm \sqrt{\frac{Kd^4}{L}} = \pm d^2 \sqrt{\frac{K}{L}}$$

16. $B = \dfrac{3gy^4}{a^2}$; for y

$Ba^2 = 3gy^4$

$$y^4 = \frac{Ba^2}{3g}$$

$$y = \pm \sqrt[4]{\frac{Ba^2}{3g}}$$

17. $A = P(1 + r)^2$; for r

$A = P + 2rP + Pr^2$
$Pr^2 + 2rP + P - A = 0$
$a = P, b = 2P, c = P - A$

$$x = \frac{-2P \pm \sqrt{4P^2 - 4(P)(P - A)}}{2P}$$

$$x = \frac{-P \pm \sqrt{AP}}{P}$$

18. $P = EI - RI^2$; for I

$RI^2 - EI + P = 0$
$a = R, b = -E, c = P$

$$I = \frac{E \pm \sqrt{E^2 - 4(R)(P)}}{2R}$$

$$I = \frac{E \pm \sqrt{E^2 - 4RP}}{2R}$$

19. $x^2 + 3bx - 10b^2 = 0$ for x

$(x + 5b)(x - 2b) = 0$
$x = -5b$
$x = 2b$

20. $y^2 - 4yw - 45w^2 = 0$ for y

$(y - 9w)(y + 5w) = 0$
$y = 9w$
$y = -5w$

21. $6a^2 + 11ab - 10b^2 = 0$ for a

$(3a - 2b)(2a + 5b) = 0$
$a = \dfrac{2b}{3}, a = -\dfrac{5b}{2}$

22. $10w^2 - 3wy = 63y^2 = 0$ for w

$10w^2 - 3wy - 63y^2 = 0$
$a = 10, b = -3y, c = -63y^2$

$$w = \frac{3y \pm \sqrt{9y^2 - 4(10)(-63y^2)}}{2(10)}$$

$$w = \frac{3y \pm 3y\sqrt{281}}{20} = \frac{3y(1 \pm \sqrt{281})}{20}$$

In problems 23–32, use the Pythagorean theorem to find the missing side.

23. $b = 7, a = \sqrt{3}$; find c

$c^2 = (7)^2 + (\sqrt{3})^2$
$c^2 = 49 + 3$
$c = \sqrt{52} = 2\sqrt{13}$

24. $a = 2\sqrt{3}, b = 3$; find c

$c^2 = (2\sqrt{3})^2 + (3)^2$
$c^2 = 12 + 9$
$c = \sqrt{21}$

25. $c = 13, b = 5$; find a

$(13)^2 = a^2 + 25$
$144 = a^2$
$12 = a$

26. $c = 17, a = 15$; find b

$(17)^2 = (15)^2 + b^2$
$64 = b^2$
$8 = b$

27. $c = \sqrt{26}, a = 3$; find b

$(\sqrt{26})^2 = 3^2 + b^2$
$17 = b^2$
$\sqrt{17} = b$

28. $c = \sqrt{17}, b = 2$; find a

$(\sqrt{17})^2 = a^2 + 2^2$
$13 = a^2$
$\sqrt{13} = a$

29. $c = 12, b = 2a$; find b and a

$12^2 = a^2 + (2a)^2$
$144 = 5a^2$

$a = \sqrt{\dfrac{144}{5}} = \dfrac{12\sqrt{5}}{5}$

$b = \dfrac{24\sqrt{5}}{5}$

30. $c = 15, a = 2b$; find b and a

$15^2 = (2b)^2 + b^2$
$225 = 5b^2$
$45 = b^2$
$b = 3\sqrt{5}$
$a = 6\sqrt{5}$

31. A right triangle has a hypotenuse of 10 inches. One leg of the triangle is 2 inches longer than the other leg. Find the length of each leg.

$10^2 = a^2 + (a + 2)^2$
$a = 6$
$a + 2 = 8$
Shorter leg $= 6$ inches
Longer leg $= 8$ inches

32. One leg of a triangle is 12 inches. The other leg is 6 inches shorter than the hypotenuse. What is its length? What is the length of the hypotenuse?

$x^2 = 12^2 + (x - 6)^2$
$x = 15$
$x - 6 = 9$
Shorter leg $= 9$ inches
Hypotenuse $= 15$ inches

33. The area of a rectangle is 91 square meters. Its length is 1 meter shorter than twice its width. Find its length and width.

Width $= x = 7$ m
Length $= 2x - 1 = 13$ m
$91 = x(2x - 1)$
$0 = 2x^2 - x - 91$
$x = -\dfrac{13}{2}, \; x = 7$

34. The area of a rectangle is 90 square meters. Its length is 3 meters longer than twice its width. Find its length and width.

Width $= x = 6$ m
Length $= 2x + 3 = 15$ m
$x(2x + 3) = 90$
$2x^2 + 3x - 90 = 0$
$x = \dfrac{-15}{2}, \; x = 6$

35. The area of a triangle is 72 square centimeters. Its altitude is 2 centimeters longer than twice its base. Find the height of the altitude and the length of the base.

Base $= x = 8$ cm
Altitude $= 2x + 2 = 18$ cm
$72 = \dfrac{1}{2}(2x + 2)x$
$72 = x^2 + x$
$x = -9, \; x = 8$

36. The area of a triangle is 96 square centimeters. Its altitude is 2 centimeters longer than five times the base. Find the lengths of the altitude and the base.

Base $= x = 6$ cm
Altitude $= 5x + 2 = 32$ cm
$96 = \dfrac{1}{2}(x)(5x + 2)$
$192 = 5x^2 + 2x$
$x = -\dfrac{32}{5}, \; x = 6$

37. Benita traveled at a constant speed for 160 miles on an old road. She then traveled 5 miles per hour faster on a newer road for 90 miles. If she drove for 6 hours, find the car's speed for each part of the trip.

Rate (Old road) $= x = 40$ mph
Rate (New road) $= x + 5 = 45$ mph
Time $= \dfrac{\text{Dist}}{\text{Rate}}$
$\dfrac{160}{x} + \dfrac{90}{x + 5} = 6 \Rightarrow 3x^2 - 110x - 400 = 0$
$x = -\dfrac{10}{3}, \; x = 40$

38. Roberto drove at a constant speed in a rainstorm for 225 miles. He took a break and the rain stopped. He then drove 150 miles at a speed that was 5 miles per hour faster than his previous speed. If he drove for 8 hours, find the car's speed for each part of the trip.

Rate (Rainstorm) $= x = 45$ mph
Rate (Clear) $= x + 5 = 50$ mph
$T = D/R$
$\dfrac{225}{x} + \dfrac{150}{x + 5} = 8$
$8x^2 - 335x - 1125 = 0$
$x = 45, \; x = -\dfrac{25}{8}$

39. Bob drove from home to work at 50 mph. After work the traffic was heavier, and he drove home at 45 mph. His driving time to and from work was 1 hour 16 minutes. How far does he live from his job?

Time (Home to work) $= x = 3/5$ hr
Time (Work to home) $= 19/15 - x = 2/3$ hr
1 hr 16 min $= 19/15$ hr
$D = RT$ Distances are equal
$50x = 45\left(\dfrac{19}{15} - x\right)$
$95x = 57$
$x = \dfrac{57}{95}$ or $\dfrac{3}{5}$ hr
$D = \dfrac{50 \text{ mi}}{\text{hr}} \cdot \dfrac{3}{5} \text{ hr} = 30$ miles

40. A driver drove his heavily loaded truck from the company warehouse to a delivery point at 35 mph. He unloaded the truck and drove back to the warehouse at 45 mph. The total trip took 5 hours 20 minutes. How far is the delivery point from the warehouse?

Time (Warehouse–Delivery) $= x = 3$ hrs
Time (Delivery–Warehouse) $= \left(5\dfrac{1}{3} - x\right) = 2\dfrac{1}{3}$ hrs
Distances are equal and $D = RT$
$35x = 45\left(\dfrac{16}{3} - x\right)$
$x = 3$
Dist $= 35(3) = 105$ miles

To Think About

41. Solve for w: $w = \dfrac{12b^2}{\dfrac{5}{2}w + \dfrac{7}{2}b + \dfrac{21}{2}}$.

$\dfrac{5}{2}w^2 + \dfrac{7}{2}bw + \dfrac{21}{2}w = 12b^2$
$5w^2 + (7b + 21)w - 24b^2 = 0$
$a = 5, \; b = 7b + 21, \; c = -24b^2$
$w = \dfrac{-7b - 21 \pm \sqrt{(7b + 21)^2 - 4(5)(-24b^2)}}{10}$
$w = \dfrac{-7b - 21 \pm \sqrt{529b^2 + 294b + 441}}{10}$

Rationalize the denominators.

42. $\dfrac{4}{\sqrt{3x}}$

$\dfrac{4}{\sqrt{3x}} \cdot \dfrac{\sqrt{3x}}{\sqrt{3x}} = \dfrac{4\sqrt{3x}}{3x}$

43. $\dfrac{5\sqrt{6}}{2\sqrt{5}}$

$\dfrac{5\sqrt{6}}{2\sqrt{5}} \cdot \dfrac{\sqrt{5}}{\sqrt{5}} = \dfrac{\sqrt{30}}{2}$

44. $\dfrac{3}{\sqrt{x}+\sqrt{y}}$

$\dfrac{3}{\sqrt{x}+\sqrt{y}} \cdot \dfrac{\sqrt{x}-\sqrt{y}}{\sqrt{x}-\sqrt{y}} = \dfrac{3(\sqrt{x}-\sqrt{y})}{x-y}$

45. $\dfrac{2\sqrt{3}}{\sqrt{3}-\sqrt{6}}$

$\dfrac{2\sqrt{3}}{\sqrt{3}-\sqrt{6}} \cdot \dfrac{\sqrt{3}+\sqrt{6}}{\sqrt{3}+\sqrt{6}} = \dfrac{6+2\sqrt{18}}{-3} = -2 - 2\sqrt{2}$

46. $\dfrac{3ab}{\sqrt[3]{8ab^2}}$

$\dfrac{3ab}{\sqrt[3]{8ab^2}} \cdot \dfrac{\sqrt[3]{a^2b}}{\sqrt[3]{a^2b}} = \dfrac{3ab\sqrt[3]{a^2b}}{2ab} = \dfrac{3\sqrt[3]{a^2b}}{2}$

Calculator Problems

Use the Pythagorean theorem to find the missing side correct to four decimal places.

47. $c = 19.3216$, $b = 14.0719$

$a = 13.2403$

48. $a = 0.7613$, $b = 0.5298$

$c = 0.9275$

For Extra Practice Exercises, turn to page 378.

Solutions to Odd-Numbered Practice Problems

1. Solve for x:

$$5x^2 - 8 = 3x^2 + 2w$$
$$5x^2 - 3x^2 = 2w + 8$$
$$2x^2 = 2w + 8$$
$$x^2 = w + 4$$
$$x = \pm\sqrt{w+4}$$

3. Solve for y: $3y^2 + 2yf - 7g = 0$. The equation does not factor. We use the quadratic formula; $a = 3$, $b = 2f$, $c = -7g$.

$$y = \dfrac{-2f \pm \sqrt{(2f)^2 - 4(3)(-7g)}}{2(3)}$$
$$= \dfrac{-2f \pm \sqrt{4f^2 + 84g}}{6}$$
$$= \dfrac{-2f \pm \sqrt{4(f^2 + 21g)}}{6} = \dfrac{-2f \pm \sqrt{4}\sqrt{f^2 + 21g}}{6}$$
$$= \dfrac{-2f \pm 2\sqrt{f^2 + 21g}}{6} = \dfrac{-f \pm \sqrt{f^2 + 21g}}{3}$$

5.

	Distance	Rate	Time
Ms. McSwiggin	100	$r + 25$	$t - 2$
Mr. McSwiggin	100	r	t

This yields by $d = rt$,

$$100 = rt \qquad (1)$$

and

$$100 = (r + 25)(t - 2) \qquad (2)$$

Solve equation (1) for t:

$$t = \dfrac{100}{r}$$

Substitute this expression into (2):

$$100 = (r + 25)\left(\dfrac{100}{r} - 2\right)$$

$$100 = (r + 25)\left(\dfrac{100 - 2r}{r}\right)$$

$$r(100) = r\left[(r + 25)\left(\dfrac{100 - 2r}{r}\right)\right]$$

$$r(100) = (r + 25)(100 - 2r)$$

$$100r = 100r + 2500 - 2r^2 - 50r$$

$$0 = 2500 - 50r - 2r^2$$

$$2r^2 + 50r - 2500 = 0$$

$$r^2 + 25r - 1250 = 0$$

$$(r + 50)(r - 25) = 0$$

$$r = -50 \quad or \quad r = 25$$

The negative speed is not used. Thus, Mr. McSwiggin traveled at 25 mph. Ms. McSwiggin traveled at 50 mph.

7. (a) $a^2 + b^2 = c^2$
$b^2 = c^2 - a^2$
For positive values of a, b, c we have
$$b = \sqrt{c^2 - a^2}$$

(b) If $c = 26$ and $a = 24$,
$$b = \sqrt{26^2 - 24^2}$$
$$= \sqrt{676 - 576} = \sqrt{100}$$
$$= 10$$

9. The length of a rectangle is 3 feet less than twice the width. Let w = the width; then $2w - 3$ = the length.

$$w(2w - 3) = 54$$
$$2w^2 - 3w = 54$$
$$2w^2 - 3w - 54 = 0$$
$$(2w + 9)(w - 6) = 0$$
$$2w = -9$$
$$w = 6 \quad or \quad w = -\frac{9}{2}$$

We do not use the negative value. Thus,

$$\text{width} = 6 \text{ feet}$$
$$\text{length} = 2w - 3 = 2(6) - 3 = 12 - 3 = 9 \text{ feet}$$

Answers to Even-Numbered Practice Problems

2. $y = \dfrac{-7w}{2},\ y = -w$ **4.** The radius should be 3 inches longer.   **6.** $h = \dfrac{-2 \pm \sqrt{4 + 8d}}{2} = -1 \pm \sqrt{1 + 2d}$

8. The legs are 5 miles and 12 miles long. The hypotenuse of the triangular piece of land is 13 miles long.
10. Carlos drove 50 mph on a secondary road and 60 mph on the better road.

EXTRA PRACTICE: EXERCISES

Section 7.1

Solve by factoring.

1. $x^2 + 8x - 33 = 0$ $3, -11$ **2.** $x^2 - 12x + 27 = 0$ $9, 3$

3. $2x^2 + 3x = 8x$ $0, \dfrac{5}{2}$ **4.** $5x^2 - 7x = 2x$ $0, \dfrac{9}{5}$

5. $9y^2 + 6y - 8 = 0$ $\dfrac{2}{3}, -\dfrac{4}{3}$ **6.** $6y^2 - 13y + 6 = 0$ $\dfrac{3}{2}, \dfrac{2}{3}$

7. $y^2 + \dfrac{10}{3} = \dfrac{17y}{3}$ $5, \dfrac{2}{3}$ **8.** $\dfrac{6}{5}y^2 + y = 5$ $-\dfrac{5}{2}, \dfrac{5}{3}$

9. $(3x + 2)(x - 1) = 7 - 7x$ **10.** $(2x + 1)^2 = 10x - 1$ $\dfrac{1}{2}, 1$

11. $3y = 2 + \dfrac{8}{y}$ $-\dfrac{4}{3}, 2$ **12.** $\dfrac{1}{y} = \dfrac{2}{y^2} - 10$ $\dfrac{2}{5}, -\dfrac{1}{2}$

13. $\dfrac{1}{2} + \dfrac{x}{2} = \dfrac{x^2 + 4}{3x + 2}$ $1, -6$ **14.** $\dfrac{1}{3} + \dfrac{2x}{3} = \dfrac{x^2 - 2}{2x - 3}$ $1, 3$

15. $\dfrac{3}{4}x^2 = 1 + \dfrac{11}{4}x$ $4, -\dfrac{1}{3}$ **16.** $\dfrac{12}{x^2} = \dfrac{5}{x} + 2$ $\dfrac{3}{2}, -4$

9. $1, -3$

17. $\dfrac{24}{x^2} + \dfrac{2}{x} - 1 = 0$ $6, -4$ **18.** $\dfrac{1}{2}x^2 - \dfrac{13}{2}x + 18 = 0$ $9, 4$

19. $5x(x - 1) - 2 + 3x = 7x^2 - 2$ $0, -1$

20. $3(2y^2 + 2y + 1) = 3 + 5y^2$ $0, -6$

21. $(y + 4)(3y - 4) = y^2 - 3y - 28$ $-\dfrac{3}{2}, -4$

22. $(2y - 3)(y + 2) = -2y + 4 + y^2$ $-5, 2$

23. $5a^2 + 9a = 2$ **24.** $3b^2 - 7b - 6 = 0$ $3, -\dfrac{2}{3}$

25. $2x^2 + 15 = 3(2x + 5)$ $0, 3$ **26.** $6(x^2 + 1) = 13x$

27. $27y^2 - 3y - 14 = 0$ **28.** $15s^2 - 4 = -17s$

29. $9x^2 + 40 = 42x$ **30.** $3(4x^2 + 2) + 25x = 8x$

31. $2(3x^2 - 1) + 7x = 18x$ $2, -\dfrac{1}{6}$ **32.** $3 - 13s = 6(s^2 - 2)$

33. $4a(8a + 7) = 15$ $-\dfrac{5}{4}, \dfrac{3}{8}$ **34.** $4r(5r + 4) = 7r + 18$

35. $x^2 - 24 = 4(x + 2)$ $8, -4$ **36.** $108 = 3a^2 + 48a$ $2, -18$

23. $\dfrac{1}{5}, -2$ **26.** $\dfrac{3}{2}, \dfrac{2}{3}$ **27.** $\dfrac{7}{9}, -\dfrac{2}{3}$ **28.** $\dfrac{1}{5}, -\dfrac{4}{3}$

29. $\dfrac{4}{3}, \dfrac{10}{3}$ **30.** $-\dfrac{3}{4}, -\dfrac{2}{3}$ **32.** $\dfrac{5}{6}, -3$ **34.** $-\dfrac{6}{5}, \dfrac{3}{4}$

Section 7.2

Solve for x by taking the square root of each side of the equation.

1. $3x^2 = 27$ ± 3 **2.** $7x^2 = 14$ $\pm\sqrt{2}$

3. $x^2 - 12 = 18$ $\pm\sqrt{30}$ **4.** $x^2 + 5 = 22$ $\pm\sqrt{17}$

5. $6x^2 + 3x = 40 + x(x + 3)$ $\pm 2\sqrt{2}$

6. $4x^2 + 5 = 41 + x^2$ $\pm 2\sqrt{3}$

7. $(2x + 1)^2 = 5$ $\dfrac{-1 \pm \sqrt{5}}{2}$ **8.** $(4x - 1)^2 = 2$ $\dfrac{1 \pm \sqrt{2}}{4}$

9. $(6x - 5)^2 = 50$ $\dfrac{5 \pm 5\sqrt{2}}{6}$ **10.** $(8x + 3)^2 = 48$ $\dfrac{-3 \pm 4\sqrt{3}}{8}$

11. $2x^2 - 4 = 4$ ± 2 **12.** $\dfrac{3x^2}{4} + 18 = 30$ ± 4

13. $\dfrac{x^2}{4} = 16$ ± 8

14. $(x + 4)^2 = 8x + 24$ $\pm 2\sqrt{2}$

15. $(x + 2)^2 = 2x(x + 2) + 12$ $\pm 2i\sqrt{2}$

16. $4x(x + 2) - 5 = 12 + 2x(4 - x)$ $\dfrac{\pm\sqrt{102}}{6}$

17. $3x^2 + 2x^2 = 45$ ± 3

18. $(x - 3)^2 + 10x = x(4 + 2x)$ ± 3

Solve by completing the square. Simplify your answers.

19. $x^2 - 8x - 14 = 0$ $4 \pm \sqrt{30}$ **20.** $x^2 - 6x - 12 = 0$

21. $x^2 + 4x + 1 = 0$ $-2 \pm \sqrt{3}$ **22.** $x^2 + 10x + 3 = 0$

20. $3 \pm \sqrt{21}$ **22.** $-5 \pm \sqrt{22}$

23. $2x^2 + 6x - 1 = 0$ **24.** $2x^2 + 8x - 3 = 0$

25. $3x^2 - x = 2$ $1, -\dfrac{2}{3}$ **26.** $2x^2 + x = 3$ $1, -\dfrac{3}{2}$

27. $\dfrac{2x^2}{3} - x + \dfrac{1}{6} = 0$ $\dfrac{3 \pm \sqrt{5}}{4}$ **28.** $\dfrac{1}{2}x^2 - \dfrac{1}{4}x - \dfrac{1}{4} = 0$

29. $8x^2 + 12x - 3 = 0$ **30.** $3x^2 - 7x - 4 = 0$

31. $0.3x^2 - 0.7x + 0.4 = 0$ $\dfrac{4}{3}, 1$ **32.** $8x^2 + 14x = 15$ $\dfrac{3}{4}, -\dfrac{5}{2}$

33. $0.2x^2 + 0.9x = 3.5$ **34.** $\dfrac{x}{12} + \dfrac{x^2 - 15}{5x} = \dfrac{x}{5}$ ± 6

35. $(x + 4)^2 = 6x + 24$ $2, -4$

23. $\dfrac{-3 \pm \sqrt{11}}{2}$ **28.** $1, -\dfrac{1}{2}$ **30.** $\dfrac{7 \pm \sqrt{97}}{6}$

24. $\dfrac{-4 \pm \sqrt{22}}{2}$ **29.** $\dfrac{-3 \pm \sqrt{15}}{4}$ **33.** $\dfrac{5}{2}, -7$

Section 7.3

Solve for the variable by using the quadratic formula. Be sure to simplify your answer. Express complex roots using i notation.

1. $x^2 + 3x - 2 = 0$ $\dfrac{-3 \pm \sqrt{17}}{2}$ **2.** $x^2 + 4x - 3 = 0$ $-2 \pm \sqrt{7}$

3. $2x^2 + x - 5 = 0$ **4.** $2x^2 + 5x - 2 = 0$

5. $6x^2 - 19x + 10 = 0$ $\dfrac{5}{2}, \dfrac{2}{3}$ **6.** $5x^2 - 23x + 12 = 0$ $4, \dfrac{3}{5}$

7. $5x^2 + x - 1 = 0$ **8.** $6x^2 - 3x - 1 = 0$

9. $y^2 = \dfrac{3}{2}y + \dfrac{1}{2}$ $\dfrac{3 \pm \sqrt{17}}{4}$ **10.** $\dfrac{1}{4}y^2 + \dfrac{3}{4}y - \dfrac{1}{4} = 0$ $\dfrac{-3 \pm \sqrt{13}}{2}$

11. $2 + \dfrac{6}{x} - \dfrac{5}{x^2} = 0$ $\dfrac{-3 \pm \sqrt{19}}{2}$ **12.** $1 - \dfrac{6}{x} - \dfrac{10}{x^2} = 0$ $3 \pm \sqrt{19}$

13. $\dfrac{2}{x - 2} + \dfrac{1}{x + 1} = 4$ $\dfrac{7 \pm \sqrt{177}}{8}$ **14.** $\dfrac{2}{x - 1} + \dfrac{1}{x + 3} = 3$

15. $x^2 - 5 = 2(x + 3) - 4$ $5, -3$ **16.** $2x(2x - 1) = 3x^2 + 11$

17. $x + 15 = 6x^2$ $\dfrac{5}{3}, -\dfrac{3}{2}$ **18.** $1 - 3x = 2x^2$

3. $\dfrac{-1 \pm \sqrt{41}}{4}$ **4.** $\dfrac{-5 \pm \sqrt{41}}{4}$ **7.** $\dfrac{1 \pm \sqrt{21}}{10}$ **8.** $\dfrac{3 \pm \sqrt{33}}{12}$ **14.** $\dfrac{-3 \pm \sqrt{177}}{6}$ **15.** $1 \pm 2\sqrt{2}$ **16.** $1 \pm 2\sqrt{3}$ **18.** $\dfrac{-3 \pm \sqrt{17}}{4}$ **22.** $\dfrac{3 \pm \sqrt{3}}{3}$ **27.** $\dfrac{-2 \pm i\sqrt{2}}{3}$

19. $3x^2 = 5x - 2$ $1, \dfrac{2}{3}$ **20.** $4 = x(3x + 2)$ $\dfrac{-1 \pm \sqrt{13}}{3}$

21. $x^2 - 5x = -3$ $\dfrac{5 \pm \sqrt{13}}{2}$ **22.** $3x^2 - 6x = -2$

23. $4x^2 - 3x - 2 = 0$ **24.** $x^2 + 4x + 1 = 0$ $-2 \pm \sqrt{3}$

25. $x^2 = -4(x + 3)$ $-2 \pm 2i\sqrt{2}$ **26.** $4(2x - 5) = x^2$ $4 \pm 2i$

27. $x(3x + 4) = -2$ **28.** $x^2 - 3.8x = 31.2$ $7.8, -4$

29. $\dfrac{1}{x + 1} + \dfrac{3}{x - 1} = \dfrac{10}{3}$ $2, -\dfrac{4}{5}$ **30.** $(2x + 1)^2 - 3(2x + 1) = (x + 3)$ $\dfrac{3 \pm \sqrt{89}}{8}$ **23.** $\dfrac{3 \pm \sqrt{41}}{8}$

31. $5x^2 - 8x + 2 = 0$ $\dfrac{4 \pm \sqrt{6}}{5}$ **32.** $2x^2 - 2x + 1 = 0$ $\dfrac{1 \pm i}{2}$

33. $(x + 5)(x + 1) = -8$ **34.** $(x - 3)(x - 1) = -10$

35. $2x = (5 - x)(1 - x)$ $4 \pm \sqrt{11}$ **36.** $(x - 4)(x - 2) = 3 - 4x$

33. $-3 \pm 2i$ **34.** $2 \pm 3i$ **36.** $1 \pm 2i$

Section 7.4

Solve and check your solution(s).

1. $\sqrt{5y - 6} = y$ $3, 2$ **2.** $\sqrt{3y + 10} = 6$ $\dfrac{26}{3}$

3. $x + 3 = \sqrt{2x + 9}$ 0 **4.** $x + 1 = \sqrt{5x + 1}$ $0, 3$

5. $\sqrt{x + 2} = 3$ 7 **6.** $\sqrt{3x - 5} = 2$ 3

7. $\sqrt{x + 11} = x - 1$ 5 **8.** $\sqrt{x + 4} = 4 - x$ $\dfrac{9 \pm \sqrt{33}}{2}$

9. $\sqrt{x^2 - 3x} = 2$ $4, -1$ **10.** $\sqrt{x^2 + 8x} = 3$ $-9, 1$

11. $\sqrt[3]{x + 2} = 4$ 62 **12.** $\sqrt[3]{2x - 1} = 3$ 14

13. $\sqrt[3]{x^2 + 3x + 4} = \sqrt[3]{3x + 12}$ $\pm 2\sqrt{2}$

14. $\sqrt[3]{x^2 - 5x + 2} = \sqrt[3]{3x + 11}$ $9, -1$

15. $\sqrt{y + 11} = 2y - 6$ 5

16. $\sqrt{3y + 6} = y + 2$ $-2, 1$

17. $\sqrt{2x + 4} = 2 + \sqrt{x - 2}$ 6

18. $\sqrt{2x + 1} = \sqrt{x - 3} + 2$ $4, 12$

19. $\sqrt{2y + 13} + \sqrt{y + 6} = 5$ -2

20. $\sqrt{3y + 7} + \sqrt{y + 5} = 4$ -1

21. $\sqrt{5x + 1} - \sqrt{x - 2} = 3$ $3, \dfrac{9}{4}$

22. $\sqrt{2x - 1} - \sqrt{x - 4} = 2$ $5, 13$

23. $\sqrt{2y - 2} = 2\sqrt{y} - \sqrt{y - 5}$ 9

24. $\sqrt{4y + 1} - \sqrt{y + 3} = \sqrt{y - 2}$ 6

25. $\sqrt{x + 3} - \sqrt{x + 5} = 2$ 4

26. $\sqrt{x - 1} + \sqrt{x + 2} = 3$ 7

27. $2x - 3\sqrt{x} = 2$ 4

28. $\sqrt{25 - 6x} + \sqrt{25 + 6x} = 8$ ± 4

29. $\sqrt{1 - 2x} - 2 = \sqrt{1 - x}$ -24

30. $\sqrt{5 - x} = \sqrt{3 + x} \cdot \sqrt{x - 5}$ 5

31. $\sqrt{x + 3} + \sqrt{4x + 1} - \sqrt{10x + 4} = 0$ 6

32. $\sqrt{3x - 5} + \sqrt{x - 9} = \sqrt{4x - 4}$ 10

33. $3\sqrt{x + 8} - \sqrt{x - 8} = 2\sqrt{2x + 2}$ 17

34. $\sqrt{x + 2} - \sqrt{16 - x} = 0$ 7

35. $\sqrt[3]{2x - 1} = 5$ 63

36. $2\sqrt[3]{3x - 9} = -4$ $\dfrac{1}{3}$

37. $\sqrt{x + 25} = 5 - x$ 0

38. $\sqrt{2x} - \sqrt{x + 1} = \dfrac{3}{\sqrt{x + 1}}$ 8

39. $x + \sqrt{x^2 - a^2} = \dfrac{a^2}{\sqrt{x^2 - a^2}}$ $x = \dfrac{2a\sqrt{3}}{3}$

Section 7.5

Solve for valid solutions only. Express any imaginary numbers using i notation.

1. $x^4 - 10x^2 + 24 = 0$ $\quad \pm\sqrt{6}, \pm 2$

2. $x^4 - 6x^2 - 27 = 0$ $\quad \pm 3, \pm i\sqrt{3}$

3. $3x^4 - 4x^2 - 7 = 0$ $\quad \dfrac{\pm\sqrt{21}}{3}, \pm i$

4. $4x^4 - 15x^2 - 4 = 0$ $\quad$ **4.** $\pm 2, \dfrac{\pm i}{2}$

5. $y^8 - 17y^4 + 16 = 0$ $\quad \pm 2, \pm 1$

6. $y^8 - 5y^4 + 4 = 0$ $\quad \pm\sqrt{2}, \pm 1$

7. $x^{2/3} + 5x^{1/3} + 6 = 0$ $\quad -27, -8$

8. $x^{2/3} + 7x^{1/3} + 12 = 0$ $\quad -64, -27$

9. $2x^{2/5} + 5x^{1/5} - 3 = 0$ $\quad$ **9.** $\dfrac{1}{32}, -243$

10. $3x^{2/5} + 4x^{1/5} - 4 = 0$ $\quad \dfrac{32}{243}, -32$

11. $3y^{1/2} = 14y^{1/4} + 5$ $\quad 625$

12. $2y^{1/2} = 5y^{1/4} + 3$ $\quad 81$

13. $9y^{-4} + 8y^{-2} - 1 = 0$ $\quad \pm 3, \pm i$

14. $40y^{-4} - 14y^{-2} + 1 = 0$ $\quad \pm 2, \pm\sqrt{10}$

15. $6(2x - 3)^2 - 5(2x - 3) + 1 = 0$ $\quad$ **15.** $\dfrac{5}{3}, \dfrac{7}{4}$

16. $(7x + 5)^2 + 2(7x + 5) - 15 = 0$ $\quad -\dfrac{2}{7}, -\dfrac{10}{7}$

17. $\dfrac{6}{(x - 1)^2} - \dfrac{5}{(x - 1)} + 1 = 0$ $\quad 4, 3$

18. $\dfrac{1}{(2x + 1)^2} - \dfrac{1}{2x + 1} = 6$ $\quad -\dfrac{3}{4}, -\dfrac{1}{3}$

19. $(3y^2 - y)^2 - 14(3y^2 - y) = -40$ $\quad -\dfrac{5}{3}, 2, \dfrac{4}{3}, -1$

20. $(3z^2 + 4z)^2 - 3(3z^2 + 4z) = 4$

21. $x^{1/2} - x^{1/4} = 6$ $\quad 81$ $\qquad$ **20.** $\dfrac{2}{3}, -2, -\dfrac{1}{3}, -1$

22. $x^4 + 17x^2 = 84$ $\quad \pm 2, \pm i\sqrt{21}$

23. $3x^4 + 5x^2 - 8 = 0$ $\quad$ **23.** $\pm 1, \pm\dfrac{2i\sqrt{6}}{3}$

24. $x + 3\sqrt{x} = 4$ $\quad 1$

25. $x^{1/3} - 3x^{1/6} = -2$ $\quad 64, 1$

26. $x^{2/3} - 4x^{1/3} = 12$ $\quad 216, -8$

27. $x^8 = 17x^4 - 16$ $\quad \pm 2, \pm 1$

28. $x - 4x^{2/3} + x^{1/3} = 0$ $\quad 0, (2 \pm \sqrt{3})^3$

29. $(x^2 + 1)^2 + 4(x^2 + 1) = 45$ $\quad$ **29.** $\pm 2, \pm i\sqrt{10}$

30. $(x - 2)^2 + 3(x - 2) = 100$ $\quad \dfrac{1}{2} \pm \dfrac{\sqrt{409}}{2}$

31. $5x^4 + 6x^2 - 11 = 0$ $\quad$ **31.** $\pm 1, \pm\dfrac{i\sqrt{55}}{5}$

32. $2x + \sqrt{x} = 15x\sqrt{x}$ $\quad \dfrac{1}{9}, 0$

33. $x + x^{1/2} - 6 = 0$ $\quad 4$

34. $x - 2\sqrt{x + 1} = 7$ $\quad 15$

Section 7.6

Solve for the specified variable.

1. $4x^2 + 2 = 5y^2$; for x $\quad x = \pm\sqrt{\dfrac{5y^2 - 2}{4}} = \pm\dfrac{\sqrt{5y^2 - 2}}{2}$

2. $2x^2 - 5 = 3y^2$; for x

3. $y^2 - 3by + 10b^2 = 0$; for y $\quad y = \dfrac{3b \pm ib\sqrt{31}}{2}$

4. $y^2 + 16by + 63b^2 = 0$; for y $\quad -7b, -9b$

5. $2a^2 + 9b^2 = 12c^2$; for b

6. $5h^2 + 16j^2 = 20k^2$; for j $\quad j = \dfrac{\pm\sqrt{20k^2 - 5h^2}}{4}$

7. $5w^2 - 2abw + 8b^2 = 0$; for w

8. $7w^2 + 3abw - 5w^2 = 0$; for w $\quad 0, -\dfrac{3ab}{2}$

9. $3kx^2 - 5kx + 12 = 0$; for x

10. $5b^2x^2 + 7bx - 10 = 0$; for x $\quad x = \dfrac{-7 \pm \sqrt{249}}{10b}$

11. $x^2 + 2bx = b^2$; for x $\quad$ **11.** $x = -b \pm b\sqrt{2}$ $\qquad$ **12.** $x = 6b$ $\quad x = -2b$

12. $x^2 - 4bx - 12b^2$; for x

13. $a^2x^2 + 2ax^2 = (a^2 - 1)^2 - x^2$; for x $\quad x = \pm(a - 1)$

14. $4x^2 + 12ax - 7a^2 = 0$; for a $\quad a = -\dfrac{2x}{7}, a = 2x$

15. $6ax^2 + abx = 2(6x + b)$; for x

16. $x^2 - (b - a)c = x(a - b + c)$; for x $\quad$ **15.** $x = \dfrac{2}{a}, x = \dfrac{-b}{6}$

17. $\dfrac{a}{x} + \dfrac{x}{a} = \dfrac{ab}{x}$; for x $\quad x = \pm a\sqrt{b - 1}$

18. $\dfrac{x}{a + b} - \dfrac{a - b}{x} = 0$; for x $\quad \pm\sqrt{a^2 - b^2}$

19. $16x^2 + 3a^2 - 16ax = 0$; for x $\quad x = \dfrac{3a}{4}, x = \dfrac{a}{4}$

20. $(c^2 + 1)x = cx^2 + c$; for x $\quad x = c, x = \dfrac{1}{c}$

21. $\dfrac{x^2 + 1}{n^2x - 2n} - \dfrac{1}{2 - nx} = \dfrac{x}{n}$; for x $\quad x = -1, x = \dfrac{n + 1}{n - 1}$

2. $x = \pm\sqrt{\dfrac{3y^2 + 5}{2}} = \pm\dfrac{\sqrt{6y^2 + 10}}{2}$ $\qquad$ **5.** $b = \dfrac{\pm\sqrt{12c^2 - 2a^2}}{3}$

7. $w = \dfrac{ab \pm b\sqrt{a^2 - 40}}{5}$ $\qquad$ **9.** $x = \dfrac{5k \pm \sqrt{25k^2 - 144k}}{6k}$

16. $x = \dfrac{a - b + c \pm \sqrt{a^2 - 2ab - 2ac + b^2 + 2bc + c^2}}{2}$ $\qquad$ **32.** 12m by 17m

Refer to the diagram of a right triangle and use the Pythagorean theorem.

22. $c = 20$, $a = 12$; find b $\quad b = 16$

23. $c = 26$, $b = 10$; find a $\quad a = 24$

24. $b = 2\sqrt{3}$, $a = 5$; find c $\quad c = \sqrt{37}$

25. $a = 3\sqrt{2}$, $b = 7$; find c $\quad c = \sqrt{67}$

26. $c = 10$, $b = \sqrt{17}$; find a $\quad a = \sqrt{83}$

27. $c = 11$, $b = \sqrt{26}$; find a $\quad a = \sqrt{95}$

28. $c = 41$, $b = 40$; find a $\quad a = 9$

29. The area of a rectangle is 154 square meters. The length is 3 meters longer than the width. Find the dimensions of the rectangle. $\quad$ 11m × 14m

30. The area of a rectangle is 117 square meters. The length is 4 meters longer than the width. Find the dimensions of the rectangle. $\quad$ 9m by 13m

31. The area of a triangle is 112 square meters. The base is 4 meters longer than four times the altitude. Find the length of both the altitude and the base of the triangle. $\quad$ 7m by 32m

32. The area of a triangle is 102 square meters. The altitude is 7 meters shorter than double the length of the base. Find the length of both the altitude and the base of the triangle.

33. Melissa took a trip in her car and drove for 7 hours. During the first 120 miles she traveled at an average speed of 5 mph slower than during the last 180 miles. How fast did she travel during the 120-mile portion? During the 180-mile portion?

34. Marcia rode in a powerboat for 4 hours. For the first 18 miles her average speed was 2 mph faster than for the last 14 miles. How fast did the boat travel during the 18-mile stretch? During the 14-mile stretch?

35. The diagonal of a rectangle is 10 feet long. If the rectangle is 2 feet longer than it is wide, find the area of the rectangle.

33. 40 mph during first 120 miles, 45 mph during last 180 miles
34. 9 mph on 18 mile stretch, 7 mph on 14 mile stretch **35.** 48 sq ft

Topic	Procedure	Examples
Standard form of a quadratic equation, p. 338	A quadratic equation in standard form is an equation of the form $ax^2 + bx + c = 0$ where a, b, and c are real numbers and $a \neq 0$. It is often necessary to remove parentheses and clear away fractions by multiplying each term of the equation by the LCD in order to obtain standard form.	Place in standard form: $$\frac{2}{x-3} + \frac{x}{x+3} = \frac{5}{x^2-9}$$ $$\left[(x+3)(x-3)\left[\frac{2}{x-3}\right] + (x+3)(x-3)\left[\frac{x}{x+3}\right]\right.$$ $$= (x+3)(x-3)\left[\frac{5}{(x+3)(x-3)}\right]$$ $$2(x+3) + x(x-3) = 5$$ $$2x + 6 + x^2 - 3x = 5$$ $$\boxed{x^2 - 1x + 1 = 0}$$
Solving a quadratic equation by factoring, p. 339	1. Put the equation in standard form. 2. Factor, if possible. 3. Set each factor equal to 0. 4. Solve each of the resulting equations.	Solve: $$(x+3)(x-2) = 5(x+3)$$ $$x^2 - 2x + 3x - 6 = 5x + 15$$ $$x^2 + x - 6 = 5x + 15$$ $$x^2 + x - 5x - 6 - 15 = 0$$ $$x^2 - 4x - 21 = 0$$ $$(x-7)(x+3) = 0$$ $$\boxed{x = 7 \quad or \quad x = -3.}$$
Solving a quadratic equation by taking the square root of each side of the equation, p. 345	If $x^2 = a$, then $x = \pm\sqrt{a}$.	Solve: $$2x^2 - 50 = 0$$ $$2x^2 = 50$$ $$x^2 = 25$$ $$x = \pm\sqrt{25}$$ $$x = \boxed{\pm 5}$$
Solving a quadratic equation by completing the square, p. 348	1. Put the equation in the form $ax^2 + bx = -c$. 2. If $a \neq 1$, divide each term of the equation by a. 3. Square half of the numerical coefficient of the linear term. Add the result to both sides of the equation. 4. Factor the left side, then take the square root of both sides of the equation. 5. Solve each resulting equation for x.	Solve: $$2x^2 - 4x - 1 = 0$$ $$2x^2 - 4x = 1$$ $$\frac{2x^2}{2} - \frac{4x}{2} = \frac{1}{2}$$ $$x^2 - 2x + \rule{1cm}{0.4pt} = \frac{1}{2} + \rule{1cm}{0.4pt}$$ $$x^2 - 2x + 1 = \frac{1}{2} + 1$$ $$(x-1)^2 = \frac{3}{2}$$ $$x - 1 = \pm\sqrt{\frac{3}{2}}$$ $$= \frac{\pm\sqrt{6}}{2}$$ $$\boxed{x = 1 \pm \frac{1}{2}\sqrt{6}}$$

Topic	Procedure	Examples
Solve a quadratic equation by using the quadratic formula, p. 352	If $ax^2 + bx + c = 0$, where $a \neq 0$, $$x = \frac{-b \pm \sqrt{b^2 - 4ac}}{2a}$$ 1. Put the equation in standard form: 2. Determine the values of a, b, and c. 3. Substitute the values of a, b, and c into the formula. 4. Simplify the result to obtain the two values of x. 5. Any imaginary solutions to the quadratic equation should be simplified by using the definition $\sqrt{-a} = i\sqrt{a}$ where $a > 0$.	Solve: $$2x^2 = 3x - 2$$ $$2x^2 - 3x + 2 = 0$$ $a = 2, b = -3, c = 2$ $$x = \frac{-(-3) \pm \sqrt{(-3)^2 - 4(2)(2)}}{2(2)}$$ $$x = \frac{3 \pm \sqrt{9 - 16}}{4}$$ $$x = \frac{3 \pm \sqrt{-7}}{4}$$ $$x = \frac{3 \pm i\sqrt{7}}{4}$$
Solving radical equations, p. 358	1. Perform algebraic operations to obtain one radical by itself on one side of the equation. 2. If the equation contains square roots, square each side of the equation. Otherwise, raise each side to the appropriate power for third- and higher-order roots. 3. Simplify, if possible. 4. If the equation still contains a radical, repeat steps 1–3. 5. Solve the resulting equation. 6. Check all apparent solutions! Solutions to radical equations must be verified.	Solve: $$x = \sqrt{2x + 9} - 3$$ $$x + 3 = \sqrt{2x + 9}$$ $$(x + 3)^2 = (\sqrt{2x + 9})^2$$ $$x^2 + 6x + 9 = 2x + 9$$ $$x^2 + 6x - 2x + 9 - 9 = 0$$ $$x^2 + 4x = 0$$ $$x(x + 4) = 0$$ $x = 0$ or $x = -4$ Check: $x = 0$: $0 \overset{?}{=} \sqrt{2(0) + 9} - 3$ $\qquad\quad 0 \overset{?}{=} \sqrt{9} - 3$ $\qquad\quad 0 = 3 - 3 \checkmark$ $x = -4$: $0 \overset{?}{=} \sqrt{2(-4) + 9} - 3$ $\qquad\qquad 0 \overset{?}{=} \sqrt{1} - 3$ $\qquad\qquad 0 \neq -2$ $x = 0$ is the only solution.
Equations that can be transferred to quadratic form, p. 362	1. Replace the variable with the smallest exponent by y. 2. If possible, replace the variable with the largest exponent by y^2. (You will need to verify that this is correct.) 3. Solve the resulting equation for y. 4. Replace y by the substitution used in step 1. 5. Solve the resulting equation for x. 6. Check your solution, in the *original* equation.	Solve: $x^{2/3} - x^{1/3} - 2 = 0$. Let $y = x^{1/3}$ and $y^2 = x^{2/3}$. $$y^2 - y - 2 = 0$$ $$(y - 2)(y + 1) = 0$$ $y = 2$ or $y = -1$ $x^{1/3} = 2$ or $x^{1/3} = -1$ $(x^{1/3})^3 = 2^3 \qquad (x^{1/3})^3 = (-1)^3$ $\quad x = 8 \qquad\qquad x = -1$ *Check:* $x = 8$: $(8)^{2/3} - (8)^{1/3} - 2 \overset{?}{=} 0$ $\qquad\quad 2^2 - 2 - 2 \overset{?}{=} 0$ $\qquad\quad 4 - 4 \overset{?}{=} 0 \checkmark$ $x = -1$: $(-1)^{2/3} - (-1)^{1/3} - 2 \overset{?}{=} 0$ $\qquad\qquad (-1)^2 - (-1) - 2 \overset{?}{=} 0$ $\qquad\qquad 1 + 1 - 2 = 0 \checkmark$ Both $x = 8$ and $x = -1$ are solutions.

Topic	Procedure	Examples
Solving quadratic equations containing two or more variables, p. 367	Treat the letter to be solved for as a variable, but treat all other letters as constants. Solve the equation by factoring, by taking the square root of each side, or by the quadratic formula.	Solve for x: (a) $6x^2 - 11xw + 4w^2 = 0$ (b) $4x^2 + 5b = 2w^2$ (c) $2x^2 + 3xz - 10z = 0$ (a) By factoring: $\quad (3x - 4w)(2x - w) = 0$ $\quad 3x - 4w = 0 \quad or \quad 2x - w = 0$ $\quad\quad 3x = 4w \quad\quad\quad 2x = w$ $\quad x = \dfrac{4w}{3}, \quad\quad\quad x = \dfrac{w}{2}$ (b) By taking a square root: $\quad 4x^2 = 2w^2 - 5b$ $\quad x^2 = \dfrac{2w^2 - 5b}{4}$ $\quad x = \pm\sqrt{\dfrac{2w^2 - 5b}{4}}$ $\quad x = \pm\dfrac{1}{2}\sqrt{2w^2 - 5b}$ (c) By the quadratic formula, $a = 2$, $b = 3z$, $c = -10z$: $\quad x = \dfrac{-3z \pm \sqrt{9z^2 - 4(2)(-10z)}}{2(2)}$ $\quad x = \dfrac{-3z \pm \sqrt{9z^2 + 80z}}{4}$
The Pythagorean theorem, p. 370	In any right triangle if c is the length of the hypotenuse while a and b are the lengths of the two legs, then $c^2 = a^2 + b^2$	Find a if $c = 7$ and $b = 5$. $49 = a^2 + 25$ $49 - 25 = a^2$ $24 = a^2$ $\sqrt{24} = a$ $2\sqrt{6} = a$

REVIEW PROBLEMS CHAPTER 7

Solve and express any complex solutions in i notation.

1. $3x^2 - 8x + 6 = 0$

$\dfrac{4 \pm i\sqrt{2}}{3}$

2. $4x^2 - 12x + 9 = 0$

$\dfrac{3}{2}$

3. $11x - 7x^2 = 2x$

$0, \dfrac{9}{7}$

4. $8x^2 - 26x + 15 = 0$

$\dfrac{3}{4}, \dfrac{5}{2}$

5. $12x^2 + 35 = 8x^2 + 15$

$\pm i\sqrt{5}$

6. $9x^2 + 27 = 0$

$\pm i\sqrt{3}$

7. $x^2 + 4x + 4 = 36$

$-8, 4$

8. $25x^2 - 10x + 1 = 1$

$0, \dfrac{2}{5}$

9. $2x^2 - 15 = -x$

$\dfrac{5}{2}, -3$

10. $6x^2 + 12x - 24 = 0$

$-1 \pm \sqrt{5}$

11. $4x^2 - 3x + 2 = 0$

$\dfrac{3 \pm i\sqrt{23}}{8}$

12. $3x^2 + 5x + 1 = 0$

$\dfrac{-5 \pm \sqrt{13}}{6}$

13. $3x(3x + 2) - 2 = 3x$

$-\dfrac{2}{3}, \dfrac{1}{3}$

14. $10x(x - 2) + 10 = 2x$

$\dfrac{11 \pm \sqrt{21}}{10}$

15. $\dfrac{(x + 2)^2}{5} + 2x = -9$

-7

16. $\dfrac{(x - 2)^2}{20} + x = -3$

-8

17. $\frac{5}{6}x^2 - x + \frac{1}{3} = 0$

$\frac{3 \pm i}{5}$

18. $\frac{4}{5}x^2 + x + \frac{1}{5} = 0$

$-\frac{1}{4}, -1$

19. $y + \frac{5}{3y} + \frac{17}{6} = 0$

$-\frac{5}{6}, -2$

20. $\frac{19}{y} - \frac{15}{y^2} + 10 = 0$

$-\frac{5}{2}, \frac{3}{5}$

21. $\frac{15}{y^2} - \frac{2}{y} = 1$

$-5, 3$

22. $y - 18 + \frac{81}{y} = 0$

9

23. $(3y + 2)(y - 1) = 7(-y + 1)$

$-3, 1$

24. $y(y + 1) + (y + 2)^2 = 4$

$0, -\frac{5}{2}$

25. $\frac{2x}{x + 3} + \frac{3x - 1}{x + 1} = 3$

$-2, 3$

26. $\frac{4x + 1}{2x + 5} + \frac{3x}{x + 4} = 2$

$-3, 2$

Solve and check your solution(s).

27. $\sqrt{2x + 1} = 2x - 5$

4

28. $1 + \sqrt{3x + 1} = x$

5

29. $\sqrt{3x + 1} - \sqrt{2x - 1} = 1$

$5, 1$

30. $\sqrt{7x + 2} = \sqrt{x + 3} + \sqrt{2x - 1}$

$1, \frac{3}{2}$

Solve for any valid real roots.

31. $x^4 - 6x^2 + 8 = 0$

$\pm 2, \pm\sqrt{2}$

32. $2x^6 - 5x^3 - 3 = 0$

$x = \frac{-\sqrt[3]{4}}{2}, \sqrt[3]{3}$

33. $3x^{1/2} - 11x^{1/4} = 4$

256

34. $x^{2/3} + 9x^{1/3} = -8$

$-512, -1$

35. $(2x - 5)^2 + 4(2x - 5) + 3 = 0$

$1, 2$

36. $1 + 4x^{-8} = 5x^{-4}$

$\pm 1, \pm\sqrt{2}$

Solve for the variable specified. Assume that all radical expressions obtained have a positive radicand.

37. $A = \frac{2B^2C}{3H}$; for B

$B = \pm\sqrt{\frac{3AH}{2C}}$

38. $PV = 5x^2 + 3y^2 + 2x$; for x

$x = \frac{-1 \pm \sqrt{1 - 15y^2 + 5PV}}{5}$

39. $20d^2 - xd - x^2 = 0$; for d

$d = \frac{x}{4}, \frac{-x}{5}$

40. $2H = 3g(a^2 + b^2)$; for b

$b = \pm\sqrt{\frac{2H}{3g} - a^2}$

Use the Pythagorean theorem to find the missing side. Assume that c is the length of the hypotenuse of a right triangle and a and b are the lengths of the legs.

41. $a = 3\sqrt{2}$, $b = 2$; find c

$c = \sqrt{22}$

42. $c = 16$, $b = 4$; find a

$a = 4\sqrt{15}$

43. The area of a rectangle is 203 square meters. Its length is 1 meter longer than four times its width. Find the length and width of the rectangle.

Width = 7m, Length = 29m

44. The area of a triangle is 70 square centimeters. Its altitude is 6 meters longer than twice the length of the base. Find the dimensions of the altitude and base.

Base = 7 cm
Alt = 20 cm

45. Jessica had driven at a constant speed for 200 miles. Then it started to rain. So for the next 90 miles she traveled 5 miles per hour slower. The entire trip took 6 hours of driving time. Find her speed for each part of the trip.

50 mph 1st part, 45 mph during rain

46. John rode in a motorboat for 60 miles at constant cruising speed to get to his fishing grounds. Then for 5 miles he trolled to catch fish. His trolling speed was 15 miles per hour slower than his cruising speed. The trip took 4 hours. Find his speed for each part of the trip.

20 mph cruising
5 mph trolling

Solve. Simplify any imaginary numbers by using i notation.

1. $6x^2 - 5x - 4 = 0$

2. $x^2 - 10x + 25 = 0$

3. $2x^2 - 98 = 0$

4. $3x^2 - 15 = 0$

5. $3x^2 - 6x - 4 = 0$

6. $2x^2 + 7x - 2 = 0$

7. $(x - 5)(x + 2) = (x + 4)(2x - 5)$

8. $2x(x - 5) = x - 12$

9. $2x^2 - \dfrac{7}{3}x = \dfrac{10}{3}$

10. $3x^2 - 6x + 15 = 0$

1. $\dfrac{4}{3}, -\dfrac{1}{2}$

2. 5

3. $7, -7$

4. $\pm\sqrt{5}$

5. $\dfrac{3 \pm \sqrt{21}}{3}$

6. $\dfrac{-7 \pm \sqrt{65}}{4}$

7. $-3 + \sqrt{19}$

8. $\dfrac{3}{2}, 4$

9. $-\dfrac{5}{6}, 2$

10. $1 \pm 2i$

11. $\dfrac{1 \pm i\sqrt{15}}{2}$

11. $3x^2 - 3x + 12 = 0$

12. $\dfrac{2}{3}x^2 + \dfrac{5}{6}x - 1 = 0$

12. $\dfrac{3}{4}, -2$

13. $\dfrac{\pm 3i\sqrt{5}}{5}$

13. $5x^2 - 7x + 12 = 3 - 7x$

14. $x(x - 3) = 18 - 3x$

14. $\pm 3\sqrt{2}$

15. $x^2 = 3(2x + 1)$

16. $4x^2 - 28x + 49 = 0$

15. $3 \pm 2\sqrt{3}$

16. $\dfrac{7}{2}$

17. $\dfrac{1}{y + 2} + \dfrac{1}{y - 4} = \dfrac{-1}{4}$

18. $\dfrac{3y - 1}{y + 3} + 3 = \dfrac{4y}{y - 3}$

17. $-8, 2$

18. $12, -1$

19. $\dfrac{7}{10y} - \dfrac{1}{10} = \dfrac{1}{y^2}$

20. $\dfrac{21}{4y^2} + \dfrac{1}{y} = \dfrac{1}{4}$

19. $5, 2$

20. $7, -3$

Solve and check your solution(s). List only valid solutions.

1. $\sqrt{x-3} = x - 5$

2. $\sqrt{5x+9} = x - 1$

3. $2 + \sqrt{x} = \sqrt{3x+4}$

4. $\sqrt{3x+1} + 1 = \sqrt{x}$

5. $\sqrt{7x-2} = \sqrt{x+1} + \sqrt{3}$

6. $\sqrt[3]{x^2+4x} = \sqrt[3]{x+4}$

Solve for any valid real roots.

7. $3x^8 - 8 = 10x^4$

8. $12x^6 = 5x^3 + 2$

9. $(x^2 + 2x)^2 - (x^2 + 2x) = 6$

10. $x^{2/3} + 3x^{1/3} = 10$

11. $2x^{1/2} - 10x^{1/4} + 12 = 0$

12. $x^{-2/3} + 2x^{-1/3} + 1 = 0$

---

1. $x = 7$

2. $x = 8$

3. $x = 0$
$x = 4$

4. No solution

5. $x = 2$

6. $x = -4$
$x = +1$

7. $x = \pm\sqrt[4]{4}$ These are the only real roots

8. $x = \dfrac{-\sqrt[3]{2}}{2}$
$x = \dfrac{\sqrt[3]{18}}{3}$

9. $x = -3, 1$ These are the only real roots

10. $x = -125, 8$

11. $x = 81, 16$

12. $x = -1$

13. $x = \pm\sqrt{\dfrac{A - 2by^2}{2b}}$

14. $a = \pm\dfrac{\sqrt{3\pi H}}{\pi}$

15. $w = \dfrac{1}{2x}, \dfrac{-5}{3x}$

$y = \dfrac{-(a + 3) \pm \sqrt{a^2 + 6a + 9 + 40x^2}}{10x^2}$
16.

17. $c = \sqrt{79}$

18. $b = 2\sqrt{6}$

Solve for the variable specified.

13. $A = 2b(x^2 + y^2)$; for x

14. $H = \dfrac{1}{3}\pi a^2$; for a

15. $6x^2w^2 + 7xw - 5 = 0$; for w

16. $5x^2y^2 + (3 + a)y - 2 = 0$; for y

Use the diagram for a right triangle for problems 17 and 18. Simplify your answers.

17. $a = 5\sqrt{3}$, $b = 2$; find c

18. $a = 5$, $c = 7$; find b

Solve the quadratic equations and simplify your answers. Use i notation for any imaginary numbers.

1. $5x^2 - 7x = 0$

2. $3x^2 + 5x = 2$

3. $\dfrac{3x}{2} - \dfrac{8}{3} = \dfrac{2}{3x}$

4. $x(x - 8) + 16 = 8(x - 6)$

5. $5x^2 - 2 = 48$

6. $\dfrac{2x}{2x + 1} - \dfrac{6}{4x^2 - 1} = \dfrac{x + 1}{2x - 1}$

7. $2x(x - 3) = -3$

Solve and check your solution(s).

8. $\sqrt{4x + 3} = 2x$

9. $2 + \sqrt{x + 10} = x$

10. $5 - \sqrt{x - 1} = \sqrt{x + 4}$

1. $0, \dfrac{7}{5}$

2. $\dfrac{1}{3}, -2$

3. $2, -\dfrac{2}{9}$

4. 8

5. $\pm\sqrt{10}$

6. $\dfrac{7}{2}, -1$

7. $\dfrac{3 \pm \sqrt{3}}{2}$

8. $\dfrac{3}{2}$

9. 6

10. 5

11. $\pm\sqrt{7}, \pm\sqrt{2}$

12. $\dfrac{1}{5}, -\dfrac{3}{4}$

13. $(1 \pm \sqrt{13})^3$

14. $z = \pm\sqrt{\dfrac{xyw}{B}}$

15. $y = \dfrac{-b \pm \sqrt{b^2 - 30w}}{5}$

16. $c = 4\sqrt{3}$

17. Width = 5 miles,
Length = 16 miles

18. 2 mph during 1st part
3 mph after lunch

Solve for any valid real roots.

11. $x^4 - 9x^2 + 14 = 0$

12. $3x^{-2} - 11x^{-1} - 20 = 0$

13. $x^{2/3} - 2x^{1/3} - 12 = 0$

Solve for the variable specified.

14. $B = \dfrac{xyw}{z^2}$; for z

15. $5y^2 + 2by + 6w = 0$; for y

16. Find the hypotenuse of a right triangle if the lengths of its legs are 6 and $2\sqrt{3}$.

17. The area of a rectangle is 80 square miles. Its length is 1 mile longer than three times its width. Find its length and width.

18. Shirley and Bill paddled a canoe at a constant speed for 6 miles. They rested, had lunch, and then paddled 1 mile per hour faster for an additional 3 miles. The entire trip took 4 hours. How fast did they paddle during each part of the trip?

Approximately one-half of this test is based on the content of Chapters 1–6. The remainder is based on the content of Chapter 7.

1. Simplify: $(-3x^{-2}y^3)^4$.

1. $\dfrac{81y^{12}}{x^8}$

2. Collect like terms:
$$\frac{1}{2}a^3 - 2a^2 + 3a - \frac{1}{4}a^3 - 6a + a^2.$$

2. $\dfrac{1}{4}a^3 - a^2 - 3a$

3. Solve for y: $a(2y + b) = 3ay - 4$.

3. $y = \dfrac{ab + 4}{a}$

4. Graph: $6x - 3y = -12$.

x	y
0	4
−2	0

4. $6x - 3y = -12$

5. Write the equation of a line parallel to $2y + x = 8$ and passing through $(6, -1)$.

6. Find the volume of a sphere of radius 2 inches.

5. $x + 2y = 4$

6. $\dfrac{32\pi}{3}$

7. Factor: $125x^3 - 27y^3$.

8. Simplify: $\sqrt{48x^4y^5}$.

7. $(5x - 3y)(25x^2 + 15xy + 9y^2)$

8. $4x^2y^2\sqrt{3y}$

9. $4\sqrt{6} + 5\sqrt{3}$

10. $\dfrac{5\sqrt{7}}{7}$

11. $0, \dfrac{3}{5}$

12. $\dfrac{1}{3}, -5$

13. $x = \dfrac{3 \pm 2\sqrt{3}}{2}$

14. $x = \dfrac{2 \pm i\sqrt{11}}{3}$

15. $x = 16$

16. $x = -27, -216$

17. $y = \dfrac{-5w \pm \sqrt{25w^2 + 56z}}{4}$

18. $y = \pm\sqrt{\dfrac{5w - 16z^2}{3}}$

19. $x = \sqrt{15}$

20. Base = 5 meters
Altitude = 18 meters

---

9. Multiply: $(3 + \sqrt{2})(\sqrt{6} + \sqrt{3})$.

10. Rationalize the denominator. $\dfrac{5}{\sqrt{7}}$

Solve and simplify your answer. Use the i notation for imaginary numbers.

11. $5x^2 + 12x = 15x$

12. $3x^2 + 14x = 5$

13. $44 = 3(2x - 3)^2 + 8$

14. $3 - \dfrac{4}{x} + \dfrac{5}{x^2} = 0$

Solve and check.

15. $\sqrt{x - 12} = \sqrt{x} - 2$

16. $x^{2/3} + 9x^{1/3} + 18 = 0$

Solve for y.

17. $2y^2 + 5wy - 7z = 0$

18. $3y^2 + 16z^2 = 5w$

19. The hypotenuse of a right triangle is $\sqrt{31}$. One leg of a triangle is 4. Find the length of the other leg.

20. A triangle has an area of 45 square meters. The altitude is 3 meters longer than three times the length of the base. Find each dimension.

Graphs and Functions

Photographing celestial bodies is an important part of astronomy. An astronomer's job, whether indoors, in an observatory, or in a laboratory, is rich in mathematics.

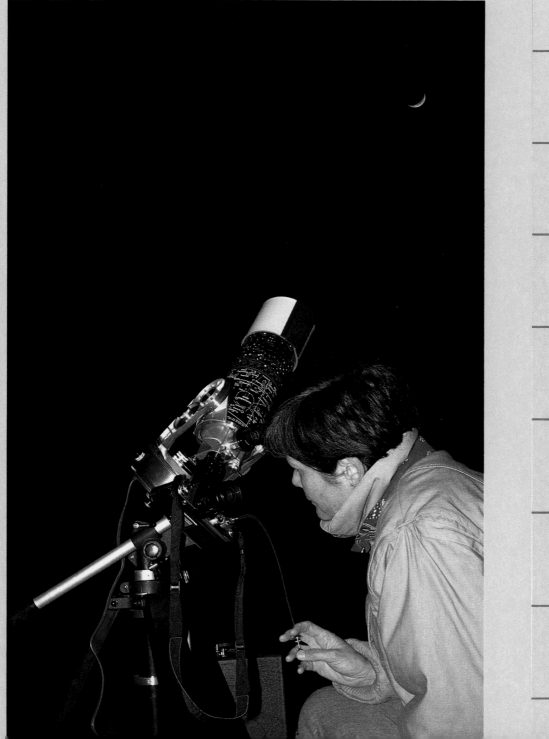

8

PRETEST CHAPTER 8

If you are familiar with the topics in this chapter, take this test now. Check your answers with those in the back of the book. If an answer was wrong or you couldn't do a problem, study the appropriate section of the chapter.

If you are not familiar with the topics in this chapter, don't take this test now. Instead, study the examples, work the practice problems, and then take the test.

This test will help you identify those concepts that you have mastered and those that need more study.

Section 8.1

1. Find the distance between $(-6, -2)$ and $(-3, 4)$. $d = 3\sqrt{5}$
2. Write the equation of a circle in standard form with a center at $(8, -2)$ and a radius of $\sqrt{7}$. $(x - 8)^2 + (y + 2)^2 = 7$
3. Put the equation of the circle $x^2 + y^2 - 2x - 4y + 1 = 0$ in standard form. Find its center and radius and sketch the graph.

Section 8.2

4. Graph the parabola $x = -2(y + 1)^2 + 4$. Label the vertex and the x-intercept.
5. Put the equation of the parabola $x^2 = y + 4x - 1$ in standard form. Determine its vertex and graph the parabola.

Section 8.3 Graph each ellipse and label the centers and four other points.

6. $4x^2 + y^2 - 36 = 0$
7. $\dfrac{(x + 3)^2}{25} + \dfrac{(y - 1)^2}{16} = 1$

Section 8.4 Locate the center and vertices of each hyperbola and graph the hyperbola.

8. $25y^2 - 49x^2 = 1225$
9. $\dfrac{(x - 2)^2}{4} - \dfrac{(y + 1)^2}{9} = 1$

Section 8.5

10. $R = \{(3, 7), (3, 8), (2, 7), (2, -7)\}$
    (a) What is the *domain* of R?
    (b) What is the *range* of R?
    (c) Is the relation R a *function*?
11. Does this graph represent a function? Yes

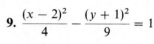

12. For $f(x) = 5x^2 + 2x - 3$, find
    (a) $f(-2)$ 13
    (b) $f(a)$ $5a^2 + 2a - 3$
    (c) $f(a + 1)$ $5a^2 + 12a + 4$

13.

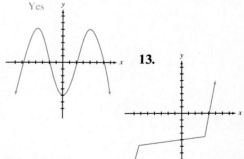

Section 8.6

13. Does this graph represent a one-to-one function? Yes
14. Determine the inverse of the function $F = \{(7, 1), (6, 3), (2, -1), (-1, -5)\}$
15. Find the inverse of $g(x) = 3 - 5x$ and graph $g(x)$ and its inverse on the same set of axes.

9.

15.

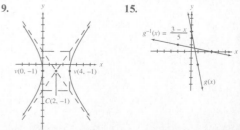

3.

$(x - 1)^2 + (y - 2)^2 = 4$
Center (1, 2)
Radius 2

4.

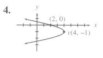
$(2, 0)$
$v(4, -1)$

5.

$(0, 1)$
$v(2, -3)$
$y = (x - 2)^2 - 3$

6.

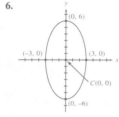
$(0, 6)$
$(-3, 0)$ $(3, 0)$
$C(0, 0)$
$(0, -6)$

7.

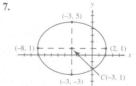
$(-3, 5)$
$(-8, 1)$ $(2, 1)$
$(-3, -3)$ $C(-3, 1)$

8.

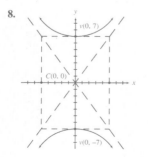
$v(0, 7)$
$C(0, 0)$
$v(0, -7)$

10. (a) $D = \{3, 2\}$ (b) $R = \{7, 8, -7\}$ (c) No
14. $F^{-1} = \{(1, 7), (3, 6), (-1, 2), (-5, -1)\}$

16. $y = x^2 + 1$ $(0, 1)$
      $4y^2 = 4 - x^2$

17. $x^2 + y^2 = 9$ $\left(\dfrac{\sqrt{35}}{5}, \dfrac{2\sqrt{65}}{5}\right)\left(\dfrac{\sqrt{35}}{5}, -\dfrac{2\sqrt{65}}{5}\right)\left(-\dfrac{\sqrt{35}}{5}, \dfrac{2\sqrt{65}}{5}\right)\left(-\dfrac{\sqrt{35}}{5}, -\dfrac{2\sqrt{65}}{5}\right)$
      $4x^2 + y^2 = 16$

INTRODUCTION

In this chapter we'll talk about four special geometric figures—the circle, the parabola, the ellipse, and the hyperbola. These shapes are called **conic sections** because they can be formed by slicing a cone with a plane. We'll discuss their equations and graphs. The equation of any conic is of degree 2.

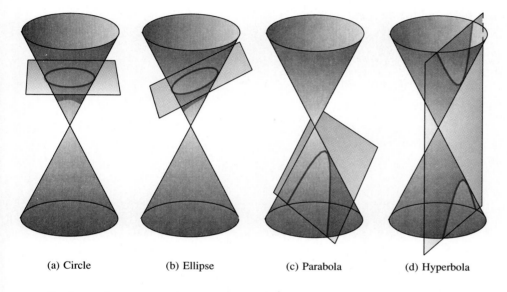

(a) Circle   (b) Ellipse   (c) Parabola   (d) Hyperbola

Conic sections are an important and interesting subject. An entire branch of mathematics, called analytic geometry, is concerned with conic sections. Physics and engineering also make extensive use of them. For example, satellite transmission "dishes" have parabolic shapes, the orbits of planets and comets are ellipses or hyperbolas; the path of a ball, rocket, or bullet is a parabola (if we neglect air resistance), and there are many other applications.

8.1 THE DISTANCE FORMULA AND THE CIRCLE

☐ After studying this section, you will be able to:

1 *Find the distance between two points*

2 *Find the center and radius of a circle and graph the circle if the equation is in standard form*

3 *Write the equation of a circle in standard form when given its center and radius*

4 *Place an equation of a circle in standard form*

1 Before we investigate the conic sections, we need to know how to find the distance between two points in the x–y plane. We will derive a *distance formula* and use it to find the equations for the conic sections.

Recall from Chapter 1 that to find the distance between two points, we simply subtract the values of the points. For example, the distance from -3 to 5 on the x-axis is

$$|5 - (-3)| = |5 + 3| = 8$$

Remember that absolute value is another name for distance. We could have written

$$|-3 - (5)| = |-8| = 8$$

Similarly, the distance from -3 to 5 on the y-axis is

$$|5 - (-3)| = 8$$

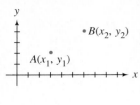

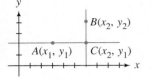

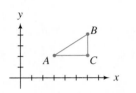

Now, we want to use this simple fact to find the distance between points in the x–y plane. For example, what is the distance between the points $(3, -1)$ and $(-4, 0)$? between $(-\frac{1}{2}, -5)$ and $(26, 10)$?

Let $A(x_1, y_1)$ and $B(x_2, y_2)$ be points on a graph. Let's find the distance from A to B. First we draw a horizontal line through A, and then we draw a vertical line through B. (We could have drawn a horizontal line through B and a vertical line through A.) The lines intersect a point $C(x_2, y_1)$. (Why are the coordinates x_2, y_1?) You should be able to see that the distance from A to C is $x_2 - x_1$, and from B to C is $y_2 - y_1$.

Now if we draw a line from A to B, we have right triangle ABC. We can use the Pythagorean theorem to find the length (distance) of the line. By the Pythagorean theorem,

$$(AB)^2 = (AC)^2 + (BC)^2$$

Let's rename the distance AB as d. Then

$$d^2 = (x_2 - x_1)^2 + (y_2 - y_1)^2$$

and

$$d = \sqrt{(x_2 - x_1)^2 + (y_2 - y_1)^2}$$

This is the distance formula.

Distance Formula

The distance between two points (x_1, y_1) and (x_2, y_2) is

$$d = \sqrt{(x_2 - x_1)^2 + (y_2 - y_1)^2}$$

Example 1 Find the distance between $(3, -4)$ and $(-2, -5)$.

$$d = \sqrt{(x_2 - x_1)^2 + (y_2 - y_1)^2} = \sqrt{[-5 - (-4)]^2 + [-2 - 3]^2}$$
$$= \sqrt{(-5 + 4)^2 + (-5)^2} = \sqrt{(-1)^2 + (-5)^2}$$
$$= \sqrt{1 + 25} = \sqrt{26} \quad \blacksquare$$

Practice Problem 1 Find the distance between $(-6, -2)$ and $(3, 1)$. Simplify your answer. $\blacksquare$

Example 2 Find x if the distance between $(x, 3)$ and $(2, 5)$ is $\sqrt{5}$.

$$\sqrt{5} = \sqrt{(2 - x)^2 + (5 - 3)^2}$$
$$\sqrt{5} = \sqrt{(2 - x)^2 + (2)^2}$$
$$\sqrt{5} = \sqrt{4 - 4x + x^2 + 4}$$
$$\sqrt{5} = \sqrt{x^2 - 4x + 8}$$

Squaring each side, we have

$$5 = x^2 - 4x + 8$$
$$0 = x^2 - 4x + 3$$
$$0 = (x - 3)(x - 1)$$
$$x = 3 \quad \text{and} \quad x = 1$$

The two solutions are $x = 3$ and $x = 1$. The points $(3, 3)$ and $(1, 3)$ are $\sqrt{5}$ units from $(2, 5)$. $\blacksquare$

Practice Problem 2 Find y if the distance between $(2, y)$ and $(1, 7)$ is $\sqrt{10}$ units. $\blacksquare$

2 The Circle

A **circle** is defined as the set of all points in a plane that are at a fixed distance from a point in that plane. The fixed distance is called the **radius**, and the point is called the **center** of the circle.

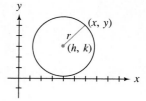

We can use the distance formula to find the equation of a circle. Let a circle of radius r have a center at (h, k). For any point (x, y) on the circle, the distance formula tells us that

$$\sqrt{(x - h)^2 + (y - k)^2} = r$$

Squaring each side gives

$$(x - h)^2 + (y - k)^2 = r^2$$

This is the equation of a circle with center at (h, k) and radius r.

> **Equation of a Circle in Standard Form**
>
> The equation of a circle with center at (h, k) and radius r is
> $$(x - h)^2 + (y - k)^2 = r^2$$

Example 3 Find the center and radius of the circle $(x - 3)^2 + (y - 4)^2 = 25$. Then sketch its graph.

From the equation of a circle, $(x - h)^2 + (y - k)^2 = r^2$, we see that $(h, k) = (3, 4)$. Thus, the center of the circle is at $(3, 4)$. Since $r^2 = 25$, the radius of the circle is $r = 5$. The sketch of this circle is shown. ■

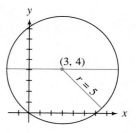

Practice Problem 3 Find the center and radius of the circle $(x + 1)^2 + (y + 2)^2 = 9$. Then sketch its graph. ■

3 Example 4 Write the equation of a circle with center $(-1, 3)$ and radius $\sqrt{5}$. Put your answer in standard form.

We are given that $(h, k) = (-1, 3)$ and $r = \sqrt{5}$. Thus, $(x - h)^2 + (y - k)^2 = r^2$ becomes

$$[x - (-1)]^2 + [y - 3]^2 = (\sqrt{5})^2$$
$$(x + 1)^2 + (y - 3)^2 = 5 \quad ■$$

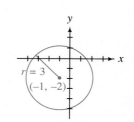

Practice Problem 4 Write the equation of a circle with center at $(-5, 0)$ and radius $= \sqrt{3}$. Leave your answer in standard form. ■

4 Example 5 Write the equation of the circle $x^2 + 2x + y^2 + 6y + 6 = 0$ in standard form. Find the radius and center of the circle and sketch its graph.

If we multiply out the terms in the equation of a circle, we get

$$(x - h)^2 + (y - k)^2 = r^2$$
$$(x^2 - 2hx + h^2) + (y^2 - 2ky + k^2) = r^2$$

Comparing this with the equation

$$(x^2 + 2x) + (y^2 + 6y) = -6$$

suggests that we can complete the square to find the equation of a circle.

$$x^2 + 2x + \underline{\quad} + y^2 + 6y + \underline{\quad} = -6$$
$$x^2 + 2x \boxed{+1} + y^2 + 6y \boxed{+9} = -6 \boxed{+1+9}$$
$$x^2 + 2x + 1 + y^2 + 6y + 9 = 4$$
$$(x + 1)^2 + (y + 3)^2 = 4$$

Thus, the center is at $(-1, -3)$ and the radius is 2. The sketch of the circle is shown. ■

Practice Problem 5 Put the equation of the circle $x^2 + 4x + y^2 + 2y - 20 = 0$ in standard form. Find its radius and center and sketch its graph. ■

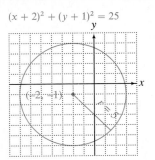

$(x + 2)^2 + (y + 1)^2 = 25$

Find the distance between each pair of points. Simplify your answer.

1. (2, 3) and (3, 5)
$d = \sqrt{(3-2)^2 + (5-3)^2} = \sqrt{5}$

2. (4, 1) and (6, 3)
$d = \sqrt{(6-4)^2 + (3-1)^2} = \sqrt{8} = 2\sqrt{2}$

3. $(-4, 1)$ and $(2, -3)$
$d = \sqrt{(2+4)^2 + (-3-1)^2} = \sqrt{52} = 2\sqrt{13}$

4. $(6, -2)$ and $(-1, 3)$
$d = \sqrt{(6+1)^2 + (-2-3)^2} = \sqrt{74}$

5. $(-7, -1)$ and $(3, -2)$
$d = \sqrt{(3+7)^2 + (-2+1)^2} = \sqrt{101}$

6. $(-2, -6)$ and $(3, -4)$
$d = \sqrt{(3+2)^2 + (-4+6)^2} = \sqrt{29}$

7. (0, 7) and (1, -3)
$d = \sqrt{(1-0)^2 + (-3-7)^2} = \sqrt{101}$

8. $(-5, -6)$ and (2, 0)
$d = \sqrt{(2+5)^2 + (0+6)^2} = \sqrt{85}$

9. $\left(\dfrac{1}{3}, \dfrac{3}{5}\right)$ and $\left(\dfrac{7}{3}, \dfrac{1}{5}\right)$
$d = \sqrt{\left(\dfrac{7}{3} - \dfrac{1}{3}\right)^2 + \left(\dfrac{1}{5} - \dfrac{3}{5}\right)^2} = \sqrt{\dfrac{104}{25}} = \dfrac{2\sqrt{26}}{5}$

10. $\left(-\dfrac{1}{4}, \dfrac{1}{7}\right)$ and $\left(\dfrac{3}{4}, \dfrac{6}{7}\right)$
$d = \sqrt{\left(\dfrac{3}{4} + \dfrac{1}{4}\right)^2 + \left(\dfrac{6}{7} - \dfrac{1}{7}\right)^2} = \dfrac{\sqrt{74}}{7}$

11. (1.3, 2.6) and $(-5.7, 1.6)$
$d = \sqrt{(1.3 + 5.7)^2 + (2.6 - 1.6)^2} = \sqrt{50} = 5\sqrt{2}$

12. (8.2, 3.5) and (6.2, -0.5)
$d = \sqrt{(8.2 - 6.2)^2 + (3.5 + 0.5)^2} = \sqrt{20} = 2\sqrt{5}$

13. $(2\sqrt{3}, -1)$ and $(\sqrt{3}, -2)$
$d = \sqrt{(2\sqrt{3} - \sqrt{3})^2 + (-1 + 2)^2} = \sqrt{4} = 2$

14. $(4, \sqrt{2})$ and $(-1, 3\sqrt{2})$
$d = \sqrt{(-1-4)^2 + (3\sqrt{2} - \sqrt{2})^2}$
$= \sqrt{(-5)^2 + (2\sqrt{2})^2}$
$= \sqrt{25 + 8} = \sqrt{33}$

Find the specified variable so that the distance between

15. (x, 1) and $(-2, 3)$ is 3
$3 = \sqrt{(x+2)^2 + (1-3)^2}$
$9 = x^2 + 4x + 8$
$0 = x^2 + 4x - 1$
$x = \dfrac{-4 \pm \sqrt{16 - 4(1)(-1)}}{2}$
$x = -2 \pm \sqrt{5}$

16. (3, y) and $(3, -5)$ is 9
$9 = \sqrt{(3-3)^2 + (y+5)^2}$
$81 = y^2 + 10y + 25$
$0 = y^2 + 10y - 56$
$0 = (y + 14)(y - 4)$
$y = 4 \quad y = -14$

17. (3, 7) and (6, y) is 5
$5 = \sqrt{(6-3)^2 + (y-7)^2}$
$0 = y^2 - 14y + 33$
$y = 3, y = 11$

18. (1, 7) and $(x, -1)$ is 10
$10 = \sqrt{(x-1)^2 + (-1-7)^2}$
$100 = x^2 - 2x + 65$
$0 = x^2 - 2x - 35$
$x = 7, x = -5$

19. (7, 3) and (x, 6) is $\sqrt{10}$
$\sqrt{10} = \sqrt{(x-7)^2 + (6-3)^2}$
$10 = x^2 - 14x + 58$
$0 = x^2 - 14x + 48$
$x = 6, x = 8$

20. (4, 5) and (2, y) is $\sqrt{5}$
$\sqrt{5} = \sqrt{(2-4)^2 + (y-5)^2}$
$5 = y^2 - 10y + 29$
$0 = y^2 - 10y + 24$
$y = 4, y = 6$

Use the following information to solve problems 21 and 22. An airport is located at point O. A short-range radar tower is located at point R. The maximum range at which the radar can detect a plane is 4 miles out from point R.

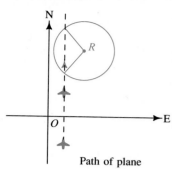

N

R

O ────► E

Path of plane

21. Assume that *R* is 5 miles east of *O* and 7 miles north of *O*. [In other words, *R* is located at the point (5, 7).] An airplane is flying parallel to and 2 miles east of the north axis. (In other words, the plane is flying along the path $x = 2$.) What is the *shortest distance north* of the airport at which the plane can be detected by the radar at *R*? (Round your answer to the nearest tenth of a mile.)

$$4 = \sqrt{(2 - 5)^2 + (y - 7)^2}$$
$$16 = y^2 - 14y + 58$$
$$0 = y^2 - 14y + 42$$
$$y = \frac{14 \pm \sqrt{28}}{2}$$
$$y \approx 4.4 \text{ miles}$$

22. Assume that *R* is 6 miles east of *O* and 6 miles north of *O*. [In other words, *R* is located at the point (6, 6).] An airplane is flying parallel to and 4 miles east of the north axis. (In other words, the plane is flying along the path $x = 4$.) What is the *greatest distance* north of the airport at which the plane can still be detected by the radar at *R*? (Round your answer to the nearest tenth of a mile.)

$$4 = \sqrt{(4 - 6)^2 + (y - 6)^2}$$
$$16 = y^2 - 12y + 40$$
$$0 = y^2 - 12y + 24$$
$$y = \frac{12 \pm \sqrt{48}}{2}$$
$$y \approx 9.5 \text{ miles}$$

Write in standard form the equation of the circle with the given center and radius.

23. Center (6, 3); $r = 8$
$(x - 6)^2 + (y - 3)^2 = 64$

24. Center (2, 5); $r = 7$
$(x - 2)^2 + (y - 5)^2 = 49$

25. Center (7, −4); $r = 2$
$(x - 7)^2 + (y + 4)^2 = 4$

26. Center (6, −9); $r = 3$
$(x - 6)^2 + (y + 9)^2 = 9$

27. Center (−3, −5); $r = \sqrt{2}$
$(x + 3)^2 + (y + 5)^2 = 2$

28. Center (−1, −7); $r = \sqrt{5}$
$(x + 1)^2 + (y + 7)^2 = 5$

29. Center (−6, 0); $r = 13$
$(x + 6)^2 + y^2 = 169$

30. Center (0, −5); $r = 11$
$x^2 + (y + 5)^2 = 121$

31. Center (0, 0); $r = 12$
$x^2 + y^2 = 144$

32. Center (0, 0); $r = 10$
$x^2 + y^2 = 100$

Give the center and radius of each circle. Then graph it.

33. $x^2 + y^2 = 9$

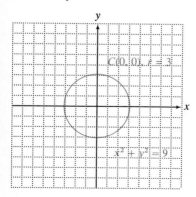

$C(0, 0), r = 3$

$x^2 + y^2 = 9$

34. $x^2 + y^2 = 25$

$C(0, 0), r = 5$

$x^2 + y^2 = 25$

35. $(x - 3)^2 + (y - 2)^2 = 4$

$C(3, 2), r = 2$

$(x - 3)^2 + (y - 2)^2 = 4$

C

36. $(x - 5)^2 + (y - 3)^2 = 16$ **37.** $(x + 2)^2 + (y - 3)^2 = 25$ **38.** $(x - 3)^2 + (y + 4)^2 = 9$

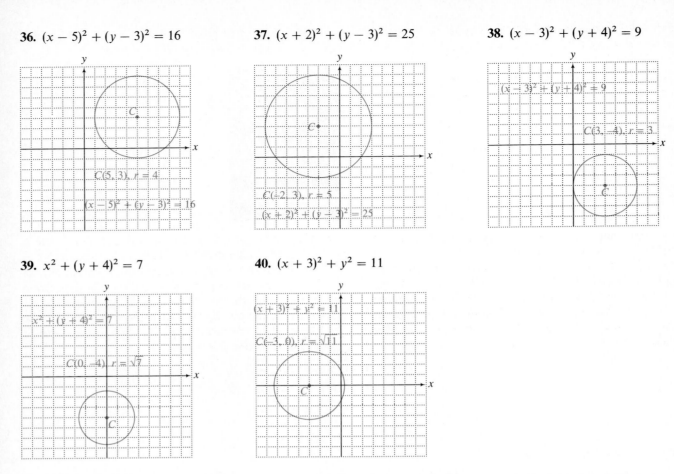

39. $x^2 + (y + 4)^2 = 7$ **40.** $(x + 3)^2 + y^2 = 11$

Put each equation in standard form, using the approach of Example 5. Find the center and radius of each circle.

41. $x^2 + y^2 + 6x - 4y - 3 = 0$

$x^2 + 6x + 9 + y^2 - 4y + 4 = 3 + 9 + 4$
$(x + 3)^2 + (y - 2)^2 = 16$
$C(-3, 2), r = 4$

42. $x^2 + y^2 + 8x - 6y - 24 = 0$

$x^2 + 8x + 16 + y^2 - 6y + 9 = 24 + 16 + 9$
$(x + 4)^2 + (y - 3)^2 = 49$
$C(-4, 3), r = 7$

43. $x^2 + y^2 + 8x + 2y - 8 = 0$

$x^2 + 8x + 16 + y^2 + 2y + 1 = 8 + 16 + 1$
$(x + 4)^2 + (y + 1)^2 = 25$
$C(-4, -1), r = 5$

44. $x^2 + y^2 + 10x + 4y + 4 = 0$

$x^2 + 10x + 25 + y^2 + 4y + 4 = -4 + 4 + 25$
$(x + 5)^2 + (y + 2)^2 = 25$
$C(-5, -2), r = 5$

45. $x^2 + y^2 + 12x + 10 = 0$

$x^2 + 12x + 36 + y^2 = -10 + 36$
$(x + 6)^2 + y^2 = 26$
$C(-6, 0), r = \sqrt{26}$

46. $x^2 + y^2 - 6x - 21 = 0$

$x^2 - 6x + 9 + y^2 = 21 + 9$
$(x - 3)^2 + y^2 = 30$
$C(3, 0), r = \sqrt{30}$

? **To Think About**

47. What is the equation of a circle with endpoints of a diameter at $(0, 1)$ and $(4, 3)$?

$d = \sqrt{(4 - 0)^2 + (3 - 1)^2} = \sqrt{20} = 2\sqrt{5}$

Radius $= \dfrac{1}{2}$ diameter $= \sqrt{5}$

$C = \text{mid pt} = \left(\dfrac{4 + 0}{2}, \dfrac{3 + 1}{2}\right) = (2, 2)$

$(x - 2)^2 + (y - 2)^2 = 5$

48. What is the equation of a circle with endpoints of a diameter at $(-3, 2)$ and $(1, 4)$?

$d = \sqrt{(-3 - 1)^2 + (2 - 4)^2} = \sqrt{20} = 2\sqrt{5}$

Radius $= \sqrt{5}$

$C = \left(\dfrac{-3 + 1}{2}, \dfrac{2 + 4}{2}\right) = (-1, 3)$

$(x + 1)^2 + (y - 3)^2 = 5$

49. Find the equation of a circle with center at $(-8, -6)$ that passes through the origin.

Radius $= \sqrt{(0 + 8)^2 + (0 + 6)^2} = 10$

$(x + 8)^2 + (y + 6)^2 = 100$

50. Find the equation of a circle with center at $(-5, 2)$ that passes through the point $(1, -4)$.

Radius $= \sqrt{(1 + 5)^2 + (-4 - 2)^2} = \sqrt{72}$

$(x + 5)^2 + (y - 2)^2 = 72$

Solve the following quadratic equations by factoring.

51. $3x^2 - 5x + 2 = 0$ $(3x - 2)(x - 1) = 0$ $x = \dfrac{2}{3}, 1$

52. $9 + \dfrac{3}{x} = \dfrac{2}{x^2}$ $(3x + 2)(3x - 1)$ $x = -\dfrac{2}{3}, \dfrac{1}{3}$

Solve the following quadratic equations by using the quadratic formula.

53. $4x^2 + 2x = 1$ $x = \dfrac{-2 \pm \sqrt{4 - 4(4)(-1)}}{8} = \dfrac{-1 \pm \sqrt{5}}{4}$

54. $5x^2 - 6x - 7 = 0$ $x = \dfrac{6 \pm \sqrt{36 - 4(5)(-7)}}{10} = \dfrac{3 \pm 2\sqrt{11}}{5}$

Calculator Problems

55. Find the distance between $(5.23, -1.67)$ and $(2.98, 3.05)$.

$D = 5.228852647$

56. Write the equation in standard form of a circle with center at $(26.8, 29.2)$ and a radius of 46.53.

$(x - 26.8)^2 + (y - 29.2)^2 = 2165.0409$

For Extra Practice Exercises, turn to page 443.

Solutions to Odd-Numbered Practice Problems

1. The distance between $(-6, -2)$ and $(3, 1)$ is

$$d = \sqrt{[3 - (-6)]^2 + [1 - (-2)]^2}$$
$$= \sqrt{(3 + 6)^2 + (1 + 2)^2}$$
$$= \sqrt{81 + 9} = \sqrt{90} = 3\sqrt{10}$$

3. $(x + 1)^2 + (y + 2)^2 = 9$

If we compare this to $(x - h)^2 + (y - k)^2 = r^2$ we can write it in the form

$$[x - (-1)]^2 + [y - (-2)]^2 = 3^2$$

Thus we see the center $(h, k) = (-1, -2)$ and the radius $r = 3$.

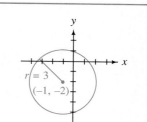

5. To put $x^2 + 4x + y^2 + 2y - 20 = 0$ in standard form, we complete the square.

$$x^2 + 4x + \underline{\quad} + y^2 + 2y + \underline{\quad} = 20$$
$$x^2 + 4x + 4 + y^2 + 2y + 1 = 20 \; +4 \; +1$$
$$(x + 2)^2 + (y + 1)^2 = 25$$

The circle has its center at $(-2, -1)$ and a radius of 5.

$(x + 2)^2 + (y + 1)^2 = 25$

Answers to Even-Numbered Practice Problems

2. $y = 4$ and $y = 10$ **4.** $(x + 5)^2 + y^2 = 3$

8.2 THE PARABOLA

1 If we pass a plane through a cone parallel to, but not touching, the edge of the cone, we form a parabola. A **parabola** is defined as the set of points that is the same distance from some fixed line (called the **directrix**) and some fixed point (called the **focus**) that is *not* on the line.

☐ After studying this section, you will be able to:

1 *Graph a parabola if the equation is in standard form*

2 *Place the equation of any horizontal or vertical parabola in standard form.*

The simplest equation of a parabola has the form

$$\text{Variable} = \text{constant} \times (\text{another variable})^2$$

We can find the equation of a parabola by using the distance formula. First let's plot a simple parabola.

Example 1   Graph: $y = x^2$.

We make a table of values, plot the points and draw a graph.

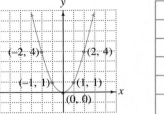

x	y
-2	4
-1	1
0	0
1	1
2	4

Graph of $y = x^2$ ■

Practice Problem 1   Graph: $y = \dfrac{1}{4}x^2$.

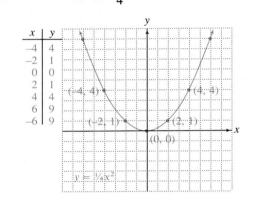

x	y
-4	4
-2	1
0	0
2	1
4	4
6	9
-6	9

■

Notice that the parabola is symmetric about the y-axis. In other words, if we folded the graph along the y-axis, the two parts of the curve would coincide. Therefore, we call the y-axis the **axis of symmetry**. Every parabola has an axis of symmetry; this axis can be *any* line. The point at which the parabola crosses the axis of symmetry is the **vertex**.

To Think About

Now let's see how we can obtain the equation for a parabola. Study this sketch. The point $F(0, c)$ is the focus. The line $y = -c$ is the directrix. (c can be any value.) By

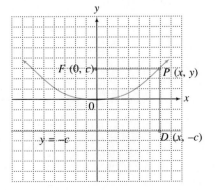

definition of the parabola, the point $P(x, y)$ must be the same distance from $F(0, c)$ as it is from $D(x, -c)$. In other words,

$$PF = PD$$

If we think of the point P as moving along the curve, then no matter where it is, the distance PF must equal the distance PD. Now we can use the distance formula.

$PF = PD$ By definition.

$\sqrt{(x - 0)^2 + (y - c)^2} = \sqrt{(x - x)^2 + (y + c)^2}$ Distance formula.

$x^2 + (y - c)^2 = (y + c)^2$

$x^2 + y^2 - 2cy + c^2 = y^2 + 2cy + c^2$ Simplifying.

$x^2 = 4cy$

Does the equation look familiar? Suppose we wrote it as

$$y = \frac{1}{4c} x^2$$

In Example 1, $\frac{1}{4c} = 1$, so we have

$$y = x^2$$

This equation describes a parabola that opens *upward*. Parabolas can also open *downward*, to the left, or to the right. We will examine all of these types. Parabolas opening up or down are called **vertical parabolas**. Those that open right or left are called **horizontal parabolas**. ■

Example 2   Graph the parabola: $y = x^2 + 3$.

Compile a table of values and plot the points. The graph looks just like the graph of $y = x^2$ but it is 3 units higher. Its vertex is $(0, 3)$ and axis of symmetry is the y-axis.

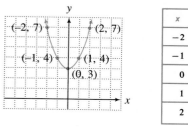

x	y
-2	7
-1	4
0	3
1	4
2	7

Graph of $y = x^2 + 3$ ■

Practice Problem 2   Graph: $y = 3 - x^2$.

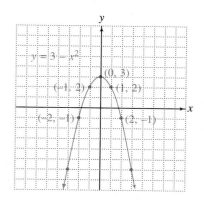

■

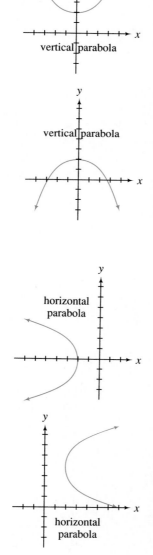

vertical parabola

vertical parabola

horizontal parabola

horizontal parabola

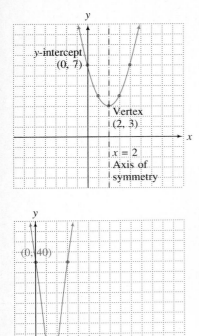

Example 3 Graph the parabola: $y = (x - 2)^2 + 3$.

This graph looks just like the graph of $y = x^2 + 3$, except that it is shifted 2 units to the right. The vertex is (2, 3). The axis of symmetry is $x = 2$. We can find the y-intercept by putting $x = 0$ in the equation, to get $y = (0 - 2)^2 + 3 = 4 + 3 = 7$. Thus, the y-intercept is (0, 7). ■

Practice Problem 3 Graph the parabola: $y = (x - 6)^2 + 4$. Label the vertex and the y-intercept. ■

Now let's summarize what we've learned.

Standard Form of Vertical Parabolas

1. The graph of $y = a(x - h)^2 + k$ is a vertical parabola if $a \neq 0$.
2. The parabola opens upward $\smile$ if $a > 0$ and downward $\frown$ if $a < 0$.
3. The vertex of the parabola is (h, k).
4. The axis of symmetry is the line $x = h$.
5. The y-intercept is the point where the parabola crosses the y-axis (where $x = 0$).

Scale: each unit = 4

We can use these steps to graph a parabola. If we want greater accuracy, we should plot a few other points also.

Example 4 Graph: $y = -\dfrac{1}{2}(x + 3)^2 - 1$.

Step 1. The equation has the form $y = a(x - h)^2 + k$, where $a = -\dfrac{1}{2}$, $h = -3$, $k = -1$, so it is a vertical parabola.

Step 2. $a < 0$; so the parabola opens downward.

Step 3. We have $h = -3$ and $k = -1$:

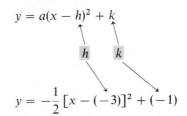

$$y = a(x - h)^2 + k$$

$$y = -\frac{1}{2}[x - (-3)]^2 + (-1)$$

Therefore, the vertex of the parabola is $(-3, -1)$.

Step 4. The axis of symmetry is the line $x = -3$.

Step 5. When $x = 0$,

$$y = -\frac{1}{2}(0 + 3)^2 - 1 = -\frac{1}{2}(9) - 1$$

$$= -4.5 - 1 = -5.5$$

Thus, the y-intercept is $(0, -5.5)$.

The graph is shown in this sketch. ■

Practice Problem 4 Graph: $y = \dfrac{1}{4}(x - 2)^2 + 3$. ■

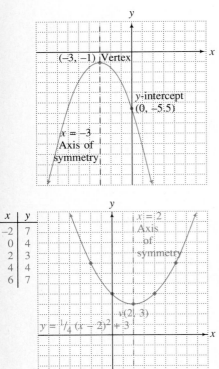

Example 5 Graph the parabola: $x = -2y^2$.

Notice that the y term is squared this time. This means that the parabola is horizontal. We chose values of y first such as $y = -2, -1, 0, 1,$ or 2. Then construct a table of values and plot the points.

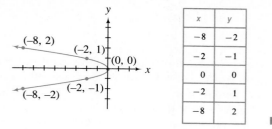

x	y
−8	−2
−2	−1
0	0
−2	1
−8	2

Practice Problem 5   Graph the parabola: $x = -2y^2 + 4$. ▪

Now we can make the same type of observations for horizontal parabolas as we did for vertical ones.

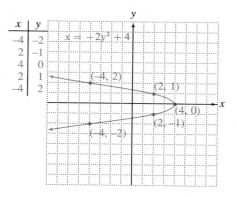

x	y
−4	−2
2	−1
4	0
2	1
−4	2

Standard Form of Horizontal Parabolas

1. The graph of $x = a(y - k)^2 + h$ is a horizontal parabola if $a \neq 0$.
2. The parabola opens to the right ⊂⊃ if $a > 0$ and opens to the left ⊂⊃ if $a < 0$.
3. The vertex of the parabola is (h, k).
4. The axis of symmetry is the line $y = k$.
5. The x-intercept is the point where the parabola crosses the x-axis (where $y = 0$).

Example 6   Graph: $x = 1(y - 3)^2 - 5$.

    Step 1. The equation has the form $x = a(y - k)^2 + h$, where $a = 1$, $k = 3$, $h = -5$, so it is a horizontal parabola.

    Step 2. $a > 0$, so the parabola open to the right.

    Step 3. We have $k = 3$ and $h = -5$:

$$x = a(y - k)^2 + h$$

$$\underset{k}{\uparrow} \qquad \underset{h}{\uparrow}$$

$$x = 1(y - 3)^2 + (-5)$$

Therefore, the vertex is $(-5, 3)$.

    Step 4. The line $y = 3$ is the axis of symmetry.

    Step 5. When $y = 0$,

$$x = 1(0 - 3)^2 - 5 = 9 - 5 = 4$$

Thus, the x-intercept is $(4, 0)$.

    The graph is shown. Notice that the graph crosses the y-axis also. We can find the y-intercepts by setting $x = 0$ and solving the quadratic equation. ▪

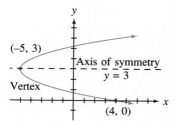

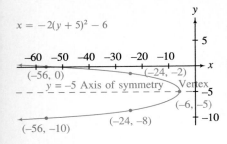

$x = -2(y + 5)^2 - 6$

Practice Problem 6 Graph the parabola: $x = -2(y + 5)^2 - 6$. Label the vertex and the x-intercept. ■

2 So far, all of the parabolas we have graphed have been in standard form. This rarely happens in the real world. How do you suppose we put a quadratic equation $y = ax^2 + bx + c$ in the standard form $y = a(x - h)^2 + k$ or a slightly different quadratic equation $x = ay^2 + by + c$ in the standard form $x = a(y - k)^2 + h$? We do it by completing the square. (We told you this was a very useful procedure.)

Example 7 Graph: $x = y^2 + 4y + 1$.

We must put the equation in standard form. Since the y term is squared, we have a horizontal parabola, so the standard form is

$$x = a(y - k)^2 + h$$

Now

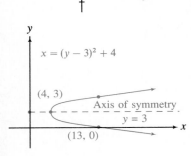

$$x = y^2 + 4y + \underline{} - \underline{} + 1$$
$$x = y^2 + 4y + \left(\frac{4}{2}\right)^2 - \left(\frac{4}{2}\right)^2 + 1 \qquad \text{Completing the square.}$$
$$x = (y^2 + 4y + 4) - 3 \qquad \text{Simplifying.}$$
$$x = (y + 2)^2 - 3 \qquad \text{Standard form.}$$

Therefore, we know that $a = 1$, $k = -2$, and $h = -3$. Hence, the vertex is $(-3, -2)$, the axis of symmetry is $y = -2$. If we let $x = 0$, we can find the x-intercept is $(1, 0)$. The parabola opens to the right. ■

Practice Problem 7 Place in standard form and graph the equation: $x = y^2 - 6y + 13$. ■

Example 8 Graph: $y = 2x^2 - 12x + 22$.

This time the x term is squared, so we have a vertical parabola. We must complete the square.

$$y = 2x^2 - 12x + 22$$
$$y = 2(x^2 - 6x) + 22 \qquad \text{We multiply by 2 because}$$
$$y = 2\left[x^2 - 6x + \left(\frac{-6}{2}\right)^2\right] - 2\left(\frac{-6}{2}\right)^2 + 22 \qquad \text{this term is multiplied by 2.}$$
$$y = 2(x - 3)^2 + 4$$

Therefore, the parabola opens up ($a > 0$), the vertex is $(3, 4)$, the axis of symmetry is $x = 3$, and the y-intercept is $(0, 22)$.

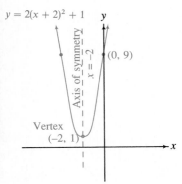

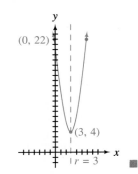

Practice Problem 8 Place in standard form and graph: $y = 2x^2 + 8x + 9$. ■

Graph each parabola and label the vertex and y-intercept. Place x and y axes at a convenient place for your graph. You may need to use a scale other than 1 square = 1 unit.

1. $y = \dfrac{1}{2}x^2$

2. $y = \dfrac{1}{3}x^2$

3. $y = -3x^2$

4. $y = -4x^2$

5. $y = x^2 - 6$

6. $y = x^2 - 5$

7. $y = -2x^2 + 4$

8. $y = -3x^2 + 1$

9. $y = (x - 4)^2 + 3$

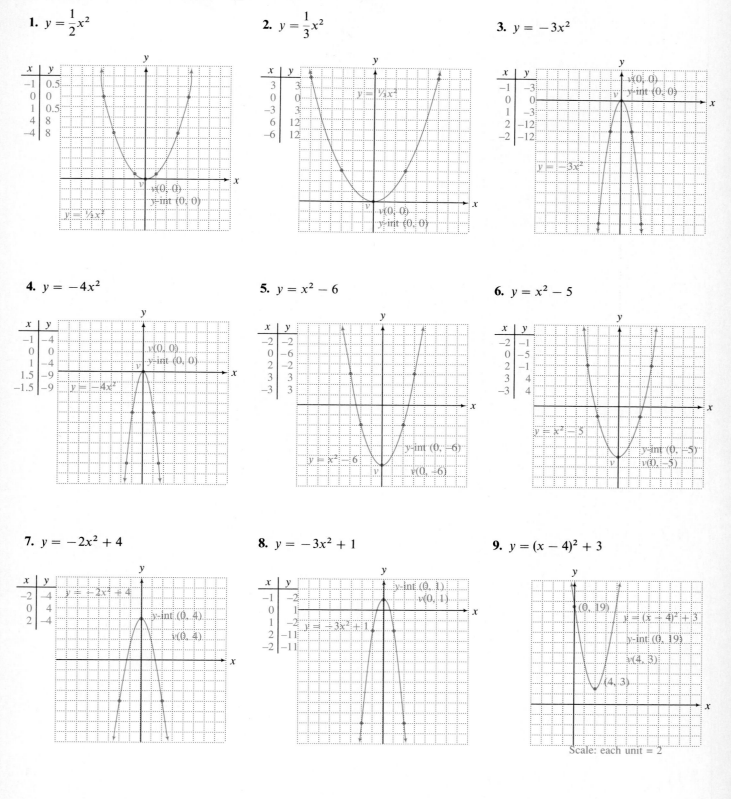

10. $y = (x - 5)^2 + 1$

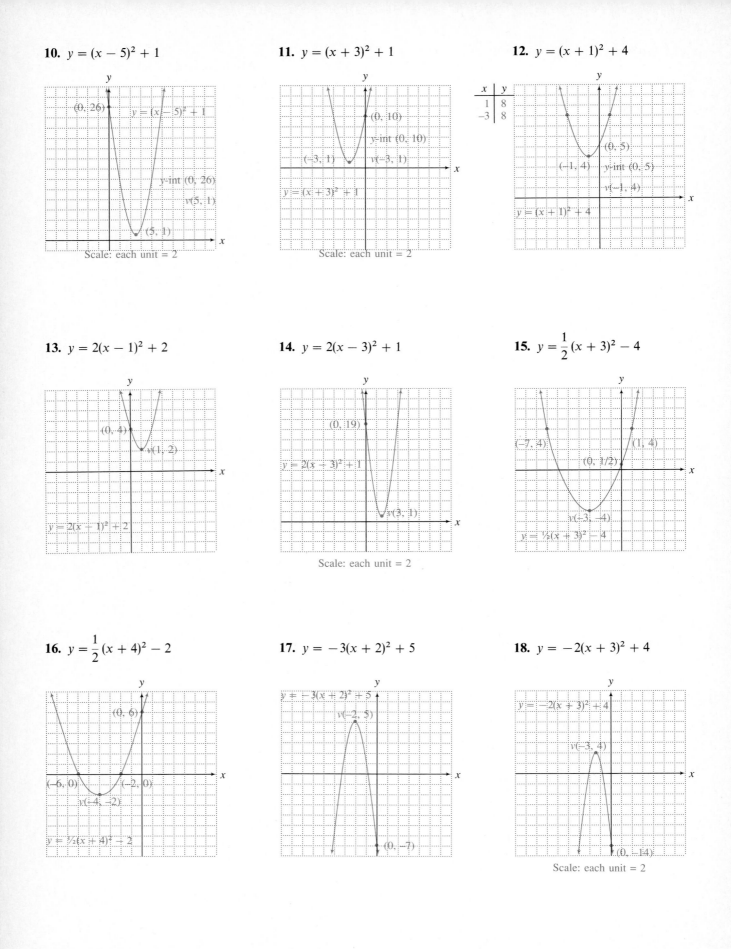

(0, 26)
$y = (x - 5)^2 + 1$
y-int (0, 26)
v(5, 1)
(5, 1)
Scale: each unit = 2

11. $y = (x + 3)^2 + 1$

(0, 10)
y-int (0, 10)
(-3, 1) v(-3, 1)
$y = (x + 3)^2 + 1$
Scale: each unit = 2

12. $y = (x + 1)^2 + 4$

x	y
1	8
-3	8

(0, 5)
(-1, 4) y-int (0, 5)
v(-1, 4)
$y = (x + 1)^2 + 4$

13. $y = 2(x - 1)^2 + 2$

(0, 4)
v(1, 2)
$y = 2(x - 1)^2 + 2$

14. $y = 2(x - 3)^2 + 1$

(0, 19)
$y = 2(x - 3)^2 + 1$
v(3, 1)
Scale: each unit = 2

15. $y = \dfrac{1}{2}(x + 3)^2 - 4$

(-7, 4) (1, 4)
(0, 1/2)
v(-3, -4)
$y = \frac{1}{2}(x + 3)^2 - 4$

16. $y = \dfrac{1}{2}(x + 4)^2 - 2$

(0, 6)
(-6, 0) (-2, 0)
v(-4, -2)
$y = \frac{1}{2}(x + 4)^2 - 2$

17. $y = -3(x + 2)^2 + 5$

$y = -3(x + 2)^2 + 5$
v(-2, 5)
(0, -7)

18. $y = -2(x + 3)^2 + 4$

$y = -2(x + 3)^2 + 4$
v(-3, 4)
(0, -14)
Scale: each unit = 2

Graph each parabola and label the vertex and x-intercept.

19. $x = \dfrac{1}{3}y^2 + 1$

20. $x = \dfrac{1}{4}y^2 + 2$

21. $x = -4y^2$

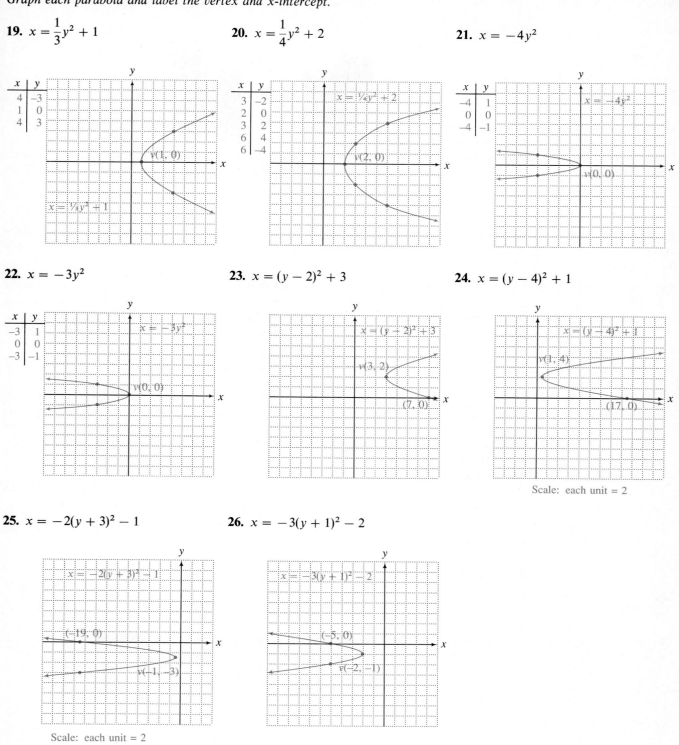

x	y
4	−3
1	0
4	3

$x = \frac{1}{3}y^2 + 1$ $v(1, 0)$

x	y
3	−2
2	0
3	2
6	4
6	−4

$x = \frac{1}{4}y^2 + 2$ $v(2, 0)$

x	y
−4	1
0	0
−4	−1

$x = -4y^2$ $v(0, 0)$

22. $x = -3y^2$

23. $x = (y - 2)^2 + 3$

24. $x = (y - 4)^2 + 1$

x	y
−3	1
0	0
−3	−1

$x = -3y^2$ $v(0, 0)$

$x = (y - 2)^2 + 3$ $v(3, 2)$ $(7, 0)$

$x = (y - 4)^2 + 1$ $v(1, 4)$ $(17, 0)$

Scale: each unit = 2

25. $x = -2(y + 3)^2 - 1$

26. $x = -3(y + 1)^2 - 2$

$x = -2(y + 3)^2 - 1$ $(-19, 0)$ $v(-1, -3)$

Scale: each unit = 2

$x = -3(y + 1)^2 - 2$ $(-5, 0)$ $v(-2, -1)$

*Put each equation in standard form. Determine **(a)** if the parabola is horizontal or vertical, **(b)** the way it opens, and **(c)** the vertex.*

27. $y = x^2 + 6x + 10$

$y = (x^2 + 6x + 9) + 1$
$y = (x + 3)^2 + 1$
(a) Vertical
(b) Opens up
(c) $v(-3, 1)$

28. $y = x^2 + 4x + 9$

$y = (x^2 + 4x + 4) + 5$
$y = (x + 2)^2 + 5$
(a) Vertical
(b) Opens up
(c) $v(-2, 5)$

29. $y = -2x^2 + 4x - 3$

$y = -2(x^2 - 2x + 1) - 3 + 2$
$y = -2(x - 1)^2 - 1$
(a) Vertical
(b) Opens down
(c) $v(1, -1)$

30. $y = -2x^2 + 4x + 5$

$y = -2(x^2 - 2x + 1) + 5 + 2$
$y = -2(x - 1)^2 + 7$
(a) Vertical
(b) Opens down
(c) $v(1, 7)$

31. $x = y^2 + 10y + 23$

$x = (y^2 + 10y + 25) - 2$
$x = (y + 5)^2 - 2$
(a) Horizontal
(b) Opens right
(c) $v(-2, -5)$

32. $x = y^2 + 8y + 9$

$x = (y^2 + 8y + 16) - 7$
$x = (y + 4)^2 - 7$
(a) Horizontal
(b) Opens right
(c) $v(7, -4)$

? To Think About

By writing a quadratic equation in the form $y = a(x - h)^2 + k$, we can find the maximum value of the equation and the value of x for which it occurs. Remember, the equation $y = a(x - h)^2 + k$ is a vertical parabola. For $a > 0$, the parabola opens up. Thus the y-coordinate of the vertex is the smallest (or minimum) value of x. Similarly, when $a < 0$, the parabola opens downward, so the y-coordinate of the vertex is the maximum value of the equation. Since the vertex occurs at (h, k), the maximum value of the equation occurs when $x = h$. Then

$$y = -a(x - h)^2 + k = -a(0) + k = k$$

For example, suppose the weekly profit of a manufacturing company in dollars is $P = -2(x - 45)^2 + 2300$ for x units manufactored. The maximum profit per week is \$2300 and is attained when 45 units are manufactured. Use this approach for problems 33–36.

33. Find the maximum monthly profit for a company that manufactures x items. The profit equation is $P = -3x^2 + 240x + 31{,}200$. How many items must be produced each month to attain maximum profit?

$P = -3(x^2 - 80x + 1600) + 31{,}200 + 4800$
$P = -3(x - 40)^2 + 36{,}000$
Maximum profit $= \$36{,}000$
items needed $= 40$

34. Find the maximum monthly profit for a company that manufactures x items. The profit equation is $P = -2x^2 + 200x + 47{,}000$. How many items must be produced each month to attain maximum profit?

$P = -2(x^2 - 100x + 2500) + 47{,}000 + 5000$
$P = -2(x - 50)^2 + 52{,}000$
Maximum profit $= \$52{,}000$
items needed $= 50$

35. The effective yield from a grove of orange trees is described by the equation $E = x(900 - x)$, where x is the number of orange trees per acre. What is the maximum effective yield? How many orange trees per acre should be planted to achieve maximum yield?

$E = -x^2 + 900x$
$E = -(x^2 - 900x + 202{,}500) + 202{,}500$
$E = -(x - 450)^2 + 202{,}500$
Maximum profit $= \$202{,}500$
items needed $= 450$

36. A research pharmacologist has determined that sensitivity (S) to a drug depends on the dosage d, given by the equation

$$S = 650d - 2d^2$$

where d is in milligrams. What is the maximum sensitivity that will occur? What dosage will produce that maximum sensitivity?

$S = -2d^2 + 650d$
$S = -2(d^2 - 325d + 26{,}406.25) + 52{,}812.50$
$S = -2(d - 162.5)^2 + 52{,}812.50$
Maximum sensitivity $= 52{,}812.5$ milligrams
Dosage $= 162.5$ milligrams

? To Think About

First write the equation in standard form. Then find the vertex. Does the parabola open up, down, right or left? Find the y-intercept for a vertical parabola and the x-intercept for a horizontal parabola.

37. $y = -\dfrac{3}{2}x^2 + \dfrac{15}{2}x + \dfrac{213}{8}$

$y = \dfrac{-12x^2 + 60x + 213}{8}$

$y = -\dfrac{12}{8}\left(x^2 - 5x + \dfrac{25}{4}\right) + \dfrac{213}{8} + \dfrac{75}{8}$

$y = -\dfrac{3}{2}\left(x - \dfrac{5}{2}\right)^2 + 36$

$v\left(\dfrac{5}{2}, 36\right)$ Parabola opens downward.

y-intercept $\left(0, \dfrac{213}{8}\right)$

38. $x = \dfrac{5}{3}y^2 + \dfrac{5}{3}y + \dfrac{53}{12}$

$x = \dfrac{20y^2 + 20y + 53}{12}$

$x = \dfrac{20}{12}\left(y^2 + y + \dfrac{1}{4}\right) + \dfrac{53}{12} - \dfrac{5}{12}$

$x = \dfrac{5}{3}\left(y + \dfrac{1}{2}\right)^2 + 4$

$v\left(4, -\dfrac{1}{2}\right)$ Parabola opens to the right.

x-intercept $\left(\dfrac{53}{12}, 0\right)$

Cumulative Review Problems

Simplify.

39. $\sqrt{50x^3}$

$\sqrt{25x^2}\sqrt{2x} = 5x\sqrt{2x}$

40. $\sqrt[3]{40x^3y^4}$

$\sqrt[3]{8x^3y^3}\sqrt[3]{5y} = 2xy\sqrt[3]{5y}$

Add.

41. $\sqrt{98x} + x\sqrt{8} - 3\sqrt{50x}$ $7\sqrt{2x} + 2x\sqrt{2} - 15\sqrt{2x}$
$2x\sqrt{2} - 8\sqrt{2x}$

42. $\sqrt[3]{16x^4} + 4x\sqrt[3]{2} - 8x\sqrt[3]{54}$ $2x\sqrt[3]{2x} + 4x\sqrt[3]{2} - 24x\sqrt[3]{2}$
$2x\sqrt[3]{2x} - 20x\sqrt[3]{2}$

Calculator Problems

Find the vertex and y-intercept of each parabola. Find the two x-intercepts by setting $y = 0$ and solving the quadratic equation.

43. $y = 2(x + 1.62)^2 - 5.38$

Vertex $(-1.62, -5.38)$
y–int -0.1312
x–intercepts 0.020121947 and -3.260121947

44. $y = -3(x - 5.61)^2 + 20.91$

Vertex $(5.61, 20.91)$
y–int -73.5063
x–intercepts $2.969824244, 8.250075756$

For Extra Practice Exercises, turn to page 444.

Solutions to Odd-Numbered Practice Problems

1. $y = \dfrac{1}{4}x^2$

3. $y = (x - 6)^2 + 4$

The vertex is $(6, 4)$ and the parabola opens upward. If $x = 0$, $y = (0 - 6)^2 + 4 = 36 + 4 = 40$, so the y-intercept is $(0, 40)$.

Scale: each unit = 4

5. $x = -2y^2 + 4$

Let y equal the values $-2, -1, 0, 1, 2$ and in each case find the corresponding values of x. Vertex is at $(9, 0)$.

7. Since the y term is squared, we have a horizontal parabola. The standard form is $x = a(y - k)^2 + h$.

$$x = y^2 - 6y + 9 \quad -9 + 13$$
$$x = (y^2 - 6y + 9) + 4$$
$$x = (y - 3)^2 + 4$$

Therefore, we know that $a = 1$, $k = 3$, and $h = 4$. The vertex is at $(4, 3)$. If $y = 0$, $x = (-3)^2 + 4 = 9 + 4 = 13$. So the x-intercept is $(13, 0)$.

2. $y = 3 - x^2$ **4.** $y = \dfrac{1}{4}(x-2)^2 + 3$ **6.** $x = -2(y+5)^2 - 6$ **8.** $y = 2x^2 + 8x + 9$
$$= 2(x+2)^2 + 1$$

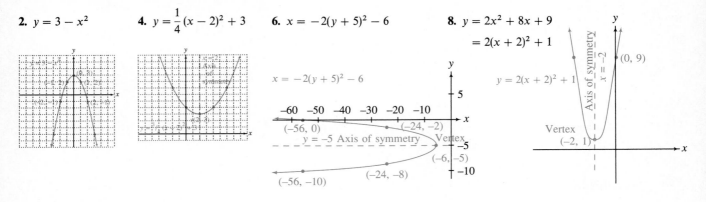

8.3   THE ELLIPSE

If a plane cuts a cone at an angle and is not perpendicular to the axis of the cone, the conic section formed is an ellipse. The orbit of a planet around the sun is approximately an ellipse. Domes in buildings are often constructed in elliptical shapes.

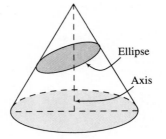

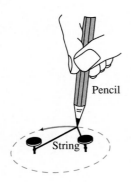

Try drawing an ellipse using two tacks, string, and a pencil. Mathematically, an **ellipse** is the set of points in a plane such that for each point in the set the *sum* of its distances to two fixed points is constant. The fixed points are called **foci** (plural of focus).

?

To Think About

Where does this equation come from? We can derive the equation of an ellipse by using the distance formula. Let's take any point $P(x, y)$. By definition of an ellipse, the *sum* of the distances of P from two fixed points (foci) $A(c, 0)$ and $B(-c, 0)$ is a constant. (See the sketch with points B, A, and P labeled.) Therefore,

$$AP + BP = K$$

where K is constant. Now by the distance formula,

$$\sqrt{(x-c)^2 + (y-0)^2} + \sqrt{(x+c)^2 + (y-0)^2} = K$$

Although solving this equation is not difficult (try it), it does involve a fair amount of work. For convenience, let's plug in some numbers and obtain the equation for one ellipse (instead of *any* ellipse).

Let the foci be $(4, 0)$, $(-4, 0)$, and let $K = 10$. Then

$$\sqrt{(x-4)^2 + y^2} + \sqrt{(x+4)^2 + y^2} = 10$$

$$\sqrt{(x+4)^2 + y^2} = 10 - \sqrt{(x-4)^2 + y^2} \qquad \text{Isolating one radical.}$$

$$(x+4)^2 + y^2 = 100 - 20\sqrt{(x-4)^2 + y^2} \qquad \text{Squaring and}$$
$$+ (x-4)^2 + y^2 \qquad \text{simplifying}$$

$$x^2 + 8x + 16 + y^2 = 100 - 20\sqrt{(x-4)^2 + y^2} \qquad \text{Multiplying}$$
$$+ x^2 - 8x + 16 + y^2$$

$$5\sqrt{(x-4)^2 + y^2} = 25 - 4x \qquad \text{Simplifying.}$$

$$25[(x-4)^2 + y^2] = (25 - 4x)^2 \qquad \text{Squaring both}$$
$$\text{sides.}$$

$$9x^2 + 25y^2 = 225 \qquad \text{Simplifying.}$$

$$\frac{x^2}{25} + \frac{y^2}{9} = 1 \qquad \text{Dividing by 225.}$$

This is the equation of the ellipse. Now we generalize it. ∎

TEACHING TIP Students at this level of course find it difficult to follow the derivation of a formula. This presentation of the derivation of the ellipse formula was particularly designed for those students who intend to take several higher-level math courses such as College Algebra and Calculus. You may want to mention to the class that this type of derivation is done in higher-level math courses and it is good to be "exposed" to a little of it in an Intermediate Algebra course.

1

> **Equation of an Ellipse in Standard Form**
>
> An ellipse with center at the origin has equation
>
> $$\frac{x^2}{a^2} + \frac{y^2}{b^2} = 1 \qquad \text{where } a, b > 0$$

To plot the ellipse, we need the x- and y-intercepts.

$$\frac{x^2}{a^2} + \frac{y^2}{b^2} = 1$$

If $x = 0$ then $\dfrac{y^2}{b^2} = 1$ $\qquad\qquad$ *If* $y = 0$ *then* $\dfrac{x^2}{a^2} = 1$

$$y^2 = b^2 \qquad\qquad\qquad x^2 = a^2$$

$$\pm\sqrt{y^2} = \pm\sqrt{b^2} \qquad\qquad \pm\sqrt{x^2} = \pm\sqrt{a^2}$$

$\pm y = \pm b$ $\;$ *or* $\;$ $\boxed{y = \pm b}$ $\qquad\qquad$ $\pm x = \pm a$ $\;$ *or* $\;$ $\boxed{x = \pm a}$

So the x-intercepts are $(a, 0)$ and $(-a, 0)$, and the y-intercepts are $(0, b)$ and $(0, -b)$ for an ellipse of the form $\dfrac{x^2}{a^2} + \dfrac{y^2}{b^2} = 1$.

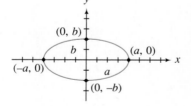

A circle is a special case of an ellipse. If $a = b$, we get

$$\frac{x^2}{a^2} + \frac{y^2}{a^2} = 1$$

$$x^2 + y^2 = a^2$$

which is the equation of a circle of radius a.

Example 1 Graph: $9x^2 + 4y^2 = 36$.

Since *both* x and y are second degree, the equation cannot represent a parabola. It must be a circle or an ellipse. We want to put the equation in standard form. We need to divide each term by 36.

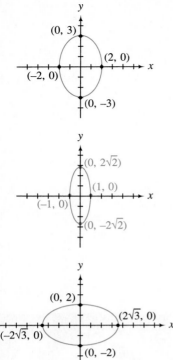

(0, 3)
(2, 0)
(−2, 0)
(0, −3)

$$\frac{9x^2}{36} + \frac{4y^2}{36} = \frac{36}{36}$$

$$\frac{x^2}{4} + \frac{y^2}{9} = 1$$

This is the equation of an ellipse with center at the origin; $a^2 = 4$ and $b^2 = 9$, so $a = 2$ and $b = 3$. Therefore, the graph crosses the x-axis at $(-2, 0)$ and $(2, 0)$, and the y-axis at $(0, 3)$ and $(0, -3)$. ■

Practice Problem 1   Graph: $\frac{x^2}{1} + \frac{y^2}{8} = 1$. ■

(0, 2√2)
(1, 0)
(−1, 0)
(0, −2√2)

Example 2   Graph: $x^2 + 3y^2 = 12$.

Put the equation in standard form.

$$\frac{x^2}{12} + \frac{3y^2}{12} = \frac{12}{12} \qquad \text{Dividing each side by 12.}$$

$$\frac{x^2}{12} + \frac{y^2}{4} = 1 \qquad \text{Simplifying.}$$

Thus,

$$a^2 = 12 \qquad \text{so} \qquad a = 2\sqrt{3}$$

$$b^2 = 4 \qquad \text{so} \qquad b = 2$$

(0, 2)
(2√3, 0)
(−2√3, 0)
(0, −2)

The x-intercepts are $(-2\sqrt{3}, 0)$ and $(2\sqrt{3}, 0)$, and the y-intercepts are $(0, 2)$ and $(0, -2)$.

■

Practice Problem 2   Place in standard form and graph: $16x^2 + 25y^2 = 400$. Label the intercepts. ■

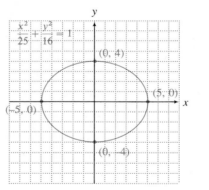

If the center of the ellipse is not at the origin but at some point (h, k), then its equation is

$$\frac{(x - h)^2}{a^2} + \frac{(y - k)^2}{b^2} = 1$$

2

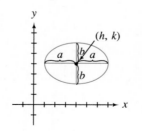

(h, k)
a
a
b

An ellipse with center at (h, k) has the equation

$$\frac{(x - h)^2}{a^2} + \frac{(y - k)^2}{b^2} = 1$$

where $a, b > 0$.

Note that a and b are *not* the x- and y-intercepts now. Why is this? Look at the sketch. You'll see that a is the horizontal distance from the center of the ellipse to a point on the ellipse (this horizontal axis is called the **major axis**). Similarly, b is the vertical distance (called the **minor axis**). Hence when the center of the ellipse is not at the origin, the ellipse may not even cross either axis.

Example 3   Graph: $\dfrac{(x-5)^2}{9} + \dfrac{(y-6)^2}{4} = 1$.

The center of the ellipse is (5, 6), $a = 3$, and $b = 2$. Therefore, we begin at (5, 6). We plot points 3 units to the left, 3 units to the right, 2 units up, and 2 units down from (5, 6).   ■

Practice Problem 3   Graph: $\dfrac{(x-2)^2}{16} + \dfrac{(y+3)^2}{9} = 1$.

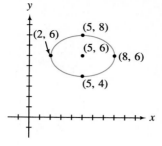

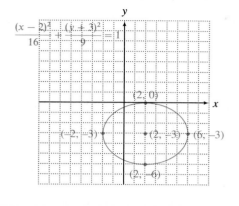

TEACHING TIP   After discussing example 3, ask students to write the equation of an ellipse that has a center at $(-4, 7)$ and has a value of $a = 5$ and $b = 6$.

$$\dfrac{(x+4)^2}{25} + \dfrac{(y-7)^2}{36} = 1 \text{ Ans.}$$

EXERCISES 8.3

Graph each ellipse. Label the intercepts. You may need to use a scale other than 1 square = 1 unit.

1. $\dfrac{x^2}{9} + \dfrac{y^2}{36} = 1$

2. $\dfrac{x^2}{4} + \dfrac{y^2}{25} = 1$

3. $\dfrac{x^2}{49} + \dfrac{y^2}{25} = 1$

4. $\dfrac{x^2}{36} + \dfrac{y^2}{4} = 1$

5. $\dfrac{x^2}{81} + \dfrac{y^2}{100} = 1$

6. $\dfrac{x^2}{121} + \dfrac{y^2}{144} = 1$

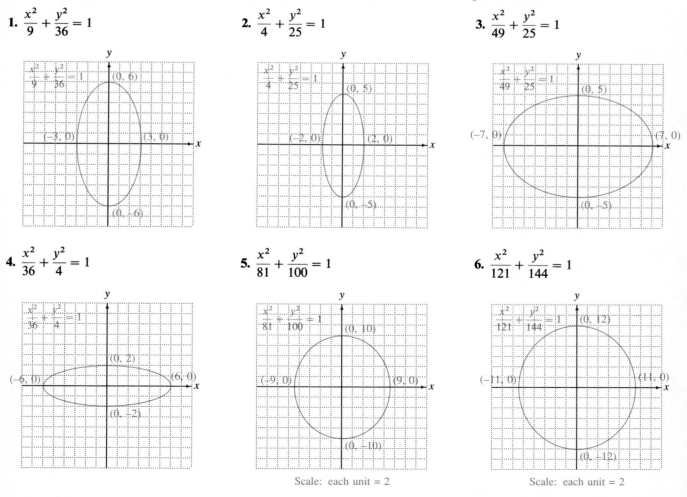

Scale: each unit = 2

Scale: each unit = 2

7. $4x^2 + y^2 - 36 = 0$

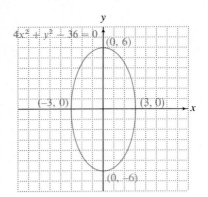

8. $x^2 + 25y^2 - 25 = 0$

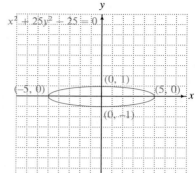

9. $64x^2 + 100y^2 = 6400$

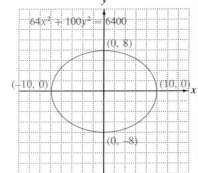

10. $49x^2 + 144y^2 = 7056$

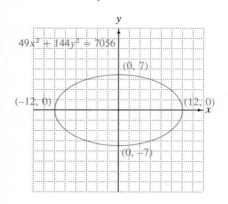

11. $x^2 + 12y^2 = 36$

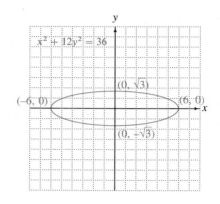

12. $8x^2 + y^2 = 16$

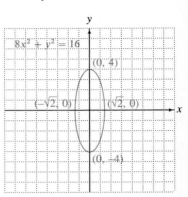

13. $7x^2 + 5y^2 = 35$

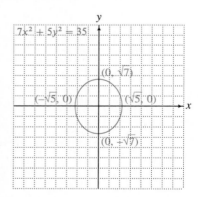

14. $5x^2 + 6y^2 = 30$

15. $\dfrac{x^2}{\frac{9}{4}} + \dfrac{y^2}{\frac{25}{4}} = 1$

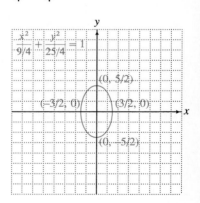

16. $\dfrac{x^2}{\frac{81}{4}} + \dfrac{y^2}{\frac{25}{16}} = 1$

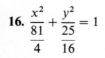

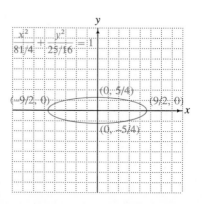

Graph each ellipse. Label the center. Place x and y axes at a convenient place for your graph. You may need to use a scale other than 1 square = 1 unit.

17. $\dfrac{(x-7)^2}{4} + \dfrac{(y-6)^2}{9} = 1$

18. $\dfrac{(x-5)^2}{9} + \dfrac{(y-2)^2}{1} = 1$

19. $\dfrac{(x+3)^2}{25} + \dfrac{(y-4)^2}{16} = 1$

20. $\dfrac{(x+2)^2}{49} + \dfrac{(y-3)^2}{25} = 1$

21. $\dfrac{(x+5)^2}{16} + \dfrac{(y+2)^2}{36} = 1$

22. $\dfrac{(x+1)^2}{36} + \dfrac{(y+4)^2}{16} = 1$

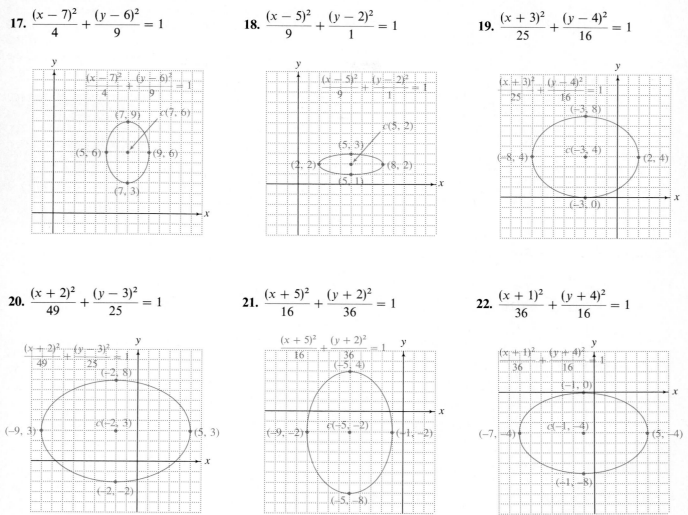

? ## To Think About

23. Write in standard form the equation of an ellipse with center at the origin, *x*-intercept at (3, 0), and *y*-intercept at (0, $\sqrt{7}$).

$\dfrac{x^2}{9} + \dfrac{y^2}{7} = 1$

24. Write in standard form the equation of an ellipse with center at the origin, *x*-intercept at ($\sqrt{5}$, 0), and *y*-intercept at (0, −6).

$\dfrac{x^2}{5} + \dfrac{y^2}{36} = 1$

25. Write in standard form the equation of an ellipse whose vertices (extreme points or turning points) are (2, 3), (6, 3), (4, 7), and (4, −1).

Center pt $\left(\dfrac{2+6}{2}, \dfrac{3+3}{2}\right)$

$C(4, 3)$

$CB = |6 - 4| = 2$

$EC = |7 - 3| = 4$

$\dfrac{(x-4)^2}{4} + \dfrac{(y-3)^2}{16} = 1$

26. Write in standard form the equation of an ellipse whose vertices are (−3, −2), (5, −2), (1, 1), and (1, −5).

Center pt $\left(\dfrac{1+1}{2}, \dfrac{1-5}{2}\right)$

$C(1, -2)$

$BC = |1 + 2| = 3$

$CD = |5 - 1| = 4$

$\dfrac{(x-1)^2}{16} + \dfrac{(y+2)^2}{9} = 1$

27. For what value of a does the ellipse

$$\frac{(x+5)^2}{4} + \frac{(y+a)^2}{9} = 1$$

pass through the point $(-4, 4)$?

$$\frac{(-4+5)^2}{4} + \frac{(4+a)^2}{9} = 1$$
$$9(1)^2 + 4(4+a)^2 = 36$$
$$4(4+a)^2 = 27$$
$$(4+a)^2 = \frac{27}{4}$$
$$4+a = \pm\frac{3\sqrt{3}}{2}$$
$$a = \frac{-8 \pm 3\sqrt{3}}{2}$$

28. Bob's backyard is a rectangle 40 meters by 60 meters. He drove two posts in the ground and fastened a rope to each post, passing it through the metal ring on his dog's collar. When the dog pulls on the rope while running, its path is an ellipse. (see the figure.) If the dog can just reach the sides of the rectangle, find the equation of the elliptical path.

28. $C\left(\dfrac{0+60}{2}, \dfrac{0+40}{2}\right) = C(30, 20)$

$$2a = 60 \qquad 2b = 40$$
$$a = 30 \qquad b = 20$$
$$\frac{(x-30)^2}{900} + \frac{(y-20)^2}{400} = 1$$

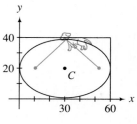

Cumulative Review Problems

Multiply and simplify.

29. $\left(2\sqrt{3} + 4\sqrt{2}\right)\left(5\sqrt{6} - \sqrt{2}\right)$
$10\sqrt{18} + 20\sqrt{12} - 2\sqrt{6} - 4\sqrt{4}$
$30\sqrt{2} + 40\sqrt{3} - 2\sqrt{6} - 8$

30. $\sqrt{3xy}\left(\sqrt{2x} + \sqrt{3y} + \sqrt{27}\right)$
$\sqrt{6x^2y} + \sqrt{9xy^2} + \sqrt{81xy}$
$x\sqrt{6y} + 3y\sqrt{x} + 9\sqrt{xy}$

Rationalize the denominator.

31. $\dfrac{3}{\sqrt{6xy}}$ $\quad \dfrac{3}{\sqrt{6xy}} \cdot \dfrac{\sqrt{6xy}}{\sqrt{6xy}} = \dfrac{3\sqrt{6xy}}{6xy} = \dfrac{\sqrt{6xy}}{2xy}$

32. $\dfrac{5}{\sqrt{2x} - \sqrt{y}}$ $\quad \dfrac{5}{\sqrt{2x} - \sqrt{y}} \cdot \dfrac{\sqrt{2x} + \sqrt{y}}{\sqrt{2x} + \sqrt{y}} = \dfrac{5\left(\sqrt{2x} + \sqrt{y}\right)}{2x - y}$

Calculator Problems

Find the four intercepts for each ellipse accurate to four decimal places.

33. $\dfrac{x^2}{12} + \dfrac{y^2}{19} = 1$

x–int $\pm\, 3.4641$
y–int $\pm\, 4.3589$

34. $\dfrac{x^2}{35} + \dfrac{y^2}{26} = 1$

x–int $\pm\, 5.9161$
y–int $\pm\, 5.0990$

For Extra Practice Exercises, turn to page 444.

Solutions to Odd-Numbered Practice Problems

1. $\dfrac{x^2}{1} + \dfrac{y^2}{8} = 1$

$$a = 1 \qquad b = \sqrt{8} = 2\sqrt{2}$$

The intercepts are $(-1, 0), (1, 0), \left(0, 2\sqrt{2}\right)$, and $\left(0, -2\sqrt{2}\right)$.

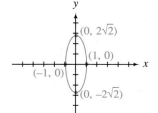

3. $\dfrac{(x-2)^2}{16} + \dfrac{(y+3)^2}{9} = 1$ and $\dfrac{(x-h)^2}{a^2} + \dfrac{(y-k)^2}{b^2} = 1$

The center is $(h, k) = (2, -3)$, $a = 4$, and $b = 3$. We thus start at $(2, -3)$ and measure to the right and to the left 4 units, and up and down 3 units.

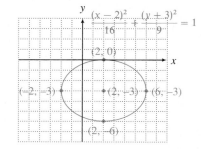

2. $16x^2 + 25y^2 = 400$

$$\frac{x^2}{25} + \frac{y^2}{16} = 1$$

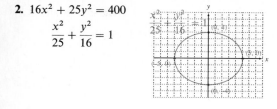

8.4 THE HYPERBOLA

By cutting a cone by a plane as shown in this sketch, we obtain the two branches of a hyperbola. A comet moving with more than enough kinetic energy to escape the sun's gravitational pull will travel in a hyperbolic path. Similarly, a rocket traveling with more than enough velocity to escape the earth's gravitational field will follow a hyperbolic path.

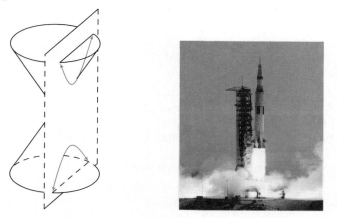

1 Mathematically, a **hyperbola** is the set of points in a plane such that for each point in the set the absolute value of the *difference* of its distances to two fixed points (called **foci**) is constant.

Notice the similarity to the definition of an ellipse. If we replace the word *difference* by *sum*, we have the definition of an ellipse. Hence, we should expect that the equation of a hyperbola will be that of an ellipse with the plus sign replaced by a minus sign. And it is. We can derive the equation just as we did for the ellipse. If the hyperbola has center at the origin, its equation is

$$\frac{x^2}{a^2} - \frac{y^2}{b^2} = 1 \qquad \text{or} \qquad \frac{y^2}{b^2} - \frac{x^2}{a^2}$$

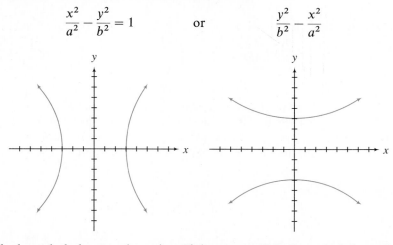

The hyperbola has two branches. If the center of the hyperbola is at the origin, then the hyperbola has two branches that have two *x*-intercepts but no *y*-intercepts or else two *y*-intercepts but no *x*-intercepts. If we graph the hyperbola

☐ After studying this section, you will be able to:

1 *Place the equation of a hyperbola whose center is at the origin in standard form and then graph the hyperbola*

2 *Graph a hyperbola whose center is at (h, k) if its equation is in standard form.*

TEACHING TIP Students find the following illustration interesting.

If a rocket travels with less than enough velocity to escape the gravitational field of earth, it will orbit the earth in an elliptical (or circular) orbit.

If the rocket has exactly the escape velocity, it will travel in a parabolic path.

If the rocket travels in excess of the escape velocity, it will travel in a hyperbolic path.

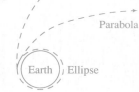

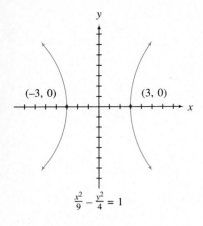

$$\frac{x^2}{9} - \frac{y^2}{4} = 1$$

by constructing a table of values and plotting points, we have this graph.

How to find the x-intercepts? Let $y = 0$. Then

$$\frac{x^2}{9} - \frac{0}{4} = 1$$

$$x^2 = 9$$

$$x = \pm 3$$

The x-intercepts are $(-3, 0), (3, 0)$. Are there any y-intercepts? According to the graph, no. Let's see why. Let $x = 0$. Then

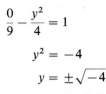

$$\frac{0}{9} - \frac{y^2}{4} = 1$$

$$y^2 = -4$$

$$y = \pm\sqrt{-4}$$

Therefore, there is no *real* value of y that satisfies this equation, so there are no y-intercepts. The intercepts are also called the **vertices** of the hyperbola.

Now let's graph

$$\frac{y^2}{9} - \frac{x^2}{4} = 1$$

You should be able to see that the y-intercepts are $(0, 3)$, $(0, -3)$ and there are no x-intercepts. The graph is shown.

We can now make some general statements.

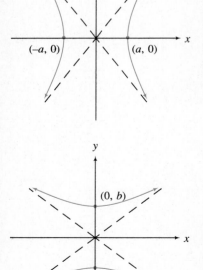

Equation of a Hyperbola in Standard Form with Center at Origin

Let a, b be any positive real numbers. A hyperbola with center at the origin and vertices $(-a, 0)$ and $(a, 0)$ has equation

$$\frac{x^2}{a^2} - \frac{y^2}{b^2} = 1$$

This is called a *horizontal hyperbola.*

A hyperbola with center at the origin and vertices $(0, b)$ and $(0, -b)$ has equation

$$\frac{y^2}{b^2} - \frac{x^2}{a^2} = 1$$

This is called a *vertical hyperbola*

You'll have noticed the diagonal lines we've drawn on the graphs of the hyperbolas. These lines called **asymptotes**. The two branches of the hyperbola come increasing close to the asymptotes as the value of $|x|$ gets very large. By drawing the asymptotes and plotting the vertices, we can easily graph a hyperbola.

Asymptotes of Hyperbolas

The asymptotes of the hyperbolas $\dfrac{x^2}{a^2} - \dfrac{y^2}{b^2} = 1$ and $\dfrac{y^2}{b^2} - \dfrac{x^2}{a^2} = 1$

$$y = \frac{b}{a}x \qquad \text{and} \qquad y = -\frac{b}{a}x$$

Note that $\dfrac{b}{a}$ and $-\dfrac{b}{a}$ are the slopes of the straight lines.

An easy way to find the asymptotes is to draw extended diagonal lines through the rectangle whose center is at the origin and whose corners are at (a, b), $(a, -b)$, $(-a, b)$, $(-a, -b)$. (This rectangle is called the fundamental rectangle.) We draw the fundamental rectangle and the asymptotes with a dashed line because they are not part of the curve.

Example 1 Graph: $\dfrac{x^2}{25} - \dfrac{y^2}{16} = 1$.

The equation has the form $\dfrac{x^2}{a^2} - \dfrac{y^2}{b^2} = 1$, so it is a horizontal hyperbola. Thus $a^2 = 25$, so $a = 5$; $b^2 = 16$, so $b = 4$. The hyperbola has vertices $(5, 0)$ and $(-5, 0)$.

To draw the asymptotes, we construct a fundamental rectangle with corners at $(5, 4)$, $(5, -4)$, $(-5, 4)$, and $(-5, -4)$. We draw extended diagonal lines through the rectangle as the asymptotes. We construct each branch of the curve passing through a vertex and getting closer to the asymptotes as the graph of the hyperbola gets farther from the origin.

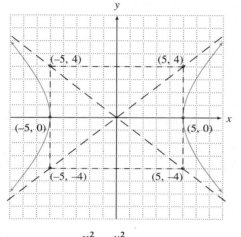

Practice Problem 1 Graph: $\dfrac{x^2}{16} - \dfrac{y^2}{25} = 1$. ∎

Example 2 Graph: $4y^2 - 7x^2 = 28$.

We see we have the standard form of a vertical hyperbola with center at the origin. To find the vertices and asymptotes, we must put the equation in standard form. Divide each term by 28.

$$\frac{4y^2}{28} - \frac{7x^2}{28} = \frac{28}{28}$$

$$\boxed{\frac{y^2}{7} - \frac{x^2}{4} = 1}$$

Here $b^2 = 7$, so $b = \sqrt{7}$; $a^2 = 4$, so $a = 2$. We have a vertical hyperbola with vertices at $(0, \sqrt{7})$ and $(0, -\sqrt{7})$. The fundamental rectangle has corners at $(2, \sqrt{7})$, $(2, -\sqrt{7})$, $(-2, \sqrt{7})$, and $(-2, -\sqrt{7})$. To aid us in graphing we measure the distance $\sqrt{7}$ as approximately 2.6. ∎

Practice Problem 2 Graph: $y^2 - 4x^2 = 4$. ∎

TEACHING TIP Students sometimes confuse horizontal and vertical hyperbolas. After discussing the formula for each and working out example 1, ask students in the class to do the following problem as classwork. Place each hyperbola in standard form and identify it as a horizontal or vertical hyperbola.

A: $2x^2 - y^2 = 72$

Ans.: $\dfrac{x^2}{36} - \dfrac{y^2}{72} = 1$ Horizontal

B: $9y^2 - x^2 = 9$

Ans.: $\dfrac{y^2}{1} - \dfrac{x^2}{9} = 1$ Vertical

C: $49x^2 - 36y^2 = 1764$

Ans.: $\dfrac{x^2}{36} - \dfrac{y^2}{49} = 1$ Horizontal

TEACHING TIP If students still seem somewhat confused after you have worked out example 2, you may want to do the following example. Place in standard form.

$$25y^2 - 16x^2 = 400$$

Ans.: $\dfrac{y^2}{16} - \dfrac{x^2}{25} = 1$

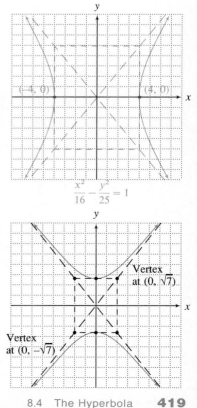

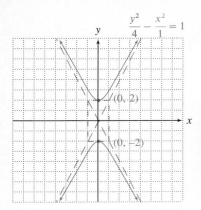

$$\frac{y^2}{4} - \frac{x^2}{1} = 1$$

$(0, 2)$

$(0, -2)$

2 If the hyperbola does not have its center at the origin, but is shifted h units to the right or left and k units up or down, the equation is as follows.

Equation of a Hyperbola in Standard Form with Center at (h, k)

A hyperbola with center at (h, k), where $a, b > 0$ is a horizontal hyperbola with equation

$$\frac{(x - h)^2}{a^2} - \frac{(y - k)^2}{b^2} = 1$$

and vertices $(h - a, k)$ and $(h + a, k)$.

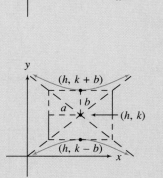

It is a vertical hyperbola with equation

$$\frac{(y - k)^2}{b^2} - \frac{(x - h)^2}{a^2} = 1$$

and vertices $(h, k + b)$ and $(h, k - b)$.

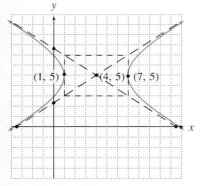

Example 3 Graph: $\dfrac{(x - 4)^2}{9} - \dfrac{(y - 5)^2}{4} = 1$.

The center is (4, 5) and the hyperbola is horizontal. We have $a = 3$ and $b = 2$, so the vertices are $(4 \pm 3, 5)$ or (7, 5) and (1, 5). We can sketch the hyperbola more readily if we can draw a fundamental rectangle. Using (4, 5) as the center, we construct a rectangle $2a$ units wide and $2b$ units high. We then draw and extend the diagonals of the rectangle. The extended diagonals are the asymptotes for the branches of the hyperbola.

In this example since $a = 3$ and $b = 2$, we draw a rectangle $2a = 6$ units wide and $2b = 4$ units high with a center at (4, 5). We draw extended diagonals through the rectangle. From the vertex at (7, 5) we draw a branch of the hyperbola opening to the right. From the vertex at (1, 5) we draw a branch of the hyperbola opening to the left. The graph of the hyperbola is shown. ■

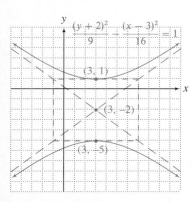

Practice Problem 3 Graph: $\dfrac{(y + 2)^2}{9} - \dfrac{(x - 3)^2}{16} = 1$. ■

Find the vertices and graph each hyperbola. If the equation is not in standard form, write it as such.

1. $\dfrac{x^2}{4} - \dfrac{y^2}{25} = 1$

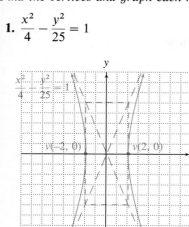

2. $\dfrac{x^2}{9} - \dfrac{y^2}{36} = 1$

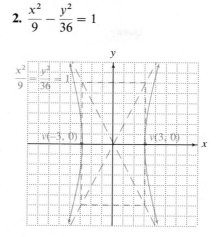

3. $\dfrac{y^2}{36} - \dfrac{x^2}{25} = 1$

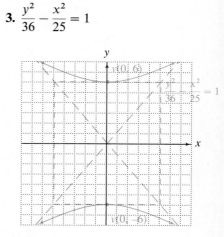

4. $\dfrac{y^2}{49} - \dfrac{x^2}{9} = 1$

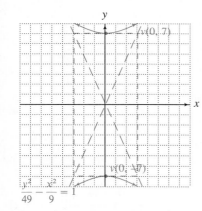

5. $\dfrac{x^2}{9} - \dfrac{y^2}{1} = 1$

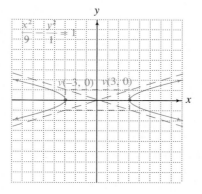 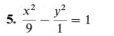

6. $\dfrac{x^2}{16} - \dfrac{y^2}{1} = 1$

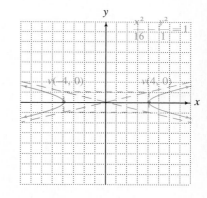

7. $9y^2 - 4x^2 = 36$ $\dfrac{y^2}{4} - \dfrac{x^2}{9} = 1$

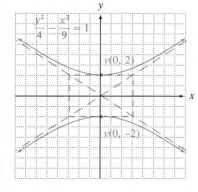

8. $4y^2 - 25x^2 = 100$ $\dfrac{y^2}{25} - \dfrac{x^2}{4} = 1$

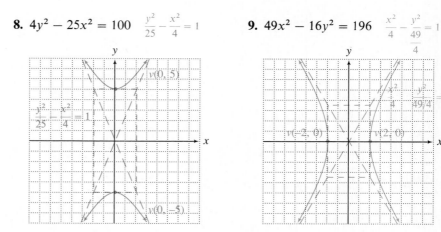

9. $49x^2 - 16y^2 = 196$ $\dfrac{x^2}{4} - \dfrac{y^2}{\frac{49}{4}} = 1$

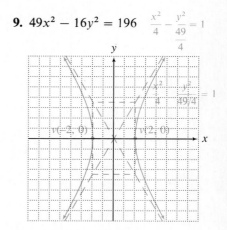 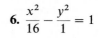

10. $16x^2 - 9y^2 = 144$ $\dfrac{x^2}{9} - \dfrac{y^2}{16} = 1$ **11.** $12x^2 - y^2 = 36$ $\dfrac{x^2}{3} - \dfrac{y^2}{36} = 1$ **12.** $8x^2 - y^2 = 16$ $\dfrac{x^2}{2} - \dfrac{y^2}{16} = 1$

13. $3y^2 - 5x^2 = 15$ $\dfrac{y^2}{5} - \dfrac{x^2}{3} = 1$ **14.** $5y^2 - 6x^2 = 30$ $\dfrac{y^2}{6} - \dfrac{x^2}{5} = 1$

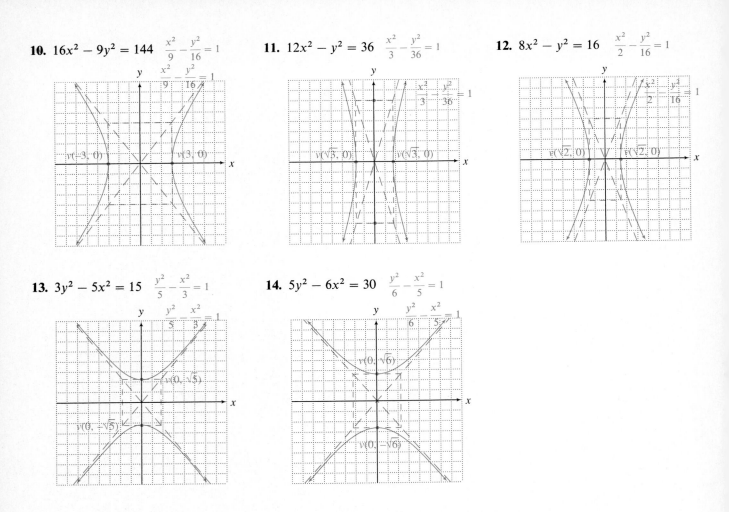

If $a = b$, the hyperbola is called an equilateral hyperbola. Graph the following equilateral hyperbolas.

15. $\dfrac{x^2}{16} - \dfrac{y^2}{16} = 1$ **16.** $\dfrac{x^2}{9} - \dfrac{y^2}{9} = 1$

17. $8y^2 - 8x^2 = 24$

$\dfrac{y^2}{3} - \dfrac{x^2}{3} = 1$ **18.** $5y^2 - 5x^2 = 10$

$\dfrac{y^2}{2} - \dfrac{x^2}{2} = 1$

Find the equation of the hyperbola with center at the origin and:

19. Vertices at $(2, 0)$ and $(-2, 0)$; asymptotes $y = \frac{3}{2}x$,

$y = -\frac{3}{2}x$ $a = 2$
$b = 3$
$\frac{x^2}{4} - \frac{y^2}{9} = 1$

20. Vertices at $(3, 0)$ and $(-3, 0)$; asymptotes $y = \frac{4}{3}x$,

$y = -\frac{4}{3}x$ $a = 3, b = 4$
$\frac{x^2}{9} - \frac{y^2}{16} = 1$

21. Vertices at $(0, 5)$ and $(0, -5)$; asymptotes $y = \frac{5}{3}x$,

$y = -\frac{5}{3}x$ $a = 3, b = 5$
$\frac{y^2}{25} - \frac{x^2}{9} = 1$

22. Vertices at $(0, 4)$ and $(0, -4)$; asymptotes $y = \frac{4}{5}x$,

$y = -\frac{4}{5}x$ $a = 5, b = 4$
$\frac{y^2}{16} - \frac{x^2}{25} = 1$

Find the center and then graph each hyperbola. Draw the axes at a convenient location. You may want to use a scale other than 1 square = 1 unit.

23. $\dfrac{(x-6)^2}{25} - \dfrac{(y-4)^2}{49} = 1$

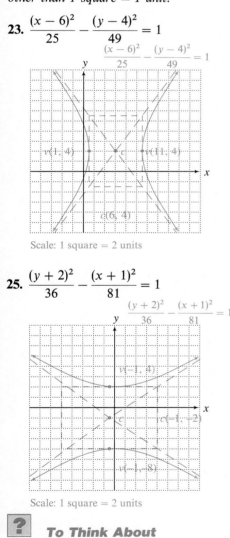

$\dfrac{(x-6)^2}{25} - \dfrac{(y-4)^2}{49} = 1$

Scale: 1 square = 2 units

24. $\dfrac{(x-7)^2}{16} - \dfrac{(y-5)^2}{25} = 1$

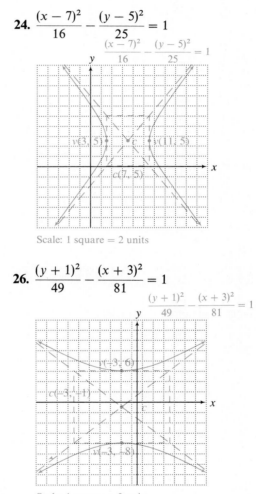

$\dfrac{(x-7)^2}{16} - \dfrac{(y-5)^2}{25} = 1$

Scale: 1 square = 2 units

25. $\dfrac{(y+2)^2}{36} - \dfrac{(x+1)^2}{81} = 1$

$\dfrac{(y+2)^2}{36} - \dfrac{(x+1)^2}{81} = 1$

Scale: 1 square = 2 units

26. $\dfrac{(y+1)^2}{49} - \dfrac{(x+3)^2}{81} = 1$

$\dfrac{(y+1)^2}{49} - \dfrac{(x+3)^2}{81} = 1$

Scale: 1 square = 2 units

? **To Think About**

27. A hyperbola center is not at the origin. Its vertices are $(5, 0)$ and $(5, 14)$, one asymptote is $y = \frac{7}{5}x$. Find the equation of the hyperbola.

$\dfrac{(y-7)^2}{49} - \dfrac{(x-5)^2}{25} = 1$

28. A rocket following a hyperbolic path turns rapidly at $(4, 0)$ and follows a path that comes closer and closer to the line $y = \dfrac{2}{3}x$ as the rocket gets farther from the tracking station. Find the equation that describes the path of the rocket if the center of the hyperbola is at $(0, 0)$.

$$\frac{x^2}{16} - \frac{y^2}{\frac{64}{9}} = 1$$

Cumulative Review Problems

Factor completely.

29. $2x^3 - 54$

$2(x^3 - 27) = 2(x - 3)(x^2 + 3x + 9)$

30. $12x^2 + x - 6$

$(4x + 3)(3x - 2)$

Combine.

31. $\dfrac{3}{x^2 - 5x + 6} + \dfrac{2}{x^2 - 4}$

$\dfrac{3}{(x - 3)(x - 2)} + \dfrac{2}{(x + 2)(x - 2)}$

$\dfrac{5x}{(x - 3)(x - 2)(x + 2)}$

32. $\dfrac{2x}{5x^2 + 9x - 2} - \dfrac{3}{5x - 1}$

$\dfrac{2x}{(5x - 1)(x + 2)} - \dfrac{3}{5x - 1}$

$\dfrac{2x - 3x - 6}{(5x - 1)(x + 2)} = \dfrac{-x - 6}{(5x - 1)(x + 2)}$ or $-\dfrac{x + 6}{(5x - 1)(x + 2)}$

Calculator Problems

33. In the hyperbola $8x^2 - y^2 = 16$, if $x = 3.5$, what are the two values of y?

$y = \pm 9.055385138$

34. In the hyperbola $x^2 - 12y^2 = 36$, if $x = 8.2$, what are the two values of y?

$y = \pm 1.613484841$

For Extra Practice Exercises, turn to page 445.

Solutions to Odd-Numbered Practice Problems

1. $\dfrac{x^2}{16} - \dfrac{y^2}{25} = 1$ is the equation of a horizontal hyperbola with center $(0, 0)$, where $a = 4$ and $b = 5$. The vertices are $(-4, 0)$ and $(4, 0)$.

3. $\dfrac{(y + 2)^2}{9} - \dfrac{(x - 3)^2}{16} = 1$ is a vertical hyperbola with center at $(3, -2)$, $a = 4$, and $b = 3$. The vertices are $(3, 1)$ and $(3, -5)$.

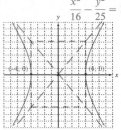

Answer to Even-Numbered Practice Problem

2. $y^2 - 4x^2 = 4$

$\dfrac{y^2}{4} - \dfrac{x^2}{1} = 1$

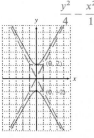

8.5 FUNCTIONS

After studying this section, you will be able to:

1 Describe what a relation is

2 Determine if a relation is a function and find the domain and range of a function

3 Determine if a given graph is or is not a function

4 Evaluate a function using functional notation

1 The concept of a function is one of the most basic and important in mathematics and science. But before we define a function, we must define a relation.

> **Definition of a Relation**
>
> A **relation** is any set of ordered pairs.

This simply means that we can relate two things, and the order in which we relate them is important. Consider a menu at a pizzeria.

Pizza	Price
Plain	$7.50
Pepperoni	$8.00
Mushroom	$8.25

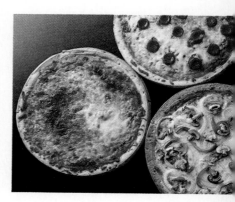

The type of pizza and its price are obviously related. We can say that they are an ordered pair. For another example, consider the formula for the area of a circle $A = \pi r^2$, where the area A and the radius r are variables. Clearly, A and r are related. For every value we give r, there is a definite value for A. If $r = 1$, then $A = \pi$; if $r = 2$, then $A = 4\pi$, and so on. If we construct a table of values

r	A
1	π
2	4π
-1	π
-2	4π

we are actually listing the ordered pairs $(1, \pi)$, $(2, 4\pi)$, $(-1, \pi)$, $(-2, 4\pi)$, and so on. The *order* is important, since $(2, 4\pi)$ is not the same as $(4\pi, 2)$.

2 We can write the ordered pairs in set notation as $\{(1, \pi), (2, 4\pi), (-1, \pi), (-2, 4\pi)\}$. All of the first items of the pair can be grouped as a set called the **domain** of the relation. The set of second items is called the **range**. In our example, the "items" are coordinates of a point. The domain is $\{1, 2, -1, -2\}$, and the range is $\{\pi, 4\}$. (Note that we need not repeat the same coordinate.)

Example 1 Find the domain and range of the relation $\{(1, 7), (2, 9), (3, 11), (4, 13)\}$.

The domain is the set of all first coordinates: $\{1, 2, 3, 4\}$. The range is the set of all second coordinates: $\{7, 9, 11, 13\}$. ■

Practice Problem 1 What are the domain and range of the relation $A = \{(2, 0), (5, 0), (6, 3), (8, 3)\}$? ■

We can now define a special type of relation.

> **Definition of a Function**
>
> A function is a relation in which no ordered pairs have the same first coordinates.

Example 2 Give the domain and range of each relation. Indicate if the relation is a function.

(a) $M = \{(1, 1), (2, 4), (3, 9), (4, 16)\}$ **(b)** $N = \{(2, 8), (2, 3), (3, 7), (3, 12)\}$

TEACHING TIP Remind students that it is important to understand what the Domain and Range are for any relation or function. Have them do the following: Find the domain and range of the relation $\{(-1, 6), (3, 6), (9, 5), (4, 5)\}$

Domain $= \{-1, 3, 4, 9\}$

Range $= \{5, 6\}$ Ans.

(c) $P = \{(6, 1), (2, 1), (3, 1), (4, 8)\}$

(a) The domain of M is $\{1, 2, 3, 4\}$. The range of M is $\{1, 4, 9, 16\}$.
The relation is a function.

(b) The domain of N is $\{2, 3\}$. The range of N is $\{3, 7, 8, 12\}$.
The relation is not a function because the ordered pairs (2, 8) and (2, 3) have the same first coordinate. Also, the ordered pairs (3, 7) and (3, 12) have the same first coordinate.

(c) The domain of P is $\{2, 3, 4, 6\}$. The range of P is $\{1, 8\}$. The relation is a function. ∎

Practice Problem 2 Give the domain and range of each relation. Indicate if the relation is a function.

(a) $Q = \{(1, -1), (2, -4), (-1, -1), (-2, -4)\}$

(b) $R = \{(1, 5), (2, 6), (3, 7), (1, 8)\}$

(c) $S = \{(3, 4), (6, 8), (5, 4), (7, 8)\}$ ■

A good way to picture a function is as follows:

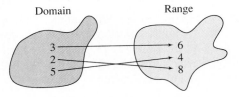

Note that for each value in the domain, there is only *one* value in the range. In this diagram, the relation is

$$\{(3, 6), (2, 8), (5, 4)\}$$

and the relation is a function. In the diagram

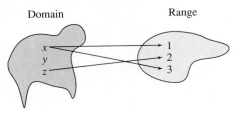

the relation is

$$\{(x, 1), (x, 3), (z, 2)\}$$

which is not a function because there are *two* values for x in the range (or there are two ordered pairs with the same first coordinate).

3 By examining the graph of a relation, we can quickly tell whether it is a function. If a vertical line drawn anywhere crosses the graph of a relation in *more* than one place, the relation is not a function. In this sketch we observe the dashed vertical line crosses the curve of a function only once.

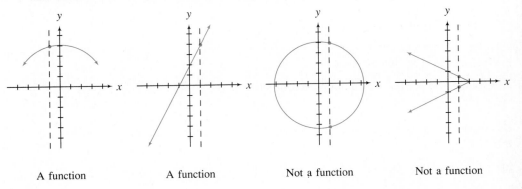

A function   A function   Not a function   Not a function

Vertical Line Test

If any vertical line can intersect the graph of a relation more than once, the relation is not a function.

TEACHING TIP After discussing the vertical line test and example 3, see if the students can do the following. Determine by the vertical line test which of the following graphs represents a function.

Ans.: B and C are functions. A is not.

Example 3 Determine if each of the following is a graph of a function.

(a)

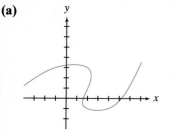

(b)

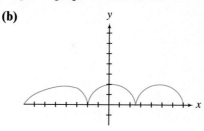

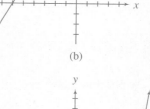

(a)

(a) By the vertical line test, this relation is not a function.

(b) By the vertical line test, this relation is a function.

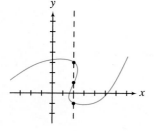

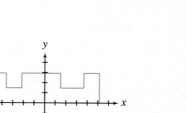

■

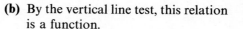

(b)

Practice Problem 3 Does this graph represent a function?

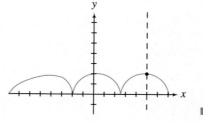

■

(c)

4 Since a function is a relation, we say that the second coordinate of the ordered pair is a function of the first. For example, $y = x^2$ describes a parabola. Here y is a function of x because every time we give a value to x, y automatically receives a value.

We use a shorthand notation to mean "y is a function of x." It is

$$y = f(x) \quad \text{or} \quad f(x) = y$$

Thus we could write $y = x^2$ or $f(x) = x^2$.

Note: The notation $f(x)$ does not mean f multiplied by x. It means that y is related to x in such a way that every time we give a value to x, we get only *one* value for y.

It may help you understand the idea of a function by imaging a "function machine" An item from the domain enters the machine—the function—and a member of the range results. We'll use $f(x) = x^2$ as an example.

If the x we put into the function machine is 3, the machine will give us 3^2, or 9.

x

Function, *f*

x^2

Example 4 If $f(x) = 2x^2 + 1$, find

(a) $f(2)$

(b) $f(-3)$

The function is described by the expression $2x^2 + 1$. This means that in order to find a value for y [where $y = f(x)$], we must take our value for x, square it, multiply by 2, and add 1. When $x = 2$, $f(x) = f(2)$; when $x = -3$, $f(x) = f(-3)$. Therefore,

(a) $f(2) = 2(2)^2 + 1 = 2(4) + 1 = 8 + 1 = 9$
(b) $f(-3) = 2(-3)^2 + 1 = 2(9) + 1 = 18 + 1 = 19$ ■

Practice Problem 4   If $f(x) = 3 - 2x^2$, find
(a) $f(1)$ **(b)** $f(-2)$ ■

Example 5   If $f(x) = 5 - 2x$, find

(a) $f(a)$ **(b)** $f(a + 2)$
(c) $f(3a)$ **(d)** $f(a + 2) - f(a)$

(a) $f(a) = 5 - 2a$
(b) $f(a + 2) = 5 - 2(a + 2) = 5 - 2a - 4 = 1 - 2a$
(c) $f(3a) = 5 - 2(3a) = 5 - 6a$
(d) Since $f(a + 2) = 1 - 2a$ and $f(a) = 5 - 2a$, we have

$$f(a + 2) - f(a) = (1 - 2a) - (5 - 2a)$$
$$= 1 - 2a - 5 + 2a$$
$$= -4$$ ■

TEACHING TIP   If after discussing example 5 with students you sense some confusion, you may want to do the following additional example.
If $g(x) = -3x - 2$
Find A: $g(a)$
    B: $g(a + 3)$
    C: $g(2a)$

Ans. A: $g(a) = -3a - 2$

Ans. B: $g(a + 3) = -3a - 11$

Ans. C: $g(2a) = -6a - 2$

Practice Problem 5   If $f(x) = 3x^2 - 4x + 1$, find
(a) $f(0)$ **(b)** $f(-1)$
(c) $f(a + 2)$ **(d)** $f(a + 2) - f(a)$ ■

EXERCISES 8.5

1. A relation is any set __Of ordered pairs__ .

2. A function is a relation in which no two ordered pairs have __The same first coordinate__ .

3. If any vertical line can intersect the graph of a relation more than once, __The relation is not a function__ .

4. The expression y is a function of x is written as __$y = f(x)$__ .

What are the domain and range of each relation? Is the relation a function?

5. $A = \{(10, 1), (12, 2), (14, 3), (16, 4)\}$
Domain = $\{10, 12, 14, 16\}$
Range = $\{1, 2, 3, 4\}$
Relation is a function

6. $B = \{(1, 4), (2, 9), (3, 16), (4, 25)\}$
Domain = $\{1, 2, 3, 4\}$
Range = $\{4, 9, 16, 25\}$
Relation is a function

7. $C = \{(1, 5), (12, 18), (3, 5), (1, 12)\}$
Domain = $\{1, 3, 12\}$
Range = $\{5, 12, 18\}$
Relation is *not* a function

8. $D = \{(0, 0), (5, 13), (7, 11), (5, 0)\}$
Domain = $\{0, 5, 7\}$
Range = $\{0, 11, 13\}$
Relation is *not* a function

9. $E = \{(3, -2), (4, -2), (5, 7), (8, -6)\}$
Domain = $\{3, 4, 5, 8\}$
Range = $\{-6, -2, 7\}$
Relation is a function

10. $F = \{(-7, 2), (-6, -1), (-3, 4), (-7, -6)\}$
Domain = $\{-7, -6, -3\}$
Range = $\{-6, -1, 2, 4\}$
Relation is *not* a function

11. $G = \{(1, 8), (3, 8), (5, 8), (7, 8)\}$
Domain = $\{1, 3, 5, 7\}$
Range = $\{8\}$
Relation is a function

12. $H = \{(2, 6), (12, 6), (-3, 6), (7, 6)\}$
Domain = $\{-3, 2, 7, 12\}$
Range = $\{6\}$
Relation is a function

13. $J = \{(3, 11), (11, 3), (-3, -11), (11, -3)\}$

    Domain $= \{-3, 3, 11\}$

    Range $= \{-11, -3, 3, 11\}$

    Relation is *not* a function

14. $K = \{(2, 14), (14, 2), (-2, -14), (14, -2)\}$

    Domain $= \{-2, 2, 14\}$

    Range $= \{-14, -2, 2, 14\}$

    Relation is *not* a function

Which of these graphs represent functions?

15.

Function

16.

Function

17.

Function

18.

Function

19.

Function

20.

Function

21.

Not a function

22.

Not a function

23.

Function

24.

Function

25.

Not a function

26.

Not a function

27.

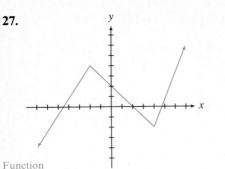

Function

28.

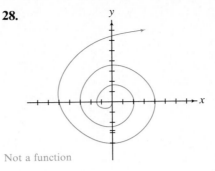

Not a function

Define the functions.

$$f(x) = x^3 \qquad g(x) = 2x^2 - 3x + 4 \qquad h(x) = 5x - 6$$

$$k(x) = 12 \qquad p(x) = x^4 - 2x^2 \qquad r(x) = (x + 3)^2$$

Find each of the following. Simplify your answers.

29. (a) $f(2)$ **(b)** $f(-3)$ **(c)** $f(0)$
  (a) $f(2) = 8$
  (b) $f(-3) = -27$
  (c) $f(0) = 0$

30. (a) $g(3)$ **(b)** $g(-1)$ **(c)** $g(0)$
  (a) $g(3) = 2(3)^2 - 3(3) + 4 = 13$
  (b) $g(-1) = 2(-1)^2 - 3(-1) + 4 = 9$
  (c) $g(0) = 4$

31. (a) $h\left(\dfrac{1}{3}\right)$ **(b)** $h(-2)$ **(c)** $h(0)$
  (a) $h\left(\dfrac{1}{3}\right) = 5\left(\dfrac{1}{3}\right) - 6 = \dfrac{5}{3} - \dfrac{18}{3} = \dfrac{-13}{3}$
  (b) $h(-2) = 5(-2) - 6 = -16$
  (c) $h(0) = 5(0) - 6 = -6$

32. (a) $k(0)$ **(b)** $k(-3)$ **(c)** $k(4)$
  (a) $k(0) = 12$
  (b) $k(-3) = 12$
  (c) $k(4) = 12$

33. (a) $p(1)$ **(b)** $p(-2)$ **(c)** $r(3)$
  (a) $p(1) = 1^4 - 2(1)^2 = -1$
  (b) $p(-2) = (-2)^4 - 2(-2)^2 = 8$
  (c) $r(3) = (3 + 3)^2 = 36$

34. (a) $f\left(\dfrac{1}{2}\right)$ **(b)** $k\left(\dfrac{1}{3}\right)$ **(c)** $h\left(\dfrac{1}{5}\right)$
  (a) $f\left(\dfrac{1}{2}\right) = \left(\dfrac{1}{2}\right)^3 = \dfrac{1}{8}$
  (b) $k\left(\dfrac{1}{3}\right) = 12$
  (c) $h\left(\dfrac{1}{5}\right) = 5\left(\dfrac{1}{5}\right) - 6 = -5$

35. (a) $g(a)$ **(b)** $g(a + 1)$
  (a) $g(a) = 2a^2 - 3a + 4$
  (b) $g(a + 1) = 2(a + 1)^2 - 3(a + 1) + 4 = 2a^2 - a + 3$

36. (a) $f(a)$ **(b)** $f(3a)$
  (a) $f(a) = a^3$
  (b) $f(3a) = (3a)^3 = 27a^3$

37. (a) $r(a)$ **(b)** $r(a - 3)$
  (a) $r(a) = (a + 3)^2 = a^2 + 6a + 9$
  (b) $r(a - 3) = (a - 3 + 3)^2 = a^2$

38. (a) $h(x + 3)$ **(b)** $h(x)$ **(c)** $h(x + 3) - h(x)$
  (a) $h(x + 3) = 5(x + 3) - 6 = 5x + 9$
  (b) $h(x) = 5x - 6$
  (c) $h(x + 3) - h(x) = 5x + 9 - (5x - 6) = 15$

39. (a) $r(x + 2)$ **(b)** $r(x)$ **(c)** $r(x + 2) - r(x)$
  (a) $r(x + 2) = (x + 2 + 3)^2 = x^2 + 10x + 25$
  (b) $r(x) = (x + 3)^2 = x^2 + 6x + 9$
  (c) $r(x + 2) - r(x) = x^2 + 10x + 25 - (x^2 + 6x + 9) = 4x + 16$

40. (a) $r(2x)$ **(b)** $r(2)$ **(c)** $r(2x) - r(2)$
  (a) $r(2x) = (2x + 3)^2 = 4x^2 + 12x + 9$
  (b) $r(2) = (2 + 3)^2 = 25$
  (c) $r(2x) - r(2) = 4x^2 + 12x + 9 - 25 = 4x^2 + 12x - 16$

? **To Think About**

In problems 41–44, find $\dfrac{f(x + h) - f(x)}{h}$.

41. $f(x) = 4x + 1$

$\dfrac{f(x + h) - f(x)}{h} = \dfrac{[4(x + h) + 1] - (4x + 1)}{h} = \dfrac{4h}{h} = 4$

42. $f(x) = 2x - 3$

$\dfrac{f(x + h) - f(x)}{h} = \dfrac{[2(x + h) - 3] - (2x - 3)}{h} = \dfrac{2h}{h} = 2$

43. $f(x) = 2x^2$

$\dfrac{2(x + h)^2 - 2x^2}{h} = \dfrac{2x^2 + 4xh + 2h^2 - 2x^2}{h} = \dfrac{h(4x + 2h)}{h} = 4x + 2h$

44. $f(x) = x^2 + x$

$\dfrac{(x + h)^2 + (x + h) - x^2 - x}{h} = \dfrac{2xh + h^2 + h}{h} = 2x + h + 1$

45. A rope 20 feet long is cut into two unequal pieces. Each piece is used to form a square. Write a function $A(x)$ that expresses the *total* area enclosed by the two squares. Assume that the shorter piece of rope is x feet long. Evaluate $A(2)$, $A(5)$, and $A(8)$.

1st piece $= x$
2nd piece $= 20 - x$

$$A(x) = \frac{x^2 + (20 - x)^2}{16}$$

$A(2) = 20.5 \text{ ft}^2$
$A(5) = 15.625 \text{ ft}^2$
$A(8) = 13.0 \text{ ft}^2$

46. In problem 45, assume that the smaller piece of rope is used to form a circle and the longer piece is used to form a square. Write a function $A(x)$ that expresses the *total* area enclosed by the circle and the square. Evaluate $A(3)$, and $A(9)$. Round answer to nearest hundredth.

$$A(x) = \frac{x^2}{4\pi} + \frac{(20 - x)^2}{16}$$

$A(3) = 18.78 \text{ ft}^2$
$A(9) = 14.01 \text{ ft}^2$

Cumulative Review Problems

Simplify.

47. $\dfrac{4x^2 + 4}{x^2 + x - 2} \cdot \dfrac{x^2 - 2x + 1}{x^3 + x}$

$\dfrac{4(x^2 + 1)}{(x + 2)(x - 1)} \cdot \dfrac{(x - 1)(x - 1)}{x(x^2 + 1)} = \dfrac{4(x - 1)}{x(x + 2)}$

48. $\dfrac{x + 3}{x^2 - 4} \div \dfrac{x^2 - x - 12}{x^3 - 8}$

$\dfrac{x + 3}{(x - 2)(x + 2)} \cdot \dfrac{(x - 2)(x^2 + 2x + 4)}{(x - 4)(x + 3)} = \dfrac{x^2 + 2x + 4}{(x + 2)(x - 4)}$

Solve for x. Check your solution.

49. $\dfrac{3}{x - 2} - \dfrac{1}{x - 1} = \dfrac{7}{x^2 - 3x + 2}$

$3(x - 1) - 1(x - 2) = 7$
$2x - 1 = 7$
$x = 4$

50. $\dfrac{2}{x + 5} = \dfrac{3}{2x - 3}$

$2(2x - 3) = 3(x + 5)$
$x = 21$

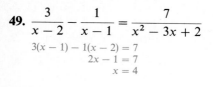

Calculator Problems

51. Find $f(-2.36)$ if $f(x) = 2x^2 - 5x + 6$.

$f(-2.36) = 28.9392$

52. Find $g(19.32)$ if $g(x) = x^3 + 3x^2 - 7x - 12$.

$g(19.32) = 8183.976768$

For Extra Practice Exercises, turn to page 446.

Solutions to Odd-Numbered Practice Problems

1. Domain of $A = \{2, 5, 6, 8\}$
Range of $A = \{0, 3\}$

3. The graph does *not* represent a function because we can draw a vertical line that intersects the graph in more than one place.

5. $f(x) = 3x^2 - 4x + 1$
  (a) $f(0) = 3(0)^2 - 4(0) + 1 = 0 - 0 + 1 = 1$
  (b) $f(-1) = 3(-1)^2 - 4(-1) + 1 = +3 + 4 + 1 = 8$
  (c) $f(a + 2) = 3(a + 2)^2 - 4(a + 2) + 1$
    $= 3(a^2 + 4a + 4) - 4a - 8 + 1$
    $= 3a^2 + 12a + 12 - 4a - 8 + 1$
    $= 3a^2 + 8a + 5$
  (d) $f(a + 2) - f(a) = (3a^2 + 8a + 5) - (3a^2 - 4a + 1)$
    $= 3a^2 + 8a + 5 - 3a^2 + 4a - 1$
    $= 12a + 4$

Answers to Even-Numbered Practice Problems

2. (a) The domain of Q is $\{-2, -1, 1, 2\}$. (The elements of the domain can be listed in any order.) The range of Q is $\{-4, -1\}$. Q is a function.
  (b) The domain of R is $\{1, 2, 3\}$. The range of R is $\{5, 6, 7, 8\}$. R is not a function since $(1, 5)$ and $(1, 8)$ have the same first coordinates.
  (c) The domain of S is $\{3, 5, 6, 7\}$. The range of S is $\{4, 8\}$. S is a function.
4. (a) $f(1) = 1$ **(b)** $f(-2) = -5$

8.6 INVERSE OF A FUNCTION

1 Even as a real number has an inverse (see Chapter 1), a function may also have an inverse. For example, if y is a function of x, we can apply the inverse function of y (written y^{-1}) to y and obtain x. The following discussion will make this clear.

First we state that not all functions have inverse functions. To have an inverse that is a function, a function must be one-to-one. This means that for every value of y, there is only one value of x. Or, in the language of ordered pairs, no ordered pairs have the same second coordinate.

> **Definition of a One-to-One Function**
>
> A one-to-one function is a function in which no ordered pairs have the same second coordinate.

Example 1 Indicate if the following functions are one-to-one.

(a) $M = \{(1, 3), (2, 7), (5, 8), (6, 12)\}$ **(b)** $P = \{(1, 4), (2, 9), (3, 4), (4, 18)\}$

(a) M is a function because no ordered pairs have the same first coordinate. M is a one-to-one function because no ordered pairs have the same second coordinate.

(b) P is a function, *but* it is not one-to-one because the ordered pairs $(1, 4)$, $(3, 4)$ have the same second coordinates.

Thus the function M has an inverse function but the function P does not.   ■

Practice Problem 1 Is the function $A = \{(-2, -6), (-3, -5), (-1, 2), (3, 5)\}$ one-to-one? ■

2 By examining the graph of a function, we can quickly tell whether it is one-to-one. If a horizontal line drawn anywhere crosses the graph of a function in *more* than one place, the function is not one-to-one.

> **Horizontal Line Test**
>
> If any horizontal line can intersect the graph of a function more than once, the function is not one-to-one.

Example 2 Determine whether each of the following is a graph of a one-to-one function.

(a)   **(b)**

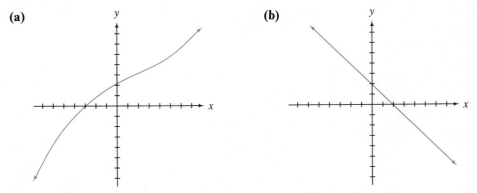

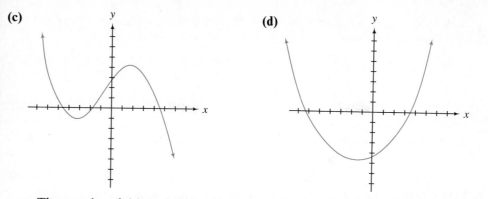

The graphs of **(a)** and **(b)** represent one-to-one functions. A horizontal line crosses the graph only once. The graphs of **(c)** and **(d)** do not represent one-to-one functions. A horizontal line crosses the graph more than once.

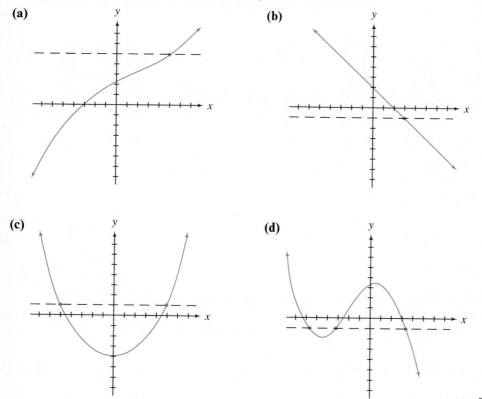

TEACHING TIP   Explain to students that we want to be able to determine if a function is a one-to-one function whether or not the graph of the function is available. That is why we have more than one way to determine if a function is a one-to-one function.

Practice Problem 2   Does the graph represent a one-to-one function?   ■

3   How do we find the inverse of a function? We simply interchange the ordered pairs. In Example 1, we said M has an inverse. What is it?

$$M = \{(1, 3), (2, 7), (5, 8), (6, 12)\}$$

The inverse of M, written M^{-1}, is

$$M^{-1} = \{(3, 1), (7, 2), (8, 5), (12, 6)\}$$

Now do you see why a function must be one-to-one to have an inverse? If not, let's look at the function P from Example 1.

$$P = \{(1, 4), (2, 9), (3, 4), (4, 18)\}$$

If P had an inverse, it would be

$$P^{-1} = \{(4, 1), (9, 2), (4, 3), (18, 4)\}$$

TEACHING TIP It usually takes the student a while to develop this concept of an inverse function. After explaining example 3, do the following additional example. If a function is defined by $6 = \{(4, 2), (7, 5), (12, 10), (14, 12)\}$. Determine the inverse of the function G.

Inverse of function $G = G^{-1} = \{(2, 4), (5, 7), (10, 12), (12, 14)\}$

But we have two ordered pairs with the same first coordinate. Therefore, P^{-1} is not a function (in other words, the inverse function does not exist).

By the way, M^{-1} does *not* mean $\dfrac{1}{M}$. Here the -1 simply means "inverse."

Example 3 Determine the inverse function of the function F if $F = \{(6, 1), (12, 2), (13, 5), (14, 6)\}$.

The inverse function of F is denoted by $F^{-1} = \{(1, 6), (2, 12), (5, 13), (6, 14)\}$. ■

Practice Problem 3 Find the inverse of the one-to-one function $B = \{(1, 2), (7, 8), (8, 7), (10, 12)\}$. ■

Suppose the function is given in the form of an equation. How do we find the inverse? Since, by definition, we interchange the ordered pairs to find the inverse of a function, this means the x values of the function become the y values of the inverse function.

Find the Inverse of a One-to-One Function

1. Replace $f(x)$ with y.
2. Interchange x and y.
3. Solve for y in terms of x.
4. Replace y with $f^{-1}(x)$.

Example 4 Find the inverse of $f(x) = 3x - 2$.

1. $y = 3x - 2$ Replacing $f(x)$ with y.
2. $x = 3y - 2$ Interchanging the variables x and y.
3. $x + 2 = 3y$ Solving for y in terms of x.

$$\frac{x + 2}{3} = y$$

4. $f^{-1}(x) = \dfrac{x + 2}{3}$ Replacing y by $f^{-1}(x)$. ■

Practice Problem 4 Find the inverse of the function $g(x) = 4 - 6x$. ■

The graphs of $f(x)$ and $f^{-1}(x)$ are symmetric about the line $y = x$.

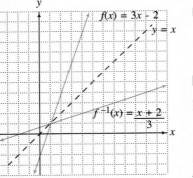

■ **Example 5** On the same set of axes, graph $f(x) = 3x - 2$ and $f^{-1}(x) = \dfrac{x + 2}{3}$.

Locate the line $y = x$.

The graph is shown. ■

Practice Problem 5 Find the inverse of the one-to-one function $f(x) = \sqrt[3]{x} + 2$. ■

EXERCISES 8.6

Complete the following:

1. A one-to-one function is a function in which no ordered pairs <u>Have same second coordinate</u>.

2. If any horizontal line can intersect the graph of a function more than once, <u>Not one to one</u>.

3. Graph of a function $f(x)$ and its inverse $f^{-1}(x)$ are symmetric to <u>$y = x$</u>.

4. Do all functions have inverse functions?

No, only those functions which are one-to-one functions

Are the following functions one-to-one?

5. $A = \{(-6, -2), (6, 2), (3, 4)\}$
Yes

6. $B = \{(0, 1), (1, 0), (10, 0)\}$
No

7. $C = \{(12, 3), (-6, 1), (6, 3)\}$
No

8. $D = \{(-6, -12), (3, 8), (6, 12)\}$
Yes

9. $E = \{(0, 7), (3, 8), (7, 0), (-8, -3)\}$
Yes

10. $F = \{(5, 0), (2, -7), (-2, 7), (0, 5)\}$
Yes

Which graphs represent one-to-one functions?

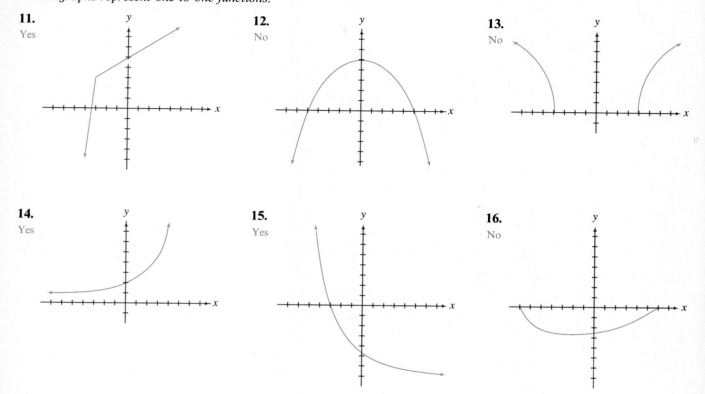

11.
Yes

12.
No

13.
No

14.
Yes

15.
Yes

16.
No

Find the inverse of each one-to-one function.

17. $G = \{(-1, 0), (5, 8)\}$
$G^{-1}\{(0, -1), (8, 5)\}$

18. $H = \{(2, 7), (-3, -1)\}$
$H^{-1} = \{(7, 2), (-1, -3)\}$

19. $J = \{(8, 2), (1, 1), (0, 0), (-8, -2)\}$
$J^{-1} = \{(2, 8), (1, 1), (0, 0), (-2, -8)\}$

20. $K = \{(-7, 1), (6, 2), (3, -1), (2, 5)\}$
$K^{-1} = \{(1, -7), (2, 6), (-1, 3), (5, 2)\}$

21. $L = \{(1, 4), (2, 9), (3, 16), (-2, -9)\}$
$L^{-1} = \{(4, 1), (9, 2), (16, 3), (-9, -2)\}$

22. $M = \{(0, 0), (-1, 1), (1, -1), (2, 8)\}$
$M^{-1} = \{(0, 0), (1, -1), (-1, 1), (8, 2)\}$

Find the inverse of each function. Graph the function and its inverse on the same set of axes.

23. $f(x) = 3x + 4$

$x = 3y + 4$
$y = \dfrac{x - 4}{3}$
$f^{-1} = \dfrac{x - 4}{3}$

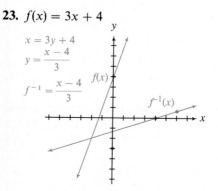

24. $g(x) = 2x + 5$

$x = 2y + 5$
$y = \dfrac{x - 5}{2}$
$g^{-1}(x) = \dfrac{x - 5}{2}$

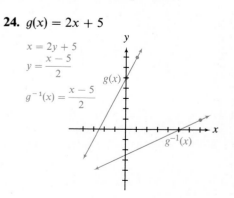

25. $h(x) = \dfrac{1}{2}x - 2$

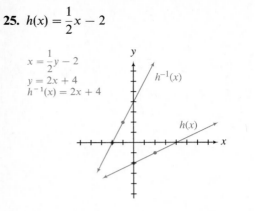

$x = \dfrac{1}{2}y - 2$

$y = 2x + 4$

$h^{-1}(x) = 2x + 4$

26. $p(x) = \dfrac{2}{3}x - 4$

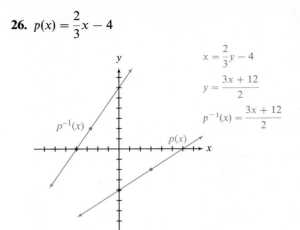

$x = \dfrac{2}{3}y - 4$

$y = \dfrac{3x + 12}{2}$

$p^{-1}(x) = \dfrac{3x + 12}{2}$

27. $k(x) = 2x - 3$

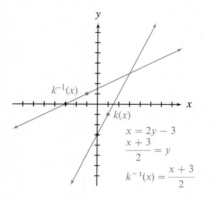

$x = 2y - 3$

$\dfrac{x + 3}{2} = y$

$k^{-1}(x) = \dfrac{x + 3}{2}$

28. $r(x) = -3x - 1$

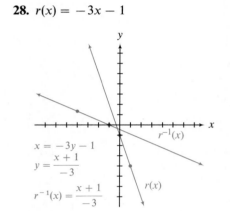

$x = -3y - 1$

$y = \dfrac{x + 1}{-3}$

$r^{-1}(x) = \dfrac{x + 1}{-3}$

29. $s(x) = 4 - 2x$

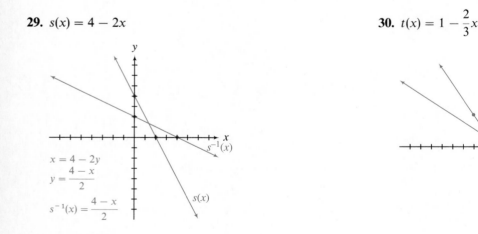

$x = 4 - 2y$

$y = \dfrac{4 - x}{2}$

$s^{-1}(x) = \dfrac{4 - x}{2}$

30. $t(x) = 1 - \dfrac{2}{3}x$

$x = 1 - \dfrac{2}{3}y$

$y = \dfrac{3 - 3x}{2}$

$t^{-1}(x) = \dfrac{3 - 3x}{2}$

Sometimes the finding of an inverse function involves taking a root of each side of the equation or raising each side of the equation to a specified power. A function written as a cube root will require a step to raise each side to the third power. A function written as a third-degree polynomial may require a step to take the cube root of each side of the equation.

Use these procedures to find the inverse of each function in Problems 31–34.

Find the inverse of each function.

31. $g(x) = \sqrt[3]{x} - 1$

$x = \sqrt[3]{y} - 1$
$x^3 = y - 1$
$y = x^3 - 1$
$g^{-1}(x) = x^3 - 1$

32. $f(x) = \sqrt[3]{x} + 2$

$x = \sqrt[3]{y} + 2$
$x^3 = y + 2$
$y = f^{-1}(x) = x^3 - 2$

33. $p(x) = x^3 + 4$

$x = y^3 + 4$
$y = \sqrt[3]{x - 4}$
$p^{-1}(x) = \sqrt[3]{x - 4}$

34. $h(x) = x^3 - 1$

$x = y^3 - 1$
$y = \sqrt[3]{x + 1}$
$h^{-1}(x) = \sqrt[3]{x + 1}$

? To Think About

If we restrict the domain of some functions, we can obtain one-to-one functions in that restricted domain. For example,
$f(x) = x^2$ *is not a one-to-one function, but* $f(x) = x^2$ *for* $x > 0$ *is a one-to-one function.*

35. The region of the ellipse $\dfrac{x^2}{4} + \dfrac{y^2}{9} = 1$, where $x \geq 0$ and $y \geq 0$, is defined by the one-to-one function

$$f(x) = 3\sqrt{1 - \frac{x^2}{4}}$$

Find the inverse function $f^{-1}(x)$.

$x = 3\sqrt{1 - \dfrac{y^2}{4}}$

$x^2 = 9\left(1 - \dfrac{y^2}{4}\right)$

$y^2 = \dfrac{36 - 4x^2}{9}$

$y = f^{-1}(x) = \dfrac{\sqrt{36 - 4x^2}}{3} = \dfrac{2\sqrt{9 - x^2}}{3}$

36. The region of the hyperbola $\dfrac{x^2}{9} - \dfrac{y^2}{16} = 1$, where $x \geq 3$ and $y \geq 0$, is defined by the one-to-one function

$$g(x) = 4\sqrt{\frac{x^2}{9} - 1}$$

Find the inverse function $g^{-1}(x)$.

$x = 4\sqrt{\dfrac{y^2}{9} - 1}$

$x^2 = 16\left(\dfrac{y^2}{9} - 1\right)$

$y^2 = \dfrac{9x^2 + 144}{16}$

$y = g^{-1}(x) = \dfrac{\sqrt{9x^2 + 144}}{4} = \dfrac{3\sqrt{x^2 + 16}}{4}$

Cumulative Review Problems

Solve for x.

37. $9x^2 - 13x = 20x$

$9x^2 - 33x = 0$
$x(9x - 33) = 0$
$x = 0$
$x = \dfrac{11}{3}$

38. $9x^2 = -3x + 2$

$9x^2 + 3x - 2 = 0$
$(3x - 1)(3x + 2) = 0$
$x = \dfrac{1}{3}, \ x = -\dfrac{2}{3}$

39. $x^{2/3} + 7x^{1/3} + 12 = 0$

$y = x^{1/3}$
$y^2 + 7y + 12 = 0$
$(y + 4)(y + 3) = 0$
$y = -4 \quad x^{1/3} = -4 \Rightarrow x = -64$
$y = -3 \quad x^{1/3} = -3 \Rightarrow x = -27$

40. $x = \sqrt{15 - 2x}$

$x^2 = 15 - 2x$
$x^2 + 2x - 15 = 0$
$(x + 5)(x - 3) = 0$
$x = -5$, extraneous value
$x = 3$

Find the inverse of each function. Express your answer in decimal form without any fractions.

41. $f(x) = -19.267x + 3.721$

$$f^{-1}(x) = \frac{3.721 - x}{19.267} = 0.1931282 - 0.0519022x$$

42. $p(x) = 0.00268x - 0.00982$

$$p^{-1}(x) = \frac{x + 0.00982}{0.00268}$$

$$= 373.13433x + 3.6641791$$

For Extra Practice Exercises, turn to page 447.

Solutions to Odd-Numbered Practice Problems

1. $A = \{(-2, -6), (-3, -5), (-1, 2), (3, 5)\}$
A is a function. No two pairs have the same second coordinates. Thus, it is a one-to-one function.

3. The inverse of B is obtained by interchanging x and y values for each ordered pair.

$$B^{-1} = \{(2, 1), (7, 8), (8, 7), (12, 10)\}$$

Note that each set contains the ordered pairs (7, 8) and (8, 7).

5. $f(x) = \sqrt[3]{x + 2}$

(A) $y = \sqrt[3]{x + 2}$	Replacing $f(x)$ with y
(B) $x = \sqrt[3]{y + 2}$	Interchanging the variables x and y
(C) $x^3 = y + 2$	Cubing each side of the equation
$x^3 - 2 = y$	Adding -2 to each side
(D) $f^{-1}(x) = x^3 - 2$	Replacing y by $f^{-1}(x)$.

Answers to Even-Numbered Practice Problems

2. A horizontal line through the graph intersects at only one point. The graph represents a one-to-one function.

4. $f^{-1}(x) = \dfrac{-x + 4}{6}$

8.7 NONLINEAR SYSTEMS OF EQUATIONS

☐ **After studying this section, you will be able to:**

1 *Solve a nonlinear system by the substitution method*

2 *Solve a nonlinear system by the addition method*

Any equation that is second degree or higher is a nonlinear equation. In other words, the equation is not a straight line (which is what the word *nonlinear* means) and can't be written in the form $y = mx + b$. A **nonlinear system** of equations includes at least one nonlinear equation.

1 Substitution Method

TEACHING TIP   After presenting example 1, you may want to do the following additional sample example.

Solve the linear system:

$x + y = -7$

$y + 5 = x^2 - 4x$

Sol. $y = -7 - x$

$(-7 - x) + 5 = x^2 - 4x$

$0 = x^2 - 3x + 2$

$x = 2, x = 1$

If $x = 2, y = -9$

If $x = 1, y = -8$

The most frequently used method for solving a nonlinear system is the method of substitution. This method works especially well when one equation of the system is linear. A sketch can often be used to verify the solution(s).

Example 1   Solve the nonlinear system:

$$x + y - 1 = 0 \qquad (1)$$
$$y - 1 = x^2 + 2x \qquad (2)$$

and verify your answer with a sketch.

We'll use the substitution method.

$y = -x + 1$	(3)	Solving for y in equation (1).
$(-x + 1) - 1 = x^2 + 2x$		Substituting (3) in equation (2).
$-x + 1 - 1 = x^2 + 2x$		

$$0 = x^2 + 3x$$ Solving the resulting quadratic equation.

$$0 = x(x + 3)$$

$$x = 0 \quad or \quad x = -3$$

Now substitute the values for x in the equation $y = -x + 1$.

For $x = -3$: $\quad y = -(-3) + 1 = +3 + 1 = 4$

For $x = 0$: $\quad y = -(0) + 1 = +1 = 1$

Thus, the solutions of the system are $(-3, 4)$ and $(0, 1)$

To sketch the system, we should first see that equation (2) describes a parabola. We can rewrite it in the form

$$y = x^2 + 2x + 1$$

$$y = (x + 1)^2$$

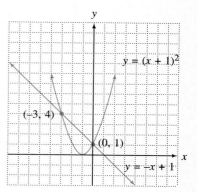

This is a parabola opening upward with a vertex at $(-1, 0)$. Equation (1) can be written as $y = -x + 1$, which is a straight line with slope $= -1$ and y intercept $(0, 1)$.

A sketch shows the two graphs intersecting at $(0, 1)$ and $(-3, 4)$. Thus, the solutions are verified. ∎

Practice Problem 1 Solve the system.

$$\frac{x^2}{4} - \frac{y^2}{4} = 1$$

$$x + y + 1 = 0 \quad \blacksquare$$

Example 2 Solve the nonlinear system:

$$y - 2x = 0 \quad (1)$$

$$\frac{x^2}{4} + \frac{y^2}{9} = 1 \quad (2)$$

and verify your answer with a sketch.

$$y = 2x \quad (3) \qquad \text{Solving equation (1) for } y.$$

$$\frac{x^2}{4} + \frac{(2x)^2}{9} = 1 \qquad \text{Substituting (3) into equation (2).}$$

$$\frac{x^2}{4} + \frac{4x^2}{9} = 1 \qquad \text{Simplifying.}$$

$$36\left(\frac{x^2}{4}\right) + 36\left(\frac{4x^2}{9}\right) = 36(1) \qquad \text{Clearing fractions.}$$

$$9x^2 + 16x^2 = 36$$

$$25x^2 = 36$$

$$x^2 = \frac{36}{25}$$

$$x = \pm\sqrt{\frac{36}{25}}$$

$$= \pm\frac{6}{5} = \pm 1.2$$

For $x = +1.2$: $\quad y = 2(1.2) = 2.4$.

For $x = -1.2$: $\quad y = 2(-1.2) = -2.4$.

Thus the solutions are $(1.2, 2.4)$ and $(-1.2, -2.4)$

TEACHING TIP After discussing example 2, ask students to do the following problem. Solve the linear system and verify your answer with a graph.

$$x^2 = y^2 + 16$$

$$y + 2 = x$$

Ans.: $x = 5, y = 3$

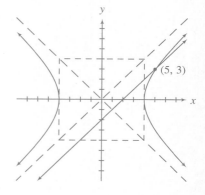

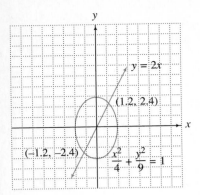

We recognize $\frac{x^2}{4} + \frac{y^2}{9} = 1$ as an ellipse with center at the origin and vertices $(0, 3), (0, -3), (2, 0), (-2, 0)$. We recognize $y = 2x$ as a straight line with slope 2 passing through the origin. The sketch shows that the points of intersection at $(1.2, 2.4)$ and $(-1.2, -2.4)$ seem reasonable. ■

Practice Problem 2   Solve the system.

$$2x - 9 = y$$
$$xy = -4 \quad ■$$

2 Addition Method

Sometimes a system may be solved more readily by adding the equations together.

Example 3   Solve:

$$4x^2 + \ \ y^2 = 1 \quad (1)$$
$$x^2 + 4y^2 = 1 \quad (2)$$

Although we could use the substitution method, it is easier to use the addition method because neither equation is linear.

$$
\begin{array}{r}
-16x^2 - 4y^2 = -4 \\
x^2 + 4y^2 = \ \ 1 \\
\hline
-15x^2 \qquad\ \ = -3
\end{array}
$$

Multiplying equation (1) by -4 and adding to equation (2).

$$x^2 = \frac{-3}{-15}$$

$$x^2 = \frac{1}{5}$$

$$x = \pm\sqrt{\frac{1}{5}}$$

If $x = +\sqrt{\frac{1}{5}}$, then $x^2 = \frac{1}{5}$. Substituting this value into equation (2) gives

$$\frac{1}{5} + 4y^2 = 1$$

$$4y^2 = \frac{4}{5}$$

$$y^2 = \frac{1}{5}$$

$$y = \pm\sqrt{\frac{1}{5}}$$

Similarly, if $x = -\sqrt{\frac{1}{5}}$, then $y = \pm\sqrt{\frac{1}{5}}$. If we rationalize each expression, the four solutions are $\left(\frac{\sqrt{5}}{5}, \frac{\sqrt{5}}{5}\right), \left(\frac{\sqrt{5}}{5}, \frac{-\sqrt{5}}{5}\right), \left(\frac{-\sqrt{5}}{5}, \frac{\sqrt{5}}{5}\right)$, and $\left(\frac{-\sqrt{5}}{5}, \frac{-\sqrt{5}}{5}\right)$. ■

Practice Problem 3   Solve the system.

$$x^2 + \ \ y^2 = 12$$
$$3x^2 - 4y^2 = \ \ 8 \quad ■$$

TEACHING TIP   After explaining example 3, try doing the following example by the addition method. Solve the system by the addition method:

$$4x^2 + y^2 = 11$$
$$y + 9 = 4x^2$$

Sol. $4x^2 + y^2 \qquad = 11$
$\underline{4x^2 \qquad - y = 9}$ Mult.
$4x^2 + y^2 \qquad = 11$ by -1
$\underline{-4x^2 \qquad + y = -9}$
$\qquad\qquad y^2 + y = 2$

$y^2 + y - 2 = 0$

$(y + 2)(y - 1) = 0$

$y = -2, y = 1$

If $y = 1$

$10 = 4x^2$

$x = \frac{\pm\sqrt{10}}{2}$

If $y = -2$

$7 = 4x^2$

$x = \frac{\pm\sqrt{7}}{2}$

Sol. are: $\left(\frac{\sqrt{7}}{2}, -2\right) \left(-\frac{\sqrt{7}}{2}, -2\right)$
$\left(\frac{\sqrt{10}}{2}, 1\right) \left(-\frac{\sqrt{10}}{2}, 1\right)$

Solve each system.

1. $y^2 = 4x$
$y = x + 1$
$(x + 1)^2 = 4x$
$x^2 + 2x + 1 = 4x$
$x^2 - 2x + 1 = 0$
$(x - 1)(x - 1) = 0$
$x = 1$
$y = 2$

2. $y^2 = 2x$
$y = -2x + 2$
$(-2x + 2)^2 = 2x \quad$ if $x = 2, y = -2$
$4x^2 - 8x + 4 = 2x \quad$ if $x = \dfrac{1}{2}, y = 1$
$4x^2 - 10x + 4 = 0$
$(x - 2)(2x - 1) = 0$
$x = 2, x = \dfrac{1}{2}$

3. $y = (x - 2)^2$
$x + y - 2 = 0$
$x + (x - 2)^2 - 2 = 0$
$x^2 - 3x + 2 = 0$
$x = 2, y = 0$
$x = 1, y = 1$

4. $y = (x - 3)^2$
$x - 1 - y = 0$
$y = x - 1$
$x - 1 = (x - 3)^2$
$x - 1 = x^2 - 6x + 9$
$0 = x^2 - 7x + 10$
$0 = (x - 5)(x - 2)$
$x = 5, x = 2$
$(5, 4)$ and $(2, 1)$

5. $y + x - 1 = 0$
$y = (x + 1)^2 - 4$
$y = -x + 1$
$-x + 1 = (x + 1)^2 - 4$
$0 = x^2 + 3x - 4$
$x = -4, y = 5$
$x = 1, y = 0$

6. $x = y + 1$
$y = -1(x + 1)^2 + 4$
$y = x - 1$
$x - 1 = -(x + 1)^2 + 4$
$x^2 + 3x - 4 = 0$
$x = -4, y = -5$
$x = 1, y = 0$

7. $x^2 + y^2 - 9 = 0$
$2y = 3 - x$
$x = 3 - 2y$
$(3 - 2y)^2 + y^2 - 9 = 0$
$5y^2 - 12y = 0$
$y = 0, x = 3$
$y = \dfrac{12}{5}, x = \dfrac{-9}{5}$

8. $x^2 + y^2 - 25 = 0$
$3y = x + 5$
$3y - 5 = x$
$(3y - 5)^2 + y^2 - 25 = 0$
$10y^2 - 30y = 0$
$y = 0, x = -5$
$y = 3, x = 4$

9. $x + 2y = 0$
$x^2 + 4y^2 = 32$
$x = -2y$
$4y^2 + 4y^2 = 32$
$y = 2, x = -4$
$y = -2, x = 4$

10. $y - 4x = 0$
$4x^2 + y^2 = 20$
$y = 4x$
$4x^2 + 16x^2 = 20$
$x = 1, y = 4$
$x = -1, y = -4$

11. $\dfrac{x^2}{4} - \dfrac{y^2}{4} = 1$
$x + y - 4 = 0$
$x = 4 - y$
$(4 - y)^2 - y^2 = 4$
$-8y = -12$
$y = \dfrac{3}{2}, x = \dfrac{5}{2}$

12. $\dfrac{x^2}{2} - \dfrac{y^2}{16} = 1$
$y - 2x = 0$
$y = 2x$
$\dfrac{x^2}{2} - \dfrac{4x^2}{16} = 1$
$x = 2, y = 4$
$x = -2, y = -4$

Find a real solution for each system. If there is no real solution, say so.

13. $xy = 4$
$x + 2y - 8 = 0$
$x = 8 - 2y$
$y(8 - 2y) = 4$
$y^2 - 4y + 2 = 0$
$y = 2 \pm \sqrt{2}$
$(4 - 2\sqrt{2}, 2 + \sqrt{2})$
$(4 + 2\sqrt{2}, 2 - \sqrt{2})$

14. $xy = 1$
$3x + y - 6 = 0$
$y = 6 - 3x$
$x(6 - 3x) = 1$
$3x^2 - 6x + 1 = 0$
$\left(\dfrac{3 + \sqrt{6}}{3}, 3 - \sqrt{6}\right)$
$\left(\dfrac{3 - \sqrt{6}}{3}, 3 + \sqrt{6}\right)$

15. $xy = 3$
$3y = 3x + 6$
$x = \dfrac{3}{y}$
$3y = \dfrac{9}{y} + 6$
$y^2 - 2y - 3 = 0 \Rightarrow y = 3, -1$
$(1, 3), (-3, -1)$

16. $xy = 5$
$2y = 2x + 8$
$y = x + 4$
$x(x + 4) = 5$
$x^2 + 4x - 5 = 0 \Rightarrow x = -5, 1$
$(-5, -1), (1, 5)$

17. $x^2 + 2y^2 = 8$
$x^2 - y^2 = 1$
$-x^2 - 2y^2 = -8$
$\underline{x^2 - y^2 = 1}$
$-3y^2 = -7 \Rightarrow y = \pm\dfrac{\sqrt{21}}{3}$
$\left(\dfrac{\sqrt{30}}{3}, \pm\dfrac{\sqrt{21}}{3}\right)\left(-\dfrac{\sqrt{30}}{3}, \pm\dfrac{\sqrt{21}}{3}\right)$

18. $2x^2 + y^2 = 8$
$x^2 + y^2 = 4$
$2x^2 + y^2 = 8$
$\underline{-x^2 - y^2 = -4}$
$x^2 \qquad = 4 \Rightarrow x = \pm 2$
$(2, 0), (-2, 0)$

19. $2x^2 - 5y^2 = -2$
$3x^2 + 2y^2 = 35$
$4x^2 - 10y^2 = -4$
$\underline{15x^2 + 10y^2 = 175}$
$19x^2 \qquad = 171$
$x = \pm 3$
$(3, \pm 2), (-3, \pm 2)$

20. $x^2 + 4y^2 = 13$
$x^2 - 3y^2 = -8$
$x^2 + 4y^2 = 13$
$\underline{-x^2 + 3y^2 = 8}$
$7y^2 = 21$
$y = \pm\sqrt{3}$
$(1, \pm\sqrt{3}), (-1, \pm\sqrt{3})$

21. $x^2 + (y - 3)^2 = 9$
$x^2 + y^2 = 4$
$x^2 = 4 - y^2$
$4 - y^2 + (y - 3)^2 = 9$
$y = \dfrac{2}{3}$
$\left(\dfrac{4\sqrt{2}}{3}, \dfrac{2}{3}\right)$
$\left(-\dfrac{4\sqrt{2}}{3}, \dfrac{2}{3}\right)$

22. $x^2 + y^2 = 9$
$(x - 2)^2 + y^2 = 21$
$y^2 = 9 - x^2$
$(x - 2)^2 + (9 - x^2) = 21$
$-4x = 8$
$x = -2$
$(-2, \pm\sqrt{5})$

23. $2x^2 + 5y^2 = 42$
$3x^2 + 4y^2 = 35$
$-6x^2 - 15y^2 = -126$
$\underline{6x^2 + 8y^2 = 70}$
$-7y^2 = -56$
$y = \pm 2\sqrt{2}$
$(1, \pm 2\sqrt{2}), (-1, \pm 2\sqrt{2})$

24. $2x^2 - 3y^2 = 5$
$3x^2 + 4y^2 = 16$
$8x^2 - 12y^2 = 20$
$\underline{9x^2 + 12y^2 = 48}$
$17x^2 \qquad = 68$
$x = \pm 2$
$(2, \pm 1), (-2, \pm 1)$

25. $x + y = 5$
$x^2 + y^2 = 4$

$x = 5 - y$
$(5 - y)^2 + y^2 = 4$
$y = \dfrac{10 \pm \sqrt{-68}}{4}$
No real sol.

26. $x^2 + y^2 = 0$
$x - y = 6$

$x = y + 6$
$(y + 6)^2 + y^2 = 0$
$y = \dfrac{-6 \pm \sqrt{-36}}{2}$
No real sol.

27. $9x^2 + 4y^2 = 36$
$x^2 + \ \ y^2 = \ \ 9$

$\begin{array}{rr} 9x^2 + 4y^2 = & 36 \\ -4x^2 - 4y^2 = & -36 \\ \hline 5x^2 \ \ \ \ \ \ = & 0 \end{array}$
$x = 0$
$(0, \pm 3)$

28. $x^2 + 2y^2 = 12$
$2x^2 + 3y^2 = 21$

$\begin{array}{rr} -2x^2 - 4y^2 = & -24 \\ 2x^2 + 3y^2 = & 21 \\ \hline -y^2 = & -3 \end{array}$
$y = \pm\sqrt{3}$
$(\sqrt{6}, \pm\sqrt{3}), (-\sqrt{6}, \pm\sqrt{3})$

? **To Think About**

29. How many solutions are possible with a system of the form $y = ax^2$ and $x^2 + y^2 = r^2$.

One or two solutions.

30. How many solutions are possible with a system of the form $\dfrac{x^2}{c^2} + \dfrac{y^2}{d^2} = 1$ and $\dfrac{x^2}{a^2} - \dfrac{y^2}{b^2} = 1$?

None, two or four sols.

31. In an experiment with a laser beam, the path of a particle orbiting a central object is described by the equation $\dfrac{x^2}{49} + \dfrac{y^2}{36} = 1$, where x and y are measured in centimeters from the center of the object. The laser beam follows the path $y = 2x - 6$. Find the coordinates at which the laser will illuminate the particle (that is, when the particle will pass through the beam).

$\dfrac{x^2}{49} + \dfrac{(2x - 6)^2}{36} = 1$
$36x^2 + 49(2x - 6)^2 = 1764$
$232x^2 - 1176x = 0$
$x = 0, y = -6$
$x = \dfrac{147}{29}, y = \dfrac{120}{29}$

Central object
Laser light
$(0, -6)$
$\left(\dfrac{147}{29}, \dfrac{120}{29}\right)$ Path of Particle
Particle

32. The area of a rectangle is 540 square meters. The diagonal of the rectangle is 39 meters long. Find the dimensions of the rectangle.

Hint: Let x and y represent the length and width and write a system of two nonlinear equations.

$\begin{array}{l} 540 = xy \\ (39)^2 = x^2 + y^2 \\ \hline 1521 = x^2 + \dfrac{291600}{x^2} \end{array}$

$x^4 - 1521x^2 + 291600 = 0$
$x^2 = 1296, x^2 = 225$
$x = 36, x = 15$ \quad Dimensions:
$y = 15, y = 36$ \quad 15 meters by 36 meters

Cumulative Review Problems

Simplify.

33. $\dfrac{x^2 - y^2}{x^3 - y^3}$

$\dfrac{(x + y)(x - y)}{(x - y)(x^2 + xy + y^2)} = \dfrac{x + y}{x^2 + xy + y^2}$

34. $\dfrac{6x^4 - 24x^3 - 30x^2}{3x^3 - 21x^2 + 30x}$

$\dfrac{6x^2(x - 5)(x + 1)}{3x(x - 5)(x - 2)} = \dfrac{2x(x + 1)}{x - 2}$

Divide.

35. $(x^3 - 3x^2 + x + 2) \div (x - 3)$

$\begin{array}{r} x^2 + 1 \\ x - 3 \overline{)\ x^3 - 3x^2 + x + 2} \\ \underline{x^3 - 3x^2} \\ x + 2 \\ \underline{x - 3} \\ +5 \end{array}$ \quad Ans. $x^2 + 1 + \dfrac{5}{x - 3}$

36. $(3x^3 - 8x^2 - 33x - 10) \div (3x + 1)$

$\begin{array}{r} x^2 - 3x - 10 \\ 3x + 1 \overline{)\ 3x^3 - 8x^2 - 33x - 10} \\ \underline{3x^3 + \ \ x^2} \\ -9x^2 - 33x \\ \underline{-9x^2 - \ \ 3x} \\ -30x - 10 \\ \underline{-30x - 10} \end{array}$ \quad Ans. $x^2 - 3x - 10$

▦ **Calculator Problems**

Find all solutions for each system. Round your answer to four decimal places.

37. $2y^2 = 5x$
$y = 1.834x - 0.982$

$x = 1.6392$ \quad and \quad $x = 0.1749$
$y = 2.0244$ \quad\quad\quad $y = -0.6612$

38. $2x^2 + 5.698y^2 = 39.768$
$3x^2 + 4.256y^2 = 34.087$

$(1.7059, \pm 2.4409)$
$(-1.7059, \pm 2.4409)$

For Extra Practice Exercises, turn to page 448.

Solutions to Odd-Numbered Practice Problems

1. $\dfrac{x^2}{4} - \dfrac{y^2}{4} = 1$ $x + y = -1$

$$x^2 - y^2 = 4 \quad (1) \quad\quad x = -1 - y \quad (2)$$
$$(-1 - y)^2 - y^2 = 4 \quad\quad \text{Substituting (2) into (1).}$$
$$1 + 2y + y^2 - y^2 = 4$$
$$1 + 2y = 4$$
$$2y = 3 \quad\quad \text{Solving for } y.$$
$$y = \frac{3}{2} = 1.5$$

If $y = 1.5$, $x = -1 - y = -1.0 - 1.5 = -2.5$

The solution is $(-2.5, 1.5)$.

3. (1) $x^2 + y^2 = 12$ $4x^2 + 4y^2 = 48$ Multiplying (1) by 4.
    (2) $3x^2 - 4y^2 = 8$ $\dfrac{3x^2 - 4y^2 = 8}{7x^2 = 56}$ Adding the equations.

$$x^2 = 8$$
$$x = \pm\sqrt{8}$$
$$= \pm 2\sqrt{2}$$

If $x = \pm 2\sqrt{2}$, then $x^2 = 8$. Substituting this value into equation (1) gives

$$8 + y^2 = 12$$
$$y^2 = 4$$
$$y = \pm\sqrt{4}$$
$$y = \pm 2$$

Thus the four solutions are $(2\sqrt{2}, 2)$, $(2\sqrt{2}, -2)$, $(-2\sqrt{2}, 2)$, $(-2\sqrt{2}, -2)$.

Answer to Even Numbered Practice Problem

2. $(0.5, -8)$ and $(4, -1)$.

EXTRA PRACTICE: EXERCISES

Section 8.1

Find the distance between each pair of points.

1. $(3, -1)$ and $(2, 7)$ $\sqrt{65}$
2. $(2, 5)$ and $(-5, 3)$ $\sqrt{53}$
3. $(-8, -2)$ and $(0, -5)$ $\sqrt{73}$
4. $(-3, 0)$ and $(-7, -1)$ $\sqrt{17}$
5. $\left(\dfrac{1}{4}, \dfrac{3}{4}\right)$ and $\left(-\dfrac{3}{4}, \dfrac{5}{4}\right)$ $\dfrac{\sqrt{5}}{2}$
6. $\left(\dfrac{1}{5}, -\dfrac{2}{5}\right)$ and $\left(\dfrac{3}{5}, \dfrac{4}{5}\right)$ $\dfrac{2\sqrt{10}}{5}$
7. $(1.8, 2.7)$ and $(1.3, 8.7)$ $\dfrac{\sqrt{145}}{2}$
8. $(2.5, 3.8)$ and $(-7.5, 2.8)$
9. $(5\sqrt{2}, 3)$ and $(\sqrt{2}, 4)$ $\sqrt{33}$
10. $(7, \sqrt{3})$ and $(2, 3\sqrt{3})$ $\sqrt{37}$
11. $(-4, 3)$ and $(4, -3)$ 10
12. $(3, -7)$ and $(-2, -7)$ 5
13. $\left(4a, \dfrac{5}{7}\right)$ and $\left(4a, -\dfrac{2}{7}\right)$ 1
14. $\left(2\dfrac{3}{5}, -1\dfrac{1}{2}\right)$ and $\left(-1\dfrac{2}{5}, 6\dfrac{1}{2}\right)$

Determine the unknown variable so that the distance between

15. $(-3, 6)$ and $(2, y)$ is 13 $-6, 18$
16. $(-3, y)$ and $(-9, -2)$ is 10 $6, -10$
17. $(x, -1)$ and $(-2, 4)$ is $\sqrt{26}$ $-3, -1$
18. $(x, -3)$ and $(-4, -1)$ is $\sqrt{13}$ $-1, -7$
19. $(6x, 4)$ and $(-2x, -2)$ is 10 ± 1
20. $(-1, 3y)$ and $(11, -2y)$ is 13 ± 1

Write in standard form the equation of a circle with the given center and radius.

21. Center $(5, 1)$, $r = 4$ $(x - 5)^2 + (y - 1)^2 = 16$
22. Center $(2, 7)$, $r = 5$ $(x - 2)^2 + (y - 7)^2 = 25$
23. Center $(-6, -2)$, $r = 3$ $(x + 6)^2 + (y + 2)^2 = 9$
24. Center $(-5, -8)$, $r = 6$ $(x + 5)^2 + (y + 8)^2 = 36$
25. Center $(-5, 7)$, $r = \sqrt{5}$ $(x + 5)^2 + (y - 7)^2 = 5$
26. Center $(2, -3)$, $r = \sqrt{13}$ $(x - 2)^2 + (y + 3)^2 = 13$

27. Center $(0, -4)$, $r = 2\sqrt{2}$ $x^2 + (y + 4)^2 = 8$
28. Center $(-3, 0)$, $r = 3\sqrt{3}$ $(x + 3)^2 + y^2 = 27$
29. Center (L, M), $r = A$ $(x - L)^2 + (y - M)^2 = A^2$
30. Center $(5, 7)$, $r = 3\sqrt{11}$ $(x - 5)^2 + (y - 7)^2 = 99$

Determine the center and radius of each circle, then sketch its graph.

31. $(x - 4)^2 + (y + 1)^2 = 25$ **32.** $(x + 2)^2 + (y - 3)^2 = 9$

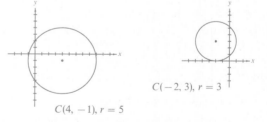

$C(4, -1)$, $r = 5$ $C(-2, 3)$, $r = 3$

Determine the center and radius of each circle.

33. $(x + 5)^2 + (y + 6)^2 = 16$ $C(-5, -6)$, $r = 4$
34. $(x + 6)^2 + (y + 1)^2 = 4$ $C(-6, -1)$. $r = 2$
35. $x^2 + (y - 3)^2 = 12$ $C(0, 3)$, $r = 2\sqrt{3}$
36. $(x + 1)^2 + y^2 = 10$ $C(-1, 0)$, $r = \sqrt{10}$
37. $(x + 3)^2 + \left(y - \dfrac{1}{2}\right)^2 = \dfrac{9}{4}$ $C\left(-3, \dfrac{1}{2}\right)$, $r = \dfrac{3}{2}$
38. $\left(x + \dfrac{1}{3}\right)^2 + \left(y - \dfrac{2}{3}\right)^2 = \dfrac{25}{9}$ $C\left(-\dfrac{1}{3}, \dfrac{2}{3}\right)$, $r = \dfrac{5}{3}$
39. $(x - 4)^2 + (y + 0.2)^2 = \dfrac{9}{25}$ $C(4, -0.2)$, $r = \dfrac{3}{5}$

8. $\sqrt{101}$ **14.** $4\sqrt{5}$

Put each equation in standard form. Find the center and radius of the circle.

40. $x^2 + y^2 + 4x - 10y + 20 = 0$ $C(-2, 5), r = 3$

41. $x^2 + y^2 + 6x - 8y + 21 = 0$ $C(-3, 4), r = 2$

42. $x^2 + y^2 - 14x - 51 = 0$ $C(7, 0), r = 10$

43. $x^2 + y^2 + 10x - 9 = 0$ $C(-5, 0), r = \sqrt{34}$

44. $x^2 + y^2 + 5x - 3y - 6 = 0$

   44. $C\left(-\dfrac{5}{2}, \dfrac{3}{2}\right), r = \dfrac{\sqrt{58}}{2}$

45. $x^2 + y^2 + 7x + 4y - 2 = 0$

46. $x^2 + 6x + y^2 - 8y - 8 = 17 - 1$ $C(-3, 4), r = 7$

47. $(x - 2)^2 + y^2 - 6y = 0$ $C(2, 3), r = 3$

   45. $C\left(-\dfrac{7}{2}, -2\right), r = \dfrac{\sqrt{73}}{2}$

Section 8.2

*Determine **(a)** if the parabola is horizontal or vertical, **(b)** the way it opens, **(c)** the vertex.*

1. $y = \dfrac{1}{4}x^2$ vertical, up, (0, 0)

2. $y = -\dfrac{1}{2}x^2$ vertical, down, (0, 0)

3. $y = -2x^2$ vertical, down, (0, 0)

4. $y = 3x^2$ vertical, up, (0, 0)

5. $y = x^2 + 3$ vertical, up, (0, 3)

6. $y = x^2 + 4$ vertical, up, (0, 4)

7. $y = 4 - 2x^2$ vertical, down, (0, 4)

8. $y = 3 - 3x^2$ vertical, down, (0, 3)

9. $y = (x - 1)^2 + 4$ vertical, up, (1, 4)

10. $y = (x - 2)^2 + 3$ vertical, up, (2, 3)

11. $y = (x + 4)^2 - 2$ vertical, up, (-4, -2)

12. $y = (x + 5)^2 - 4$ vertical, up, (-5, -4)

13. $y = -2(x - 1)^2 - 3$ vertical, down, (1, -3)

14. $y = -2(x - 3)^2 - 1$ vertical, down, (3, -1)

15. $x = 3y^2$ horizontal, right, (0, 0)

16. $x = -2y^2$ horizontal, left, (0, 0)

17. $x = 5 - y^2$ horizontal, left, (5, 0)

18. $x = 4y^2 - 6$ horizontal, right, (-6, 0)

19. $x = (y + 1)^2 - 3$ horizontal, right, (-3, -1)

20. $x = (y - 4)^2 + 3$ horizontal, right, (3, 4)

21. $x = (y - 2)^2 + 6$ horizontal, right, (6, -2)

22. $x = (y + 4)^2 - 5$ horizontal, right, (-5, -4)

23. $(x - 2)^2 = 8y$ vertical, up, (2, 0)

24. $(y - 1)^2 = 4(x + 1)$ horizontal, right, (-1, 1)

25. $x + 2 = 4y^2$ horizontal, right, (-2, 0)

26. $x - 2 = 2y^2 + 8y + 8$ horizontal, right, (2, -2)

27. $x^2 + x = 2(y - 1)^2 + x^2$ horizontal, right, (0, 1)

28. $6(2y - y^2) = 4(x - 1)^2 - 6y^2$ vertical, up, (1, 0)

29. $y = x^2 - 2$ vertical, up, (0, -2)

30. $y^2 + 4 = x$ horizontal, right, (4, 0)

Graph each parabola. Label the vertex and one other point.

31. $x - 2 = -4(y - 1)^2$ **32.** $y = -8(x + 1)^2 + 3$

*Put each equation in standard form. Determine **(a)** if the parabola is horizontal or vertical, **(b)** the way it opens, and **(c)** the vertex.*

33. $y = x^2 + 4x + 7$ $y = (x + 2)^2 + 3$, vertical, up, (-2, 3)

34. $y = x^2 + 6x + 13$ $y = (x + 3)^2 + 4$, vertical, up, (-3, 4)

35. $y = -x^2 + 6x - 8$ $y = -1(x - 3)^2 + 1$, vertical, down, (3, 1)

36. $y = -x^2 + 4x - 9$ $y = -1(x - 2)^2 - 5$, vertical, down, (2, -5)

37. $x = y^2 - 8y + 9$ $x = (y - 4)^2 - 7$, horizontal, right, (-7, 4)

38. $x = y^2 - 10y + 14$ $x = (y - 5)^2 - 11$, horizontal, right, (-11, 5)

39. $x = y^2 - y - 6$

40. $y = x^2 - 2x - 8$ $y = (x - 1)^2 - 9$, vertical, up, (1, -9)

41. $y + 4 = x^2$ $y = x^2 - 4$, vertical, up, (0, -4)

42. $x = y^2 - 3y - 10$ $x = \left(y - \dfrac{3}{2}\right)^2 - \dfrac{49}{4}$, vertical, up, $\left(-\dfrac{49}{4}, \dfrac{3}{2}\right)$

39. $x = \left(y - \dfrac{1}{2}\right)^2 - \dfrac{25}{4}$, horizontal, right, $\left(-\dfrac{25}{4}, \dfrac{1}{2}\right)$

Section 8.3

Determine the intercepts of each ellipse.

1. $\dfrac{x^2}{25} + \dfrac{y^2}{1} = 1$ $(\pm 5, 0), (0, \pm 1)$ **2.** $\dfrac{x^2}{36} + \dfrac{y^2}{49} = 1$ $(\pm 6, 0), (0, \pm 7)$

3. $x^2 + 9y^2 = 36$ $(\pm 6, 0), (0, \pm 2)$ **4.** $4x^2 + y^2 = 16$ $(\pm 2, 0), (0, \pm 4)$

5. $\dfrac{x^2}{18} + \dfrac{y^2}{9} = 1$ $(\pm 3\sqrt{2}, 0), (0, \pm 3)$ **6.** $\dfrac{x^2}{7} + \dfrac{y^2}{16} = 1$ $(\pm \sqrt{7}, 0), (0, \pm 4)$

7. $16x^2 + 3y^2 = 48$

8. $9x^2 + 5y^2 = 45$

9. $7x^2 + 8y^2 = 56$

10. $6x^2 + 7y^2 = 42$

11. $\dfrac{x^2}{1} + \dfrac{y^2}{\frac{1}{4}} = 1$

12. $\dfrac{x^2}{9} + \dfrac{y^2}{\frac{1}{4}} = 1$ $\left(\pm\dfrac{3}{2}, 0\right), (0, \pm 1)$

13. $x^2 + 4y^2 = 1$ $(\pm 1, 0), \left(0, \pm\dfrac{1}{2}\right)$ **14.** $\dfrac{x^2}{4} + \dfrac{y^2}{9} = 1$

15. $\dfrac{x^2}{2} + \dfrac{y^2}{8} = 2$ $(\pm 2, 0), (0, \pm 4)$ **16.** $4x^2 + 9y^2 = 36$

17. $3x^2 + 4y^2 = 27$

18. $\dfrac{x^2}{4} + \dfrac{y^2}{\frac{1}{9}} = 1$

19. $4x^2 + 4x + y^2 = 4x + 1$

20. $0.1x^2 + 0.4y^2 = 0.4$

21. $0.9x^2 + 0.4y^2 = 3.6$

14. $(\pm 2, 0), (0, \pm 3)$

16. $(\pm 3, 0), (0, \pm 2)$

17. $(\pm 3, 0), \left(0, \pm\dfrac{3\sqrt{3}}{2}\right)$

18. $\left(\pm\dfrac{2}{3}, 0\right), \left(0, \pm\dfrac{1}{3}\right)$

19. $\left(\pm\dfrac{1}{2}, 0\right), (0, \pm 1)$

20. $(\pm 2, 0), (0, \pm 1)$

21. $(\pm 2, 0), (0, \pm 3)$

7. $(\pm\sqrt{3}, 0), (0, \pm 4)$

8. $(\pm\sqrt{5}, 0), (0, \pm 3)$

9. $(\pm 2\sqrt{2}, 0), (0, \pm\sqrt{7})$

10. $(\pm\sqrt{7}, 0), (0, \pm\sqrt{6})$

11. $(\pm 1, 0), \left(0, \pm\dfrac{1}{2}\right)$

Find the coordinates of the four vertices and the center of each ellipse.

22. $\dfrac{(x-1)^2}{4} + \dfrac{(y-2)^2}{9} = 1$ $(-1, 2), (1, 5), (3, 2), (1, -1), C = (1, 2)$

23. $\dfrac{(x-3)^2}{9} + \dfrac{(y-2)^2}{25} = 1$ $(0, 2), (3, 7), (6, 2), (3, -3), C = (3, 2)$

24. $\dfrac{(x+4)^2}{25} + \dfrac{(y-1)^2}{36} = 1$ $(-9, 1), (-4, 7), (1, 1), (-4, -5),$ $C = (-4, 1)$

25. $\dfrac{(x-2)^2}{4} + \dfrac{(y+5)^2}{36} = 1$ $(0, -5), (2, 1), (4, -5), (2, -11),$ $C = (2, -5)$

26. $\dfrac{(x+2)^2}{1} + \dfrac{(y+5)^2}{9} = 1$ $(-3, -5), (-2, -2), (1, -5),$ $(-2, -8), C = (-2, -5)$

27. $\dfrac{(x+3)^2}{4} + \dfrac{(y+3)^2}{49} = 1$ $(-5, -3), (-3, 4), (-1, -3), (-3, -10),$ $C = (-3, -3)$

28. $\dfrac{(x-1)^2}{9} + y^2 = 1$ $(-2, 0), (1, 1), (4, 0), (1, -1), C = (1, 0)$

29. $\dfrac{x^2}{4} + \dfrac{(y-2)^2}{9} = 1$ $(-2, 2), (0, 5), (2, 2), (0, -1), C = (0, 2)$

30. $\dfrac{(x-1)^2}{25} + \dfrac{(y-1)^2}{4} = 1$ $(-4, 1), (1, 3), (6, 1), (1, -1), C = (1, 1)$

31. $\dfrac{(x-4)^2}{25} + \dfrac{(y-1)^2}{9} = 1$ $(-1, 1), (4, 4), (9, 1), (4, -2), C = (4, 1)$

Write in standard form an equation of an ellipse with a center at the origin and

32. x-intercept at $(-5, 0)$ and y-intercept at $(0, -\sqrt{2})$

33. x-intercept at $(-\sqrt{3}, 0)$ and y-intercept at $(0, 8)$

32. $\dfrac{x^2}{25} + \dfrac{y^2}{2} = 1$ **33.** $\dfrac{x^2}{3} + \dfrac{y^2}{64} = 1$

Section 8.4

Determine if the hyperbola is horizontal or vertical. Find the coordinates of the two vertices.

1. $\dfrac{x^2}{9} - \dfrac{y^2}{4} = 1$ horizontal, $(\pm 3, 0)$

2. $\dfrac{x^2}{16} - \dfrac{y^2}{9} = 1$ horizontal, $(\pm 4, 0)$

3. $\dfrac{x^2}{36} - \dfrac{y^2}{25} = 1$ horizontal, $(\pm 6, 0)$

4. $\dfrac{x^2}{49} - \dfrac{y^2}{36} = 1$ horizontal, $(\pm 7, 0)$

5. $\dfrac{y^2}{9} - \dfrac{x^2}{1} = 1$ vertical, $(0, \pm 3)$

6. $\dfrac{y^2}{4} - \dfrac{x^2}{1} = 1$ vertical, $(0, \pm 2)$

7. $4y^2 - 9x^2 = 36$ vertical, $(0, \pm 3)$

8. $25y^2 - 4x^2 = 100$ vertical, $(0, \pm 2)$

9. $9x^2 - 16y^2 = 144$ horizontal, $(\pm 4, 0)$

10. $16x^2 - 49y^2 = 196$ horizontal, $\left(\pm\dfrac{7}{2}, 0\right)$

11. $5y^2 - 3x^2 = 15$ vertical, $(0, \pm\sqrt{3})$

12. $6y^2 - 5x^2 = 30$ vertical, $(0, \pm\sqrt{5})$

13. $3x^2 - y^2 = 48$ horizontal, $(\pm 4, 0)$

14. $12x^2 - y^2 = 48$ horizontal, $(\pm 2, 0)$

15. $\dfrac{x^2}{25} - \dfrac{y^2}{25} = 1$ horizontal, $(\pm 5, 0)$

16. $\dfrac{x^2}{36} - \dfrac{y^2}{36} = 1$ horizontal, $(\pm 6, 0)$

17. $6y^2 - 6x^2 = 30$ vertical, $(0, \pm\sqrt{5})$

18. $7y^2 - 7x^2 = 21$ vertical, $(0, \pm\sqrt{3})$

19. $2x^2 - \dfrac{y^2}{2} = 2$ horizontal, $(\pm 1, 0)$

20. $\dfrac{y^2}{9} - \dfrac{x^2}{16} = -1$ horizontal, $(\pm 4, 0)$

21. $x^2 - \dfrac{y^2}{9} = -1$ vertical, $(0, \pm 3)$

22. $\dfrac{x^2}{4} - \dfrac{y^2}{4} = 4$ horizontal, $(\pm 4, 0)$

23. $\dfrac{x^2}{2} - \dfrac{y^2}{2} = -8$ vertical, $(0, \pm 4)$

24. $9y^2 - 4x^2 = 36$ vertical, $(0, \pm 2)$

25. $36x^2 - 9y^2 = 36$ horizontal, $(\pm 1, 0)$

26. $4x^2 - y^2 = -4$ vertical, $(0, \pm 2)$

27. $5x^2 - 5y^2 = 125$ horizontal, $(\pm 5, 0)$

28. $3y^2 - 3x^2 = 27$ vertical, $(0, \pm 3)$

Put each equation in standard form. Find the vertices and graph each hyperbola.

29. $\dfrac{x^2}{4} - \dfrac{y^2}{9} - 1 = 0$

30. $3x^2 - 12y^2 + 12 = 0$

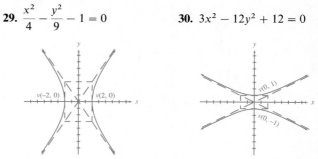

31. Find the equation of the hyperbola with its center at the origin, vertices at $(0, 6)$ and $(0, -6)$, and asymptotes $y = \dfrac{6}{7}x$ and $y = -\dfrac{6}{7}x$. $\dfrac{y^2}{36} - \dfrac{x^2}{49} = 1$

32. Find the equation of the hyperbola with its center at the origin, vertices at $(-4, 0)$ and $(4, 0)$, and asymptotes $y = 2x$ and $y = -2x$. $\dfrac{x^2}{16} - \dfrac{y^2}{64} = 1$

Determine the vertices and the center of each hyperbola.

33. $\dfrac{(x-2)^2}{4} - \dfrac{(y+5)^2}{16} = 1$ $(0, -5), (4, -5), C = (2, -5)$

34. $\dfrac{(x+3)^2}{25} - \dfrac{(y-2)^2}{9} = 1$ $(-8, 2), (2, 2), C = (-3, 2)$

35. $\dfrac{(y+1)^2}{36} - \dfrac{(x+4)^2}{25} = 1$ $(-4, 5), (-4, -7), C = (-4, -1)$

36. $\dfrac{(y+5)^2}{9} - \dfrac{(x+3)^2}{49} = 1$ $(-3, -2), (-3, -8), C = (-3, -5)$

37. $\dfrac{(x-2)^2}{4} - \dfrac{(y+3)^2}{9} = -1$ $(2, -6), (2, 0), C = (2, -3)$

38. $(x+2)^2 - (y-1)^2 = -9$ $(-2, 4), (-2, -2), C = (-2, 1)$

39. $\dfrac{(x-2)^2}{4} - (y+1)^2 = -4$ $(2, 1), (2, -3), C = (2, -1)$

40. $x^2 - (y-2)^2 = 9$ $(-3, 2), (3, 2), C = (0, 2)$

Section 8.5

What are the domain and range of each relation? Is the relation a function?

1. $\{(6, 0.1), (7, 0.3), (8, 0.5), (9, 0.1)\}$

2. $\{(0.3, 1), (0.4, -2), (0.5, 1), (0.6, 2)\}$

3. $\{(100, 1), (20, 2), (10, 6), (100, 5)\}$

4. $\{(36, 9), (14, 2), (18, 3), (14, -7)\}$

5. $\{(-3, -2), (3, 2), (3, -2), (6, -4)\}$

6. $\{(6, 1), (-6, 3), (1, 6), (3, -6)\}$

7. $\{(4, -1), (16, -3), (8, -2), (4, -1)\}$

8. $\{(-3, -7), (-7, -3), (0, -7), (-7, 3)\}$

9. $\{(0, 0), (4, 0), (5, 0)\}$

10. $\{(-1, 1), (-1, 2), (-1, 3)\}$

11. $\left\{(1, 0.2), (2, 3), \left(1, \dfrac{1}{5}\right)\right\}$

12. $\left\{(-1, 0), \left(2, \dfrac{1}{2}\right), \left(3, \dfrac{1}{2}\right), (4, -1)\right\}$

13. $\left\{\left(0.1, \dfrac{1}{2}\right), \left(0.2, \dfrac{1}{3}\right)\right\}$

14. $\left\{(0.3, 0.1), \left(\dfrac{1}{2}, \dfrac{1}{10}\right), (-5, 6), (-2, -2)\right\}$

1. $D = \{6, 7, 8, 9\}$
$R = \{0.1, 0.3, 0.5\}$
Yes

2. $D = \{0.3, 0.4, 0.5, 0.6\}$
$R = \{1, -2, 2\}$
Yes

3. $D = \{100, 20, 10\}$
$R = \{1, 2, 6, 5\}$
No

4. $D = \{36, 14, 18\}$
$R = \{9, 2, 3, -7\}$
No

5. $D = \{-3, 3, 6\}$
$R = \{-2, 2, -4\}$
No

6. $D = \{6, -6, 1, 3\}$
$R = \{1, 3, 6, -6\}$
Yes

7. $D = \{4, 16, 8\}$
$R = \{-1, -3, -2\}$
Yes

8. $D = \{-3, -7, 0\}$
$R = \{-7, -3, 3\}$
No

Which of these graphs represent functions?

15.

Yes

16.

No

Define the functions.

$f(x) = 4 - 2x \qquad g(x) = \dfrac{1}{3} - \dfrac{1}{2}x \qquad h(x) = 2x^2 - 3x + 1$

$k(x) = 2x^3 \qquad p(x) = x^4 + 3x^2 \qquad r(x) = (x - 2)^2$

9. $D = \{0, 4, 5\}$
$R = \{0\}$
Yes

10. $D = \{-1\}$
$R = \{1, 2, 3\}$
No

11. $D = \{1, 2\}$
$R = \{0.2, 3\}$
Yes

12. $D = \{-1, 2, 3, 4\}$
$R = \left\{0, \dfrac{1}{2}, -1\right\}$
Yes

13. $D = \{0.1, 0.2\}$
$R = \left\{\dfrac{1}{2}, \dfrac{1}{3}\right\}$
Yes

14. $D = \left\{0.3, \dfrac{1}{2}, -5, -2\right\}$
$R = \left\{0.1, \dfrac{1}{10}, 6, -2\right\}$
Yes

Find each of the following. Simplify your answer.

17. (a) $f(-2)$ 8
(b) $f(0)$ 4
(c) $f(3)$ -2

18. (a) $g(4)$ $-\dfrac{5}{3}$
(b) $g(0)$ $\dfrac{1}{3}$
(c) $g(-2)$ $\dfrac{4}{3}$

19. (a) $h(3)$ 10
(b) $h(-1)$ 6
(c) $h(-2)$ 15

20. (a) $r(-3)$ 25
(b) $r(2)$ 0
(c) $r(1)$ 1

21. (a) $k(2)$ 16
(b) $k(-2)$ -16
(c) $k(2a)$ $16a^3$

22. (a) $p(0)$ 0
(b) $p(-2)$ 28
(c) $p(2a)$ $16a^4 + 12a^2$

23. (a) $f(a)$ $4 - 2a$
(b) $r(a + 2)$ a^2
(c) $h(a + 1)$ $2a^2 + a$

24. (a) $g(a)$ $\dfrac{1}{3} - \dfrac{1}{2}$
(b) $h(a + 2)$ $2a^2 + 5a + 3$
(c) $k(a)$ $2a^3$

25. (a) $p\left(\dfrac{1}{2}\right)$ $\dfrac{13}{16}$
(b) $r\left(\dfrac{1}{3}\right)$ $\dfrac{25}{9}$
(c) $h\left(\dfrac{1}{2}\right)$ 0

26. (a) $k\left(\dfrac{1}{3}\right)$ $\dfrac{2}{27}$
(b) $f\left(\dfrac{1}{4}\right)$ $\dfrac{7}{2}$
(c) $h\left(\dfrac{1}{3}\right)$ $\dfrac{2}{9}$

27. (a) $g(a + 1)$
(b) $g(4a)$
(c) $f(a - 3)$

28. (a) $g(a + 2)$
(b) $h(a - 1)$
(c) $f(a + 1)$

29. (a) $r(2x)$ $4x^2 - 8x + 4$
(b) $r(x)$ $x^2 - 4x + 4$
(c) $r(2x) - r(x)$ $3x^2 - 4x$

30. (a) $h(2x)$ $8x^2 - 6x + 1$
(b) $h(x)$ $2x^2 - 3x + 1$
(c) $h(2x) - h(x)$ $6x^2 - 3x$

31. $f(0) + g(0) - h(1)$ $\dfrac{13}{3}$

32. $2f(0) + 3k(1)$ 14

33. $3k(1) + r(2)$ 6

34. $k(2) - 3f(1)$ 10

Find $\dfrac{f(x + h) - f(x)}{h}$.

35. $f(x) = 3 - 4x$ -4

36. $f(x) = \dfrac{1}{2} + 2x$ 2

37. $f(x) = 2x^2 + x$ $4x + 2h + 1$

38. $f(x) = x^2 - 5x + 6$ $2x + h - 5$

39. $f(x) = x^3$ $3x^2 + 3xh + h^2$

40. $f(x) = 17$ 0

27. (a) $-\dfrac{1}{2}a - \dfrac{1}{6}$
(b) $\dfrac{1}{3} - 2a$
(c) $10 - 2a$

28. (a) $-\dfrac{1}{2}a - \dfrac{2}{3}$
(b) $2a^2 - 7a + 6$
(c) $2 - 2a$

Are the following functions one-to-one?
1. $A = \{(1, 9), (2, 16), (3, 25), (-1, -9)\}$ Yes
2. $B = \{(1, 1), (2, 8), (3, 27), (-2, -8)\}$ Yes
3. $C = \{(-5, -2), (-3, -1), (2, -3), (4, -2)\}$ No
4. $D = \left\{\left(\frac{1}{2}, -1\right), \left(\frac{3}{2}, -2\right), \left(\frac{5}{2}, -3\right), \left(\frac{7}{2}, -2\right)\right\}$ No
5. $E = \{(0, 8), (-8, 0), (1, 81), (-81, 1)\}$ Yes
6. $F = \{(12, 0), (36, 3), (-3, 36), (-12, 0)\}$ No
7. $G = \{(0, 0), (2.1, 6), (3, 0)\}$ No
8. $H = \left\{(4, -1), \left(\frac{1}{3}, -2\right), (2, -1), (3, 0)\right\}$ No
9. $I = \{(6, -2), (-2, 6), (3.1, 0.4)\}$ Yes

Which graphs represent one-to-one functions?
10.

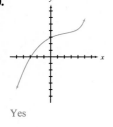

Yes

11.

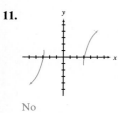

No

Find the inverse of each one-to-one function.
12. $G = \{(1, 9), (2, 12), (-4, -3), (0, 0)\}$
13. $H = \{(6, 1), (7, 2), (8, -3), (10, 10)\}$
14. $J = \{(-2, 3), (7, 4), (0, 8), (3, -2)\}$
15. $K = \{(1, 6), (-3, -5), (-5, 7), (6, 1)\}$
16. $L = \{(-12, -6), (-6, -3), (-3, -1.5), (8, 16)\}$
17. $M = \{(0, -5), (3, 7), (2, -8), (-2, 8)\}$
18. $R = \{(-1, -1), (2, 2), (3, 3)\}$
19. $S = \{(2, -6), (-6, 2), (5, 6), (1, 1), (3, -1)\}$

Find the inverse of each function. Graph the function and its inverse.
20. $f(x) = 4x - 5$

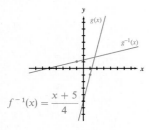

$f^{-1}(x) = \dfrac{x + 5}{4}$

21. $g(x) = 3x - 4$

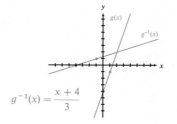

$g^{-1}(x) = \dfrac{x + 4}{3}$

22. $h(x) = \dfrac{1}{2}x + 5$

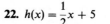
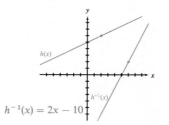

$h^{-1}(x) = 2x - 10$

23. $p(x) = \dfrac{5}{6}x + 2$

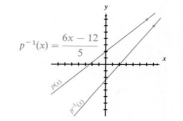

$p^{-1}(x) = \dfrac{6x - 12}{5}$

Find the inverse of each function.
24. $g(x) = \sqrt[3]{x + 3}$ $g^{-1}(x) = x^3 - 3$
25. $f(x) = \sqrt[3]{x - 2}$ $f^{-1}(x) = x^3 + 2$
26. $p(x) = x^3 + 7$ $p^{-1}(x) = \sqrt[3]{x - 7}$
27. $h(x) = x^3 - 5$ $h^{-1}(x) = \sqrt[3]{x + 5}$
28. $f_1(x) = x^3$ $f_1^{-1}(x) = \sqrt[3]{x}$
29. $f_2(x) = x^5 - 1$ $f_2^{-1}(x) = \sqrt[5]{x + 1}$
30. $g_1(x) = x$ $g_1^{-1}(x) = x$
31. $g_2(x) = -x$ $g_2^{-1}(x) = -x$
32. $h_1(x) = 5 + x$ $h_1^{-1}(x) = x - 5$
33. $h_2 = \sqrt[5]{x + 1}$ $h_2^{-1}(x) = x^5 - 1$

12. $G^{-1} = \{(9, 1), (12, 2), (-3, -4), (0, 0)\}$
13. $H^{-1} = \{(1, 6), (2, 7), (-3, 8), (10, 10)\}$
14. $J^{-1} = \{(3, -2), (4, 7), (8, 0), (-2, 3)\}$
15. $K^{-1} = \{(6, 1), (-5, -3), (7, -5), (1, 6)\}$
16. $L^{-1} = \{(-6, -12), (-3, -6), (-1.5, -3), (16, 8)\}$
17. $M^{-1} = \{(-5, 0), (7, 3), (-8, 2), (8, -2)\}$
18. $R^{-1} = \{(-1, -1), (2, 2), (3, 3)\}$
19. $S^{-1} = \{(-6, 2), (2, -6), (6, 5), (1, 1), (-1, 3)\}$

Find a real solution for each system. If there is no real solution, say so.

1. $x = 2y^2$ (8, 2), (2, −1)
$x − 2y = 4$

2. $x = 3y^2$ (27, −3), (12, 2)
$x + 3y = 18$

3. $y = (x − 3)^2 − 2$
$2x − 3y = 7$ (2, −1), $\left(\dfrac{14}{3}, \dfrac{7}{9}\right)$

4. $y = (x − 2)^2 + 3$ (0, 7), (3, 4)
$x + y = 7$

5. $x^2 + y^2 − 16 = 0$
$y = 4x − 4$ (0, −4), $\left(\dfrac{32}{17}, \dfrac{60}{17}\right)$

6. $x^2 + y^2 − 4 = 0$
$y = \dfrac{1}{2}x + 1$ (−2, 0), $\left(\dfrac{6}{5}, \dfrac{8}{5}\right)$

7. $x^2 + 4y^2 = 16$ $(2\sqrt{2}, −\sqrt{2})$,
$x + 2y = 0$ $(−2\sqrt{2}, \sqrt{2})$

8. $4x^2 + y^2 = 20$ $\left(\dfrac{\sqrt{10}}{2}, \sqrt{10}\right), \left(−\dfrac{\sqrt{10}}{2}, −\sqrt{10}\right)$
$y − 2x = 0$

9. $\dfrac{x^2}{9} − \dfrac{y^2}{4} = 1$ No real sol.
$y = 2x$

10. $\dfrac{x^2}{4} − \dfrac{y^2}{9} = 1$ No real sol.
$y = 3x$

11. $x^2 + y^2 = 34$ (3, 5), (5, 3)
$x + y = 8$

12. $x + y = 7$
$3x^2 + y^2 = 43$ (3, 4), $\left(\dfrac{1}{2}, \dfrac{13}{2}\right)$

13. $2x + y = 5$
$3x^2 − 7y^2 = 5$ (2, 1), $\left(\dfrac{18}{5}, −\dfrac{11}{5}\right)$

14. $x^2 − 2y^2 = 7$ (5, −3), (27, 19)
$x − y = 8$

15. $x^2 + y^2 = 25$ (4, −3), (−4, 3)
$3x + 4y = 0$

16. $x^2 − 3y^2 = 13$
$x − 2y = 1$ (−11, −6), (5, 2)

17. $3y^2 − x^2 = 8$ (−2, 2), (−10, 6)
$2y − 2 = −x$

18. $2x + 3y = 14$
$x^2 − y^2 = 12$ (4, 2), $\left(−\dfrac{76}{5}, \dfrac{74}{5}\right)$

19. $x + 2y = 10$ (0, 5), (4, 3)
$x^2 + y^2 = 25$

20. $2x − y = 4$ (3, 2), (−1, −6)
$xy = 6$

Find a real solution for each system, if possible. If there is no real solution, say so.

21. $xy = −2$ (2, −1), $\left(\dfrac{1}{2}, −4\right)$
$2x − y = 5$

22. $xy = 1$ $\left(\dfrac{7}{4}, \dfrac{4}{7}\right)$, (−1, −1)
$4x − 7y = 3$

23. $5x^2 + 3y^2 = 12$ $\left(\dfrac{3}{2}, ±\dfrac{1}{2}\right), \left(−\dfrac{3}{2}, ±\dfrac{1}{2}\right)$
$3x^2 − 7y^2 = 5$

24. $4x^2 − y^2 = 7$ (2, ±3), (−2, ±3)
$x^2 + 3y^2 = 31$

25. $x^2 + y^2 = 16$ (−4, 0)
$(x − 2)^2 + y^2 = 36$

26. $x^2 + y^2 = 9$ (−3, 0)
$(x + 7)^2 + y^2 = 16$

27. $y^2 = x − 3$ (7, 2), (4, −1)
$y^2 = 3y − 2x + 12$

28. $x^2 = y + 4$ $(±\sqrt{2}, −2), \left(±\dfrac{\sqrt{39}}{3}, \dfrac{1}{3}\right)$
$x^2 = 6 − 4y − 3y^2$

29. $3x^2 + 4y^2 = 16$ (2, ±1), (−2, ±1)
$0 = 5 − 2x^2 + 3y^2$

30. $5 + y^2 − x^2 = 0$ (3, ±2), (−3, ±2)
$x^2 + 2y^2 = 17$

31. $x^2 + y^2 = 10$ (1, ±3), (−1, ±3)
$16x^2 + y^2 = 25$

32. $x^2 + y^2 − 4 = 0$ $\left(\dfrac{4\sqrt{7}}{7}, ±\dfrac{2\sqrt{21}}{7}\right), \left(−\dfrac{4\sqrt{7}}{7}, ±\dfrac{2\sqrt{21}}{7}\right)$
$x^2 + 8y^2 − 16 = 0$

33. $x^2 + y^2 = 25$ No real sol.
$\dfrac{x^2}{4} + \dfrac{y^2}{9} = 1$

34. $x^2 − y^2 = 1$ (1, 0), (−1, 0)
$x^2 + y^2 = 1$

35. $y = x^2 − 4$ $(±\sqrt{3}, −1), (±2, 0)$
$x^2 + y^2 = 4$

CHAPTER ORGANIZER

Topic	Procedure	Examples
Distance between two points, p. 394	The distance d between points (x_1, y_1) and (x_2, y_2) is $$d = \sqrt{(x_2 − x_1)^2 + (y_2 − y_1)^2}$$	Find the distance between $(−6, −3)$ and $(5, −2)$. $$d = \sqrt{[5 − (−6)]^2 + [−2 − (−3)]^2}$$ $$= \sqrt{(5 + 6)^2 + (−2 + 3)^2}$$ $$= \sqrt{121 + 1}$$ $$= \sqrt{122}$$
Standard form of the equation of a circle, p. 395	The standard form of the equation of a circle with center at (h, k) and radius r is $$(x − h)^2 + (y − k)^2 = r^2$$	Graph: $(x − 3)^2 + (y + 4)^2 = 16$. Center at $(h, k) = (3, −4)$, radius = 4

Topic	Procedure	Examples
Standard form of vertical hyperbola with center at (h, k), p. 420	The vertical hyperbola with center at (h, k) and vertices $(h, k + b)$ and $(h, k - b)$ has equation $$\frac{(y - k)^2}{b^2} - \frac{(x - h)^2}{a^2} = 1$$	Graph: $\dfrac{(y - 5)^2}{9} - \dfrac{(x - 4)^2}{4} = 1$. Center at $(4, 5)$, $b = 3$, $a = 2$.
Relations, functions, and one-to-one functions, p. 425, 432	A *relation* is any set of ordered pairs. A *function* is a relation in which no ordered pairs have the same first coordinate. A *one-to-one function* is a function in which no ordered pairs have the same second coordinate.	Is $\{(3, 6), (2, 8), (9, 1), (4, 6)\}$, a one-to-one function? No, since $(3, 6)$ and $(4, 6)$ have the same second coordinate.
Vertical and horizontal line tests, p. 427, 432	If vertical line intersects the graph of a relation more than once, the relation is not a function. If a horizontal line intersects the graph of a function more than once, the function is not one-to-one.	Does this graph represent a function? No, because a vertical line intersects the curve more than once. Does this graph represent a one-to-one function? Yes, a horizontal line only crosses it once.
Inverse of a function, p. 434	Any one-to-one function has an inverse function. To find the equation of an inverse function $f^{-1}(x)$ when the equation of a one-to-one function $f(x)$ is given: 1. Replace $f(x)$ with y. 2. Interchange x and y. 3. Solve for y in terms of x. 4. Replace y with $f^{-1}(x)$.	Find the inverse of $f(x) = (x + 3)^3$. $$y = (x + 3)^3$$ $$x = (y + 3)^3$$ $$\sqrt[3]{x} = \sqrt[3]{(y + 3)^3}$$ $$\sqrt[3]{x} = y + 3$$ $$\sqrt[3]{x} - 3 = y$$ $$f^{-1}(x) = \sqrt[3]{x} - 3$$

Topic	Procedure	Examples
Nonlinear systems of equations, p. 438	We can solve a nonlinear system by the substitution method or the addition method. In the addition method, we multiply one or more equations by a numerical value, then add them together so that one variable is eliminated. In the substitution method we solve one equation for one variable and substitute that expression into the other equation.	Solve by substitution: $$2x^2 + y^2 = 18$$ $$xy = 4$$ $$y = \frac{4}{x}$$ $$2x^2 + \left(\frac{4}{x}\right)^2 = 18$$ $$2x^2 + \frac{16}{x^2} = 18$$ $$2x^4 + 16 = 18x^2$$ $$2x^4 - 18x^2 + 16 = 0$$ $$x^4 - 9x^2 + 8 = 0$$ $$(x^2 - 1)(x^2 - 8) = 0$$ $x^2 - 1 = 0 \qquad x^2 - 8 = 0$ $x^2 = 1 \qquad\quad x^2 = 8$ $x = \pm 1 \qquad\quad x = \pm 2\sqrt{2}$ Since $xy = 4$, if $x = 1$ then $y = 4$ if $x = -1$ then $y = -4$ if $x = 2\sqrt{2}$ then $y = \sqrt{2}$ if $x = -2\sqrt{2}$ then $y = -\sqrt{2}$ The solutions are $(1, 4)$, $(-1, -4)$, $(2\sqrt{2}, \sqrt{2})$, and $(-2\sqrt{2}, -\sqrt{2})$.

REVIEW PROBLEMS CHAPTER 8

In problems 1 and 2, find the distance between the points.

1. $(-7, 3)$ and $(-2, -1)$
$\sqrt{41}$

2. $(10.5, -6)$ and $(7.5, -4)$
$\sqrt{13}$

3. Write in standard form the equation of a circle with center at $(0, -7)$ and radius 5.
$x^2 + (y + 7)^2 = 25$

4. Write in standard form the equation of a circle with center at $(-6, 3)$ and radius $\sqrt{15}$.
$(x + 6)^2 + (y - 3)^2 = 15$

Put each equation in standard form. Find the center and the radius of each circle.

5. $x^2 + y^2 - 6x - 8y + 3 = 0$ $\quad (x - 3)^2 + (y - 4)^2 = 22$
$C(3, 4), r = \sqrt{22}$

6. $x^2 + y^2 - 10x + 12y + 52 = 0$ $\quad (x - 5)^2 + (y + 6)^2 = 9$
$C(5, -6), r = 3$

Graph each parabola. Label its vertex and plot at least one intercept.

7. $x = \frac{1}{3}y^2$

8. $y = -2(x + 1)^2 - 3$

9. $x = \frac{1}{2}(y - 2)^2 + 4$

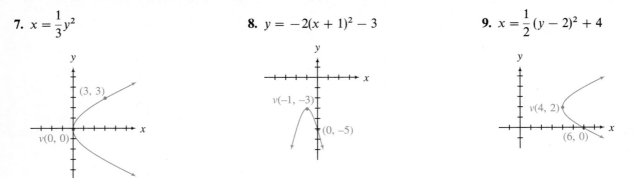

Put each equation in standard form. Find the vertex and determine in which direction the parabola opens.

10. $x^2 + 6x = y - 4$ $y = (x + 3)^2 - 5$
vertex at $(-3, -5)$
Parabola opens upward.

11. $x + 8y = y^2 + 10$ $x = (y - 4)^2 - 6$
vertex at $(-6, 4)$
Parabola opens to the right.

Graph each ellipse. Label its center and four other points.

12. $\dfrac{x^2}{\frac{1}{4}} + \dfrac{y^2}{1} = 1$

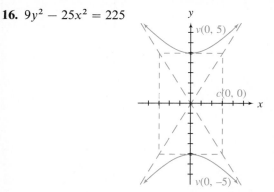

13. $16x^2 + y^2 - 32 = 0$

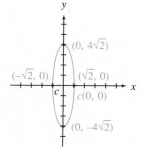

Scale: each unit is $\sqrt{2}$ units

Determine the vertices and the center of each ellipse.

14. $\dfrac{(x + 1)^2}{9} + \dfrac{(y - 2)^2}{16} = 1$

$C = (-1, 2); v = (2, 2), (-4, 2), (-1, 6), (-1, -2)$

15. $\dfrac{(x + 5)^2}{4} + \dfrac{(y + 3)^2}{25} = 1$

$C = (-5, -3); v = (-3, -3), (-7, -3), (-5, 2), (-5, -8)$

Find the center and vertices of each hyperbola and graph it.

16. $9y^2 - 25x^2 = 225$

17. $x^2 - 4y^2 - 16 = 0$

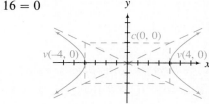

Determine the vertices and the center of each hyperbola.

18. $\dfrac{(x - 2)^2}{4} - \dfrac{(y + 3)^2}{25} = 1$ $(0, -3), (4, -3)$
$C = (2, -3)$

19. $9(y - 2)^2 - (x + 5)^2 - 9 = 0$ $(-5, 3), (-5, 1)$
$C = (-5, 2)$

*For each set, determine **(a)** the domain, **(b)** the range, **(c)** if the set defines a function, and, **(d)** if the set defines a one-to-one function.*

20. $A = \{(100, 10), (200, 20), (300, 30), (400, 10)\}$

(a) $D = \{100, 200, 300, 400\}$
(b) $R = \{10, 20, 30\}$
(c) Yes
(d) No

21. $B = \{(3, 7), (7, 3), (0, 8), (0, -8)\}$

(a) $D = \{0, 3, 7\}$
(b) $R = \{-8, 3, 7, 8\}$
(c) No
(d) No

22. $C = \{(12, 6), (0, 6), (0, -1), (-6, -12)\}$

(a) $D = \{12, 0, -6\}$
(b) $R = \{-1, -12, 6\}$
(c) No
(d) No

23. $D = \left\{\left(\dfrac{1}{2}, 2\right), \left(\dfrac{1}{4}, 4\right), \left(-\dfrac{1}{3}, -3\right), \left(4, \dfrac{1}{4}\right)\right\}$

(a) $D = \left\{\dfrac{1}{2}, \dfrac{1}{4}, -\dfrac{1}{3}, 4\right\}$

(b) $R = \left\{2, 4, -3, \dfrac{1}{4}\right\}$

(c) Yes
(d) Yes

24. $E = \{(0, 1), (1, 2), (2, 9), (-1, -2)\}$
  (a) $D = \{0, 1, 2, -1\}$
  (b) $R = \{1, 2, 9, -2\}$
  (c) Yes
  (d) Yes

25. $F = \{(3, 7), (2, 1), (0, -3), (1, 1)\}$
  (a) $D = \{3, 2, 0, 1\}$
  (b) $R = \{7, 1, -3\}$
  (c) Yes
  (d) No

*For each graph, determine (**a**) if the graph represents a function and (**b**) if the graph represents a one-to-one function.*

26.
  (a) Yes
  (b) No

27.
  (a) No
  (b) No

28.
  (a) Yes
  (b) Yes

29.
  (a) Yes
  (b) No

30.
  (a) No
  (b) No

31.
  (a) Yes
  (b) Yes

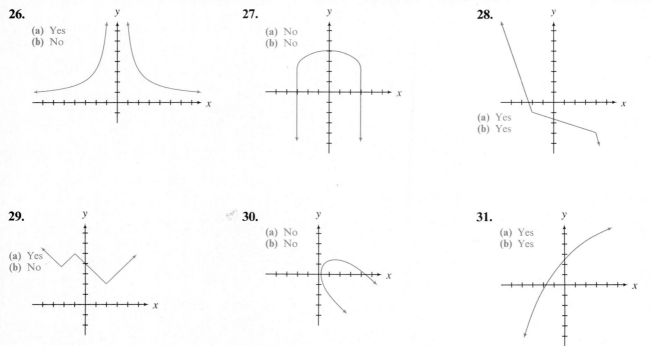

Find the inverses of the functions.

32. $A = \{(0.5, 3), (0.8, 4), (1.2, 5), (4, 0.8)\}$
$A^{-1} = \{(3, 0.5), (4, 0.8), (5, 1.2), (0.8, 4)\}$

33. $B = \{(-10, 1), (1, 10), (3, -7), (4, 3)\}$
$B^{-1} = \{(1, -10), (10, 1), (-7, 3), (3, 4)\}$

Find the equation for the inverse of each function.

34. $f(x) = \dfrac{1}{2}x - \dfrac{3}{4}$ $f^{-1}(x) = \dfrac{4x + 3}{2}$

35. $g(x) = \sqrt[3]{2 - x}$
$g^{-1}(x) = 2 - x^3$

Evaluate the following functions.

36. $h(x) = 2x^2 - 5x + 3$
Find $h(-2)$, $h(3)$, $h(a + 1)$.
  (a) 21
  (b) 6
  (c) $2a^2 - a$

37. $j(x) = x^3 + 5x$
Find $j(-3)$, $j\left(\dfrac{1}{2}\right)$, $j(2a)$.
  (a) -42
  (b) $\dfrac{21}{8}$
  (c) $8a^3 + 10a$

Solve each nonlinear system.

38. $x^2 + y = 9$
$y - x = 3$
$(-3, 0), (2, 5)$

39. $y^2 - x^2 = 3$
$x - 2y = 1$
No real sol.

Solve each nonlinear system.

40. $2x^2 + y^2 = 17$
$x^2 + 2y^2 = 22$
$(2, \pm 3), (-2, \pm 3)$

41. $xy = -2$
$x^2 + y^2 = 5$
$(2, -1), (-2, 1), (1, -2), (-1, 2)$

42. $3x^2 - 4y^2 = 12$
$7x^2 - y^2 = 8$
No real sol.

1. Find the distance between $(3.6, -4)$ and $(-5.4, 2)$.

2. Write in standard form the equation of a circle with center at $(5, -7)$ and has radius $\sqrt{11}$.

3. Put the equation $x^2 + y^2 - 2x + 10y - 10 = 0$ in the standard form. Find its center and radius.

Put the equation in standard form if it is not. Then graph each parabola, labeling the vertex and one other point.

4. $x = \dfrac{1}{2}y^2 - 2$

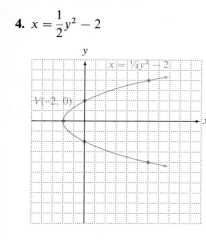

5. $y = -2(x + 1)^2 + 3$

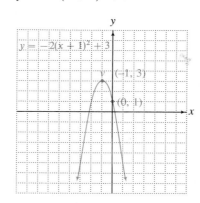

6. $x - 1 + 4y = y^2$

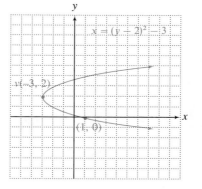

Put each equation in standard form if it is not. Then graph each ellipse, labeling the center and four other points.

7. $25x^2 + 16y^2 = 400$

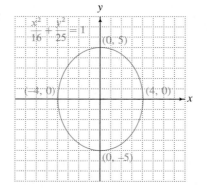

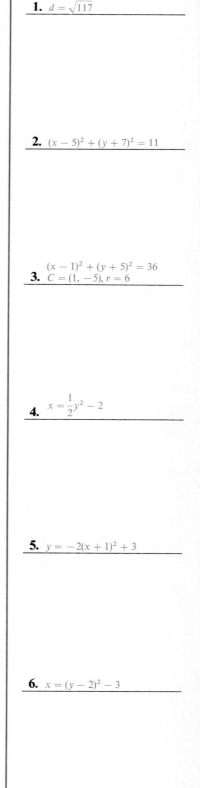

1. $d = \sqrt{117}$

2. $(x - 5)^2 + (y + 7)^2 = 11$

3. $(x - 1)^2 + (y + 5)^2 = 36$
$C = (1, -5), r = 6$

4. $x = \dfrac{1}{2}y^2 - 2$

5. $y = -2(x + 1)^2 + 3$

6. $x = (y - 2)^2 - 3$

7. $\dfrac{x^2}{16} + \dfrac{y^2}{25} = 1$

8. $\dfrac{\dfrac{y^2}{4}}{9} + \dfrac{x^2}{1} = 1$

9. $\dfrac{(x-2)^2}{36} + \dfrac{(y-1)^2}{49} = 1$

10. $\dfrac{y^2}{4} - \dfrac{x^2}{9} = 1$

11. $\dfrac{x^2}{1} - \dfrac{y^2}{8} = 1$

12. $\dfrac{(x+5)^2}{9} - \dfrac{(y+2)^2}{25} = 1$

---

8. $\dfrac{\dfrac{y^2}{4}}{9} + \dfrac{x^2}{1} = 1$

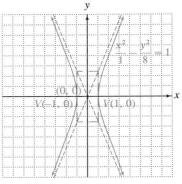

9. $\dfrac{(x-2)^2}{36} + \dfrac{(y-1)^2}{49} = 1$

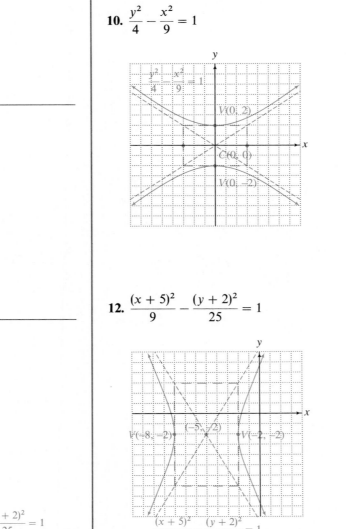

Put each equation in standard form if it is not. Then graph each hyperbola, labeling the center and the two vertices.

10. $\dfrac{y^2}{4} - \dfrac{x^2}{9} = 1$

11. $8x^2 - y^2 = 8$

12. $\dfrac{(x+5)^2}{9} - \dfrac{(y+2)^2}{25} = 1$

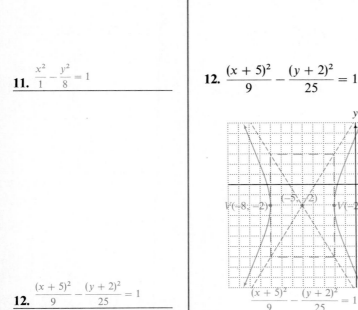

*For each set determine **(a)** the domain, **(b)** the range, **(c)** if the set defines a function, and **(d)** if the set defines a one-to-one function.*

1. $A = \left\{ \left(\frac{1}{2}, \frac{1}{4} \right), \left(\frac{1}{3}, \frac{1}{6} \right), (0, 0), \left(\frac{1}{2}, \frac{1}{8} \right) \right\}$

(a) $D = \left\{ \frac{1}{2}, \frac{1}{3}, 0, \right\}$
(b) $R = \left\{ \frac{1}{4}, \frac{1}{6}, 0, \frac{1}{8} \right\}$
1. (c) No   (d) No

2. $B = \{(-2, 3), (-7, -18), (2, 3), (7, 18)\}$

(a) $D = \{-2, -7, 2, 7\}$
(b) $R = \{3, 18, -18\}$
(c) Yes
2. (d) No

3. $C = \{(12, 0), (-12, 3), (-3, 12), (3, -12)\}$

(a) $D = \{12, -12, -3, 3\}$
(b) $R = \{0, 3, 12, -12\}$
(c) Yes
3. (d) Yes

4. $D = \{(3.6, 1.2), (2.4, 4.8), (-4.8, 2.2), (-2.6, 1.2)\}$

(a) $D = \{3.6, 2.4, -4.8, -2.6\}$
(b) $R = \{1.2, 4.8, 2.2, 1.2\}$
(c) Yes
4. (d) Yes

*For each graph determine **(a)** if the graph represents a function and **(b)** if the graph represents a one-to-one function.*

5.

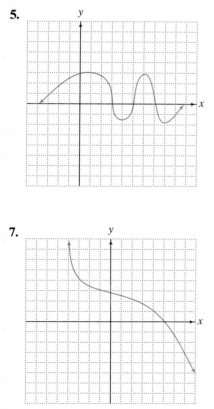

6.

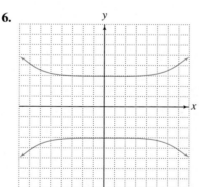

(a) Yes
5. (b) No

(a) No
6. (b) No

7.

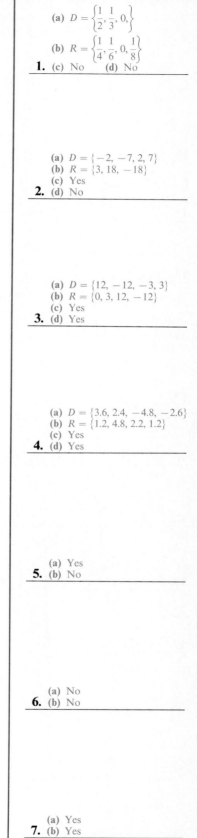

(a) Yes
7. (b) Yes

$p(2) = 14$
$g(3) = 43$
8. $s(-2) = 6$

$p(-3) = -51$
$g(2) = 16$
9. $s\left(\dfrac{1}{2}\right) = \dfrac{19}{4}$

10. -5

11. 42

12. (a) $5a^2 + 12a - 1$
(b) $\dfrac{14 - a}{2}$

13. (a) $16a^3 - 2a$
(b) $5a^2 - 18a + 8$

14. -1

15. 3

16. $A^{-1} = \{(-5, 1), (-3, 2),\ (-2, 3), (6, -1)\}$

17. $B^{-1} = \{(5, 0), (6, -5),\ (7, 1), (1, 1)\}$

18. $f^{-1}(x) = \dfrac{4 - x}{3}$

19. $g^{-1}(x) = \sqrt[3]{x + 2}$

20. $(0, 1)$
$(\sqrt{5}, 6)$
$(-\sqrt{5}, 6)$

21. $(1, \pm 2)$
$(-1, \pm 2)$

22. $(1, 4)$
$(-1, -4)$
$(2\sqrt{2}, \sqrt{2})$
$(-2\sqrt{2}, -\sqrt{2})$

Define $p(x) = 2x^3 - x$, $\quad g(x) = 5x^2 + 2x - 8$, $\quad$ *and* $s(x) = 5 - \dfrac{1}{2}x$. *Find*

8. $p(2)$, $g(3)$, $s(-2)$

9. $p(-3)$, $g(2)$, $s\left(\dfrac{1}{2}\right)$

10. $p(0) + g(-1)$

11. $p(-1) + g(3)$

12. $g(a + 1)$, $s(a - 4)$

13. $p(2a)$, $g(a - 2)$

14. $s(a + 3) - s(a + 1)$

15. $s(a - 4) - s(a + 2)$

Find the inverse.

16. $A = \{(1, -5), (2, -3), (3, -2), (-1, 6)\}$

17. $B = \{(0, 5), (-5, 6), (1, 7), (1, 1)\}$

Find the equation for the inverse of the function given.

18. $f(x) = 4 - 3x$

19. $g(x) = x^3 - 2$

20. Solve the nonlinear system.

$$y = x^2 + 1$$
$$x^2 + y^2 - 8y + 7 = 0$$

Solve each nonlinear system.

21. $\quad y^2 - 2x^2 = 2$
$\qquad 2y^2 - 3x^2 = 5$

22. $2x^2 + y^2 = 18$
$\qquad xy = 4$

1. Find the distance between $(-6, -8)$ and $(-2, 5)$.

Place the equation in standard form. Find the center or vertex, plot at least one other point, identify the conic, and sketch the curve.

2. $x^2 + y^2 + 6x - 4y + 9 = 0$

3. $y^2 - 6y - x + 13 = 0$

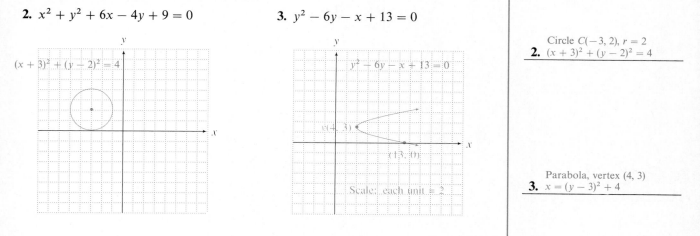

Identify and graph each conic section. Label the center and/or vertex as appropriate.

4. $\dfrac{x^2}{10} - \dfrac{y^2}{9} = 1$

5. $\dfrac{x^2}{25} + \dfrac{y^2}{1} = 1$

6. $y = -2(x + 3)^2 + 4$

7. $\dfrac{(x + 2)^2}{16} + \dfrac{(y - 5)^2}{4} = 1$

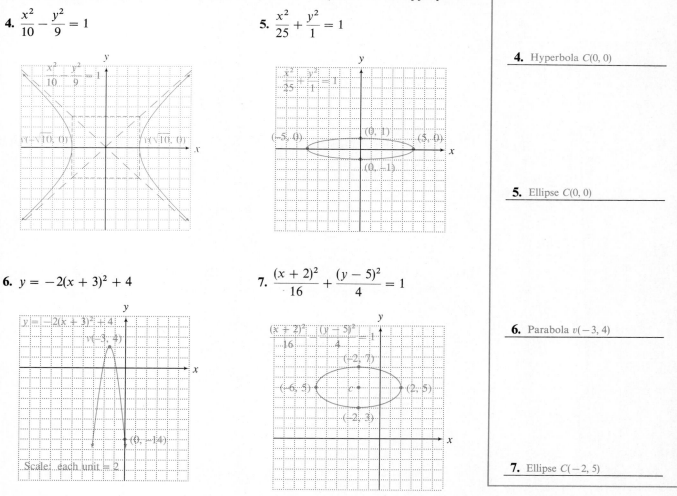

1. $\sqrt{185}$

2. Circle $C(-3, 2)$, $r = 2$
$(x + 3)^2 + (y - 2)^2 = 4$

3. Parabola, vertex $(4, 3)$
$x = (y - 3)^2 + 4$

4. Hyperbola $C(0, 0)$

5. Ellipse $C(0, 0)$

6. Parabola $v(-3, 4)$

7. Ellipse $C(-2, 5)$

8. Hyperbola $C(0, 0)$

(a) $D = \{1, 2, -3\}$
(b) $R = \{1, 2, -3, -2\}$
(c) No
9. (d) No

(a) Yes
10. (b) No

$f(-2) = 20$
$f(1) = 5$
$f(a) = 3a^2 - 2a + 4$
11. $f(a + 2) = 3a^2 + 10a + 12$

$f^{-1} = \{(1.6, -2), (5.5, -1),$
12. $\quad\quad\quad (1.1, 3), (2, 1.6)\}$

13. $f^{-1}(x) = \dfrac{10x + 2}{5}$

14. $(0, 5), (-4, -3)$

15. $(1, 0), (-1, 0)$

$(\sqrt{3}, -\sqrt{3}), (-\sqrt{3}, \sqrt{3}),$
16. $\left(\dfrac{\sqrt{6}}{2}, -\sqrt{6}\right), \left(-\dfrac{\sqrt{6}}{2}, \sqrt{6}\right)$

---

8. $7y^2 - 7x^2 = 28$

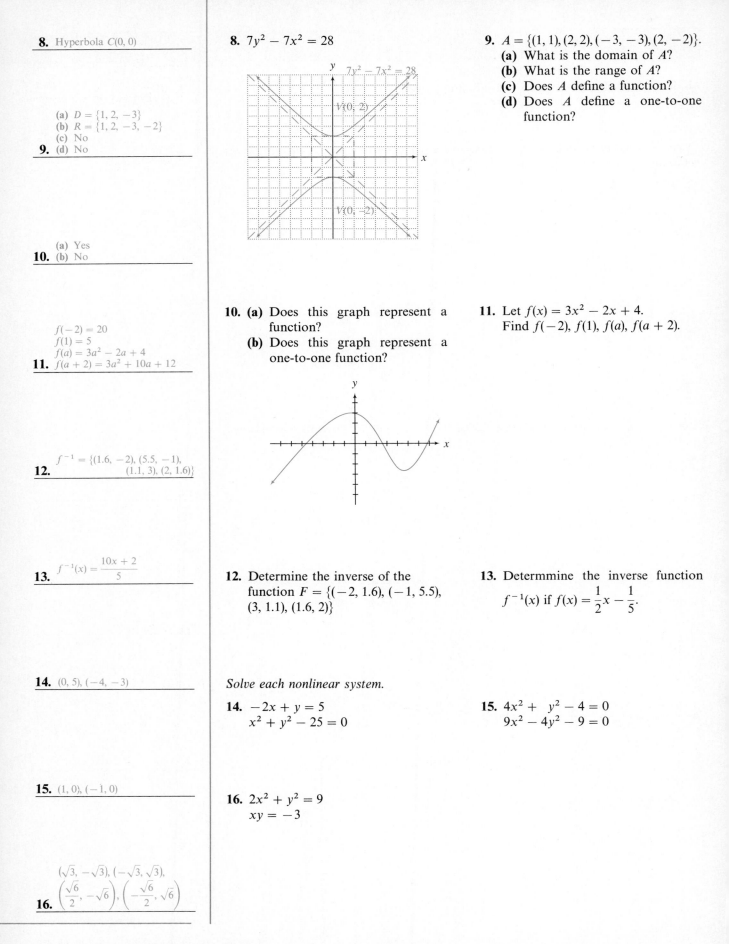

10. (a) Does this graph represent a function?
(b) Does this graph represent a one-to-one function?

12. Determine the inverse of the function $F = \{(-2, 1.6), (-1, 5.5), (3, 1.1), (1.6, 2)\}$

Solve each nonlinear system.

14. $-2x + y = 5$
$\quad\ x^2 + y^2 - 25 = 0$

16. $2x^2 + y^2 = 9$
$\quad\ xy = -3$

---

9. $A = \{(1, 1), (2, 2), (-3, -3), (2, -2)\}$.
(a) What is the domain of A?
(b) What is the range of A?
(c) Does A define a function?
(d) Does A define a one-to-one function?

11. Let $f(x) = 3x^2 - 2x + 4$.
Find $f(-2), f(1), f(a), f(a + 2)$.

13. Determmine the inverse function $f^{-1}(x)$ if $f(x) = \dfrac{1}{2}x - \dfrac{1}{5}$.

15. $4x^2 + \ \ y^2 - 4 = 0$
$\quad\ 9x^2 - 4y^2 - 9 = 0$

Approximately one-half of this test covers the content of Chapters 1–7. The remainder covers the content of Chapter 8.

1. Identify the property illustrated by the equation $5(-3) = -3(5)$.

2. Evaluate: $3(4 - 6)^3 + \sqrt{25}$.

3. Simplify: $2\{x - 3[x - 2(x + 1)]\}$

4. Solve for p: $A = 3bt + prt$

5. Factor: $x^3 + 125$.

6. Add: $\dfrac{3}{x - 4} + \dfrac{6}{x^2 - 16}$.

7. Solve for x:

$$\frac{3}{2x + 3} = \frac{1}{2x - 3} + \frac{2}{4x^2 - 9}.$$

8. Solve for (x, y, z):

$$3x - 2y - 9z = 9$$
$$x - y + z = 8$$
$$2x + 3y - z = -2$$

9. Simplify: $\sqrt{8x} + 3x\sqrt{50} - 4x\sqrt{32}$.

10. Multiply and simplify:
$(\sqrt{2} + \sqrt{3})(2\sqrt{6} - \sqrt{3})$.

11. Find the distance between $(6, -1)$ and $(-3, -4)$.

Identify and graph each equation.

12. $y = -\dfrac{1}{2}(x + 2)^2 - 3$

13. $25x^2 + 25y^2 = 125$

Circle with radius $\sqrt{5}$

1. Commutative property for multiplication

2. -19

3. $8x + 12$

4. $p = \dfrac{A - 3bt}{rt}$

5. $(x + 5)(x^2 - 5x + 25)$

6. $\dfrac{3x + 18}{(x + 4)(x + 4)}$

7. $x = \dfrac{7}{2}$

8. $x = 4, y = -3, z = 1$

9. $2\sqrt{2x} - x\sqrt{2}$

10. $4\sqrt{3} + 6\sqrt{2} - \sqrt{6} - 3$

11. $3\sqrt{10}$

12. Parabola $V(-2, -3)$

13. Circle $C(0, 0)$ radius $= \sqrt{5}$

14. $16x^2 - 4y^2 = 64$

15. $\dfrac{(x - 2)^2}{25} + \dfrac{(y - 3)^2}{16} = 1$

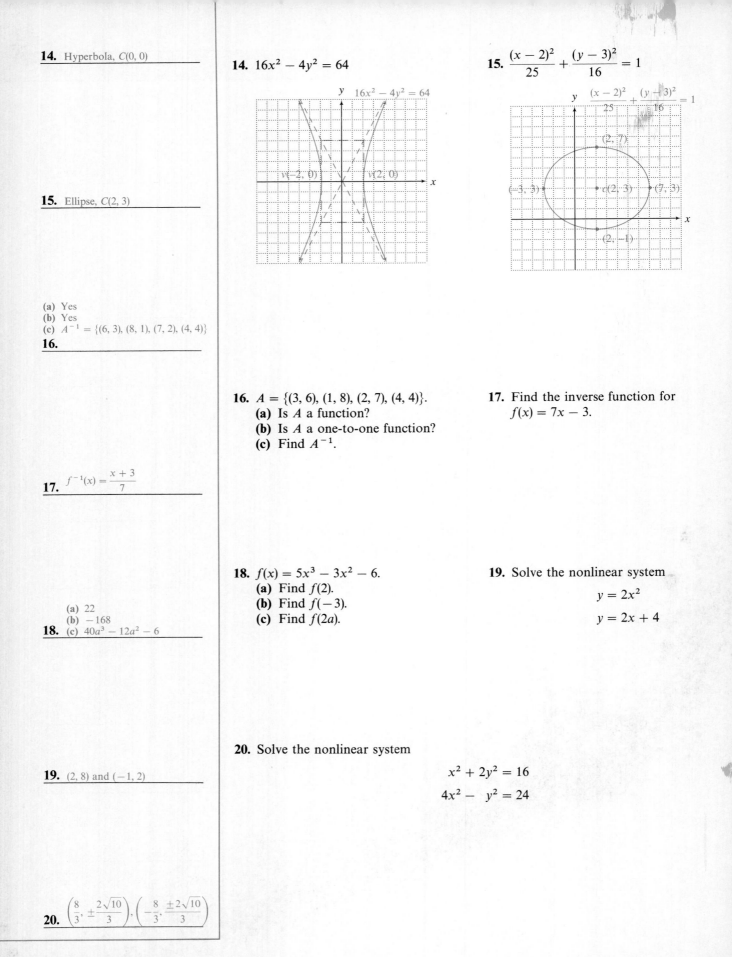

16. $A = \{(3, 6), (1, 8), (2, 7), (4, 4)\}$.
   (a) Is A a function?
   (b) Is A a one-to-one function?
   (c) Find A^{-1}.

17. Find the inverse function for
   $f(x) = 7x - 3$.

18. $f(x) = 5x^3 - 3x^2 - 6$.
   (a) Find $f(2)$.
   (b) Find $f(-3)$.
   (c) Find $f(2a)$.

19. Solve the nonlinear system

$$y = 2x^2$$
$$y = 2x + 4$$

20. Solve the nonlinear system

$$x^2 + 2y^2 = 16$$
$$4x^2 - y^2 = 24$$

Exponential and Logarithmic Functions

Geologists apply mathematical formulas in their study of earthquakes. No reliable prediction method currently exists, but mathematics is helping make their predictions more accurate.

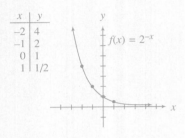

$$
\begin{array}{c|c}
x & y \\
\hline
-2 & 4 \\
-1 & 2 \\
0 & 1 \\
1 & 1/2
\end{array}
$$

$f(x) = 2^{-x}$

PRETEST CHAPTER 9

If you are familiar with the topics in this chapter, take this test now. Check your answers with those in the back of the book. If an answer was wrong or you couldn't do a problem, study the appropriate section of the chapter.

If you are not familiar with the topics in this chapter, don't take this test now. Instead, study the examples, work the practice problems, and then take the test.

This test will help you identify those concepts that you have mastered and those that need more study.

Section 9.1

1. Sketch the graph of $f(x) = 2^{-x}$. Plot at least four points.
2. Solve for x: $3^{2x-1} = 27$. $x = 2$
3. The amount of money A due after t years when a principal amount P is invested at interest rate r is given by the equation $A = P(1 + r)^t$. How much money will Nancy have in four years if she invests $10,000 in a mutual fund that pays 12% interest compounded annually? $10,000 $(1.12)^4$ or $15,735.19

Section 9.2

4. Write in logarithmic form: $\dfrac{1}{36} = 6^{-2}$. $\log_6 \dfrac{1}{36} = -2$
5. Solve for x: $\log_4 x = 3$. $x = 64$
6. Evaluate: $\log_{10}(10{,}000)$. 4

Section 9.3

7. Write the logarithm in terms of $\log_5 x$, $\log_5 y$, and $\log_5 z$: $\log_5\left(\dfrac{x^2 y^5}{z^3}\right)$
   $2\log_5 x + 5\log_5 y - 3\log_5 z$
8. Express as one logarithm: $\dfrac{1}{2}\log_4 x - 3\log_4 w$. $\log_4 \dfrac{\sqrt{x}}{w^3}$
9. Find x if $\log_3 x + \log_3 2 = 4$. $x = \dfrac{81}{2}$

Section 9.4

10. Use a scientific calculator or Table B–3[†] to find an approximate value of x in the equation $\log x = 3.9170$. $x = 8260.4$
11. Use a scientific calculator, or Table B–3 and the value $\log e \approx 0.4343$, to approximate $\ln 4.79$. 1.57
12. Use a scientific calculator or Table B–2 to find an approximate value of x in the equation $\ln x = 0.24$. $x = 1.27$
13. Using a scientific calculator or Table B–3, find $\log_6 5.02$. 0.9005

Section 9.5

14. Solve the following logarithmic equation and check your solution.
$$\log x - \log(x + 3) = -1 \quad x = \frac{1}{3}$$
15. Solve the exponential equation $4^{2x+1} = 9$. $x = 0.2925$
16. How long would it take for $2000 to grow to $7000 at 6% annual interest compounded yearly? Round your answer to the nearest year. 21 yrs.

[†] Reference tables B–1 (Square Roots), B–2 (Exponential Values), and B–3 (Common Logarithms) are found in Appendix B, p. 578.

9.1 THE EXPONENTIAL FUNCTION

☐ After studying this section, you will be able to:

1 Graph an exponential equation

2 Solve an elementary exponential equation

3 Solve an applied problem requiring the use of an exponential function

We have defined 2^x for any rational number x. For example,

$$2^{-2} = \frac{1}{4}$$

$$2^{1/2} = \sqrt{2}$$

$$2^{1.7} = 2^{17/10} = \sqrt[10]{2^{17}}$$

We can also define $y = 2^x$ when x is an irrational number, such as π or $\sqrt{2}$. The actual definition is too advanced for this course. But we evaluate 2^x by approximating x to several decimal places for many values of x. Then we evaluate 2^x.

For example, to find $y = 2^{\sqrt{2}}$, we would evaluate

$$2^1 = 2, \quad 2^{1.4} = 2.6390, \quad 2^{1.41} = 2.6573, \quad 2^{1.414} = 2.6647$$

and so on. We are really replacing the irrational number $\sqrt{2}$ by rational numbers that approximate the value of $\sqrt{2}$. The approximations get closer and closer to the actual value $\sqrt{2}$, but *never* quite reach it.

1 We can now define an **exponential function** for all real values of x.

Definition of Exponential Function

The function $f(x) = b^x$, where $b > 0$, $b \neq 1$, and x is a real number, is called the **exponential function**.

The number b is called the **base** of the function. Now let's look at some graphs of exponential functions.

Example 1 Graph: $f(x) = 2^x$.

We make a table of values for x and evaluate $f(x)$.

$$f(-1) = 2^{-1} = \frac{1}{2} \qquad f(0) = 2^0 = 1 \qquad f(1) = 2^1 = 2$$

Can you verify the other values in this table? We will now draw the graph.

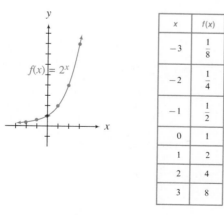

x	f(x)
−3	$\frac{1}{8}$
−2	$\frac{1}{4}$
−1	$\frac{1}{2}$
0	1
1	2
2	4
3	8

TEACHING TIP   Students who have difficulty with these graphs usually are making errors in evaluating the function values. After explaining examples 1 and 2, ask students to complete the following: Fill in the chart

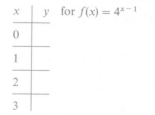

Then graph the function $f(x)$

Notice how the curve of $f(x) = 2^x$ comes *very close to* the x-axis but *never* touches it. The x-axis is an asymptote for an exponential function. You should also see that $f(x)$ is always positive, so the range of $f(x)$ includes *all* positive real numbers (the domain includes *all* real numbers). As x increases, $f(x)$ increases faster and faster (the curve gets steeper). ■

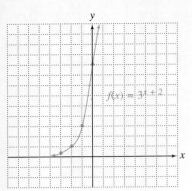

Practice Problem 1   Graph: $f(x) = 3^{x+2}$ ■

Example 2   Graph: $f(x) = \left(\dfrac{1}{2}\right)^x$.

We can write $\left(\dfrac{1}{2}\right)^x$ as $f(x) = \left(\dfrac{1}{2}\right)^x = (2^{-1})^x = 2^{-x}$ and evaluate it for a few values of x. We will now draw the graph.

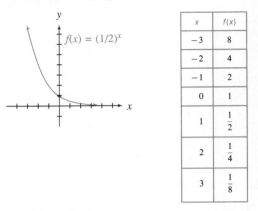

x	$f(x)$
-3	8
-2	4
-1	2
0	1
1	$\dfrac{1}{2}$
2	$\dfrac{1}{4}$
3	$\dfrac{1}{8}$

Note that as x increases, $f(x)$ decreases.   ■

Practice Problem 2   Graph: $f(x) = \left(\dfrac{1}{3}\right)^x$.   ■

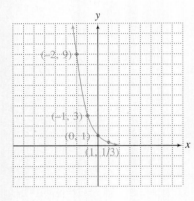

2 All of the usual laws of exponents are true for exponential functions. We also have the following important property to help us solve exponential equations.

Property of Exponential Equations

If $b^x = b^y$, then $x = y$ for $b > 0$ and $b \ne 1$.

Example 3   Solve: $2^x = \dfrac{1}{16}$.

To use the property of exponential equations, we must have the same base on each side of the equation.

$$2^x = \frac{1}{16}$$

$$2^x = \frac{1}{2^4} \qquad \text{Because } 2^4 = 16.$$

$$2^x = 2^{-4} \qquad \text{Because } \frac{1}{2^4} = 2^{-4}.$$

$$x = -4 \qquad \text{Property of exponential equations.} \quad ■$$

Practice Problem 3   Solve: $2^x = \dfrac{1}{32}$.   ■

TEACHING TIP After solving example 3, you may want to do the following additional example. Solve for x:

$$10^x = 0.0001$$

Sol.: $10^x = \dfrac{1}{10000} = \dfrac{1}{10^4}$

$$10x = 10^{-4}$$
$$x = -4$$

An extremely useful function is the exponential function e^x, where $e \approx 2.718281828459\ldots$. We usually obtain values for e^x by using a calculator or a computer. If you have a scientific calculator, use the $\boxed{e^x}$ button. If you don't have a scientific calculator, use $e \approx 2.7183$ as an approximate value. If you don't have any calculator, use Table B–2 in the appendix.

Example 4   Graph: $f(x) = e^x$.

Using a calculator or Table B–2, we obtain the following table of values (rounded to nearest hundredth). From the table of values we will draw a graph.

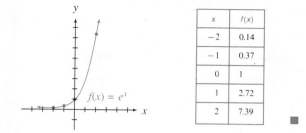

x	f(x)
−2	0.14
−1	0.37
0	1
1	2.72
2	7.39

Practice Problem 4   Graph: $f(x) = e^{x-2}$.   ■

3 Applications of Exponential Functions

The exponential function is frequently used in biology, statistics, and many other fields. An exponential function is used to describe radioactive decay. The equation $A = Ce^{kt}$ tells us how much of a radioactive element is left after a specified time.

Example 5   The radioactive decay of the chemical element americum 241 can be described by the equation

$$A = Ce^{-0.0016008t}$$

where A is the amount remaining, C the original amount, t the time elapsed in years, and $k = -0.0016008$, the decay constant for americum. If 10 mg are sealed in a laboratory container today, how much americum would theoretically be present in 2000 years? Round your answer to the nearest hundredth.

Here $C = 10$ and $t = 2000$.

$$A = 10e^{-0.0016008(2000)} = 10e^{-3.2016}$$

Using a calculator or Table B–2, we have

$$A \approx 10(0.040697) \approx 0.40697 \approx 0.41 \text{ mg}   ■$$

Practice Problem 5   If 20 milligrams of americum 241 is present now, how much will theoretically be present in 5000 years? Round your answer to the nearest thousandth.   ■

An exponential function can be used to solve compound interest problems. If a principal P is invested at an annual interest rate r, the amount of money A accumulated after t years is $A = P(1 + r)^t$.

Example 6   If a young married couple invests $5000 in a mutual fund that pays 16% interest compounded annually, how much will they have in three years?

Here $P = 5000$, $r = 0.16$, and $t = 3$.

$$\begin{aligned} A &= P(1 + r)^t \\ &= 5000(1 + 0.16)^3 \\ &= 5000(1.16)^3 \\ &= 5000(1.560896) \\ &\approx 7804.48 \end{aligned}$$

The couple will have $7804.48.   ■

Note: If you have a scientific calculator, you can find $(1.16)^3$ by using the $\boxed{y^x}$ button, as follows:

$$1.16 \ \boxed{y^x} \ 3 \ \boxed{=} \ 1.560896$$

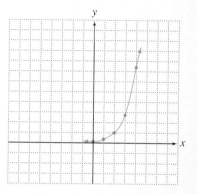

If you don't have a scientific calculator, use the sequence

$$1.16 \boxed{\times} 1.16 \boxed{\times} 1.16 \boxed{=} 1.560896$$

Practice Problem 6 If Uncle Jose invests $4000 in a mutual fund that pay 11% interest compounded annually, how much will he have in two years? ■

Example 7 If you invest $8000 in a fund that pays 15% annual interest compounded monthly, how much will you have after six months?

Here $P = 8000$, but the compounding is done each *month*, so $t = 6$. Since the annual rate is 15%, the monthly rate is $\frac{15}{12} = 1.25\%$. So $r = 0.0125$. Thus,

$$
\begin{aligned}
A &= 8000(1 + 0.0125)^6 \\
&= 8000(1.0125)^6 \\
&= 8000(1.077383) \\
&\approx 8619.07
\end{aligned}
$$

Rounding to the nearest cent you would have $8619.07 ■

Practice Problem 7 How much money would a woman have if she invested $1500 for 13 weeks at a 13% annual interest rate compounded weekly? ■

EXERCISES 9.1

1. The exponential function is an equation of the form

_____

$F(x) = b^x$

2. The irrational number e is a number that is approximately _____.

2.7183

Graph each function.

3. $f(x) = 4^x$

x	y
−1	1/4
0	1
1	4
2	16

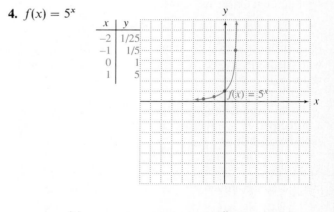

Scale: 1 square = 2 units

4. $f(x) = 5^x$

x	y
−2	1/25
−1	1/5
0	1
1	5

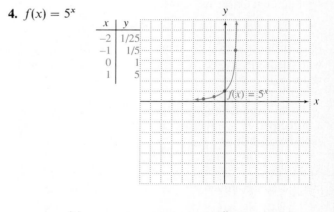

5. $f(x) = \left(\dfrac{1}{3}\right)^x$

x	y
−2	9
−1	3
0	1
1	1/3

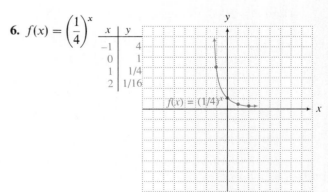

6. $f(x) = \left(\dfrac{1}{4}\right)^x$

x	y
−1	4
0	1
1	1/4
2	1/16

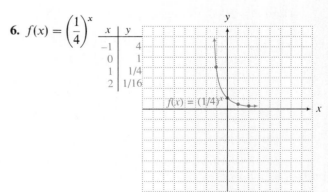

7. $f(x) = 4^{-x}$

x	y
-2	16
-1	4
0	1
1	1/4

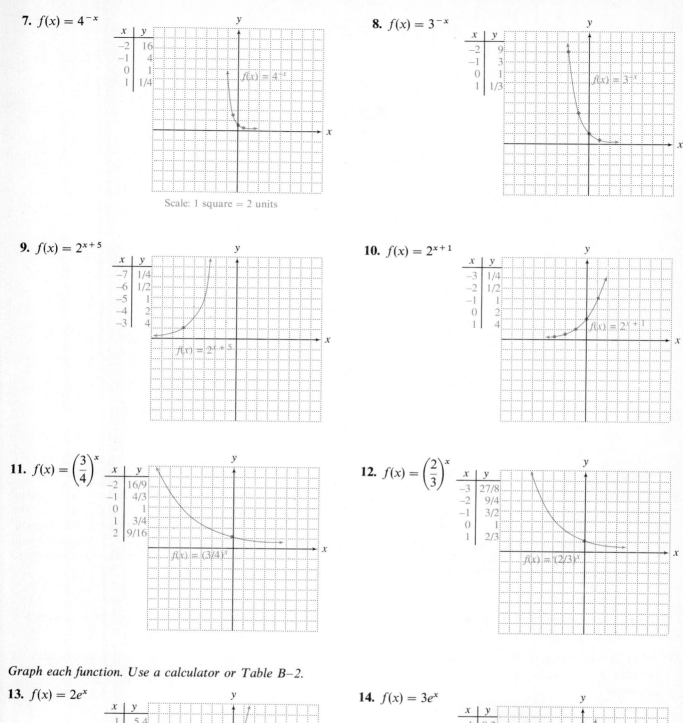

$f(x) = 4^{-x}$

Scale: 1 square = 2 units

8. $f(x) = 3^{-x}$

x	y
-2	9
-1	3
0	1
1	1/3

$f(x) = 3^{-x}$

9. $f(x) = 2^{x+5}$

x	y
-7	1/4
-6	1/2
-5	1
-4	2
-3	4

$f(x) = 2^{x+5}$

10. $f(x) = 2^{x+1}$

x	y
-3	1/4
-2	1/2
-1	1
0	2
1	4

$f(x) = 2^{x+1}$

11. $f(x) = \left(\dfrac{3}{4}\right)^x$

x	y
-2	16/9
-1	4/3
0	1
1	3/4
2	9/16

$f(x) = (3/4)^x$

12. $f(x) = \left(\dfrac{2}{3}\right)^x$

x	y
-3	27/8
-2	9/4
-1	3/2
0	1
1	2/3

$f(x) = (2/3)^x$

Graph each function. Use a calculator or Table B–2.

13. $f(x) = 2e^x$

x	y
1	5.4
0	2
-1	0.7
-2	0.3

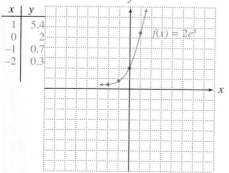

$f(x) = 2e^x$

14. $f(x) = 3e^x$

x	y
1	8.2
0	3
-1	1.1
-2	0.4

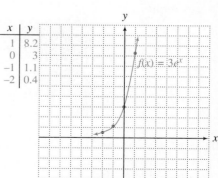

$f(x) = 3e^x$

15. $f(x) = e^{1-x}$

x	y
-1	7.4
0	2.7
1	1
2	0.4

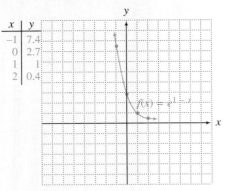

$f(x) = e^{1-x}$

16. $f(x) = e^{2-x}$

x	y
-1	20.1
0	7.4
1	2.7
2	1
3	0.4

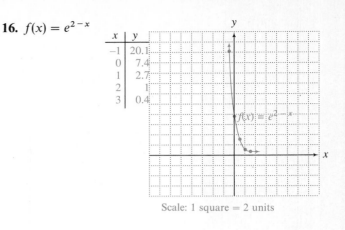

$f(x) = e^{2-x}$

Scale: 1 square = 2 units

Solve for x.

17. $3^{-x} = \dfrac{1}{3}$

$3^{-x} = 3^{-1} \Rightarrow x = 1$

18. $4^{-x} = \dfrac{1}{16}$

$4^{-x} = 4^{-2} \Rightarrow x = 2$

19. $4^x = 256$

$4^x = 4^4 \Rightarrow x = 4$

20. $3^x = 243$

$3^x = 3^5 \Rightarrow x = 5$

21. $2^x = \dfrac{1}{8}$

$2^x = 2^{-3} \Rightarrow x = -3$

22. $2^x = \dfrac{1}{16}$

$2^x = 2^{-4} \Rightarrow x = -4$

23. $5^{x+1} = 25$

$5^{x+1} = 5^2$
$x + 1 = 2$
$x = 1$

24. $6^{2x} = 36$

$6^{2x} = 6^2$
$2x = 2$
$x = 1$

25. $3^{4x+1} = 27$

$3^{4x+1} = 3^3$
$4x + 1 = 3$
$x = \dfrac{1}{2}$

26. $5^{2x+3} = 25$

$5^{2x+3} = 5^2$
$2x + 3 = 2$
$x = -\dfrac{1}{2}$

27. $10^{x-1} = 0.001$

$10^{x-1} = 10^{-3}$
$x - 1 = -3$
$x = -2$

28. $10^{x+6} = 0.01$

$10^{x+6} = 10^{-2}$
$x + 6 = -2$
$x = -8$

Use an exponential equation to solve each problem.

29. The radioactive decay of radium 226 can be described by the equation $A = Ce^{-0.0004279t}$, where A is the amount of radium remaining, C the original amount, and t the elapsed time in years. If 6 milligrams of radium is sealed in a container now, how much radium would be in the container after 1000 years?

$A = 6e^{-0.0004279(1000)}$
$A = 3.91$ mg

30. The radioactive decay of radon 222 can be described by the equation $A = Ce^{-0.1813t}$, where A is the amount of radon remaining, C is the original amount, and t the elapsed time in days. If 1.5 milligrams is in a laboratory container, how much was in there 10 days ago?

$C = \dfrac{1.5}{e^{-1.813}}$
$C = 9.19$ mg

Use the following information for problems 31 and 32. The atmospheric pressure measured in pounds per square inch is given by the equation $P = 14.7e^{-0.21d}$, where d is the distance in miles above sea level.

31. What is the pressure in pounds per square inch experienced by a man on a mountain 2 miles above sea level?

$p = 14.7e^{-0.21(2)}$
$p = 9.66$ lbs/sq inch

32. What is the pressure in pounds per square inch on a jet plane flying 10 miles above sea level?

$p = 14.7e^{-0.21(10)}$
$p = 1.80$ lbs/sq inch

33. How much money will Sue have in four years if she invests $6000 at a 14% annual rate of interest compounded annually?

$A = 6000(1.14)^4$
$A = \$10,133.76$

34. How much money will Barbara have in five years if she invests $5000 at an 8% annual rate of interest compounded annually?

$A = 5000(1.08)^5$
$A = \$7346.64$

35. How much money will Frank have in three years if he invests $2000 at a 15% annual rate of interest compounded quarterly? How much will he have if it is compounded monthly?

Quarterly

$r = \dfrac{15}{4} = 3.75\%$

$r = 0.0375$

$A = 2000(1 + 0.0375)^{12}$

$A = \$3110.91$

Monthly

$r = \dfrac{15}{12} = 1.25$

$A = 2000(1 + 0.0125)^{36}$

$A = \$3127.89$

36. How much money will Hank have in two years if he invests $7000 at an 18% annual rate if it is compounded quarterly? compounded monthly?

Quarterly

$\dfrac{18}{4} = 4.5,\ r = 0.045$

$A = 7000(1.045)^8$

$A = \$9954.70$

Monthly

$\dfrac{18}{12} = 1.5,\ r = .015$

$A = 7000(1.015)^{24}$

$A = \$10,006.52$

37. **(a)** Sketch the graph of the exponential function. $f(x) = -2^x$.
(b) How is this different from $f(x) = (-2)^x$?
(c) Why is $f(x) = (-2)^x$ not an exponential function?

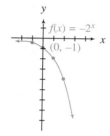

(a)

(b) In the first equation 2 is raised to a power. In the second equation -2 is raised to a power.
(c) The definition of $f(x) = b^x$ requires that $b > 0$.

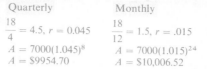

To Think About

38. **(a)** Sketch the graph of the exponential function $f(x) = -3^x$.
(b) How is this different from $f(x) = (-3)^x$?
(c) Why is $f(x) = (-3)^x$ not an exponential function?

(a)

(b) In the first equation 3 is raised to a power. In the second equation -3 is raised to a power.
(c) The definition of $f(x) = b^x$ requires that $b > 0$

39. The number of bacteria in a culture given by $B(t) = 4000(2^t)$, where t is the time in hours. How many bacteria will grow in the culture in 3 hours? in 9 hours?

3 hrs

$B(t) = 4000(2^3)$

$B(t) = 32,000$

9 hrs

$B(t) = 4000(2^9)$

$B(t) = 2,048,000$

40. The equation $C(t) = P(1.04)^t$ forecasts tuition cost, where t is time in years and P is the present cost in dollars. If the cost of a college education is increasing 4% per year, how much will a college now charging $3000 for tuition charge in 10 years? How much will a college now charging $12,000 tuition charge in 15 years?

10 years

$C(t) = 3000(1.04)^{10}$

$C(t) = \$4440.73$

15 years

$C(t) = 12000(1.04)^{15}$

$C(t) = \$21,611.32$

41. Let $f(x) = \dfrac{e^x + e^{-x}}{2}$. Evaluate $f(x)$ when $x = -1$, $-0.5, 0, 0.5, 1, 1.5, 2$. Now use these values to graph the function. [$f(x)$ defines a special function called the hyperbolic cosine. This function is used in advanced mathematics and science to study a variety of technical applications.]

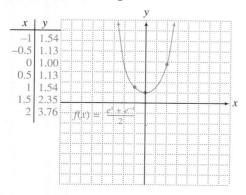

x	y
-1	1.54
-0.5	1.13
0	1.00
0.5	1.13
1	1.54
1.5	2.35
2	3.76

42. Let $g(x) = \dfrac{e^x - e^{-x}}{2}$. Evaluate $g(x)$ when $x = -2$, $-1, -0.5, 0, 0.5, 1, 1.5, 2$. Now graph $g(x)$ using these values. [$g(x)$ defines a special function called the hyperbolic sine.]

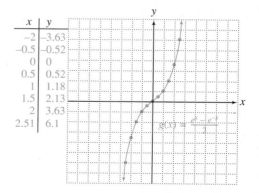

x	y
-2	-3.63
-0.5	-0.52
0	0
0.5	0.52
1	1.18
1.5	2.13
2	3.63
2.51	6.1

Cumulative Review Problems

Solve for x.

43. $3x + 5x + 8 = 9 + 4x - 12$

$8x + 8 = 4x - 3$

$x = -\dfrac{11}{4}$

44. $\dfrac{1}{2}x - 5 = \dfrac{2}{3}x - 3 - \dfrac{5}{6}x$

$3x - 30 = 4x - 18 - 5x$

$4x = 12$

$x = 3$

45. $\dfrac{1}{5}(5 - 2x) + \dfrac{1}{10}(x - 4) = \dfrac{3}{10}$

$2(5 - 2x) + (x - 4) = 3$

$10 - 4x + x - 4 = 3$

$3 = 3x$

$1 = x$

46. $2[5 - 3(2 - x)] = 3x$

$2[-1 + 3x] = 3x$

$-2 + 6x = 3x$

$x = \dfrac{2}{3}$

Calculator Problems

47. Evaluate $f(x) = 4.623e^x$; $x = 1.63, 2.95, -3.04$.

$f(1.63) = 23.59521283$

$f(2.95) = 88.32682408$

$f(-3.04) = 0.221140694$

48. Evaluate $f(x) = (0.52)^x$; $x = 2.5, 3.6, -1.2$.

$f(2.5) = 0.194988213$

$f(3.6) = 0.094975598$

$f(-1.2) = 2.191775094$

For Extra Practice Exercises, turn to page 498.

Solutions to Odd-Numbered Practice Problems

1. $f(x) = 3^{x+2}$

$f(-4) = 3^{-4+2} = 3^{-2} = \dfrac{1}{3^2} = \dfrac{1}{9}$

$f(-3) = 3^{-3+2} = 3^{-1} = \dfrac{1}{3}$

$f(-2) = 3^{-2+2} = 3^0 = 1$

$f(-1) = 3^{-1+2} = 3$

$f(0) = 3^{0+2} = 3^2 = 9$

x	$f(x)$
-4	$\dfrac{1}{9}$
-3	$\dfrac{1}{3}$
-2	1
-1	3
0	9

3. $2^x = \dfrac{1}{32}$

$2^x = \dfrac{1}{2^5}$ $(2^5 = 32)$

$2^x = 2^{-5}$

$x = -5$

5. $A = Ce^{-0.0016008t}$ where $C = 20$ and $t = 5000$.

$A = 20e^{-0.0016008(5000)}$

$= 20e^{-8.004}$

$\approx 20(0.0003341) \approx 0.006682 \approx 0.007$ mg

7. $A = P(1 + r)^t$, $P = \$1500$, and $t = 13$ weeks. An annual rate of 13% compounded weekly means a weekly rate of $\dfrac{13}{52} = 0.25\%$. Therefore, $r = 0.0025$.

$A = 1500(1 + 0.0025)^{13}$

$= 1500(1.0025)^{13}$

$\approx 1500(1.032991997) \approx 1549.49$

The woman would have \$1549.49 after 13 weeks.

Answers to Even-Numbered Practice Problems

2. $f(x) = \left(\dfrac{1}{3}\right)^x$

x	$f(x)$
-2	9
-1	3
0	1
1	$\dfrac{1}{3}$
2	$\dfrac{1}{9}$

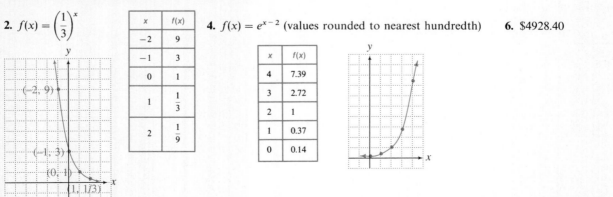

4. $f(x) = e^{x-2}$ (values rounded to nearest hundredth)

x	$f(x)$
4	7.39
3	2.72
2	1
1	0.37
0	0.14

6. \$4928.40

9.2 THE LOGARITHMIC FUNCTION

☐ After studying this section, you will be able to:

1 *Write exponential equations in logarithmic form*

2 *Write logarithmic equations in exponential form*

3 *Solve elementary logarithmic equations*

4 *Graph logarithmic equations*

Logarithms were invented about 400 years ago by the Scottish mathematician, John Napier. Napier's amazing invention reduced complicated problems to simple subtraction and addition. Astronomers quickly saw the immense value of logarithms and began using them. The work of Johannes Kepler, Isaac Newton, and others would have been much harder without logarithms.

1 The key property you must remember is that a logarithm is an exponent. We write $\log_b x = y$ to mean that the logarithm of x to the base b is equal to y.

Definition of Logarithm

The **logarithm** of a *positive* number x is the power (exponent) to which the base b must be raised to produce x. That is, $y = \log_b x$ is the same as $x = b^y$ where $b > 0$, $b \neq 1$.

This definition is extremely important and useful. You will need to convert logarithmic expressions to exponential ones, and vice versa, often to solve equations.

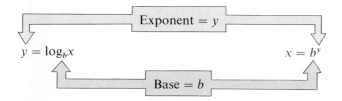

Example 1 Write in logarithmic form.

(a) $4 = 2^2$
(b) $81 = 3^4$
(c) $\dfrac{1}{100} = 10^{-2}$

We use the property that $x = b^y$ is equivalent to $\log_b x = y$.

(a) $4 = 2^2$
Here $x = 4$, $b = 2$, $y = 2$, so $\quad 2 = \log_2 4$

(b) $81 = 3^4$
Here $x = 81$, $b = 3$, $y = 4$, so $\quad 4 = \log_3 81$

(c) $\dfrac{1}{100} = 10^{-2}$

Here $x = \dfrac{1}{100}$, $b = 10$, $y = -2$, so $\quad -2 = \log_{10}\left(\dfrac{1}{100}\right)$ ■

Practice Problem 1 Write in logarithmic form.

(a) $49 = 7^2$
(b) $\dfrac{1}{64} = 4^{-3}$
(c) $1000 = 10^3$ ■

2 Example 2 Write in exponential form.

(a) $2 = \log_5 25$
(b) $3 = \log_{1/4}\left(\dfrac{1}{64}\right)$
(c) $-4 = \log_{10}\left(\dfrac{1}{10,000}\right)$

(a) $2 = \log_5 25$
Here $y = 2$, $b = 5$, $x = 25$. Thus, since $x = b^y$, $\quad 25 = 5^2$

(b) $y = 3$, $b = \frac{1}{4}$, $x = \frac{1}{64}$, so $\quad \frac{1}{64} = \left(\frac{1}{4}\right)^3$

(c) $y = -4$, $b = 10$, $x = \frac{1}{10,000}$, so $\quad \frac{1}{10,000} = 10^{-4}$ ∎

Practice Problem 2   Write in exponential form.

(a) $3 = \log_5 125$ **(b)** $4 = \log_{1/2}\left(\frac{1}{16}\right)$ **(c)** $-2 = \log_6\left(\frac{1}{36}\right)$ ∎

3 We can solve logarithmic equations easily sometimes by writing them in exponential form.

Example 3   Solve for the variable.

(a) $\log_5 x = -3$ **(b)** $\log_{1/3} 81 = y$ **(c)** $\log_a 16 = 4$

(a) $5^{-3} = x$

$\dfrac{1}{5^3} = x$

$\dfrac{1}{125} = x$

(b) $\left(\dfrac{1}{3}\right)^y = 81$

$(3^{-1})^y = 3^4$

$3^{-y} = 3^4$

$-y = 4$

$y = -4$

(c) $a^4 = 16$

$a^4 = 2^4$

$a = 2$ ∎

Practice Problem 3   Solve for the variable.

(a) $\log_6 y = -2$ **(b)** $\log_b 125 = 3$ **(c)** $\log_{1/2} 32 = x$ ∎

Example 4   Evaluate: $\log_3 81$.

Let $\log_3 81 = x$. Then

$$81 = 3^x$$

$$3^4 = 3^x$$

$$x = 4$$

Thus, $\log_3 81 = 4$. ∎

Practice Problem 4   Evaluate: $\log_{10} 0.1$. ∎

4 The logarithmic function is the **inverse** of the exponential function. If we graph the function $y = 2^x$ and $y = \log_2 x$ on the same set of axes, the graph of one is the reflection of the other about the line $y = x$.

Example 5   Graph: $y = \log_2 x$.

If we write $y = \log_2 x$ in exponential form, we have $x = 2^y$. We make a table of values and graph the function $x = 2^y$.

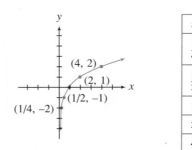

x	y
$\frac{1}{4}$	-2
$\frac{1}{2}$	-1
1	0
2	1
4	2

∎

TEACHING TIP It is important that students be able to rapidly switch from log equations to exponential equations in order to solve the equations presented in example 3. After discussing the three equations in example 3, ask them to do the following problems as a class exercise. Solve for x

A: $\log_3 x = 4$ B: $\log_x 121 = 2$

Ans. A: $x = 81$, B: $x = 11$

TEACHING TIP Remind students as they look at the graph in example 5 that x is never negative in the graph. We cannot take the log of a negative number. They will need to remember this when they are solving more involved logarithmic equations later in the chapter.

Practice Problem 5 Graph: $y = \log_{1/2}x$. ■

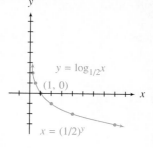

$f(x) = a^x$ and $f(x) = \log_a x$ are inverse functions. As such they have all the properties of inverse functions. We will examine a few of this properties as we study the graphs of two inverse functions $y = 2^x$ and $y = \log_2 x$.

Example 6 Compare the graphs of $y = \log_2 x$ and $y = 2^x$.

Make a table of values (ordered pairs) for each equation.

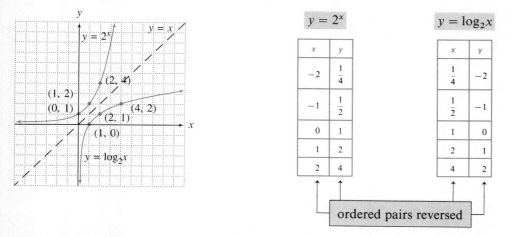

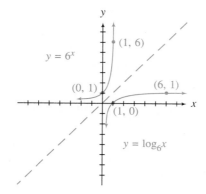

So $y = \log_2 x$ is the inverse of $y = 2^x$ because the ordered pairs (x, y) are reversed. The sketch of the two equations shows the inverse property. If we reflect the graph of $y = 2^x$ about the line $y = x$, it will coincide with the graph of $y = \log_2 x$. ■

Practice Problem 6 Compare the graphs of $y = \log_6 x$ and $y = 6^x$. ■

EXERCISES 9.2

1. A logarithm is really just an _____Exponent_____.

2. In the equation $y = \log_b x$ the value b is called the _____Base_____.

3. In the equation $y = \log_b x$ what is the domain (the permitted values of x)?

$x > 0$

4. In the equation $y = \log_b x$, what are the permitted values of b?

$b > 0$

Write in logarithmic form.

5. $64 = 4^3$
$\log_4 64 = 3$

6. $125 = 5^3$
$\log_5 125 = 3$

7. $100 = 10^2$
$\log_{10} 100 = 2$

8. $36 = 6^2$
$\log_6 36 = 2$

9. $\dfrac{1}{25} = 5^{-2}$
$\log_5\left(\dfrac{1}{25}\right) = -2$

10. $0.01 = 10^{-2}$
$\log_{10}(0.01) = -2$

11. $32 = 2^5$
$\log_2 32 = 5$

12. $64 = 2^6$
$\log_2 64 = 6$

13. $y = e^3$
$\log_e y = 3$

14. $y = e^{-4}$
$\log_e y = -4$

Write in exponential form.

15. $2 = \log_3 9$
$3^2 = 9$

16. $2 = \log_2 4$
$2^2 = 4$

17. $4 = \log_5 625$
$5^4 = 625$

18. $4 = \log_3 81$
$3^4 = 81$

19. $3 = \log_{10} 1000$
$10^3 = 1000$

20. $2 = \log_{10} 100$
$10^2 = 100$

21. $-2 = \log_{10}(0.01)$
$10^{-2} = 0.01$

22. $-3 = \log_{10}(0.001)$
$10^{-3} = 0.001$

23. $-4 = \log_3\left(\dfrac{1}{81}\right)$
$3^{-4} = \dfrac{1}{81}$

24. $-5 = \log_2\left(\dfrac{1}{32}\right)$
$2^{-5} = \dfrac{1}{32}$

25. $5 = \log_e x$
$e^5 = x$

26. $6 = \log_e x$
$e^6 = x$

Solve.

27. $\log_2 x = 4$
$2^4 = x$
$16 = x$

28. $\log_2 x = 6$
$2^6 = x$
$64 = x$

29. $\log_{10} x = -3$
$10^{-3} = x$
$\dfrac{1}{1000} = x$

30. $\log_{10} x = -2$
$10^{-2} = x$
$x = \dfrac{1}{100}$

31. $\log_5 625 = y$
$5^y = 625$
$5^y = 5^4$
$y = 4$

32. $\log_6 216 = y$
$6^y = 216$
$6^y = 6^3$
$y = 3$

33. $\log_7\left(\dfrac{1}{49}\right) = y$
$7^y = \dfrac{1}{49}$
$7^y = 7^{-2}$
$y = -2$

34. $\log_4\left(\dfrac{1}{64}\right) = y$
$4^y = \dfrac{1}{64}$
$4^y = 4^{-3}$
$y = -3$

35. $\log_a 32 = 5$
$a^5 = 32$
$a^5 = 2^5$
$a = 2$

36. $\log_a 81 = 4$
$a^4 = 81$
$a^4 = 3^4$
$a = 3$

37. $\log_a 1000 = 3$
$a^3 = 1000$
$a^3 = 10^3$
$a = 10$

38. $\log_a 100 = 2$
$a^2 = 100$
$a^2 = 10^2$
$a = 10$

39. $\log_8 2 = w$
$8^w = 2$
$2^{3w} = 2^1$
$3w = 1$
$w = \dfrac{1}{3}$

40. $\log_{25} 5 = w$
$25^w = 5$
$5^{2w} = 5^1$
$2w = 1$
$w = \dfrac{1}{2}$

41. $\log_3\left(\dfrac{1}{3}\right) = w$
$3^w = 3^{-1}$
$w = -1$

42. $\log_2\left(\dfrac{1}{32}\right) = w$
$2^w = 2^{-5}$
$w = -5$

43. $\log_{10} w = 3$
$10^3 = w$
$w = 1000$

44. $\log_{10} w = -3$
$w = 10^{-3}$
$w = 0.001$

45. $\log_w 25 = -2$
$w^{-2} = 25$
$\dfrac{1}{w^2} = \dfrac{1}{5^2}$
$w = \dfrac{1}{5}$

46. $\log_w 64 = -6$
$w^{-6} = 64$
$\dfrac{1}{w^6} = 2^6$
$w = \dfrac{1}{2}$

47. $\log_e w = 4$
$w = e^4$

48. $\log_e w = 7$
$w = e^7$

Evaluate.

49. $\log_{10} 10$
$10^x = 10$
$x = 1$

50. $\log_{10} 100$
$10^x = 10^2$
$x = 2$

51. $\log_{10}(0.001)$
$10^x = .001$
$10^x = 10^{-3}$
$x = -3$

52. $\log_{10}(0.0001)$
$10^x = 10^{-4}$
$x = -4$

53. $\log_3 81$
$3^x = 81$
$3^x = 3^4$
$x = 4$

54. $\log_2 32$
$2^x = 32$
$2^x = 2^5$
$x = 5$

55. $\log_8 64$
$8^x = 64$
$8^x = 8^2$
$x = 2$

56. $\log_5 125$
$5^x = 125$
$5^x = 5^3$
$x = 3$

57. $\log_6 \sqrt{6}$
$6^x = \sqrt{6}$
$6^x = 6^{1/2}$
$x = \dfrac{1}{2}$

58. $\log_7 \sqrt{7}$
$7^x = \sqrt{7}$
$7^x = 7^{1/2}$
$x = \dfrac{1}{2}$

Graph.

59. $\log_3 x = y$ $\quad 3^y = x$

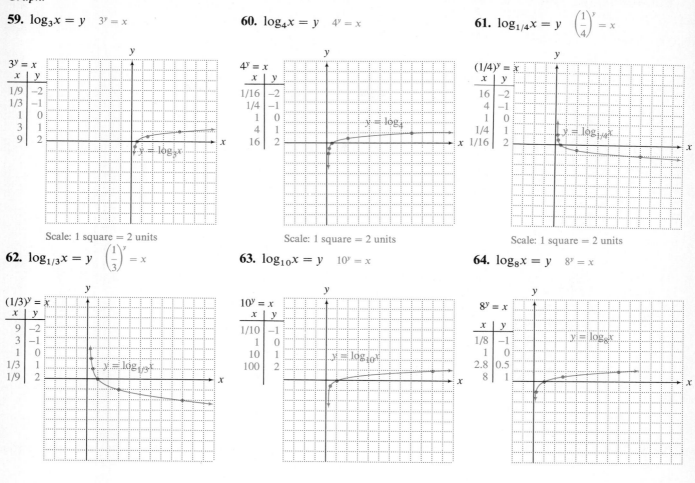

$3^y = x$

x	y
1/9	−2
1/3	−1
1	0
3	1
9	2

$y = \log_3 x$

Scale: 1 square = 2 units

60. $\log_4 x = y$ $\quad 4^y = x$

$4^y = x$

x	y
1/16	−2
1/4	−1
1	0
4	1
16	2

$y = \log_4 x$

Scale: 1 square = 2 units

61. $\log_{1/4} x = y$ $\quad \left(\dfrac{1}{4}\right)^y = x$

$(1/4)^y = x$

x	y
16	−2
4	−1
1	0
1/4	1
1/16	2

$y = \log_{1/4} x$

Scale: 1 square = 2 units

62. $\log_{1/3} x = y$ $\quad \left(\dfrac{1}{3}\right)^y = x$

$(1/3)^y = x$

x	y
9	−2
3	−1
1	0
1/3	1
1/9	2

$y = \log_{1/3} x$

63. $\log_{10} x = y$ $\quad 10^y = x$

$10^y = x$

x	y
1/10	−1
1	0
10	1
100	2

$y = \log_{10} x$

64. $\log_8 x = y$ $\quad 8^y = x$

$8^y = x$

x	y
1/8	−1
1	0
2.8	0.5
8	1

$y = \log_8 x$

? **To Think About**

To determine if a solution is an acid or a base, chemists check the solution's pH. *A solution is an acid if its* pH *is less than 7 and a base if its* pH *is greater than 7. The* pH *is defined by* $pH = -\log_{10}[H^+]$, *where* $[H^+]$ *is the concentration of the hydrogen ion in the solution.*

65. The concentration of hydrogen ions in grapefruit is approximately 10^{-1}. What is the pH of the grapefruit?

$pH = -\log_{10}[10^{-1}]$
$-pH = \log_{10}[10^{-1}]$
$10^{-pH} = 10^{-1}$
$pH = 1$

66. The concentration of hydrogen ions in vinegar is approximately 10^{-3}. What is the pH of the vinegar?

$pH = -\log_{10}[10^{-3}]$
$-pH = \log_{10}[10^{-3}]$
$10^{-pH} = 10^{-3}$
$pH = 3$

67. A chemist has mixed a solution with a pH of 9. Find the concentration of hydrogen ions $[H^+]$ in the solution.

$9 = -\log_{10}[H^+]$
$-9 = \log_{10}[H^+]$
$[H^+] = 10^{-9}$

68. Alice found a cleaning solvent with a pH of 8. Find the concentration of hydrogen ions $[H^+]$ in the solution.

$8 = -\log_{10}[H^+]$
$-8 = \log_{10}[H^+]$
$10^{-8} = [H^+]$

69. Evaluate: $5^{\log_5 4}$.

$5^{\log_5 4} = y,\ \log_5 y = \log_5 4,\ y = 4$

70. Evaluate: $\log_2 \sqrt[4]{2}$. $\quad \log_2 2^{1/4} = x$
$\qquad\qquad 2^x = 2^{1/4}$
$\qquad\qquad x = \dfrac{1}{4}$

71. Graph: $y = -\dfrac{2}{3}x + 5$.

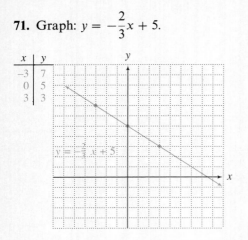

x	y
-3	7
0	5
3	3

$y = -\dfrac{2}{3}x + 5$

72. Graph: $6x + 3y = -6$.

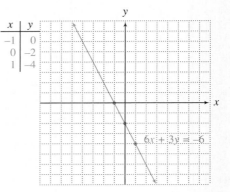

x	y
-1	0
0	-2
1	-4

$6x + 3y = -6$

73. Find the slope of a line containing $(-6, 3)$ and $(-1, 2)$.

$$m = \frac{3 - 2}{-6 - (-1)} = \frac{1}{-6 + 1} = \frac{1}{-5}$$

74. Find the equation of a line perpendicular to $y = -\dfrac{2}{3}x + 4$ that contains $(-4, 1)$.

$$m_{\text{Given line}} = -\frac{2}{3}; \; m_\perp = \frac{3}{2}$$

$$y - 1 = \frac{3}{2}(x + 4)$$

$$2y - 2 = 3x + 12$$

$$y = \frac{3x + 14}{2}$$

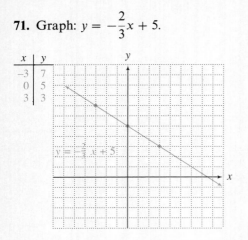 **Calculator Problems**

75. A chemist has a solution with a pH of 8.3. Find the concentration of hydrogen ions $[H^+]$ in the solution.

$[H^+] = 5.011872 \times 10^{-9}$

76. The concentration of hydrogen ions in a certain citric acid is 1.23×10^{-3}. What is the pH?

pH = 2.910094889

For Extra Practice Exercises, turn to page 499.

Solutions to Odd-Numbered Practice Problems

1. (a) If $49 = 7^2$, then $2 = \log_7 49$. **(b)** If $\dfrac{1}{64} = 4^{-3}$, then $-3 = \log_4\left(\dfrac{1}{64}\right)$. **(c)** If $1000 = 10^3$, then $3 = \log_{10} 1000$.

3. (a) $\log_6 y = -2$; then $y = 6^{-2}$

$$y = \frac{1}{6^2}$$

$$\boxed{y = \frac{1}{36}}$$

(b) $\log_b 125 = 3$; then $125 = b^3$

$$5^3 = b^3$$

Thus, $b = 5$.

(c) $\log_{1/2} 32 = x$; then $32 = \left(\dfrac{1}{2}\right)^x$

$$2^5 = \left(\frac{1}{2}\right)^x$$

$$\frac{1}{2^{-5}} = \left(\frac{1}{2}\right)^x$$

$$\left(\frac{1}{2}\right)^{-5} = \left(\frac{1}{2}\right)^x$$

Thus, $x = -5$.

5. To graph $y = \log_{1/2} x$, we first write $x = \left(\dfrac{1}{2}\right)^y$. We make a table of values.

x	y
$\dfrac{1}{2}$	1
1	0
2	-1
4	-2

$y = \log_{1/2} x$

$(1, 0)$

$x = (1/2)^y$

2. (a) $125 = 5^3$ **(b)** $\dfrac{1}{16} = \left(\dfrac{1}{2}\right)^4$ **(c)** $\dfrac{1}{36} = 6^{-2}$

4. $\log_{10}(0.1) = -1$

6. $y = \log_6 x$ $\qquad$ $y = 6^x$

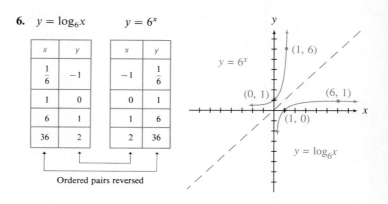

Ordered pairs reversed

9.3 PROPERTIES OF LOGARITHMS

1 We have already said that logarithms reduce complex expressions to addition and subtraction. The following properties show us how to use logarithms this way.

> **Property 1**
>
> For any positive numbers M and N and any base $b \neq 1$,
> $$\log_b MN = \log_b M + \log_b N$$

After studying this section, you will be able to:

1 Use the property $\log_b MN = \log_b M + \log_b N$

2 Use the property $\log_b\left(\dfrac{M}{N}\right) = \log_b M - \log_b N$

3 Use the property $\log_b M^p = p \log_b M$

4 Solve simple logarithmic equations

To see that this property is true, we let

$$\log_b M = x \qquad \text{and} \qquad \log_b N = y$$

where x and y are any values. Now we write the expressions in exponential notation:

$$b^x = M \qquad \text{and} \qquad b^y = N$$

Then

$$MN = b^x b^y = b^{x+y} \qquad \text{Laws of exponents.}$$

If we convert this equation to logarithmic form, then we must have

$$\log_b MN = x + y \qquad\qquad \text{Definition of logarithm.}$$

$$\log_b MN = \log_b M + \log_b N \qquad \text{By substitution.}$$

Note that the logarithms must have the same base.

Example 1 Write $\log_3 XZ$ as a sum of logarithms.

By property 1, $\log_3 XZ = \log_3 X + \log_3 Z$ ■

Practice Problem 1 Write as a sum of logarithms: $\log_4 WXY$. ■

Example 2 Write as a single logarithm: $\log_{10}11 + \log_{10}7$.

$$\log_b MN = \log_b M + \log_b N$$

Thus,

$$\log_{10}11 + \log_{10}7 = \log_{10}(11 \cdot 7)$$

$$\log_{10}11 + \log_{10}7 = \log_{10}77 \qquad ■$$

Practice Problem 2 Write as a single logarithm: $\log_9 12 + \log_9 5$. ■

Example 3   Write as a single logarithm: $\log_3 16 + \log_3 x + \log_3 y$.

If we extend our rule: $\log_b MNP = \log_b M + \log_b N + \log_b P$

Thus, $\log_3 16 + \log_3 x + \log_3 y = \log_3 16xy$ ∎

Practice Problem 3   Write as a single logarithm: $\log_7 w + \log_7 8 + \log_7 x$.   ∎

2   A similar property is true for the logarithm of a quotient.

Property 2

For any positive numbers M and N and any base $b \neq 1$,

$$\log_b\left(\frac{M}{N}\right) = \log_b M - \log_b N$$

We can prove this property in the same way as we did property 1.

Note: Be sure you understand property 2 $\dfrac{\log_b M}{\log_b N} \neq \log_b M - \log_b N$.

Example 4   Write as the difference of two logarithms: $\log_3\left(\dfrac{29}{7}\right)$.

$$\log_3\left(\frac{29}{7}\right) = \log_3 29 - \log_3 7$$ ∎

Practice Problem 4   Write as the difference of two logarithms: $\log_3\left(\dfrac{17}{5}\right)$.   ∎

3

Property 3

For any positive number M, any real number p, and any base $b \neq 1$,

$$\log_b M^p = p \log_b M$$

Example 5   Write with no exponent: $\log_3 26^5$.

$$\log_3 26^5 = 5 \log_3 26$$ ∎

Practice Problem 5   Write with no exponent: $\log_7 16^9$.   ∎

Example 6   Write as a single logarithm: $\dfrac{1}{3}\log_b x + 2\log_b w - 3\log_b z$.

First, we must eliminate the coefficients of the log terms

$$\log_b x^{1/3} + \log_b w^2 - \log_b z^3 \qquad \text{by property 3}$$

Now we can combine either the sum or difference of the logarithms. We'll do the sum.

$$= \log_b x^{1/3} w^2 - \log_b z^3 \qquad \text{by property 1}$$

Now we combine the difference.

$$= \log_b\left(\frac{x^{1/3} w^2}{z^3}\right) \qquad\qquad \text{by property 2}$$ ∎

Practice Problem 6   Write as one logarithm: $\dfrac{1}{3}\log_7 x - 5\log_7 y$.   ∎

TEACHING TIP   When you have finished example 6, ask students to do this problem as a class problem. Write as a single logarithm:

$$2\log_b w + \frac{1}{2}\log_b z - \frac{1}{3}\log_b y$$

Ans.: $\log_b\left(\dfrac{w^2 z^{1/2}}{y^{1/3}}\right)$

TEACHING TIP   When you have finished discussing example 9, ask students to do the following problem for classwork. Solve for x:

$$\log_3 x + \log_3 7 = 2$$

Ans.: $x = \dfrac{9}{7}$

Example 7 Write as three logarithms: $\log_b\left(\dfrac{x^4y^3}{z^2}\right)$.

$$\log_b\left(\frac{x^4y^3}{z^2}\right) = \log_b x^4y^3 - \log_b z^2 \qquad \text{by property 2}$$

$$= \log_b x^4 + \log_b y^3 - \log_b z^2 \qquad \text{by property 1}$$

$$= 4\log_b x + 3\log_b y - 2\log_b z \qquad \text{by property 3} \quad \blacksquare$$

Practice Problem 7 Write as three logarithms: $\log_3\left(\dfrac{x^4y^5}{z}\right)$. $\quad \blacksquare$

We can use properties 1–3 to prove three logarithmic identities.

4

> For all positive values of $b \neq 1$ and all positive values of x and y
>
> **1.** $\log_b b = 1$.
> **2.** $\log_b 1 = 0$.
> **3.** If $\log_b x = \log_b y$, then $x = y$.

To Think About

?

Let's think how we can prove that these 3 identities are true.

1. Let
$$\log_b b = y$$
$$b = b^y \qquad \text{by definition of logarithm.}$$

Therefore, y must be 1. Thus $\log_b b = 1$.

2. Let
$$\log_b 1 = y$$
$$1 = b^y$$

The only value of y for which this equation holds is $y = 0$ because $b^0 = 1$. Thus $\log_b 1 = 0$.

3. Let
$$\log_b x = X \qquad \log_b y = Y$$

By the definition of a logarithm,
$$x = b^X \qquad y = b^Y$$

If $b^X = b^Y$, then $X = Y$, by the property of exponential equations. Since $X = \log_b x$ and $Y = \log_b y$, we have $\log_b x = \log_b y$ only if $x = y$. $\quad \blacksquare$

Example 8

(a) Evaluate: $\log_7 7$.   **(b)** Evaluate: $\log_5 1$.
(c) Find x if $\log_3 x = \log_3 17$.

(a) $\log_7 7 = 1$ because $\log_b b = 1$ **(b)** $\log_5 1 = 0$ because $\log_b 1 = 0$
(c) If $\log_3 x = \log_3 17$, then $x = 17$. $\quad \blacksquare$

Practice Problem 8 Evaluate.
(a) $\log_7 1$ **(b)** $\log_8 8$ $\quad \blacksquare$

If we have a logarithmic equation, these properties are useful in combining separate logarithms together.

Example 9 Find x if $\log_2 x + \log_2 5 = 3$.

$$\log_2 5x = 3$$
$$5x = 2^3 \qquad \text{Converting to exponential form.}$$
$$5x = 8$$
$$x = \frac{8}{5} \quad \blacksquare$$

Practice Problem 9 Find x if $\log_4 x + \log_4 5 = 2$. $\blacksquare$

TEACHING TIP If after presenting example 10 you see the students are somewhat confused, consider doing the following additional example. Solve for x:

$$2\log_5 2 + 2\log_5 7 = \log_5 x$$

Sol.: $\log_5 2^2 + \log_5 7^2 = \log_5 x$

$\log_5 4 + \log_5 4a = \log_5 x$

$\log_5 196 = \log_5 x$

$196 = x$

Example 10 Find x if $2\log_7 3 - 4\log_7 2 = \log_7 x$.

$$2\log_7 3 = \log_7 3^2 = \log_7 9$$
$$4\log_7 2 = \log_7 2^4 = \log_7 16$$

Therefore,

$$\log_7 9 - \log_7 16 = \log_7 x$$
$$\log_7 \frac{9}{16} = \log_7 x$$

Hence

$$x = \frac{9}{16} \quad \blacksquare$$

Practice Problem 10 Find x if $\log_3 2 - \log_3 5 = \log_3 6 + \log_3 x$. $\blacksquare$

EXERCISES 9.3

Write each expression as the sum or difference of single logarithms of x, y, and z.

1. $\log_5 \sqrt{x}\, y^3$
$\log_5 \sqrt{x} + \log_5 y^3$
$\frac{1}{2}\log_5 x + 3\log_5 y$

2. $\log_3 x^4 \sqrt{y}$
$\log_3 x^4 + \log_3 y^{1/2}$
$4\log_3 x + \frac{1}{2}\log_3 y$

3. $\log_7\left(\dfrac{2x}{y}\right)$
$\log_7(2x) - \log_7 y$
$\log_7 2 + \log_7 x - \log_7 y$

4. $\log_8\left(\dfrac{3y}{x^2}\right)$
$\log_8(3y) - \log_8 x^2$
$\log_8 3 + \log_8 y - 2\log_8 x$

5. $\log_2\left(\dfrac{7x^3 y^2}{z^5}\right)$
$\log_2 7 + \log_2 x^3 + \log_2 y^2 - \log_2 z^5$
$\log_2 7 + 3\log_2 x + 2\log_2 y - 5\log_2 z$

6. $\log_5\left(\dfrac{6x^4 y}{z^6}\right)$
$\log_5 6 + \log_5 x^4 + \log_5 y - \log_5 z^6$
$\log_5 6 + 4\log_5 x + \log_5 y - 6\log_5 z$

7. $\log_b \sqrt[3]{\dfrac{x}{y^2 z}}$
$\frac{1}{3}\log_b\left(\dfrac{x}{y^2 z}\right) = \frac{1}{3}[\log_b x - (\log_b y^2 + \log_b z)]$
$= \frac{1}{3}\log_b x - \frac{2}{3}\log_b y - \frac{1}{3}\log_b z$

8. $\log_b \sqrt[4]{\dfrac{z}{x^2 y^3}}$
$\frac{1}{4}[\log_b z - (\log_b x^2 + \log_b y^3)] = \frac{1}{4}[\log_b z - 2\log_b x - 3\log_b y]$
$= \frac{1}{4}\log_b z - \frac{1}{2}\log_b x - \frac{3}{4}\log_b y$

9. $\log_e e^5 x y^2$
$\log_e e^5 + \log_e x + \log_e y^2 = 5 + \log_e x + 2\log_e y$

10. $\log_e e^{-4} y^3 z$
$\log_e e^{-4} + \log_e y^3 + \log_e z = -4 + 3\log_e y + \log_e z$

Write as a single logarithm.

11. $\log_5 x + \log_5 7 + \log_5 3$
$\log_5(x)(7)(3) = \log_5 21x$

12. $\log_5 7 + \log_5 11 + \log_5 y$
$\log_5(7)(11)(y) = \log_5 77y$

13. $5\log_3 x - \log_3 7$
$\log_3 x^5 - \log_3 7 = \log_3\left(\dfrac{x^5}{7}\right)$

14. $3 \log_8 5 - \log_8 z$

$\log_8 5^3 - \log_8 z = \log_8 \dfrac{125}{z}$

15. $\dfrac{1}{2} \log_b x + \dfrac{1}{3} \log_b y - 4 \log_b z$

$\log_b x^{1/2} + \log_b y^{1/3} - \log_b z^4$

$\log_b \dfrac{\sqrt{x} \sqrt[3]{y}}{z^4}$

16. $7 \log_b x + 3 \log_b y - \dfrac{1}{3} \log_b z$

$\log_b x^7 + \log_b y^3 - \log_b z^{1/3}$

$\log_b \dfrac{x^7 y^3}{\sqrt[3]{z}}$

17. $\dfrac{1}{2} (\log_3 7 - \log_3 x - \log_3 y)$

$\log_3 \sqrt{\dfrac{7}{xy}}$

18. $\dfrac{1}{3} (\log_4 x - \log_4 2 - \log_4 z^2)$

$\log_4 \sqrt[3]{\dfrac{x}{2z^2}}$

Find x in each of the following.

19. $\log_3 1 = x$
$x = 0$

20. $\log_8 1 = x$
$x = 0$

21. $\log_7 7 = x$
$x = 1$

22. $\log_5 5 = x$
$x = 1$

23. $\log_{10} 10^3 = x$
$x = 3$

24. $\log_{10} 10^{-4} = x$
$x = -4$

25. $\log_e e^{-4} = x$
$x = -4$

26. $\log_e e^8 = x$
$x = 8$

Solve.

27. $\log_{10} x + \log_{10} 25 = 2$
$\log_{10} 25x = 2$
$25x = 100$
$x = 4$

28. $\log_{10} x + \log_{10} 5 = 1$
$\log_{10} 5x = 1$
$5x = 10$
$x = 2$

$\log_7 5 = \log_7 15x$
$5 = 15x$
$x = \dfrac{1}{3}$

29. $\log_7 5 = \log_7 x + \log_7 15$

30. $\log_3 6 = \log_3 x + \log_3 2$
$\log_3 6 = \log_3 2x$
$6 = 2x$
$3 = x$

31. $\log_6 24 - \log_6 4 = \log_6 3x$
$\log_b \dfrac{24}{4} = \log_6 3x$
$3x = 6$
$x = 2$

32. $\log_5 80 - \log_5 40 = \log_5 4x$
$\log_5 \dfrac{80}{40} = \log_5 4x$
$4x = 2$
$x = \dfrac{1}{2}$

33. $\log_e x - \log_e 2 = 2$
$\log_e \dfrac{x}{2} = 2$
$\dfrac{e^2}{1} = \dfrac{x}{2}$
$x = 2e^2$

34. $\log_e x + \log_e 3 = 1$
$\log_e 3x = 1$
$3x = e$
$x = \dfrac{e}{3}$

35. Show that $\log_{10} A = \log_{10}(10{,}000)(1.07^x)$ can be written as $\log_{10} A = 4 + x \log_{10}(1.07)$ and that $\dfrac{\log_{10} A - 4}{\log_{10}(1.07)} = x$

$\log_{10} A = \log_{10} 10^4 + x \log 1.07$
$\log_{10} A = 4 + x \log_{10} 1.07$
$\dfrac{\log_{10} A - 4}{\log_{10} 1.07} = x$

36. Show that $\log_{10} A = \log_{10}(1000)(1.12)^x$ can be written as $\log_{10} A = 3 + x \log_{10}(1.12)$ and that $\dfrac{\log_{10} A - 3}{\log_{10}(1.12)} = x$

$\log_{10} A = \log_{10} 10^3 + x \log_{10} 1.12$
$\log_{10} A = 3 + x \log_{10} 1.12$
$\log_{10} A - 3 = x \log_{10} 1.12$
$\log_{10} A - 3 = x \log_{10} 1.12$
$\dfrac{\log_{10} A - 3}{\log_{10} 1.12} = x$

To Think About

37. Prove that $\log_b \left(\dfrac{M}{N} \right) = \log_b M - \log_b N$ by using an argument similar to the proof of property 1.

Let $\log_b M = x$, $\log_b N = y$
So, $b^x = M$, $b^y = N$
$\dfrac{M}{N} = \dfrac{b^x}{b^y} = b^{x-y}$
Thus, $\log_b \dfrac{M}{N} = \log_b b^{x-y}$
but $\log_b b^{x-y} = x - y$
Thus, $\log_b \dfrac{M}{N} = x - y$

Subst. for x, y, $\log_b \dfrac{M}{N} = \log_b M - \log_b N$

38. Prove that $\log_b M^p = p \log_b M$ by using an argument similar to the proof of property 1.

Let $\log_b M = x \Rightarrow b^x = M$
$(b^x)^p = M^p$
$\log_b (b^x)^p = \log_b (M^p)$
$p \log_b b^x = \log_b M^p$
$px = \log_b M^p$
substitute for x
$p \log_b M = \log_b M^p$

39. It can be shown that $y = b^{\log_b y}$. Use this property to evaluate $5^{\log_5 4} + 3^{\log_3 2}$.

$4 + 2 = 6$

40. It can be shown that $x = \log_b b^x$. Use this property to evaluate $\log_7 \sqrt[4]{7} + \log_6 \sqrt[12]{6}$.

$\log_7 7^{1/4} = \dfrac{1}{4}$

$\log_6 6^{1/12} = \dfrac{1}{12}$

$\dfrac{1}{4} + \dfrac{1}{12} = \dfrac{4}{12} = \dfrac{1}{3}$

Cumulative Review Problems

41. Find the area of a circle whose radius is 4 meters.

$A = \pi(4)^2$
$A = 50.27$ sq m

42. Find the volume of a cylinder with a radius of 2 meters and a height of 5 meters. $\quad V = \pi(2)^2(5)$
$\qquad\qquad V = 62.83$ cu m

43. Solve for (x, y): $5x + 3y = 9$

$\begin{aligned} 10x + 6y &= 18 \\ 21x - 6y &= 75 \\ \hline 31x &= 93 \end{aligned}$ $\qquad 7x - 2y = 25$

$x = 3$
$y = -2$

44. Solve for (x, y, z): $2x - y + z = 3$

$$x + 2y + 2z = 1$$

$$4x + y + 2z = 0$$

Elim. y $\boxed{1+3}$ $\quad 2x + z = 1$

Elim. y $\boxed{1+2}$ $\quad 5x + 4z = 7 \quad$ $\times(-4)$

$\qquad\qquad\qquad \underline{-8x - 4z = -4}$

$\qquad\qquad x = -1, y = -2, z = 3$

$\qquad\qquad (-1, -2, 3)$

For Extra Practice Exercises, turn to page 500.

Solutions to Odd-Numbered Practice Problems

1. Property 1 can be extended to three logarithms:

$$\log_b MNP = \log_b M + \log_b N + \log_b P$$

Thus

$$\log_4 WXY = \log_4 W + \log_4 X + \log_4 Y$$

3. $\log_b M + \log_b N + \log_b P = \log_b MNP$
Therefore,

$$\log_7 w + \log_7 8 + \log_7 x = \log_7(w \cdot 8 \cdot x) = \log_7 8wx$$

5. $\log_b M^p = p \log_b M$
Therefore,

$\log_7 16^9 = 9 \log_7 16$

7. $\log_3\left(\dfrac{x^4 y^5}{z}\right) = \log_3 x^4 + \log_3 y^5 - \log_3 z$
$\qquad\qquad\quad = 4 \log_3 x + 5 \log_3 y - \log_3 z$

9. $\log_4 x + \log_4 5 = 2$
$\qquad \log_4 5x = 2$
Converting to exponent form, we have

$$4^2 = 5x$$

$$16 = 5x \qquad \dfrac{16}{5} = x$$

Answers to Even-Numbered Practice Problems

2. $\log_9(12)(5) = \log_9 60$ **4.** $\log_3 17 - \log_3 5$ **6.** $\log_7\left(\dfrac{\sqrt[3]{x}}{y^5}\right)$ **8. (a)** $\log_7 1 = 0$ **(b)** $\log_8 8 = 1$ **10.** $x = \dfrac{1}{15}$

After studying this section, you will be able to:

1 *Find a common logarithm on a scientific calculator*

2 *Find an antilogarithm of a common logarithm on a scientific calculator*

3 *Find a common logarithm using a table*

4 *Find an antilogarithm of a common logarithm using a table*

5 *Find a natural logarithm on a scientific calculator*

6 *Find an antilogarithm of a natural logarithm on a scientific calculator*

(objectives continue on next page.)

9.4 LOGARITHMS TO DIFFERENT BASES

Although we can find a logarithm of a number to any positive base except 1, the most frequently used bases are 10 and e. Logarithms to base 10 are called **common logarithms** and are usually written with no subscript.

> **Definition**
>
> The common logarithm of a number x is
>
> $$\log x = \log_{10} x \qquad \text{for all } x > 0$$

We use a scientific calculator or a table of common logarithms to evaluate logarithms.

1 **Finding Common Logarithms on a Scientific Calculator**

To find the common logarithm of a number on a scientific calculator, enter the number and then press the $\boxed{\log x}$ or $\boxed{\log}$ key. (On some calculators you have to press two keys: The 2nd Fn or INV key, and then the log x or log key. Consult the instruction manual for your calculator.)

7 *Find a natural logarithm in a table*

8 *Find an antilogarithm of a natural logarithm using a table*

9 *Evaluate a logarithm to a base other than 10 or e*

Example 1 On a scientific calculator find a decimal approximation for

(a) log 7.32 **(b)** log 73.2 **(c)** log 5632 **(d)** log 0.314

Note: Your calculator may display fewer digits in the answer.

(a) 7.32 log x 0.864511081 ← Note that the only difference
(b) 73.2 log x 1.864511081 ← in the two answers is the
(c) 5632 log x 3.750662646 1 before the decimal point.
(d) 0.314 log x −0.503070351 ∎

Practice Problem 1 On a scientific calculator find a decimal approximation for
(a) log 4.36 **(b)** log 436 **(c)** log 1279 **(d)** log 0.2418 ∎

To Think About

Why is the difference in the solutions to Example 1 (a) and (b) only 1.00? Can you show why this should be true? Consider the following:

$$\log 73.2 = \log(7.32 \times 10^1) \quad \text{Using scientific notation.}$$
$$= \log 7.32 + \log 10^1 \quad \text{By property of logs.}$$
$$= \log 7.32 + 1 \quad \text{Because } \log_b b = 1.$$
$$= 0.864511081 + 1 \quad \text{Using a calculator.}$$
$$= 1.864511081 \quad \text{Adding the decimals.} \quad ∎$$

TEACHING TIP This section can be taught introducing logs from a table only, from a calculator only, or a mixture of both. You may need to modify it slightly depending on the emphasis you wish to make. Most faculty prefer to emphasize using calculators.

2 **Finding Antilogarithms on a Scientific Calculator**

Suppose that we want to solve for x in the following situation. This is sometimes called finding an **antilogarithm**.

Example 2 Find an approximate value for x if log x = 4.326.

Here we are given the value of the logarithm, and we want to find the number that has that logarithm. In other words, we want the **antilogarithm**. We know that $\log_{10} x = 4.326$ is equivalent to $10^{4.326} = x$. So to solve this problem, we want to find a number to a certain power. In this case we want to evaluate 10 to the 4.326 power. Using a calculator, we have

$$4.326 \boxed{10^x} \quad 21183.61135$$

(If your scientific calculator does not have a $\boxed{10^x}$ key, you can usually use 2nd Fn log x or INV log x to perform the operation.) ∎

Practice Problem 2 Using a scientific calculator find an approximate value for x if log x = 2.913. ∎

Example 3 Using a scientific calculator, find an approximate value for x.

(a) log x = 1.156 **(b)** log x = 0.07318 **(c)** log x = −3.1621

(a) log x = 1.156 is equivalent to $10^{1.156} = x$, and

$$1.156 \boxed{10^x} \quad 14.32187899$$

(b) log x = 0.07318 is equivalent to $10^{0.07318} = x$, and

$$0.07318 \boxed{10^x} \quad 1.183531987$$

(c) $\log x = -3.1621$ is equivalent to $10^{-3.1621} = x$, and

$$3.1621 \boxed{+/-} \boxed{10^x} \quad 0.0006884937466$$

(Some calculators may give the answer in scientific notation as $6.884937466 \times 10^{-4}$. This is displayed on the calculator screen as $6.884937466 -4$.) ∎

Practice Problem 3 Using a scientific calculator, find an approximate value for x.
(a) $\log x = 1.823$ **(b)** $\log x = 0.06134$ **(c)** $\log x = -4.6218$
∎

❸ Finding Common Logarithms with Table B–3

If we use Table B–3 to find a common logarithm of a number, that number must be in scientific notation. The table is valid only for logarithms of numbers N, where $1.00 \le N < 9.99$.

Example 4 Using Table B–3, find approximate values for

(a) $\log 123$ **(b)** $\log 0.00111$

For each logarithm we need to use a portion of Table B–3.

COMMON LOGARITHMS (PORTION)

N	0	1	2	3
1.0	0.0000	0.0043	0.0086	0.0128
1.1	0.0414	0.0453	0.0492	0.0531
1.2	0.0792	0.0828	0.0864	0.0899

(a) $\log 123 = \log(1.23 \times 10^2)$ Writing in scientific notation.
             $= \log 1.23 + \log 10^2$ Using property of logs.
             $= 0.0899 + \log 10^2$ Using table with 1.2 row and 3 column.
             $= 0.0899 + 2$ Since $\log_b b^2 = 2\log_b b = 2 \cdot 1 = 2$.
             $= 2.0899$ Adding decimals.

(b) $\log 0.00111 = \log(1.11 \times 10^{-3})$ Writing in scientific notation.
                 $= \log 1.11 + \log 10^{-3}$ Using property of logs.
                 $= 0.0453 + \log 10^{-3}$ Using table with 1.1 row and 1 column.
                 $= 0.0453 - 3$ Property that $\log_{10} 10^{-3} = -3$.
                 $= 0.0453 - 3.000$ Adding zeros for convenience.
                 $= -2.9547$ Combining two decimals.

(*Note:* We sometimes leave the answer as $0.0453 - 3$. In this case the 0.0453 is called the **mantissa** and the -3 is called the **characteristic**.) ∎

Practice Problem 4 Using Table B–3, find approximate values for
(a) $\log 113$ **(b)** $\log 0.121$ ∎

Finding Antilogarithms with Table B–3

In order to solve for x in the equation $\log x = 0.0128$, we have to find the 0.0128 in the inside of the table and read to the outside labels. If the exact value does not appear, we pick the value in the table that is closest to it.

❹ Example 5 Using Table B–3, find an approximate value of x in each equation.

(a) $\log x = 0.0128$ **(b)** $\log x = 3.0864$

(a) If $\log x = 0.0128$, we look inside the table to find 0.0128. It lies on the 1.0 row and under the 3 column. Thus $\log 1.03 = 0.0128$, so $x = 1.03$
(b) Our table does not allow for values such as 3.0846. Therefore, we write it as

TEACHING TIP Whether a student uses a calculator or a table, it is important that he or she be able to find x in the two problems of example 5. Take a few minutes to make sure the student understands what the equation represents.

$0.0864 + 3$. To solve the equation $\log x = 0.0846$, we use the 1.2 row and the 2 column. Thus $\log 1.22 = 0.0846$. Now

$$\log 1220 = \log(1.22 \times 10^3)$$
$$= \log 1.22 + \log 10^3$$
$$= 0.0846 + 3$$
$$= 3.0846$$

Thus, $x = 1220$ ■

Practice Problem 5 Using Table B–3, find an approximate value of x in each equation.
(a) $\log x = 0.0414$ **(b)** $\log x = 2.0492$ ■

Example 6 Using Table B–3, find an approximate value for x if $\log x = 0.0453 - 4$.

First we solve the equation $\log x = 0.0453$. The value 0.0453 lies in the 1.1 row and under the 1 column. Thus, $\log 1.11 = 0.0453$. Now

$$\log(1.11 \times 10^{-4}) = 0.0453 - 4$$

Thus, $x = 1.11 \times 10^{-4}$ or 0.000111 ■

Practice Problem 6 Using Table B–3, find an approximate value of x if $\log x = 0.0899 - 3$. ■

5 Natural Logarithms

For most theoretical work in mathematics and other sciences the most useful base for logarithms is e. Logarithms with base e are known as **natural logarithms** and are usually written $\ln x$.

> **Definition**
>
> The natural logarithm of a number x is
> $$\ln x = \log_e x \qquad \text{for all } x > 0$$

On a scientific calculator we can usually approximate natural logarithms with the $\boxed{\ln x}$ or $\boxed{\ln}$ key.

Example 7 On a scientific calculator, approximate the following values.

(a) $\ln 7.21$ **(b)** $\ln 72.1$ **(c)** $\ln 0.0356$

(a) $7.21 \boxed{\ln x}$ 1.975468951 **(b)** $72.1 \boxed{\ln x}$ 4.278054044
(c) $0.0356 \boxed{\ln x}$ -3.335409641
Note that there is no simple relationship between the answers to parts (a) and (b) Do you see why this is different from common logarithms? ■

Practice Problem 7 On a scientific calculator, approximate the following values.
(a) $\ln 4.82$ **(b)** $\ln 48.2$ **(c)** $\ln 0.0793$ ■

6 Finding Antilogarithms of a Natural Logarithm on a Scientific Calculator

Example 8 On a scientific calculator find an approximate value of x for each equation.

(a) $\ln x = 2.9836$ **(b)** $\ln x = -1.5619$

(a) If $\ln x = 2.9836$, then $e^{2.9836} = x$. On a scientific calculator,

$$2.9836 \boxed{e^x} \quad 19.75882051$$

(b) If $\ln x = -1.5619$, then $e^{-1.5619} = x$. On a scientific calculator,

$$1.5619 \boxed{+/-} \boxed{e^x} \quad 0.209737191 \quad \blacksquare$$

Practice Problem 8 On a scientific calculator, find an approximate value of x for each equation.

(a) $\ln x = 3.1628$ **(b)** $\ln x = -2.0573$ $\blacksquare$

⑦ Using a Table for Natural Logarithms

If you're going to do extensive work with natural logarithms, you should get a scientific calculator. You could also use a table of natural logarithms, found in a book of mathematical tables in the reference section of your college or local library, or the formula

$$\ln x = \frac{\log x}{\log e} \approx \frac{\log x}{0.4343}$$

Example 9 Use Table B–3 and the formula $\ln x \approx \dfrac{\log x}{0.4343}$ to evaluate the logarithms to four significant digits.

(a) $\ln 5.62$ **(b)** $\ln 36.2$

(a) $\ln 5.62 \approx \dfrac{\log 5.62}{0.4343} = \dfrac{0.7497}{0.4343} = 1.726$

(b) $\ln 36.2 \approx \dfrac{\log 36.2}{0.4343} = \dfrac{\log 3.62 + 1}{0.4343}$

$$= \dfrac{0.5587 + 1.000}{0.4343} = \dfrac{1.5587}{0.4343} = 3.589 \quad \blacksquare$$

Practice Problem 9 Use Table B–3 and the formula $\ln x \approx \dfrac{\log x}{0.4343}$ to evaluate logarithms to four significant digits.

(a) $\ln 3.82$ **(b)** $\ln 41.8$ $\blacksquare$

⑧ Finding Antilogarithms of Natural Logarithms with Table B–2

To find the antilogarithm of natural logarithms, we can use Table B–2, the table of values of e^x.

Example 10 Using Table B–2, find an approximate value of x: $\ln x = 4.4$.

The equation $\ln x = 4.4$ is equivalent to $e^{4.4} = x$. Using Table B–2, we have $e^{4.4} = 81.451$ $\blacksquare$

Practice Problem 10 Using Table B–2, find an approximate value of x: $\ln x = 2.6$. $\blacksquare$

⑨ Change of Base Formula

A scientific calculator has a separate key to find common logarithms (base 10) and natural logarithms (base e). There is no direct way to find a logarithm with a base 3 or a base 7. What do we do in such cases? The logarithm of a number to a base other than 10 or e can be found from the following formula.

Change of Base Formula

$$\log_b x = \frac{\log_a x}{\log_a b}$$

where $a, b, x > 0$ and $a \neq 1$, $b \neq 1$.

Let's see how this formula would work. If you wanted to use common logarithms to find $\log_3 56$, the value of b in the formula would be 3. You could then write $\log_3 56 = \dfrac{\log_{10} 56}{\log_{10} 3} = \dfrac{\log 56}{\log 3}$. Do you see why?

Example 11   Evaluate.   **(a)** $\log_7 3.67$ **(b)** $\log_3 5.12$

(a) $\log_7 3.67 = \dfrac{\log 3.67}{\log 7}$

On a calculator, we perform

3.67 $\boxed{\log x}$ $\boxed{\div}$ 7 $\boxed{\log x}$ $\boxed{=}$ 0.668166339

(b) $\log_3 5.12 = \dfrac{\log 5.12}{\log 3}$

On a calculator, we perform

5.12 $\boxed{\log x}$ $\boxed{\div}$ 3 $\boxed{\log x}$ $\boxed{=}$ 1.486561234

If you don't have a calculator, use Table B–3 to find each common logarithm and then divide the decimals. ∎

Practice Problem 11   Evaluate.   **(a)** $\log_6 5.28$ **(b)** $\log_9 3.76$ ∎

TEACHING TIP   After discussing example 11 you might want to mention that the problem could have been solved equally as well using natural logs. Students usual appreciately the fact that either the $\boxed{\log x}$ or the $\boxed{\ln x}$ key can be used on the calculator.

$$\log_7 3.67 = \frac{\log 3.67}{\log 7} \text{ or } \frac{\ln 3.67}{\ln 7}$$

EXERCISES 9.4

Use a scientific calculator or Table B–3 to approximate.

1. log 7.36
0.866877814

2. log 2.19
0.340444115

3. log 3.56
0.551449998

4. log 8.96
0.95230801

5. log 356
2.551449998

6. log 896
2.95230801

7. log 125,000
5.096910013

8. log 78,500
4.894869657

9. log 0.0123
−1.910094889

10. log 0.567
−0.246416941

11. log 0.891
−0.050122296

12. log 0.0354
−1.450996738

13. Try to find log(−5.08). What happens? Why?
Error. You cannot take the log of a negative number.

14. Try to find log(−6.63). What happens? Why?
Error. You cannot take the log of a negative number.

Find the approximate value of x, using a scientific calculator or Table B–3.

15. log x = 0.1614
1.450106836

16. log x = 0.2480
1.770108958

17. log x = 0.5821
3.820322269

18. log x = 0.5922
3.910209261

19. log x = 1.7860
61.09420249

20. log x = 1.7896
61.60273583

21. log x = 3.9304
8519.223264

22. log x = 3.9576
9069.847815

23. log x = 6.4683
2939679.609

24. log x = 5.6274
424033.3354

25. log x = 0.5353 − 2
0.034300464

26. log x = 0.9974 − 3
0.009940312

27. log x = −3.3893
0.000408037

28. log x = −4.0458
0.000089991

29. log x = 2.6516
448.3322704

30. log x = 2.7104
513.3339644

Use a scientific calculator or Table B–3 and the formula $\ln x \approx \dfrac{\log x}{0.4343}$ to approximate.

31. ln 5.62
1.726331664

32. ln 8.81
2.17588744

33. ln 56.2
4.028916757

34. ln 88.1
4.478472533

35. ln 136,000
11.82041016

36. ln 129,000
11.76756768

37. ln 0.0167
−4.09234656

38. ln 0.0362
−3.31869616

39. ln 8.93
2.189416395

40. ln 5.64
1.729884066

Find an approximate value of x, using a scientific calculator or Table B–2.

41. ln $x = 0.95$
2.585709659

42. ln $x = 0.55$
1.733253018

43. ln $x = 2.4$
11.02317638

44. ln $x = 4.4$
81.45086866

45. ln $x = 14$
1202604.284

46. ln $x = 12$
162754.7914

47. ln $x = -0.13$
0.878095431

48. ln $x = -0.18$
0.835270211

49. ln $x = -5.5$
0.004086771

50. ln $x = -7.0$
0.000911882

Use a scientific calculator or Table B–3 to find

51. $\log_3 5.01$
1.466792181

52. $\log_2 6.13$
2.615887074

53. $\log_9 8.66$
0.98247341

54. $\log_8 7.98$
0.998796249

55. $\log_6 0.127$
−1.151699337

56. $\log_5 0.173$
−1.090109579

57. $\log_{14} 156$
1.913507505

58. $\log_{15} 243$
2.028419355

To Think About

59. In the equation $\log_{10} x = y$, y can have negative values but x must be greater than zero. Explain.

x represents the number that results when the base 10 is raised to an exponent, y. 10 to any power, positive or negative, will always be a positive number.

60. In the equation $\log_e x = y$, y can have negative values but x must be greater than zero. Explain.

x represents the number that results when the base e is raised to an exponent, y. $e \approx 2.7$ raised to any power, positive or negative, will always be a positive number.

61. Evaluate: $\log 17 + \log_3 17 + \ln 17$.
6.642564189

62. Evaluate: $\log_2 56 + \log 56 + \ln 56$.
11.58089464

Cumulative Review Problems

Solve the quadratic equations. Simplify your answer.

63. $17x^2 - 7x = 0$ $\quad x(17x - 7) = 0$

$$x = 0, \; x = \frac{7}{17}$$

64. $3x^2 - 11x - 5 = 0$ $\quad a = 3, b = -11, c = -5$

$$x = \frac{11 \pm \sqrt{121 - 4(3)(-5)}}{2(3)} = \frac{11 \pm \sqrt{181}}{6}$$

65. $2y^2 + 4y - 3 = 0$

$a = 2, b = 4, c = -3$

$$y = \frac{-4 \pm \sqrt{16 - 4(2)(-3)}}{4} = \frac{-4 \pm \sqrt{40}}{4} = \frac{-2 \pm \sqrt{10}}{2}$$

66. $3y^2 + 5y + 1 = 0$

$a = 3, b = 5, c = 1$

$$y = \frac{-5 \pm \sqrt{25 - 4(3)(1)}}{2(3)} = \frac{-5 \pm \sqrt{13}}{6}$$

For Extra Practice Exercises, turn to page 500.

Solutions to Odd-Numbered Practice Problems

1. (a) 4.36 $\boxed{\log x}$ 0.639486489

(b) 436 $\boxed{\log x}$ 2.639486489

(c) 1279 $\boxed{\log x}$ 3.106870544

(d) 0.2418 $\boxed{\log x}$ −0.616543703

3. (a) $\log x = 1.823$ is equivalent to $10^{1.823} = x$.

1.823 $\boxed{10^x}$ 66.52731562

(b) $\log x = 0.06134$ is equivalent to $10^{0.06134} = x$.

0.06134 $\boxed{10^x}$ 1.151701679

(c) $\log x = -4.6218$ is equivalent to $10^{-4.6218} = x$.

4.6218 $\boxed{+/-}$ $\boxed{10^x}$ 0.00002388911164 [or $2.388911164 \times 10^{-5}$]

5. (a) If $\log x = 0.0414$, we look inside the table to find 0.0414. It lies on the 1.1 row and under the 0 column. Thus $x = 1.10$.

(b) We write $\log x = 2.0492$ as $\log x = 0.0492 + 2$. Now we locate 0.0492 on the 1.1 row and under the 2 column. Thus $\log 1.12 = 0.0492$. Now

$$\log 112 = \log 1.12 \times 10^2$$
$$= 0.0492 + 2$$
$$= 2.0492$$

Thus $x = 112$.

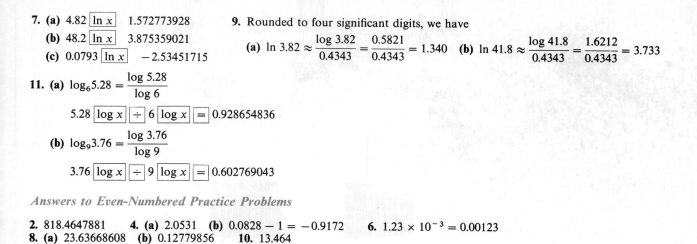

7. (a) 4.82 $\boxed{\ln x}$ 1.572773928

   (b) 48.2 $\boxed{\ln x}$ 3.875359021

   (c) 0.0793 $\boxed{\ln x}$ -2.53451715

9. Rounded to four significant digits, we have

  (a) $\ln 3.82 \approx \dfrac{\log 3.82}{0.4343} = \dfrac{0.5821}{0.4343} = 1.340$ **(b)** $\ln 41.8 \approx \dfrac{\log 41.8}{0.4343} = \dfrac{1.6212}{0.4343} = 3.733$

11. (a) $\log_6 5.28 = \dfrac{\log 5.28}{\log 6}$

      5.28 $\boxed{\log x}$ $\boxed{\div}$ 6 $\boxed{\log x}$ $\boxed{=}$ 0.928654836

  (b) $\log_9 3.76 = \dfrac{\log 3.76}{\log 9}$

      3.76 $\boxed{\log x}$ $\boxed{\div}$ 9 $\boxed{\log x}$ $\boxed{=}$ 0.602769043

Answers to Even-Numbered Practice Problems

2. 818.4647881   **4. (a)** 2.0531   **(b)** $0.0828 - 1 = -0.9172$ **6.** $1.23 \times 10^{-3} = 0.00123$

8. (a) 23.63668608   **(b)** 0.12779856   **10.** 13.464

9.5   EXPONENTIAL AND LOGARITHMIC EQUATIONS

☐ **After studying this section, you will be able to:**

1 *Solve logarithmic equations*

2 *Solve exponential equations*

3 *Solve applied problems requiring the use of logarithmic and exponential equations*

1 To solve logarithmic equations, the first step we try to accomplish is to try to get the logarithms on one side of the equation and the numerical values on the other.

Example 1   Solve: $\log_2 2x + \log_2 4 = 8$.

$$\log_2(2x)(4) = 8$$
$$\log_2(8x) = 8$$
$$8x = 2^8$$
$$8x = 256$$
$$x = 32 \quad \blacksquare$$

Practice Problem 1   Solve: $2 + \log_3 2x = \log_3(3x + 15)$.   ∎

After looking at our results from Example 1 we can describe a general procedure.

1. If an equation contains some logarithms and some terms without logarithms, try to get one logarithm alone on one side and one numerical value on the other.
2. Then convert to an exponential equation using the definition of a logarithm.
3. Solve the equation.

Example 2   Solve: $\log 5 = 2 - \log(x + 3)$.

$$\log 5 + \log(x + 3) = 2$$
$$\log[5(x + 3)] = 2$$
$$\log(5x + 15) = 2$$
$$5x + 15 = 10^2$$
$$5x + 15 = 100$$
$$5x = 85$$
$$x = 17 \quad \blacksquare$$

TEACHING TIP After solving example 2, you may want to check the knowledge of your students by asking them to solve the following problem at their seats. Solve for *x*:

$$\log(x - 1) + \log(x - 4) = 1$$

Ans.: $x = 6$ only [$x = -1$ cannot be used for we cannot take the log of a negative number]

Practice Problem 2   Solve: $\log(x + 5) = 2 - \log 5$.   ∎

If the equation contains only logarithms, use the properties of logarithms to get one logarithm on each side and then use the property

$$\boxed{\text{If } \log_b M = \log_b N, \text{ then } M = N.}$$

What if one of our possible solutions gives the logarithm of a negative number? Can we evaluate the logarithm of a negative number? Look again at the graph of log x on page 474. Note that the domain of log x is $x > 0$. (The graph is on the positive side of the x-axis.) Therefore, the logarithm of a negative number is *not defined.*

You should be able to see this by using the definition of logarithms. If $\log(-2)$ were valid, we could write

$$y = \log_{10}(-2)$$
$$10^y = -2$$

Obviously, no value of y makes this equation two. So we see a reason why we can never take the logarithm of a negative number.

TEACHING TIP After solving example 3, you may find it helpful to do the following additional example showing the solutions of log equations. Solve for *x:*

$$\log_4 x - \log_4 18 = \log_4(x - 3)$$

Sol.: $\log_4\left(\dfrac{x}{18}\right) = \log_4 x - 3$

$$\frac{x}{18} = x - 3$$

$$x = 18x - 54$$

$$-17x = -54$$

$$x = \frac{54}{17} \text{ Ans.}$$

Example 3 Solve: $\log(x + 6) + \log(x + 2) = \log(x + 20)$.

$$\log(x + 6)(x + 2) = \log(x + 20)$$
$$\log(x^2 + 8x + 12) = \log(x + 20)$$
$$x^2 + 8x + 12 = x + 20$$
$$x^2 + 7x - 8 = 0$$
$$(x + 8)(x - 1) = 0$$
$$x + 8 = 0 \qquad x - 1 = 0$$
$$x = -8 \qquad x = 1$$

Check: $\log(x + 6) + \log(x + 2) = \log(x + 20)$

$x = 1$: $\log(1 + 6) + \log(1 + 2) \overset{?}{=} \log(1 + 20)$

$$\log(7) + \log(3) \overset{?}{=} \log(21)$$

$$\log(7 \cdot 3) = \log 21 \checkmark$$

$x = -8$: $\log(-8 + 6) + \log(-8 + 2) \overset{?}{=} \log(-8 + 20)$

$$\log(-2) + \log(-6) \neq \log(12)$$

Only $x = 1$ is a solution. ■

Practice Problem 3 Solve: $\log 5 - \log x = \log(6x - 7)$. Check your solution. ■

To Think About

Now, suppose that we tried to check the value $x = -8$ for Example 3 and did the following:

$$\log(-2) + \log(-6) \overset{?}{=} \log 12$$
$$\log[(-2)(-6)] \overset{?}{=} \log 12$$
$$\log 12 = \log 12$$

Have we proven that $x = -8$ is a solution? No, because you cannot take the log of a negative number. The expressions $\log(-2)$ and $\log(-6)$ are not defined. ■

2 To solve for the variable in an exponential equation, we usually have to take the logarithm of each side of the equation.

If $M, N > 0$, then $M = N$ if $\log_b M = \log_b N$, where $b > 0$ and $b \neq 1$.

Example 4   Solve: $2^x = 7$.

$$\log 2^x = \log 7$$

$$x \log 2 = \log 7$$

$$x = \frac{\log 7}{\log 2}$$

We could approximate this answer as $x \approx 2.807354922$ ∎

Practice Problem 4   Solve: $3^x = 5$.   ∎

Example 5   Solve for x: $3^x = 7^{x-1}$.

$$\log 3^x = \log 7^{(x-1)}$$

$$x \log 3 = (x - 1) \log 7$$

$$x \log 3 = x \log 7 - \log 7$$

$$x \log 3 - x \log 7 = -\log 7$$

$$x(\log 3 - \log 7) = -\log 7$$

$$x = \frac{-\log 7}{\log 3 - \log 7}$$

Using a calculator, we could approximate this answer as $x \approx 2.296606943$ ∎

Practice Problem 5   Solve for x: $2^{3x+1} = 9^{x+1}$.   ∎

3 Example 6   If an amount of money earns interest at 12% compounded annually, the amount available after t years is $A = P(1 + 0.12)^t$, where P is the principal invested. How many years will it take for $300 to grow to $1500? Round your answer to the nearest whole year.

$$A = P(1.12)^t$$

$$1500 = 300(1.12)^t$$

$$\frac{1500}{300} = (1.12)^t$$

$$5 = (1.12)^t$$

$$\log 5 = \log(1.12)^t$$

$$\log 5 = t(\log 1.12)$$

$$\frac{\log 5}{\log 1.12} = t$$

On a scientific calculator

$$5 \boxed{\log x} \div 1.12 \boxed{\log x} = 14.20150519$$

Thus it would take approximately 14 years   ∎

Practice Problem 6   The growth of the world's population can be measured by the equation $A = A_0 e^{rt}$. If the growth rate is 2% per year, the equation becomes $A = A_0 e^{0.02t}$, where t is the number of years, A_0 is the population of the world at time $t = 0$, and A is the population at time t. How many years will it take for the world's population to triple? (Round your answer to the nearest whole year.)   ∎

TEACHING TIP   After solving example 5, show students how taking the natural logarithm of each side of the equation will simplify the computation by doing the following example. Solve for x: Round to nearest hundredth.

$$e^{-1.4x} = 5.82$$

Sol.: $\ln e^{-1.4x} = \ln 5.82$

$$-1.4x \ln e = \ln 5.82$$

$$-1.4x = \ln 5.82$$

$$x = \frac{\ln 5.82}{-1.4}$$

Using a calculator: $x \approx -1.26$ Ans.

Example 7 The magnitude of an earthquake is measured by the formula $M = \log\left(\dfrac{I}{I_0}\right)$, where I is the intensity of the earthquake and I_0 is the minimum measurable intensity. The 1964 earthquake in Anchorage, Alaska, had a magnitude of 8.4. The 1906 earthquake in Taiwan had a magnitude of 7.1. How much more energy was released from the Anchorage earthquake than from the Taiwan earthquake?

Let I_A = intensity of Alaska earthquake. Then

$$8.4 = \log\left(\frac{I_A}{I_0}\right) = \log I_A - \log I_0$$

Solving for $\log I_0$ gives

$$\log I_0 = \boxed{\log I_A - 8.4}$$

Let I_T = intensity of Taiwan earthquake. Then

$$7.1 = \log\left(\frac{I_T}{I_0}\right) = \log I_T - \log I_0$$

Solving for $\log I_0$ gives

$$\log I_0 = \boxed{\log I_T - 7.1}$$

Therefore,

$$\boxed{\log I_A - 8.4 = \log I_T - 7.1}$$

$$\log I_A - \log I_T = 8.4 - 7.1$$

$$\log \frac{I_A}{I_T} = 1.3$$

$$10^{1.3} = \frac{I_A}{I_T}$$

$$19.95262315 = \frac{I_A}{I_T} \qquad \text{Using a calculator.}$$

$$20 = \frac{I_A}{I_T} \qquad \text{Rounding to the nearest whole number.}$$

$$20 I_T = I_A$$

The Alaska earthquake had approximately 20 times the intensity of the Taiwan earthquake. ■

Practice Problem 7 The 1933 earthquake in Japan had a magnitude of 8.9. The 1989 earthquake in San Francisco had a magnitude of 7.1. How much more energy was released from the Japan earthquake than the San Francisco earthquake? ■

EXERCISES 9.5

Solve each logarithmic equation and check your solution.

1. $1 + \log x = \log(9x + 1)$

$1 = \log(9x + 1) - \log x$

$1 = \log\left(\dfrac{9x + 1}{x}\right)$

$\dfrac{9x + 1}{x} = 10^1$

$x = 1$

2. $1 + \log(4 - x) = \log(3x + 1)$

$1 = \log(3x + 1) - \log(4 - x)$

$1 = \log\left(\dfrac{3x + 1}{4 - x}\right)$

$\dfrac{3x + 1}{4 - x} = 10^1$

$x = 3$

3. $\log_6(x - 9) + \log_6 x = 2$

$\log(x - 9)(x) = 6^2$

$x^2 - 9x = 36$

$x = 12$

4. $1 + \log(x - 3) = \log x$

$1 = \log x - \log(x - 3)$

$1 = \log \dfrac{x}{x - 3}$

$\dfrac{x}{x - 3} = 10^1 \quad \boxed{x = \dfrac{10}{3}}$

5. $\log_2(3x + 7) - \log_2(2x - 5) = 5$

$\log_2 \dfrac{3x + 7}{2x - 5} = 5$

$\dfrac{3x + 7}{2x - 5} = 2^5$

$\boxed{x = \dfrac{167}{61}}$

6. $\log_2(x + 5) - 2 = \log_2 x$

$\log_2(x + 5) - \log_2 x = 2$

$\log_2 \dfrac{x + 5}{x} = 2$

$\dfrac{x + 5}{x} = 2^2$

$\boxed{x = \dfrac{5}{3}}$

7. $\log_3(x - 1) - 3 = \log_3(2x + 1)$

$\log_3(x - 1) - \log_3(2x + 1) = 3$

$\log_3 \dfrac{x - 1}{2x + 1} = 3$

$\dfrac{x - 1}{2x + 1} = 3^3$

$x = \dfrac{-28}{53}$, not a solution

8. $\log_3(x + 6) = 3 - \log_3 x$

$\log_3(x + 6) + \log_3 x = 3$

$\log_3 x(x + 6) = 3$

$x(x + 6) = 3^3$

$\boxed{x = 3} \qquad x = -9$ not a solution

9. $2 \log_7 x = \log_7(x + 4) + \log_7 2$

$\log_7 x^2 = \log_7 2(x + 4)$

$x^2 = 2x + 8$

$\boxed{x = 4} \qquad x = -2$, not a solution

10. $\log x + \log(x - 1) = \log 12$

$\log x(x - 1) = \log 12$

$x^2 - x = 12$

$\boxed{x = 4} \qquad x = -3$, not a solution

11. $\log 2 - \log(3x - 5) = \log x \qquad \log \dfrac{2}{3x - 5} = \log x$

$\dfrac{2}{3x - 5} = x$

$\boxed{x = 2} \qquad x = -\dfrac{1}{3}$, not a solution

12. $\log_7(2x - 1) = \log_7(x + 2) + \log_7(x - 2)$

$\log_7(2x - 1) = \log_7(x + 2)(x - 2)$

$2x - 1 = x^2 - 4$

$\boxed{x = 3} \qquad x = -1$, not a solution

13. $2 \log(x + 3) = \log(x + 1) + \log(x + 4)$

$\log(x + 3)^2 = \log(x + 1)(x + 4)$

$x^2 + 6x + 9 = x^2 + 5x + 4$

$x = -5$, not a solution

14. $\log(x + 6) = \log(x + 20) - \log(x + 2)$

$\log(x + 6) = \log \dfrac{x + 20}{x + 2}$

$x + 6 = \dfrac{x + 20}{x + 2}$

$\boxed{x = 1} \qquad x = -8$, not a solution

15. $\log 2 + \log(2x - 5) = \log(x - 2) + \log(x - 1)$

$\log x(2x - 5) = \log(x - 2)(x - 1)$

$2x^2 - 5x = x^2 - 3x + 2$

$\boxed{x = 1 + \sqrt{3}} \qquad x = 1 - \sqrt{3}$, not a solution

16. $\log 2 + \log(x - 2) = \log(x^2 + 17) - \log(x + 2)$

$\log 2(x - 2) = \log \dfrac{x^2 + 17}{x + 2}$

$2x^2 - 8 = x^2 + 17$

$x^2 = 25$

$\boxed{x = 5} \qquad x = -5$, not a solution

Solve each exponential equation.

17. $9^x = 11$

$x \log 9 = \log 11$

$x = \dfrac{\log 11}{\log 9} = 1.091329169$

18. $7^x = 13$

$x \log 7 = \log 13$

$x = \dfrac{\log 13}{\log 7}$

$x = 1.318123223$

19. $5^{x + 1} = 9$

$(x + 1) \log 5 = \log 9$

$x = \dfrac{\log 9}{\log 5} - 1$

$x = 0.365212389$

20. $4^{x + 2} = 7$

$(x + 2) \log 4 = \log 7$

$x = \dfrac{\log 7}{\log 4} - 2$

$x = -0.596322539$

21. $2^{3x + 4} = 17$

$(3x + 4) \log 2 = \log 17$

$3x \log 2 + 4 \log 2 = \log 17$

$3x \log 2 = \log 17 - 4 \log 2$

$x = \dfrac{\log 17 - 4 \log 2}{3 \log 2}$

$x = 0.02915428$

22. $5^{2x - 1} = 11$

$(2x - 1) \log 5 = \log 11$

$2x \log 5 - \log 5 = \log 11$

$x = \dfrac{\log 11 + \log 5}{2 \log 5}$

$x = 1.244948051$

23. $3^x = 2^{x + 3}$

$x \log 3 = (x + 3) \log 2$

$x = \dfrac{3 \log 2}{\log 3 - \log 2}$

$x = 5.128533874$

24. $5^x = 4^{x + 1}$

$x \log 5 = (x + 1) \log 4$

$x = \dfrac{\log 4}{\log 5 - \log 4}$

$x = 6.212567439$

25. $8^x = 9^{x-2}$

$x \log 8 = (x-2) \log 9$

$x = \dfrac{-2 \log 9}{\log 8 - \log 9}$

$x = 37.30969515$

26. $9^x = 7^{x+3}$

$x \log 9 = (x+3) \log 7$

$x = \dfrac{3 \log 7}{\log 9 - \log 7}$

$x = 23.22879147$

27. $e^x = 37$

$x = \ln 37$

$x = 3.610917913$

28. $e^x = 43$

$x = \ln 43$

$x = 3.761200116$

29. $e^{-x} = 0.12$

$-x = \ln 0.12$

$x = -\ln 0.12$

$x = 2.120263536$

30. $e^{-x} = 0.18$

$-x = \ln 0.18$

$x = -\ln 0.18$

$x = 1.714798428$

The growth of the world's population can be measured by the equation $A = A_0 e^{rt}$, where t is the number of years, A_0 is the population of the world at time $t = 0$, r is the rate of increase per year, and A is the population at time t. Assume that $r = 2\%$ per year. Use this information to solve problems 31–34. Round your answers to the nearest whole year.

31. How long will it take a population of 6 billion to increase to 9 billion?

$9 = 6 e^{.02t}$

$\dfrac{9}{6} = e^{.02t}$

$0.02t = \ln 9 - \ln 6$

$t = \dfrac{\ln 9 - \ln 6}{0.02}$

$t = 20$ yrs.

32. How long will it take a population of 7 billion to increase to 12 billion?

$12 = 7 e^{0.02t}$

$\dfrac{12}{7} = e^{0.02t}$

$t = \dfrac{\ln 12 - \ln 7}{0.02}$

$t = 27$ yrs.

33. How long will it take for the world's population to double?

$2A_0 = A_0 e^{0.02t}$

$\ln 2 = 0.002t$

$t = \dfrac{\ln 2}{0.02}$

$t = 35$ yrs.

34. How long will it take for the world's population to quadruple (become four times as large)?

$4A_0 = A_0 e^{0.02t}$

$\ln 4 = 0.02t$

$t = \dfrac{\ln 4}{0.02}$

$t = 69$ yrs.

When a principal P earns interest at $r\%$ compounded annually, the amount A after t years is $A = P(1 + r)^t$. Use this information to solve problems 35–38. Round all answers to the nearest whole year.

35. How long will it take \$1000 to grow to \$4500 at 7% annual interest?

$4500 = 1000(1 + 0.07)^t$

$4.5 = (1.07)^t$

$\log 4.5 = t \log 1.07$

$t = \dfrac{\log 4.5}{\log 1.07}$

$t = 22$ yrs.

36. How long will it take \$1500 to grow to \$5000 at 8% annual interest?

$5000 = 1500(1.08)^t$

$\log 5000 - \log 1500 = t \log 1.08$

$\dfrac{\log 5000 - \log 1500}{\log 1.08} = t$

$t = 16$ yrs.

37. How long will it take for a principal to triple at 6% annual interest?

$3A = A(1 + 0.06)^t$

$\log 3 = t \log 1.06$

$t = \dfrac{\log 3}{\log 1.06}$

$t = 19$ yrs.

38. How long will it take for a principal to double at 5% annual interest?

$2A = A(1.05)^t$

$\log 2 = t \log 1.05$

$t = \dfrac{\log 2}{\log 1.05}$

$t = 14$ yrs.

? To Think About

The magnitude of an earthquake (amount of energy released) is measured by the formula $M = \log\left(\dfrac{I}{I_0}\right)$, where I is the intensity of the earthquake and I_0 is the minimum measurable intensity. Use this formula to solve problems 39 and 40.

39. The 1906 earthquake in San Francisco had a magnitude of 8.3. In 1971 an earthquake in Japan, measured 6.8. How much more energy was released from the San Francisco earthquake than from the Japan earthquake?

$8.3 = \log\left(\dfrac{I_S}{I_0}\right) = \log I_S - \log I_0$

$6.8 = \log\left(\dfrac{I_J}{I_0}\right) = \log I_J - \log I_0$

$8.3 - \log I_S = 6.8 - \log I_J$

$8.3 - 6.8 = \log I_S - \log I_J$

$1.5 = \log \dfrac{I_S}{I_J}$

$32 \approx \dfrac{I_S}{I_J} \Rightarrow I_S = 32 I_J$

32 times greater

40. The 1933 Japan earthquake had a magnitude of 8.9. In Turkey a 1975 earthquake had a magnitude of 6.7. How much more energy was released from the Japan earthquake than from the Turkey earthquake?

$8.9 = \log\left(\dfrac{I_J}{I_0}\right)$; $6.7 = \log\left(\dfrac{I_T}{I_0}\right)$

$2.2 = \log\left(\dfrac{I_J}{I_T}\right)$

$158 \approx \dfrac{I_J}{I_T}$

$I_J = 158 I_T$ 158 times greater

Cumulative Review Problems

Simplify.

41. $\sqrt{98x^3y^2}$
$7xy\sqrt{2x}$

42. $\sqrt[3]{81x^6y^9}$
$3x^2y^3\sqrt[3]{3}$

43. $(\sqrt{3} + 2\sqrt{2})(\sqrt{6} - \sqrt{2})$
$\sqrt{18} + 2\sqrt{12} - \sqrt{6} - 2(2)$
$3\sqrt{2} + 4\sqrt{3} - \sqrt{6} - 4$

44. $2\sqrt{50x} + 3\sqrt{72x} - 4\sqrt{128x}$
$10\sqrt{2x} + 18\sqrt{2x} - 32\sqrt{2x} = -4\sqrt{2x}$

Calculator Problems

Solve for x. Round your answers to four decimal places.

45. $(6.213)^x = 5.817$
$x = 0.96394524$

46. $(4.62)^x = (3.51)^{x+2}$
$x = 9.139108542$

For Extra Practice Exercises, turn to page 501.

Solutions to Odd-Numbered Practice Problems

1. $2 + \log_3 2x = \log_3(3x + 15)$
$2 = \log_3(3x + 15) - \log_3 2x$
$2 = \log_3\left(\dfrac{3x + 15}{2x}\right)$
$3^2 = \dfrac{3x + 15}{2x}$
$9 = \dfrac{3x + 15}{2x}$
$18x = 3x + 15$
$15x = 15$
$x = 1$

3. $\log 5 - \log x = \log(6x - 7)$
$\log\left(\dfrac{5}{x}\right) = \log(6x - 7)$
$\dfrac{5}{x} = 6x - 7$
$5 = 6x^2 - 7x$
$0 = 6x^2 - 7x - 5$
$0 = (3x - 5)(2x + 1)$

$3x - 5 = 0 \quad or \quad 2x + 1 = 0$
$3x = 5 \qquad\qquad 2x = -1$
$x = \dfrac{5}{3} \qquad\qquad x = -\dfrac{1}{2}$

Check: $\log 5 - \log x = \log(6x - 7)$

$x = \dfrac{5}{3}: \quad \log 5 - \log\left(\dfrac{5}{3}\right) \overset{?}{=} \log\left[6\left(\dfrac{5}{3}\right) - 7\right]$

$\log 5 - \log\dfrac{5}{3} \overset{?}{=} \log 3$

$\log\left[\dfrac{5}{\frac{5}{3}}\right] \overset{?}{=} \log 3$

$\log 3 = \log 3 \checkmark$

$x = -\dfrac{1}{2}: \quad \log 5 - \log\left(-\dfrac{1}{2}\right) \overset{?}{=} \log\left[6\left(-\dfrac{1}{2}\right) - 7\right]$

Since logarithms of negative numbers do not exist, $x = -\dfrac{1}{2}$ is not a valid solution.

The only solution is $x = \dfrac{5}{3}$.

5.
$2^{3x+1} = 9^{x+1}$
$\log 2^{3x+1} = \log 9^{x+1}$
$(3x + 1)\log 2 = (x + 1)\log 9$
$3x\log 2 + \log 2 = x\log 9 + \log 9$
$3x\log 2 - x\log 9 = \log 9 - \log 2$
$x(3\log 2 - \log 9) = \log 9 - \log 2$

$x = \dfrac{\log 9 - \log 2}{3\log 2 - \log 9}$ (We could approximate this answer as $x \approx -12.76989838$.

7. The 1933 Japan earthquake had a magnitude of 8.9. The 1989 San Francisco earthquake had a magnitude of 7.1.

$$8.9 = \log\left(\frac{I_J}{I_0}\right) = \log I_J - \log I_0$$

$$\log I_0 = \log I_J - 8.9$$

$$7.1 = \log\left(\frac{I_S}{I_0}\right) = \log I_S - I_0$$

$$\log I_0 = \log I_S - 7.1$$

Therefore,

$$\log I_J - 8.9 = \log I_S - 7.1$$

$$\log I_J - \log I_S = 8.9 - 7.1$$

$$\log \frac{I_J}{I_S} = 1.8$$

$$10^{1.8} = \frac{I_J}{I_S} \qquad \text{We evaluate } 10^{1.8} \text{ on a calculator.}$$

$$63.09573445 = \frac{I_J}{I_S}$$

Rounding to the nearest whole number gives us

$$63 = \frac{I_J}{I_S}$$

$$63 I_S = I_J$$

The Japan earthquake had approximately 63 times the intensity of the San Francisco earthquake.

Answers to Even-Numbered Practice Problems

2. 15 **4.** $x = \dfrac{\log 5}{\log 3}$ (we could approximate this as $x \approx 1.464973521$)

6. $t = \dfrac{\ln 3}{0.02}$ years

To the nearest whole year it will be 55 years for the population to triple.

EXTRA PRACTICE: EXERCISES

Section 9.1

Graph each function.

1. $f(x) = 6^x$

2. $f(x) = 7^x$

3. $f(x) = \left(\dfrac{1}{4}\right)^x$

4. $f(x) = \left(\dfrac{1}{3}\right)^x$

5. $f(x) = 2^{x+3}$

6. $f(x) = 2^{x+4}$

7. $f(x) = 3^{2-x}$

8. $f(x) = 3^{3-x}$

Graph each function. Use a calculator or Table B–2.

9. $f(x) = \dfrac{1}{3}e^x$

10. $f(x) = \dfrac{1}{2}e^x$

11. $f(x) = e^{2+x}$

12. $f(x) = e^{x-2}$

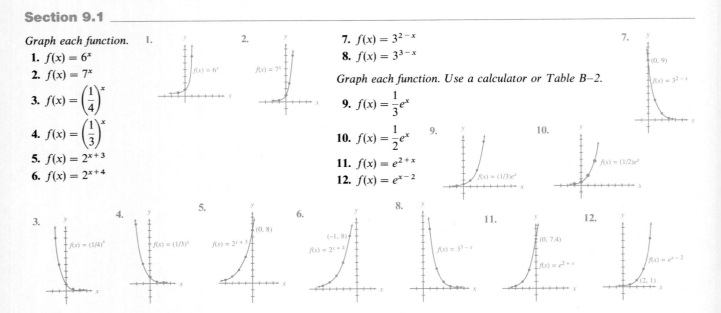

Solve for x.

13. $3^{-x} = \dfrac{1}{9}$ $x = 2$

14. $4^{-x} = \dfrac{1}{64}$ $x = 3$

15. $4^x = 16$ $x = 2$

16. $3^x = 27$ $x = 3$

17. $2^x = 64$ $x = 6$

18. $2^x = 128$ $x = 7$

19. $5^{x+3} = 25$ $x = -1$

20. $6^{x+4} = 36$ $x = -2$

21. $10^{2x} = 0.01$ $x = -1$

22. $10^{3x} = 0.001$ $x = -1$

23. $2 \cdot 3^x = 18$ $x = 2$

24. $3 \cdot 2^{-x} = \dfrac{6}{32}$ $x = 4$

25. $10^{-x} = \dfrac{1}{1000}$ $x = 3$

26. $\left(\dfrac{2}{3}\right)^x = \dfrac{9}{4}$ $x = -2$

27. $\left(\dfrac{2}{5}\right)^{x+1} = \dfrac{125}{8}$ $x = -4$

28. $\left(\dfrac{3}{7}\right)^{2x+1} = \dfrac{81}{2401}$ $x = \dfrac{3}{2}$

For problems 29–30, use the following equation. A calculator will be helpful. The atmospheric pressure measured in pounds per square inch is given by the equation $P = 14.7e^{-0.21d}$, where d is the distance in miles above sea level.

29. What is the pressure in pounds per square inch experienced by a man on a mountain 1.5 miles above sea level?

30. What is the pressure in pounds per square inch on a jet flying 5 miles above sea level?   5.14 lbs/sq in.

31. How much money will Marcia have in three years if she invests $9000 at a 7% annual rate of interest compounded annually? $11,025.39

32. How much money will Melissa have in four years if she invests $7000 at a 6% annual rate of interest compounded annually? $8837.34

33. How much money will Johnny have in five years if he invests $10,000 at a 12% annual rate of interest compounded quarterly? How much will he have if the interest is compounded monthly?   **(a)** $18,061.11   **(b)** $18,166.97

34. How much money will Roger have in three years if he invests $15,000 at an 18% annual rate of interest compounded quarterly? How much will he have if the interest is compounded monthly?   **(a)** $25,438.22   **(b)** $25,637.09

29. 10.7 lbs/sq in.

Section 9.2

Write each expression in logarithmic form.

1. $81 = 9^2$ $\log_9 81 = 2$

2. $49 = 7^2$ $\log_7 49 = 2$

3. $1024 = 4^5$ $\log_4 1024 = 5$

4. $625 = 5^4$ $\log_5 625 = 4$

5. $\dfrac{1}{125} = 5^{-3}$ $\log_5\left(\dfrac{1}{125}\right) = -3$

6. $\dfrac{1}{64} = 4^{-3}$ $\log_4\left(\dfrac{1}{64}\right) = -3$

7. $y = e^5$ $\log_e y = 5$

8. $y = e^8$ $\log_e y = 8$

9. $8^{-2/3} = \dfrac{1}{4}$ $\log_8 \dfrac{1}{4} = -\dfrac{2}{3}$

10. $\left(\dfrac{2}{3}\right)^5 = \dfrac{32}{243}$ $\log_{2/3} \dfrac{32}{343} = 5$

11. $x^n = b$ $\log_x b = n$

12. $3^{-5} = \dfrac{1}{243}$ $\log_3 \dfrac{1}{243} = -5$

Write in exponential form.

13. $2 = \log_4 16$ $4^2 = 16$

14. $2 = \log_5 25$ $5^2 = 25$

15. $4 = \log_{10} 10,000$ $10^4 = 10,000$

16. $5 = \log_{10} 100,000$

17. $-3 = \log_{10}(0.001)$

18. $-2 = \log_{10}(0.01)$

19. $-4 = \log_3\left(\dfrac{1}{81}\right)$ $3^{-4} = \dfrac{1}{81}$

20. $-6 = \log_2\left(\dfrac{1}{64}\right)$

21. $8 = \log_e x$ $e^8 = x$

22. $7 = \log_e x$ $e^7 = x$

23. $\log_2 16 = 4$ $2^4 = 16$

24. $\log_{10}(0.00001) = -5$

25. $\log_b c = n$ $b^n = c$

26. $\log_3\left(\dfrac{1}{243}\right) = -5$

Solve for the variable.

27. $\log_2 x = 5$ $x = 32$

28. $\log_3 x = 4$ $x = 81$

29. $\log_{10} x = -4$

30. $\log_{10} x = -5$

31. $\log_7 343 = y$ $= 3$

32. $\log_8 512 = y$ $y = 3$

33. $\log_3\left(\dfrac{1}{9}\right) = y$ $y = -2$

34. $\log_2\left(\dfrac{1}{8}\right) = y$ $y = -3$

35. $\log_a 81 = 4$ $a = 3$

36. $\log_a 64 = 6$ $a = 2$

16. $10^5 = 100,000$ **17.** $10^{-3} = 0.001$ **18.** $10^{-2} = 0.01$

20. $2^{-6} = \dfrac{1}{64}$ **24.** $10^{-5} = 0.00001$ **26.** $3^{-5} = \dfrac{1}{243}$

29. $x = 10^{-4} = 0.0001$ **30.** $x = 10^{-5} = 0.00001$

37. $\log_a 1,000,000 = 6$ $a = 10$

38. $\log_a 100,000 = 5$ $a = 10$

39. $\log_6\left(\dfrac{1}{36}\right) = w$ $w = -2$

40. $\log_5\left(\dfrac{1}{125}\right) = w$ $w = -3$

41. $\log_w 81 = -4$ $w = \dfrac{1}{3}$

42. $\log_w 32 = -5$ $w = \dfrac{1}{2}$

43. $\log_e w = 3$ $w = e^3$

44. $\log_e w = 5$ $w = e^5$

45. $\log_2 \dfrac{1}{32} = z$ $z = -5$

46. $\log_{2/3}\left(\dfrac{16}{81}\right) = x$ $x = 4$

Evaluate.

47. $\log_{10} 1000$ 3

48. $\log_{10} 10,000$ 4

49. $\log_{10}(0.01)$ -2

50. $\log_{10}(0.001)$ -3

51. $\log_4 64$ 3

52. $\log_3 243$ 5

53. $\log_8 \sqrt{8}$ $\dfrac{1}{2}$

54. $\log_5 \sqrt{5}$ $\dfrac{1}{2}$

55. $\log_{2/3}\left(\dfrac{243}{32}\right)$ -5

56. $\log_3 \sqrt[3]{9}$ $\dfrac{2}{3}$

57. $\log_2 \sqrt[5]{2^3}$ $\dfrac{3}{5}$

58. $\log_3 \sqrt[4]{243}$ $\dfrac{5}{4}$

In problems 59–62, graph each function.

59. $\log_5 x = y$

60. $\log_6 x = y$

61. $\log_{1/6} x = y$

62. $\log_{1/7} x = y$

In chemistry, a solution is an acid if its pH is lower than 7. It is a base if its pH is greater than 7. The pH is defined by $pH = -\log_{10}[H^+]$ where $[H^+]$ is the concentration of hydrogen ions in the solution.

63. The concentration of hydrogen ions in a juice is approximately 10^{-2}. What is the pH?   pH = 2

64. The concentration of hydrogen ions in a solution is approximately 10^{-5}. What is the pH?   pH = 5

59. $y = \log_5 x$ (5, 1) (1, 0)   **60.** $y = \log_6 x$ (6, 1) (1, 0)   **61.** $y = \log_{1/6} x$ (1, 0) (6, −1)   **62.** $y = \log_{1/7} x$ (1, 0) (7, −1)

65. A certain fluid has a pH of 10. Find the concentration of hydrogen ions $[H^+]$ in the solution. $[H^+] = 10^{-10}$

66. Melinda has a cleaning solvent with a pH of 11. Find the concentration of hydrogen ions $[H^+]$ in the solution. $[H^+] = 10^{-11}$

Section 9.3

Write each expression as a sum or difference of $\log x$, $\log y$, and $\log z$. For example, $\log \dfrac{xy}{z} = \log x + \log y - \log z$.

1. $\log_5 x^2 \sqrt{y}$

2. $\log_3 x^6 y^3$ $6\log_3 x + 3\log_3 y$

3. $\log_6 \dfrac{3x}{z^4}$

4. $\log_8 \dfrac{5y}{\sqrt{x}}$ $\log_8 5 + \log_8 y - \dfrac{1}{2}\log_8 x$

5. $\log_b \sqrt[4]{\dfrac{y^2}{5x}}$

6. $\log_b \sqrt[3]{\dfrac{z^2}{4x}}$

7. $\log_e e^4 x^3 y^2$

8. $\log_e e^{-2} x^4 y^7$ $-2 + 4\log_e x + 7\log_e y$

9. $\log_2 \left(\dfrac{xy}{z}\right)$

10. $\log_2 8x^2 z$ $3 + 2\log_2 x + \log_2 z$

11. $\log_5 \left(\dfrac{125yz}{x^2}\right)$

12. $\log_{10} 0.001x^2 y$

Use the properties of logarithms to express each of the following as a single logarithm.

13. $\log_5 2 + \log_5 x + \log_5 20$ $\log_5 40x$

14. $\log_4 z + \log_4 13 + \log_4 5$ $\log_4 65z$

15. $4\log_3 x - \log_3 5$ $\log_3 \dfrac{x^4}{5}$

16. $6\log_8 2 - \log_8 z$ $\log_8 \dfrac{2^6}{z}$

17. $2\log_b z + \dfrac{1}{4}\log_b y + \dfrac{1}{3}\log_b x$ $\log_b z^2 y^{1/4} x^{1/3}$ or $\log_b z^2 \sqrt[12]{x^4 y^3}$

18. $6\log_b y + \dfrac{1}{2}\log_b z + \dfrac{1}{3}\log_b x$ $\log_b y^6 z^{1/2} x^{1/3}$ or $\log_b y^6 \sqrt[6]{x^2 z^3}$

19. $\dfrac{1}{4}(\log_3 2 - \log_3 x - \log_3 5)$ $\log_3 \sqrt[4]{\dfrac{2}{5x}}$

20. $\dfrac{1}{5}(\log_4 7 - \log_4 z - \log_4 2)$ $\log_4 \sqrt[5]{\dfrac{7}{2z}}$

21. $\log_2 6 + \log_2 5 - 4$

22. $81 - 2\log_3 12$ $81 - \log_3 144$

23. $2(\log_a x + \log_a y)$ $\log_a (xy)^2$

24. $\log_b \left(\dfrac{x^6}{y^{3/2}}\right)$

24. $3\left(2\log_b x - \dfrac{1}{2}\log_b y\right)$

21. $\log_2 30 - 4$

Evaluate.

25. $\log_6 1$ 0

26. $\log_7 1$ 0

27. $\log_8 8$ 1

28. $\log_6 6$ 1

29. $\log_{10} 10^7$ 7

30. $\log_{10} 10^5$ 5

31. $\log_e e^{-2}$ -2

32. $\log_e e^{-3}$ -3

33. $\log_3 243$ 5

34. $\log_{2/3} \dfrac{243}{32}$ -5

35. $4\log_4 2$ 2

36. $\log_{1/3} 9$ -2

Solve each equation.

37. $\log_{10} x + \log_{10} 50 = 3$ 20

38. $\log_{10} x + \log_{10} 2 = 2$ 50

39. $\log_6 21 = \log_6 x + \log_6 3$ 7

40. $\log_9 42 = \log_9 x + \log_9 7$ 6

41. $\log_{11} 35 - \log_{11} 7 = \log_{11} 10x$ $\dfrac{1}{2}$

42. $\log_7 50 - \log_7 10 = \log_7 20x$ $\dfrac{1}{4}$ **41.** $\dfrac{1}{2}$

43. $\log_e x - \log_e 3 = 3$ $3e^3$

44. $\log_e x + \log_e 5 = 2$ $\dfrac{e^2}{5}$

45. It can be shown that $y = b^{\log_b y}$. Use this property to evaluate $8^{2\log_8 2} + 3^{4\log_3 4}$. 260

46. It can be shown that $x = \log_b b^x$. Use this property to evaluate $\log_5 \sqrt[4]{5} + \log_8 \sqrt[7]{8}$. $\dfrac{11}{28}$

47. If $\log_b 5 = a$ and $\log_b 3 = c$, find $\log_b 75b^2$ in terms of a and c. $2a + c + 2$

1. $2\log_5 x + \dfrac{1}{2}\log_5 y$ **5.** $\dfrac{1}{2}\log_b y - \dfrac{1}{4}\log_b 5 - \dfrac{1}{4}\log_b x$

3. $\log_6 3 + \log_6 x - 4\log_6 z$ **6.** $\dfrac{2}{3}\log_b z - \dfrac{1}{3}\log_b 4 - \dfrac{1}{3}\log_b x$ **7.** $4\log_e e + 3\log_e x + 2\log_e y$ **9.** $\log_2 x + \log_2 y - \log_2 z$ **11.** $3 + \log_5 y + \log_5 z - 2\log_5 x$

12. $-3 + 2\log_{10} x + \log_{10} y$

    $4 + 3\log_e x + 2\log_e y$

Section 9.4

Use a scientific calculator or Table B–3 to approximate the logarithms in problems 1–14.

1. $\log 4.38$ 0.641474111

2. $\log 5.17$ 0.713490543

3. $\log 1723$ 3.236285277

4. $\log 1894$ 3.277379975

5. $\log 89,200$ 4.950364854

6. $\log 936,000$ 5.971275849

7. $\log 0.763$ -0.117475462

8. $\log 0.668$ -0.175223538

9. $\log 0.00514$ -2.289036881

10. $\log 0.0478$ -1.320572103

11. $\log 0.00862$ -2.064492734

12. $\log 261,000,000$ 8.416640507

13. $\log 4.32$ 0.635483747

14. $\log 0.461$ -0.336299075

15. What happens when we try to find $\log(-9.13)$? Why?

16. What happens when we try to find $\log(-5.79)$? Why?

Using a scientific calculator or Table B–3, approximate x.

17. $\log x = 0.4713$ 2.960056495

18. $\log x = 0.5353$ 3.430046439

19. $\log x = 1.9782$

20. $\log x = 1.9375$

21. $\log x = 5.8209$

22. $\log x = 4.6972$

23. $\log x = 0.7110 - 3$

24. $\log x = 0.9965 - 2$

25. $\log x = -4.7077$

26. $\log x = -5.1925$

27. $\log x = 8.6632 - 10$

28. $\log x = 7.3102 - 10$

29. $\log x = 3.4128$

30. $\log x = 0.6132$

Approximate using a scientific calculator or Table B–3 and the relationship $\log e \approx 0.4343$.

31. $\ln 8.34$ 2.121063216

32. $\ln 4.71$ 1.549687908

33. $\ln 83.4$ 4.423648309

34. $\ln 47.1$ 3.852273001

35. $\ln 0.0432$ -3.141914784

36. $\ln 0.0813$ -2.509609262

37. $\ln 176,000$ 12.07823927

38. $\ln 192,000$ 12.16525065

39. $\ln 0.0028$ -5.878135862

40. $\ln 14,000$ 9.546812609

Using a scientific calculator or Table B–2, approximate x.

41. $\ln x = 0.19$ 1.209249598

42. $\ln x = 0.13$ 1.138828383

43. $\ln x = 2.6$ 13.46373803

44. $\ln x = 3.8$ 44.70118449

45. $\ln x = 15$ 3269017.373

46. $\ln x = 13$ 442413.392

47. $\ln x = -0.45$ 0.637628152

48. $\ln x = -0.28$ 0.755783741

49. $\ln x = 0.116$ 1.122995872

50. $\ln x = 4.4343$ 84.29309906

51. $\ln x = 2.46$ 11.70481154

52. $\ln x = -0.061$ 0.94082324

15. Error—we can only take logs of numbers greater than zero.
16. Error—we can only take logs of numbers greater than zero.
19. 95.10426641   **21.** 662064.0403   **23.** 0.005140437   **25.** 0.000019602   **27.** 0.046046858   **29.** 2587.021273
20. 86.59643233   **22.** 49796.63542   **24.** 0.099197334   **26.** 0.000006419   **28.** 0.002042678   **30.** 4.103930525

For problems 53–58, use a scientific calculator or Table B–3 to find

53. $\log_3 8.61$ 1.959676167

54. $\log_2 7.35$ 2.87774425

55. $\log_8 0.164$ −0.86941076

56. $\log_6 0.129$ −1.142978681

57. $\log_{16} 183$ 1.87892496

58. $\log_{17} 134$ 1.728722551

59. In the equation $\log_3 x = y$, explain why y can have negative values but x must be greater than zero.

60. In the equation $\log_5 x = y$, explain why y can have negative values but x must be greater than zero.

See #59. Base here is "5".

59. y is an exponent and as such can be a positive or negative number. However, with a positive base (3), the number x will be positive because 3 raised to either a pos. or neg. no. remains positive.

Section 9.5

Solve each equation and check your solution.

1. $\log_5(x - 2) + \log_5 3 = 2$ $\dfrac{31}{3}$

2. $\log_6(x + 3) + \log_6 4 = 2$ 6

3. $\log_9(x - 8) = 1 - \log_9 x$ 9

4. $\log_5(x + 1) + \log_5(x - 3) = 1$ 4

5. $\log_2(x - 2) + \log_2(x + 5) = 3$ 3

6. $\log_3(2x - 1) = 2 - \log_3 4$ $\dfrac{13}{8}$

7. $\log_3 x^2 + \log_3 6x = 3$ $\sqrt[3]{36}$

8. $\log_2 x^2 + \log_2 2x = 3$ $\sqrt[3]{4}$ $\dfrac{\sqrt[3]{36}}{2}$

9. $\log_8 3 + \log_8(x - 2) = \log_8(x + 1)$ $\dfrac{7}{2}$

10. $\log_2 5 + \log_2(2x - 1) = \log_2(4x + 7)$ 2

11. $\log(x - 3) = \log(7x - 23) - \log(x + 1)$ 4, 5

12. $\log(x - 3) = \log(3x - 8) - \log x$ 4

13. $\log_9 x + \log_9(2x - 3) = \log_9 2$ 2

14. $\log_6 x + \log_6(3x - 5) = \log_6 2$ 2

15. $\log_7(2x + 1) + \log_7 3 = \log_7 5 - \log_7 x$ $\dfrac{-3 + \sqrt{129}}{12}$

16. $\log_8 2 + \log_8(x - 4) = \log_8 6 + \log_8 x$ No sol.

17. $\log(17x + 2) - 2 \log x = 1$ **17.** $\dfrac{17 + 3\sqrt{41}}{20}$

18. $\log(5x + 7) - \log 3x = 2$

19. $\log(2t + 3) + \log(4t - 1) = 2 \log 3$ $\dfrac{3}{4}$ **18.** $\dfrac{7}{295}$

20. $\log(2t + 4) - \log(3t + 1) = \log 6$

21. $\log(x^2 - 30x) = 3$ 50, −20   **20.** $-\dfrac{1}{8}$

22. $\log(3t + 1) - \log(2t + 3) = \log 2$ No sol.

Solve each exponential equation.

23. $3^x = 14$ 2.402173503

24. $4^x = 11$ 1.729715809

25. $5^{x+3} = 13$ −1.406307359

26. $6^{x+2} = 17$ −0.418753525

27. $17 = 2^{2x-3}$ 3.543731421

28. $15 = 4^{3x-1}$ 0.984481766

29. $5^x = 4^{x+2}$ 12.42513488

30. $8^x = 5^{x+3}$ 10.27292863

31. $26 = e^x$ 3.258096538

32. $35 = e^x$ 3.555348061

33. $e^{-x} = 0.17$ 1.771956842

34. $e^{-x} = 0.25$ 1.386294361

35. $9^{2x} = 321$ 1.313348026

36. $2^x = 65$ 6.022367813

37. $4^x = \dfrac{1}{32}$ $-\dfrac{5}{2}$

38. $(1.3)^x = 54$ 15.2039915

39. $2^x = 1878$ 10.87498135

40. $(2.1)^x = 1765$ 10.07619582

41. $(2.3)^{-x} = 0.0018$ 7.587824938

The growth of the world's population can be measured by the equation $A = A_0 e^{rt}$, where t is the number of years, A_0 is the population of the world at time $t = 0$, r is the rate of population increase per year, and A is the population at time t. Assume $r = 2\%$ per year. Round your answers to the nearest whole year. Use this information to solve problems 42–45.

42. How long will it take a population of 7 billion to increase to 16 billion?   41 yrs.

43. How long will it take a population of 6 billion to increase to 10 billion?   26 yrs.

44. If the population rate of increase was $r = 1\%$, how long will it take the world population to double?   69 yrs.

45. If the population rate of increase was $r = 3\%$, how long will it take the world population to double?   23 yrs.

The amount A of money after t years when a principal P is invested at $r\%$ is $A = P(1 + r)^t$. Round all answers to nearest whole year. Use this formula to solve problems 46–49.

46. How long would it take $2000 to grow to $7000 at 5% annual interest?   26 yrs.

47. How long will it take $3000 to grow to $8000 at 6% annual interest?   17 yrs.

48. How long will it take a principal to double at 7% annual interest?   10 yrs.

49. How long will it take a principal to triple at 5% annual interest?   23 yrs.

CHAPTER ORGANIZER

Topic	Procedure	Examples
Exponential function p. 465	$f(x) = b^x$, where $b > 0$ and $b \neq 1$ and x is a real number.	Graph: $f(x) = \left(\dfrac{2}{3}\right)^x$.

Table for $f(x) = \left(\dfrac{2}{3}\right)^x$:

x	$f(x)$
−2	2.25
−1	1.5
0	1
1	0.$\overline{6}$
2	0.$\overline{4}$

$f(x) = (2/3)^x$ (0, 1)

Topic	Procedure	Examples
Properties of exponential functions p. 466	When $b > 0$ and $b \neq 1$, if $b^x = b^y$, then $x = y$.	Solve for x: $2^x = \dfrac{1}{32}$. $$2^x = \frac{1}{2^5}$$ $$2^x = 2^{-5}$$ Thus $x = -5$.
Definition of logarithm p. 473	$y = \log_b x$ if and only if $x = b^y$, where $b > 0$ and $b \neq 1$.	Write in exponential form: $\log_3 17 = 2x$. $$3^{2x} = 17$$ Write as a logarithmic equation: $18 = 3^x$. $$\log_3 18 = x$$ Solve for x: $\log_6\left(\dfrac{1}{36}\right) = x$. $$6^x = \frac{1}{36}$$ $$6^x = 6^{-2}$$ So $x = -2$.
Properties of logarithms p. 479	Where $M > 0$, $N > 0$, and $b \neq 1$: $$\log_b MN = \log_b M + \log_b N$$ $$\log_b\left(\frac{M}{N}\right) = \log_b M - \log_b N$$ $$\log_b M^p = p \log_b M$$ $$\log_b b = 1$$ $$\log_b 1 = 0$$ If $\log_b M = \log_b N$, then $M = N$.	Write as separate logarithms of x, y, w: $\log_3\left(\dfrac{x^2 \sqrt[3]{y}}{w}\right)$. $$2\log_3 x + \frac{1}{3}\log_3 y - \log_3 w$$ Write as one logarithm: $5\log_6 x - 2\log_6 w - \dfrac{1}{4}\log_6 z$. $$\log_6\left(\frac{x^5}{w^2 \sqrt[4]{z}}\right)$$
Finding logarithms p. 484	Use a scientific calculator or Table B–3. $$\log x = \log_{10} x \quad \text{for all } x > 0.$$ $$\ln x = \log_e x \quad \text{for all } x > 0.$$	$\log 3.82 = 0.5820634$ $\ln 52.8 = 1.7226339$
Finding antilogarithms p. 485	If $\log x = b$, then $10^b = x$. If $\ln x = b$, then $e^b = x$. Use a calculator or a table to evaluate.	Find x if $\log x = 2.1416$. $$10^{2.1416} = x$$ 2.1416 $\boxed{10^x}$ 138.54792 Find x if $\ln x = 0.6218$. $$e^{0.6218} = x$$ 0.6218 $\boxed{e^x}$ 1.8622771
Finding a logarithm to a different base p. 489	Change of base formula: $$\log_b x = \frac{\log_a x}{\log_a b} \quad \text{where } a, b, x > 0 \text{ but } a \neq 1, b \neq 1$$	Evaluate: $\log_7 1.86$. $$\frac{\log 1.86}{\log 7}$$ 1.86 $\boxed{\log}$ $\boxed{\div}$ 7 $\boxed{\log}$ $\boxed{=}$ 0.3189132

Topic	Procedure	Examples
Solving logarithmic equations p. 491	1. If an equation contains some logarithms and some terms without logarithms, try to change the logarithms to one single logarithm on one side and one numerical value on the other. Then convert the equation to exponential form. 2. If an equation contains only logarithms, try to get only one logarithm on each side of the equation. Then use the property that if $\log_b M = \log_b N$, then $M = N$. *Note:* Always check your solutions when solving logarithmic equations.	1. Solve for x: $\log_5 3x - \log_5(x^2 - 1) = \log_5 2$. $$\log_5 3x = \log_5 2 + \log_5(x^2 - 1)$$ $$\log_5 3x = \log_5 2(x^2 - 1)$$ $$3x = 2x^2 - 2$$ $$0 = 2x^2 - 3x - 2$$ $$0 = (2x + 1)(x - 2)$$ $$2x + 1 = 0 \qquad x - 2 = 0$$ not valid $\quad x = -\dfrac{1}{2} \qquad x = 2 \checkmark$ valid *Check:* $x = 2$: $\quad \log_5 3(2) - \log_5(2^3 - 1) \overset{?}{=} \log_5 2$ $$\log_5 6 - \log_5 3 \overset{?}{=} \log_5 2$$ $$\log_5\left(\frac{6}{3}\right) \overset{?}{=} \log_5 2$$ $$\log_5 2 = \log_5 2 \checkmark$$ $x = -\dfrac{1}{2}$: For the expression $\log_5(3x)$ we would obtain $\log_5(-1.5)$. You cannot take a log of a negative number. $x = -\dfrac{1}{2}$ is not a solution.
Solving exponential equations p. 493	1. See if each expression can be written so that only one base appears on one side of the equation and the same base appears on the other side. Then use the property that if $b^x = b^y$, then $x = y$. 2. If you can't do step 1, take the logarithm of each side of the equation and use the properties of logarithms to solve for the variable.	1. Solve for x: $\quad 2^{x-1} = 7$. $$\log 2^{x-1} = \log 7$$ $$(x - 1) \log 2 = \log 7$$ $$x \log 2 - \log 2 = \log 7$$ $$x \log 2 = \log 7 + \log 2$$ $$x = \frac{\log 7 + \log 2}{\log 2}$$ (We can approximate the answer as $x \approx 3.8073549$.)

REVIEW PROBLEMS CHAPTER 9

Graph the function in problems 1 and 2.

1. $f(x) = 4^{3+x}$ $\quad f(x) = 4^{3+x}$

$f(x) = 4^{3+x}$

$(-3, 1)$

2. $f(x) = e^{x-3}$ $\quad f(x) = e^{x-3}$

$f(x) = e^{x-3}$

$(3, 1)$

3. Solve: $5^{x+2} = 125$.

1

4. Change to logarithmic form: $\dfrac{1}{32} = 2^{-5}$.

$\log_2 \dfrac{1}{32} = -5$

5. Write in exponential form: $-3 = \log_{10}(0.001)$.

$10^{-3} = 0.001$

Solve problems 6–15.

6. $\log_3 x = -2$
$\dfrac{1}{9}$

7. $\log_w 16 = 4$
2

8. $\log_7 w = -1$
$\dfrac{1}{7}$

9. $\log_8 x = 0$
1

10. $\log_w 27 = 3$
3

11. $\log_{10} w = -3$
0.001

12. $\log_{10} 1000 = x$
3

13. $\log_2 64 = x$
6

14. $\log_2\left(\dfrac{1}{4}\right) = x$
-2

15. $\log_5 125 = x$
3

16. Graph the equation: $\log_3 x = y$.
$\log_3 x = y$

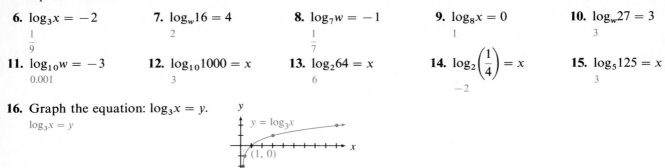

Write each expression as the sum or difference of $\log_2 x$, $\log_2 y$, $\log_2 z$.

17. $\log_2 x^3 \sqrt{y}$ $3\log_2 x + \dfrac{1}{2}\log_2 y$

18. $\log_2\left(\dfrac{5x}{\sqrt{w}}\right)$ $\log_2 5 + \log_2 x - \dfrac{1}{2}\log_2 w$

Write as a single logarithm.

19. $\log_3 x + \log_3 w^{1/2} - \log_3 2$ $\log_3 \dfrac{x\sqrt{w}}{2}$

20. $4\log_8 w - \dfrac{1}{3}\log_8 z$ $\log_8 \dfrac{w^4}{\sqrt[3]{z}}$

21. Evaluate: $\log_e e^6$.
6

Solve.

22. $\log_8 x + \log_8 3 = \log_8 75$
25

23. $\log_5 100 - \log_5 x = \log_5 4$
25

Find the value with a scientific calculator or Table B–2 or B–3.

24. $\log 23.8$
1.376576957

25. $\log 0.0817$
-1.087777943

26. $\ln 3.92$
1.366091654

27. $\ln 803$
6.688354714

28. Find n if $\log n = 1.1367$.
13.69935122

29. Find n if $\ln n = 1.7$.
5.473947392

30. $\log_8 2.81$
0.49685671

Solve the equation and check your solution.

31. $\log_7(x + 3) + \log_7(5) = 2$ $x = \dfrac{34}{5}$

32. $\log_3(2x + 3) = \log_3(2) - 3$ $x = \dfrac{-79}{54}$

33. $2\log_3(x + 3) - \log_3(x + 1) = 3\log_3 2$
$x = 1$

34. $\log_5(x + 1) - \log_5 8 = \log_5 x$
$x = \dfrac{1}{7}$

Solve the equation.

35. $3^{x+1} = 7$
0.771243749

36. $2^{3x+1} = 5^x$
-1.474769847

37. $e^{3x-4} = 20$
2.331910758

38. $(1.03)^x = 20$
101.3482295

39. How much money would Chou Lou have after four years if he invested $5000 at 6% annual interest?
$6312.38

40. How long will it take Frances to double her money if the annual interest rate is 8%?
9 yrs.

41. An earthquake's magnitude is given by $M = \log\left(\dfrac{I}{I_0}\right)$, where I is the intensity of the earthquake and I_0 is the minimum measurable intensity. The 1964 earthquake in Anchorage, Alaska, had a magnitude of 8.4. The 1975 earthquake in Turkey had a magnitude of 6.7. How much more energy was released from the Alaska earthquake than from the Turkey earthquake?
50.1 times as much

42. The work W done by a volume of gas expanding at a constant temperature from volume V_0 to volume V_1 is given by $W = p_0 V_0 \ln\left(\dfrac{V_1}{V_0}\right)$, where p_0 is the pressure at volume V_0.
(a) Find W when $p_0 = 40$ pounds per cubic inch, $V_0 = 15$ cubic inches, and $V_1 = 24$ cubic inches.
(b) If the amount of work is 100 pound-inch, $V_0 = 8$ cubic inches, and $V_1 = 40$ cubic inches, find p_0.
(a) 282   **(b)** 7.77

1. Sketch the graph of $f(x) = 2^{x-3}$.

2. Solve: $3^{x+2} = \dfrac{1}{27}$.

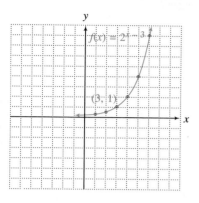

3. How much money will Anne have in four years if she invests $3000 at a 6% annual rate of interest compounded annually?

4. Write in logarithmic form: $\dfrac{1}{49} = 7^{-2}$.

5. Write in exponential form: $-4 = \log_{10}(0.0001)$.

Solve for the variable in problems 6–8.

6. $\log_w 256 = 4$

---

1. $f(x) = 2^{x-3}$

2. $x = -5$

3. $3787.43

4. $\log_7\left(\dfrac{1}{49}\right) = -2$

5. $0.0001 = 10^{-4}$

6. $w = 4$

7. $x = 10^{-6}$

7. $\log_{10} x = -6$

8. $\log_7 49 = w$

8. $w = 2$

9. Write the expression as the sum or difference of $\log_6 x$, $\log_6 y$, $\log_6 2$, and $\log_6 5$: $\log_6 \left(\dfrac{2x^3}{5\sqrt{y}} \right)$.

$\log_6 2 + 3\log_6 x - \log_6 5 - \dfrac{1}{2}\log_6 y$
9.

10. Write as a single logarithm: $\log_5 x + \log_5 2 - \dfrac{1}{2}\log_5 z$.

10. $\log_5 \dfrac{2x}{\sqrt{z}}$

11. Evaluate without a table or calculator: $\log_8 8^3$.

11. 3

12. Solve: $\log_5 x + \log_5 10 = 2$.

12. $x = \dfrac{5}{2}$

Approximate using a scientific calculator or Table B–3 and the relation $\log e \approx 0.4343.$

1. $\log 5.04$ **2.** $\log 0.00217$ **3.** $\ln 8.61$

4. $\ln 156,000$ **5.** $\log_8 2.91$ **6.** $\log_3 82.4$

Use a scientific calculator or Table B–2 or B–3 to approximate x.

7. $\log x = 0.9053$ **8.** $\log x = 1.9647$

9. $\ln x = 0.15$ **10.** $\ln x = 1.9$

1. 0.702430536

2. −2.663540266

3. 2.152924318

4. 11.95761129

5. 0.513673051

6. 4.015598116

7. $x = 8.040813701$

8. $x = 92.19343574$

9. $x = 1.161834243$

10. $x = 6.68589442$

11. $x = 2$ _____

Solve the equation and check your solution.

11. $\log_7(4x + 7) - \log_7(2x - 1) = \log_7 5$

12. $\log_4(x + 2) + \log_4 3 = 2$

12. $x = \dfrac{10}{3}$ _____

Solve the equation.

13. $e^{x + 2} = 12$

13. $x = 0.48490665$ _____

14. $5^{4x + 1} = 11^{2x}$

14. $x = -0.980192471$ _____

15. How many years will it take for \$4000 to grow to \$9000 at 6% annual interest compounded yearly?

15. 14 yrs. _____

16. If the world's population is increasing according to the equation $A = A_0 e^{0.02t}$ where A_0 is the original population at $t = 0$ and A is the new population at time t, how long does it take for a population of 7 billion to increase to 14 billion.? Round your answer to nearest whole year.

16. 35 yrs. _____

1. Graph: $f(x) = 3^{4-x}$

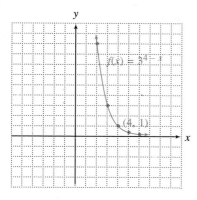

In problems 3 and 4, solve for the variable.

3. $\log_8 x = -2$

5. Write as a single logarithm: $\log_8 x + \log_8 w - \dfrac{1}{4}\log_8 3$.

Evaluate using a calculator or Table B–3 and the relation $\log e \approx 0.4343$.

6. $\log 23.6$ **7.** $\ln 5.99$ **8.** $\log_3 1.62$

2. Solve: $4^{x+3} = 64$.

4. $\log_w 125 = 3$

---

1. $f(x) = 3^{4-x}$

2. $x = 0$

3. $\dfrac{1}{64}$

4. $w = 5$

5. $\log_8 \dfrac{xw}{\sqrt[4]{3}}$

6. 1.372912003

7. 1.790091412

8. 0.439123205

9. 5350.569382

10. 1.150273799

11. $x = \dfrac{16}{3}$

12. $x = \dfrac{3}{7}$

13. $x = -1.413208524$

14. $2938.66

Use a scientific calculator or Table B–2 or B–3 to approximate x.

9. $\log x = 3.7284$

10. $\ln x = 0.14$

Solve the equation and check your solution.

11. $\log_8 2x + \log_8 6 = 2$

12. $\log_8(x + 3) - \log_8 2x = \log_8 4$

13. Solve: $5^{3x+6} = 17$.

14. How much money will Henry have if he invests $2000 for five years at 8% annual interest compounded annually?

15. How long will it take for Barb to double her money if she invests it at 5% compounded annually? Round to nearest whole year.

Approximately one-half of this test covers the content of Chapters 1–8. The remainder covers the content of Chapter 9.

1. Evaluate: $2(-3) + 12 \div (-2) + 3\sqrt{36}$.

2. Solve for x: $H = 3bx - 2ay$.

3. Graph: $y = -\dfrac{2}{3}x + 4$.

4. Factor: $5ax + 5ay - 7wx - 7wy$.

5. Solve for (x, y, z):
$$3x - y + z = 6$$
$$2x - y + 2z = 7$$
$$x + y + z = 2$$

6. Simplify: $(5\sqrt{2} + \sqrt{3})(\sqrt{5} - 2\sqrt{6})$.

7. Solve: $x^4 - 5x^2 - 6 = 0$.

8. Solve for (x, y):
$$2x - y = 4$$
$$4x - y^2 = 0$$

9. Solve: $2x - 3 = \sqrt{7x - 3}$.

1. 6

2. $x = \dfrac{H + 2ay}{3b}$

3. $y = -\dfrac{2}{3}x + 4$

4. $(x + y)(5a - 7w)$

5. $x = 1, y = -1, z = 2$

6. $5\sqrt{10} + \sqrt{15} - 20\sqrt{3} - 6\sqrt{2}$

7. $x = \pm\sqrt{6}$
$x = \pm i$

8. $x = 4 \quad x = 1$
$y = 4 \quad y = -2$

9. $x = 4$
($x = \frac{3}{4}$ is an extraneous solution)

10. $\dfrac{5\sqrt[3]{4x^2y}}{2xy}$

11. $f(x) = 2^{3-2x}$

12. $x = \dfrac{3}{2}$

13. $x = \dfrac{1}{4}$

14. 0.403120521

15. $x = 66.20640403$

16. 1.771243749

17. $x = 9$

18. $x = 2$

19. $x = -0.535026479$

20. $4234.74

---

10. Rationalize the denominator:
$$\dfrac{5}{\sqrt[3]{2xy^2}}.$$

11. Graph: $f(x) = 2^{3-2x}$.

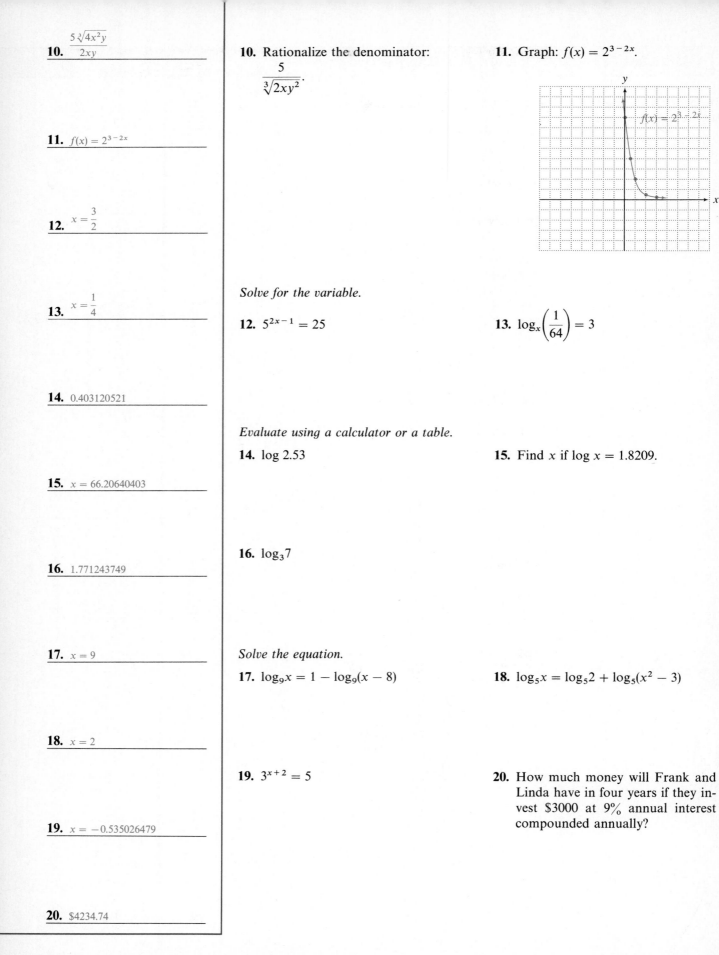

Solve for the variable.

12. $5^{2x-1} = 25$

13. $\log_x\left(\dfrac{1}{64}\right) = 3$

Evaluate using a calculator or a table.

14. $\log 2.53$

15. Find x if $\log x = 1.8209$.

16. $\log_3 7$

Solve the equation.

17. $\log_9 x = 1 - \log_9(x - 8)$

18. $\log_5 x = \log_5 2 + \log_5(x^2 - 3)$

19. $3^{x+2} = 5$

20. How much money will Frank and Linda have in four years if they invest $3000 at 9% annual interest compounded annually?

Inequalities

A Coast Guard Officer is in charge of a search for a missing boat and its crew. A knowledge of mathematical equations defining this region is often needed in order to establish boundaries for the search.

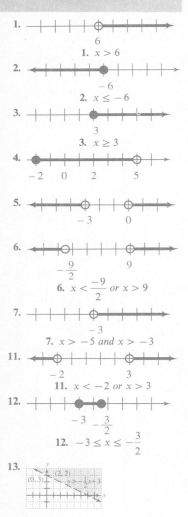

1.
   1. $x > 6$

2.
   2. $x \le -6$

3.
   3. $x \ge 3$

4.

5.

6.
   6. $x < \dfrac{-9}{2} \text{ or } x > 9$

7.
   7. $x > -5 \text{ and } x > -3$

11.
   11. $x < -2 \text{ or } x > 3$

12.
   12. $-3 \le x \le -\dfrac{3}{2}$

13.

14.

15.
   $\dfrac{x^2}{1} - \dfrac{y^2}{25} \le 1$

PRETEST CHAPTER 10

If you are familiar with the topics in this chapter, take this test now. Check your answers with those in the back of the book. If an answer was wrong or you couldn't do a problem, study the appropriate section of the chapter.

If you are not familiar with the topics in this chapter, don't take this test now. Instead, study the examples, work the practice problems, and then take the test.

This test will help you identify those concepts that you have mastered and those that need more study.

Section 10.1   Solve and graph your solution.

1. $7x + 12 < 9x$ $x > 6$ 2. $3(x - 5) - 5x \ge 2x + 9$ $x \le -6$
3. $\dfrac{2}{3}x - \dfrac{5}{6}x - 3 \le \dfrac{1}{2}x - 5$ $x \ge 3$

Section 10.2

4. Graph the region: $-2 \le x < 5$.   5. Graph when $x < -3 \text{ or } x > 0$.
6. Solve for x and graph when $2x + 3 < -6 \text{ or } x - 2 > 7$. $x < -\dfrac{9}{2} \text{ or } x > 9$
7. Solve for x and graph when $x + 1 > -4 \text{ and } -x + 4 < 7$. $x > -5 \text{ and } x > -3$

Section 10.3   Solve for x.

8. $|3x + 2| < 8$ $x < 2 \text{ and } x > -\dfrac{10}{3}$ 9. $\left|\dfrac{2}{3}x - \dfrac{1}{2}\right| \le 3$ $x \le \dfrac{21}{4} \text{ and } x \ge -15$
10. $|2 - 5x - 4| > 13$ $x < -3 \text{ or } x > \dfrac{11}{5}$

Section 10.4   Solve each quadratic inequality and graph your solution.

11. $x^2 - x - 6 > 0$ $x < -2 \text{ or } x > 3$ 12. $2x^2 + 9x \le -9$ $-3 \le x \le -\dfrac{3}{2}$

Section 10.5   Graph the region described by the inequality.

13. $y > -\dfrac{1}{2}x + 3$ 14. $2x - 3y \le -15$

Section 10.6

15. Graph the region described by the quadratic inequality: $25x^2 - y^2 \le 25$.

Graph each system. $\dfrac{x^2}{1} - \dfrac{y^2}{25} \le 1$

16. $2y < x + 6$ 17. $y \ge (x + 1)^2 - 2$
    $3y < -2x + 3$ $x + 2y \le 4$

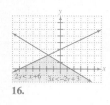

16.

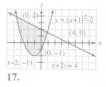

17.

10.1 LINEAR INEQUALITIES

1 An **inequality** means that the expressions in a mathematical statement are not *necessarily* equal. One expression *may* be equal to another, or it may be less than the other. For example, "five is less than eight" is an inequality; "x is less than or equal to $\sqrt{5}$" is also an inequality. We use symbols shown in the following table to denote inequalities.

SYMBOLS OF INEQUALITY

Symbol	Meaning	Example
$\neq$	is not equal to	$3 \neq 9$
$>$	is greater than	$100 > 99$
$<$	is less than	$6 < 55$
$\geq$	is greater than or equal to	$9 \geq 7$
$\leq$	is less than or equal to	$12 \leq 12$
$\not>$	is not greater than	$5 \not> 8$
$\not<$	is not less than	$8 \not< 5$
$\not\geq$	is not greater than or equal to	$2 \not\geq 200$
$\not\leq$	is not less than or equal to	$15 \not\leq 1$

We can use the number line to visualize the concept of inequality. We say that a first number is less than a second number if the first number lies to the *left* of the second number on the number line.

Since -1 lies to the left of 3 on the number line, we say that $-1 < 3$.

We say that a first number is greater than a second number if the first number lies to the *right* of the second number on the number line.

Since 1 lies to the right of -3 on the number line, we say that $1 > -3$.

Example 1 Insert the proper symbol between the numbers.

(a) 8 _____ 6 **(b)** -2 _____ 3 **(c)** -4 _____ -2 **(d)** $\dfrac{1}{2}$ _____ $\dfrac{1}{3}$

(e) $(5-8)$ _____ $(2-3)$ **(f)** $(1-7)$ _____ $(-4-12)$

(g) 0.56 _____ 0.561 **(h)** -0.033 _____ -0.0329

(a) $8 > 6$ because 8 is to the right of 6

(b) $-2 < 3$ because -2 is to the left of 3

(c) $-4 < -2$ because -4 is to the left of -2

(d) $\dfrac{1}{2} > \dfrac{1}{3}$ because $\dfrac{3}{6} > \dfrac{2}{6}$

(e) $(5-8) < (2-3)$ because $(-3) < (-1)$

(f) $(1-7) > (-4-12)$ because $(-6) > (-16)$

(g) $0.56 < 0.561$ because $0.560 < 0.561$

(h) $-0.033 < -0.0329$ because $-0.0330 < -0.0329$ ■

Practice Problem 1 Insert the symbol $<$ or $>$ between the two numbers.

(a) -1 __$>$__ -2 **(b)** $\dfrac{5}{2}$ __$>$__ $\dfrac{4}{2}$

(c) -0.56 __$<$__ -0.5 **(d)** $(-8-2)$ __$>$__ $(-3-12)$ ■

2 We also use the number line to graph inequalities. For example, we graph $x > 4$ by shading in an area to the right of 4. The open circle at 4 means that the graph does not include the point $x = 4$.

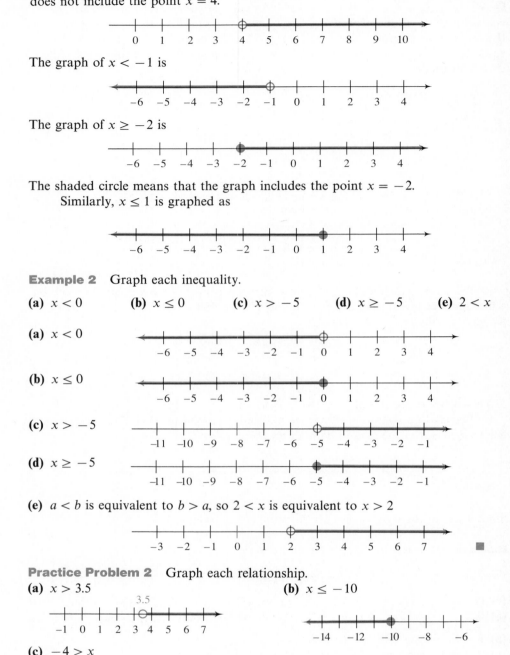

The graph of $x < -1$ is

The graph of $x \geq -2$ is

The shaded circle means that the graph includes the point $x = -2$.
Similarly, $x \leq 1$ is graphed as

TEACHING TIP Students sometimes do not totally understand the less than or equal to statement. If we say x is less than or equal to 5, it means that x can be 5 or any number less than 5. Later on students will need to be able to check to see if the statement x is less than or equal to 5 is true when x has the value -3. This of course would be true, but some students need assistance at this point.

Example 2 Graph each inequality.

(a) $x < 0$ **(b)** $x \leq 0$ **(c)** $x > -5$ **(d)** $x \geq -5$ **(e)** $2 < x$

(a) $x < 0$

(b) $x \leq 0$

(c) $x > -5$

(d) $x \geq -5$

(e) $a < b$ is equivalent to $b > a$, so $2 < x$ is equivalent to $x > 2$

Practice Problem 2 Graph each relationship.

(a) $x > 3.5$ **(b)** $x \leq -10$

(c) $-4 > x$

3 We know that a linear equation can be written as $ax + by = c$. Similarly, a **linear inequality** can be written as $ax + by < c$ (or $>$, $\leq$, $\geq$, etc.). Solving first-degree inequalities is similar to solving first-degree equations. We use various properties of real numbers.

The same number can be added or subtracted from both sides of an inequality without changing the direction of the inequality. (Remember, any inequality symbol can be used. We use $<$ for convenience.)

Example 3 Solve the inequalities and graph their solutions.

(a) $x - 8 < 15$ **(b)** $5x \geq 4x - 2$

(a)
$$x - 8 < 15$$
$$x - 8 \boxed{+ 8} < 15 \boxed{+ 8} \qquad \text{Adding } +8 \text{ to each side.}$$
$$x < 23 \qquad\qquad \text{Simplifying.}$$

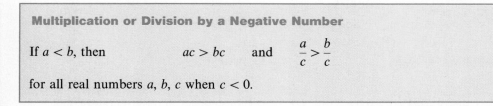

(b)
$$5x \geq 4x - 2$$
$$5x \boxed{- 4x} \geq 4x \boxed{- 4x} - 2 \qquad \text{Subtracting } 4x \text{ from each side.}$$
$$x \geq -2 \qquad\qquad\qquad \text{Simplifying.} \quad \blacksquare$$

Practice Problem 3 Solve the inequalities and graph their solutions.

(a) $x + 2 > -12$ **(b)** $12x \leq 11x + 5$

$\blacksquare$

When we multiply or divide both sides of an inequality by a positive number, the direction of the inequality is not changed. If $5x < -15$ and we divide both sides by 5 we obtain $x < -3$.

When we multiply or divide both sides of an inequality by a *negative number*, the direction of the inequality is *reversed*. Therefore if we divide both sides of $-3x < 21$ by -3 we obtain $x > -7$. If we divide both sides of $-4x \geq -16$ by -4 we obtain $x \leq 4$.

Example 4   Solve and graph your solution: $6x + 3 \leq 2x - 5$.

$$6x + 3 \leq 2x - 5$$

$6x + 3 - 3 \leq 2x - 5 - 3$	Subtracting 3 from each side.
$6x \leq 2x - 8$	Simplifying.
$6x - 2x \leq 2x - 2x - 8$	Subtracting $2x$ from each side.
$4x \leq -8$	Simplifying.
$\dfrac{4x}{4} \leq \dfrac{-8}{4}$	Dividing each side by 4. The inequality is not reversed.

$$x \leq -2$$

(number line from -7 to 3, shaded to the left with closed circle at -2)

Practice Problem 4   Solve the inequality and graph your solution: $8x - 8 \geq 5x + 1$. ∎

(number line from -1 to 7, closed circle at 3)

TEACHING TIP   After doing sample example 5, ask students to do the following problem for classwork. Solve and graph your solution:

$$3(x - 2) < 5x - 3$$

Sol.: $x > -1.5$

(number line with open circle at -1.5, shaded right; marks at -2, -1, 0)

TEACHING TIP   After discussing example 6, you may want to do the following additional example. Solve and graph your solution:

$$\frac{x}{3} - 1 \leq \frac{x}{5} - \frac{1}{5}$$

Sol.:

LCD = 15

$$15\left(\frac{x}{3}\right) - 15(1) \leq 15\left(\frac{x}{5}\right) - 15\left(\frac{1}{5}\right)$$

$$5x - 15 \leq 3x - 3$$

$$2x \leq 12$$

$$x \leq 6$$

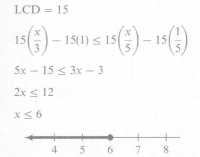

(number line with closed circle at 6; marks at 4, 5, 6, 7, 8)

Example 5   Solve for x: $\dfrac{1}{7}(x + 5) > \dfrac{1}{5}(x + 1)$.

$$\frac{1}{7}(x + 5) > \frac{1}{5}(x + 1)$$

$$\frac{x}{7} + \frac{5}{7} > \frac{x}{5} + \frac{1}{5}$$

$$35\left(\frac{x}{7}\right) + 35\left(\frac{5}{7}\right) > 35\left(\frac{x}{5}\right) + 35\left(\frac{1}{5}\right)$$

$5x + 25 > 7x + 7$	Removing parentheses.
$5x + 25 - 25 > 7x + 7 - 25$	Subtracting 25 from each side.
$5x > 7x - 18$	Simplifying.
$5x - 7x > 7x - 7x - 18$	Subtracting $7x$ from each side.
$-2x > -18$	Simplifying.
$\dfrac{-2x}{-2} < \dfrac{-18}{-2}$	Dividing each side by -2. This reverses the direction of the inequality.

$$x < 9 \qquad ∎$$

Practice Problem 5   Solve for x: $2 - 3x > 7(1 - x)$. ∎

Example 6   Solve: $\dfrac{x}{4} - \dfrac{3}{4} - 1 \leq \dfrac{x}{2}$.

$4\left(\dfrac{x}{4}\right) - 4\left(\dfrac{3}{4}\right) - 4(1) \leq 4\left(\dfrac{x}{2}\right)$	Multiplying each term by the LCD 4.
$x - 3 - 4 \leq 2x$	Simplifying.
$x - 7 \leq 2x$	Combining like terms.
$x - x - 7 \leq 2x - x$	Adding $-x$ to each side.

$$-7 \le 1x \qquad \text{Simplifying.}$$
$$\boxed{x \ge -7} \qquad \text{Because } a < b \text{ is equivalent to } b > a. \quad \blacksquare$$

Practice Problem 6 Solve for x: $\dfrac{1}{5} - \dfrac{1}{10}x \le \dfrac{3}{10}x + 1.$ $\quad \blacksquare$

EXERCISES 10.1

True or false?

1. The statement $6 < 9$ conveys the same information as $9 > 6$.

True

2. The inequality $x \le -2$ conveys the same information as $-2 \ge x$.

True

Insert the symbol $<$ or $>$ between each pair of numbers.

3. 12 _____ -4

$>$

4. -3 _____ 7

$<$

5. -6 _____ -5

$<$

6. -2 _____ -8

$>$

7. $\dfrac{3}{4}$ _____ $\dfrac{2}{3}$

$>$

8. $\dfrac{5}{6}$ _____ $\dfrac{5}{7}$

$>$

9. -3.4 _____ -3.41

$>$

10. -2.69 _____ -2.7

$>$

11. $(5 - 8)$ _____ $(3 - 2)$

$<$

12. $(-12 + 6)$ _____ $(18 - 3)$

$<$

Graph each relationship.

13. $x \ge -2$

14. $x \ge -4$

15. $x < 6$

16. $x < 9$

17. $x > \dfrac{5}{4}$

18. $x < \dfrac{2}{3}$

19. $x \le -4.5$

20. $x \ge -7.5$

Solve for x and graph your solution.

21. $3x + 5 \le 20$ $\quad x \le 5$

22. $2x - 8 \le 10$ $\quad x \le 9$

23. $5x + 6 > -7x - 6$ $\quad x > -1$

24. $2x + 5 > 4x - 5$ $\quad x < 5$

25. $3x - 9 < 5x - 7$ $\quad x > -1$

26. $15 - 3x < -x - 5$ $\quad x > 10$

Solve for x.

27. $9x - 16 + 6x \ge 11 + 4x - 5$ $\quad x \ge 2$

28. $7 - 9x - 12 \ge 3x + 5 - 8x$ $\quad x \le -\dfrac{5}{2}$

29. $-2(x + 3) < -9$ $\quad x > \dfrac{3}{2}$

30. $2x - 11 + 3(x + 2) < 0$

$x < 1$

31. $-4(x + 2) - 3x - 20 > 0$

$x < -4$

32. $1 - (x + 3) + 2x > 4$

$x > 6$

33. $1 + \dfrac{1}{8}x \le \dfrac{1}{4}x - \dfrac{3}{4} + \dfrac{1}{8}x$

$x \ge 7$

34. $\dfrac{7}{6} - \dfrac{1}{3}x + \dfrac{5}{6}x \le 1x - \dfrac{4}{3}$

$x \ge 5$

35. $\dfrac{1}{3}(x + 2) \ge 3x - 5(x - 2)$

$x \ge 4$

36. $\dfrac{1}{4}(x + 3) \ge 4x - 2(x - 3)$

$x \le -3$

37. $x - 6 + \dfrac{1}{3}x < \dfrac{1}{4}(x + 2)$

$x < 6$

38. $\dfrac{1}{2}x - x + \dfrac{9}{2} < \dfrac{1}{5}(x + 5)$

$x > 5$

? To Think About

For problems 39 to 42, describe the situation with a linear inequality and then solve it.

39. A newspaper carrier earns $5 per week plus 25¢ per week for each newspaper delivered to a home. How many home deliveries must the carrier make to earn more than $12.50 per week?

$\$5 + \$0.25x > \$12.50$
$x =$ No. of deliveries $x > 30$

40. A waitress earns $3 per hour plus an average tip of $4 for every table served. How many tables must she serve to earn more than $52 for a 4-hour shift?

$x =$ No. of tables
$\$12 + \$4x > \$52$
$x > \dfrac{40}{4}$
$x > 10$
She would have to serve more than 12 tables.

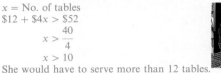

41. An automaker sells its cars for an average of $10,000 each. The company's fixed costs are $2,000,000 per month. The average car sold by the company costs $7300 to build. The chairperson wants to sell enough cars each month to realize a profit of more than $3,000,000 per month. How many cars must be sold each month?

$x =$ No. of cars sold
$\$10,000x - (\$2,000,000 + \$7300x) > \$3,000,000$
$2700x > 5,000,000$
$x > 1851.9$
More than 1851 must be sold each month

42. A man invested $5600 in a mutual fund for one year. The fund pays simple interest for one year. If the investor wants to earn more than $280 interest for the year, what interest rate is required?

$I = prt$. Let $r =$ rate
$\$5600(r)(1) > \$280$
$r > \dfrac{280}{5600}$
$r > 0.05$ or 5%

Cumulative Review Problems

Simplify.

43. $\dfrac{3x^2y^6}{-18x^3y^4}$ $\dfrac{-y^2}{6x}$

44. $(2x^2y^{-3})^2$

$4x^4y^{-6}$ or $\dfrac{4x^4}{y^6}$

45. $(5x^{1/2}y^{2/3})(4x^{3/2}y^{1/4})$

$20x^2y^{11/12}$

46. $\dfrac{(3x^{1/3}y^{1/6})^{-6}}{(3x^{1/4}y^{1/2})^{-4}}$

$\dfrac{3^{-6}x^{-2}y^{-1}}{3^{-4}x^{-1}y^{-2}} = \dfrac{y}{3^2x} = \dfrac{y}{9x}$

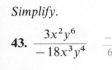

Calculator Problems

Solve for x. Round final answer to nearest hundredth.

47. $156.98x - 32.73 < 181.23x + 77.32$

$x > -4.54$

48. $1.92(6.3x + 4.9) \ge 7.06x - 4.371$

$x > -2.74$

For Extra Practice Exercises, turn to page 550.

Solutions to Odd-Numbered Practice Problems

1. (a) $-1 > -2$ **(b)** $\dfrac{5}{2} > \dfrac{4}{2}$ **(c)** $-0.56 < -0.50$ **(d)** $(-8 - 2) > (-3 - 12)$ since $(-10) > (-15)$

3. (a)
$x + 2 > -12$
$x + 2 - 2 > -12 - 2$
$x > -14$

(b)
$12x \le 11x + 5$
$12x - 11x \le 11x - 11x + 5$
$x \le 5$

5.
$2 - 3x > 7(1 - x)$
$2 - 3x > 7 - 7x$
$2 - 3x + 7x > 7 - 7x + 7x$
$2 + 4x > 7$
$2 - 2 + 4x > 7 - 2$
$4x > 5$
$x > \dfrac{5}{4}$ *or* $x > 1\dfrac{1}{4}$

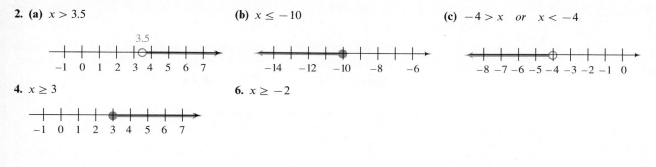

2. (a) $x > 3.5$ **(b)** $x \leq -10$ **(c)** $-4 > x$ *or* $x < -4$

4. $x \geq 3$ **6.** $x \geq -2$

10.2 COMPOUND INEQUALITIES

Some inequalities consist of two inequalities connected by the word *and* or the word *or*. They are called **compound inequalities**. The solution of a compound inequality using the connective *and* includes all the numbers that make both parts true at the same time.

☐ After studying this section, you will be able to:

1 *Graph a compound inequality using the connective and*

2 *Graph a compound inequality using the connective or*

3 *Solve a compound inequality and graph the solution*

① Compound Inequalities Using the Word AND

Example 1   Graph the values of x where $7 < x$ *and* $x < 12$.

In order for 7 to be less than x and x to be less than 12, x must be between 7 and 12. Numbers that are greater than 7 and less than 12 can be written as $7 < x < 12$.

Practice Problem 1   Graph the values of x where $-8 < x$ *and* $x < -2$. ■

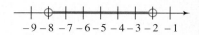

Example 2   Graph the values of x where $-6 \leq x \leq 2$.

Here we have -6 is less than or equal to x and x is less than or equal to 2.

Practice Problem 2   Graph the values of x where $-1 \leq x \leq 5$. ■

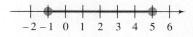

Example 3   Graph the region where $-8.5 \leq x < -1$.

Note the shaded circle at -8.5 and the open circle at -1. ■

Practice Problem 3   Graph the region $-10 \leq x \leq -5.5$ ■

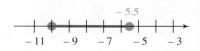

Example 4   Graph the values of x when $x < 5$ *and* $x > -2$.

In order for x to be less than 5 and more than -2, it must be between -2 and 5 but not including those endpoints.

Practice Problem 4   Graph the values of x when $x < 6$ *and* $x > -1$. ■

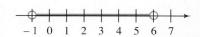

TEACHING TIP After discussing examples 6 and 7, give the following problem as a class exercise. Graph each of the following regions:

A: $x < -4$ *or* $x > -1$

B: $x \le -3$ *or* $x > 3$

C: $x < 7$ *or* $x \ge 10$

A.

−6 −5 −4 −3 −2 −1 0 1

B.

−5 −4 −3 −2 −1 0 1 2 3 4 5

C.

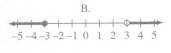

 5 6 7 8 9 10 11 12

Example 5 Graph the salary range (s) of the full-time employees of Tentron Corporation. The salary of each person is greater than or equal to $190 weekly. The salary of each person is less than or equal to $800 weekly.

The salary of each person is greater than or equal to $190 weekly. We write $s \ge 190$. The salary of each person is less than or equal to $800 weekly. We write $s \le 800$. Thus s may be between 190 and 800 and may include those endpoints.

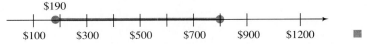

$100 $300 $500 $700 $900 $1200

Practice Problem 5 Graph the salary range if each person earns at least $200 per week but never more than $950 per week.

200   400   600   800   1000

2 Compound Inequalities Using the Word OR

The solution of a compound inequality using the connective *or* includes all the numbers that belong to either of the two inequalities.

Example 6 Graph the region where $x < 3$ *or* $x > 6$.

−3 −2 −1   0   1   2   3   4   5   6   7

The solution consists of all those numbers x that are less than 3 or all those numbers that are greater than 6. Any given x value lies in one side *or* the other, but not in both at the same time.

Practice Problem 6 Graph the region where $x < 8$ *or* $x > 12$.

Example 7 Graph the region where $x > -2$ *or* $x \le -5$.

Note the shaded circle at -5 and the open circle at -2.

−7 −6 −5 −4 −3 −2 −1   0   1   2   3

Practice Problem 7 Graph the region where $x \le -6$ *or* $x > 3$.

Example 8 Male applicants for the state police force in Fred's home state are ineligible for the force if they are shorter than 60 inches or taller than 76 inches. Graph these regions.

The rejected applicants' height h will be less than 60 inches ($h < 60$) *or* will be greater than 76 inches ($h > 76$).

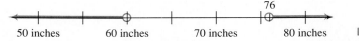

50 inches   60 inches   70 inches   80 inches

Practice Problem 8 Graph the region if female applicants are ineligible if they are shorter than 56 inches or taller than 70 inches.

50 in   60 in   70 in   80 in

3 Solving Compound Inequalities

When asked to solve for x in two compound inequalities, we normally solve each one separately.

Example 9 Solve for x where $3x + 2 > 14$ *or* $2x - 1 < -7$. Graph your solution.

We solve for each inequality separately.

$$3x + 2 > 14 \quad \text{or} \quad 2x - 1 < -7$$

$$3x > 12 \qquad\qquad 2x < -7 + 1$$

$$x > 4 \qquad\qquad 2x < -6$$

$$\qquad\qquad\qquad\qquad x < -3$$

The solution is $x < -3$ *or* $x > 4$.

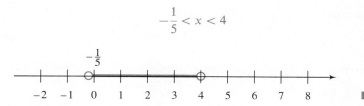

Practice Problem 9 Solve for x and graph where $3x - 4 < -1$ *or* $2x + 3 > 13$.

Example 10 Solve for x and graph when $5x - 1 > -2$ *and* $3x - 4 < 8$.

We solve for each inequality separately.

$$5x - 1 > -2 \qquad \text{and} \qquad 3x - 4 < 8$$

$$5x > -2 + 1 \qquad\qquad\qquad 3x < 8 + 4$$

$$5x > -1 \qquad\qquad\qquad\qquad 3x < 12$$

$$x > -\frac{1}{5} \qquad\qquad\qquad\qquad x < 4$$

The solution is all the numbers between $-\dfrac{1}{5}$ and 4, not including these endpoints.

$$-\frac{1}{5} < x < 4$$

Practice Problem 10 Solve for x when $3x + 6 > -6$ *and* $4x + 5 < 1$.

Example 11 Solve and graph: $2x + 5 \le 11$ *and* $-3x > 18$.

We solve each inequality separately.

$$2x + 5 \le 11 \qquad \text{and} \qquad -3x > 18$$

$$2x \le 6 \qquad\qquad\qquad\qquad x < -\frac{18}{3}$$

$$x \le 3 \qquad\qquad\qquad\qquad x < -6$$

The solution is then $x < -6$ *and* at the same time $x \le 3$.

Notice this can be described by *one* region. The only numbers x that satisfy both statements $x \le 3$ *and* $x < -6$ at the same time would be in the region $x < -6$.

TEACHING TIP After discussing example 11, have students do the following problem as a class exercise. Solve and graph your solution:

$3x - 4 \ge -7$ *and* $-2x + 1 \le -9$

Sol.: $x \ge 5$

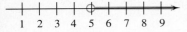

Practice Problem 11 Solve for x when $-2x + 3 < -7$ and $7x - 1 > -15$. ■

Example 12 Solve: $-3x - 2 < -5$ and $4x + 6 < -12$.

We solve each inequality separately.

$$-3x - 2 < -5 \qquad \text{and} \qquad 4x + 6 < -12$$

$$-3x - 2 + 2 < -5 + 2 \qquad\qquad 4x + 6 - 6 < -12 - 6$$

$$-3x < -3 \qquad\qquad\qquad 4x < -18$$

$$\boxed{\frac{-3x}{-3} > \frac{-3}{-3}} \qquad\qquad\qquad \frac{4x}{4} < \frac{-18}{4}$$

$$x > 1 \qquad\qquad\qquad x < -4\frac{1}{2}$$

Now clearly it is impossible for one number to be greater than 1 *and* at the same time less than $-4\frac{1}{2}$.

There is *no solution*. We express this by the notation $\varnothing$, which is an empty set. ■

Practice Problem 12 Solve for x when $-3x - 11 < -26$ and $5x + 4 < 14$. ■

EXERCISES 10.2

Graph the values of x that satisfy the conditions given.

1. $3 < x$ and $x < 8$

2. $5 < x$ and $x < 10$

3. $-4 < x$ and $x < 2$

4. $-7 < x$ and $x < 1$

5. $7 < x < 9$

6. $3 < x < 5$

7. $-2 \le x \le 5$

8. $-1 \le x \le 6$

9. $x > 5$ or $x < 3$

10. $x > 7$ or $x < 2$

11. $x < -3$ or $x > 6$

12. $x < -2$ or $x > 4$

13. $x \le -1$ or $x \ge 4$

14. $x \le -6$ or $x \ge 2$

Solve for x without graphing.

15. $3x + 1 < -2$ and $x \ge -5$
$-5 \le x < -1$

16. $4x - 1 < 7$ and $x \ge -1$
$-1 \le x < 2$

17. $x + 4 > 6$ or $x - 2 \le -7$
$x < -5$ or $x > 2$

18. $x + 1 \geq 5$ *or* $x - 3 < -6$
  $x < -3 \text{ or } x \geq 4$

19. $x < 8$ *and* $x > 10$
  No sol. $\varnothing$

20. $x < 6$ *and* $x > 9$
  No sol. $\varnothing$

Express as an inequality.

21. The manufactured part (p) was defective if it was longer than 9.5 centimeters or less than 9.0 centimeters.
  $p > 9.5 \text{ or } p < 9.0$

22. The bottle was not filled properly if the contents (c) were more than 12.2 ounces or less than 11.8 ounces.
  $c > 12.1 \text{ or } c < 11.8$

23. The pay raise r was acceptable to the bus drivers' union if at least 3% but not more than 6%.
  $0.03 \leq r \leq 0.06$

24. The number of cars c driving over Interstate 91 during the evening hours during January was always at least 5000 but never more than 12,000.
  $5000 \leq c \leq 12{,}000$

Solve the compound inequality.

25. $x - 3 > -5$ *and* $2x + 4 < 8$
  $-2 < x < 2$

26. $x + 3 < 7$ *and* $x - 2 < -3$
  $x < -1$

27. $5x - 7 \geq 3$ *and* $4x - 8 \leq 0$
  $x \geq 2 \text{ and } x \leq 2$ Sol.: $x = 2$

28. $2x - 5 \geq 1$ *and* $3x - 3 \leq 6$
  $x \geq 3 \text{ and } x \leq 3$ Sol.: $x = 3$

29. $2x - 5 < -11$ *or* $5x + 1 \geq 6$
  $x < -3 \text{ or } x \geq 1$

30. $-3x - 1 < 5$ *or* $5x + 4 < 14$
  $x > -2 \text{ or } x < 2$ Sol.: All real numbers

31. $3x - 4 > -1$ *or* $2x + 1 < 15$
  $x > 1 \text{ or } x < 7$ Sol.: All real numbers

32. $4x + 3 < -1$ *or* $2x - 3 > -11$
  $x < -1 \text{ or } x > -4$ Sol.: All real numbers

33. $7x + 2 \geq 2$ *and* $2x + 7 \geq 19$
  $x \geq 6$

34. $5x - 6 < 14$ *and* $6x + 5 < -1$
  $x < -1$

35. $2x + 5 < 3$ *and* $3x - 1 > -1$
  $x < -1 \text{ and } x > 0$ No sol. $\varnothing$

36. $6x - 10 < 8$ *and* $2x + 1 > 9$
  $x < 3 \text{ and } x > 4$ No sol. $\varnothing$

? To Think About

Solve the compound inequality.

37. $x \geq 3$ *and* $x > -2$ *and* $x \leq 8$ *and* $x < 12$
  $3 \leq x \leq 8$

38. $x > -2.5$ *and* $x > 6$ *and* $x < 3.5$ *and* $x \leq 14$
  $x > 6 \text{ and } x < 3.5$ No sol. $\varnothing$

Solve the compound inequality.

39. $\dfrac{1}{4}(x + 2) + \dfrac{1}{8}(x - 3) \leq 1$ *and* $\dfrac{3}{4}(x - 1) > -\dfrac{1}{4}$
  $\dfrac{2}{3} < x \leq \dfrac{7}{3}$

40. $\dfrac{x - 4}{6} - \dfrac{x - 2}{9} \leq \dfrac{5}{18}$ *or* $-\dfrac{2}{5}(x + 3) < -\dfrac{6}{5}$
  $x \leq 13 \text{ or } x > 0$ Sol.: All real numbers

Cumulative Review Problems

Factor completely.

41. $x^3 - 8x^2 + 15x$
  $x(x - 5)(x - 3)$

42. $17x^2 - 17x$
  $17x(x - 1)$

43. $3ax - 2b + 2a - 3bx$
  $(3ax - 3bx) + (2a - 2b)$
  $3x(a - b) + 2(a - b)$
  $(3x + 2)(a - b)$

44. $2x^2 + x - 21$
  $(2x + 7)(x - 3)$

Calculator Problems

Solve for x. Round your answer to two decimal places.

45. $1.29x + 3.47 < 9.63$ *and* $-2.62x - 3.79 < 8.93$
  $-4.85 < x < 4.78$

46. $2.35x + 6.62 \geq 5.04x - 1.23$ *or* $9.28x \geq 52.71$
  $x \leq 2.92 \text{ or } x \geq 5.68$

For Extra Practice Exercises, turn to page 550.

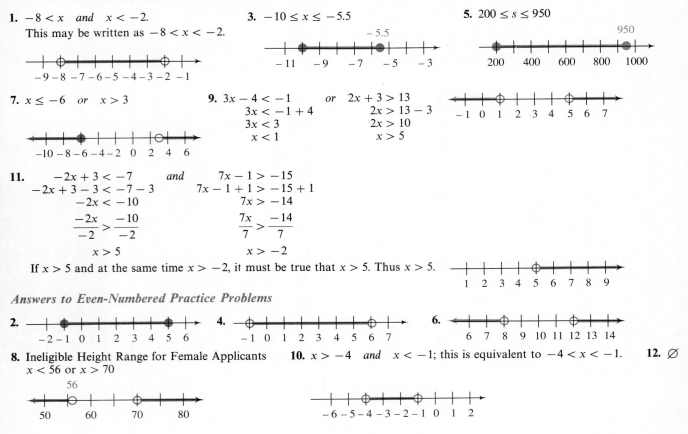

1. $-8 < x$ *and* $x < -2$.
This may be written as $-8 < x < -2$.

3. $-10 \leq x \leq -5.5$

5. $200 \leq s \leq 950$

7. $x \leq -6$ *or* $x > 3$

9.
$$3x - 4 < -1 \qquad or \qquad 2x + 3 > 13$$
$$3x < -1 + 4 \qquad\qquad 2x > 13 - 3$$
$$3x < 3 \qquad\qquad 2x > 10$$
$$x < 1 \qquad\qquad x > 5$$

11.
$$-2x + 3 < -7 \qquad and \qquad 7x - 1 > -15$$
$$-2x + 3 - 3 < -7 - 3 \qquad 7x - 1 + 1 > -15 + 1$$
$$-2x < -10 \qquad\qquad 7x > -14$$
$$\frac{-2x}{-2} > \frac{-10}{-2} \qquad\qquad \frac{7x}{7} > \frac{-14}{7}$$
$$x > 5 \qquad\qquad x > -2$$

If $x > 5$ and at the same time $x > -2$, it must be true that $x > 5$. Thus $x > 5$.

Answers to Even-Numbered Practice Problems

2.

4.

6.

8. Ineligible Height Range for Female Applicants
$x < 56$ or $x > 70$

10. $x > -4$ *and* $x < -1$; this is equivalent to $-4 < x < -1$.

12. $\varnothing$

10.3 ABSOLUTE VALUE INEQUALITIES

□ After studying this section, you will be able to:

1 Solve absolute value inequalities of the form $|bx + c| < a$

2 Solve absolute value inequalities of the form $|bx + c| > a$

1 Recall from Chapter 2 how we solved absolute value equations. We use the same principles to solve absolute value inequalities.

If we write $|x| < 3$, we mean that $-3 < x < 3$. Do you see why? Try it for a few values of x. The expression $|x| < 3$ actually means that x is less than 3 units from zero on the number line.

Thus we conclude that $|x| < 3$ and $-3 < x < 3$ are equivalent statements.

> **Definition**
>
> If a is a positive real number, when $|x| < a$, then $-a < x < a$.

Example 1 Solve: $|x + 5| \leq 10$. Graph your solution.

What values of x make the distance from 0 of $x + 5$ less than *or* equal to 10? We have

$$-10 \leq x + 5 \leq 10$$

We can solve this triple inequality by adding -5 to each part.

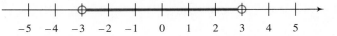

$$-10 \; \boxed{-5} \leq x + 5 \; \boxed{-5} \leq 10 \; \boxed{-5}$$

$$-15 \leq x \leq 5$$

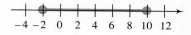

The solution is thus $-15 \leq x \leq 5$ ■

Practice Problem 1   Solve: $|x - 4| \leq 6$. Graph your solution.   ■

To Think About

Do you see why $|x + 5| \leq 10$ is equivalent to $-10 \leq x + 5 \leq 10$? Could you write the problem another way?

We could also solve it by saying that $-10 \leq x + 5$ and $x + 5 \leq 10$. Solving this compound inequality separately, we have

$$-10 < x + 5 \qquad and \qquad x + 5 < 10$$
$$-10 - 5 < x + 5 - 5 \qquad x + 5 - 5 < 10 - 5$$
$$-15 < x \qquad\qquad x < 5$$

Therefore, $-15 < x < 5$, which is the solution that we obtained to Example 1. ■

Example 2   Solve: $\left| x - \dfrac{2}{3} \right| \leq \dfrac{5}{2}$.

$$-\frac{5}{2} \leq x - \frac{2}{3} \leq \frac{5}{2} \qquad\qquad \text{If } |x| < a, \text{ then } -a < x < a.$$

$$6\left(-\frac{5}{2}\right) \leq 6(x) - 6\left(\frac{2}{3}\right) \leq 6\left(\frac{5}{2}\right) \qquad \text{Multiplying each part of the triple inequality by 6.}$$

$$-15 \leq 6x - 4 \leq 15 \qquad\qquad \text{Simplifying.}$$

$$-15 \; +4 \leq 6x - 4 \; +4 \leq 15 \; +4 \qquad \text{Adding 4 to each part.}$$

$$-11 \leq 6x \leq 19 \qquad\qquad \text{Simplifying.}$$

$$-\frac{11}{6} \leq \frac{6x}{6} \leq \frac{19}{6} \qquad\qquad \text{Dividing each part by 6.}$$

$$-1\frac{5}{6} \leq x \leq 3\frac{1}{6} \qquad\qquad \text{Changing to mixed fractions to facilitate graphing.} \quad ■$$

Practice Problem 2   Solve: $\left| x + \dfrac{3}{4} \right| \leq \dfrac{7}{6}$.

Example 3   Solve: $|2(x - 1) + 4| < 8$. Graph your solution.

First we may simplify the quantity within the absolute value expression.

$$|2x - 2 + 4| < 8$$
$$|2x + 2| < 8$$
$$-8 < 2x + 2 < 8 \qquad\qquad \text{If } |x| < a, \text{ then } -a < x < a.$$
$$-8 - 2 < 2x + 2 - 2 < 8 - 2 \qquad \text{Adding } -2 \text{ to each part.}$$
$$-10 < 2x < 6 \qquad\qquad \text{Simplifying.}$$
$$\frac{-10}{2} < \frac{2x}{2} < \frac{6}{2} \qquad\qquad \text{Dividing each part by 2.}$$
$$-5 < x < 3 \quad ■$$

TEACHING TIP   After discussing example 3, have students do the following problem as a class exercise. Solve and graph your solution:

$$|3 - 2(4 - x)| < 12$$

Sol.: $-3.5 < x < 8.5$

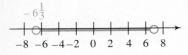

$-6\frac{1}{3}$

Practice Problem 3   Solve and graph: $|2 + 3(x - 1)| < 20$.   ■

2   Now we consider the case when the absolute value is greater than a positive real number. If we write $|x| > 3$, we mean that x is more than 3 units from zero on the number line.

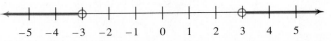

Thus $x > 3$ or $x < -3$. This gives evidence to show that $|x| > 3$ is equivalent to the compound inequality $x > 3$ *or* $x < -3$. In a more general case, we state the following:

> **Definition**
>
> If a is a positive real number when $|x| > a$, then $x > a$ *or* $x < -a$.

Example 4   Solve and graph: $|x - 4| > 7$.

By definition, when $|x| > a$, then $x > a$ *or* $x < -a$. Therefore,

$$x - 4 > 7 \quad or \quad x - 4 < -7$$

Solving each inequality separately, we have

$$x - 4 + 4 > 7 + 4 \qquad x - 4 + 4 < -7 + 4$$
$$x > 11 \qquad\qquad x < -3$$

Our solution is $x > 11$ *or* $x < -3$

Practice Problem 4   Solve and graph: $|x + 6| > 2$.   ■

Example 5   Solve: $|-3x + 6| > 18$.

By definition, we have the compound

$$-3x + 6 > 18 \qquad\qquad or \qquad\qquad -3x + 6 < -18$$
$$-3x > 12 \qquad\qquad\qquad\qquad\qquad -3x < -24$$
$$\boxed{\frac{-3x}{-3} < \frac{12}{-3}} \longrightarrow \begin{array}{c}\text{Division by negative}\\ \text{number reverses inequality.}\end{array} \longrightarrow \boxed{\frac{-3x}{-3} > \frac{-24}{-3}}$$
$$x < -4 \qquad\qquad\qquad\qquad\qquad\qquad x > 8$$

The solution is $x < -4$ *or* $x > 8$

Practice Problem 5   Solve and graph: $|-5x - 2| > 13$.   ■

Example 6   Solve: $\left|3 - \frac{2}{3}x\right| \geq 5$.

By definition, we have the compound inequality.

$$3 - \frac{2}{3}x \geq 5 \qquad or \qquad 3 - \frac{2}{3}x \leq -5$$

$$3(3) - 3\left(\frac{2}{3}x\right) \geq 3(5) \qquad\qquad 3(3) - 3\left(\frac{2}{3}x\right) \leq 3(-5)$$

$$9 - 2x \geq 15 \qquad\qquad\qquad 9 - 2x \leq -15$$

$$-2x \geq 6 \qquad\qquad\qquad -2x \leq -24$$

$$\boxed{\frac{-2x}{-2} \leq \frac{6}{-2}} \qquad\qquad\qquad \boxed{\frac{-2x}{-2} \geq \frac{-24}{-2}}$$

$$x \leq -3 \qquad\qquad\qquad\qquad x \geq 12$$

The solution is $x \leq -3 \ or \ x \geq 12$

Practice Problem 6   Solve and graph: $\left|4 - \frac{3}{4}x\right| \geq 5$. ■

EXERCISES 10.3

Solve and graph the solutions.

1. $|x| \leq 8$ $\quad -8 \leq x \leq 8$

2. $|x| < 6$ $\quad -6 < x < 6$

3. $|x| > 5$ $\quad x > 5 \ or \ x < -5$

4. $|x| \geq 7$ $\quad x \geq 7 \ or \ x \leq -7$

5. $|x + 4| < 13$ $\quad -17 < x < 9$

6. $|x + 6| < 3$ $\quad -9 < x < -3$

Solve for x.

7. $|x - 6| \leq 4$
$2 \leq x \leq 10$

8. $|x - 7| \leq 10$
$-3 \leq x \leq 17$

9. $|2x + 3| \leq 17$
$-10 \leq x \leq 7$

10. $|3x + 2| \leq 12$
$-\frac{14}{3} \leq x \leq \frac{10}{3}$

11. $|3x - 5| \leq 1$
$\frac{4}{3} \leq x \leq 2$

12. $|2x - 7| \leq 3$
$2 \leq x \leq 5$

13. $\left|x - \frac{1}{2}\right| < \frac{5}{2}$
$-2 < x < 3$

14. $\left|x - \frac{3}{2}\right| < \frac{1}{2}$
$1 < x < 2$

15. $\left|\frac{1}{4}x + 2\right| < 6$
$-32 < x < 16$

16. $\left|\frac{1}{5}x + 1\right| < 5$
$-30 < x < 20$

17. $|-1 + 3(x + 1)| \leq 5$
$-\frac{7}{3} \leq x \leq 1$

18. $|-3 + 4(x + 1)| \leq 3$
$-1 \leq x \leq \frac{1}{2}$

19. $\left|\frac{4}{5}(x - 1)\right| < 8$
$-9 < x < 11$

20. $\left|\frac{3}{4}(x - 1)\right| < 6$
$-7 < x < 9$

21. $\left|\frac{2x + 6}{3}\right| < 2$
$-6 < x < 0$

22. $\left|\frac{5x - 3}{2}\right| < 4$
$-1 < x < \frac{11}{5}$

23. $|x + 2| > 5$
$x > 3 \ or \ x < -7$

24. $|x + 4| > 7$
$x > 3 \ or \ x < -11$

25. $|x - 2| \geq 3$
$x \geq 5$ or $x \leq -1$

26. $|x - 1| \geq 2$
$x \geq 3$ or $x \leq -1$

27. $|3x - 8| \geq 7$
$x \geq 5$ or $x \leq \frac{1}{3}$

28. $|5x - 2| \geq 13$
$x \geq 3$ or $x \leq -\frac{11}{5}$

29. $\left|3 - \frac{3}{4}x\right| > 9$
$x < -8$ or $x > 16$

30. $\left|3 - \frac{2}{3}x\right| > 5$
$x < -3$ or $x > 12$

31. $\left|\frac{1}{5}x - \frac{1}{10}\right| > 2$
$x < -\frac{19}{2}$ or $x > \frac{21}{2}$

32. $\left|\frac{1}{4}x - \frac{3}{8}\right| > 1$
$x > \frac{11}{2}$ or $x < -\frac{5}{2}$

33. $|5 - 7x| \geq 9$
$x \leq -\frac{4}{7}$ or $x \geq 2$

34. $|11 - 6x| \geq 7$
$x \leq \frac{2}{3}$ or $x \geq 3$

35. $\left|\frac{1}{3}(x - 2)\right| > 5$
$x > 17$ or $x < -13$

36. $\left|\frac{2}{5}(x - 2)\right| > 4$
$x > 12$ or $x < -8$

In a certain company the measured thickness m of a helicopter blade must differ from the exact standard s by not more than 0.12 millimeters. The manufacturing engineer expresses this as $|m - s| \leq 0.12$.

37. Find the limits of m if the standard s is 18.65 millimeters.
$|m - 18.65| \leq 0.12$
$18.53 \leq m \leq 18.77$

38. Find the limits of m if the standard s is 17.48 millimeters.
$|m - 17.48| \leq 0.12$
$17.36 \leq m \leq 17.60$

A small computer microchip has dimension requirements. The manufacturing engineer has written the specification that the new length n of the chip can differ from the previous length p by only 0.05 centimeter or less. The equation is

$$|n - p| \leq 0.05 \text{ centimeter.}$$

39. Find the limits of the new length if the previous length is 9.68 centimeters.
$|n - 9.68| \leq 0.05$
$9.63 \leq n \leq 9.73$

40. Find the limits of the new length if the previous length is 7.84 centimeters.
$|n - 7.84| \leq 0.05$
$7.79 \leq n \leq 7.89$

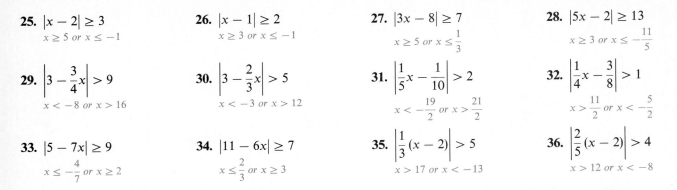

? To Think About

41. A student tried to solve the inequality $|4x - 8| > 12$. Instead of writing $4x - 8 > 12$ or $4x - 8 < -12$, which he should have done, he made a mistake. In error he wrote $12 < 4x - 8 < -12$. What is wrong with his approach?
$12 < 4x - 8 < -12$
$12 < \boxed{4x - 8} < -12$
Ignoring box—statement says $12 < -12$ which is a false statement.

42. A student tried to write a solution to a triple inequality $6 < 4 - 3x < 19$. He made an error and got the wrong answer. He did the following steps

Step 1 $\quad 6 - 4 < 4 - 4 - 3x < 19 - 4$

Step 2 $\quad 2 < -3x < 15$

Step 3 $\quad \dfrac{2}{-3} < \dfrac{-3x}{-3} < \dfrac{15}{-3}$

Step 4 $\quad \dfrac{-2}{3} < x < -5$

Step 2: $2 < -3x < 15$
Next step: Divide by -3, *but* remember the reverse inequality symbol. Next step should read
Step 3: $\dfrac{2}{-3} > \dfrac{-3x}{-3} > \dfrac{15}{-3}$

What *serious error* did he make?

Cumulative Review Problems

43. Solve for (x, y):

$$5x + 2y = 9$$
$$x + 3y = 4$$

$5x + 2y = 9$
$-5x - 15y = -20$
─────────────
$y = \dfrac{11}{13}, \ x = \dfrac{19}{13}$
$\left(\dfrac{19}{13}, \dfrac{11}{13}\right)$

44. Solve for (x, y, z):

$$4x + 3y + 2z = 11$$
$$3x + 4y - z = -1$$
$$2x - y + 4z = 17$$

$\boxed{1 \ \& \ 2}$ Elim. "z": $10x + 11y = 9$
$\boxed{2 \ \& \ 3}$ Elim. "z": $14x + 15y = 13$
─────────────
Elim. "x": $4y = -4$
$y = -1$

$(2, -1, 3)$

45. Solve for (x, y):

$$x^2 + (x^2 - 10)^2 = 16 \qquad x^2 + y^2 = 16$$
$$x^4 - 19x^2 + 84 = 0$$
$$(x^2 - 12)(x^2 - 7) = 0 \qquad y = x^2 - 10$$
$$x = \pm 2\sqrt{3}, y = 2$$
$$x = \pm\sqrt{7}, y = -3$$
$$(\pm 2\sqrt{3}, 2), (\pm\sqrt{7}, -3)$$

46. Solve for (x, y):

$$3x^2 + 4y^2 = 28$$
$$x^2 + y^2 = 8$$

$$\begin{array}{r} 3x^2 + 4y^2 = 28 \\ -4x^2 - 4y^2 = -32 \\ \hline x = \pm 2, y = \pm 2 \end{array}$$
$$(2, \pm 2), (-2, \pm 2)$$

Calculator Problems

Solve for x. Round your answers to two decimal places.

47. $|5.24 - 3.25x| \le 16.75$
  $-3.54 \le x \le 6.77$

48. $|0.293x + 0.77| > 4.08$
  $x < -16.55 \text{ or } x > 11.30$

For Extra Practice Exercises, turn to page 551

Solutions to Odd-Numbered Practice Problems

1.
$$|x - 4| \le 6$$
$$-6 \le x - 4 \le 6$$
$$-6 + 4 \le x - 4 + 4 = 6 + 4$$
$$-2 \le x \le 10$$

3.
$$|2 + 3(x - 1)| < 20$$
$$|2 + 3x - 3| < 20$$
$$|-1 + 3x| < 20$$
$$-20 < -1 + 3x < 20$$
$$-20 + 1 < -1 + 1 + 3x < 20 + 1$$
$$-19 < 3x < 21$$
$$\frac{-19}{3} < \frac{3x}{3} < \frac{21}{3}$$
$$-6\frac{1}{3} < x < 7$$

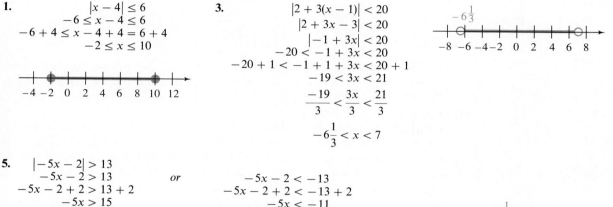

5.
$$|-5x - 2| > 13$$

$-5x - 2 > 13$	*or*	$-5x - 2 < -13$
$-5x - 2 + 2 > 13 + 2$		$-5x - 2 + 2 < -13 + 2$
$-5x > 15$		$-5x < -11$

$$\frac{-5x}{-5} < \frac{15}{-5} \quad \longleftarrow \text{Reverse Direction} \longrightarrow \quad \frac{-5x}{-5} > \frac{-11}{-5}$$

$$x < -3 \qquad\qquad x > \frac{11}{5}$$
$$x > 2\frac{1}{5}$$

Answers to Even-Numbered Practice Problems

2. $-\dfrac{23}{12} \le x \le \dfrac{5}{12}$

4. $x > -4 \text{ or } x < -8$

6. $x \le -1\dfrac{1}{3} \text{ or } x \ge 12$

10.4 QUADRATIC INEQUALITIES

After studying this section, you will be able to:

1 We now want to solve quadratic inequalities such as $x^2 - 2x - 3 > 0$ and $2x^2 + x - 15 < 0$. A quadratic inequality has the form $ax^2 + bx + c < 0$ (or replace $<$ by $>$, $\le$, $\ge$); where $a \ne 0$, and a, b, and c are real numbers. We use our knowledge of solving quadratic equations to solve quadratic inequalities.

1 *Solve a factorable quadratic inequality*

2 *Solve a nonfactorable quadratic inequality*

Let's solve the inequality $x^2 - 2x - 3 > 0$. We want to find two points called the critical points. To do this we replace the inequality by an equals sign and solve the resulting equation.

$$x^2 - 2x - 3 = 0$$

$$(x + 1)(x - 3) = 0 \qquad \text{Factoring.}$$

$$x + 1 = 0 \quad or \quad x - 3 = 0 \qquad \text{Zero-product rule.}$$

$$x = -1 \qquad\qquad x = 3$$

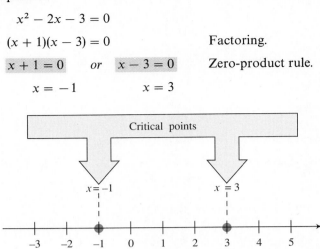

These two solutions form critical points that divide the number line into three segments. You will show as an exercise that all values of x in a given segment produce results that are greater than zero, or else all values of x in a given segment produce results that are less than zero.

To solve the quadratic inequality, we pick an arbitrary test point in each region and see if it is greater than zero since we want to find where $x^2 - 2x - 3$ is > 0. If one point in a region satisfies the inequality, then *all* points in the region satisfy the inequality. We will test $x^2 - 2x - 3$ for three values of x.

Region I: $x = -2$

$$(-2)^2 - 2(-2) - 3 = 4 + 4 - 3 = 5 > 0$$

Region II: $x = 0$

$$(0)^2 - 2(0) - 3 = 0 + 0 - 3 = -3 < 0$$

Region III: $x = 4$

$$(4)^2 - 2(4) - 3 = 16 - 8 - 3 = 5 > 0$$

Thus we see $x^2 - 2x - 3 > 0$ when $x < -1$ *or* $x > 3$. No points in region II satisfy the inequality. The graph of the solution is

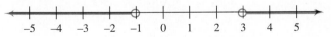

We summarize our method.

Solving a Quadratic Inequality

1. Replace the inequality symbol by an equals sign. Solve the resulting equation to find the critical points.
2. Separate the number line into three distinct regions on each side of these critical points.
3. Evaluate the quadratic expression at a test point in each region.
4. Determine which regions satisfy the original conditions of the quadratic inequality.

Example 1   Solve and graph: $x^2 - 10x + 24 > 0$.

1. Replace the inequality symbol by an equals sign. Solve the resulting equation to find the critical points $x = 4$ and $x = 6$.

$$x^2 - 10x + 24 = 0$$
$$(x - 4)(x - 6) = 0$$
$$x - 4 = 0 \quad or \quad x - 6 = 0$$
$$x = 4 \qquad\qquad x = 6$$

2. Separate the number line into distinct regions on each side of the critical points.

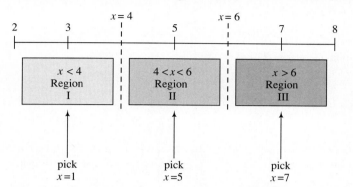

TEACHING TIP   Students sometimes get confused about how to pick the test points in step 3 of the procedure. Remind them that they may pick any convenient point except for the critical points that are the roots of the quadratic equation. Emphasize that we want to test one point that we have selected that is in each of the three regions.

3. Evaluate the quadratic expression at an arbitrary test point in each of the regions.

$$x^2 - 10x + 24$$

Region I: $x = 1$

$$(1)^2 - 10(1) + 24 = 1 - 10 + 24 = 15 \;>0$$

Region II: $x = 5$

$$(5)^2 - 10(5) + 24 = 25 - 50 + 24 = -1 \;<0$$

Region III: $x = 7$

$$(7)^2 - 10(7) + 24 = 49 - 70 + 24 = 3 \;>0$$

4. Determine which regions satisfy the original conditions of the quadratic inequality.

$$x^2 - 10x + 24 > 0 \text{ when } x < 4 \; or \text{ when } x > 6$$

The graph of the solution is

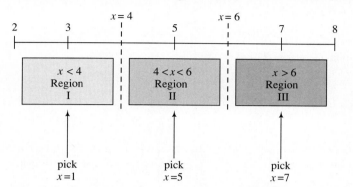

Practice Problem 1   Solve and graph $x^2 - 2x - 8 < 0$.   ∎

Example 2   Solve and graph: $2x^2 + x - 6 \leq 0$.

$$2x^2 + x - 6 = 0$$
$$(2x - 3)(x + 2) = 0$$
$$2x - 3 = 0 \quad or \quad x + 2 = \;\; 0$$
$$2x = 3 \qquad\qquad x = -2$$
$$x = \frac{3}{2} = 1.5$$

TEACHING TIP   After explaining examples 1 and 2, ask students to do the following problem as a class exercise. Solve and graph:

$$2x^2 + x - 15 \geq 0$$

Sol.: $x \leq -2.5 \; or \; x \geq 3$

The critical points are $x = -2$ and $x = 1.5$. Now we arbitrarily pick a test point in each region.

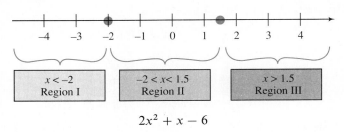

$$2x^2 + x - 6$$

Region I: $x = -3$

$$2(-3)^2 + (-3) - 6 = 18 - 3 - 6 = 9 \; \boxed{> 0}$$

Region II: $x = 0$

$$2(0)^2 + (0) - 6 = 0 + 0 - 6 = -6 \; \boxed{< 0}$$

Region III: $x = 2$

$$2(2)^2 + (2) - 6 = 8 + 2 - 6 = 4 \; \boxed{> 0}$$

Since our inequality is $\leq$ and not just $<$, we include the critical points. Thus $2x^2 + x - 6 \leq 0$ when $-2 \leq x \leq 1.5$. The graph of our solution is

Practice Problem 2   Solve: $2x^2 + 9x - 5 \geq 0$. ■

2 Sometimes the quadratic expression needs to be put in standard form. If it does not factor, use the quadratic formula.

TEACHING TIP After discussing example 3, you may want to show the students the following additional example. Solve and graph. Round your answers to the nearest tenth.

$$3x^2 - 6x + 2 < 0$$

Sol.: $x = \dfrac{-(-6) \pm \sqrt{(-6)^2 - 4(3)(2)}}{2(3)}$

$x = \dfrac{6 \pm \sqrt{12}}{6} = \dfrac{3 \pm \sqrt{3}}{3}$

on a calculator $\sqrt{3} \doteq 1.732$

$x = \dfrac{3 + \sqrt{3}}{3} \doteq 1.6 \quad x = \dfrac{3 - \sqrt{3}}{3} \doteq 0.4$

Ans.: $0.4 < x < 1.6$

Example 3   Solve: $x^2 + 4x > 6$.

First we write $x^2 + 4x - 6 > 0$. Now $x^2 + 4x - 6 = 0$ does not factor, so we use the quadratic formula to find the critical points.

$$x = \frac{-4 \pm \sqrt{4^2 - 4(1)(-6)}}{2(1)} = \frac{-4 \pm \sqrt{16 + 24}}{2}$$

$$= \frac{-4 \pm \sqrt{40}}{2} = \frac{-4 \pm 2\sqrt{10}}{2} = -2 \pm \sqrt{10}$$

Using a calculator or our table of square roots, we find that

$$-2 + \sqrt{10} = -2 + 3.162 = 1.162 \text{ or about } 1.2$$

$$-2 - \sqrt{10} = -2 - 3.162 = -5.162 \text{ or about } -5.2$$

Region I: $x = -6$

$$(-6)^2 + 4(-6) - 6 = 36 - 24 - 6 = 6 \; \boxed{> 0}$$

Region II: $x = 0$

$$(0)^2 + 4(0) - 6 = 0 + 0 - 6 = -6 \boxed{< 0}$$

Region III: $x = 2$

$$(2)^2 + 4(2) - 6 = 4 + 8 - 6 = 6 \boxed{> 0}$$

Thus $x^2 + 4x > 6$ when $x^2 + 4x - 6 > 0$, and that occurs when $x < -2 - \sqrt{10}$ or $x > -2 + \sqrt{10}$. ∎

Practice Problem 3 Solve and graph: $x^2 + 2x < 7$.

---

1. In solving a quadratic inequality, why is it necessary to find the critical points?

The critical points divide the number line into segments. All values of x in a given segment produce results that are greater than zero, or else all the values of x in a given segment produce results that are less than zero.

2. In solving a quadratic inequality what is the difference between solving a problem like $ax^2 + bx + c > 0$ and a problem like $ax^2 + bx + c \geq 0$?

Solving a problem such as $ax^2 + bx + c \geq$ indicates that the endpoints of an interval are included in the solution. The endpoints are not included when $ax^2 + bx + c > 0$.

Solve and graph.

3. $x^2 + x - 12 < 0$

$(x + 4)(x - 3) = 0$
$-4 < x < 3$

4. $x^2 + 2x - 15 < 0$

$(x + 5)(x - 3) = 0$
$-5 < x < 3$

5. $x^2 - 2x - 24 > 0$

$(x - 6)(x + 4) = 0$
$x < -4 \ or \ x > 6$

6. $x^2 - 3x - 40 > 0$

$(x + 5)(x - 8) = 0$
$x < -5 \ or \ x > 8$

7. $2x^2 + x - 3 < 0$

$(2x + 3)(x - 1) = 0$
$-\dfrac{3}{2} < x < 1$

8. $6x^2 - 5x + 1 < 0$

$(3x - 1)(2x - 1) = 0$
$\dfrac{1}{3} < x < \dfrac{1}{2}$

9. $x^2 + 7x + 10 \geq 0$

$(x + 5)(x + 2) = 0$
$x \leq -5 \ or \ x \geq -2$

10. $x^2 + 8x + 12 \geq 0$

$(x + 6)(x + 2) = 0$
$x \leq -6 \ or \ x \geq -2$

Solve.

11. $2x^2 \leq 11x + 6$

$(2x + 1)(x - 6) = 0$
$-\dfrac{1}{2} \leq x \leq 6$

12. $2x^2 \leq -13x + 7$

$(2x - 1)(x + 7) = 0$
$-7 \leq x \leq \dfrac{1}{2}$

13. $x^2 - 6x \leq -9$

$(x - 3)(x - 3) = 0$
$x = 3$

14. $x^2 - 4x \leq -4$

$(x - 2)(x - 2) = 0$
$x = 2$

15. $x^2 - 2x > 4$

$x = \dfrac{2 \pm \sqrt{20}}{2} = 1 \pm \sqrt{5}$

$1 - \sqrt{5} \ or \approx -1.2 \quad 1 + \sqrt{5} \ or \approx 3.2$
Ans. $x < (1 - \sqrt{5}) \ or \ x > (1 + \sqrt{5})$
Approx. $x < -1.2 \ or \ x > 3.2$

16. $x^2 + 6x > 8$

$x = \dfrac{-6 \pm \sqrt{68}}{2} = -3 \pm \sqrt{17}$

$-3 - \sqrt{17} \ or \approx -7.1 \quad -3 + \sqrt{17} \ or \approx 1.1$
Ans. $x < (-3 - \sqrt{17}) \ or \ x > (-3 + \sqrt{17})$
Approx. $x < -7.1 \ or \ x > 1.1$

17. $x^2 - 6x < -7$

$x = \dfrac{+6 \pm \sqrt{8}}{2} = 3 \pm \sqrt{2}$

$3 - \sqrt{2} \ or \approx 1.6 \quad 3 + \sqrt{2} \ or \approx 4.4$
Ans. $3 - \sqrt{2} < x < 3 + \sqrt{2}$
Approx. $1.6 < x < 4.4$

18. $x^2 < 2x + 1$

$x = \dfrac{2 \pm \sqrt{8}}{2} = 1 \pm \sqrt{2}$

$1 - \sqrt{2} \ or \approx -0.4 \quad 1 + \sqrt{2} \ or \approx 2.4$
Ans. $1 - \sqrt{2} < x < 1 + \sqrt{2}$
Approx. $-0.4 < x < 2.4$

19. $x^2 + x - 20 < 0$

$(x + 5)(x - 4) = 0$
$-5 < x < 4$

20. $x^2 + 3x - 28 < 0$

$(x + 7)(x - 4) = 0$
$-7 < x < 4$

21. $2x^2 + 7x - 4 \le 0$

$(2x - 1)(x + 4) = 0$

$-4 \le x \le \dfrac{1}{2}$

22. $5x^2 + 13x - 6 \le 0$

$(5x - 2)(x + 3) = 0$

$-3 \le x \le \dfrac{2}{5}$

23. $6x^2 - 5x > 6$

$(2x - 3)(3x + 2) = 0$

$x < \dfrac{-2}{3} \; or \; x > \dfrac{3}{2}$

24. $3x^2 + 17x > -10$

$(3x + 2)(x + 5) = 0$

$x < -5 \; or \; x > -\dfrac{2}{3}$

25. $4x^2 \ge 6x - 1$

$x = \dfrac{+6 \pm \sqrt{20}}{8} = \dfrac{+3 \pm \sqrt{5}}{4}$

Ans. $x \le \dfrac{3 - \sqrt{5}}{4} \; or \; x \ge \dfrac{3 + \sqrt{5}}{4}$

Approx. $x \le 0.2 \; or \; x \ge 1.3$

26. $2x^2 \ge 6x - 3$

$x = \dfrac{6 \pm \sqrt{12}}{4} = \dfrac{3 \pm \sqrt{3}}{2}$

$\dfrac{3 - \sqrt{3}}{2} \; or \; \approx 0.6 \qquad \dfrac{3 + \sqrt{3}}{2} \; or \; \approx 2.4$

Ans. $x \le \dfrac{3 - \sqrt{3}}{2} \; or \; x \ge \dfrac{3 + \sqrt{3}}{2}$

Approx. $x \le 0.6 \; or \; x \ge 2.4$

27. $-x^2 - 5x + 36 \ge 0$

$-(x^2 + 5x - 36) \ge 0$

$x^2 + 5x - 36 \le 0$

$(x + 9)(x - 4) = 0$

$-9 \le x \le 4$

28. $-x^2 - 7x + 44 \ge 0$

$-(x^2 - 7x + 44) \ge 0$

$x^2 + 7x - 44 \le 0$

$(x + 11)(x - 4) = 0$

$-11 \le x \le 4$

29. $x^2 + 3x + 8 \le 0$

$x = \dfrac{-3 \pm \sqrt{-23}}{2}$

Real no. line has no intervals

Sol.: $\varnothing$

30. $x^2 + 2x + 6 \le 0$

$x = \dfrac{-2 \pm \sqrt{-20}}{2}$

Real no. line has no intervals

Sol.: $\varnothing$

? **To Think About**

31. Verify that all values of $x < -1$ make $x^2 - 2x - 3 > 0$ by substituting $x = -5, -4, -3, -2$ into $x^2 - 2x - 3$, and find the values of the quadratic expression.

x	y
-5	32
-4	21
-3	12
-2	5

32. Verify that all values of $-1 < x < 3$ make $x^2 - 2x - 3 < 0$ by substituting $x = 0$, $x = 0.5$, $x = 1$, $x = 2$ into $x^2 - 2x - 3$, and find the values of the quadratic expression.

x	y
0	-3
0.5	-3.75
1	-4
2	-3

In problems 33 and 34, the profit of a manufacturing company is determined by the number x of units manufactured each day. **(a)** *Find when the profit is greater than zero.* **(b)** *Find the daily profit when 50 units are manufactured.* **(c)** *Find the daily profit when 60 units are manufactured.*

33. Profit $= -20(x^2 - 220x + 2400)$

$-20(x^2 - 220x + 2400) > 0$

$x^2 - 220x + 2400 < 0$

$x = \dfrac{220 \pm \sqrt{38800}}{2} \approx 208.5 \; or \; 11.5$

(a)

    $\approx 11.5 < x < 208.5$

(b) \$122,000

(c) \$144,000

34. Profit $= -25(x^2 - 280x + 4000)$

$-25(x^2 - 280x + 4000) > 0$

$x^2 - 280x + 4000 < 0$

$x = \dfrac{280 \pm \sqrt{62400}}{2} \approx 264.9 \; or \; 15.1$

(a)

    $\approx 15.1 < x < 264.9$

(b) \$187,500

(c) \$230,000

Solve.

35. $(x - 4)(x + 2)(x + 6) < 0$

$(x - 4)(x + 2)(x + 6) = 0$

$x < -6 \; or \; -2 < x < 4$

36. $(x + 5)(x - 2)(x - 3) > 0$

$(x + 5)(x - 2)(x - 3) = 0$

$x > 3 \; or \; -5 < x < 2$

Cumulative Review Problems

Graph each equation.

37. $y = \dfrac{2}{3}x - 3$

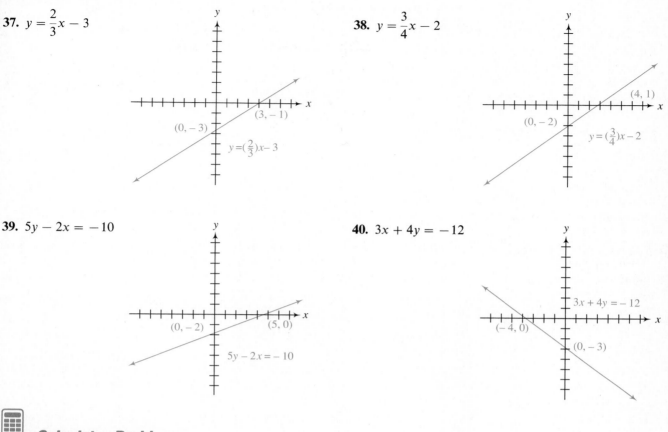

38. $y = \dfrac{3}{4}x - 2$

39. $5y - 2x = -10$

40. $3x + 4y = -12$

Calculator Problems

Solve by the quadratic formula. Round your answer to the nearest tenth.

41. $12.3x^2 + 4.9x - 2.8 > 0$
  $x > 0.3 \text{ or } x < -0.7$

42. $3.9x^2 - 6.8x - 4.6 \leq 0$
  $-0.5 \leq x \leq 2.3$

For Extra Practice Exercises, turn to page 551.

Solutions to Odd-Numbered Practice Problems

1. $x^2 - 2x - 8 < 0$
  $(x - 4)(x + 2) = 0$
  $x = 4 \qquad x = -2$

$$x^2 - 2x - 8$$

Region I $x < -2$ $x = -3$: $(-3)^2 - 2(-3) - 8 = 9 + 6 - 8 = 7 > 0$
Region II $2 < x < 4$ $x = 0$: $(0)^2 - 2(0) - 8 = 0 - 0 - 8 = -8 < 0$
Region III $x > 4$ $x = 5$: $(5)^2 - 2(5) - 8 = 25 - 10 - 8 = 7 > 0$

Thus, $x^2 - 2x - 8 < 0$ when $-2 < x < 4$.

3. $x^2 + 2x < 7$
  $x^2 + 2x - 7 < 0$
  $x^2 + 2x - 7 = 0$

$$x = \frac{-2 \pm \sqrt{(2)^2 - 4(1)(-7)}}{2(1)} = \frac{-2 \pm \sqrt{4 + 28}}{2} = \frac{-2 \pm \sqrt{32}}{2}$$

$$= \frac{-2 \pm 4\sqrt{2}}{2} = -1 \pm 2\sqrt{2}$$

When $\sqrt{2} \approx 1.414$,

$$x = -1 + 2(1.414) = -1 + 2.828 = 1.828 \quad \text{about } 1.8$$
$$x = -1 - 2(1.414) = -1 - 2.828 = -3.828 \quad \text{about } -3.8$$
$$x^2 + 2x - 7$$

Region I $\quad x < -3.8 \quad x = -5: \quad (-5)^2 + 2(-5) - 7 = 25 - 10 - 7 = 8 > 0$
Region II $\quad -3.8 < x < 1.8 \quad x = 0: \quad (0)^2 + 2(0) - 7 = 0 + 0 - 7 = -7 < 0$
Region III $\quad x > 1.8 \quad x = 3: \quad (3)^2 + 2(3) - 7 = 9 + 6 - 7 = 8 > 0$

Thus, $x^2 + 2x < 7$ when $x^2 + 2x - 7 < 0$ when $-1 - 2\sqrt{2} < x < -1 + 2\sqrt{2}$.

Answer to Even-Numbered Practice Problem

2. $x \leq -5 \quad or \quad x \geq 0.5$

□ After studying this section, you will be able to:

1 *Graph a linear inequality in two variables*

2 *Graph a linear absolute value inequality*

10.5 LINEAR INEQUALITIES IN TWO VARIABLES

1 A linear inequality is similar to a linear equation, but the equals sign is replaced by $<$, $\leq$, $>$, or $\geq$. The graph of a linear inequality is a half-plane that lies above or below a line, and includes the line if the inequality contains $\leq$ or $\geq$ symbols.

> **Procedure for Graphing Linear Inequalities**
>
> 1. Replace the inequality symbol by an equals sign. This equation will be a boundary for the desired region.
> 2. Graph the line obtained in step 1. Use a dashed line if the original inequality contains $<$ or $>$ symbols. Use a solid line if the original inequality contains $\leq$ or $\geq$ symbols.
> 3. Choose a test point that does not lie on the boundary line. Substitute the coordinates into the original inequality. If you obtain an inequality that is true, shade the region on the side of the line containing the test point. If you obtain a false inequality, shade the region on the opposite side of the line from the test point.

If the boundary line does not pass through $(0, 0)$, that is usually a good test point to use.

TEACHING TIP Students will sometimes raise questions about example 1 and step 3 of the solution. They sometimes wonder if they have to pick $(0, 0)$ as the test point. Remind them that they may pick any test point that is not on the line. In fact, some students like to pick two test points, one above the line and one below. That way one point will fail the test and the other point will not. This gives further assurance that the correct side of the line is being shaded in.

Example 1 Graph: $y < 2x + 3$.

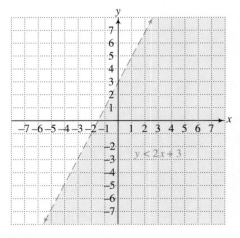

1. The boundary line is $y = 2x + 3$.
2. Graph $y = 2x + 3$ using a dashed line because the inequality contains $<$.

3. Since the line does not pass through $(0, 0)$, we can use it as a test point. Substituting $(0, 0)$ into $y < 2x + 3$, we have

$$0 < 2(0) + 3$$
$$0 < 3$$

This inequality is true. We therefore shade the region on the same side of the line as $(0, 0)$. See the sketch. The solution is the shaded region *not including* the dashed line. ■

Practice Problem 1   Graph: $y > 3x + 1$.   ■

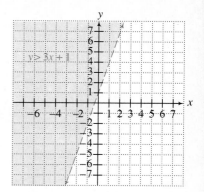

Example 2   Graph: $3x + 2y \geq 4$.

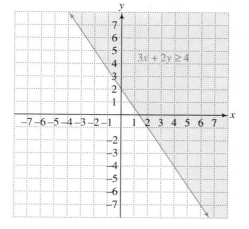

1. The boundary line is $3x + 2y = 4$.

2. Graph the boundary line with a solid line because the inequality contains $\geq$.

3. Since the line does not pass through $(0, 0)$, we can use it as a test point. Substituting $(0, 0)$ into $3x + 2y \geq 4$ gives

$$3(0) + 2(0) \geq 4$$
$$0 + 0 \geq 4$$
$$0 \geq 4$$

This inequality is false. We therefore shade the region on the opposite side of the line from $(0, 0)$. See the sketch. The solution is the shaded region *including* the boundary line.   ■

Practice Problem 2   Graph: $-4x + 5y \leq -10$.   ■

Example 3   Graph: $4x - y < 0$.

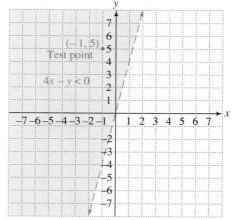

1. The boundary line is $4x - y = 0$.

2. Graph the boundary line with a dashed line.

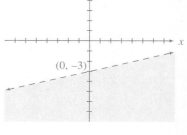

TEACHING TIP   After explaining examples 1 and 2, ask students to do the following problem as classwork. Graph $3y - x + 9 < 0$.

Sol.:

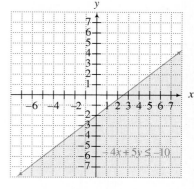

3. Since $(0, 0)$ lies on the line, we cannot use it as a test point. We may choose any other point. Let's pick $(-1, 5)$. Substituting $(-1, 5)$ into $4x - y < 0$ gives

$$4(-1) - 5 < 0$$
$$-4 - 5 < 0$$
$$-9 < 0$$

This is true. We therefore shade the same side of the boundary line as $(-1, 5)$. See the sketch. The solution is the shaded region above the dashed line but *not including* the dashed line. ■

Practice Problem 3   Graph: $3y + x < 0$. ■

2 **Example 4**   Graph: $|x| < 2$.

From Section 10.3 we know that $|x| < 2$ is equivalent to $-2 < x < 2$. On the x-axis we graph this as

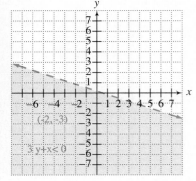

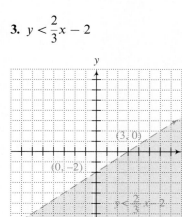

If we extend our graph to include the y-axis, then $-2 < x < 2$ for any value of y. We draw a dashed line for $x = 2$ and $x = -2$. The shaded region in this sketch is our answer. ■

Practice Problem 4   Graph: $|x - 2| < 5$. ■

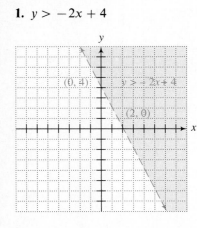

EXERCISES 10.5

Graph each region.

1. $y > -2x + 4$

2. $y > -3x + 2$

3. $y < \dfrac{2}{3}x - 2$

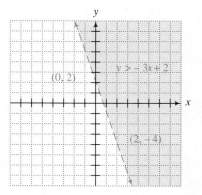

4. $y < \dfrac{3}{4}x - 3$

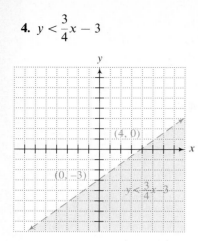

5. $y \le -\dfrac{3}{5}x + 1$

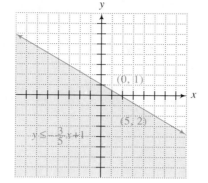

6. $y \le -\dfrac{2}{3}x + 4$

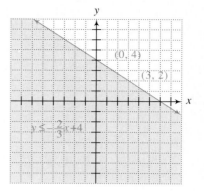

7. $-x + 2y \le 10$

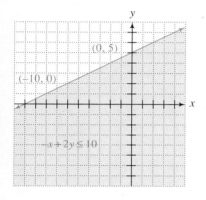

8. $-x + 3y \le 12$

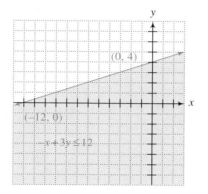

9. $y < -2x$

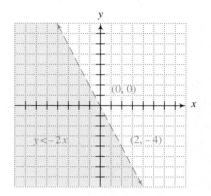

10. $y > -3x$

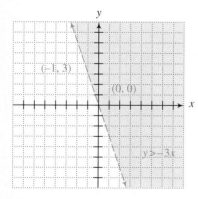

11. $3x - 2y \ge 0$

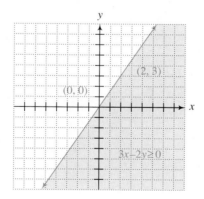

12. $4x - 3y \ge 0$

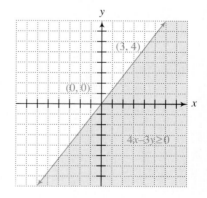

To Think About

13. When we graph the inequality $3x - 2y \ge 0$ in problem 11, why can't we use $(0, 0)$ as a test point?

Pt. $(0, 0)$ is on the line

14. When we graph the inequality $4x - 3y \ge 0$ in problem 12, why can't we use $(0, 0)$ as a test point?

Pt. $(0, 0)$ is on the line

Graph each inequality in the Cartesian plane.

15. $|x + 1| < 3$
$-4 < x < 2$

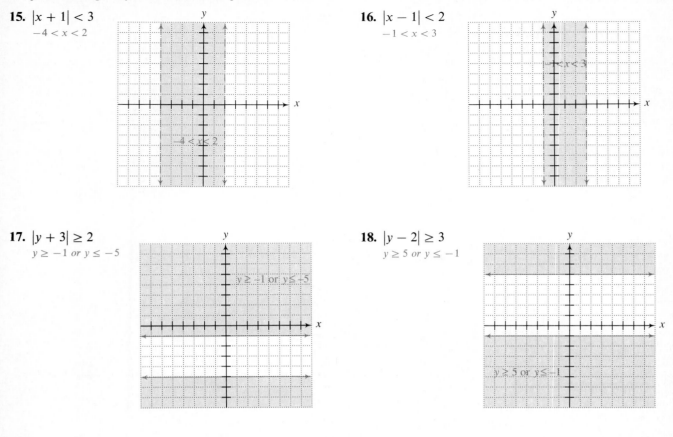

16. $|x - 1| < 2$
$-1 < x < 3$

17. $|y + 3| \geq 2$
$y \geq -1 \ or \ y \leq -5$

18. $|y - 2| \geq 3$
$y \geq 5 \ or \ y \leq -1$

? **To Think About**

19. What *one* region should be shaded to satisfy the inequalities $x + y \leq 3$, $x \geq 0$, and $y \geq 0$?

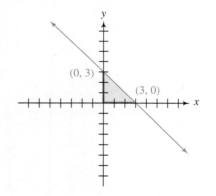

20. What *one* region should be shaded to satisfy the inequalities $x \geq 1$, $y \geq 2$, $x \leq 4$, and $y \leq 5$?

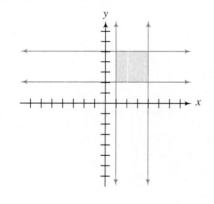

Cumulative Review Problems

Determine if each of the following equations determines a circle, ellipse, parabola or hyperbola.

21. $x^2 + y^2 = 25$
Circle

22. $y = x^2 + 2$
Parabola

23. $\dfrac{x^2}{9} + \dfrac{y^2}{4} = 1$
Ellipse

24. $\dfrac{x^2}{25} - \dfrac{y^2}{16} = 1$
Hyperbola

For Extra Practice Exercises, turn to page 552.

1. The boundary line is $y = 3x + 1$. We use a dashed line since the $>$ symbol is present. Substituting $(0, 0)$ into $y > 3x + 1$ gives $0 > 1$, which is false. Thus, we shade on the opposite side of the boundary from $(0, 0)$.

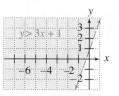

3. The boundary line is $3y + x = 0$. We use a dashed line. We cannot use $(0, 0)$ to test the inequality, let's pick $(-2, -3)$. Substituting $(-2, -3)$ into $3y + x < 0$ yields $-11 < 0$, which is true. Therefore, we shade on the same side of the line as $(-2, -3)$.

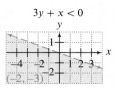

Answers to Even-Numbered Practice Problems

2. $-4x + 5y \le -10$

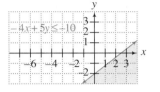

4. $|x - 2| < 5$

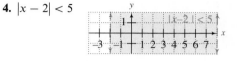

10.6 SYSTEMS OF INEQUALITIES

After studying this section, you will be able to:

1 *Graph a second-degree inequality in two variables*

2 *Graph a system of inequalities in two variables*

1 Second-Degree Inequalities

We can use the same procedure as in Section 10.5 to graph a second-degree inequality such as $\dfrac{x^2}{9} + \dfrac{y^2}{16} < 1$.

Example 1 Graph the region: $\dfrac{x^2}{9} + \dfrac{y^2}{16} < 1$.

1. Replace the inequality by an equal sign. The boundary line is $\dfrac{x^2}{9} + \dfrac{y^2}{16} = 1$, which is an ellipse with center at $(0, 0)$, $a = 3$, and $b = 4$.

2. Graph the boundary using a dashed line because the inequality contains $<$.

3. We can use $(0, 0)$ as a test point because the curve does not pass through the origin. Substituting $(0, 0)$ in $\dfrac{x^2}{9} + \dfrac{y^2}{16} < 1$ gives

$$\frac{0}{9} + \frac{0}{16} < 1$$

$$0 + 0 < 1$$

$$0 < 1$$

which is true. Thus, we shade the interior of the curve. See the sketch.

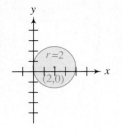

TEACHING TIP After
discussing examples 1 and 2,
ask students to do the
following problem for
classwork. Graph

$$\frac{y^2}{36} - \frac{x^2}{9} \leq 1$$

Sol.:

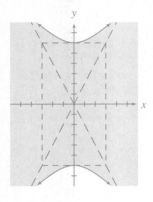

Practice Problem 1   Graph the region: $(x - 2)^2 + y^2 \leq 4$.   ▪

Example 2   Graph: $\frac{x^2}{9} - \frac{y^2}{25} \geq 1$.

1. Replace the inequality by an equal sign. The boundary line is a horizontal hyperbola with center at $(0, 0)$, $a = 3$, and $b = 5$. It has two branches, one opening to the right, the other to the left.

2. Graph the boundary with a solid line.

3. Test the inequality with $(0, 0)$.

$$\frac{x^2}{9} - \frac{y^2}{25} \geq 1$$

$$\frac{0}{9} - \frac{0}{25} \geq 1$$

$$0 \geq 1 \qquad \text{False}$$

Thus, we shade the other side of each branch of the boundary line from $(0, 0)$. The graph is the shaded region and the boundary lines in the sketch.

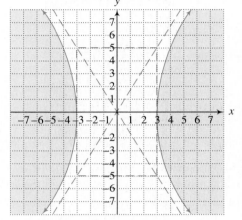

Practice Problem 2   Graph the region: $\frac{x^2}{25} - \frac{y^2}{16} > 1$.

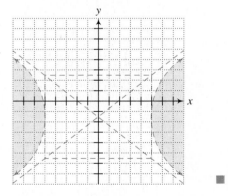

Example 3   Graph: $y > (x - 2)^2 - 4$.

1. The boundary line is the parabola $y = (x - 2)^2 - 4$, which opens upward and has a vertex at $(2, -4)$.

2. Since the inequality contains $>$, we use a dashed line.

3. The parabola passes through $(0, 0)$, so we select another test point, one not on the boundary line. We choose $(5, -5)$, which is clearly below the boundary line.

$$y > (x - 2)^2 - 4$$
$$-5 > (5 - 2)^2 - 4$$
$$-5 > 9 - 4$$
$$-5 > 5 \qquad \text{False}$$

Thus we shade above the boundary line. The shaded region lies on the opposite side of the parabola from $(5, -5)$. The solution is shown in the sketch.

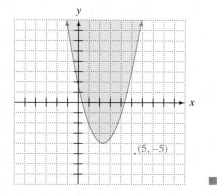

Practice Problem 3 Graph the region: $y > (x + 1)^2 - 3$. ∎

▣ Systems of Inequalities

The solution to a system of inequalities is the intersection of the solution sets of the individual inequalities.

Example 4 Graph the solution of:

$$y \leq -3x + 2$$
$$-2x + y \geq -1$$

We first graph each inequality separately. The graph of $y \leq -3x + 2$ is the region below the line $y = -3x + 2$ and the line itself. The graph of $-2x + y \geq -1$ is the region above $-2x + y = -1$ and the line itself. The graph of the intersection of these two graphs is the area that is common to both graphs.

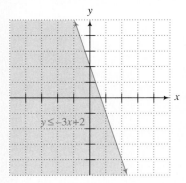

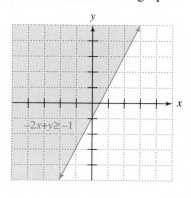

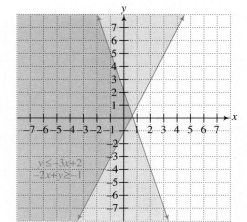

TEACHING TIP After discussing example 4, ask students to do the following problem for classwork. Graph the solution of

$$2y + 4 \leq x$$
$$2x + y \leq -2$$

Sol.:

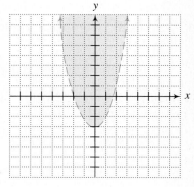

TEACHING TIP After
discussing example 5, ask
students to do the following
problem for classwork. Graph
the solution of

$$y - 3 \geq (x - 2)^2$$

$$y - 5 \leq 2x$$

Sol.:

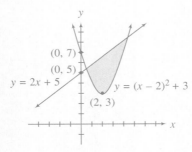

Practice Problem 4   Graph the region of the solution of

$$-2x + y \leq -3$$

$$x + 2y \geq 4$$

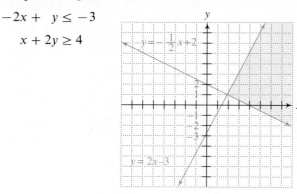

Example 5   Graph the solution of

$$-x + y \leq 3$$

$$x^2 + y^2 \leq 25$$

The graph of $-x + y = 3$ is a straight line. The region $-x + y \leq 3$ is the line itself and the region below. The graph of $x^2 + y^2 = 25$ is a circle of radius 5 with center at the origin. The shaded region of $x^2 + y^2 \leq 25$ is the region *inside* the circle. Using a test point such as $(0, 0)$ shows that $0 + 0 \leq 25$ is true. Therefore, to shade the region described by $x^2 + y^2 \leq 25$, we shade *inside* the circle and the circle itself. The solution to the system is the region common to both graphs.

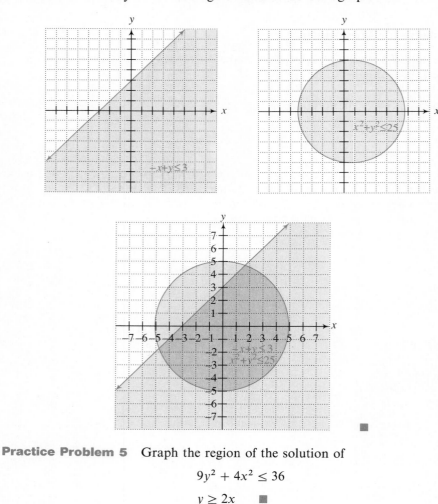

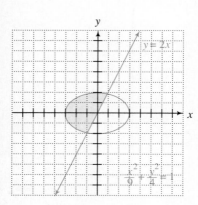

Practice Problem 5   Graph the region of the solution of

$$9y^2 + 4x^2 \leq 36$$

$$y \geq 2x$$

Graph each region.

1. $x^2 + y^2 \leq 49$ Circle $r = 7$

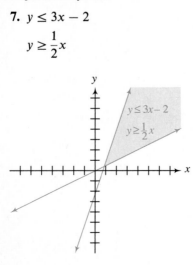

2. $x^2 + y^2 \geq 4$ Circle $r = 2$

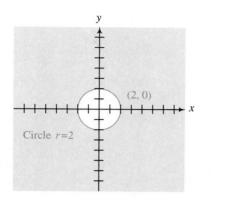

3. $\dfrac{x^2}{4} + \dfrac{y^2}{49} \leq 1$ Ellipse $C(0, 0)$

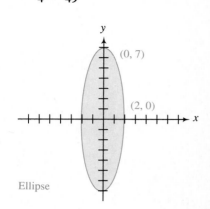

4. $\dfrac{x^2}{25} - \dfrac{y^2}{4} \geq 1$ Hyperbola

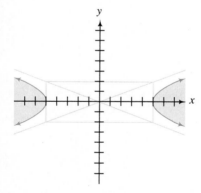

5. $y < (x + 3)^2 - 2$

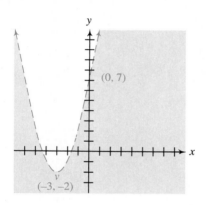

6. $y > (x - 2)^2 + 5$

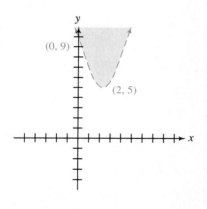

Graph each system.

7. $y \leq 3x - 2$
$\quad y \geq \dfrac{1}{2}x$

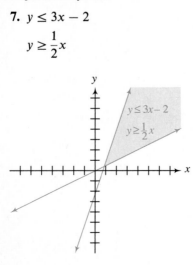

8. $y \geq 2x - 3$
$\quad y \leq \dfrac{2}{3}x$

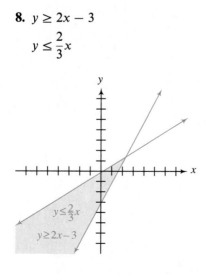

9. $y < (x - 2)^2 - 4$
$\quad y > -2x - 3$

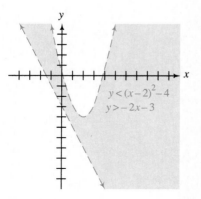

10. $y < (x + 3)^2 - 2$

$y > \dfrac{1}{2}x - 4$

11. $\dfrac{x^2}{9} + \dfrac{y^2}{16} \leq 1$

$2x + y \leq 2$

12. $\dfrac{x^2}{4} + \dfrac{y^2}{25} \leq 1$

$x + 3y \leq 3$

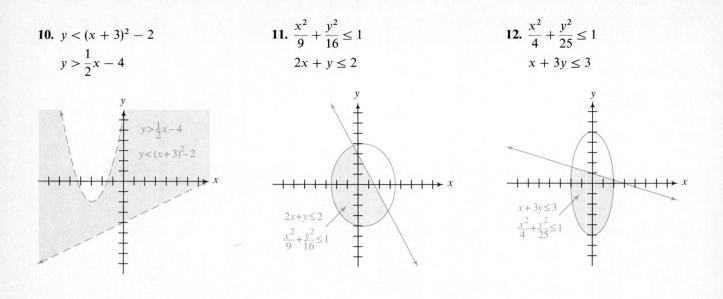

? To Think About

Coast Guard personnel are preparing for a search and recovery mission on a disabled boat reported to be missing. Draw a sketch of the region if the north, east, south, and west directions are imposed on the x, y axes if:

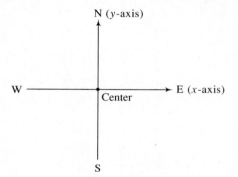

Graph each system.

13. The search must be within a 5-mile radius $(x^2 + y^2 < 25)$ of the search center and must be less than 3 miles north $(y < 3)$ of the search center.

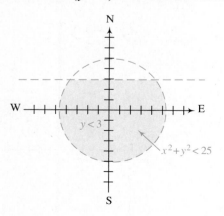

14. The search must be south of the parabolic shape of how objects float in the tide $(y < 3 - 2x^2)$ and must be less than 2 miles east of the search center $(x < 2)$.

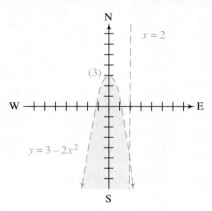

Cumulative Review Problems

15. Solve for x: $\dfrac{8}{x-1} - 1 = \dfrac{x}{x-2}$.

$8(x-2) - (x-1)(x-2) = x(x-1)$
$0 = 2x^2 - 12x + 18$
$x = 3$

16. Solve for w: $H = \dfrac{2}{3}(w - 4x)$.

$3H = 2w - 8x$
$w = \dfrac{3H + 8x}{2}$

Calculator Problems

Find the values of (x, y) to the nearest tenth where the ellipse boundary and straight-line boundary intersect in the following systems.

17. $\dfrac{x^2}{9} + \dfrac{y^2}{16} \le 1$ $\quad$ $(-0.9, 3.8)$
$\qquad\qquad\qquad\quad$ $(2.3, -2.6)$

$\quad$ $2x + y \le 2$

18. $\dfrac{x^2}{4} + \dfrac{y^2}{25} \le 1$ $\quad$ $(2.0, 0.3)$
$\qquad\qquad\qquad\quad$ $(-1.9, 1.6)$

$\quad$ $x + 3y \le 3$

For Extra Practice Exercises, turn to page 552.

Solutions to Odd-Numbered Practice Problems

1. The boundary line is the circle defined by $(x-2)^2 + y^2 = 4$, which has center at $(2, 0)$ and radius 2. Since the curve passes through $(0, 0)$, we select a different test point, such as $(1, 1)$, which we can clearly see is inside the circle. Testing it, we have

$$(1-2)^2 + (1)^2 < 4$$
$$(-1)^2 + 1 < 4$$
$$2 < 4$$

Because $2 < 4$ is true, we shade the interior of the circle. The solution is the circle itself and the shaded region:

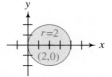

3. The parabola defined by $y = (x+1)^2 - 3$ has a vertex at $(-1, -3)$ and opens upward. We draw a dashed line because of the $>$ symbol.

$\qquad$ If we use $(0, 0)$ as a test point, $y > (x+1)^2 - 3$ becomes $0 > (0+1)^2 - 3$, $0 > -2$, which is true. So we shade on the $(0, 0)$ side of the curve.

5. $y \ge 2x$: We want the region above the line $y = 2x$ and in the line itself. The boundary is $9y^2 + 4x^2 = 36$.

$$\frac{4x^2}{36} + \frac{9y^2}{36} = 1$$
$$\frac{x^2}{9} + \frac{y^2}{4} = 1$$

This is an ellipse with center at $(0, 0)$ and $a = 3$, $b = 2$. The point $(0, 0)$ satisfies the inequality $9y^2 + 4x^2 \le 36$, so we want to shade inside the ellipse. The final solution is the shaded region.

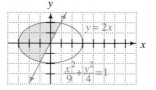

2. $\dfrac{x^2}{25} - \dfrac{y^2}{16} > 1$

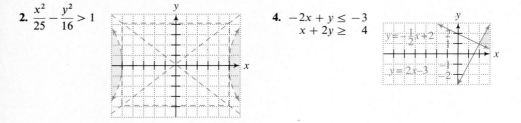

4. $-2x + y \le -3$
$x + 2y \ge 4$

EXTRA PRACTICE: EXERCISES

Section 10.1

Insert the symbol < or > between each pair of numbers.

1. -8 _____ -3 $\quad <$ **2.** -2 _____ -7 $\quad >$

3. -5 _____ 3 $\quad <$ **4.** 4 _____ -2 $\quad >$

5. -4.8 _____ -4.81 $\quad >$

6. -3.198 _____ -3.20 $\quad >$

7. $(12 - 7)$ _____ $(4 - 6)$ $\quad >$

8. $(-11 - 3)$ _____ $(-2 - 3)$ $\quad <$

9. $-\dfrac{3}{7}$ _____ $-\dfrac{4}{7}$ $\quad >$ **10.** 6.2 _____ 6.245 $\quad <$

11. $-\dfrac{12}{17}$ _____ $\dfrac{-9}{14}$ $\quad <$ **12.** $-\dfrac{27}{5}$ _____ $-\dfrac{21}{4}$ $\quad <$

Solve for x and graph your solution.

13. $4 - 3x < -2$ $\quad x > 2$

14. $2x - 7 \le 3x$ $\quad x \ge -7$

15. $2(x - 3) < 8$ $\quad x < 7$

16. $3x - 5 \le -4 + 2(x - 1)$ $\quad x \le -1$

Solve for x.

17. $4x - 5(x + 3) \ge 2x - 3$ $\quad x \le -4$

18. $1 + 6(x + 2) \ge -3(2 - x) + 1$ $\quad x \ge -6$

19. $\dfrac{1}{3}x < \dfrac{2}{5}(x + 2)$ $\quad x > -12$

20. $\dfrac{1}{2}x < \dfrac{3}{4}(x + 4)$ $\quad x > -12$

21. $x - \dfrac{1}{2} \le \dfrac{x}{3} + 7$ $\quad x \le \dfrac{45}{4}$

22. $2x - 3(x - 2) \le \dfrac{1}{2}(x + 1)$ $\quad x \ge \dfrac{11}{3}$

23. $\dfrac{x}{5} - \dfrac{2}{3}x + \dfrac{1}{2} \ge \dfrac{1}{3}(x - 4)$ $\quad x \le \dfrac{55}{24}$

24. $\dfrac{2}{3}(x - 3) + \dfrac{1}{4}x + 1 \ge 16 - \dfrac{1}{2}x$ $\quad x \ge 12$

25. $0.2x - 1 < 0.3(4 - x)$ $\quad x < \dfrac{22}{5}$

26. $\dfrac{2x}{5} - \dfrac{x}{3} \le 1$ $\quad x \le 15$

27. $-4(3 - x) \ge (-6 + x)2$ $\quad x \ge 0$

28. $0.1x - 0.2(x + 1) < 0.4x + 3$ $\quad x > -\dfrac{32}{5}$

29. $\dfrac{2(x - 1)}{3} - \dfrac{3(x + 1)}{2} \le 1$ $\quad x \ge -\dfrac{19}{5}$

Describe the situation with a linear inequality, and then solve it.

30. A truck driver earns \$100 per week plus \$5 for each package he delivers. How many deliveries must he make per week to earn at least \$1140 per month? (Assume 4 weeks in a month.)

31. A waiter earns \$3 per hour plus an average of \$5 for every table he serves. To earn more than \$415 for a 35-hour week, how many tables will he need to serve?

13.
14.
15.
16.

30. He must deliver at least 37 packages.

31. Number of tables must be greater than 62.

Section 10.2

Graph the values of x that satisfy the conditions given.

1. $4 < x$ *and* $x < 7$

2. $2 < x$ *and* $x < 5$

3. $4 < x \le 6.5$

4. $0 \le x < 2.5$

5. $x > 3$ *or* $x < -4$

6. $x > 7$ *or* $x < -1$

7. $x + 2 \ge 6$ *or* $x - 2 < -4$

8. $x + 5 > 7$ *or* $x - 3 \le -8$

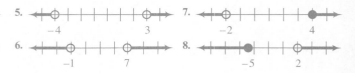

Solve the compound inequality.

9. $x + 2 < 6$ *and* $x - 3 < -4$ $x < -1$

10. $x - 4 > -6$ *and* $2x + 3 < 7$ $-2 < x < 2$

11. $2x - 6 \geq 0$ *and* $3x - 2 \leq 5$ No sol. $\varnothing$

12. $5x - 8 \geq 2$ *and* $4x - 9 \leq -1$ $x = 2$

13. $-3x - 2 < 4$ *or* $5x + 3 < 13$ All real numbers

14. $2x - 6 < -12$ *or* $5x + 2 \geq 7$ $x < -3 \text{ or } x \geq 1$

15. $5x - 6 < 14$ *and* $6x + 7 < 1$ $x < -1$

16. $7x + 3 \geq 13$ *and* $2x + 9 \geq 21$ $x \geq 6$

17. $6x - 11 < 7$ *and* $2x + 3 > 11$ No sol. $\varnothing$

18. $2x + 7 < 5$ *and* $3x - 3 > -5$ No sol. $\varnothing$

Section 10.3

Solve.

1. $|x| \geq 9$ $x \geq 9 \text{ or } x \leq -9$

2. $|x| > 8$ $x > 8 \text{ or } x < -8$

3. $|x| < 4$ $-4 < x < 4$

4. $|x| \leq 7$ $-7 \leq x \leq 7$

5. $|x + 6| < 9$ $-15 < x < 3$

6. $|x + 10| < 3$ $-13 < x < -7$

7. $|x + 2| \leq 16$ $-18 \leq x \leq 14$

8. $|x + 3| \leq 14$ $-17 \leq x \leq 11$

9. $|2x - 8| \leq 10$ $-1 \leq x \leq 9$

10. $|3x - 5| \leq 10$ $-\dfrac{5}{3} \leq x \leq 5$

11. $\left|x + \dfrac{3}{5}\right| \leq 4$ $-\dfrac{23}{5} \leq x \leq \dfrac{17}{5}$

12. $\left|x + \dfrac{2}{3}\right| \leq 6$ $-\dfrac{20}{3} \leq x \leq \dfrac{16}{3}$

13. $|-2 + 3(x - 1)| \leq 5$ $0 \leq x \leq \dfrac{10}{3}$

14. $|-2 + 4(x - 1)| \leq 6$ $0 \leq x \leq 3$

15. $\left|\dfrac{2x - 3}{2}\right| < 4$ $-\dfrac{5}{2} < x < \dfrac{11}{2}$

16. $\left|\dfrac{3x - 1}{3}\right| < 3$ $-\dfrac{8}{3} < x < \dfrac{10}{3}$

17. $|x| > 8$ $x > 8 \text{ or } x < -8$

18. $|x| \geq 6$ $x \geq 6 \text{ or } x \leq -6$

19. $|x + 2| \geq 5$ $x \geq 3 \text{ or } x \leq -7$

20. $|x + 4| \geq 11$ $x \geq 7 \text{ or } x \leq -15$

21. $|3x - 5| \geq 7$ $x \geq 4 \text{ or } x \leq -\dfrac{2}{3}$

22. $|4x - 3| \geq 13$ $x \geq 4 \text{ or } x \leq -\dfrac{5}{2}$

23. $\left|2 + \dfrac{1}{2}x\right| > 5$ $x > 6 \text{ or } x < -14$

24. $\left|3 + \dfrac{1}{4}x\right| > 3$ $x > 0 \text{ or } x < -24$

25. $\left|\dfrac{1}{3}x - \dfrac{1}{6}\right| \geq 3$ $x \geq \dfrac{19}{2} \text{ or } x \leq \dfrac{-17}{2}$

26. $\left|\dfrac{1}{4}x - \dfrac{1}{8}\right| \geq 2$ $x \geq \dfrac{17}{2} \text{ or } x \leq \dfrac{-15}{2}$

27. $|6 - 5x| \geq 2$ $x \leq \dfrac{4}{5} \text{ or } x \geq \dfrac{8}{5}$

28. $|8 - 3x| \geq 5$ $x \leq 1 \text{ or } x \geq \dfrac{13}{3}$

29. $\left|\dfrac{3}{4}(x - 5)\right| > 4$ $x > \dfrac{31}{3} \text{ or } x < \dfrac{-1}{3}$

30. $\left|\dfrac{3}{5}(x - 4)\right| > 3$ $x > 9 \text{ or } x < -1$

Section 10.4

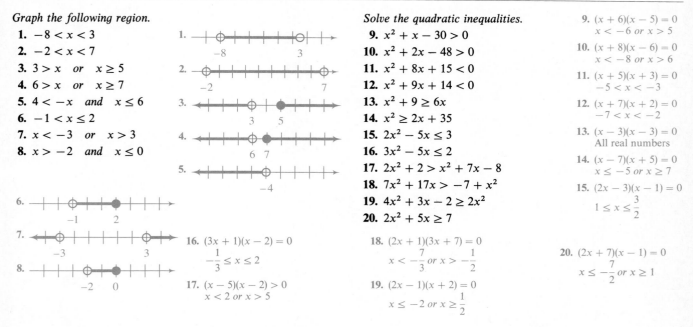

Graph the following region.

1. $-8 < x < 3$

2. $-2 < x < 7$

3. $3 > x$ *or* $x \geq 5$

4. $6 > x$ *or* $x \geq 7$

5. $4 < -x$ *and* $x \leq 6$

6. $-1 < x \leq 2$

7. $x < -3$ *or* $x > 3$

8. $x > -2$ *and* $x \leq 0$

16. $(3x + 1)(x - 2) = 0$
$-\dfrac{1}{3} \leq x \leq 2$

17. $(x - 5)(x - 2) > 0$
$x < 2 \text{ or } x > 5$

Solve the quadratic inequalities.

9. $x^2 + x - 30 > 0$

10. $x^2 + 2x - 48 > 0$

11. $x^2 + 8x + 15 < 0$

12. $x^2 + 9x + 14 < 0$

13. $x^2 + 9 \geq 6x$

14. $x^2 \geq 2x + 35$

15. $2x^2 - 5x \leq 3$

16. $3x^2 - 5x \leq 2$

17. $2x^2 + 2 > x^2 + 7x - 8$

18. $7x^2 + 17x > -7 + x^2$

19. $4x^2 + 3x - 2 \geq 2x^2$

20. $2x^2 + 5x \geq 7$

18. $(2x + 1)(3x + 7) = 0$
$x < -\dfrac{7}{3} \text{ or } x > -\dfrac{1}{2}$

19. $(2x - 1)(x + 2) = 0$
$x \leq -2 \text{ or } x \geq \dfrac{1}{2}$

9. $(x + 6)(x - 5) = 0$
$x < -6 \text{ or } x > 5$

10. $(x + 8)(x - 6) = 0$
$x < -8 \text{ or } x > 6$

11. $(x + 5)(x + 3) = 0$
$-5 < x < -3$

12. $(x + 7)(x + 2) = 0$
$-7 < x < -2$

13. $(x - 3)(x - 3) = 0$
All real numbers

14. $(x - 7)(x + 5) = 0$
$x \leq -5 \text{ or } x \geq 7$

15. $(2x - 3)(x - 1) = 0$
$1 \leq x \leq \dfrac{3}{2}$

20. $(2x + 7)(x - 1) = 0$
$x \leq -\dfrac{7}{2} \text{ or } x \geq 1$

21. $36x - 6x^2 < 0$ **21.** $6x(6-x)=0$ **22.** $5x(5-x)=0$

$\qquad\qquad\qquad\qquad x < 0 \ or \ x > 6 \qquad x < 0 \ or \ x > 5$

22. $25x - 5x^2 < 0$

23. $-3x^2 + 11x + 20 > 0$ **23.** $-(3x^2-11x-20)>0$

24. $-4x^2 - 9x > 2$ $\qquad\qquad 3x^2 - 11x - 20 < 0$

25. $5x^2 \leq 2 - 9x$ $\qquad\qquad (3x+4)(x-5)=0$

26. $3x^2 > 7x + 6$ $\qquad\qquad\qquad -\dfrac{4}{3} < x < 5$

27. $6x^2 \geq 5x - 1$

28. $15x^2 - 4 < -17x$

24. $-(4x^2 + 9x + 2) > 0$ **25.** $(5x-1)(x+2)=0$ **26.** $(3x+2)(x-3)=0$ **27.** $(3x-1)(2x-1)=0$ **28.** $(3x+4)(5x-1)=0$ **31.** $(8x-3)(4x+5)=0$

$\quad 4x^2 + 9x + 2 < 0 \qquad\quad -2 \leq x \leq \dfrac{1}{5} \qquad\quad x > 3 \ or \ x < -\dfrac{2}{3} \qquad\quad x \leq \dfrac{1}{3} \ or \ x \geq \dfrac{1}{2} \qquad\quad -\dfrac{4}{3} < x < \dfrac{1}{5} \qquad\quad -\dfrac{5}{4} \leq x \leq \dfrac{3}{8}$

$\quad (4x+1)(x+2) < 0$

$\quad -2 < x < -\dfrac{1}{4}$

29. $9x^2 + 40 \geq 42x$ **29.** $(3x-10)(3x-4)=0$

30. $3(4x^2 + 2) - 8x \geq -25x$ $\qquad x \leq \dfrac{4}{3} \ or \ x \geq \dfrac{10}{3}$

31. $4x(8x + 7) \leq 15$

32. $x^2 - 24 \leq 4(x + 2)$ **30.** $(3x+2)(4x+3)=0$

Solve. $\qquad\qquad x \leq -\dfrac{3}{4} \ or \ x \geq -\dfrac{2}{3}$

33. $(2-x)(x+3)(x+4) < 0$ $-4 < x < -3 \ or \ x > 2$

34. $(x+6)(x-4)(1-x) > 0$ $x < -6 \ or \ 1 < x < 4$

32. $(x-8)(x+4)=0$

$\qquad -4 \leq x \leq 8$

Section 10.5

Graph the solution set of each linear inequality in two variables.

1. $2y < -x - 2$

2. $y \geq x + 1$

3. $2y < 3x - 6$

4. $4y \geq -3x + 12$

5. $x + y \geq 7$

6. $2x + y \leq 11$

7. $2x - y \geq -10$

8. $3x - y \leq 4$

9. $x \leq 6$

10. $x \geq -2$

Section 10.6

Graph each quadratic inequality in two variables.

1. $y \geq (x-2)^2 + 1$

2. $y \leq (x-3)^2 + 2$

3. $x^2 + (y-2)^2 \leq 36$

4. $(x+3)^2 + y^2 \leq 25$

5. $\dfrac{x^2}{9} - \dfrac{y^2}{4} \leq 1$

6. $\dfrac{y^2}{25} - \dfrac{x^2}{4} \geq 1$

7. $x^2 + 9y^2 \leq 9$

8. $25x^2 + y^2 \geq 25$

Graph the solution sets of each system of equations.

9. $3x - y > 0$

$\quad x < y$

10. $4y - 3x < 12$

$\quad 2x - y < 0$

11. $2x - y \leq 1$

$\quad 3x + y \geq 4$

12. $4x - y \leq 3$

$\quad x + 2y \leq 6$

13. $x + y \leq 5$

$\quad y \leq (x+3)^2 - 2$

14. $x + y \leq 6$

$\quad y \leq (x-1)^2 - 3$

15. $\dfrac{x^2}{4} + \dfrac{y^2}{9} \geq 1$

$\quad y \leq \dfrac{2}{3}x - 1$

16. $\dfrac{x^2}{25} + \dfrac{y^2}{4} \geq 1$

$\quad y \leq \dfrac{3}{4}x - 2$

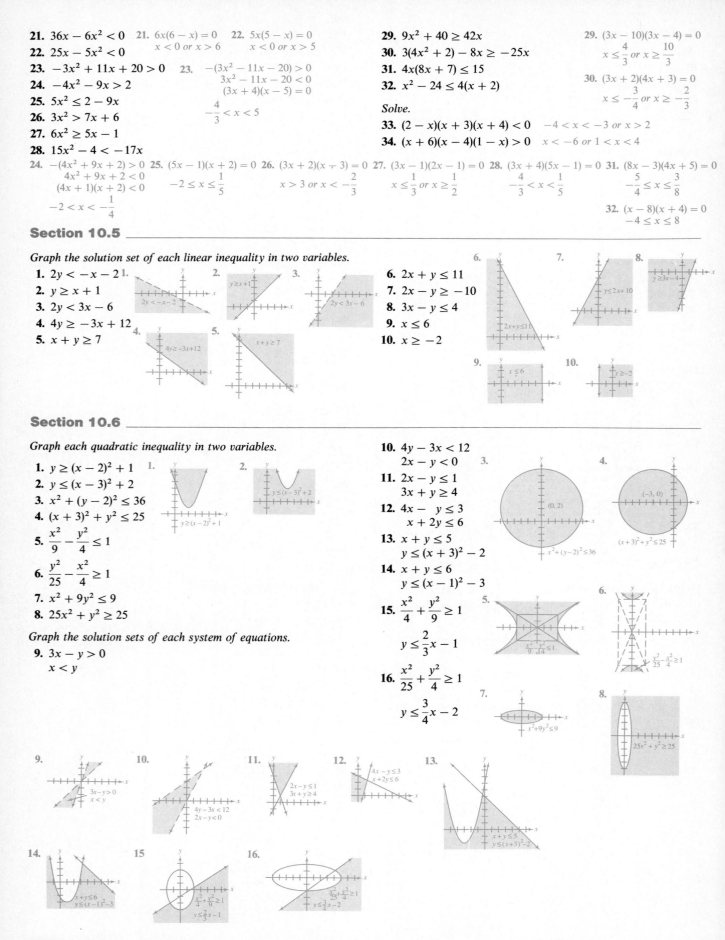

552   Chap. 10   Inequalities

CHAPTER ORGANIZER

Topic	Procedure	Examples
Solving linear inequalities, p. 517	**1.** If $a < b$, then for all real numbers a, b, c, $$a + c < b + c \quad \text{and} \quad a - c < b - c$$ **2.** If $a < b$, then for all real numbers a, b when $c > 0$, $$ac < bc \quad \text{and} \quad \frac{a}{c} < \frac{b}{c}$$ Multiplying or dividing both sides of an inequality by a positive number does NOT reverse the inequality. **3.** If $a < b$, then for all real numbers a, b when $c < 0$, $$ac > bc \quad \text{and} \quad \frac{a}{c} > \frac{b}{c}$$ Multiplying or dividing both sides of an inequality REVERSES THE DIRECTION of the inequality symbol.	Solve and graph: $3(2x - 4) + 1 \geq 7$. $$6x - 12 + 1 \geq 7$$ $$6x - 11 \geq 7$$ $$6x \geq 18$$ $$x \geq 3$$ Solve and graph: $\frac{1}{4}(x + 3) \leq \frac{1}{3}(x - 2)$ $$\frac{1}{4}x + \frac{3}{4} \leq \frac{1}{3}x - \frac{2}{3}$$ $$3x + 9 \leq 4x - 8$$ $$-1x + 9 \leq -8$$ $$-1x \leq -17$$ $$\frac{-1x}{-1} \geq \frac{-17}{-1}$$ $$x \geq 17$$
Solving compound inequalities containing **and**, p. 521	The solution is the desired region containing all values of x that meet both conditions.	Graph the values of x satisfying $x + 6 > -3$ and $2x - 1 < -4$. $$x + 6 - 6 > -3 - 6 \quad \text{and} \quad 2x < -3$$ $$x > -9 \quad \text{and} \quad x < -1.5$$
Solving compound inequalities containing **or**, p. 522	The solution is the desired region containing all values of x that meet either of the two conditions.	Graph the values of x satisfying $-3x + 1 \leq 7$ or $3x + 1 \leq -11$. $$-3x + 1 - 1 \leq 7 - 1 \quad \text{or} \quad 3x + 1 - 1 \leq -11 - 1$$ $$-3x \leq 6 \quad \text{or} \quad 3x \leq -12$$ $$\frac{-3x}{-3} \geq \frac{6}{-3} \quad \text{or} \quad \frac{3x}{3} \leq \frac{-12}{3}$$ $$x \geq -2 \quad \text{or} \quad x \leq -4$$
Solving absolute value inequalities involving $<$ or $\leq$, p. 526	When a is a positive real number: If $|x| < a$, then $-a < x < a$. If $|x| \leq a$, then $-a \leq x \leq a$.	Solve and graph: $|3x - 2| < 19$. $$-19 < 3x - 2 < 19$$ $$-19 + 2 < 3x - 2 + 2 < 19 + 2$$ $$-17 < 3x < 21$$ $$-\frac{17}{3} < \frac{3x}{3} < \frac{21}{3}$$ $$-5\frac{2}{3} < x < 7$$

Topic	Procedure	Examples
Solving absolute value inequalities involving $>$ or $\geq$, p. 528	When a is a positive real number: If $\lvert x \rvert > a$, then $x > a$ or $x < -a$. If $\lvert x \rvert \geq a$, then $x \geq a$ or $x \leq -a$.	Solve and graph: $\left\lvert \frac{1}{3}(x-2) \right\rvert \geq 2$. $\frac{1}{3}(x-2) \geq 2 \qquad or \qquad \frac{1}{3}(x-2) \leq -2$ $\frac{1}{3}x - \frac{2}{3} \geq 2 \qquad\qquad \frac{1}{3}x - \frac{2}{3} \leq -2$ $x - 2 \geq 6 \qquad\qquad\quad x - 2 \leq -6$ $x \geq 6 + 2 \qquad\qquad\quad x \leq -6 + 2$ $x \geq 8 \qquad or \qquad\quad x \leq -4$
Solving quadratic inequalities in one variable, p. 532	1. Replace the inequality by an equals sign. Solve the resulting equation to find the critical points. 2. Separate the number line into distinct regions on each side of these critical points. 3. Evaluate the quadratic expression at a test point in each region. 4. Determine which regions satisfy the original conditions of the quadratic inequality.	Solve and graph: $3x^2 + 5x - 2 > 0$. 1. $3x^2 + 5x - 2 = 0$ $(3x - 1)(x + 2) = 0$ $3x - 1 = 0 \qquad x + 2 = 0$ $x = \frac{1}{3} \qquad\qquad x = -2$ Critical points are -2 and $\frac{1}{3}$. 2. 3. Pick $x = -3$ \qquad Pick $x = 0$ \qquad Pick $x = 3$ $3x^2 + 5x - 2$ *Region I:* $x = -3$ $3(-3)^2 + 5(-3) - 2 = 27 - 15 - 2 = 10 > 0$ *Region II:* $x = 0$ $3(0)^2 + 5(0) - 2 = 0 + 0 - 2 = -2 < 0$ *Region III:* $x = 3$ $3(3)^2 + 5(3) - 2 = 27 + 15 - 2 = 40 > 0$ 4. We know that the expression is greater than zero (that is, $3x^2 + 5x - 2 > 0$) when $x < -2$ or $x > \frac{1}{3}$.

Topic	Procedure	Examples
Graphing the solution for linear inequalities in two variables, p. 538	1. Replace the inequality symbol by an equals sign. This equation will be a boundary for the desired region. 2. Graph the line obtained in step 1, using a solid line if the original inequality contains the $\leq$ or $\geq$ symbols, and a dashed line if the original inequality contains $<$ or $>$ symbols. 3. Pick any point that does not lie on the boundary line. Substitute the coordinates into the original inequality. If you obtain a true inequality, shade the region on the side of the line containing the point. If you obtain a false inequality, shade the region on the side of the line opposite from the test point.	Graph the solution for $3y - 4x \geq 6$. 1. The boundary line is $3y - 4x = 6$. 2. The line passes through $(0, 2)$ and $(-1.5, 0)$. The inequality includes the boundary; draw a solid line 3. Pick $(0, 0)$ as a test point. $$3y - 4x \geq 6$$ $$3(0) - 4(0) \overset{?}{\geq} 6$$ $$0 - 0 \overset{?}{\geq} 6$$ $$0 \not\geq 6$$ Our test point fails. We shade on the side that does not contain $(0, 0)$.
Graphing the solution for a quadratic inequality in two variables, p. 543	The boundary line is usually curved, such as a parabola, circle, hyperbola, or ellipse. Use the procedure for graphing linear inequalities in two variables, except that one boundary line is a curved line.	Graph: $y + 2 > \frac{1}{2}x^2$. 1. We write $y = \frac{1}{2}x^2 - 2$. 2. We graph the dashed line because the boundary line is not included. 3. Let us pick $(0, 1)$ as a test point. $$y + 2 > \frac{1}{2}x^2$$ $$1 + 2 > \frac{1}{2}(0)^2$$ $$3 > 0 \quad \text{True}$$ Thus we shade on the side of the parabola containing $(0, 1)$.
Graphing the solution for a system of inequalities in two variables, p. 545	1. Replace the inequality symbol by an equals sign. 2. Sketch each boundary line. 3. Determine the region that satisfies each inequality individually. 4. Shade the common region that satisfies all the inequalities.	Graph: $$3x + 2y \leq 10$$ $$-1x + 2y \geq 2$$ 1–2. $3x + 2y \leq 10$ can be graphed more easily as $y \leq -\frac{3}{2}x + 5$. We draw a solid line. $-1x + 2y \geq 2$ can be graphed more easily as $y \geq \frac{1}{2}x + 1$. We draw a solid line. 3. We shade above $y \geq \frac{1}{2}x + 1$ and below $y \leq -\frac{3}{2}x + 5$ and include the boundary lines. 4. The common region is shaded.

Solve for x.

1. $8x + 3 < 5x$
$x < -1$

2. $7x + 5 < 2x$
$x < -1$

3. $2 - x \geq 3x + 10$
$x \leq -2$

4. $2 - 3x \geq 10 - 7x$
$x \geq 2$

5. $4x - 1 < 3(x + 2)$
$x < 7$

6. $3(3x - 2) < 4x - 16$
$x < -2$

7. $(x + 6) - (2x + 7) \leq 3x - 9$
$x \geq 2$

8. $(4x - 3) - (2x + 7) \leq 5 - x$
$x \leq 5$

9. $\dfrac{1}{9}x + \dfrac{2}{9} > \dfrac{1}{3}$
$x > 1$

10. $\dfrac{3}{4}x - \dfrac{1}{4} < 2$
$x < 3$

11. $\dfrac{6}{5} - x \geq \dfrac{3}{5}x + \dfrac{14}{5}$
$x \leq -1$

12. $\dfrac{7}{4} - 2x \geq -\dfrac{3}{2}x - \dfrac{5}{4}$
$x \leq 6$

13. $\dfrac{1}{3}(x - 2) < \dfrac{1}{4}(x + 5) - \dfrac{5}{3}$
$x < 3$

14. $\dfrac{1}{3}(x + 2) > 3x - 5(x - 2)$
$x > 4$

Graph the values of x that satisfy the conditions given.

15. $-3 \leq x < 2$

16. $-4 < x \leq 5$

17. $-8 \leq x \leq -4$

18. $-9 \leq x \leq -6$

19. $x < -2$ *or* $x \geq 5$

20. $x < -3$ *or* $x \geq 6$

21. $x > -5$ *and* $x < -1$

22. $x > -8$ *and* $x < -3$

23. $x + 3 > 8$ *or* $x + 2 < 6$

Solve for x.

24. $x - 2 > 7$ *or* $x + 3 < 2$
$x > 9 \text{ or } x < -1$

25. $x + 3 > 8$ *and* $x - 4 < -2$
No sol. $\varnothing$

26. $x + 5 > 7$ *and* $x + 3 < -8$
No sol. $\varnothing$

27. $3x - 5 \geq 0$ *and* $4x - 1 \leq 2$
No. sol. $\varnothing$

28. $2x - 7 < 3$ *and* $5x - 1 \geq 8$
$\dfrac{9}{5} < x < 5$

29. $4x - 2 < 8$ *or* $3x + 1 > 4$
All real numbers

30. $8x - 3 < 5$ *or* $2x - 3 > 5$
$x < 1 \text{ or } x > 4$

Solve for x.

31. $|x + 3| < 10$
$-13 < x < 7$

32. $|x + 4| < 3$
$-7 < x < -1$

33. $|2x - 1| \leq 15$
$-7 \leq x \leq 8$

34. $|3x - 2| \leq 19$
$-\dfrac{17}{3} \leq x \leq 7$

35. $\left|\dfrac{1}{2}x + 2\right| < \dfrac{7}{4}$
$-\dfrac{15}{2} < x < -\dfrac{1}{2}$

36. $\left|\dfrac{1}{5}x + 3\right| < \dfrac{11}{5}$
$-26 < x < -4$

37. $|2x - 1| \geq 9$
$x \geq 5 \text{ or } x \leq -4$

38. $|3x - 1| \geq 2$
$x \geq 1 \text{ or } x \leq -\dfrac{1}{3}$

39. $|3(x - 1)| \geq 5$
$x \geq \frac{8}{3}$ or $x \leq -\frac{2}{3}$

40. $|2(x - 3)| \geq 4$
$x \geq 5$ or $x \leq 1$

41. $|7 + x - 3| > 10$
$x < -14$ or $x > 6$

42. $|8 + x - 7| > 7$
$x < -8$ or $x > 6$

Solve.

43. $x^2 + 7x - 18 < 0$
$-9 < x < 2$

44. $x^2 + 4x - 21 < 0$
$-7 < x < 3$

45. $x^2 - 9x + 20 > 0$
$x < 4$ or $x > 5$

46. $x^2 - 11x + 28 > 0$
$x < 4$ or $x > 7$

47. $3x^2 - 5x - 2 \leq 0$
$-\frac{1}{3} \leq x \leq 2$

48. $2x^2 - 5x - 3 \leq 0$
$-\frac{1}{2} \leq x \leq 3$

49. $4x^2 + 12x + 9 < 0$
$(2x + 3)^2 < 0$
No sol.

50. $9x^2 + 6x + 1 < 0$
$(3x + 1)^2 < 0$
No sol.

51. $9x^2 - 4 > 0$
$x < -\frac{2}{3}$ or $x > \frac{2}{3}$

52. $16x^2 - 25 > 0$
$x < -\frac{5}{4}$ or $x > \frac{5}{4}$

53. $x^2 + 13x > 16 + 7x$
$x < -8$ or $x > 2$

54. $x^2 - 9x > 4 - 7x$
$x < (1 - \sqrt{5})$ or $x > (1 + \sqrt{5})$

55. $4x^2 - 8x \leq 12 + 5x^2$
$x \leq -6$ or $x \geq -2$

56. $-2x^2 + 7x + 12 \leq -3x^2 + x$
No sol. $\varnothing$

57. $(x + 4)(x - 2)(3 - x) > 0$
$x < -4$ or $2 < x < 3$

58. $(x + 1)(x + 4)(2 - x) < 0$
$-4 < x < -1$ or $x > 2$

Graph the region described by the inequality.

59. $y < 3x + 2$

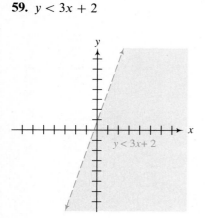

60. $y < 2x + 4$

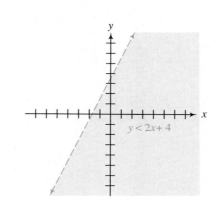

61. $y > -\frac{1}{2}x + 3$

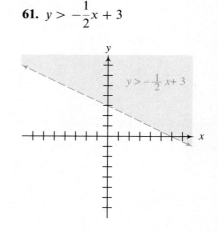

62. $y > -\frac{2}{3}x + 1$

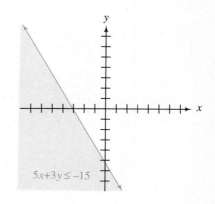

63. $3x + 4y \leq -12$

64. $5x + 3y \leq -15$

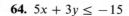

65. $5y - 2x - 20 < 0$

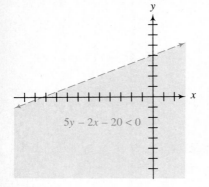

66. $4x - 3y - 24 < 0$

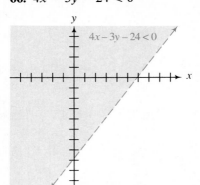

67. $y < (x + 2)^2 - 3$

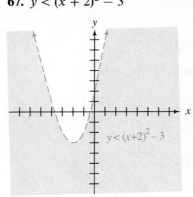

68. $y < (x - 2)^2 + 3$

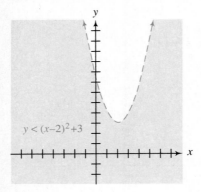

69. $x^2 - 4y^2 < 100$

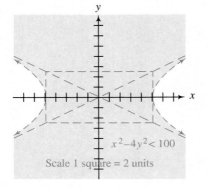

70. $x^2 - 9y^2 > 81$

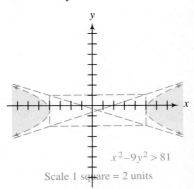

71. $25x^2 + 4y^2 \geq 100$

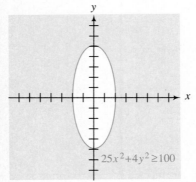

72. $16x^2 + y^2 \leq 16$

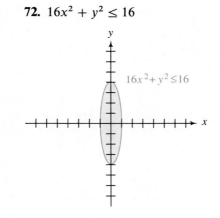

Graph the region described by each system of inequalities.

73. $x + y < 6$
 $x - y > 2$

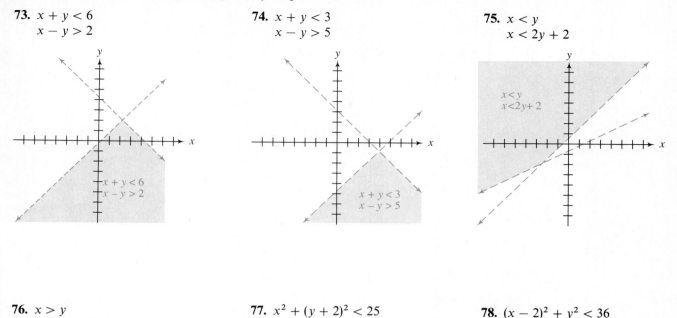

74. $x + y < 3$
 $x - y > 5$

75. $x < y$
 $x < 2y + 2$

$x < y$
$x < 2y + 2$

$x + y < 6$
$x - y > 2$

$x + y < 3$
$x - y > 5$

76. $x > y$
 $x > 3y - 3$

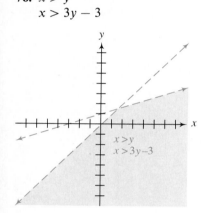

77. $x^2 + (y + 2)^2 < 25$
 $y < -1$

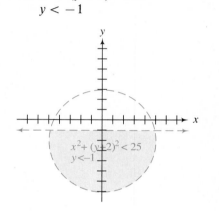

78. $(x - 2)^2 + y^2 < 36$
 $x < 2$

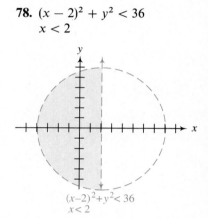

$x > y$
$x > 3y - 3$

$x^2 + (y+2)^2 < 25$
$y < -1$

$(x-2)^2 + y^2 < 36$
$x < 2$

79. $x + y \leq 2$
 $y \leq (x + 1)^2 - 2$

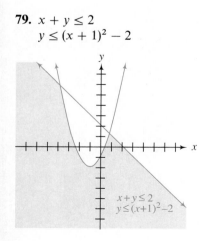

80. $x + y \leq 4$
 $y \geq (x - 1)^2 - 1$

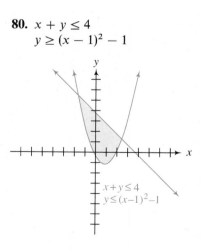

$x + y \leq 2$
$y \leq (x+1)^2 - 2$

$x + y \leq 4$
$y \leq (x-1)^2 - 1$

Graph each relationship.

1. $x > -3$

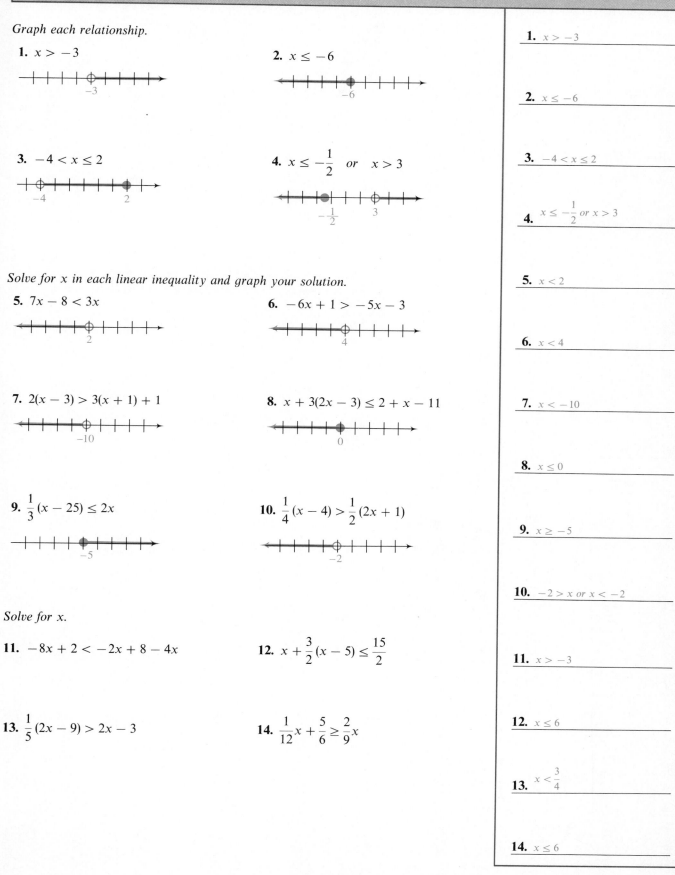

2. $x \le -6$

3. $-4 < x \le 2$

4. $x \le -\dfrac{1}{2}$ or $x > 3$

Solve for x in each linear inequality and graph your solution.

5. $7x - 8 < 3x$

6. $-6x + 1 > -5x - 3$

7. $2(x - 3) > 3(x + 1) + 1$

8. $x + 3(2x - 3) \le 2 + x - 11$

9. $\dfrac{1}{3}(x - 25) \le 2x$

10. $\dfrac{1}{4}(x - 4) > \dfrac{1}{2}(2x + 1)$

Solve for x.

11. $-8x + 2 < -2x + 8 - 4x$

12. $x + \dfrac{3}{2}(x - 5) \le \dfrac{15}{2}$

13. $\dfrac{1}{5}(2x - 9) > 2x - 3$

14. $\dfrac{1}{12}x + \dfrac{5}{6} \ge \dfrac{2}{9}x$

1. $x > -3$

2. $x \le -6$

3. $-4 < x \le 2$

4. $x \le -\dfrac{1}{2}$ or $x > 3$

5. $x < 2$

6. $x < 4$

7. $x < -10$

8. $x \le 0$

9. $x \ge -5$

10. $-2 > x$ or $x < -2$

11. $x > -3$

12. $x \le 6$

13. $x < \dfrac{3}{4}$

14. $x \le 6$

Graph the values of x that satisfy the conditions given.

15. $x \geq -8 \quad or \quad x > -4$

16. $x < 2 \quad and \quad x \leq -3$

17. $x + 1 > 3 \quad and \quad x - 3 < 10$

18. $x - 3 < -6 \quad or \quad x + 1 > 3$

19. $-3x + 2 \leq -4 \quad and \quad x + 3 \geq 0$

20. $2x + 2 > 0 \quad and \quad 5x - 6 < 9$

Find the solution for each absolute value inequality.

21. $|3x - 1| \leq 14$

22. $|5x + 2| > 7$

23. $\left| \dfrac{4x + 2}{3} \right| > 4$

24. $\left| \dfrac{1}{2}(x - 2) \right| \leq 3$

25. $\left| \dfrac{3}{5}(x + 1) \right| < 2$

26. $|3 + 2x - 8| > 5$

Solve.

1. $x^2 - 5x + 6 > 0$

2. $2x^2 - 5x - 3 < 0$

3. $2x^2 + 7x - 4 \leq 0$

4. $x^2 - x - 30 \geq 0$

5. $x^2 - 6x + 12 < 19$

6. $3x^2 < 2x + 1 + 2x^2$

7. $-x^2 + 9x + 36 \geq 0$

8. $x^2 > -4(2x + 3)$

Graph the regions.

9. $2x - 3y \geq -6$

10. $x + 8y < -16$

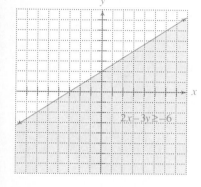

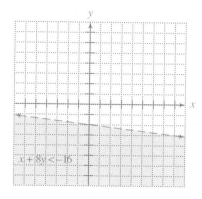

11. $5x - 6 \leq 2y + 5x$

12. $5y + 3x > 15$

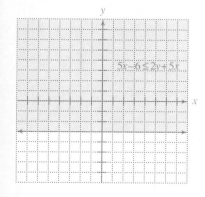

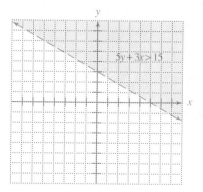

13. $(x - 4)^2 + (y + 2)^2 < 9$

14. $y + 3 > (x - 4)^2$

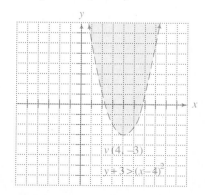

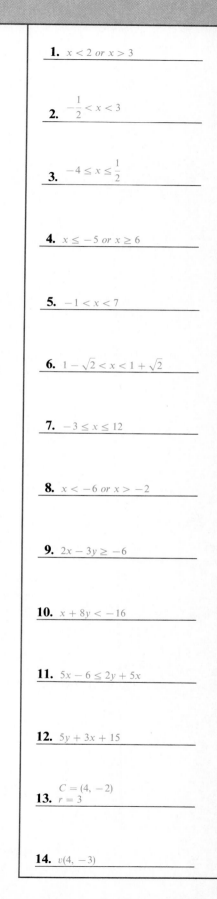

1. $x < 2 \text{ or } x > 3$

2. $-\frac{1}{2} < x < 3$

3. $-4 \leq x \leq \frac{1}{2}$

4. $x \leq -5 \text{ or } x \geq 6$

5. $-1 < x < 7$

6. $1 - \sqrt{2} < x < 1 + \sqrt{2}$

7. $-3 \leq x \leq 12$

8. $x < -6 \text{ or } x > -2$

9. $2x - 3y \geq -6$

10. $x + 8y < -16$

11. $5x - 6 \leq 2y + 5x$

12. $5y + 3x + 15$

13. $C = (4, -2)$
$r = 3$

14. $v(4, -3)$

15. $36y^2 - 9x^2 \leq -36$

16. $\dfrac{x^2}{25} + \dfrac{y^2}{25} \geq 1$

17. $x \geq 3;\ y \leq -2$

18. $y \leq 2x + 1$

19. $\dfrac{x^2}{9} + \dfrac{y^2}{4} < 1;\ y > \dfrac{3}{2}x - 2$

20. $\dfrac{x^2}{4} - \dfrac{y^2}{4} \leq 1;\ y \leq -\dfrac{1}{2}x + 2$

15. $36y^2 - 9x^2 \leq -36$

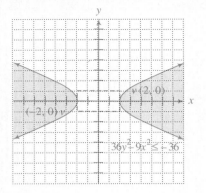

16. $5x^2 + 5y^2 \geq 125$

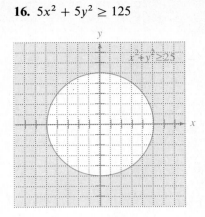

Graph the region described by each system of inequalities.

17. $x \geq 3$
$\quad\ y \leq -2$

18. $x + y \geq -4$
$\quad\ y \leq 2x + 1$

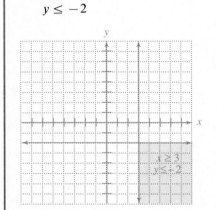

19. $y > \dfrac{3}{2}x - 2$

$\quad\ \dfrac{x^2}{9} + \dfrac{y^2}{4} < 1$

20. $y \leq -\dfrac{1}{2}x + 2$

$\quad\ \dfrac{x^2}{4} - \dfrac{y^2}{4} \leq 1$

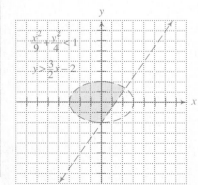

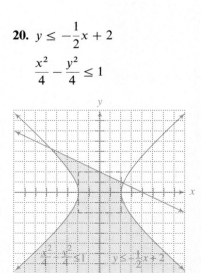

Solve and graph.

1. $5 - 6x < 2x + 21$

2. $-\dfrac{1}{2} + \dfrac{1}{3}(2 - 3x) \geq \dfrac{1}{2}x + \dfrac{5}{3}$

Find the values of x that satisfy the given conditions.

3. $2x + 4 > -6$ *and* $5x < -15$

4. $x - 4 \leq -6$ *or* $2x + 1 \geq 3$

Solve each absolute value inequality.

5. $|7x - 3| \leq 18$

6. $|3x + 1| > 7$

Solve.

7. $x^2 < 2(x + 4)$

8. $-3x^2 + 10x + 8 \geq 0$

---

1. $x > -2$

2. $x \leq -1$

3. $-5 < x < -3$

4. $x \leq -2 \; or \; x \geq 1$

5. $-\dfrac{15}{7} \leq x \leq 3$

6. $x < -\dfrac{8}{3} \; or \; x > 2$

7. $-2 < x < 4$

8. $-\dfrac{2}{3} \leq x \leq 4$

9. $y \geq -4x$

10. $4x - 2y < -6$

11. $-\dfrac{x^2}{36} + \dfrac{y^2}{9} \leq 1$

12. $y + 4 \geq (x - 5)^2$

$y \leq \dfrac{1}{2}x - 3$
13. $4y + 3x \leq 4$

$25x^2 + 9y^2 \leq 225$
14. $2x - y - 1 \geq 0$

Graph the regions.

9. $y \geq -4x$

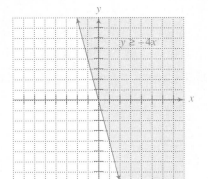

10. $4x - 2y < -6$

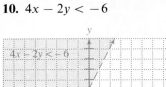

11. $-\dfrac{x^2}{36} + \dfrac{y^2}{9} \leq 1$

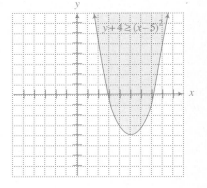

12. $y + 4 \geq (x - 5)^2$

Graph the solution of each system of inequalities.

13. $y \leq \dfrac{1}{2}x - 3$

   $4y + 3x \leq 4$

14. $25x^2 + 9y^2 \leq 225$
   $2x - y - 1 \geq 0$

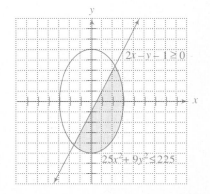

Approximately one-half of this test covers the content of Chapters 1–9. The remainder covers the content of Chapter 10.

1. Simplify: $\dfrac{3x^{-6}y^{-2}}{-9x^{-8}y^5}$

2. Solve for x: $A = \dfrac{x+y}{2}$

3. Factor completely: $3x^3 + 81$

4. Solve for x: $\dfrac{2}{x-2} + \dfrac{5}{x^2-4} = \dfrac{3}{x+2}$

5. Graph: $7x - 2y = -14$.

6. Find the area of a trapezoid with an altitude of 12 meters and bases of 9 meters and 15 meters.

7. Solve for (x, y, z):

$$2x - \ y - 2z = -1$$
$$x + \ y + \ z = \ \ 4$$
$$x - 2y - \ z = \ \ 1$$

8. Solve for x: $3x^2 + 7x - 2 = 0$.

9. Solve for x:
$$\log 12 = \log(x+1) + \log x$$

10. Simplify: $\sqrt{98x} + 3\sqrt{8x} - 4\sqrt{50x}$.

Solve and graph.

11. $-4 - 3x < -2x + 6$

12. $\dfrac{1}{3}(x+2) \le \dfrac{1}{5}(x+6)$

1. $\dfrac{-x^2}{3y^7}$

2. $x = 2A - y$

3. $3(x+3)(x^2 - 3x + 9)$

4. $x = 15$

5. $7x - 2y = -14$

6. 144 sq. meters

7. $x = 2$
$y = -1$
$z = 3$

8. $x = \dfrac{-7 \pm \sqrt{73}}{6}$

9. $x = 3$

10. $-7\sqrt{2x}$

11. $x > -10$

12. $x \le 4$

13. $-2 < x < 4$

14. $x \le -9 \text{ or } x \ge -2$

15. $-20 \le x \le 12$

16. $x < -\dfrac{7}{3} \text{ or } x > 5$

17. $x < -\dfrac{1}{2} \text{ or } x > 3$

18. $3x - 4y < 6$

19. $\dfrac{y^2}{9} - \dfrac{x^2}{16} \ge 1$

20. $x + 2y \ge 4$
$x^2 + y^2 \le 25$

Find the value of x that satisfies the conditions given.

13. $3x + 7 > 2x + 5$ *and* $3x < 12$

14. $x + 5 \le -4$ *or* $2 - 7x \le 16$

Solve each absolute value inequality.

15. $\left| \dfrac{1}{2}x + 2 \right| \le 8$

16. $|3x - 4| > 11$

17. Solve:
$2x^2 - 5x - 3 > 0.$

18. Graph the region: $3x - 4y \le 6$.

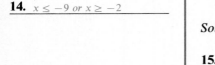

19. Graph the region: $\dfrac{y^2}{9} - \dfrac{x^2}{16} \ge 1$.

20. Graph the solution of the system of inequalities:

$x + 2y \ge 4$
$x^2 + y^2 \le 25$

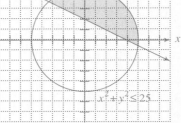

Please review the content areas of chapters 1–10. Then try to solve the problems in this Practice Final Examination.

Chapter 1

1. Evaluate $(4 - 3)^2 + \sqrt{9} \div (-3) + 4$

2. Simplify $\left(\dfrac{2x^3y^{-2}}{3x^4y^{-3}}\right)^{-2}$

3. Simplify
$5a - 2ab - 3a^2 - 6a - 8ab + 2a^2$

4. Solve for y: $\dfrac{1}{3}y - 4 = \dfrac{1}{2}y + 1$

5. Solve for C: $F = \dfrac{9}{5}C + 32$

Chapter 2

6. Graph the line $7x - 2y = -14$

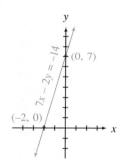

7. Find the slope of the line passing through $(1, 5)$ and $(-2, -3)$

8. Write the equation of a straight line in standard form that is parallel to $3x + 2y = 8$ and passes through $(-1, 4)$.

9. A man invested $4000 part at 12% interest, and part at 14% interest. After one year he had earned $508 in interest. How much was invested at each interest rate?

10. A piece of land is rectangular and has a perimeter of 1760 meters. The length is 200 meters less than twice the width. Find the dimensions of the land.

Chapter 3

11. Solve for x and y:

$\dfrac{1}{2}x + \dfrac{2}{3}y = 1$

$\dfrac{1}{3}x + y = -1$

12. Solve for x and y:
$4x - 3y = 12$
$3x - 4y = 2$

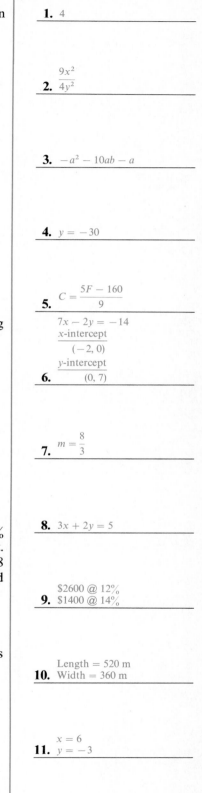

1. 4

2. $\dfrac{9x^2}{4y^2}$

3. $-a^2 - 10ab - a$

4. $y = -30$

5. $C = \dfrac{5F - 160}{9}$

6. $7x - 2y = -14$
x-intercept
$(-2, 0)$
y-intercept
$(0, 7)$

7. $m = \dfrac{8}{3}$

8. $3x + 2y = 5$

9. $2600 @ 12%
$1400 @ 14%

10. Length $= 520$ m
Width $= 360$ m

11. $x = 6$
$y = -3$

12. $x = 6$
$y = 4$

13. Solve for x, y and z:
$$2x + 3y - z = 16$$
$$x - y + 3z = -9$$
$$5x + 2y - z = 15$$

14. Solve for x, y, and z:
$$y + z = 2$$
$$x + z = 5$$
$$x + y = 5$$

15. Solve for z only by using Cramer's Rule.
$$2x - y + 5z = -2$$
$$x + 3y - z = 6$$
$$4x + y + 3z = -2$$

Chapter 4

16. Multiply and simplify your answer. $(3x - 2)(2x^2 - 4x + 3)$

17. Divide $(25x^3 + 9x + 2) \div (5x + 1)$

Factor completely the following:

18. $8x^3 - 27$

19. $x^3 + 2x^2 - 4x - 8$

20. $2x^3 + 15x^2 - 8x$

Chapter 5

Simplify the following:

21. $\dfrac{9x^3 - x}{3x^2 - 8x - 3}$

22. $\dfrac{x^2 - 9}{2x^2 + 7x + 3} \div \dfrac{x^2 - 3x}{2x^2 + 11x + 5}$

23. $\dfrac{3x}{x + 5} - \dfrac{2}{x^2 + 7x + 10}$

24. $\dfrac{\dfrac{3}{2x + 1} + 2}{1 - \dfrac{2}{4x^2 - 1}}$

25. Solve for x: $\dfrac{x - 1}{x^2 - 4} = \dfrac{2}{x + 2} + \dfrac{4}{x - 2}$

26. Simplify: $\dfrac{5x^{-4}y^{-2}}{15x^{-1/2}y^3}$

27. Simplify: $\sqrt[3]{40x^4y^7}$

28. Combine like terms:
$5\sqrt{2} - 3\sqrt{50} + 4\sqrt{98}$

29. Rationalize the denominator:
$$\dfrac{2\sqrt{3} + 1}{3\sqrt{3} - \sqrt{2}}$$

30. Simplify and add together:
$i^3 + \sqrt{-25} + \sqrt{-16}$

Chapter 7

31. Solve for x: $5x(x + 1) = 1 + 6x$

32. Solve for x: $5x^2 - 9x = -12x$

33. Solve for x and check your solution:
$\sqrt{2x + 9} = x + 3$

34. Solve for x: $x^{2/3} + 5x^{1/3} - 14 = 0$

35. The area of a rectangle is 52 square centimeters. The length of the rectangle is 1 meter longer than 3 times its width. Find the dimensions of the rectangle.

Chapter 8

36. Place the equation of the circle in standard form. Find its center and radius.
$x^2 + y^2 + 6x - 4y = -9$

Identify and graph:

37. $\dfrac{x^2}{16} + \dfrac{y^2}{25} = 1$

38. $\dfrac{x^2}{4} - \dfrac{y^2}{9} = 1$

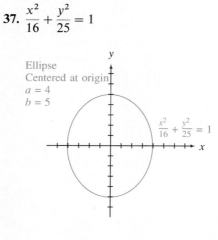

Ellipse
Centered at origin
$a = 4$
$b = 5$
$\dfrac{x^2}{16} + \dfrac{y^2}{25} = 1$

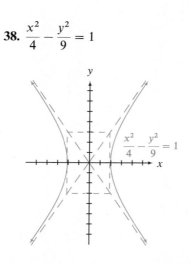

$\dfrac{x^2}{4} - \dfrac{y^2}{9} = 1$

26. $\dfrac{1}{3x^{7/2}y^5}$

27. $2xy^2\sqrt[3]{5xy}$

28. $18\sqrt{2}$

29. $\dfrac{18 + 2\sqrt{6} + 3\sqrt{3} + \sqrt{2}}{25}$

30. $8i$

31. $x = \dfrac{1 \pm \sqrt{21}}{10}$

32. $x = 0, x = -\dfrac{3}{5}$

33. $x = 0$

34. $x = 8, x = -343$

35. Width $= 4$ cm
Length $= 13$ cm

36. $(x + 3)^2 + (y - 2)^2 = 4$
Center at $(-3, 2)$
Radius $= 2$

37. $\dfrac{x^2}{16} + \dfrac{y^2}{25} = 1$
Ellipse

38. $\dfrac{x^2}{4} - \dfrac{y^2}{9} = 1$
Hyperbola

39. Parabola opening right

40.
$$f(-1) = 10$$
$$f(a) = 3a^2 - 2a + 5$$
$$f(a + 2) = 3a^2 + 10a + 13$$

41.
$f(x) = 2^{1-x}$

x	0	1	-2	4	-1
y	2	1	8	$\frac{1}{8}$	4

42. $0.0016 = x$ or $\frac{1}{625} = x$

43. $21 = x$

44. $y = -2$

45. $x = 8$

46. $x < 1$

47. $x \leq -9$ or $x \geq -2$

48. $-\frac{5}{2} < x < \frac{15}{2}$

49. $x \leq -\frac{1}{3}$ or $x \geq 4$

50. $y \geq 3x - 4$
$2x + 3y \leq -6$

---

39. $x = 2(y - 3)^2 + 5$

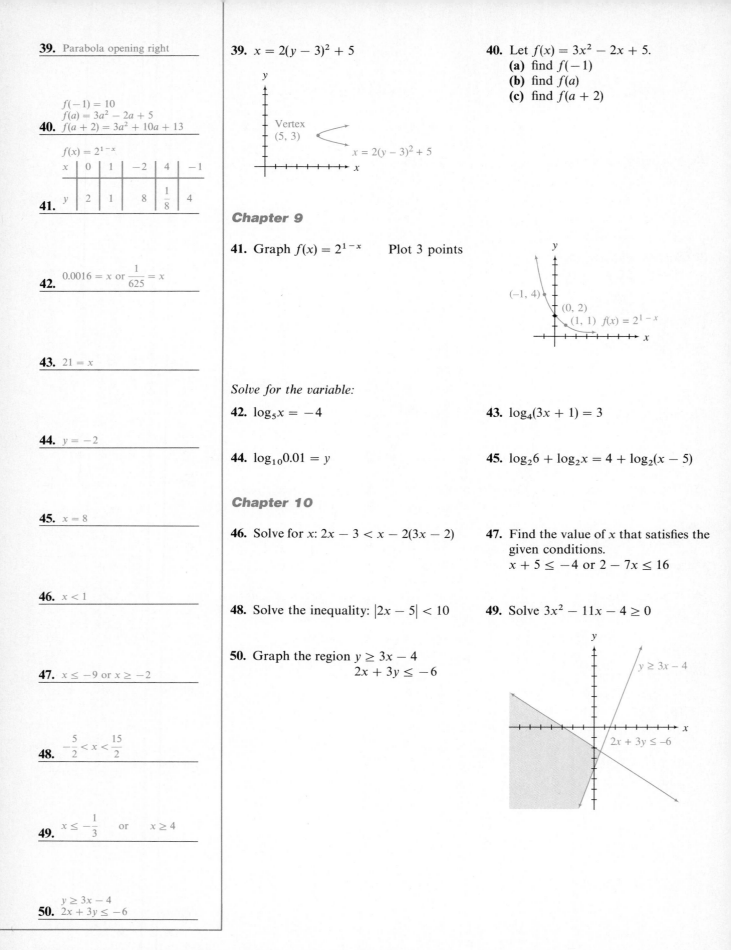

Vertex (5, 3)

$x = 2(y - 3)^2 + 5$

Chapter 9

41. Graph $f(x) = 2^{1-x}$ Plot 3 points

$(-1, 4)$
$(0, 2)$
$(1, 1)$ $f(x) = 2^{1-x}$

Solve for the variable:

42. $\log_5 x = -4$

44. $\log_{10} 0.01 = y$

Chapter 10

46. Solve for x: $2x - 3 < x - 2(3x - 2)$

48. Solve the inequality: $|2x - 5| < 10$

50. Graph the region $y \geq 3x - 4$
$$2x + 3y \leq -6$$

---

40. Let $f(x) = 3x^2 - 2x + 5$.
  (a) find $f(-1)$
  (b) find $f(a)$
  (c) find $f(a + 2)$

43. $\log_4(3x + 1) = 3$

45. $\log_2 6 + \log_2 x = 4 + \log_2(x - 5)$

47. Find the value of x that satisfies the given conditions.
$$x + 5 \leq -4 \text{ or } 2 - 7x \leq 16$$

49. Solve $3x^2 - 11x - 4 \geq 0$

$y \geq 3x - 4$

$2x + 3y \leq -6$

On Variation

VARIATION

After studying this section, you will be able to:

1 Solve problems requiring the use of a direct variation equation

2 Solve problems requiring the use of an inverse variation equation

3 Solve problems requiring the use of joint or combined variation

1 Direct Variation

There are many times in daily life when we observe how a change in one variable quantity produces a change in another. If we order one large pepperoni pizza, we pay $8.95. If we order two of the same pizza, we pay $17.90. For three of the same pizza, it is $26.85. The change in the variable number of pizzas we order results in a corresponding change in the price we pay.

If one variable is a constant multiple of the other, the two variables are said to vary directly. In equation form we have, if y varies directly as x, then $y = kx$, where k represents a constant, some real number that will stay the same over a certain range of problems. If we want to work with such an equation, we will first want to find the value of k.

Example 1 If y varies directly as x and $y = 25$ when $x = 15$, find y when $x = 20$.

We first find the constant by substituting in the known values of $x = 15$ and $y = 25$.

$$y = kx$$

$$25 = k(15)$$

$$\frac{25}{15} = \frac{15k}{15} \qquad \text{Dividing each side by 15.}$$

$$\frac{5}{3} = k$$

Next we use the equation with the k value known.

$$y = \frac{5}{3}x$$

We want to find y when $x = 20$.

$$y = \frac{5}{3}(20)$$

$$y = \frac{100}{3} \quad \blacksquare$$

Practice Problem 1 If y varies directly as x and $y = 9$ when $x = \frac{1}{2}$, find the value of y when $x = \frac{2}{3}$. $\blacksquare$

Example 2 The time of a pendulum's swing varies directly as the square root of its length. If the pendulum is 1 foot long when the time is 0.2 second, find the time if the length is 4 feet.

Let t = the time and L = the length. We then have the equation

$$t = k\sqrt{L}$$

We can evaluate k by substituting $L = 1$ and $t = 0.2$ into the equation.

$$0.2 = k(\sqrt{1})$$
$$0.2 = k \qquad \text{Because } \sqrt{1} = 1.$$

Now we know the value of k and can write the equation more completely.

$$t = 0.2\sqrt{L}$$

When $L = 4$ we have

$$t = 0.2\sqrt{4}$$
$$t = (0.2)(2)$$
$$t = 0.4 \text{ second} \qquad \blacksquare$$

Practice Problem 2 In some racing cars the maximum speed varies directly as the square root of the horsepower of the engine. If the maximum speed of a car with 256 horsepower is 128 miles per hour, what is the maximum speed of a car with 225 horsepower? $\blacksquare$

2 Inverse Variation

In some cases when one variable increases, another variable decreases. For example, as the amount of money you earn each year increases, the percentage of your income that you get to keep after taxes decreases. If one variable is a constant multiple of the reciprocal of the other, the two variables are said to vary inversely. If y varies inversely as x, we can express this by the equation $y = \dfrac{k}{x}$, where k is the constant of variation.

Example 3 If y varies inversely as x and $y = 12$ when $x = 5$, find y when $x = 14$.

If y varies inversely as x, we can write the equation $y = \dfrac{k}{x}$. We can find the value of k by substituting the values $y = 12$ and $x = 5$.

$$12 = \frac{k}{5}$$
$$60 = k$$

We can thus write the equation

$$y = \frac{60}{x}$$

To find the value of y when $x = 14$, we substitute into that equation.

$$y = \frac{60}{14}$$
$$y = \frac{30}{7} \qquad \blacksquare$$

Practice Problem 3 If y varies inversely as x and $y = 45$ when $x = 16$, find the value of y when $x = 36$. $\blacksquare$

Example 4   The amount of light from a light source varies inversely as the square of the distance to the light source. If an object receives 6.25 lumens when the light source is 8 meters away, how much light will it receive if it is 4 meters away?

Let L = the amount of light and d = the distance to the light source. Since the amount of light varies inversely as the square of the distance to the light source, we have

$$L = \frac{k}{d^2}$$

Substituting the know values of $L = 6.25$ when $d = 8$, we can find the value of k.

$$6.25 = \frac{k}{8^2}$$

$$6.25 = \frac{k}{64}$$

$$400 = k$$

We are now able to write a more specific equation,

$$L = \frac{400}{d^2}.$$

We will use this to find L when $d = 4$ meters.

$$L = \frac{400}{4^2}$$

$$L = \frac{400}{16}$$

$$L = 25 \text{ lumens} \quad \blacksquare$$

Practice Problem 4   If the amount of power in an electrical circuit is held constant, the resistance in the circuit varies inversely as the square of the amount of current. If the amount of current is 0.01 ampere, the resistance is 800 ohms. What is the resistance if the amount of current is 0.04 ampere? $\blacksquare$

3 Joint Variation and Combined Variation

Sometimes a quantity depends on the variation of two or more other quantities.

Example 5 y varies directly as x and z and inversely as d^2. When $x = 7$, $z = 3$, and $d = 4$, the value of y is 20. Find the value of y when $x = 5$, $z = 6$, and $d = 2$.

We can write the equation $y = \dfrac{kxz}{d^2}$. To find the value of k we substitute into the equation $y = 20$, $x = 7$, $z = 3$, and $d = 4$.

$$20 = \frac{k(7)(3)}{4^2}$$

$$20 = \frac{21k}{16}$$

$$320 = 21k$$

$$\frac{320}{21} = k$$

Now we can use the equation

$$y = \frac{\dfrac{320}{21}xz}{d^2} \qquad \text{or} \qquad y = \frac{320xz}{21d^2}$$

We want to find y when $x = 5$, $z = 6$, and $d = 2$.

$$y = \frac{320(5)(6)}{21(2)^2}$$

$$y = \frac{\overset{80}{\cancel{320}}(5)(\overset{2}{\cancel{6}})}{\underset{7}{\cancel{21}}(\underset{1}{\cancel{4}})}$$

$$y = \frac{800}{7} \quad \blacksquare$$

Practice Problem 5 y varies directly as z and w^2 and inversely as x. $y = 20$ when $z = 3$, $w = 5$, and $x = 4$. Find y when $z = 4$, $w = 6$, and $x = 2$.

EXERCISES

Round all answers to nearest tenth.

1. If y varies directly as x and $y = 8$ when $x = 20$, find y when $x = 4$.
   $y = 1.6$

2. If y varies directly as x and $y = 30$ when $x = 2$, find y when $x = 5$.
   $y = 75$

3. If y varies directly as x^2 and $y = 18$ when $x = 2$, find y when $x = 3$.
   $y = 40.5$

4. If y varies directly as x^3 and $y = 32$ when $x = 4$, find y when $x = 7$.
   $y = 171.5$

5. The time it takes to fill a cubic box with a shipment of dominoes varies directly as the cube of the side of the box. A box that is 9 inches on each side takes 243 seconds. How long will it take to fill a box that is 12 inches on each side?
   576 seconds

6. The distance to stop a car varies directly as the square of its speed. A car that is traveling 30 miles per hour can stop in 40 feet. How long will it take to stop if it is traveling 60 miles per hour?
   160 ft

7. If y varies inversely as x and $y = 18$ when $x = 6$, find y when $x = 13$.
   $y = 8.3$

8. If y varies inversely as x and $y = 20$ when $x = 25$, find y when $x = 16$.
   $y = 31.3$

9. If y varies inversely as the cube of x and $y = 20$ when $x = 4$, find y when $x = 3$.
   $y = 47.4$

10. If y varies inversely as the square of x and $y = 30$ when $x = 6$, find y when $x = 8$.
    $y = 16.9$

11. The volume of gas varies inversely as the pressure of the gas on the container holding it. When the pressure is 25 pounds, the volume is 96 cubic feet. When the volume is 100 cubic feet, what is the pressure?
    $p = 24$ lbs

12. The weight of an object on the earth's surface varies inversely as the square of its distance from the center of the earth. An object weighs 1000 pounds on the earth's surface. This is approximately 4000 miles from the center of the earth. How much would an object weigh 4500 miles from the center of the earth?
    790.1 lbs

13. y varies directly as x and z^2 and inversely as w. Now $y = 20$ when $x = 6$ and $z = 2$ and $w = 10$. Find y when $x = 8$, $z = 3$, and $w = 5$.

$y = 120$

14. y varies directly as x and z and inversely as the square root of w. Now $y = 10$ when $x = 6$, $z = 3$, and $w = 4$. Find y when $x = 8$, $z = 10$, and $w = 9$.

$y = 8.8$

15. y varies jointly as w and z. If $y = 100$ when $w = \dfrac{1}{2}$ and $z = 38$, find y when $w = 4$ and $z = 6$. (*Hint:* Use $y = kwz$.)

$y = 126.3$

16. y varies jointly as w, z, and h. If $y = 50$ when $w = 3$, $z = 4$, and $h = 6$, find y when $w = 2$, $z = 3$, and $h = 5$. (*Hint:* Use $y = kwzh$.)

$y = 20.8$

17. The weight of a cylindrical paperweight varies jointly as the height and the square of the radius. A paperweight that is 2 centimeters high and has a radius of 3 centimeters weighs 90 kilograms. How much does a paperweight weigh that is 3 centimeters high and has a radius of 4 centimeters?

240 kg

18. The attraction F of two masses m_1 and m_2 varies directly as the product of m_1 and m_2 and inversely as the square of the distance between the two bodies. If a force of 10 pounds attracts two bodies weighing 80 tons and 100 tons that are 100 miles apart, how great will be the force if the two bodies weighed 8 tons and 15 tons and were 20 miles apart?

3.8 lbs

Solutions to Odd-Numbered Practice Problems

1. $y = kx$

$9 = (k)\left(\dfrac{1}{2}\right)$

$18 = k$

$y = 18x$

$\quad = 18\left(\dfrac{2}{3}\right)$

$\quad = 12$

3. $y = \dfrac{k}{x}$

$45 = \dfrac{k}{16}$

$720 = k$

$y = \dfrac{720}{x}$

$\quad = \dfrac{720}{36}$

$\quad = 20$

5. $y = \dfrac{kzw^2}{x}$

$20 = \dfrac{k(3)(5)^2}{4}$

$20 = \dfrac{k(3)(25)}{4}$

$80 = 75k$

$\dfrac{80}{75} = k$

$\dfrac{16}{15} = k$

$y = \dfrac{\left(\dfrac{16}{15}\right)(4)(6)^2}{2}$

$\quad = \dfrac{(16)(\overset{2}{\cancel{4}})(\overset{12}{\cancel{36}})}{(\underset{5}{\cancel{15}})(2)}$

$\quad = \dfrac{1024}{10} = 102.4$

Answers to Even-Numbered Practice Problems

2. 120 miles per hour   **4.** 50 ohms

TABLE B-1: TABLE OF SQUARE ROOTS

Square root values ending in 0.000 are exact. All other values are approximate and are rounded to the nearest thousandth.

x	$\sqrt{x}$	x	$\sqrt{x}$	x	$\sqrt{x}$	x	$\sqrt{x}$	x	$\sqrt{x}$
1	1.000	41	6.403	81	9.000	121	11.000	161	12.689
2	1.414	42	6.481	82	9.055	122	11.045	162	12.728
3	1.732	43	6.557	83	9.110	123	11.091	163	12.767
4	2.000	44	6.633	84	9.165	124	11.136	164	12.806
5	2.236	45	6.708	85	9.220	125	11.180	165	12.845
6	2.449	46	6.782	86	9.274	126	11.225	166	12.884
7	2.646	47	6.856	87	9.327	127	11.269	167	12.923
8	2.828	48	6.928	88	9.381	128	11.314	168	12.961
9	3.000	49	7.000	89	9.434	129	11.358	169	13.000
10	3.162	50	7.071	90	9.487	130	11.402	170	13.038
11	3.317	51	7.141	91	9.539	131	11.446	171	13.077
12	3.464	52	7.211	92	9.592	132	11.489	172	13.115
13	3.606	53	7.280	93	9.644	133	11.533	173	13.153
14	3.742	54	7.348	94	9.695	134	11.576	174	13.191
15	3.873	55	7.416	95	9.747	135	11.619	175	13.229
16	4.000	56	7.483	96	9.798	136	11.662	176	13.266
17	4.123	57	7.550	97	9.849	137	11.705	177	13.304
18	4.243	58	7.616	98	9.899	138	11.747	178	13.342
19	4.359	59	7.681	99	9.950	139	11.790	179	13.379
20	4.472	60	7.746	100	10.000	140	11.832	180	13.416
21	4.583	61	7.810	101	10.050	141	11.874	181	13.454
22	4.690	62	7.874	102	10.100	142	11.916	182	13.491
23	4.796	63	7.937	103	10.149	143	11.958	183	13.528
24	4.899	64	8.000	104	10.198	144	12.000	184	13.565
25	5.000	65	8.062	105	10.247	145	12.042	185	13.601
26	5.099	66	8.124	106	10.296	146	12.083	186	13.638
27	5.196	67	8.185	107	10.344	147	12.124	187	13.675
28	5.292	68	8.246	108	10.392	148	12.166	188	13.711
29	5.385	69	8.307	109	10.440	149	12.207	189	13.748
30	5.477	70	8.367	110	10.488	150	12.247	190	13.784
31	5.568	71	8.426	111	10.536	151	12.288	191	13.820
32	5.657	72	8.485	112	10.583	152	12.329	192	13.856
33	5.745	73	8.544	113	10.630	153	12.369	193	13.892
34	5.831	74	8.602	114	10.677	154	12.410	194	13.928
35	5.916	75	8.660	115	10.724	155	12.450	195	13.964
36	6.000	76	8.718	116	10.770	156	12.490	196	14.000
37	6.083	77	8.775	117	10.817	157	12.530	197	14.036
38	6.164	78	8.832	118	10.863	158	12.570	198	14.071
39	6.245	79	8.888	119	10.909	159	12.610	199	14.107
40	6.325	80	8.944	120	10.954	160	12.649	200	14.142

TABLE B-2: EXPONENTIAL VALUES

x	e^x	e^{-x}	x	e^x	e^{-x}
0.00	1.0000	1.0000	**1.6**	4.9530	0.2019
0.01	1.0101	0.9900	**1.7**	5.4739	0.1827
0.02	1.0202	0.9802	**1.8**	6.0496	0.1653
0.03	1.0305	0.9704	**1.9**	6.6859	0.1496
0.04	1.0408	0.9608	**2.0**	7.3891	0.1353
0.05	1.0513	0.9512	**2.1**	8.1662	0.1225
0.06	1.0618	0.9418	**2.2**	9.0250	0.1108
0.07	1.0725	0.9324	**2.3**	9.9742	0.1003
0.08	1.0833	0.9231	**2.4**	11.023	0.0907
0.09	1.0942	0.9139	**2.5**	12.182	0.0821
0.10	1.1052	0.9048	**2.6**	13.464	0.0743
0.11	1.1163	0.8958	**2.7**	14.880	0.0672
0.12	1.1275	0.8869	**2.8**	16.445	0.0608
0.13	1.1388	0.8781	**2.9**	18.174	0.0550
0.14	1.1503	0.8694	**3.0**	20.086	0.0498
0.15	1.1618	0.8607	**3.1**	22.198	0.0450
0.16	1.1735	0.8521	**3.2**	24.533	0.0408
0.17	1.1853	0.8437	**3.3**	27.113	0.0369
0.18	1.1972	0.8353	**3.4**	29.964	0.0334
0.19	1.2092	0.8270	**3.5**	33.115	0.0302
0.20	1.2214	0.8187	**3.6**	36.598	0.0273
0.21	1.2337	0.8106	**3.7**	40.447	0.0247
0.22	1.2461	0.8025	**3.8**	44.701	0.0224
0.23	1.2586	0.7945	**3.9**	49.402	0.0202
0.24	1.2712	0.7866	**4.0**	54.598	0.0183
0.25	1.2840	0.7788	**4.1**	60.340	0.0166
0.26	1.2969	0.7711	**4.2**	66.686	0.0150
0.27	1.3100	0.7634	**4.3**	73.700	0.0136
0.28	1.3231	0.7558	**4.4**	81.451	0.0123
0.29	1.3364	0.7483	**4.5**	90.017	0.0111
0.30	1.3499	0.7408	**4.6**	99.484	0.0101
0.35	1.4191	0.7047	**4.7**	109.95	0.0091
0.40	1.4918	0.6703	**4.8**	121.51	0.0082
0.45	1.5683	0.6376	**4.9**	134.29	0.0074
0.50	1.6487	0.6065	**5.0**	148.41	0.0067
0.55	1.7333	0.5769	**5.5**	244.69	0.0041
0.60	1.8221	0.5488	**6.0**	403.43	0.0025
0.65	1.9155	0.5220	**6.5**	665.14	0.0015
0.70	2.0138	0.4966	**7.0**	1,096.6	0.0009
0.75	2.1170	0.4724	**7.5**	1,808.0	0.00055
0.80	2.2255	0.4493	**8.0**	2,981.0	0.00034
0.85	2.3396	0.4274	**8.5**	4,914.8	0.00020
0.90	2.4596	0.4066	**9.0**	8,103.1	0.00012
0.95	2.5857	0.3867	**9.5**	13,360	0.000075
1.0	2.7183	0.3679	**10**	22,026	0.000045
1.1	3.0042	0.3329	**11**	59,874	0.000017
1.2	3.3201	0.3012	**12**	162,754	0.0000061
1.3	3.6693	0.2725	**13**	442,413	0.0000023
1.4	4.0552	0.2466	**14**	1,202,604	0.0000008
1.5	4.4817	0.2231	**15**	3,269,017	0.0000003

TABLE B-3: COMMON LOGARITHMS

x	0	1	2	3	4	5	6	7	8	9
1.0	.0000	.0043	.0086	.0128	.0170	.0212	.0253	.0294	.0334	.0374
1.1	.0414	.0453	.0492	.0531	.0569	.0607	.0645	.0682	.0719	.0755
1.2	.0792	.0828	.0864	.0899	.0934	.0969	.1004	.1038	.1072	.1106
1.3	.1139	.1173	.1206	.1239	.1271	.1303	.1335	.1367	.1399	.1430
1.4	.1461	.1492	.1523	.1553	.1584	.1614	.1644	.1673	.1703	.1732
1.5	.1761	.1790	.1818	.1847	.1875	.1903	.1931	.1959	.1987	.2014
1.6	.2041	.2068	.2095	.2122	.2148	.2175	.2201	.2227	.2253	.2279
1.7	.2304	.2330	.2355	.2380	.2405	.2430	.2455	.2480	.2504	.2529
1.8	.2553	.2577	.2601	.2625	.2648	.2672	.2695	.2718	.2742	.2765
1.9	.2788	.2810	.2833	.2856	.2878	.2900	.2923	.2945	.2967	.2989
2.0	.3010	.3032	.3054	.3075	.3096	.3118	.3139	.3160	.3181	.3201
2.1	.3222	.3243	.3263	.3284	.3304	.3324	.3345	.3365	.3385	.3404
2.2	.3424	.3444	.3464	.3483	.3502	.3522	.3541	.3560	.3579	.3598
2.3	.3617	.3636	.3655	.3674	.3692	.3711	.3729	.3747	.3766	.3784
2.4	.3802	.3820	.3838	.3856	.3874	.3892	.3909	.3927	.3945	.3962
2.5	.3979	.3997	.4014	.4031	.4048	.4065	.4082	.4099	.4116	.4133
2.6	.4150	.4166	.4183	.4200	.4216	.4232	.4249	.4265	.4281	.4298
2.7	.4314	.4330	.4346	.4362	.4378	.4393	.4409	.4425	.4440	.4456
2.8	.4472	.4487	.4502	.4518	.4533	.4548	.4564	.4579	.4594	.4609
2.9	.4624	.4639	.4654	.4669	.4683	.4698	.4713	.4728	.4742	.4757
3.0	.4771	.4786	.4800	.4814	.4829	.4843	.4857	.4871	.4886	.4900
3.1	.4914	.4928	.4942	.4955	.4969	.4983	.4997	.5011	.5024	.5038
3.2	.5051	.5065	.5079	.5092	.5105	.5119	.5132	.5145	.5159	.5172
3.3	.5185	.5198	.5211	.5224	.5237	.5250	.5263	.5276	.5289	.5302
3.4	.5315	.5328	.5340	.5353	.5366	.5378	.5391	.5403	.5416	.5428
3.5	.5441	.5453	.5465	.5478	.5490	.5502	.5514	.5527	.5539	.5551
3.6	.5663	.5575	.5587	.5599	.5611	.5623	.5635	.5647	.5658	.5670
3.7	.5682	.5694	.5705	.5717	.5729	.5740	.5752	.5763	.5775	.5786
3.8	.5798	.5809	.5821	.5832	.5843	.5855	.5866	.5877	.5888	.5899
3.9	.5911	.5922	.5933	.5944	.5955	.5966	.5977	.5988	.5999	.6010
4.0	.6021	.6031	.6042	.6053	.6064	.6075	.6085	.6096	.6107	.6117
4.1	.6128	.6138	.6149	.6160	.6170	.6180	.6191	.6201	.6212	.6222
4.2	.6232	.6243	.6253	.6263	.6274	.6284	.6294	.6304	.6314	.6325
4.3	.6335	.6345	.6355	.6365	.6375	.6385	.6395	.6405	.6415	.6425
4.4	.6435	.6444	.6454	.6464	.6474	.6484	.6493	.6503	.6513	.6522
4.5	.6532	.6542	.6551	.6561	.6571	.6580	.6590	.6599	.6609	.6618
4.6	.6628	.6637	.6646	.6656	.6665	.6675	.6684	.6693	.6702	.6712
4.7	.6721	.6730	.6739	.6749	.6758	.6767	.6776	.6785	.6794	.6803
4.8	.6812	.6821	.6830	.6839	.6848	.6857	.6866	.6875	.6884	.6893
4.9	.6902	.6911	.6920	.6928	.6937	.6946	.6955	.6964	.6972	.6981
5.0	.6990	.6998	.7007	.7016	.7024	.7033	.7042	.7050	.7059	.7067
5.1	.7076	.7084	.7093	.7101	.7110	.7118	.7126	.7135	.7143	.7152
5.2	.7160	.7168	.7177	.7185	.7193	.7202	.7210	.7218	.7226	.7235
5.3	.7243	.7251	.7259	.7267	.7275	.7284	.7292	.7300	.7308	.7316
5.4	.7324	.7332	.7340	.7348	.7356	.7364	.7372	.7380	.7388	.7396

x	0	1	2	3	4	5	6	7	8	9
5.5	.7404	.7412	.7419	.7427	.7435	.7443	.7451	.7459	.7466	.7474
5.6	.7482	.7490	.7497	.7505	.7513	.7520	.7528	.7536	.7543	.7551
5.7	.7559	.7566	.7574	.7582	.7589	.7597	.7604	.7612	.7619	.7627
5.8	.7634	.7642	.7649	.7657	.7664	.7672	.7679	.7686	.7694	.7701
5.9	.7709	.7716	.7723	.7731	.7738	.7745	.7752	.7760	.7767	.7774
6.0	.7782	.7789	.7796	.7803	.7810	.7818	.7825	.7832	.7839	.7846
6.1	.7853	.7860	.7868	.7875	.7882	.7889	.7896	.7903	.7910	.7917
6.2	.7924	.7931	.7938	.7945	.7952	.7959	.7966	.7973	.7980	.7987
6.3	.7993	.8000	.8007	.8014	.8021	.8028	.8035	.8041	.8048	.8055
6.4	.8062	.8069	.8075	.8082	.8089	.8096	.8102	.8109	.8116	.8122
6.5	.8129	.8136	.8142	.8149	.8156	.8162	.8169	.8176	.8182	.8189
6.6	.8195	.8202	.8209	.8215	.8222	.8228	.8235	.8241	.8248	.8254
6.7	.8261	.8267	.8274	.8280	.8287	.8293	.8299	.8306	.8312	.8319
6.8	.8325	.8331	.8338	.8344	.8351	.8357	.8363	.8370	.8376	.8382
6.9	.8388	.8395	.8401	.8407	.8414	.8420	.8426	.8432	.8439	.8445
7.0	.8451	.8457	.8463	.8470	.8476	.8482	.8488	.8494	.8500	.8506
7.1	.8513	.8519	.8525	.8531	.8537	.8543	.8549	.8555	.8561	.8567
7.2	.8573	.8579	.8585	.8591	.8597	.8603	.8609	.8615	.8621	.8627
7.3	.8633	.8639	.8645	.8651	.8657	.8663	.8669	.8675	.8681	.8686
7.4	.8692	.8698	.8704	.8710	.8716	.8722	.8727	.8733	.8739	.8745
7.5	.8751	.8756	.8762	.8768	.8774	.8779	.8785	.8791	.8797	.8802
7.6	.8808	.8814	.8820	.8825	.8831	.8837	.8842	.8848	.8854	.8859
7.7	.8865	.8871	.8876	.8882	.8887	.8893	.8899	.8904	.8910	.8915
7.8	.8921	.8927	.8932	.8938	.8943	.8949	.8954	.8960	.8965	.8971
7.9	.8976	.8982	.8987	.8993	.8998	.9004	.9009	.9015	.9020	.9025
8.0	.9031	.9036	.9042	.9047	.9053	.9058	.9063	.9069	.9074	.9079
8.1	.9085	.9090	.9096	.9101	.9106	.9112	.9117	.9122	.9128	.9133
8.2	.9138	.9143	.9149	.9154	.9159	.9165	.9170	.9175	.9180	.9186
8.3	.9191	.9196	.9201	.9206	.9212	.9217	.9222	.9227	.9232	.9238
8.4	.9243	.9248	.9253	.9258	.9263	.9269	.9274	.9279	.9284	.9289
8.5	.9294	.9299	.9304	.9309	.9315	.9320	.9325	.9330	.9335	.9340
8.6	.9345	.9350	.9355	.9360	.9365	.9370	.9375	.9380	.9385	.9390
8.7	.9395	.9400	.9405	.9410	.9415	.9420	.9425	.9430	.9435	.9440
8.8	.9445	.9450	.9455	.9460	.9465	.9469	.9474	.9479	.9484	.9489
8.9	.9494	.9499	.9504	.9509	.9513	.9518	.9523	.9528	.9533	.9538
9.0	.9542	.9547	.9552	.9557	.9562	.9566	.9571	.9576	.9581	.9586
9.1	.9590	.9595	.9600	.9605	.9609	.9614	.9619	.9624	.9628	.9633
9.2	.9638	.9643	.9647	.9652	.9657	.9661	.9666	.9671	.9675	.9680
9.3	.9685	.9689	.9694	.9699	.9703	.9708	.9713	.9717	.9722	.9727
9.4	.9731	.9736	.9741	.9745	.9750	.9754	.9759	.9763	.9768	.9773
9.5	.9777	.9782	.9786	.9791	.9795	.9800	.9805	.9809	.9814	.9818
9.6	.9823	.9827	.9832	.9836	.9841	.9845	.9850	.9854	.9859	.9863
9.7	.9868	.9872	.9877	.9881	.9886	.9890	.9894	.9899	.9903	.9908
9.8	.9912	.9917	.9921	.9926	.9930	.9934	.9939	.9943	.9948	.9952
9.9	.9956	.9961	.9965	.9969	.9974	.9978	.9983	.9987	.9991	.9996

Note: To use this table to find approximate values for Natural Logarithms use the formula

$$\ln x \approx \frac{\log x}{0.4343}$$

For example

$$\ln 9.51 \approx \frac{\log 9.51}{0.4343} \approx \frac{0.9782}{0.4343} \approx 2.2524$$

A

Absolute value inequalities (10.3)   Inequalities that contain at least one absolute value expression.

Absolute value of a number (1.2)   **The distance between the number and 0 on the number line. The absolute value of a number x is written as $|x|$. The absolute value can be determined by**

$$|x| = \begin{cases} x & \text{if } x > 0 \\ 0 & \text{if } x = 0 \\ -x & \text{if } x < 0 \end{cases}$$

Algebraic expression (1.5)   A collection of numerical values, variables, and operation symbols is called an algebraic expression. $3x - 6y + 3yz$ and $\sqrt{5xy}$ are algebraic expressions.

Algebraic fraction (5.1)   An algebraic fraction is an expression of the form P/Q where P and Q are polynomials and Q is not zero. Algebraic fractions are also called rational expressions. For example, $\dfrac{x + 3}{x - 4}$ and $\dfrac{5x^2 + 1}{6x^3 - 5x}$ are algebraic fractions.

Approximate value (1.3)   **A value that is not exact. The approximate value of $\sqrt{3}$ correct to the nearest tenth is 1.7. The symbol $\approx$ or $\doteq$ is used to indicate "is approximately equal to."**

Associative property of addition (1.1)   For all real numbers $a,b,$ $a + (b + c) = (a + b) + c.$

Associative property of multiplication (1.1)   For all real numbers $a,b,c,$ $a(bc) = (ab)c.$

Asymptote (8.4)   A line that a curve gets continually closer to in some region, but the curve does not actually touch the line in that region. Often an asymptote is a helpful reference in making a sketch of a curve, such as a hyperbola.

Axis of symmetry of a parabola (8.2)   A line passing through the focus and the vertex of a parabola about which the two sides of the parabola are symmetric. See the sketch.

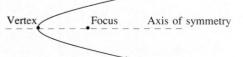

Vertex   Focus   Axis of symmetry

B

Base (1.3)   The number or variable that is raised to a power. In the expression 2^3, the number 2 is the base.

Base of an exponential function (9.1)   The number b is called the base of the function $f(x) = b^x$.

Binomial (4.1)   A polynomial of two terms. For example, $z^2 - 9$ is a binomial.

C

Cartesian coordinate system (2.1)   Another name for the rectangular coordinate system named after its inventor, Rene Descartes.

Characteristic of a logarithm (9.4)   The integer part of a logarithm. If $\log 0.00111 = 0.0453 - 3$, then the characteristic of the logarithm is -3.

Circle (1.6)   A geometric figure that consists of a collection of points that are of equal distance from a fixed point called the center.

Center

Circumference of a circle (1.6)   The distance around a circle. The circumference of a circle is given by the formulas $C = \pi d$ and $C = 2\pi r$, where d is the diameter of the circle and r is the radius of the circle.

Closure property of addition (1.1)   For all real numbers $a,b,$ the sum $a + b$ is a real number.

Closure property of multiplication (1.1)   For all real numbers $a,b,$ the product ab is a real number.

Coefficient (1.5)   Any factor or group of factors in a term may be called the coefficient of the term. In the term $8xy$, the coefficient of xy is 8. However, the coefficient of x is $8y$. In the term $abcd$, the coefficient of $abcd$ is 1.

Collect like terms (1.5)   Collecting like terms is the process of adding and subtracting like terms. If we collect like terms in the expression $5x - 8y - 7x - 12y$, we obtain $-2x - 20y$.

Combined variation (Appendix)   If y varies directly as

x and z and inversely as d^2, we can write the equation $y = kxz/d^2$ where k is the constant of variation.

Common denominator (1.2)   Two fractions that have the same number in the denominator are said to have a common denominator. The fractions $\dfrac{4}{13}$ and $\dfrac{7}{13}$ have a common denominator of 13.

Common logarithm (9.4)   The common logarithm of a number x is given by $\log x = \log_{10} x$ for all $x > 0$. A common logarithm is a logarithm to base 10.

Commutative property of addition (1.1)   For all real numbers a,b, $a + b = b + a$.

Commutative property of multiplication (1.1)   For all real numbers a,b, $ab = ba$.

Complex fraction (5.4)   A fraction made up of polynomials or numerical values in which the numerator or the denominator contains at least one fraction. Examples of complex fractions are:

$$\dfrac{\dfrac{1}{3} + \dfrac{1}{5}}{\dfrac{2}{7}} \quad \text{and} \quad \dfrac{\dfrac{1}{x} + 3}{2 + \dfrac{5}{x}}$$

Complex number (6.5)   A number that can be written in the form $a + bi$ where a and b are real numbers and $i = \sqrt{-1}$.

Compound inequalities (10.2)   Two inequality statements connected together by the word "and" or connected together by the word "or".

Conjugate of a binomial with radicals (6.4)   The expressions $a\sqrt{x} + b\sqrt{y}$ and $a\sqrt{x} - b\sqrt{y}$ are called conjugates. The conjugate of $2\sqrt{3} + 5\sqrt{2}$ is $2\sqrt{3} - 5\sqrt{2}$. The conjugate of $4 - \sqrt{x}$ is $4 + \sqrt{x}$.

Conjugate of a complex number (6.5)   The expressions $a + bi$ and $a - bi$ are called conjugates. The conjugate of $5 + 2i$ is $5 - 2i$. The conjugate of $7 - 3i$ is $7 + 3i$.

Coordinates of a point (2.1)   An ordered pair of numbers (x, y) that specify the location of a point on a rectangular coordinate system.

Counting numbers (1.1)   The counting numbers are the natural numbers. They are the numbers in the infinite set $\{1, 2, 3, 4, 5, 6, 7, \ldots\}$.

Critical points of a quadratic inequality (10.3)   The critical points of a quadratic inequality of the form $ax^2 + bx + c > 0$ or $ax^2 + bx + c < 0$ are those points where $ax^2 + bx + c = 0$.

D

The degree of a polynomial (4.1)   The degree of a polynomial is the degree of the highest degree term in the polynomial. The polynomial $5x^3 + 4x^2 - 3x + 12$ is of degree three.

The degree of a term (4.1)   The degree of a term is the sum of the exponents of its variables. The term $5x^2y^2$ is of degree 4.

Denominator (5.1)   The bottom expression in a fraction. The denominator of $\dfrac{5}{11}$ is 11. The denominator of $\dfrac{x - 7}{x + 8}$ is $x + 8$.

Descending order for a polynomial (4.1)   A polynomial is written in descending order if the term of the highest degree is first, the term of the next to highest degree is second, and so on, with each each succeeding term of less degree. The polynomial $5y^4 - 3y^3 + 7y^2 + 8y - 12$ is in descending order.

Determinant (3.4)   A determinant is a square array of numbers written between vertical lines. For example $\begin{vmatrix} 1 & 5 \\ 2 & 4 \end{vmatrix}$ is a 2×2 determinant. It is also called a second–order determinant. $\begin{vmatrix} 1 & 7 & 8 \\ 2 & -5 & -1 \\ -3 & 6 & 9 \end{vmatrix}$ is a 3×3 determinant. It is also called a third–order determinant.

Different signs (1.2)   When one number is positive and one number is negative, the two numbers are said to have different signs. The numbers 5 and -9 have different signs.

Direct variation (Appendix)   If a variable y varies directly as x, we can write the equation $y = kx$ where k represents some real number that will stay the same over a range of problems. This value k is called the constant of variation.

Discriminant of a quadratic equation (7.3)   In the equation $ax^2 + bx + c = 0$ and $a \neq 0$ then the expression $b^2 - 4ac$ is called the discriminant. It can be used to determine the nature of the roots of the quadratic equation. If the discriminant is *positive*, then there are two rational or irrational roots. The two roots will be rational only if the discriminant is a perfect square. If the discriminant is *zero*, then there is only one rational root. If the discriminant is *negative*, then there are two complex roots.

Distance between two points (8.1)   The distance between point (x_1, y_1) and point (x_2, y_2) is given by the formula $d = \sqrt{(x_2 - x_1)^2 + (y_2 - y_1)^2}$.

Distributive property of multiplication over addition (1.1)   For any real numbers a, b, c, $a(b + c) = ab + ac$.

Dividend (4.2)   The expression that is being divided by another. In the problem $12 \div 4 = 3$, the dividend is 12. In the problem $x - 5 \overline{)\,5x^2 + 10x - 3}$, the dividend is $5x + 10x - 3$.

Divisor (4.2)   The expression that is divided into another. In the problem $12 \div 4 = 3$ the divisor is 4. In the problem $x + 3 \overline{)\,2x^2 - 5x - 14}$, the divisor is $x + 3$.

Domain of a relation or a function (8.5)   If all of the ordered pairs of the relation or the function are listed, all of the different first items of each pair is called the domain.

E

e (9.1)   The number e is an irrational number. It can be approximated by the value $e \approx 2.7183$.

Elements (1.1) The objects that are in a set are called elements.

Ellipse (8.3) An ellipse is the set of points in a plane such that for each point in the set the sum of its distances to two fixed points is constant. Each of the fixed points is called a focus. Each of the following graphs is an ellipse.

Equation (1.7) A mathematical statement that two quantities are equal.

Equations that are quadratic in form (7.5) An equation that can be transformed to an equation that is quadratic. Examples of equations that are quadratic in form are: $9x^4 - 25x^2 + 16 = 0$, $8x^{1/2} + 7x^{1/4} - 1 = 0$.

Equilateral hyperbola (8.4) A hyperbola for which $a = b$ in the equation of the hyperbola.

Equivalent equations (1.7) Equations that have the same solution(s).

Even integers (1.3) Integers that are exactly divisible by 2, such as $\ldots -4, -2, 0, 2, 4, 6, \ldots$

Exponent (1.3) The number that indicates the power of a base. If the number is a positive integer it tells us how many factors of the base occur. In the expression 2^3, the exponent is 3. The number 3 tells us that there are 3 factors each of which is 2 since $2^3 = 2 \cdot 2 \cdot 2$. If an exponent is negative, use the property that $x^{-n} = \dfrac{1}{x^n}$. If an exponent is zero, use the property that $x^0 = 1$ where $x \neq 0$.

Exponential function (9.1) The exponential function is $f(x) = b^x$ where $b > 0$, $b \neq 1$, and x is any real number.

Expression (1.3) Any combination of mathematical operation symbols with numbers or variables or both is a mathematical expression. Examples of mathematical expressions are $2x + 3y - 6z$ and $\sqrt{7xyz}$.

Extraneous solution to an equation (5.5) A correctly-obtained solution to an equation, which when substituted back into the original equation, does not yield a true statement. For example $x = 2$ is an extraneous solution to the equation

$$\frac{x}{x - 2} - 4 = \frac{2}{x - 2}$$

An extraneous solution is also called an extraneous root.

F

Factor (1.5) and (4.4) When two or more numbers, variables, or algebraic expressions are multiplied, each of them is called a factor. In the expression $5st$, the factors are 5, s, and t. In the expression $(x - 6)(x + 2)$, the factors are $(x - 6)$ and $(x + 2)$.

First degree equation in one variable (1.7) An equation such as $x = 5 - 3x$ or $12x - 3(x + 5) = 22$ in which only one kind of variable appears and that variable has an exponent of one. It is also called a linear equation in one variable.

First degree equation (1.7) A mathematical equation such as $2x - 8 = 4y + 9$ or $7x = 21$ in which each variable has an exponent of one. It is also called a linear equation.

Focus of a parabola (8.2) The focus point of a parabola has many properties. For example the focus point of a parabolic mirror is the point to which all incoming light rays that are parallel to the axis of symmetry will collect. A parabola is a set of points that is the same distance from a fixed line called the directrix and a fixed point. This fixed point is the focus.

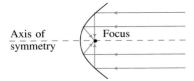

Formula (1.6) A formula is a rule for finding the value of a variable when the values of other variables in the expression are known. For example, the formula for finding the Fahrenheit temperature when the Celsius Temperature is known is $F = 1.8C + 32$.

Fractional equation (5.5) An equation that contains a rational expression. Examples of fractional equations are

$$\frac{x}{3} + \frac{x}{4} = 7 \quad \text{and} \quad \frac{2}{3x - 3} + \frac{1}{x - 1} = \frac{-5}{12}$$

Function (8.5) A relation in which no ordered pairs have the same first coordinates.

G

Graph of a function (8.5) The graph of a function is a graph in which a vertical line will never cross in more than one place. The following sketches represent the graphs of functions:

Graph of a linear inequality in two variables (10.5) The graph of a linear inequality in two variables is a shaded region in two dimensional space. It may or may not include the boundary line. If the line is to be included the sketch will show a solid line. If it is not to be included the sketch will show a dashed line. Two sketches are shown below.

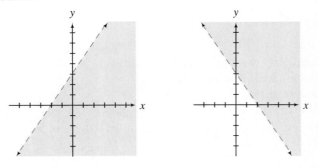

Graph of a one–to–function (8.6) The graph of a one–to–one function is a graph of a function that has the additional property that a horizontal line will never cross the graph in more than one place. The following sketches represent the graphs of one–to–one functions.

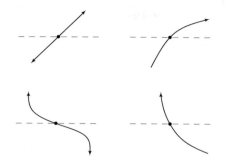

Graph of a system of inequalities in two variables (10.6) The graph is a shaded region that satisfies all the conditions of every inequality at the same time. Some examples are illustrated below:

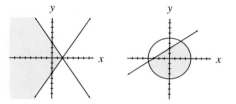

Greater than or equal to symbol (10.1) The symbol $\geq$ means greater than or equal to.

Greater than symbol (1.2) The $>$ symbol means greater than. $5 > 3$ is read "5 is greater than 3."

Greatest common factor of a polynomial (4.4) The greatest common factor of a polynomial is a common factor of each term of the polynomial which has the largest possible numerical coefficient and the largest possible exponent for each of the variables. For example, the greatest common factor of $50x^4y^5 - 25x^3y^4 + 75x^5y^6$ is $25x^3y^4$.

H

Higher–order equations (7.5) Equations that contain variables raised to the third or a higher power are called higher–order equations. Examples of higher-order equations are the following:

$$x^4 - 29x^2 + 100 = 0, \qquad x^3 + 3x^2 - 4x - 12 = 0$$

Higher–order roots (6.2) Cube Roots, Fourth Roots, and Roots with an index greater than two are called higher–order roots.

Horizontal line (2.1) A horizontal line is a straight line that is parallel to the x-axis. A horizontal line has a slope of zero. The equation of any horizontal line can be written in the form $y = b$ where b is a constant. A sketch is shown.

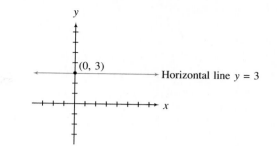

Horizontal parabolas (8.2) Parabolas that open to the right or to the left. The following graphs represent horizontal parabolas.

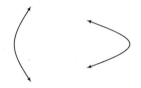

Hyperbola (8.4) A hyperbola is the set of points in a plane such that for each point in the set the absolute value of the difference of its distances to two fixed points is constant. Each of these fixed points is called a focus. Each of the following sketches represents the graph of a hyperbola.

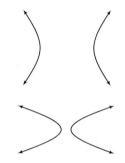

Hypotenuse of a right triangle (7.6) The side opposite the right angle in any right triangle. The hypotenuse is always the longest side of a triangle. In the following sketch the hypotenuse is side c.

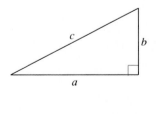

I

Identity property for addition (1.1) For any real number a, $a + 0 = a = 0 + a$.

Identity property for multiplication (1.1) For any real number a, $a(1) = a = 1(a)$.

Imaginary number (6.5) The imaginary number i is defined as $i = \sqrt{-1}$ and $i^2 = -1$.

Inconsistent system of equations (3.1) A system of equations for which no solution is possible.

Index of a radical (6.2) The index of a radical indicates what type of a root is being taken. The index of a cube root is 3. When we write $\sqrt[3]{x}$, the 3 is called the index of the radical. When we write $\sqrt[4]{y}$, the index is 4. The index of a square root is 2, but the index is not written in the square root symbol such as $\sqrt{x}$.

Inequality (10.1) An inequality is a mathematical statement expressing an order relationship. The following are inequalities:

$$x < 3, \qquad x \geq 4.5, \qquad 2x + 3 \leq 5x - 7,$$
$$x + 2y < 8, \qquad 2x^2 - 3x > 0$$

Infinite set (1.1) A set that has no end to the numbers of elements that are within it. An infinite set is often indicated by placing an ellipsis (...) after listing some of the elements of the set.

Interest (2.5) Interest is the charge made for borrowing money or the income received from investing money. Simple interest is calculated by the formula $I = prt$ where p is the principal which is borrowed, r is the rate of interest, and t is the amount of time the money is borrowed.

Integers (1.1) The integers are the numbers in the infinite set

$$\{\ldots -3, -2, -1, 0, 1, 2, 3, \ldots\}$$

Inverse function of a one–to–one function (8.6) The inverse of a one-to-one function is that function obtained by interchanging the first and second coordinates in each ordered pair of the function.

Inverse property for addition (1.1) For any real number a, $a + (-a) = 0 = (-a) + a$.

Inverse property for multiplication (1.1) For any real number $a \neq 0$, $a\left(\dfrac{1}{a}\right) = 1 = \left(\dfrac{1}{a}\right)a$.

Inverse variation (Appendix) If a variable y varies inversely as x we can write the equation $y = \dfrac{k}{x}$ where k is the constant of variation.

Irrational numbers (1.1) Numbers whose decimal forms are nonterminating and nonrepeating.

J

Joint variation (Appendix) If a variable y varies jointly as x and z, we can write the equation $y = kxz$ where k is the constant of variation.

L

Least common denominator of algebraic fraction (5.3) The least common denominator (LCD) of two or more algebraic fractions is a product of all the different prime factors of each denominator with any factor that is repeated in any denominator being repeated in the LCD with the highest power that factor has in any one fraction.

For example, The LCD of $\dfrac{5}{2(x + 2)(x - 3)^2}$ and $\dfrac{3}{(x - 3)^4}$ is $2(x + 2)(x - 3)^4$. The LCD of $\dfrac{5}{(x + 2)(x - 3)}$ and $\dfrac{7}{(x - 3)(x + 4)}$ is $(x + 2)(x - 3)(x + 4)$.

Least common denominator of numerical fractions (1.7) The smallest whole number that is exactly divisible by all the denominators of a group of fractions. The least common denominator (LCD) of $\dfrac{1}{7}, \dfrac{9}{21}, \dfrac{3}{14}$ is 42. The number 42 is the smallest number that can be exactly divided by 7, by 21, and by 14. The least common denominator is sometimes called the lowest common denominator.

Leg of a right triangle (7.6) One of the two shortest sides of a right triangle. In the following sketch, side a and side b are the legs of the right triangle.

Less than symbol (1.2) The $<$ symbol means less than. $2 < 8$ is read "2 is less than 8."

Less than or equal to symbol (10.1) The symbol $\leq$ means less than or equal to.

Like signs (1.2) Two numbers with the same sign are said to have like signs. The numbers -8 and -15 have like signs. The numbers 4 and 3.5 have like signs.

Like terms (1.5) Terms that have identical variables and also have identical exponents. In the mathematical expression $5x - 8syz + 7x + 15syz$, the terms $5x$ and $7x$ are like terms and the terms $-8syz$ and $15syz$ are like terms.

Linear equation (1.7) An mathematical equation such as $3x + 7 = 5x - 2$ or $5x + 7y = 9$ in which each variable has an exponent of one. It is also called an equation of the first degree.

Linear equation in one variable (1.7) An equation such as $4x = 12$ or $5x + 7 = 3x - 2$ in which only one kind of variable appears and that variable has an exponent of one.

Linear inequality (10.1) An inequality statement involving variables with an exponent of 1 and no variables in the denominator in any expression. Some examples of linear inequalities are the following:

$$2x + 3 > 5x - 6, \qquad y < 2x + 1, \qquad x < 8$$

Literal equation (1.8) An equation that has other variables in it besides the variable that you wish to solve for. $I = prt$, $7x + 3y - 6z = 12$, and $P = 2w + 2l$ are examples of literal equations.

Logarithm (9.2) The logarithm of a positive number x is the power to which the base b must be raised to produce x. That is, $y = \log_b x$ is the same as $x = b^y$ where $b > 0$, $b \neq 1$. A logarithm is an exponent.

Logarithm equation (9.2) An equation which contains at least one logarithm.

M

Magnitude of an earthquake (9.5) The magnitude of an earthquake is measured by the formula $M = \log\left(\dfrac{I}{I_0}\right)$ where I is the intensity of the earthquake and I_0 is the minimum measurable intensity.

Mantissa of a logarithm (9.4) The decimal part of a logarithm. If $\log 0.00111 = 0.0453 - 3$, then the mantissa of the logarithm is 0.0453.

Minor of an element of a third order determinant (3.4) The second order determinant that remains after you delete the row and column in which the element appears. The minor of the element 6 in the determinant $\begin{vmatrix} 1 & 2 & 3 \\ 7 & 6 & 8 \\ -3 & 5 & 9 \end{vmatrix}$ is the second order determinant $\begin{vmatrix} 1 & 3 \\ -3 & 9 \end{vmatrix}$.

Monomial (4.1) A polynomial of one term. For example, $3a$ is a monomial.

N

Natural logarithm (9.4) The natural logarithm of a number x is $\ln x = \log_e x$ for all $x > 0$. A natural logarithm is a logarithm with a base of the number e.

Negative integers (1.1) The negative integers are the numbers in the infinite set

$$\{-1, -2, -3, -4, -5, -6, -7, \ldots\}$$

Nonlinear system of equations (8.7) A system of equations in which at least one equation is not a linear equation.

Nonzero (1.4) A nonzero value is a value other than zero. If we say the variable x is nonzero we mean that x cannot have the value of zero.

Numerator (5.1) The top expression in a fraction. The numerator of $\dfrac{3}{19}$ is 3. The numerator of $\dfrac{x+5}{x^2+25}$ is $x + 5$.

Numerical coefficient (1.5) The numerical value multiplied by the variables in a term. The numerical coefficient of $-8xyw$ is -8. The numerical coefficient of abc is 1.

O

Odd integer (1.3) Integers that are not exactly divisible by 2, such as $\ldots -3, -1, 1, 3, 5, 7, \ldots$.

One–to–one function (8.6) A one–to–one function is a function in which no ordered pairs have the same second coordinate.

Opposite of a number (1.2) The opposite of a number is that number with the same absolute value but a different sign. The opposite of -7 is 7. The opposite of 13 is -13.

Ordered pair (2.1) A pair of numbers represented in a specified order. An ordered pair is used to specify the location of a point. Every point on a rectangular coordinate system can be represented by an ordered pair (x, y).

Origin (2.1) The point determined by the intersection of the x-axis and the y-axis. It has the coordinates $(0, 0)$.

P

Parabola (8.2) A parabola is defined as the set of points that is the same distance from some fixed line (called the directrix) and some fixed point (called the focus) that is not on the line. The graph of any equation of the form $y = ax^2 + bx + c$ or $x = ay^2 + by + c$ where a, b, c are real numbers and $a \neq 0$ is a parabola. Some examples of the graphs of parabolas are shown below.

Parallel lines (2.2) Two straight lines are parallel if they never intersect. Parallel lines have the same slope.

Parallelogram (1.6) A four–sided geometric figure with opposite sides parallel. The opposite sides of a parallelogram are equal.

Percent (1.6) Hundredths or "per one hundred;" indicated by the % symbol. Thirty-seven hundredths means thirty seven percent. $\dfrac{37}{100} = 37\%$.

Perfect square (1.3) If x is a real number and a is a positive real number such that $a = x^2$ then x is a square root of a and a is a perfect square. Some numbers that are perfect squares are 1, 4, 9, 16, 25, 36, 49, 64, 81, and 100.

Perfect square trinomials (4.6) are trinomials of the form $a^2 + 2ab + b^2$ or $a^2 - 2ab + b^2$.

Perpendicular lines (2.2) Two straight lines are perpendicular if they meet at a 90 degree angle. If two nonvertical lines have slopes m_1 and m_2 and $m_1, m_2 \neq 0$, then the lines are perpendicular if and only if $m_1 = -\dfrac{1}{m_2}$.

pH of a solution (9.2) The pH of a solution is defined by the equation $\text{pH} = -\log_{10}(\text{H}^+)$ where H^+ is the concentration of the hydrogen ion in the solution. The solution is an acid if the pH is less than 7 and is a base if the pH is greater than 7.

Pi (1.6) An irrational number, denoted by the symbol π, which is approximately equal to 3.141592654. In most cases, 3.14 can be used as a sufficiently accurate approximation for π.

Point–slope form of the equation of a straight line (2.3) The point–slope form of the equation of a straight line passing through the point (x_1, y_1) and having slope m is $y - y_1 = m(x - x_1)$.

Polynomials (1.5) and (4.1) Polynomials are variable expressions that contain terms with nonnegative integer exponents. A polynomial must contain no division by a variable. Some examples of polynomials are $5y^2 - 8y + 3$, $-12xy$, $12a - 14b$, and $7x$.

Positive integers (1.1) The positive integers are the numbers in the infinite set $\{1, 2, 3, 4, 5, 6, 7, \ldots\}$. The positive integers are the natural numbers.

Power (1.4) When a number is raised to a power it means a number with an exponent of that power. Thus, two to the third power means 2^3. The power is the exponent, which is three. In the expression x^5, we say "x is raised to the fifth power."

Prime factors of a number (5.3) The prime factors of a number are those factors of a number which are prime. To write the number 40 as a product of prime factors we would write $40 = 5 \times 2^3$. To write the number 462 as the product of prime factors we would write $462 = 2 \times 3 \times 7 \times 11$.

Prime factors of a polynomial (5.3) When a polynomial is completely factored it is written as a product of prime factors. Thus, the prime factors of $x^4 - 81$ are written as $x^4 - 81 = (x^2 + 9)(x - 3)(x + 3)$.

Prime number (5.3) A positive integer that is greater than 1 and that has no factors other than 1 and itself is a prime number. The first ten prime numbers are: 2, 3, 5, 7, 11, 13, 17, 19, 23, and 29.

Prime polynomial (4.7) A prime polynomial is a polynomial that cannot be factored using the methods of intermediate algebra. Examples of prime polynomials are $2x^2 + 100x - 19$, $25x^2 + 9$, and $x^2 - 3x + 5$.

Principal (1.6) In monetary problems, the principal is the original amount of money invested or borrowed.

Principal square root (1.3) The positive square root of a number is called the principal square root. The symbol to find the principal square root is $\sqrt{\ }$. Thus, $\sqrt{4}$ means to find the principal square root of 4 which is 2.

Proportion (5.6) A proportion is an equation stating that two ratios are equal. For example $\dfrac{a}{b} = \dfrac{c}{d}$ is a proportion.

Pythagorean theorem (7.6) In any right triangle, if c is the length of the hypotenuse and a and b are the lengths of the two legs, then $c^2 = a^2 + b^2$.

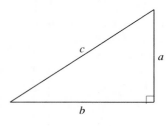

Q

Quadrants (2.1) The four regions into which the x-axis and the y-axis divide the rectangular coordinate system.

Quadratic equation in standard form (7.1) An equation of the form $ax^2 + bx + c = 0$, where a, b, c are real numbers and $a \neq 0$, is a quadratic equation in standard form. A quadratic equation is classified as a second-degree equation.

Quadratic formula (7.3) If $ax^2 + bx + c = 0$ and $a \neq 0$, then the roots to the equation are found by the formula
$$x = \frac{-b \pm \sqrt{b^2 - 4ac}}{2a}.$$

Quadratic inequalities (10.3) A quadratic inequality can be placed in the form $ax^2 + bx + c > 0$ where $a \neq 0$ and a, b, c are real numbers. The $>$ symbol may be replaced by a $<$, $\geq$, or a $\leq$ symbol.

Quotient (1.4) The result of dividing one number or expression by another. In the problem $12 \div 4 = 3$, the quotient is 3.

R

Radicand (1.3) The expression beneath the radical sign is called the radicand. The radicand of $\sqrt{7x}$ is $7x$.

Radical equation (7.4) An equation that contains one or more radicals is called a radical equation. The following are examples of radical equations.
$$\sqrt{9x - 20} = x, \qquad 4 = \sqrt{x - 3} + \sqrt{x + 5}$$

Radical sign (1.3) The symbol $\sqrt{\ }$ is used to indicate the root of a number and is called a radical sign.

Radius of a circle (1.6) The distance from any point on the circle to the center of the circle.

Range of a relation or a function (8.5) If all of the ordered pairs of the relation or the function are listed, all of the different second items of each pair is called the range.

Ratio (5.6) The ratio of two values is the first value divided by the second. The ratio of a to b where $b \neq 0$ is written as $\dfrac{a}{b}$, a/b, $a \div b$ or $a:b$.

Rational equation (5.5) A fractional equation that has at least one variable in one or more denominators. Examples of rational equations are $\dfrac{x + 6}{3x} = \dfrac{x + 8}{5}$ and $\dfrac{x + 3}{x} - \dfrac{x + 4}{x + 5} = \dfrac{15}{x^2 + 5x}$.

Rational exponents (6.2) When the exponent is a rational number we understand this is equivalent to a radical expression in the following way: $x^{m/n} = (\sqrt[n]{x})^m = \sqrt[n]{x^m}$. Thus, $x^{3/7} = (\sqrt[7]{x})^3 = \sqrt[7]{x^3}$.

Rational expressions (5.1) A rational expression is a fraction of the form $\dfrac{P}{Q}$ where P and Q are polynomials and Q is not zero. Rational expressions are also called algebraic fractions. For example, $\dfrac{7}{x - 8}$ and $\dfrac{3x - 5}{2x^2 + 1}$ are rational expressions.

Rational numbers (1.1) The rational numbers are an

infinite set of numbers containing all the integers and all exact quotients of two integers where the denominator is not zero. In set notation, the rational numbers are the set of numbers $\left\{\dfrac{a}{b} \,\middle|\, a \text{ and } b \text{ are integers but } b \neq 0\right\}$.

Rationalizing the denominator (6.4)   The process of transforming a fraction that contains one or more radicals in the denominator to an equivalent fraction that does not contain one. When we rationalize the denominator of $\dfrac{5}{\sqrt{3}}$ we obtain $\dfrac{5\sqrt{3}}{3}$. When we rationalize the denominator of $\dfrac{-2}{\sqrt{11}-\sqrt{7}}$ we obtain $\dfrac{\sqrt{11}+\sqrt{7}}{2}$.

Rationalizing the numerator (6.4)   The process of transforming a fraction that contains one or more radicals in the numerator to an equivalent fraction that does not contain any radicals in the numerator. When we rationalize the numerator of $\dfrac{\sqrt{5}}{x}$, we obtain $\dfrac{5}{x\sqrt{5}}$.

Real numbers (1.1)   Numbers that are rational or irrational.

Real number line (1.2)   A number line on which all the real numbers are placed. Positive numbers lie to the right of 0 on the number line. Negative numbers lie to the left of 0 on the number line.

Real number line

Reciprocal (1.2)   The reciprocal of a number is 1 divided by that number. Therefore, the reciprocal of 12 is $\dfrac{1}{12}$. The reciprocal of $\dfrac{3}{4}$ is $\dfrac{4}{3}$. The reciprocal of $-\dfrac{5}{8}$ is $-\dfrac{8}{5}$.

Rectangle (1.6)   A four–sided figure with opposite sides parallel and all interior angles measuring 90 degrees. The opposite sides of a rectangle are equal.

Rectangular solid (1.6)   A three–dimensional object in which each side is a rectangle. A rectangular solid has the shape of a "box."

Reduce a fraction (5.1)   To use the basic rule of fractions to simplify a fraction. The basic rule of fractions is: For any polynomials a, b, c where $b, c \neq 0$ $\dfrac{ac}{bc} = \dfrac{a}{b}$. To reduce

the fraction $\dfrac{5(x-3)}{(x+9)(x-3)}$ we obtain $\dfrac{5}{x+9}$. An additional example is: To reduce the fraction $\dfrac{x^2-16}{2x+8}$ we have $\dfrac{(x+4)(x-4)}{2(x+4)} = \dfrac{x-4}{2}$.

Relation (8.5)   Any set of ordered pairs.

Remainder (4.2)   The amount left after the final subtraction when working out a division problem. In the problem

$$15\overline{)64}$$
$$\underline{60}$$
$$\boxed{4} \longleftarrow \text{The remainder is 4.}$$

In the problem

$$x-2\overline{)2x^2 - 7x + 9}$$

with $2x - 3$ above, $2x^2 - 4x$, $-3x + 9$, $-3x + 6$, and $\boxed{3} \longleftarrow$ The remainders is 3.

Repeating decimal (1.1)   A number that in decimal form has one or more digits which continue to repeat. The numbers $0.33333\ldots$ and $0.128128128\ldots$ are repeating decimals.

Reversing an inequality (10.1)   Multiplying or dividing both sides of an inequality by a negative number changes a "greater than" symbol to a "less than" symbol and changes a "less than" symbol to a "greater than" symbol. This is called reversing the direction of an inequality. For example, to solve $-3x < 9$, we divide each side by -3. $\dfrac{-3x}{-3} > \dfrac{9}{-3}$ so $x > -3$. The $<$ symbol was reversed to $>$ by dividing both sides by -3.

Rhombus (1.6)   A parallelogram with four equal sides is called a rhombus.

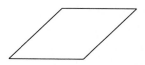

Right circular cylinder (1.6)   A three–dimensional object shaped like a tin can.

Right triangle (7.6)   A triangle which contains one right angle. A right angle is an angle which measures exactly

90 degrees. It is indicated by the small rectangle at the corner of the angle.

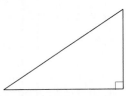

Root of an equation (1.7)   A number which, when substituted into a given equation, yields a true mathematical statement. The root of an equation is also called the solution of an equation.

S

Scientific notation (1.4)   A positive number is written in scientific notation if it is in the form $a \times 10^n$ where $1 \leq a < 10$ and n is an integer.

Set (1.1)   A collection of objects.

Signed numbers (1.2)   Numbers that are either positive, negative, or zero. Positive signed numbers such as 5, 9, or 124 are usually written without a positive sign. Negative signed numbers such as -5, -3.3, or -178 are always written with a negative sign.

Similar radicals (6.3)   Two radicals are said to be similar if they are simplified, have the same radicand, and the same index. $2\sqrt[3]{7xy^2}$ and $-5\sqrt[3]{7xy^2}$ are similar radicals. Usually similar radicals are referred to as *like radicals*.

Similar triangles (5.6)   Two triangles are similar if their corresponding sides are proportional. For example, the following two triangles are proportional.

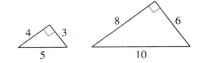

Simplifying a radical (6.3)   To simplify a radical when the root cannot be found exactly, we use the product rule for radicals $\sqrt[n]{ab} = \sqrt[n]{a}\,\sqrt[n]{b}$ for $a \geq 0$, $b \geq 0$, if n is even, in such a way that $\sqrt[n]{a}$ can be found exactly.
To simplify $\sqrt{20}$ we have $= \sqrt{4}\sqrt{5} = 2\sqrt{5}$.
To simplify $\sqrt[3]{16x^4}$ we have $= \sqrt[3]{8x^3}\sqrt[3]{2x} = 2x\sqrt[3]{2x}$.

Simplifying imaginary numbers (6.5)   Imaginary numbers are simplified by using the property that for all positive real numbers a, $\sqrt{-a} = \sqrt{-1}\sqrt{a} = i\sqrt{a}$. Thus, to simplify $\sqrt{-7}$ we have $\sqrt{-7} = \sqrt{-1}\sqrt{7} = i\sqrt{7}$.

Slope of a straight line (2.2)   The slope of a straight line that passes through the points (x_1, y_1) and (x_2, y_2) is

$$\text{Slope} = m = \frac{y_2 - y_1}{x_2 - x_1} \qquad \text{where } x_1 \neq x_2.$$

Slope-intercept form of the equation of a straight line (2.3)   The slope-intercept form of the equation of a straight line with slope m and y-intercept b is $y = mx + b$.

Solution of an equation (1.7)   A number which, when substituted into a given equation, yields a true mathe-

matical statement. The solution of an equation is also called the root of an equation.

Sphere (1.6)   A perfectly round three-dimensional object shaped like a ball.

Square root (1.3)   If x is a real number and a is a positive real number such that $a = x^2$, then x is a square root of a and a is a perfect square. One square root of 16 is 4 since $4^2 = 16$. Another square root of 16 is -4 since $(-4)^2 = 16$.

Standard form of the equation of a circle (8.1)   A circle with a center at (h, k) and a radius of r is in standard form if it is written as $(x - h)^2 + (y - k)^2 = r$.

Standard form of the equation of an ellipse (8.3)   An ellipse with its center at the origin has an equation of the form:

$$\frac{x^2}{a^2} + \frac{y^2}{b^2} = 1 \qquad a, b > 0$$

This ellipse has intercepts at $(a, 0)$, $(-a, 0)$, $(0, b)$, and $(0, -b)$.

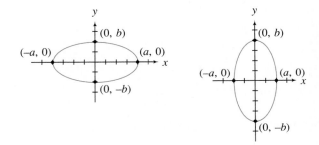

An ellipse with its center at (h, k) has an equation of the form:

$$\frac{(x - h)^2}{a^2} + \frac{(y - k)^2}{b^2} = 1 \qquad a, b > 0$$

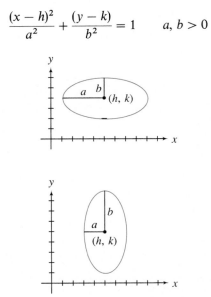

Standard form of the equation of a hyperbola with its center at the origin (8.4)   A horizontal hyperbola with its center at the origin has an equation in standard form of $\frac{x^2}{a^2} - \frac{y^2}{b^2} = 1$ where $a,b > 0$. The vertices are at $(-a, 0)$ and $(a, 0)$.

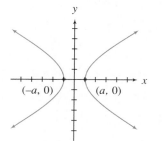

A vertical hyperbola with its center at the origin has an equation in standard form of $\frac{y^2}{b^2} - \frac{x^2}{a^2} = 1$ where $a,b > 0$. The vertices are at $(0, b)$ and $(0, -b)$.

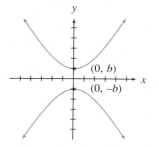

Standard form of the equation of a hyperbola with its center at point (h, k) (8.4)   A horizontal hyperbola with its center at (h, k) has an equation in standard form of $\frac{(x - h)^2}{a^2} - \frac{(y - k)^2}{b^2} = 1$ where $a,b > 0$. The vertices are $(h - a, k)$ and $(h + a, k)$.

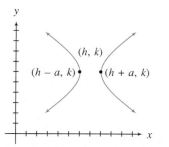

A vertical hyperbola with its center at (h, k) has an equation in standard form of $\frac{(y - k)^2}{b^2} - \frac{(x - h)^2}{a^2} = 1$ where

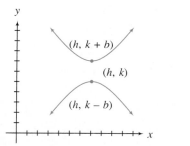

$a,b > 0$. The vertices are at $(h, k + b)$ and $(h, k - b)$.

Standard form of the equation of a parabola (8.2)   The standard form of the equation of a vertical parabola with its vertex at (h, k) is $y = a(x - h)^2 + k$ where $a \neq 0$. The standard form of the equation of a horizontal parabola with its vertex at (h, k) is $x = a(y - k)^2 + h$ where $a \neq 0$.

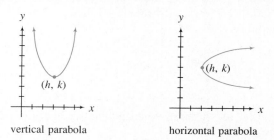

vertical parabola   horizontal parabola

Standard form of the equation of a straight line (2.3)   The equation of a straight line is expressed in standard form if it is written in the form $Ax + By = C$ where A, B, and C are real numbers.

Standard form of the quadratic equation (7.1)   The standard form of the quadratic equation is $ax^2 + bx + c = 0$, where a,b,c, are real numbers and $a \neq 0$. A quadratic equation is classified as a second–degree equation.

Subset (1.1)   A subset of a set is a set whose elements are all members of another set. For example, the Whole Numbers are a subset of the Integers.

System of dependent equations (3.1)   A system of n linear equations in n variables in which some equations are dependent will not have a unique solution. Such a system will have an infinite number of solutions.

System of equations (3.1)   A system of equations is a set of two or more equations that must be considered together. The solution to a system of equations is a value for each variable of the system that will satisfy each equation.

$$x + 3y = -7$$
$$4x + 3y = -1$$

is a system of two equations in two unknowns. The solution to this system is $(2, -3)$ or the values $x = 2$, $y = -3$.

System of inequalities (10.6)   If two inequalities in two variables are considered at one time we have a system of inequalities. The solution to a system of inequalities in two variables is that region that satisfies every inequality at one time. Some examples of systems of inequalities are;

$$y \leq 3x - 2 \qquad\qquad \frac{x^2}{4} + \frac{y^2}{25} < 1$$
$$\text{and}$$
$$y \geq \frac{1}{2}x \qquad\qquad x + 3y < 3$$

T

Term (1.5)   A term is a real number, a variable, or a product or quotient of numbers and variables. The expression $5xyz$ is one term. The expression $7x + 5y + 6z$ has three terms.

Terminating decimal (1.1) A number in decimal form such as 0.18 or 0.3462. The number of nonzero digits in a terminating decimal is finite.

Trapezoid (1.6) A four–sided geometric figure with two sides parallel. The parallel sides are called the bases of the trapezoid.

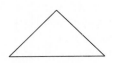

Triangle (1.6) A three–sided geometric figure is called a triangle.

Trinomial (4.1) A polynomial of three terms. For example, $2x^2 + 3x - 4$ is a trinomial.

U

Unknown (1.7) A variable or constant whose value is not known.

V

Value of a second order determinant (3.4) The value of the second order determinant $\begin{vmatrix} a & b \\ c & d \end{vmatrix}$ is defined to be $ad - cb$.

Value of a third order determinant (3.4) The value of the third order determinant $\begin{vmatrix} a_1 & b_1 & c_1 \\ a_2 & b_2 & c_2 \\ a_3 & b_3 & c_3 \end{vmatrix}$ is defined to be $a_1b_2c_3 + b_1c_2a_3 + c_1a_2b_3 - a_3b_2c_1 - b_3c_2a_1 - c_3a_2b_1$.

Variable (1.1) When a letter is used to represent a number it is called a variable.

Vertex of a parabola (8.2) The vertex of a vertical parabola is the lowest point on a parabola opening upward, or the highest point on a parabola opening downward.

The vertex of a horizontal parabola is the left most point on a parabola opening to the right, or the right most point on a parabola opening to the left.

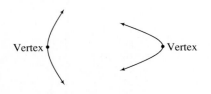

Vertical line (2.1) A vertical line is a straight line that is parallel to the y-axis. A vertical line has no slope. The equation of a vertical line can be written in the form $x = a$ where a is a constant. A sketch of a vertical line is shown.

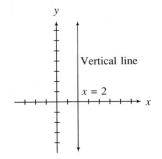

Vertical parabolas (8.2) Parabolas that open up or down. The following graphs represent vertical parabolas.

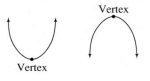

W

Whole numbers (1.1) The whole numbers are the set of numbers containing the natural numbers as well as the number 0. The whole numbers can be written as the infinite set $\{0, 1, 2, 3, 4, 5, 6, 7 \ldots\}$.

X

x-Intercept (2.1) The number a is the x-intercept of a line if the line crosses the x-axis at $(a, 0)$. The x-intercept of the line shown below is 5.

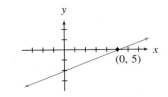

Y

y-Intercept (2.1) The number b is the y-intercept of a line if the line crosses the y-axis at $(0, b)$. The y-intercept of the line shown below is 4.

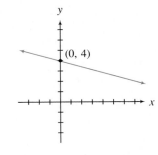

Selected Answers

CHAPTER 1 Basic Concepts

Pretest Chapter 1

1. $\pi, \sqrt{3}$ **2.** 2, 0 **3.** identity property for addition **4.** -16 **5.** $-\dfrac{2}{3}$ **6.** 10 **7.** -50 **8.** $36x^{-1}y^2z$

9. $\dfrac{125}{4x^{12}y}$ **10.** $\dfrac{y^7}{-3x}$ **11.** $\dfrac{16}{9a^2b^6}$ **12.** $\dfrac{y^9}{-27x^6}$ **13.** 7.23×10^{-8} **14.** $3x^3 - 14x^2 - 7x$

15. $-10x^4y + 15x^3y^2 - 5x^2y$ **16.** $21x + 18y$ **17.** -33 **18.** 113.04 sq. meters **19.** -3.7 **20.** -18

21. $x = -2.4$ **22.** $\dfrac{15 - 5x}{-8}$ or $\dfrac{5x - 15}{8}$ or $\dfrac{15 - 5x}{8}$ **23.** $a = \dfrac{b + 24}{11b}$ **24. (a)** $r = \dfrac{A - P}{Pt}$ **(b)** 0.06 **25.** $x = 3, x = -\dfrac{5}{3}$

26. $x = 4, x = 12$ **27.** $x = 2.5, x = -5.5$ **28.** $x = 5, x = 0.75$

Exercises 1.1

1. rational, real **3.** integer, rational, real **5.** rational, real **7.** irrational, real **9.** rational, real

11. $-25, -\dfrac{18}{5}, -0.763, -0.333\ldots, 0, \dfrac{1}{10}, \dfrac{2}{7}, 9, \dfrac{283}{5}, 52.8$ **13.** 9 **15.** $-25, -\dfrac{18}{5}, -\pi, -0.763, -0.333\ldots$ **17.** 9

19. 1, 2, 3, 4, 5, 6, 7 **21.** $-4, -3, -2$ **23.** True **25.** True **27.** associative property for addition
29. inverse property for multiplication **31.** identity property for addition **33.** commutative property for multiplication
35. closure property for multiplication **37.** commutative property for addition **39.** inverse property for multiplication
41. associative property for multiplication **43.** associative property for addition **45.** commutative property for addition

47. closure property for multiplication **49.** inverse property for addition **51.** $-82, -\dfrac{156}{3}, -\dfrac{5}{7}, -0.\overline{16}, -\dfrac{1}{10}, 0$

Exercises 1.2

1. -3 **3.** -5 **5.** -3 **7.** $-\dfrac{5}{3}$ or $-1\dfrac{2}{3}$ **9.** 5 **11.** -42 **13.** $-\dfrac{10}{21}$ **15.** $\dfrac{1}{32}$ **17.** -10 **19.** 7 **21.** 0

23. 7 **25.** 55 **27.** 1 **29.** -30 **31.** One or three of the quantities a, b, c, must be negative. In other words, when

multiplying an odd number of negative numbers, the answer will be negative. **33.** $\dfrac{5}{4}$ or $1\dfrac{1}{4}$

35. commutative property for addition **37.** -0.678197169

Exercises 1.3

1. 2^8 **3.** x^6 **5.** $(-6)^5$ **7.** 81 **9.** -64 **11.** -64 **13.** 216 **15.** 81 **17.** negative **19.** 5 **21.** 9

23. -4 **25.** $\dfrac{5}{7}$ **27.** Does not exist **29.** 0.3 **31.** 7 **33.** 0 **35.** -20 **37.** 6 **39.** 40 **41.** -35

43. -14 **45.** 2 **47.** 3 **49.** 3 **51.** 24 **53.** commutative property for multiplication **55.** 7685.702373

Exercises 1.4

1. x^{12} **3.** x^{18} **5.** 3^{17} **7.** $-6x^6$ **9.** $36x^8y^3$ **11.** $-10xy^5z^9$ **13.** $-6a^{-3}b^{-3}$ **15.** $-12y^{-11}$ **17.** x^5

19. $\dfrac{1}{a^5}$ or a^{-5} **21.** 8 **23.** $\dfrac{2}{x^5}$ or $2x^{-5}$ **25.** $4y^2z$ **27.** $\dfrac{2}{3a^{15}b}$ or $\dfrac{2}{3}a^{-15}b^{-1}$ **29.** $\dfrac{-7}{4}a^3b^{10}$ **31.** x^{16} **33.** $81a^{20}b^4$

35. $\dfrac{x^{12}y^{18}}{z^6}$ **37.** $-8y^6z^3$ **39.** $\dfrac{9a^2c^6}{16b^{12}}$ **41.** $\dfrac{1}{8x^{12}y^{18}}$ **43.** $\dfrac{x^7y^{12}}{27}$ **45.** $\dfrac{-256}{a^3b^{17}}$ **47.** $\dfrac{2a^4}{b^7}$ **49.** $\dfrac{y^4}{9x^8}$ **51.** $\dfrac{x^6}{y^8}$

53. $\dfrac{1}{a^{15}b^5}$ **55.** $\dfrac{1}{4x^2}$ **57.** $\dfrac{7}{5}$ **59.** 4.7×10^2 **61.** 1.73×10^6 **63.** 1.7×10^{-2} **65.** 8.346×10^{-6} **67.** $713{,}000$

69. 0.01863 **71.** 0.000000901 **73.** 36×10^{-8} **75.** 3×10^{-3} **77.** $\dfrac{729}{64}x^{6n-18}y^{-24n-72}z^{18n+18}$ **79.** 24 **81.** -15

83. $-9460.906704x^{21}y^{28}$

Exercises 1.5

1. $-5x^2$ **3.** $1, 2, 3$ **5.** $5, -3, 1$ **7.** $18, -12, 1$ **9.** $5x^3, -6x^2, +4x, +8$ **11.** $11ab$ **13.** $6x - 8y$

15. $-7x^2 + 10x$ **17.** $\dfrac{a}{6}$ **19.** $\dfrac{-3a^2}{10} + 2b$ **21.** $-7.7x^2 - 3.6x$ **23.** $-3a^2b - 14ab - 5ab^2$ **25.** $2x^2 + 2xy$

27. $x^4 - 3x^3 - 5x^2$ **29.** $-10a^2 + 15a + 40$ **31.** $2x^3y - 6x^2y^2 + 8xy^3$ **33.** $\dfrac{2}{3}x + 2xy - 4$ **35.** $\dfrac{x^3}{6} + \dfrac{5x^2}{6} - \dfrac{3x}{2}$

37. $2a^6b - 6a^5b + 2a^3b - 4a^2b$ **39.** $7x - 2xy - 15y$ **41.** $-y - 12z$ **43.** $2x + 8$ **45.** $4x - 5y$ **47.** $18x + 16$

49. $5a^2 + 6a - 22$ **51.** $\dfrac{47}{20}x^3 + \dfrac{19}{9}y^3 + \dfrac{3}{4}x - \dfrac{1}{6}x^2 - 2y$ **53.** 10 **55.** $-\dfrac{9}{5}$ **57.** $-22.7x^3 - 2.573y^3$

Exercises 1.6

1. -5 **3.** -7 **5.** -12 **7.** 10 **9.** -55 **11.** 4 **13.** 14 **15.** 8 **17.** 400 **19.** $\dfrac{18}{5}$ **21.** $50°C$

23. 12.56 sq. in **25.** 84 sq. meters **27.** 40 sq. yards **29.** 0.035 sq. meters **31.** 0.28 meters **33. (a)** 197.82 cu. ft

(b) 131.88 sq. ft **35.** $A = \$2950$ **37.** $S = 114$ **39.** $R = \dfrac{15}{79}$ ohm **41.** $-12x$ **43.** $\dfrac{25x^4}{4y^6}$ **45.** 48.414387

Exercises 1.7

1. $x = 59$ **3.** $x = -7$ **5.** $x = 4$ **7.** $y = -10$ **9.** $y = \dfrac{2}{3}$ **11.** $x = -5$ **13.** $a = -2$ **15.** $y = 27$

17. $x = \dfrac{16}{3}$ **19.** $a = 20$ **21.** $y = -1$ **23.** $x = 6$ **25.** $x = 8$ **27.** $x = 0$ **29.** $y = 4$ **31.** $x = -1$

33. $x = 2$ **35.** $x = \dfrac{29}{2}$ **37.** Yes **39.** $x = -\dfrac{3}{2}$ **41.** $-5x + 4$ **43.** $10x^2 + 45x - 30$ **45.** $x = -0.8901$

Exercises 1.8

1. $x = \dfrac{7}{3a}$ **3.** $x = \dfrac{y}{3}$ **5.** $x = \dfrac{4y}{ab}$ **7.** $x = \dfrac{8 - 3y}{5}$ **9.** $x = \dfrac{3y + 12}{2}$ **11.** $x = \dfrac{3a - 3b}{2}$ **13.** $t = \dfrac{d}{r}$ **15.** $y = \dfrac{x}{2}$

17. $b = \dfrac{4cd}{5ax}$ **19.** $y = \dfrac{5 - 3b}{15}$ **21. (a)** $a = \dfrac{2A}{b}$ **(b)** $a = 10$ **23. (a)** $n = \dfrac{A - a + d}{d}$ **(b)** $n = 6$

25. (a) $a = \dfrac{2D - 2Vt}{t^2}$ **(b)** $a = 3$ **27.** $y = -\dfrac{31x - 36}{10}$ **29.** $\dfrac{x^6}{4y^2}$ **31.** $x = 4$ **33.** $x = \dfrac{A + 3966.9228}{3318.7328}$

Exercises 1.9

1. $x = 14, x = -14$ **3.** $x = 5, x = -9$ **5.** $x = 9, x = -4$ **7.** $x = \dfrac{8}{3}, x = -8$ **9.** $x = 10, x = 2$ **11.** $x = 2, x = 8$

13. $x = 7, x = -10$ **15.** $x = 4, x = \dfrac{-3}{2}$ **17.** $x = \dfrac{-8}{3}, x = \dfrac{16}{3}$ **19.** $x = 9, x = -1$ **21.** $x = 5, x = -1$

23. $x = -4, x = 4$ **25.** $x = \dfrac{-5}{3}, x = \dfrac{-1}{3}$ **27.** $x = 5$ **29.** No solution **31.** $x = 13, x = -17$ **33.** $x = -3$

35. $x = -8$ **37.** $x = -0.59, x = -3.29$ **39.** $x = 0.12, x = -5.18$

Extra Practice: Exercises

Section 1.1 **1.** $\dfrac{1}{3}, 3\pi, \sqrt{2}$ **3.** 0 **5.** $-6, 0$ **7.** $\dfrac{1}{3}, -\dfrac{2}{5}$ **9.** $-5, -3, -1, 1, 3, 5$ **11.** $-4, -2, 0, 2, 4, 6 \ldots$

13. identity property for multiplication **15.** associative property for multiplication
17. commutative property for multiplication **19.** commutative property for addition **21.** closure property for addition
23. closure property for multiplication **25.** distributive property of multiplication over addition *Section 1.2* **1.** -16

3. $-\dfrac{3}{2}$ **5.** -36 **7.** -3 **9.** $-\dfrac{5}{24}$ **11.** -13 **13.** 48 **15.** 0 **17.** 0 **19.** -26 **21.** 10 **23.** 0 **25.** 4

27. 0   *Section 1.3*   **1.** -32 **3.** $\frac{2}{3}$ **5.** -16 **7.** $\frac{5}{12}$ **9.** -216 **11.** 1   **13.** -8 **15.** 89   **17.** 0   **19.** 990

21. 3   **23.** 5   *Section 1.4*   **1.** $-18x^2$ **3.** $\frac{1}{2x^4}$ **5.** $24x^4y^6z^8$ **7.** $-6x^6y^{-1}z^3$ **9.** $\frac{1}{3x^{14}}$ **11.** $-3x^8y^{11}$ **13.** $7x^{12}$

15. $\frac{6x^{10}z^3}{y^2}$ **17.** $\frac{1}{16y^4z^{24}}$ **19.** $\frac{d^4}{25b^2}$ **21.** $\frac{64x^6}{y^9}$ **23.** $\frac{x^4}{9y^6}$ **25.** $\frac{8x^6}{27y^{15}}$ **27.** $\frac{9x}{4y^2}$ **29.** 5.3721×10^{11}

31. 4.32×10^5 *Section 1.5*   **1.** $2b - ab$ **3.** $-\frac{3}{2}a^2 + \frac{1}{2}b^2$ **5.** $7xy - 4xy^2$ **7.** $15x - 6y$ **9.** $-3a^2b + 6ab^2 - 15ab$

11. $2x - \frac{4}{3}y + \frac{10}{3}$ **13.** $8a^2x^2 - 12a^2x + 6ax^2$ **15.** $9x^2y^2 - 3x^2y^3 + 6xy^4$ **17.** $-3x - 17y$

19. $-3a + a^3 + a^2b - a^3b$ **21.** $12x + 30y$ **23.** $-4x^2 - 18x$ **25.** $18 - 21a + 27b + 3ab$ **27.** $0.01x^2 + 0.12x$

Section 1.6   **1.** -14 **3.** 6   **5.** 7   **7.** 4   **9.** -1 **11.** 0   **13.** 2   **15.** $Z = \frac{9}{5}$ **17.** 50.24 cu. m   **19.** \$4140

21. 78   **23.** 400   **25.** 38,808   *Section 1.7*   **1.** $x = 7$ **3.** $x = -1$ **5.** $x = -\frac{1}{2}$ **7.** $x = \frac{24}{7}$ **9.** $x = 2$

11. $x = \frac{17}{5}$ **13.** $y = 3$ **15.** $x = 97$ **17.** $y = -\frac{40}{7}$ **19.** $y = \frac{1}{2}$ **21.** $a = 4$ **23.** $x = \frac{-22}{21}$ **25.** $x = 16$

Section 1.8   **1.** $x = \frac{-3y - 5}{7}$ **3.** $x = \frac{4y - 2}{3ay}$ **5.** $x = \frac{5b}{2}$ **7.** $x = \frac{-2a - 38}{17a}$ **9.** $x = \frac{3 + 2bc}{7a}$ **11.** $x = \frac{3}{22b}$

13. $c = \frac{7 - ab}{2ab}$ **15.** $y = \frac{6x - 7}{80}$ **17.** $y = \frac{z + 2 - 3x}{2}$ **19.** $g = \frac{2s}{t^2}$ **21.** $b_2 = \frac{2a - hb_1}{h}$

23. (a) $\frac{2S + nd - dn^2}{2n}$ (b) $a = 3$ **25.** (a) $a = \frac{2S - nl}{n}$ (b) $a = 4$ *Section 1.9*   **1.** $x = 3, x = -\frac{8}{3}$ **3.** $x = 18, x = -6$

5. $x = -\frac{2}{3}, x = 2$ **7.** $x = \frac{3}{2}, x = -\frac{13}{2}$ **9.** $x = 6, x = -\frac{4}{7}$ **11.** $x = -1, x = \frac{2}{3}$ **13.** $x = 0, x = -\frac{12}{5}$

Review Problems Chapter 1

1. 0, 2, 4, 6, 8, 10   **3.** associative property for multiplication   **5.** 11   **7.** 18   **9.** -9 **11.** $\frac{2}{3}$ **13.** $-24x^4y^6$

15. $25x^2y^{-2}$ **17.** $\frac{81y^4}{16x^4z^8}$ or $\frac{81}{16}x^{-4}y^4z^{-8}$ **19.** $\frac{a^6}{8b^{12}}$ or $2^{-3}a^6b^{-12}$ **21.** $\frac{9x^5}{4y^4}$ or $\frac{9}{4}x^5y^{-4}$ **23.** 7.21×10^{-3}

25. $-ab - 2a^2b - 6b^2 + 5b^3$ **27.** $-3a^2 - 36a$ **29.** 28   **31.** $x = -2$ **33.** $x = \frac{10}{3}$ **35.** $x = 15$ **37.** $y = \frac{4x - 5}{8}$

39. (a) $W = \frac{P - 2L}{2}$ (b) 29.5 m   **41.** $x = 7, x = -9$ **43.** $x = 3, x = -\frac{1}{2}$ **45.** $x = 12, x = -\frac{4}{3}$ **47.** $x = 44, x = -20$

49. $x = -\frac{1}{5}, x = \frac{13}{5}$

Quiz Sections 1.1–1.4

1. $0, \frac{12}{3}$ **2.** $-2\sqrt{3}, \pi$ **3.** True   **4.** identity property for addition   **5.** commutative property for addition   **6.** 75

7. 21   **8.** $-\frac{3}{2}$ **9.** 2^{32} **10.** $\frac{1}{6x^5}$ or $\frac{x^{-5}}{6}$ **11.** $-30x^3$ **12.** $\frac{3y^4}{5xz}$ or $\frac{3}{5}x^{-1}y^4z^{-1}$ **13.** $\frac{1}{81x^8y^4}$ or $\frac{1}{81}x^{-8}y^{-4}$

14. $\frac{1}{8x^{24}y^{15}}$ or $\frac{1}{8}x^{-24}y^{-15}$ **15.** $-\frac{x^{10}}{32y^{15}}$ **16.** $\frac{a^2}{b^4c^{10}}$ **17.** $\frac{27x^2}{y^{13}}$ **18.** $\frac{16}{a^{22}b^2}$ **19.** 3.13×10^{-7} **20.** 6.42×10^{16}

Quiz Sections 1.5–1.9

1. $-\frac{3}{2}x + 8x^2$ **2.** $-3ab - 9b^2 + 3ab^2$ **3.** $-3x^2 + 6xy + 3$ **4.** $-4x^4y + 12x^3y - 16x^2y$ **5.** $-10a + 24ab - 6b$

6. $20 - 21x$ **7.** 75   **8.** 25   **9.** 46 cm   **10.** 113.04 ft³   **11.** -13 **12.** $y = 68$ **13.** $x = -\frac{11}{5}$ **14.** $y = \frac{8x + 12}{5}$

15. (a) $y = \frac{5H - B}{Bx}$ (b) $y = 3$ **16.** $x = -4, x = 8$ **17.** $x = 3, x = -\frac{9}{5}$ **18.** $x = 2, x = \frac{1}{3}$

Test Chapter 1

1. $-\pi, \sqrt{7}, 3\sqrt{2}$ **2.** $16, 13, \dfrac{8}{2}, \dfrac{15}{15}, 0$ **3.** associative property for multiplication.   **4.** 4   **5.** -2

6. $-36a^{-1}b^{-1}$ or $\dfrac{-36}{ab}$ **7.** $-\dfrac{4}{5}x^{-1}yz^{-13}$ or $\dfrac{-4y}{5xz^{13}}$ **8.** $9a^{10}b^{-4}$ or $\dfrac{9a^{10}}{b^4}$ **9.** $-x^2 - 16x$ **10.** $-2a^2 - 4a - 11b$

11. $6a^2b^2 + 4ab^3 - 12a^4b^2$ **12.** $14x + 60$ **13.** 38   **14.** 9   **15.** 78 sq. m   **16.** 113.04 sq. m   **17.** $x = 1$

18. $x = \dfrac{1}{2}$ **19.** $x = -5$ **20.** $n = \dfrac{L - a + d}{d}$ **21.** $C = \dfrac{5F - 160}{9}$ **22.** $C = 40°$ **23.** $r = \dfrac{4H - 12b + 1}{2}$

24. 2.186×10^{-6} **25.** $x = -7, x = \dfrac{39}{5}$ **26.** $x = 6, x = -18$

CHAPTER 2   Applications of Linear Equations

Pretest Chapter 2

1. $a = -\dfrac{24}{5}$ **2.**   **3.**   **4.** $m = \dfrac{14}{3}$ **5.** $m_\perp = -\dfrac{9}{2}$

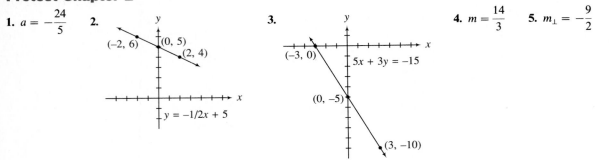

6. $2x + y = 11$ **7.** $y = 2x$ **8.** 9 cm $\times$ 23 cm   **9.** 26   **10.** 80 gms @ 77% pure copper, 20 gms @ 92% pure copper
11. $25,500 @ 10%, $14,500 @ 15%

Exercises 2.1

1. $y = -13$ **3.** $x = -5$ **5.** $y = -2$ **7.** $x = \dfrac{7}{2}$ **9.**   **11.**

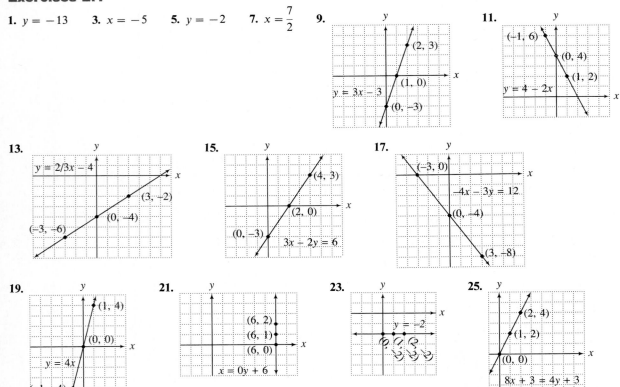

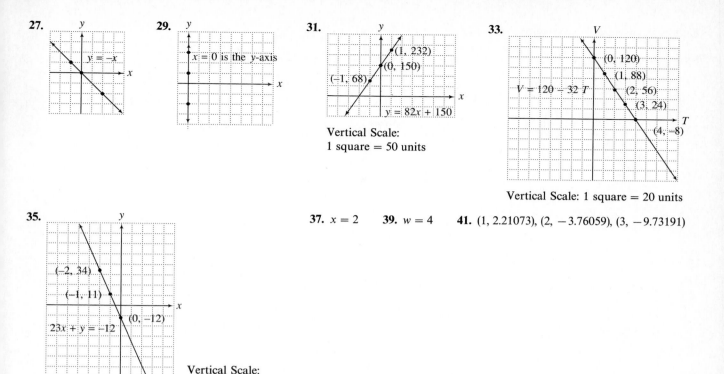

27. $y = -x$

29. $x = 0$ is the y-axis

31. $(1, 232)$ $(0, 150)$ $(-1, 68)$ $y = 82x + 150$

Vertical Scale:
1 square = 50 units

33. $V = 120 - 32\ T$ $(0, 120)$ $(1, 88)$ $(2, 56)$ $(3, 24)$ $(4, -8)$

Vertical Scale: 1 square = 20 units

35. $(-2, 34)$ $(-1, 11)$ $(0, -12)$ $23x + y = -12$

Vertical Scale:
1 square = 10 units

37. $x = 2$ **39.** $w = 4$ **41.** $(1, 2.21073), (2, -3.76059), (3, -9.73191)$

Exercises 2.2

1. $m = -7$ **3.** $m = \dfrac{3}{5}$ **5.** $m = 4$ **7.** $m = 0$ **9.** No, division by zero is undefined.   **11.** Yes   **13.** $m = -2$

15. $m = -\dfrac{4}{3}$ **17.** $m = 0$ **19.** $m_\perp = -\dfrac{2}{3}$ **21.** $m_\perp = \dfrac{1}{4}$ **23.** $m_\perp = -\dfrac{4}{3}$

25. Since $m_{AB} = m_{BC}$ and B is a common point, then all the points lie on one straight line.   **27.** $m_{AD} = m_{BC} = -\dfrac{1}{6}$,

$m_{AB} = m_{CD} = 1$ **29.** $m_l = \dfrac{10}{7}$ and $m_h = \dfrac{10}{7}$. Thus $l \parallel h$.   **31.** -56 **33.** $\dfrac{-10x^3}{y^{12}}$ **35.** 0.389728097

Exercises 2.3

1. $2x + 7y = 35$ **3.** $x - 5y = -20$ **5.** $y = -5x + 2, m = -5, b = 2$ **7.** $y = \dfrac{2}{3}x + \dfrac{8}{3}, m = \dfrac{2}{3}, b = \dfrac{8}{3}$

9. $y = -\dfrac{1}{8}x + \dfrac{5}{4}, m = -\dfrac{1}{8}, b = \dfrac{5}{4}$ **11.** $y = -\dfrac{7}{11}x - \dfrac{10}{11}, m = -\dfrac{7}{11}, b = -\dfrac{10}{11}$ **13.** $y = 3x - 9$ **15.** $y = 5x + 33$

17. $y = -\dfrac{2}{3}x - \dfrac{8}{3}$ **19.** $x - 3y = -11$ **21.** $x - 8y = 23$ **23.** $13x + 2y = 12$ **25.** $y = -3$ **27.** $x = -6$

29. $3x + 4y = -15$ **31.** $4x + y = -42$ **33.** $x + 5y = -6$ **35.** $3x + 5y = 23$ **37.** $x = 5$

39. $595x + 36y = -143$ **41.** $5, -6, 2, 1.333\ldots, -\dfrac{1}{4}, 0$ **43.** $-\dfrac{3}{2}x^2 - 9xy - 3y^2$ **45.** $y = -2.063x + 21.473$

Exercises 2.4

1. $x = 210$ **3.** $x = 23$ **5.** (Wally's, $8400), (Bob's, $14,800)   **7.** 260 miles   **9.** 80 hours
11. (1st, 62), (2nd, 64), (3rd, 66)   **13.** (1st, 8), (2nd, 16), (3rd, 48)   **15.** 275 m wide by 827 m long
17. (1st, 56 in), (2nd, 28 in), (3rd, 14 in)   **19.** (1st, 50°), (2nd, 30°), (3rd, 100°)   **21.** 75°   **23.** identity property for addition
25. $9x + 21$ **27.** 327 miles

Exercises 2.5

1. 3000   **3.** $12,500   **5.** 540   **7.** (1st, 21), (2nd, 25)   **9.** (shorter, 7 linear feet), (longer, 9 linear feet)
11. $1300 @ 6%, $1700 @ 9%   **13.** $12,000 @ 12%, $18,000 @ 15%   **15.** 10 qts of 60% acid, 20 qts of 30% acid

17. 36 lbs @ $6.00/lb, 108 lbs @ $8.00/lb   **19.** 200 lbs   **21.** 35 mph   **23.** Each ran $\dfrac{1}{2}$ hr or 30 min.   **25.** $30,000

27. 15   **29.** 18   **31.** 50,000

Extra Practice: Exercises

Section 2.1 **1.** $5, -2$ **3.** $0, \dfrac{-20}{3}$ **5.** $3, -2$ **7.** $0.4, 0.2$ **9.**   **11.**

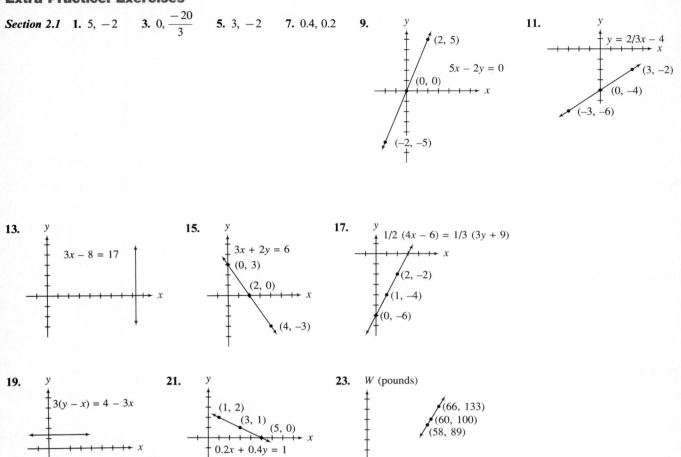

25.

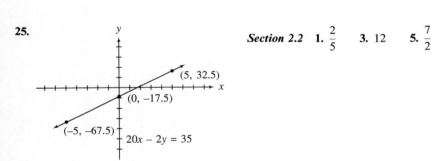

Section 2.2 **1.** $\dfrac{2}{5}$ **3.** 12 **5.** $\dfrac{7}{2}$

7. $-\dfrac{11}{6}$ **9.** Yes. $m = -3$ using points 1 and 2, and points 2 and 3   **11.** 0 **13.** $\dfrac{1}{25}$ or 0.04 **15.** $m = 0$ **17.** $-\dfrac{b}{a}$

19. $m = -1$ **21.** Yes. $m = \dfrac{4}{3}$ **23.** Yes. $m_1 = m_2 = \dfrac{10}{3}$ **Section 2.3** **1.** $x - 3y = 12$ **3. (a)** $y = x - \dfrac{5}{2}$

(b) $m = 1, b = -\dfrac{5}{2}$ **5.** $x - 2y = -9$ **7.** $x = 8$ **9.** $5x - 2y = -14$ **11.** $a = 5, b = 6$ **13.** $2x - 3y = 3$

15. $x = -3$ **17.** $y = 4$ **19.** $2x - 3y = 22$ **21.** $2x + 3y = 19$ **23.** $a = 3, b = 4$ **Section 2.4** **1.** 56 **3.** 350
5. (Anita's, $16,500), (Marcia's, $30,000)   **7.** (1st, 6), (2nd, 18), (3rd, 36)   **9.** $129, 131, 133$ **11.** 11 ft   **13.** $40°, 140°$
15. 7 **17.** 8 **19.** 1.20 **21.** 60 **23.** 5 **Section 2.5** **1.** 1600 **3.** $23, 41$ **5.** 2500 @ 14%, 2500 @ 11%

7. 75 lbs @ $5.00, 225 lbs @ $3.00   **9.** $16\dfrac{2}{3}$ liters @ 24%, $33\dfrac{1}{3}$ liters @ 18% **11.** 13.5 miles   **13.** 45 ounces

15. 45 mph   **17.** 4000

Review Problems Chapter 2

1. -1 **3.**

5. $m = \dfrac{1}{10}$ **7.** no slope

9. No, slope 1st two points $= -6$, slope 2nd two points $= -\dfrac{9}{4}$ **11.** $2x - 3y = 12$ **13.** $13x - 12y = -7$

15. $3x - 2y = 13$ **17.** 464 **19.** 350 miles **21.** width $= 9$ mm, length $= 35$ mm **23.** 2650

25. $4500 @ 12%, $2500 @ 8% **27.** 12 lbs @ $4.25, 18 lbs @ $4.50

Quiz Sections 2.1–2.3

1. $b = -\dfrac{7}{2}$ **2.**

3.

4. $m = \dfrac{5}{4}$ **5.** No. $m = 2$, $m = \dfrac{5}{3}$

6. $y = \dfrac{8}{3}x + \dfrac{8}{3}$, $m = \dfrac{8}{3}$, $b = \dfrac{8}{3}$ **7.** $y = -\dfrac{3}{2}x + \dfrac{7}{2}$ **8.** $3x + 5y = -12$ **9.** $14x - 8y = 5$ **10.** $x = -1$

11.

Quiz Sections 2.4–2.5

1. 185 **2.** 250 miles **3.** 1st $= 35°$, 2nd $= 80°$, 3rd $= 65°$ **4.** (Paul's, $34,500), (Richard's, $24,000)

5. $2600 @ 8%, $5400 @ 14% **6.** 12.5 liters @ 70%, 37.5 liters @ 30%

Test Chapter 2

1.

2. 2 **3.** $-\dfrac{3}{8}$ **4.** $x + 8y = -11$ **5.** $7x + 6y = -12$ **6.** $y = 2$

7. 1st $= 16$ m, 2nd $= 32$ m, 3rd $= 21$ m **8.** 900 hrs **9.** 2.5 gal @ 90%, 7.5 gal @ 50% **10.** $1800 @ 6%, $3200 @ 10%

Cumulative Test Chapters 1–2

1. $-12, -3, 0, \dfrac{1}{4}, 2.16, 2.333\ldots, -\dfrac{5}{8}, 3$ **2.** associative property for addition **3.** 58 **4.** $\dfrac{x^6}{4y^8}$ **5.** $\dfrac{b^5}{-2a^4}$

6. 54 cm   **7.** 153.86 sq. in   **8.** $30x^3 - 4x^2 - 8x$ **9.** 3   **10.** $b = \dfrac{3h - 2d}{2}$ **11.**

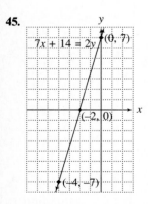

12. $\dfrac{1}{2}$

13. $2x + y = 11$ **14.** $3x + 2y = -12$ **15.** (1st, 25 m), (2nd, 35 m), (3rd, 45 m)   **16.** 340 miles
17. \$2000 @ 12%, \$4500 @ 10%   **18.** 6 gals @ 80%, 3 gals @ 50%

CHAPTER 3   Systems of Linear Equations

Pretest Chapter 3
1. $x = 1, y = 2$ **2.** $x = 2, y = -3$ **3.** infinite number of solutions-dependent equations   **4.** $x = 3, y = 0, z = 2$
5. $x = 4, y = -3, z = 1$ **6.** \$12 per shirt, \$17 per pants   **7.** Packet A = 3, Packet B = 2, Packet C = 4   **8.** -3
9. -34 **10.** 0   **11.** -45 **12.** $x = 3, y = -1$ **13.** $x = -4$

Exercises 3.1

1. $x = 1, y = 2$ **3.** $x = 23, y = -43$ **5.** $x = 4, y = -2$ **7.** $a = -3, b = -2$ **9.** $x = \dfrac{3}{7}, y = \dfrac{13}{7}$ **11.** $x = 3, y = -2$

13. $x = 0, y = 1$ **15.** $a = 1, b = -1$ **17.** $s = 1, t = \dfrac{5}{3}$ **19.** $x = 1, y = -3$ **21.** $x = 5, y = 1$

23. $x = -1, y = 3$ **25.** $x = 6, y = -8$ **27.** $x = -12, y = -12$ **29.** $a = \dfrac{4}{3}, b = -\dfrac{16}{9}$ **31.** $x = 5, y = -3$

33. no solution; inconsistent system of eqs.   **35.** $x = 4, y = -1$ **37.** $y = \dfrac{c - ae}{b - ad}, x = \dfrac{eb - cd}{b - ad}$

39. $a = \dfrac{15}{14}, b = -\dfrac{19}{14}, x = \dfrac{14}{15}, y = -\dfrac{14}{19}$ **41.** $a = \dfrac{46}{69}, b = \dfrac{1}{6}, x = \dfrac{69}{46}, y = 6$ **43.**

45.

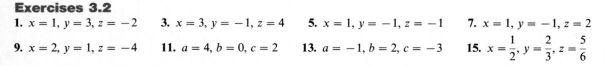

47. $x = 1.6867, y = -3.7662$

Exercises 3.2
1. $x = 1, y = 3, z = -2$ **3.** $x = 3, y = -1, z = 4$ **5.** $x = 1, y = -1, z = -1$ **7.** $x = 1, y = -1, z = 2$

9. $x = 2, y = 1, z = -4$ **11.** $a = 4, b = 0, c = 2$ **13.** $a = -1, b = 2, c = -3$ **15.** $x = \dfrac{1}{2}, y = \dfrac{2}{3}, z = \dfrac{5}{6}$

17. $x = 1, y = 3, z = 5$ **19.** $a = 2, b = 4, c = 4$ **21.** $x = 4, y = -5, z = 3$ **23.** $a = 5, b = -3, c = 2, x = \dfrac{1}{5}, y = -\dfrac{1}{3}, z = \dfrac{1}{2}$

25. $a = 2, b = -3, c = 4, x = \dfrac{1}{2}, y = -\dfrac{1}{3}, z = \dfrac{1}{4}$ **27.** infinite number of solutions-dependent eqs.

29. no solution; inconsistent system of eqs.   **31.** $m = -\dfrac{5}{6}$ **33.** $x - 3y = -11$ **35.** $x = 1.10551, y = 2.93991, z = 1.73307$

Exercises 3.3

1. 310 mezzanine tickets, 220 orchestra tickets   **3.** 51 letter stamps, 95 postcard stamps
5. 300 full-time students, 220 part-time students   **7.** 150 basic detectors, 120 advanced detectors
9. 9 packets of mixture 1, 12 packets of mixture 2   **11.** boat speed = 35 mph, current speed = 7 mph
13. plane speed in still air = 195 mph, wind speed = 15 mph   **15.** 36 A packages, 20 B packages, 19 C packages
17. pump A = 10,000 gal/hr, pump B = 12,000 gal/hr, pump C = 15,000 gal/hr

19. A packets $= 2, B$ packets $= 1, C$ packets $= 5, D$ packets $= 3$ **21.** $x = \dfrac{7}{18}$ **23.** 681 tickets @ \$9.95, 306 tickets @ \$12.95

Exercises 3.4

1. -7 **3.** 15   **5.** $-\dfrac{47}{4}$ **7.** 47   **9.** 18   **11.** 0   **13.** 0   **15.** -0.6 **17.** 39   **19.** -27 **21.** -39

23. 12   **25.** 0   **27.** $x = -\dfrac{11}{4}$ **29.** $x = -7$ **31.** $x = -\dfrac{2}{5}$ **33.** $A = 6$ **35.** $A = 18$ **37.** 147

39. $-25x^3 - 10x^2$ **41.** $\dfrac{-24y^7z^2}{x}$ **43.** 7882.2841

Exercises 3.5

1. $x = 2, y = 3$ **3.** $x = -3, y = 4$ **5.** $x = 4, y = 0$ **7.** $x = 4, y = -16$ **9.** $x = -1, y = -1$ **11.** $x = 4, y = -2$

13. infinite number of solutions-dependent eqs.   **15.** $x = \dfrac{2}{7}, y = \dfrac{1}{7}$ **17.** $x = 3, y = -1$ **19.** $x = 2, y = 6$

21. $x = 1, y = 1, z = 1$ **23.** $x = -1, y = 1, z = 2$ **25.** $x = 4, y = -2, z = 1$ **27.** $x = -3, y = -2, z = 2$ **29.** $z = 3$
31. $y = -7$ **33.** infinite number of solutions   **35.** $z = -3$ **37.** 190 miles   **39.** $x = 1.5795, y = -0.0902$

Extra Practice: Exercises

Section 3.1   **1.** $x = 2, y = -4$ **3.** $x = -2, y = -1$ **5.** $x = 3, y = 2$ **7.** $x = 2, y = -3$ **9.** $x = 4, y = 3$

11. $x = -7, y = -6$ **13.** $x = 5, y = 2$ **15.** $x = \dfrac{4}{3}, y = -\dfrac{1}{2}$ **17.** no solution; inconsistent system of eqs.

19. $x = 4, y = -2$ **21.** $x = 6, y = 0$ **23.** infinite number of solutions-dependent eqs.   **25.** $a = -3, b = -1$
27. $s = 2, t = -3.5$ **29.** $x = 6, y = 9$ **31.** $a = -1, b = -3$ **33.** no solution; inconsistent eqs.
35. no solution; inconsistent eqs.   *Section 3.2*   **1.** $x = 2, y = -1, z = 1$ **3.** $x = 1, y = 2, z = 3$
5. $x = 3, y = -1, z = 4$ **7.** $x = 3, y = -6, z = -5$ **9.** $x = 2, y = 3, z = 4$ **11.** $x = 4, y = 1, z = -3$

13. $x = 1, y = 2, z = 3$ **15.** $x = 39, y = 21, z = 12$ **17.** $x = 2, y = 3, z = 4$ **19.** $x = \dfrac{7}{2}, y = \dfrac{11}{2}, z = \dfrac{3}{2}$

21. $x = 8, y = 4, z = 2$ **23.** $x = 4, y = -5, z = 3$ **25.** $x = 12, y = 6, z = 0$ **27.** no solution; inconsistent system of eqs.
Section 3.3   **1.** 270 reserved seats, 260 general admission   **3.** subcompacts = \$400, compacts = \$500
5. wind = 2.5 mph, without wind = 17.5 mph   **7.** A = 300 gals., B = 150 gals., C = 275 gals.   **9.** $A = 7, B = 5, C = 3$
11. 5 hrs @ 30 mph, 6 hrs @ 25 mph   **13.** lighter cat = 7 lbs   **15.** \$650   **17.** 930 ft   **19.** 100 balloons   **21.** 40
Section 3.4   **1.** 27   **3.** -23 **5.** -0.33 **7.** 0   **9.** 0   **11.** -0.26 **13.** -2200 **15.** 0   **17.** -84 **19.** 0

21. -109 **23.** 43   **25.** $-\dfrac{1}{12}$ **27.** $x = -\dfrac{1}{14}$ **29.** $x = 4, y = 4$ **31.** area = 32 sq. units

Section 3.5   **1.** $x = 1, y = 1$ **3.** $x = 9, y = 5$ **5.** $x = -3, y = 4$ **7.** $x = 6, y = -2$

9. infinite number of solutions-dependent eqs.   **11.** $x = 3, y = -1$ **13.** $x = 2, y = -\dfrac{3}{2}$ **15.** $x = 0, y = 0$

17. $x = 4, y = 2$ **19.** $x = -\dfrac{3}{2}, y = 2$ **21.** $x = 14, y = 14$ **23.** $x = 1, y = -1, z = 2$ **25.** $x = 4, y = 3, z = 2$

27. $x = -3, y = 1, z = 5$ **29.** $z = -2$ **31.** $z = \dfrac{1}{5}$

Review Problems Chapter 3

1. no solution; inconsistent system of eqs.   **3.** $x = 2, y = -4$ **5.** $x = 0, y = 3$ **7.** $a = \dfrac{4}{3}, b = -\dfrac{1}{2}$ **9.** $x = 0, y = \dfrac{2}{3}$

11. $x = 1, y = 1, z = -2$ **13.** $x = 5, y = -3, z = 8$ **15.** speed of wind = 24 mph, speed of plane in still air = 264 mph

17. hats = \$3, shirts = \$15, pants = \$12   **19.** -1 **21.** -34 **23.** 16   **25.** $x = \dfrac{20}{3}, y = \dfrac{10}{3}$ **27.** $y = -5$

Quiz Sections 3.1–3.3
1. $x = 5, y = -4$ **2.** $x = 6, y = 0$ **3.** $a = 6, b = -2$ **4.** $a = 3, b = 7$ **5.** no solutions; inconsistent system of eqs.
6. infinite number of solutions-dependent eqs.   **7.** $x = 1, y = -1, z = 2$ **8.** $x = 6, y = -2, z = -1$
9. 250 advance tickets, 130 tickets sold at door   **10.** machine $A = 56$, machine $B = 73$, machine $C = 60$

Quiz Sections 3.4–3.5
1. 10   **2.** -36 **3.** $\dfrac{51}{2}$ or 25.5   **4.** 27   **5.** -2 **6.** -12 **7.** $x = 3, y = 3$ **8.** $x = 11, y = 7$

9. $x = 3, y = -2, z = 1$ **10.** $x = -5$

Test Chapter 3
1. $x = 2, y = 7$ **2.** $x = \dfrac{3}{2}, y = 0$ **3.** $a = -\dfrac{3}{4}, b = \dfrac{13}{12}$ **4.** no solution; inconsistent system of eqs.

5. $x = 3, y = -2, z = 1$ **6.** $x = -3, y = 7, z = 4$ **7.** speed of wind = 50 mph, speed of plane in still air = 450 mph
8. 4 station wagons, 6 two-door sedans, 6 four-door sedans   **9.** $x = 2, y = 2$ **10.** $x = 1, y = 2$ **11.** $z = -1$

Cumulative Test Chapters 1–3
1. identity property for addition   **2.** 2   **3.** $15x^{-6}y^2$ or $\dfrac{15y^2}{x^6}$ **4.** $22x + 12$ **5.** $P = \dfrac{A}{3 + 4rt}$ **6.** $x = 68$

7.
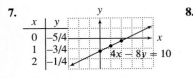

8. $m = \dfrac{1}{10}$ **9.** $6x - 5y = 27$ **10.** 1st side = 17 m, 2nd side = 24 m, 3rd side = 28 m

11. \$1500 @ 7%, \$4500 @ 9%   **12.** $x = 2, y = -4$ **13.** $x = 2, y = -1, z = -1$ **14.** shirts = \$21, slacks = \$30
15. $x = 5, y = 3$ **16.** $z = -2$ **17.** infinite number of solutions-dependent eqs.

CHAPTER 4   Polynomials

Pretest Chapter 4
1. $x^2 - 11x + 4$ **2.** $30a^2 - 48aw - 35az + 56wz$ **3.** $2x^4 - 5x^3y - 13x^2y^2 + 2xy^3 + 8y^4$ **4.** $5x - 6y - 10$

5. $3y^2 + y + 4 + \dfrac{7}{y - 2}$ **6.** $x^3 + 2x^2 - x - 2$ **7.** $12a^3b^2(2 + 3a - 5b)$ **8.** $(4x - 3y)(3x - 2)$ **9.** $(5w + 3z)(2x - 5y)$
10. $(x - 5y)(x - 2y)$ **11.** $(2y - 5)(2y + 3)$ **12.** $(7x - 3y)(4x - y)$ **13.** $(6x - 5y)^2$ **14.** $(11x - 1)(11x + 1)$
15. $(2x - y)(4x^2 + 2xy + y^2)$ **16.** $(4x + 3)(16x^2 - 12x + 9)$ **17.** $y^3(x - 3y)(x^2 + 3xy + 9y^2)$ **18.** $2x(x - 4)(x + 3)$
19. prime   **20.** $a(9a + 7y)^2$

Exercises 4.1
1. binomial, 4th degree   **3.** monomial, 9th degree   **5.** trinomial, 8th degree   **7.** (a) $5x^3 - 3x^2 + 3x - 19$
(b) $-x^4 + x^3 + 2x^2 - 5x + 3$ **(c)** $x^4 - 6x^3 + 7x^2 - 8x + 2$ **9.** $6x^2 - 8x - 4$ **11.** $2x^3 - 9x^2 + 2x + 13$
13. $5a^3 - 4a^2 + 2a + 9$ **15.** $6x^3 - 10x^2 + 2x$ **17.** $-6x^2y + 18xy^2 - 45xy$ **19.** $x^2 - x - 30$ **21.** $6x^2 + 7x + 2$
23. $28x^2 - 45x + 18$ **25.** $15aw + 6ad - 20bw - 8bd$ **27.** $-12x^2 + 11xy - 2y^2$ **29.** $10r^2 - 8rs^2 - 18s^4$
31. $5x^3 + 4x^2 - 11x + 2$ **33.** $6x^3 - 7x^2y - 10xy^2 + 6y^3$ **35.** $2x^4 - 17x^3 + 34x^2 - 17x + 2$
37. $5a^4 - 18a^3 + 11a^2 - 10a + 12$ **39.** $3r^4 + 5r^3s - 20r^2s^2 + 2rs^3 + 4s^4$ **41.** $25x^2 - 64y^2$ **43.** $25a^2 - 20ab + 4b^2$
45. $64x^2 + 144x + 81$ **47.** $4x^4 - 1$ **49.** $4a^4b^4 - 12a^2b^2 + 9$ **51.** $2x^3 - 7x^2 - 7x + 30$ **53.** $3a^3 - a^2 - 22a + 24$
55. $15x^{5n} + 20x^{3n} - 6x^{2n} - 8$ **57.** $6a^{3-n} + 12a^{3-2n} + 12a^n + 24$ **59.** $6x^3 + 25x^2 + 49x + 40$ cm^2 **61.** $-10x - 12y$
63. $2x^3 - 4x^2 - 8x + 6$ **65.** $10.732x^2 - 10.729x$

Exercises 4.2
1. $3x^2 + 4x - 6$ **3.** $4x^2 - 5x - 4$ **5.** $x^2 - 2x + 5$ **7.** $9a^2 + 6a - 2$ **9.** $3x + 2$ **11.** $6x - 1$

13. $2a - 7 + \dfrac{5}{3a + 5}$ **15.** $x^2 - 2x + 13 - \dfrac{14}{x + 1}$ **17.** $2x^2 + 3x + 6 + \dfrac{5}{x - 2}$ **19.** $x^2 - 2x + 3$ **21.** $x^2 - 3x + 9$

23. $x^3 - 7x^2 + 70x - 351 + \dfrac{1756}{x + 5}$ **25.** $5a^2 + a + 3 + \dfrac{a + 7}{3a^2 - 1}$ **27.** $2t^2 - 3t + 2$ **29.** $3x^2 + 5x - 2$ miles per hour

31. $3x^n y^5 + 5x^8 y^4 - 2x^3$ **33.** $x = 2$ **35.** $x = 6$ **37.** $58.9x^2 - 9.87x + 258.1$

Exercises 4.3

1. $x + 9$ **3.** $2x + 1 + \dfrac{-2}{x - 6}$ **5.** $2x^2 - 4x + 13 - \dfrac{40}{x + 4}$ **7.** $x^2 + 4x + 5$ **9.** $x^2 + 6x + 11 + \dfrac{27}{x - 2}$

11. $x^2 - 4x + 8 - \dfrac{8}{x + 2}$ **13.** $6x^3 + 3x^2 - 6x - 16 + \dfrac{26}{x + 2}$ **15.** $x^3 - 7x^2 + 8x - 8 - \dfrac{1}{x + 1}$

17. $3x^3 - 4x^2 + 6x - 13 + \dfrac{12}{x + 1}$ **19.** $2x^4 + 11x^3 + 31x^2 + 95x + 283 + \dfrac{852}{x - 3}$

21. $x^5 + x^4 + 2x^3 + 2x^2 + 2x + 1 + \dfrac{1}{x - 1}$ **23.** $x^2 - 2x + 4$ **25.** $b = -\dfrac{13}{3}$

27. **(a) (b)** results are the same: $x^3 - 3x^2 + 5x - 2$ **(c)** in about half the time   **29.** $x^2 + 3.7x + 0.84$ R 6.408

Exercises 4.4

1. $5(4 - y)$ **3.** $xy(y - 3x)$ **5.** $b(bx^2 + x + 1)$ **7.** $2x(x^2 - 4x + 6)$ **9.** $9ab(ab - 4 + 5b)$
11. $2ab^2 c(2a^2 - 4ac + 3c^2)$ **13.** There is no common factor.   **15.** $12xy^2(y - 2x^2 + 3xy^2 - 5x^3 y)$ **17.** $(x + y)(3x - 2)$
19. $(a - 3b)(5b + 8)$ **21.** $(a + 3b)(8x + 1)$ **23.** $(3x - y)(2a^2 - 5b^3)$ **25.** $(5x + y)(3x - 8y - 1)$ **27.** $(x + 5)(x^2 + 3)$
29. $(x + 2y)(4 - 3w)$ **31.** $(a - 3)(a + y)$ **33.** $(x - 3y)(5a - 2b)$ **35.** $(t^2 - 5)(y + 5)$ **37.** $(7x + 2y^2)(4x + 3w)$
39. $(4a - c)(3a^2 - c^2)$ **41.** $21x^m y^n(7x^2 y^n - 5x + 8y^{n-1})$ **43.**   **45.** $m = -1$

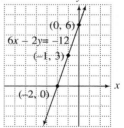

47. $7.37(2x - 3y + 8)$

Exercises 4.5

1. $(x + 3)(x + 1)$ **3.** $(x + 9)(x - 2)$ **5.** $(x + 6)(x - 5)$ **7.** $(x + 6)(x + 2)$ **9.** $(a - 5)(a + 3)$ **11.** $(a + 9)(a - 5)$
13. $(x - 4y)(x - 5y)$ **15.** $(x + 7y)(x - 2y)$ **17.** $(x^2 - 8)(x^2 + 5)$ **19.** $(x + 3)(x - 3)(x^2 - 7)$ **21.** $(2x - 1)(x - 3)$
23. $(5x + 4)(x + 2)$ **25.** $(3x - 5)(2x + 1)$ **27.** $(3a - 5)(a - 1)$ **29.** $(4a + 9)(2a - 1)$ **31.** $(3x - 2)(2x - 3)$
33. $(2x + 3)(x + 5)$ **35.** $(3x^2 + 1)(x^2 - 3)$ **37.** $(3x + y)(2x + 11y)$ **39.** $(x + 10)(x - 2)$ **41.** $(3x + 2)(2x - 1)$
43. $(3x^2 - 5)(x^2 + 1)$ **45.** $(5x + 2)(3x - 1)$ **47.** $(3x + 5)(2x + 5)$ **49.** $(7x - y)(x - 3y)$ **51.** $(x^3 - 13)(x^3 + 3)$
53. $(x^n + 7)(x^n + 31)$ **55.** $(7x^n + 2)(3x^n - 8)$ **57.** $A = 28.26$ in^2 **59.** $x + 3y = -6$

Exercises 4.6

1. $(6x - 5y)(6x + 5y)$ **3.** $(1 - 9xy)(1 + 9xy)$ **5.** $(w - z)(w + z)(w^2 + z^2)$ **7.** $(7m - 3n)(7m + 3n)$ **9.** $2(4x + 3)(4x - 3)$
11. $x(11x + 2)(11x - 2)$ **13.** $(7x - 1)^2$ **15.** $(w - 3)^2$ **17.** $(3x^2 + y)^2$ **19.** $(9w + 2t)^2$ **21.** $(5x - 4y)^2$
23. $2(2x + 3)^2$ **25.** $x(6x - 7)^2$ **27.** $(2x + 3)(4x^2 - 6x + 9)$ **29.** $(4x - 1)(16x^2 + 4x + 1)$
31. $(5x - 2)(25x^2 + 10x + 4)$ **33.** $(m - 2n)(m^2 + 2mn + 4n^2)(m + 2n)(m^2 - 2mn + 4n^2)$ **35.** $(4x + 5)(16x^2 - 20x + 25)$
37. $2(3y - 2)(9y^2 + 6y + 4)$ **39.** $x(4x + 3)(16x^2 - 12x + 9)$ **41.** $x^2(x - 2y)(x^2 + 2xy + 4y^2)$ **43.** $(5w^3 - 1)(5w^3 + 1)$
45. $(2w^3 - 1)^2$ **47.** $(2a - 3b)(4a^2 + 6ab + 9b^2)$ **49.** $(5m + 2n)(25m^2 - 10mn + 4n^2)$ **51.** $(3x - 10y)(3x + 10y)$
53. $(2w - 5z)^2$ **55.** $9(2a - 3b)(2a + 3b)$ **57.** $(4x + yz)(16x^2 - 4xyz + y^2 z^2)$ **59.** $(9x^2 - 2)^2$
61. $(4x^2 + 9y^2)(2x - 3y)(2x + 3y)$ **63.** $2[5(2)] = 20$, not 25; $(5x + 4)(5x + 1)$ **65.** $2[2(3)] = 12$, not 15; $(4x - 3)(x - 3)$
67. $(9x^8 + 16)(3x^4 - 4)(3x^4 + 4)$ **69.** $(11x^8 - 5y^{10})^2$ **71.** 1st side $= 20$ cm, 2nd side $= 30$ cm, 3rd side $= 16$ cm

Exercises 4.7

1. remove a common factor if possible   **3.** $(8x - 1)(8x + 1)$ **5.** $(2x - 1)(x + 3)$ **7.** $(2x - 5y)(4x^2 + 10xy + 25y^2)$
9. $x(x + 2y - z)$ **11.** $2a(b + 5)(b - 5)$ **13.** $3x(3x + 2)(2x - 1)$ **15.** $(6x + 1)(x - 4)$ **17.** $(x - 1)(x - y)$
19. $2x(2x - 1)(4x^2 + 2x + 1)$ **21.** $2x(x - 3)(x + 3)(x^2 + 1)$ **23.** $3x^2(x^2 + 9)$ **25.** $3x(2x - 5)(x + 1)$
27. $2(2x^2 - 4x - 3)$ **29.** $3y(3y - 2)^2$ **31.** $2(a - 7)(a - 5)$ **33.** $a(-3 + a)(x + 2y)$ or $a(a - 3)(2y + x)$
35. $y(8 - 7y)(8 + 7y)$ **37.** $(2x^2 - 5)(x^2 + 1)$ **39.** prime   **41.** $2y^6(3x^2 - 1)(9x^4 + 3x^2 + 1)$ **43.** $(2x^2 + 5y^4)^2$
45. $b = 2$ **47.** $(x^{2n} - 12a^{2n})(x^{2n} + 11a^{2n})$ **49.** $x = -1$, $y = -2$ **51.** $x = 6$, $y = 2$, $z = 4$

Extra Practice: Exercises

Section 4.1 **1. (a)** trinomial **(b)** 4th degree **3.** $-4a^3 - 9a^2 + a + 1$ **5.** $x^3 + 5x^2 - x - 7$ **7.** $21x^3 - 3x^2 - 4x + 1$
9. $12x^5 - 4x^4 - 4x^3 + 2x^2 + 3x - 6$ **11.** $10x^2 - 51x + 56$ **13.** $2x^3 + 3x^2 - 17x + 12$ **15.** $9y^4 + 12x^2y^2 + 4x^4$
17. $16x^2 - 121y^2$ **19.** $x^3 - 3x^2 + 3x - 1$ **21.** $x^4 - 16$ **23.** $12x^3 + x^2 - 9x + 2$ **Sections 4.2 and 4.3** **1.** $4x^2 - x + 2$

3. $x + 11 + \dfrac{72}{3x - 4}$ **5.** $y^2 + 2y - 1 + \dfrac{8}{2y - 3}$ **7.** $x^4 + x - 3 + \dfrac{27}{x + 3}$ **9.** $4x^2 - 6x + 9$ **11.** $2x^2 + x - 1$

13. $x + 2$ **15.** $(a + b)$ **17.** $x^2 - 1$ **19.** $2x^2 - 3x + 4 + \dfrac{7}{2x - 5}$ **21.** $x^2 - 1 + \dfrac{5}{x^2 - 3x + 1}$ **23.** $2x^2 + 4$

25. $(x - 1)$ **27.** $x + 2 + \dfrac{3}{x + 2}$ **29.** $x^2 + 2x + 2$ **31.** $x^2 - 10x + 29 - \dfrac{84}{x + 3}$ **33.** $x^3 - 3x^2 + 2x - 3$

35. $x^4 - 5x^3 + 10x^2 - 18x + 36 - \dfrac{77}{x + 2}$ **Section 4.4** **1.** $a(y + a)$ **3.** $3x^3y^4(3x^3 - 5y - 2x)$ **5.** $7x^3y^2(2 - 3x^3y - 5y^2)$
7. $(x - 2y)(3 + 5x)$ **9.** $(y + 1)(x - 2y)$ **11.** $(a - b)(a + 1)$ **13.** $(2x^2 - 1)(7 + 4y^4)$ **15.** $a^2(a + 5)(b^3 + 2)$ **17.** $3bc$
19. $4b(2a^2c - 3a + 4c)$ **21.** $x(x^3 + x^2 - x + 1)$ **23.** $(a - b)(5x + 4y + 3z)$ **25.** $(x - 4a)(2x + 3n)$
27. $2(2m + n)(4a - 3b)$ **29.** $(b - c)(ax^2 - by^2)$ **Section 4.5** **1.** $(x + 6)(x + 8)$ **3.** $(x + 9)(x - 7)$ **5.** $(2x + 3)(x + 2)$
7. $(5x - 2)(3x + 1)$ **9.** $(x^2 - 3)(x^2 + 8)$ **11.** $(2x - 7y)(x + 3y)$ **13.** $(3a - 4b)(a - 5b)$ **15.** $(3x^2 - 5)(2x^2 - 1)$
17. $(7x + 10)(x - 1)$ **19.** $(3x + 2y)(4x - 7y)$ **21.** $(2x + 9)(x + 2)$ **23.** $(a^2 + 2b^2)^2$ **25.** $(2a + 3b)(a - 4b)$
27. $(3a + 2b)(5a - 12b)$ **29.** prime **31.** $(2m - 3)(m - 8)$ **Section 4.6** **1.** $(a - 10)(a + 10)$ **3.** $(11b - 7d)(11b + 7d)$
5. $(2x - 3y)^2$ **7.** $(10x + 3)^2$ **9.** $(4x - 3y)(16x^2 + 12xy + 9y^2)$ **11.** $(3a + 5b)(9a^2 - 15ab + 25b^2)$
13. $(8x^4 + 1)(8x^4 - 1)$ **15.** $(3w^2 - 4z^2)(9w^4 + 12w^2z^2 + 16z^4)$ **17.** $(7x - 3y)^2$ **19.** $(4x - 9y^2)^2$ **21.** prime
23. $(m^2n^2 + 9x^2)(mn + 3x)(mn - 3x)$ **25.** $(6x - 5y)(36x^2 + 30xy + 25y^2)$ **27.** $(x^3 + 3)^2$ **29.** $(5x - y)(25x^2 + 5xy + y^2)$
31. $(x + 2)^2(x - 2)^2$ **Section 4.7** **1.** $7x^2y^3(3 - xy^2)$ **3.** $2a(a - 2b)(a^2 + 2ab + 4b^2)$ **5.** $(x + 7)(x - 4)$ **7.** $2(x - 7)^2$
9. $2x(3x - 2)(9x^2 + 6x + 4)$ **11.** $(2y - 3)(x + 4)$ **13.** prime **15.** $(3 - x)(d + cx)$ **17.** $a^4(5 - x)(25 + 5x + x^2)$
19. $(7x - 8y)^2$ **21.** $2x(x^2 - 3x + 15)$ **23.** $27(5 - a)(5 + a)$ **25.** $2(2x^n - 3)(x^n + 5)$ **27.** $4ax(a + 3x)$ **29.** $(4x + 3)^2$
31. $2(4r - s)(r + 3s)$ **33.** $3(2y + 1)(y - 6)$ **35.** $(x + 4)(x^2 + 5)$

Review Problems Chapter 4

1. (a) $5x^4 + 6x^3 + 5x^2 + x - 1$ **(b)** $5x^4 - 8x^3 - 5x^2 + 5x - 3$ **3.** $-x^3 - 7x^2 + 3x + 3$ **5.** $6x^3 - 3x^2 + 2x - 1$

7. $2x^3 - 7x^2 - 7x + 30$ **9.** $-5x^2 + 3x + 20$ **11.** $2x^2 - 3x - 4$ **13.** $5a^2 - a + 3 + \dfrac{-a + 7}{3a^2 - 1}$ **15.** $2x^3 - 3x^2 + x - 4$

17. $4x^3 - x + 2 - \dfrac{4}{x + 3}$ **19.** $(x + 3)(x + 12)$ **21.** $(3x - 11)(3x + 11)$ **23.** $(x + 4w)(x - 2y)$ **25.** prime

27. $x(3x - 1)(9x^2 + 3x + 1)$ **29.** $-a^2b^3(3a - 2b + 1)$ **31.** $(3x^2 + 1)(x^2 - 2)$ **33.** $b(3a + 7)(3a - 2)$ **35.** $3(2x + 1)^2$
37. $y^2(y + 7)(y - 5)$ **39.** $(3x^2 + 2)(x^2 - 3)$ **41.** $(2x + 3)(x + 2)(x - 2)$ **43.** $4(2 - x)(a + b)$ **45.** $2x(2x - 1)(x + 3)$
47. $(4x^2y - 7)^2$ **49.** $13xy(2x^2 - y^2 + 4xy^3)$ **51.** $3ab(3c - 2)(3c + 2)$ **53.** $2x^2(25x^2 - 50x + 32)$

Quiz Sections 4.1–4.4

1. (a) $5x^3 - 4x^2 - 6x - 15$ **(b)** $5x^3 - 8x^2 + 6x - 1$ **2.** $4x^2 + 2x + 2$ **3.** $2x^4 - 8x^3 - 3x^2 + 15x + 1$
4. $-6x^3 + 4x^2y^2 - 2x^2y$ **5.** $x^2 - 49$ **6.** $7x^3 - 21x^2 + 2x - 6$ **7.** $2x^3 + 11x^2 - 10x - 24$ **8.** $2x^3 - 5x^2 + x + 2$
9. $4x^4 + 12x^2y + 9y^2$ **10.** $8xy - 4x + 2$ **11.** $y^2 - 3y - 5$ **12.** $x^3 - 4$ **13.** $3(3a^3 - 6a^2b - 5b^2)$
14. $10xy(6x^2 - 1)$ **15.** $(a - 3b)(5x + 2y)$ **16.** $(a - 3)(4b + 5a)$ **17.** $(5a - 2x^2)(7y - 3x)$

Quiz Sections 4.5–4.7

1. $(y + 3)^2$ **2.** $(5y - 2)(2y + 1)$ **3.** $(x - 16y)(x - y)$ **4.** $(7x + 1)(7x - 1)$ **5.** $(x^2 - 6)(x^2 + 2)$ **6.** $(2x - 5y)^2$
7. $(3x^2 + 4)^2$ **8.** $(3x + 2)(2x - 5)$ **9.** $(3y - 4)(1 - x)$ **10.** $2(3x + 5y)(2x - y)$ **11.** $2x(5x - 1)(5x + 1)$
12. $4a(2a^2 - 5)(a^2 + 3)$ **13.** $3(2x - 3y)^2$ **14.** $81(x^2 + 1)(x - 1)(x + 1)$ **15.** prime **16.** $2(w + 5)(x - 2)$
17. $2x(2x - 3)(4x^2 + 6x + 9)$ **18.** $(2x + 3)(x + 3)(x - 3)$ **19.** $2y(3y - 4)(y - 2)$ **20.** $(8y + 3)(2y + 3)$

Test Chapter 4

1. $-4x^2y - 1$ **2.** $5a^2 - 9a - 2$ **3.** $2x^3 - 6x^2y$ **4.** $4x^2 - 12xy^2 + 9y^4$ **5.** $x^4 + 3x^3 - 24x^2 - 18x + 8$

6. $5x^2 + 4x - 7$ **7.** $x^3 - x^2 + x - 2$ **8.** $x^2 - 3x + 1$ **9.** $x^3 - 1 - \dfrac{2}{x + 1}$ **10.** $2x^4 + x^3 + 4x^2 + x + 3 + \dfrac{17}{x - 4}$

11. $(11x - 5y)(11x + 5y)$ **12.** $(3x + 5y)^2$ **13.** $x(x - 2)(x - 24)$ **14.** $2(4x - 1)(3x + 2)$ **15.** $4x^2y(x + 2y + 1)$
16. $(x + 3y)(x - 2w)$ **17.** prime **18.** $3x^2(x + 2)(x + 10)$ **19.** $3(6x - 5)(x + 1)$ **20.** $y^4(5x - 4)(5x + 4)$
21. $2a(3a - 2)(9a^2 + 6a + 4)$ **22.** $x(3x^2 - y)^2$ **23.** $(3x^2 + 2)(x^2 + 5)$ **24.** $(x - 6y)(x - 2y)$ **25.** $(x + 2y)(3 - 5a)$
26. $(4x^2 + 1)(2x + 1)(2x - 1)$

Cumulative Test Chapters 1–4

1. associative property for multiplication **2.** 2 **3.** 29 **4.** $x = \dfrac{2 - 7y}{5}$ **5.** $x = 0$ **6.** $m = \dfrac{8}{3}$

7.

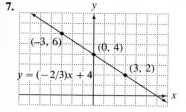

$(-3, 6)$ $(0, 4)$ $(3, 2)$ $y = (-2/3)x + 4$

8. width $= 6$ m, length $= 17$ m   **9.** $x = 2, y = -4$ **10.** $x = 2, y = 3, z = 6$

11. $5a^2 - 9ab + 12b^2$ **12.** $-6x^2y^2 - 9xy^3 + 15x^2y^3$ **13.** $10x^3 - 19x^2 - 14x + 8$ **14.** $-3x^2 + 2x - 4$

15. $2x^2 + x + 5 + \dfrac{6}{x - 2}$ **16.** $2x^2(x - 5)$ **17.** $(8x + 7)(8x - 7)$ **18.** $x(3x - 4)^2$ **19.** $(5x + 6)^2$ **20.** $3(x - 7)(x + 2)$

21. $2(x + 2)(x + 10)$ **22.** prime   **23.** $x(3x + 1)(2x + 3)$ **24.** $x(3x + 4)(9x^2 - 12x + 16)$ **25.** $(2m + 1)(7n + 5p)$

CHAPTER 5   Fractional Algebraic Expressions and Equations

Pretest Chapter 5

1. $\dfrac{7x + 3y}{x + y}$ **2.** $\dfrac{2x^2 + 3x - 1}{1 - 5x - 6x^2}$ **3.** $2(a - 5)$ **4.** $\dfrac{15(x - 5y)}{2y^4(x + 5y)}$ **5.** $\dfrac{x^2 - 4x + 8}{3x(x - 2)}$ **6.** $\dfrac{12x + 5}{(x + 5)(x - 5)}$

7. $\dfrac{10y - 6}{(y + 3)(y - 3)(y + 4)}$ **8.** $\dfrac{21x}{8}$ **9.** $\dfrac{x}{(2x - 1)(6x + 1)}$ **10.** $x = \dfrac{25}{2}$ or 12.5 **11.** $y = 5$ **12.** $d_2 = \dfrac{d_1 w_2}{w_1}$

13. $n = \dfrac{IR}{E - Ir}$ **14.** 31.5 ft   **15.** 8 ft by $13\dfrac{1}{3}$ ft

Exercises 5.1

1. $\dfrac{2}{x - 5}$ **3.** $\dfrac{y}{y + 2}$ **5.** $y - 2$ **7.** $\dfrac{3x}{2y}$ **9.** $\dfrac{a + 2}{a + 4}$ **11.** $\dfrac{x - 2}{x + y}$ **13.** $\dfrac{2(y + 3)}{y + 4}$ **15.** $\dfrac{x + 6}{x + 4}$ **17.** $\dfrac{-2}{x^2}$

19. $-\dfrac{2y + 5}{3 + y}$ **21.** $\dfrac{(a - 4)(a + 3)}{(2a - 3)(a + 4)}$ The fraction cannot be reduced.   **23.** $\dfrac{x^2 + 1}{x + 1}$ **25.** $\dfrac{x - y}{2}$ **27.** $\dfrac{x + 5}{3 - x}$

29. $\dfrac{x(2x + 3)}{3(x + 1)}$ **31.** $\dfrac{2(x^2 - y^2)}{x^2 + y^2}$ **33.** $-\dfrac{2(a + 3x)}{b^2 + 3y^2}$ **35.** $\dfrac{125y^3}{8x^6}$ **37.** $w = \dfrac{1}{2}$

Exercises 5.2

1. $a(a - 2)$ **3.** $\dfrac{1}{2}$ **5.** $\dfrac{2}{5xy^6}$ **7.** $\dfrac{x + 7}{x + 2}$ **9.** $\dfrac{y + 3}{y + 4}$ **11.** $\dfrac{y(x - 5)}{x^2}$ **13.** $\dfrac{y^2}{2(y - 2)}$ **15.** $\dfrac{(4a + 5)(a - 4)}{3a + 2}$

17. $\dfrac{x - 3y}{x(x^2 + 2)}$ **19.** $\dfrac{-5}{2}$ **21.** $\dfrac{a + 3b}{a - 3b}$ **23.** $\dfrac{(y + 1)(y - 2)}{(y - 1)(y + 2)}$ **25.** $\dfrac{5x^2 - 13x - 15}{(x - 3)(2x - 3)}$ **27.** $\dfrac{x + 5}{x - 6}$

29.

$y = (-3/2)x + 4$

$(-2, 7)$ $(0, 4)$ $(2, 1)$

x	y
-2	7
0	4
2	1

31. $4x - y = -5$ **33.** $\dfrac{7x(x + 2)}{2x - 5}$

Exercises 5.3

1. $6xy^2$ **3.** $(x + 6y)(x - 2y)$ **5.** $(x + 3y)(x + 4y)$ **7.** $(x + 6)(2x + 5)^3$ **9.** $x(5x - 7)(x - 1)$ **11.** $(3y + 7)(3y - 7)^2$

13. $24x^2(x + 3)(x - 8)$ **15.** $\dfrac{7x + 6}{2x(x + 2)}$ **17.** $\dfrac{12y + 2x}{5x^2y}$ **19.** $\dfrac{-5x + 18}{(x - 4)(x - 3)}$ **21.** $\dfrac{28x + 15y}{(7x - 5y)(7x + 5y)}$ **23.** $\dfrac{3y - 4}{(y + 2)(y - 3)}$

25. $\dfrac{2a^2 + 5a - 10}{2a(a + 2)(a - 2)}$ **27.** $\dfrac{y^2 - 3y + 18}{(2y - 3)(y + 3)}$ **29.** $\dfrac{-2x^2 + 6xy - 2y^2}{xy}$ **31.** $\dfrac{x^2 - x}{(x + 5)(x - 2)(x + 3)}$ **33.** $\dfrac{3}{(3x + 4y)(3x + 2y)}$

35. $\dfrac{4}{y + 4}$ **37.** $\dfrac{3a^2 + 4a - 13}{3a - 5}$ **39.** $\dfrac{3x + y}{(x + 2y)(x + y)(x - 2y)}$ **41.** $\dfrac{27x^3 - 37x^2 + 26x - 8}{(3x - 2)^2}$ **43.** $\dfrac{x + 2}{x}$

45. 40 liters of 15% acid solution, 20 liters of 30% acid solution   **47.** \$1700 @ 7%, \$1300 @ 9%   **49.** $\dfrac{-0.0132x - 0.1917}{6x^2 + 7x - 20}$

Exercises 5.4

1. $\dfrac{xy(x+y)}{2}$ **3.** $\dfrac{3x+2}{5x-6}$ **5.** $\dfrac{y-5}{y}$ **7.** $\dfrac{y^2-3}{3}$ **9.** $\dfrac{2(y+3)}{3y-8}$ **11.** $\dfrac{4(7-2x)}{x(x^2+1)}$ **13.** $-\dfrac{(2y+1)(y-1)}{y}$ **15.** $\dfrac{x(2x+5)}{5(2x+3)}$

17. $\dfrac{2ab(5a+b)}{(a+b)(a-b)(3a+b)}$ **19.** $\dfrac{1}{y-4}$ **21.** $\dfrac{-1}{y-3}$ **23.** $x=\dfrac{9}{13},\ y=\dfrac{59}{13}$ **25.** $x=1,\ y=-2,\ z=4$

Exercises 5.5

1. $y=-1$ **3.** $x=-1$ **5.** $x=\dfrac{5}{4}$ **7.** $y=-3$ (no sol.) **9.** $x=5$ **11.** $x=-5$ **13.** $x=-9$ **15.** $y=1$

17. $z=\dfrac{34}{3}$ **19.** $y=7$ **21.** $z=3$ (no sol.) **23.** $x=-3$ **25.** no sol., $0\neq 3$

27. when the denominator of any fraction equals zero and when the variable drops out **29.** $x=0$ **31.** $7(x+3)(x-3)$
33. $(4x-3y)(16x^2+12xy+9y^2)$ **35.** $x=2.951127594$

Exercises 5.6

1. $R=\dfrac{E}{I}$ **3.** $t=\dfrac{A-P}{Pr}$ **5.** $x=\dfrac{ab}{W}$ **7.** $t=\dfrac{2S}{V_1+V_2}$ **9.** $T_1=\dfrac{P_1V_1T_2}{P_2V_2}$ **11.** $n=\dfrac{IR}{E-Ir}$ **13.** $x_1=\dfrac{mx_2-y_2+y_1}{m}$

15. $h=\dfrac{3V}{\pi r^2}$ **17.** $t_2=\dfrac{kAt_1-QL}{kA}$ **19.** $T=\dfrac{V-V_0+bV_0T_0}{bV_0}$ **21.** $R_1=\dfrac{LR_2-dR_2}{d}$ **23.** 13.75 miles **25.** ≈ 68.18 mph.

27. 21 defectives **29.** 250 deer **31.** 180 km **33.** 10.5 in. **35.** 125 kg **37.** 34 detectives, 153 officers **39.** 282 ft
41. $\approx 23.68\times 36.32$ ft **43.** prime **45.** $(5x-9y)^2$ **47.** $T=T_0+0.1702\,(V/V_0)+0.1656$

Extra Practice: Exercises

Section 5.1 **1.** $\dfrac{2(3y+1)}{2y+3}$ **3.** $\dfrac{2x+3}{x+8}$ **5.** $\dfrac{6a^2}{25b^3}$ **7.** $\dfrac{3y-1}{2y-3}$ **9.** $\dfrac{x+4}{4}$ **11.** $\dfrac{x^2+2}{3x+1}$ **13.** $\dfrac{a(a+b)}{a-b}$ **15.** $\dfrac{3(3-x)}{2x^2(x-2)}$

17. $-\dfrac{5x^2}{4}$ **19.** $\dfrac{x}{x+y}$ **21.** $\dfrac{x-2}{x-3}$ **23.** $\dfrac{x-3}{5x}$ **25.** $\dfrac{a-c}{a+c}$ **27.** $\dfrac{b(a+2b)}{2(a^2+2ab+4b^2)}$ **29.** $\dfrac{x^2-2xy+4y^2}{x}$

31. $\dfrac{4x^2+10xy+25y^2}{x(2x+5y)}$ **Section 5.2** **1.** $\dfrac{2x^2}{y}$ **3.** -3 **5.** $\dfrac{(x-y)^2}{(2x+y)(x+y)}$ **7.** $\dfrac{1}{2x}$ **9.** $\dfrac{3}{2(x-5)}$

11. $\dfrac{2x^2(x+1)(x-1)}{15(x+2)}$ **13.** $-\dfrac{x-2y}{3}$ **15.** $\dfrac{24}{5y(x-5y)}$ **17.** $\dfrac{x}{x-4}$ **19.** $4a^2+2a+1$ **21.** 1 **23.** x **25.** $\dfrac{3}{x-2}$

27. $\dfrac{(a-b)^2}{b}$ **Section 5.3** **1.** $2a^3b^2$ **3.** $2(x+4)(x+3)(x-3)$ **5.** $(5x+1)(2x+3)^3$ **7.** $\dfrac{21x+4}{3x(3x+2)}$

9. $\dfrac{43x^2+80x-75}{5(x+2)(x-5)(x+5)}$ **11.** $\dfrac{8y-21}{(y-2)(y-3)}$ **13.** $\dfrac{3x}{(x+4)(x+1)}$ **15.** $\dfrac{5(x^2+6x+6)}{x(x+2)(x+5)}$ **17.** $\dfrac{2x^2+5x+6}{2x+1}$

19. $\dfrac{2a^2+1}{(2a-1)(a+2)(a-1)}$ **21.** $\dfrac{2ab}{a^2-b^2}$ **23.** $\dfrac{6ab+5b^2-30b+10}{10b}$ **25.** $\dfrac{5}{a+3}$ **27.** $\dfrac{-18b^2}{2a+3b}$ **29.** $\dfrac{3a-7b}{(a+b)(a-b)}$

31. $\dfrac{ay+c-bx}{xy}$ **33.** 0 **Section 5.4** **1.** $\dfrac{5}{b(2a+3b)}$ **3.** $\dfrac{1}{2y(y+3)}$ **5.** $\dfrac{4y+7}{2y+7}$ **7.** $\dfrac{46}{90x+105}$ **9.** $\dfrac{a^2-a-3}{a^3+3a^2-a}$

11. $-\dfrac{y^2}{4}$ **13.** $\dfrac{2(4x-5)}{(8x-7)(2x-3)}$ **15.** $\dfrac{m^2(x-3)}{x^2(m-1)}$ **17.** $\dfrac{x}{x-3}$ **19.** $\dfrac{x+2}{x(x+3)}$ **21.** $\dfrac{1}{2a^2-1}$ **23.** $x+y$

25. $6x+24y$ **Section 5.5** **1.** $x=3$ **3.** $y=5$ **5.** no sol. **7.** $x=2$ **9.** $x=2$ **11.** $y=-4$ **13.** no sol.

15. $x=29$ **17.** $x=\dfrac{2}{5}$ **19.** $x=\dfrac{3}{4}$ **21.** $s=6$ **23.** $y=-1$ **25.** $x=-3$ **27.** $x=-3$ **Section 5.6**

1. $r=\dfrac{E-CR}{C}$ **3.** $B=\dfrac{AC}{A-C}$ **5.** $P=\dfrac{S}{rt+1}$ **7.** $y=mx-mx_0+y_0$ **9.** $T=\dfrac{CN}{C-V}$ **11.** $A=\dfrac{QL}{kt_1-kt_2}$

13. $b=\dfrac{V-V_0}{V_0T-V_0T_0}$ **15.** $t_1=\dfrac{H+Smt_2}{Sm}$ **17.** $r=\dfrac{S-a}{S-l}$ **19.** $R=\dfrac{em-Cnr}{C}$ **21.** $x=\dfrac{2a+5}{2}$ **23.** $x=\dfrac{11h-6k}{5}$

25. 225 miles **27.** 787.4 in, 2.54 m **29.** 350 cups **31.** 200 miles **33.** 22 **35.** $30°,\ 60°,\ 90°$ **37.** 70 **39.** $\dfrac{100PD}{100C}$

Review Problems Chapter 5

1. $\dfrac{x}{2}$ **3.** $\dfrac{4b}{5a^3}$ **5.** $-\dfrac{y+7}{y-7}$ **7.** $\dfrac{(a+1)(a-1)}{a^2+2}$ **9.** $\dfrac{x(2x-1)}{x-2}$ **11.** $\dfrac{y-5}{y-4}$ **13.** $\dfrac{x+6}{3(x+2)}$ **15.** $-\dfrac{(y+1)^2(y+3)}{y+5}$

17. $\dfrac{2y+5}{2y-5}$ **19.** $\dfrac{4x+3y-2}{x^2y^2}$ **21.** $\dfrac{-7x+20}{4x(x+4)}$ **23.** $\dfrac{7y-18}{(y+5)(y-5)}$ **25.** $-\dfrac{y+2}{y+3}$ **27.** $\dfrac{a-2}{a+3}$ **29.** $\dfrac{4a^2+17a+11}{a+4}$

31. $\dfrac{2y + 3x}{7}$ **33.** $\dfrac{x}{x - 5}$ **35.** $\dfrac{y^2 + y + 1}{y^2 - y - 1}$ **37.** $\dfrac{2(2x - 1)}{3x}$ **39.** $\dfrac{y^2}{2y - 1}$ **41.** $x = 6$ **43.** $x = -1$ **45.** $a = -6$

47. $y = \dfrac{3}{4}$ **49.** $a = -\dfrac{1}{2}$ **51.** $x = \dfrac{3}{4}$ **53.** $M = \dfrac{mV}{N} - N$ **55.** $T_1 = \dfrac{P_1 V_1 T_2}{P_2 V_2}$ **57.** $t = \dfrac{2S}{V_1 + V_2}$ **59.** $R_2 = \dfrac{dR_1}{L - d}$

61. 57 **63.** 5.6 hrs **65.** 15 cm

Quiz Sections 5.1–5.3

1. $-\dfrac{y}{4x}$ **2.** $\dfrac{3x + 2}{4x - 3}$ **3.** $\dfrac{y}{y - 3}$ **4.** $\dfrac{x}{2y^2}$ **5.** $\dfrac{(x + 7)(x + 8)}{8x(x - 3)}$ **6.** $\dfrac{x + 6y}{3x - 4y}$ **7.** $\dfrac{10x + 5y - 6xy}{2xy(2x + y)}$ **8.** $\dfrac{3x + 15}{(x + 3)(x + 2)}$

9. $-\dfrac{3x + 4}{x(x - 4)(x - 2)}$ **10.** $\dfrac{11y - 9}{(2y + 1)(y - 3)}$ **11.** $\dfrac{6x - 4}{x - 1}$ **12.** $\dfrac{-4x - 9}{(2x + 3)(4x^2 - 6x + 9)}$

Quiz Sections 5.4–5.6

1. $\dfrac{1}{y - 1}$ **2.** $\dfrac{y - 5}{y}$ **3.** $\dfrac{-1}{3x + 5}$ **4.** $y = -1$ **5.** $y = -11$ **6.** $x = -4$ **7.** no sol. **8.** $C_1 = \dfrac{CC_2}{C_2 - C}$

9. $t_1 = \dfrac{QL + kAt_2}{kA}$ **10.** $A = \pi r S + \pi r^2$ **11.** 22.5 in. **12.** 2280 students **13.** 12.1 meters

Test Chapter 5

1. $\dfrac{x + 2}{x - 3}$ **2.** $\dfrac{y - 2}{y^2 - 2y + 4}$ **3.** $\dfrac{2(2y - 1)}{3y + 5}$ **4.** $\dfrac{-6}{(2x - 1)(x + 1)}$ **5.** $\dfrac{-2x - 17}{(x + 5)(x - 5)}$ **6.** $\dfrac{3x^2 + 8x + 6}{(x + 3)^2(x + 2)}$ **7.** $-\dfrac{2}{5}$

8. $-x + 1$ **9.** $x = \dfrac{7}{2}$ **10.** $y = 5$ **11.** $W = \dfrac{S - 2Lh}{2h + 2L}$ **12.** 52.5 minutes

Cumulative Test Chapters 1–5

1. $\dfrac{x^4 z^8}{9y^6}$ **2.** $x = \dfrac{55}{24}$ **3.**

x	y
0	-6
1	-3
2	0

$-6x + 2y = -12$

(2, 0)

(1, −3)

(0, −6)

4. $5x - 6y = 13$ **5.** \$700 @ 5% interest, \$6300 @ 8% interest

6. $x = -2, y = -3$ **7.** $x = 2, y = -1, z = 4$ **8.** $(3x + 5y)(9x^2 - 15xy + 25y^2)$ **9.** $x(9x - 5y)^2$ **10.** $\dfrac{7(x - 2)}{x + 4}$

11. $\dfrac{x(x + 1)}{2x + 5}$ **12.** $\dfrac{(x^2 - 3x + 9)(2x + 5)}{(x - 3)^2}$ **13.** $-\dfrac{x + 25}{2(x - 4)(x - 5)}$ **14.** $\dfrac{2(x + 1)(2x - 1)}{16x^2 - 7}$ **15.** $x = -4$ **16.** $x = -2$

17. $b = \dfrac{5H - 2x}{3 + 4H}$ **18.** 8250 cars

CHAPTER 6 Rational Exponents and Radicals

Pretest Chapter 6

1. $\dfrac{10y^{1/2}}{x^{1/12}}$ **2.** $\dfrac{8x^6}{y^3}$ **3.** $-5x^{3/2}y$ **4.** $\dfrac{-27x^{3/4}}{y}$ **5.** $\dfrac{1}{8}$ **6.** 8 **7.** $5a^2b^7c^3$ **8.** $2xy^3\sqrt[4]{3x^3}$ **9.** $x\sqrt{3x} - \sqrt[3]{3}$

10. $132 - 54\sqrt{2}$ **11.** $\dfrac{\sqrt[3]{2x}}{x}$ **12.** $\dfrac{2\sqrt{3} + 3\sqrt{2} + 2 + \sqrt{6}}{4}$ **13.** $9 - 7i$ **14.** $6i$ **15.** $21 - 20i$ **16.** $2 - i$

Exercises 6.1

1. $x^{5/6}y$ **3.** $-14x^{7/12}y^{1/12}$ **5.** $\dfrac{1}{5^{1/2}}$ **7.** $2x^{7/10}$ **9.** $\dfrac{-4y}{x^{1/6}}$ **11.** $2ab$ **13.** $\dfrac{a^3}{27b^6}$ **15.** $49x^{4/3}y^{1/2}z^3$ **17.** $25x^2yz^3$

19. $x^2 - y^{13/15}$ **21.** $a^{1/3} + 3a^{31/30}$ **23.** $a^{1/20}b^{1/6}$ **25.** $x^{41/24}$ **27.** 32 **29.** $a = -\dfrac{3}{8}$ **31.** $3x^{1/2}(-4x + 2x^2)$

33. $2a(3a^{1/3} - 4a^{1/2})$ **35.** $\dfrac{3y + 1}{y^{1/2}}$ **37.** $\dfrac{1 + 4^{1/3}y^{2/3}}{y^{2/3}}$ **39.** $\dfrac{x^{n/3}}{y^{2n/3}}$ **41.** x^{3n+1} **43.** $2a^{3n}b^n$

45. $x + x^{2/3}y^{1/3} + x^{1/3}y^{-1/3} + 1$ **47.** $3x^{3/4} - 2x^{1/2}y^{1/3} - 3x^{1/4}y^{2/3} + 2y$ **49.** $10x^{4n} + 2x^{5n/2}y^{4/3} - 5x^{3n/2}y^{1/2} - y^{11/6}$

51. $x = -\dfrac{3}{2}$ **53.** $b = \dfrac{2A - ah}{h}$ **55.** $-17.92628036x^{3/2}y^{-2}$

Exercises 6.2

1. A sq. root of a number is one of that number's two equal factors. **3.** $9^{1/3}$ **5.** $(2x)^{1/5}$ **7.** $(a + b)^{3/7}$

9. $x^{1/6}$ **11.** $(3x)^{5/6}$ **13.** $(\sqrt[4]{x})^3$ **15.** $\dfrac{1}{(\sqrt[3]{7})^2}$ **17.** $(\sqrt[7]{2a + b})^5$ **19.** $(\sqrt[5]{-x})^3$ **21.** 12 **23.** 12 **25.** $-\dfrac{1}{3}$

27. 3 **29.** -5 **31.** 5 **33.** -2 **35.** -2 **37.** not a real number **39.** 8 **41.** 5 **43.** $\dfrac{1}{8}$ **45.** -2

47. $\dfrac{8}{27}$ **49.** $5x^2$ **51.** $9x^2y^4$ **53.** $6x^3y^4z^5$ **55.** $6ab^3c^4$ **57.** $5x^2y^3$ **59.** $2z^2|xy^3|$ **61.** cost = \$1215 per day

63. $\sqrt[4]{256} = 4$, but $(\sqrt[4]{-16})^2$ is not a real number **65.** $-\dfrac{488}{109}$ **67.** $-\dfrac{1}{4}x^2 - \dfrac{5}{2}xy$ **69.** 10 **71.** 23 **73.** -7

Exercises 6.3

1. $5\sqrt{2}$ **3.** $4\sqrt{3}$ **5.** $2\sqrt{30}$ **7.** 9 **9.** $3x\sqrt{x}$ **11.** $2a^2b^2\sqrt{15b}$ **13.** $2y^4z\sqrt{6xz}$ **15.** 2 **17.** $3\sqrt[3]{4}$ **19.** $2\sqrt[3]{7}$
21. $2ab^2\sqrt[3]{b^2}$ **23.** $2x^3y^4\sqrt[3]{7x}$ **25.** $-2a^2bc^4\sqrt[3]{2}$ **27.** $2x^2y^3\sqrt[4]{3y}$ **29.** $3p^5\sqrt[4]{kp^3}$ **31.** $-2xy\sqrt[5]{y}$
33. $xy^2\sqrt[6]{8}$ or $xy^2\sqrt{2}$ **35.** $a = 4$ **37.** 17 **39.** $6\sqrt{3}$ **41.** $3\sqrt{3}$ **43.** $-11\sqrt{2}$ **45.** 0 **47.** $\sqrt{7x}$ **49.** $-13x\sqrt{5}$
51. $11\sqrt[3]{2}$ **53.** $-10xy\sqrt[3]{y} + 6xy^2$ **55.** $-27x\sqrt{2xy} + 13x\sqrt[3]{3xy}$ **57.** $7y\sqrt[6]{2xy^4z^3}$ **59.** $x = 4$ **61.** $y(9x + 5)(9x - 5)$
63. $0.258x^{3/2}y^3$

Exercises 6.4

1. $\sqrt{15}$ **3.** $-12\sqrt{3}$ **5.** $30x^2y^2\sqrt{3}$ **7.** $5\sqrt{2} + 30$ **9.** $6x - 8\sqrt{5x}$ **11.** $-3\sqrt{2}$ **13.** $4 - 6\sqrt{6}$ **15.** $74 + 11\sqrt{35}$
17. $x - 6\sqrt{x} + 8$ **19.** $\sqrt{15} + 2\sqrt{10} + 3 + 2\sqrt{6}$ **21.** $-11x$ **23.** $29 - 4\sqrt{30}$ **25.** $3x + 13 + 6\sqrt{3x + 4}$
27. $4a - 20\sqrt{ab} + 25b$ **29.** In the form of $(a + b)(a^2 - ab + b^2)$, $(\sqrt[3]{6})^3 + (\sqrt[3]{5})^3 = 6 + 5 = 11$, which equals $a^3 + b^3$
31. $\dfrac{3\sqrt{2}}{2}$ **33.** $\dfrac{\sqrt{2x}}{4}$ **35.** $\dfrac{\sqrt{5y}}{5y}$ **37.** $\dfrac{3\sqrt{2x}}{2x}$ **39.** $\dfrac{\sqrt{35y}}{7x}$ **41.** $\dfrac{2(\sqrt{6} - \sqrt{3})}{3}$ **43.** $\dfrac{7 + \sqrt{7}}{6}$ **45.** $\dfrac{x\sqrt{3} - \sqrt{2x}}{3x - 2}$

47. $4 + \sqrt{15}$ **49.** $\dfrac{3x - 2\sqrt{3xy} + y}{3x - y}$ **51.** $\dfrac{3\sqrt{6} + 4}{2}$ **53.** $8 - 3\sqrt{5}$ **55.** $6x^2\sqrt[4]{3}$ **57.** $3x\sqrt[3]{4} - 4x^2\sqrt[3]{x}$

59. $3\sqrt[3]{x^2} + 3x\sqrt[3]{2} - \sqrt[3]{4x^2} - 2x$ **61.** $\dfrac{3\sqrt[4]{8x}}{2x}$ **63.** $\dfrac{x\sqrt[3]{147}}{7}$ **65.** $x\sqrt[5]{8x^3y}$ **67.** $\dfrac{5}{7\sqrt{5}}$ **69.** $\dfrac{-25}{8(\sqrt{3} - 2\sqrt{7})}$

71. cost = \$2.92 **73.** $\dfrac{5\sqrt{2a} + 5\sqrt{3a} + 4\sqrt{5a}}{5a}$ **75.** $x = 2, y = 3$ **77.** $y = -5, z = 3$
79. $3.555345x - 1.732923\sqrt{xy} - 2.5707y$

Exercises 6.5

1. $7i$ **3.** $i\sqrt{19}$ **5.** $5i\sqrt{2}$ **7.** $3i\sqrt{7}$ **9.** $x = 3, y = -5\sqrt{2}$ **11.** $x = -6, y = 3$ **13.** $x = -3, y = -\dfrac{7}{2}$

15. $-5 - 12i$ **17.** $-26 - 4i$ **19.** $7 - 6i$ **21.** -21 **23.** $7 + 4i$ **25.** $29 + 22i$ **27.** $34 - 6i$ **29.** $-10 - 12i$

31. $27 - 36i$ **33.** i **35.** 1 **37.** 0 **39.** $\dfrac{1 + i}{2}$ **41.** $\dfrac{13 + i}{10}$ **43.** $-\dfrac{8i + 6}{3}$ **45.** $\dfrac{35 + 42i}{61}$

47. $\sqrt{-3}$ and $\sqrt{-27}$ are not real numbers; -54 **49.** $-44 - 117i$ **51.** $\dfrac{-x + 1}{(x + 3)(x + 1)}$ **53.** $x = -3$ **55.** $y = -2$

Extra Practice: Exercises

Section 6.1 **1.** $-6x^{3/4}y^{3/4}$ **3.** $3^{1/10}$ **5.** $\dfrac{6y^{3/4}}{x^{5/6}}$ **7.** $\dfrac{1}{64a^3b^6}$ **9.** $2^2x^{3/2}y^{5/2}z^{1/2}$ **11.** $\dfrac{1}{a^{5/12}} + \dfrac{2}{a^{1/3}}$ **13.** 91

15. $x^{65/12}$ **17.** -2 **19.** $m^6n^2x^{1/2}$ **21.** $\dfrac{104}{315}$ **23.** $\dfrac{2}{x^3}$ **25.** $an^{1/2}$ **27.** $3x^{1/3}(x^2 - 2x)$ or $3x^{1/3}(x^{6/3} - 2x^{3/3})$

29. $6a^{1/2}(2a^{5/2} - 3a^2)$ **31.** $\dfrac{x^{3/2} + 2^{1/2}}{2^{1/2}x^{3/2}}$ **33.** $\dfrac{3^nx^{n/4}}{y^{2n/3}}$ **35.** $\dfrac{3y^{3n}}{x^n}$ **37.** 2^{4n} **39.** $6a^{3/8} + 3a^{1/4}b^{2/3} - 4a^{1/8}b^{1/3} - 2b$

Section 6.2 **1.** $(3x)^{1/7}$ **3.** $(2y)^{5/8}$ **5.** $x^{1/8}$ **7.** $(2x^2)^{1/2}$ **9.** $(x^3z)^{1/4}$ **11.** $\sqrt[8]{x^7}$ **13.** $\sqrt[4]{(x + 2y)^3}$ **15.** $\sqrt[8]{16x^4}$ or $\sqrt{2x}$

17. 18   **19.** $-\dfrac{5}{6}$ **21.** 5   **23.** $-\dfrac{1}{2}$ **25.** 2   **27.** 0   **29.** not a real no.   **31.** 0   **33.** 5   **35.** $\dfrac{1}{5}$ **37.** 27

39. $10x^3$ **41.** $25a^2b^8$ **43.** $12x^4yz^5$ **45.** $-2a^4c^3$ **47.** $12ax^3$ **49.** $7x^2y^4$ **51.** $-xy^2z^3$ **53.** $3x^3y^5z^2$

Section 6.3   **1.** $5x^2y^3\sqrt{3x}$ **3.** $2a^4b^2\sqrt{17}$ **5.** $-3xy^4z^4\sqrt[3]{3z^2}$ **7.** $2x^5y^4z^5\sqrt[3]{5yz^2}$ **9.** not a real no.   **11.** $2x^5y^3\sqrt[4]{5y}$

13. $-2x^3y^3\sqrt[5]{2y^3}$ **15.** $x^3yz^2\sqrt[6]{5x^2z^3}$ **17.** $3xyz\sqrt[4]{yz^2}$ **19.** $-2y^2z\sqrt[5]{xz}$ **21.** $12yz\sqrt{2xz}$ **23.** $x^4\sqrt[5]{3105x}$

25. $7\sqrt{3}$ **27.** 0   **29.** $32\sqrt{3}$ **31.** $y\sqrt{7y}$ **33.** $-x^2y^2\sqrt{xy}$ **35.** $19\sqrt[3]{2}$ **37.** $11x\sqrt[3]{x}$ **39.** $-11\sqrt{2ab}$

41. $-7\sqrt{7}$ **43.** $-3\sqrt[3]{7x}+16\sqrt[3]{2x}$ **45.** $-6\sqrt[5]{x}$ ***Section 6.4***   **1.** $-30\sqrt{2}$ **3.** $8x^2y^3\sqrt{3}$ **5.** $-3\sqrt{10}-24$

7. $-4x^2$ **9.** $3\sqrt{30}-2$ **11.** $4x-10\sqrt{2xy}+12y$ **13.** $28+20\sqrt{5}$ **15.** $26+2x-10\sqrt{2x+1}$ **17.** $53+10\sqrt{6}$

19. $56-15\sqrt{x}+x$ **21.** $9a-4b$ **23.** -115 **25.** -105 **27.** $a-b$ **29.** 1   **31.** $3\sqrt{11}/11$ **33.** $\sqrt{3x}/3$

35. $\dfrac{8\sqrt{11x}}{11x}$ **37.** $\dfrac{\sqrt{3x}}{4x}$ **39.** $\dfrac{w\sqrt{5x}}{4x}$ **41.** $-x(\sqrt{5}-\sqrt{6})$ **43.** $5+2\sqrt{5}$ **45.** $\dfrac{y\sqrt{2}+\sqrt{5y}}{2y-5}$

47. $-\sqrt{15}+\sqrt{10}+3\sqrt{2}-2\sqrt{3}$ **49.** $\dfrac{14+5\sqrt{10}}{18}$ **51.** $\dfrac{7+2\sqrt{10}}{3}$ **53.** $\dfrac{6\sqrt{x}+2\sqrt{2}}{9x-2}$ **55.** $24x\sqrt[4]{x^3}$

57. $6x\sqrt[3]{2}-9x\sqrt[3]{4x}$ **59.** 6   **61.** $\dfrac{7\sqrt[4]{3x}}{3x}$ **63.** $\dfrac{\sqrt[3]{75}}{5x}$ **65.** $\dfrac{\sqrt[3]{3x^2y}}{y}$ ***Section 6.5***   **1.** $11i$ **3.** $3i\sqrt{11}$ **5.** $9i\sqrt{3}$

7. $2ix\sqrt{y}$ **9.** $x=-3,\ y=7$ **11.** $x=-21,\ y=-\dfrac{1}{5}$ **13.** $x=\dfrac{1}{3},\ y=-\dfrac{1}{2}$ **15.** $5-5i$ **17.** $-11-10i$

19. $-84-8i$ **21.** $22+29i$ **23.** $18+21i$ **25.** 85   **27.** $-i$ **29.** $-i$ **31.** $\dfrac{-23+i}{53}$ **33.** $\dfrac{13-i}{10}$ **35.** $\dfrac{20-9i}{13}$

37. $\dfrac{-4-5i}{2}$ **39.** $\dfrac{8+6i}{25}$ **41.** $\dfrac{15-112i}{113}$

Review Problems Chapter 6

1. $-6a^{5/6}b^{3/4}$ **3.** $\dfrac{x}{32y^{1/2}z^4}$ **5.** $2a^{19/20}-3a^{3/10}$ **7.** $3x^{n+1}$ **9.** $\dfrac{2x+1}{x^{2/3}}$ **11.** $(2x)^{1/10}$ **13.** 8   **15.** $\dfrac{1}{81}$

17. $3xy^3z^5\sqrt{11x}$ **19.** $2x^2z^2\sqrt[4]{y^3z^3}$ **21.** $12x^5y^6$ **23.** $11\sqrt{2}$ **25.** $2-6\sqrt[3]{2}$ **27.** $11\sqrt{2x}-x\sqrt{2}$ **29.** $90\sqrt{2}$

31. $4-9\sqrt{6}$ **33.** $74-12\sqrt{30}$ **35.** $\dfrac{x\sqrt{3y}}{y}$ **37.** $\sqrt{3}$ **39.** $\dfrac{3x-\sqrt{xy}}{9x-y}$ **41.** $\dfrac{2+3\sqrt{2}}{7}$ **43.** $\dfrac{3x+4\sqrt{xy}+y}{x-y}$

45. $4i+3i\sqrt{5}$ **47.** $-9-11i$ **49.** $29-29i$ **51.** $6i-8$ **53.** -1 **55.** $\dfrac{11+13i}{10}$ **57.** $\dfrac{18+30i}{17}$

Quiz Sections 6.1–6.2

1. $\dfrac{-6y^{1/2}}{x^{1/20}}$ **2.** $-2x^{5/12}y^{1/4}$ **3.** $\dfrac{b}{4a^6}$ **4.** $8x^6y^9$ **5.** $4x(x^{1/2}-3x^{-1/2})$ **6.** $\dfrac{4x+1}{x^{1/2}}$ **7.** 5   **8.** -2 **9.** $\dfrac{3}{2}$

10. $\dfrac{1}{81}$ **11.** $10x^3z^4$ **12.** $-3x^2y^4$ **13.** $2a^5b^8c$ **14.** 9

Quiz Sections 6.3–6.5

1. $5xy^2\sqrt{3x}$ **2.** $-2ab^3c^4\sqrt[3]{5b}$ **3.** $2a^2c^2\sqrt[4]{2b^3c^3}$ **4.** $-2x\sqrt[5]{x}$ **5.** $19\sqrt{2}$ **6.** $-\sqrt{2}+5\sqrt[3]{2}$ **7.** $20x\sqrt{2x}$

8. $11a\sqrt[3]{2ab}$ **9.** $36x\sqrt{6}$ **10.** $4\sqrt{3}-4\sqrt{15}$ **11.** 12   **12.** $187-20\sqrt{21}$ **13.** $\dfrac{3\sqrt{5}}{5}$ **14.** $\dfrac{2\sqrt[3]{9x}}{3x}$ **15.** $\dfrac{\sqrt{5}-1}{2}$

16. $\dfrac{27+7\sqrt{6}}{29}$ **17.** $8+3i$ **18.** $5i$ **19.** $7-26i$ **20.** $\dfrac{6i-4}{3}$ **21.** $\dfrac{1+7i}{10}$ **22.** $13-84i$

Test Chapter 6

1. $-6x^{8/15}y^{3/4}$ **2.** $\dfrac{5x^{3/2}}{3}$ **3.** $2^{2/3}x^{1/6}$ **4.** $\dfrac{1}{16}$ **5.** 729   **6.** $3xy^3\sqrt[3]{3x^2}$ **7.** $10x^2y^3\sqrt{y}$ **8.** $4a^2b^5\sqrt{3a}$

9. $-20\sqrt{2}+8x\sqrt[3]{2x}$ **10.** $14\sqrt{2}$ **11.** $30\sqrt{6}-54\sqrt{2}$ **12.** $60-55\sqrt{2}$ **13.** $\dfrac{\sqrt[3]{4x}}{x}$ **14.** $\dfrac{\sqrt{5x}}{x}$ **15.** $2+\sqrt{3}$

16. $5+11i$ **17.** $6i$ **18.** $-1-18i$ **19.** $\dfrac{11+10i}{17}$ **20.** $27+36i$

Cumulative Test Chapters 1–6

1. associative property for addition   **2.** $6a^4-3a^3+15a^2-8a$ **3.** -64 **4.** $x=\dfrac{3y+24}{2}$

5.

x	y
0	−3
5	0
10	3

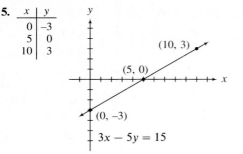

(10, 3)

(5, 0)

(0, −3)

$3x - 5y = 15$

6. $8(2x - 1)(x + 2)$ **7.** $x = 2, y = 1, z = -4$ **8.** $\dfrac{5x - 6}{(x - 5)(x + 3)}$

9. width = 7 m, length = 17 m   **10.** $b = \dfrac{26x + 1}{4}$ **11.** $\dfrac{1}{2x^{1/2}y^{15/2}}$ **12.** $\dfrac{x^{1/6}}{3^{1/3}y^{2/3}}$ **13.** $\dfrac{1}{4}$ **14.** $2xy^3 \sqrt[3]{5x^2}$ **15.** $4\sqrt{5x}$

16. $-34 + 3\sqrt{6}$ **17.** $\dfrac{16 + 9\sqrt{3}}{-13}$ **18.** $12i$ **19.** $-5 + 12i$ **20.** $\dfrac{13 + i}{10}$

CHAPTER 7   Quadratic Equations

Pretest Chapter 7

1. $\dfrac{2}{3}, -\dfrac{3}{4}$ **2.** $0, \dfrac{7}{4}$ **3.** $\dfrac{-2}{3}, 3$ **4.** $\pm 2\sqrt{3}$ **5.** $\dfrac{2 \pm \sqrt{10}}{2}$ **6.** $\dfrac{1 \pm 2\sqrt{2}}{2}$ **7.** $\dfrac{1 \pm \sqrt{21}}{10}$ **8.** $\dfrac{-3 \pm 2i\sqrt{2}}{2}$ **9.** -3

10. $5, 13$ **11.** $2, -1$ **12.** $\pm 8, \pm 2\sqrt{2}$ **13.** $x = \dfrac{-2w - 5b \pm \sqrt{4w^2 + 20wb + 25b^2 + 96w}}{6}$ **14.** $w = 4$ m, $l = 13$ m

Exercises 7.1

1. $x = -10, x = -1$ **3.** $x = 9, x = 4$ **5.** $x = 0, x = \dfrac{6}{5}$ **7.** $x = \dfrac{5}{2}, x = 1$ **9.** $x = \dfrac{-4}{3}, x = 2$ **11.** $x = \dfrac{2}{3}, x = \dfrac{-5}{2}$

13. $x = \dfrac{3}{8}, x = 1$ **15.** $x = 9, x = -3$ **17.** $x = -7, x = 3$ **19.** $x = 0, x = -1$ **21.** $x = 0, x = \dfrac{1}{8}$ **23.** $x = 6, x = 2$

25. $x = 5, x = -2$ **27.** $x = 7, x = -3$ **29.** $x = 4, x = -3$ **31.** $x = -3, x = \dfrac{-5}{4}$ **33.** $x = 12, x = -1$

35. $x = 0, x = \dfrac{2}{11}$ **37.** 10 units   **39.** $b = 1, x^2 + x - 12 = 0$ **41.** $x = \dfrac{11}{8}, x = \dfrac{-4}{5}$ **43.** $200x^{11}y^{10}$ **45.** $\dfrac{x^4}{9y^8z^2}$

47. $2.193(x + 4)(x + 2) = 0, x = -2, -4$

Exercises 7.2

1. $x = \pm 11$ **3.** $x = \pm 2\sqrt{5}$ **5.** $x = \pm\sqrt{13}$ **7.** $x = \pm 3$ **9.** $x = \pm 6$ **11.** $x = 3 \pm 2\sqrt{3}$ **13.** $x = \dfrac{-1 \pm \sqrt{7}}{2}$

15. $x = \dfrac{9}{4}, \dfrac{-3}{4}$ **17.** $x = \dfrac{4 \pm 2\sqrt{2}}{3}$ **19.** $x = 1 \pm \sqrt{6}$ **21.** $x = -5 \pm 2\sqrt{5}$ **23.** $x = 4 \pm \sqrt{33}$ **25.** $x = 3 \pm \sqrt{5}$

27. $x = \dfrac{-5 \pm \sqrt{3}}{2}$ **29.** $x = \dfrac{3}{2}, x = \dfrac{-1}{2}$ **31.** $y = 3, y = \dfrac{-5}{2}$ **33.** $x = \dfrac{-3 \pm \sqrt{33}}{12}$ **35.** $x = \dfrac{-7 \pm \sqrt{65}}{8}$

37. $y = \dfrac{\pm\sqrt{10} - \sqrt{2}}{2}$ **39.** $x = \dfrac{-13 \pm \sqrt{313}}{8}$ **41.** 15 seconds   **43.** 8   **45.** 40   **47.** $x = \pm 4.2817$

Exercises 7.3

1. $x = \dfrac{-3 \pm \sqrt{89}}{2}$ **3.** $x = \dfrac{1 \pm \sqrt{21}}{10}$ **5.** $x = \dfrac{-5 \pm \sqrt{37}}{2}$ **7.** $x = -4 \pm \sqrt{3}$ **9.** $x = \dfrac{1}{2}, x = \dfrac{-1}{3}$ **11.** $x = \dfrac{-3 \pm \sqrt{41}}{8}$

13. $x = \dfrac{2 \pm \sqrt{13}}{3}$ **15.** $x = \dfrac{4 \pm \sqrt{6}}{2}$ **17.** $x = \pm 1$ **19.** $x = \dfrac{1 \pm \sqrt{29}}{2}$ **21.** $x = \dfrac{-7 \pm \sqrt{17}}{4}$ **23.** $x = \dfrac{5 \pm \sqrt{73}}{2}$

25. $y = \dfrac{9 \pm \sqrt{129}}{2}$ **27.** $y = 9, y = 5$ **29.** 2 complex roots   **31.** 2 complex roots   **33.** 2 rational roots

35. $x = 2 \pm 2i$ **37.** $x = \dfrac{-1 \pm i}{2}$ **39.** $x = \dfrac{4 \pm i\sqrt{5}}{3}$ **41.** $x = \dfrac{1 \pm i\sqrt{47}}{6}$ **43.** $a = 2$ **45.** $x = \dfrac{-d \pm \sqrt{d^2 - 60f}}{10}$

47. $7 + 4\sqrt{3} = 7 + 4\sqrt{3}$ **49.** $-3x^2 - 10x + 11$ **51.** $6x^2 - 11x$ **53.** $x = -2.7554, 1.0888$

Exercises 7.4

1. Isolate one of the radicals on one side of the equation.　　**3.** $x = 7$, $x = -1$ (extraneous)　　**5.** $x = 12$, $x = 4$ (extraneous)

7. $y = 7$, $y = 4$ (extraneous)　　**9.** $y = 1$ (extraneous), $y = -2$　　**11.** $x = -5$, $x = 4$　　**13.** $x = 9$, $x = -1$　　**15.** $x = \dfrac{5}{2}$

17. $x = -5$, $x = 2$　　**19.** $x = -9$　　**21.** $x = \dfrac{-17}{15}$ (no sol.)　　**23.** $x = 5$, $x = 8$　　**25.** $x = 5$, $x = 13$　　**27.** $x = 6$

29. $x = \dfrac{3}{2}$, $x = -1$ (extraneous)　　**31.** $x = 2$, $x = 7$ (extraneous)　　**33.** $y = 0$, $y = 4$　　**35.** $c = 9$　　**37.** $x = -3$, $x = -2$

39. $16x^4$　　**41.** $-6x^2y^3$　　**43.** $x = 4.9232$ or 0.4028

Exercises 7.5

1. $x = \pm\sqrt{5}$, $x = \pm 2$　　**3.** $x = \pm\dfrac{\sqrt{6}}{2}$, $x = \pm i$　　**5.** $x = \pm\dfrac{i\sqrt{6}}{3}$, $x = \pm 2$　　**7.** $x = \sqrt[3]{4}$, $x = \sqrt[3]{3}$　　**9.** $x = -\dfrac{\sqrt[3]{4}}{2}$, $x = \sqrt[3]{4}$

11. $x = \pm\sqrt[4]{2}$, $x = \pm 1$　　**13.** $x = \pm\dfrac{\sqrt[4]{54}}{3}$ These are the only real roots　　**15.** $x = -64$, $x = 8$　　**17.** $x = 343$, $x = 27$

19. $x = \dfrac{1}{16}$ (extraneous), $x = 81$　　**21.** $x = \dfrac{1}{4096}$, $x = 1$ (extraneous)　　**23.** $x = -32$, $x = 1$

25. $x = -2$, $x = \dfrac{-1 \pm \sqrt{13}}{2}$, $x = 1$　　**27.** $x = 49$, $x = 9$ (extraneous)　　**29.** $x = -5$, $x = -2$　　**31.** $x = \dfrac{1}{2}$, $x = 3$

33. $x = \dfrac{5}{6}$, $x = \dfrac{3}{2}$　　**35.** $-15\sqrt{2x}$　　**37.** $3\sqrt{10} - 12\sqrt{3}$

Exercises 7.6

1. $x = \pm\sqrt{3H}$　　**3.** $y = \dfrac{\pm\sqrt{2A - 5}}{2}$　　**5.** $V = \pm\sqrt{\dfrac{Fr}{kb}}$　　**7.** $r = \pm\sqrt{\dfrac{V - \pi R^2 h}{\pi h}}$　　**9.** $x = \dfrac{5 \pm \sqrt{25 + 12abB}}{6ab}$

11. $x = \dfrac{-5 \pm \sqrt{25 - 8aw - 8w}}{2a + 2}$　　**13.** $w = \dfrac{-b \pm \sqrt{b^2 + 40}}{5}$　　**15.** $h = \pm d^2\sqrt{\dfrac{K}{L}}$　　**17.** $x = \dfrac{-P \pm \sqrt{AP}}{P}$

19. $x = -5b$, $x = 2b$　　**21.** $a = \dfrac{2b}{3}$, $a = \dfrac{-5b}{2}$　　**23.** $c = 2\sqrt{13}$　　**25.** $a = 12$　　**27.** $b = \sqrt{17}$　　**29.** $a = \dfrac{12\sqrt{5}}{5}$, $b = \dfrac{24\sqrt{5}}{5}$

31. shorter = 6 in., longer = 8 in.　　**33.** width = 7 m, length = 13 m　　**35.** base = 8 cm, altitude = 18 cm

37. rate (old road) = 40 mph, rate (new road) = 45 mph　　**39.** 30 miles　　**41.** $w = \dfrac{-7b - 21 \pm \sqrt{529b^2 + 294b + 441}}{10}$

43. $\dfrac{\sqrt{30}}{2}$　　**45.** $-2 - 2\sqrt{2}$　　**47.** $a = 13.2403$

Extra Practice: Exercises

Section 7.1　**1.** $3, -11$　　**3.** $0, \dfrac{5}{2}$　　**5.** $\dfrac{2}{3}, \dfrac{-4}{3}$　　**7.** $5, \dfrac{2}{3}$　　**9.** $1, -3$　　**11.** $\dfrac{-4}{3}, 2$　　**13.** $1, -6$　　**15.** $4, -\dfrac{1}{3}$　　**17.** $6, -4$

19. $0, -1$　　**21.** $-\dfrac{3}{2}, -4$　　**23.** $\dfrac{1}{5}, -2$　　**25.** $0, 3$　　**27.** $\dfrac{7}{9}, -\dfrac{2}{3}$　　**29.** $\dfrac{4}{3}, \dfrac{10}{3}$　　**31.** $2, \dfrac{-1}{6}$　　**33.** $-\dfrac{5}{4}, \dfrac{3}{8}$　　**35.** $8, -4$

Section 7.2　**1.** ± 3　　**3.** $\pm\sqrt{30}$　　**5.** $\pm 2\sqrt{2}$　　**7.** $\dfrac{-1 \pm \sqrt{5}}{2}$　　**9.** $\dfrac{5 \pm 5\sqrt{2}}{6}$　　**11.** ± 2　　**13.** ± 8　　**15.** $\pm 2i\sqrt{2}$

17. ± 3　　**19.** $4 \pm \sqrt{30}$　　**21.** $-2 \pm \sqrt{3}$　　**23.** $\dfrac{-3 \pm \sqrt{11}}{2}$　　**25.** $1, -\dfrac{2}{3}$　　**27.** $\dfrac{3 \pm \sqrt{5}}{4}$　　**29.** $\dfrac{-3 \pm \sqrt{15}}{4}$　　**31.** $\dfrac{4}{3}, 1$

33. $\dfrac{5}{2}, -7$　　**35.** $2, -4$　　*Section 7.3*　**1.** $\dfrac{-3 \pm \sqrt{17}}{2}$　　**3.** $\dfrac{-1 \pm \sqrt{41}}{4}$　　**5.** $\dfrac{5}{2}, \dfrac{2}{3}$　　**7.** $\dfrac{1 \pm \sqrt{21}}{10}$　　**9.** $\dfrac{3 \pm \sqrt{17}}{4}$

11. $\dfrac{-3 \pm \sqrt{19}}{2}$　　**13.** $\dfrac{7 \pm \sqrt{177}}{8}$　　**15.** $1 \pm 2\sqrt{2}$　　**17.** $\dfrac{5}{3}, -\dfrac{3}{2}$　　**19.** $1, \dfrac{2}{3}$　　**21.** $\dfrac{5 \pm \sqrt{13}}{2}$　　**23.** $\dfrac{3 \pm \sqrt{41}}{8}$　　**25.** $-2 \pm 2i\sqrt{2}$

27. $\dfrac{-2 \pm i\sqrt{2}}{3}$　　**29.** $2, -\dfrac{4}{5}$　　**31.** $\dfrac{4 \pm \sqrt{6}}{5}$　　**33.** $-3 \pm 2i$　　**35.** $4 \pm \sqrt{11}$　　*Section 7.4*　**1.** $3, 2$　　**3.** 0　　**5.** 7　　**7.** 5

9. $4, -1$　　**11.** 62　　**13.** $\pm 2\sqrt{2}$　　**15.** 5　　**17.** 6　　**19.** -2　　**21.** $3, \dfrac{9}{4}$　　**23.** 9　　**25.** 4　　**27.** 4　　**29.** -24

31. 6　　**33.** 17　　**35.** 63　　**37.** 0　　**39.** $x = \dfrac{2a\sqrt{3}}{3}$　　*Section 7.5*　**1.** $\pm\sqrt{6}, \pm 2$　　**3.** $\dfrac{\pm\sqrt{21}}{3}, \pm i$　　**5.** $\pm 2, \pm 1$

7. $-27, -8$　　**9.** $\dfrac{1}{32}, -243$　　**11.** 625　　**13.** $\pm 3, \pm i$　　**15.** $\dfrac{5}{3}, \dfrac{7}{4}$　　**17.** $4, 3$　　**19.** $-\dfrac{5}{3}, 2, \dfrac{4}{3}, -1$　　**21.** 81

23. $\pm 1, \pm\dfrac{2i\sqrt{6}}{3}$ **25.** 64, 1   **27.** $\pm 2, \pm 1$ **29.** $\pm 2, \pm i\sqrt{10}$ **31.** $\pm 1, \pm\dfrac{i\sqrt{55}}{5}$ **33.** 4   *Section 7.6* **1.** $\pm\dfrac{\sqrt{5y^2 - 2}}{2}$

3. $y = \dfrac{3b \pm ib\sqrt{31}}{2}$ **5.** $b = \dfrac{\pm\sqrt{12c^2 - 2a^2}}{3}$ **7.** $w = \dfrac{ab \pm b\sqrt{a^2 - 40}}{5}$ **9.** $x = \dfrac{5k \pm \sqrt{25k^2 - 144k}}{6k}$ **11.** $x = -b \pm b\sqrt{2}$

13. $x = \pm(a - 1)$ **15.** $x = \dfrac{2}{a}, x = \dfrac{-b}{6}$ **17.** $x = \pm a\sqrt{b - 1}$ **19.** $x = \dfrac{3a}{4}, x = \dfrac{a}{4}$ **21.** $x = -1, x = \dfrac{n + 1}{n - 1}$

23. $a = 24$ **25.** $c = \sqrt{67}$ **27.** $a = \sqrt{95}$ **29.** 11 m by 14 m   **31.** 7 m by 32 m
33. 40 mph during 120 miles, 45 mph during 180 miles   **35.** 48 sq. ft

Review Problems Chapter 7

1. $\dfrac{4 \pm i\sqrt{2}}{3}$ **3.** $0, \dfrac{9}{7}$ **5.** $\pm i\sqrt{5}$ **7.** $-8, 4$ **9.** $\dfrac{5}{2}, -3$ **11.** $\dfrac{3 \pm i\sqrt{23}}{8}$ **13.** $-\dfrac{2}{3}, \dfrac{1}{3}$ **15.** $-7, \pm i$ **17.** $\dfrac{3 \pm i}{5}$

19. $-\dfrac{5}{6}, -2$ **21.** $-5, 3$ **23.** $-3, 1$ **25.** $-2, 3$ **27.** 4   **29.** 5, 1   **31.** $\pm 2, \pm\sqrt{2}$ **33.** 256   **35.** 1, 2

37. $B = \pm\sqrt{\dfrac{3AH}{2C}}$ **39.** $d = \dfrac{x}{4}, \dfrac{-x}{5}$ **41.** $c = \sqrt{22}$ **43.** width = 7 m, length = 29 m

45. 50 mph during 1st part, 45 mph during rain

Quiz Sections 7.1–7.3

1. $\dfrac{4}{3}, \dfrac{-1}{2}$ **2.** 5   **3.** 7, -7 **4.** $\pm\sqrt{5}$ **5.** $\dfrac{3 \pm \sqrt{21}}{3}$ **6.** $\dfrac{-7 \pm \sqrt{65}}{4}$ **7.** $-3 + \sqrt{19}$ **8.** $\dfrac{3}{2}, 4$ **9.** $\dfrac{-5}{6}, 2$

10. $1 \pm 2i$ **11.** $\dfrac{1 \pm i\sqrt{15}}{2}$ **12.** $\dfrac{3}{4}, -2$ **13.** $\dfrac{\pm 3i\sqrt{5}}{5}$ **14.** $\pm 3\sqrt{2}$ **15.** $3 \pm 2\sqrt{3}$ **16.** $\dfrac{7}{2}$ **17.** $-8, 2$

18. 12, -1 **19.** 5, 2   **20.** 7, -3

Quiz Sections 7.4–7.6

1. $x = 7$ **2.** $x = 8$ **3.** $x = 0, x = 4$ **4.** no sol.   **5.** $x = 2$ **6.** $x = -4, x = +1$

7. $x = \pm\sqrt[4]{4}$ These are the only real roots   **8.** $x = \dfrac{-\sqrt[3]{2}}{2}, x = \dfrac{\sqrt[3]{18}}{3}$ **9.** $x = -3, 1$. These are the only real roots

10. $x = -125, 8$ **11.** $x = 81, 16$ **12.** $x = -1$ **13.** $x = \pm\sqrt{\dfrac{A - 2by^2}{2b}}$ **14.** $a = \pm\dfrac{\sqrt{3\pi H}}{\pi}$ **15.** $w = \dfrac{1}{2x}, \dfrac{-5}{3x}$

16. $y = \dfrac{-(a + 3) \pm \sqrt{a^2 + 6a + 9 + 40x^2}}{10x^2}$ **17.** $c = \sqrt{79}$ **18.** $b = 2\sqrt{6}$

Test Chapter 7

1. $0, \dfrac{7}{5}$ **2.** $\dfrac{1}{3}, -2$ **3.** $2, \dfrac{-2}{9}$ **4.** 8   **5.** $\pm\sqrt{10}$ **6.** $\dfrac{7}{2}, -1$ **7.** $\dfrac{3 \pm \sqrt{3}}{2}$ **8.** $\dfrac{3}{2}$ **9.** 6   **10.** 5

11. $\pm\sqrt{7}, \pm\sqrt{2}$ **12.** $\dfrac{1}{5}, \dfrac{-3}{4}$ **13.** $(1 \pm \sqrt{13})^3$ **14.** $z = \pm\sqrt{\dfrac{xyw}{B}}$ **15.** $y = \dfrac{-b \pm \sqrt{b^2 - 30w}}{5}$ **16.** $c = 4\sqrt{3}$

17. width = 5 miles, length = 16 miles   **18.** 2 mph during 1st part, 3 mph after lunch

Cumulative Test Chapters 1–7

1. $\dfrac{81y^{12}}{x^8}$ **2.** $\dfrac{1}{4}a^3 - a^2 - 3a$ **3.** $y = \dfrac{ab + 4}{a}$ **4.**

x	y
0	4
-2	0

5. $x + 2y = 4$ **6.** $\dfrac{32\pi}{3}$

7. $(5x - 3y)(25x^2 + 15xy + 9y^2)$ **8.** $4x^2y^2\sqrt{3y}$ **9.** $4\sqrt{6} + 5\sqrt{3}$ **10.** $\dfrac{5\sqrt{7}}{7}$ **11.** $0, \dfrac{3}{5}$ **12.** $\dfrac{1}{3}, -5$

13. $x = \dfrac{3 \pm 2\sqrt{3}}{2}$ **14.** $x = \dfrac{2 \pm i\sqrt{11}}{3}$ **15.** $x = 16$ **16.** $x = -27, -216$ **17.** $y = \dfrac{-5w \pm \sqrt{25w^2 + 56z}}{4}$

18. $y = \pm\sqrt{\dfrac{5w - 16z^2}{3}}$ **19.** $x = \sqrt{15}$ **20.** base = 5 m, altitude = 18 m

CHAPTER 8   Graphs and Functions

Pretest Chapter 8

1. $d = 3\sqrt{5}$ **2.** $(x - 8)^2 + (y + 2)^2 = 7$ **3.**

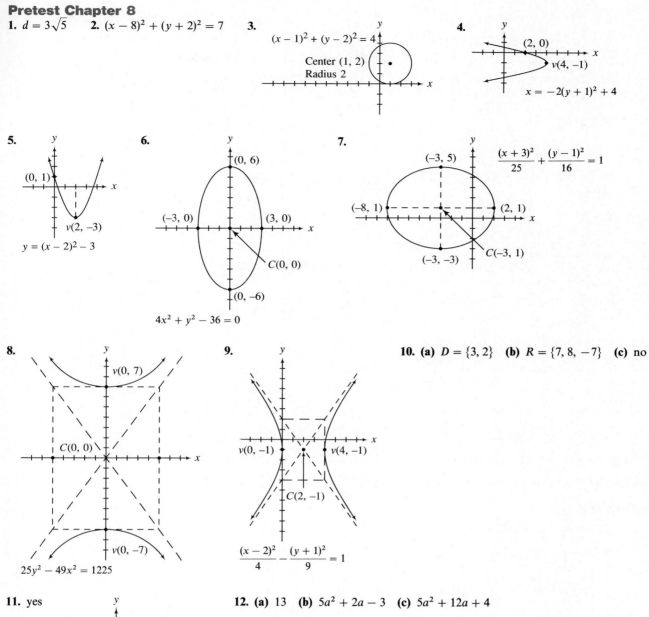

3. $(x - 1)^2 + (y - 2)^2 = 4$
Center (1, 2)
Radius 2

4. $x = -2(y + 1)^2 + 4$; $v(4, -1)$; $(2, 0)$

5. $y = (x - 2)^2 - 3$; $(0, 1)$; $v(2, -3)$

6. $4x^2 + y^2 - 36 = 0$; $(0, 6)$; $(-3, 0)$; $(3, 0)$; $(0, -6)$; $C(0, 0)$

7. $\dfrac{(x + 3)^2}{25} + \dfrac{(y - 1)^2}{16} = 1$; $(-3, 5)$; $(-8, 1)$; $(2, 1)$; $(-3, -3)$; $C(-3, 1)$

8. $25y^2 - 49x^2 = 1225$; $v(0, 7)$; $v(0, -7)$; $C(0, 0)$

9. $\dfrac{(x - 2)^2}{4} - \dfrac{(y + 1)^2}{9} = 1$; $v(0, -1)$; $v(4, -1)$; $C(2, -1)$

10. (a) $D = \{3, 2\}$ **(b)** $R = \{7, 8, -7\}$ **(c)** no

11. yes

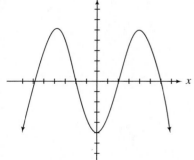

12. (a) 13   **(b)** $5a^2 + 2a - 3$ **(c)** $5a^2 + 12a + 4$

13. yes

14. $F^{-1} = \{(1, 7), (3, 6), (-1, 2), (-5, -1)\}$ **15.**

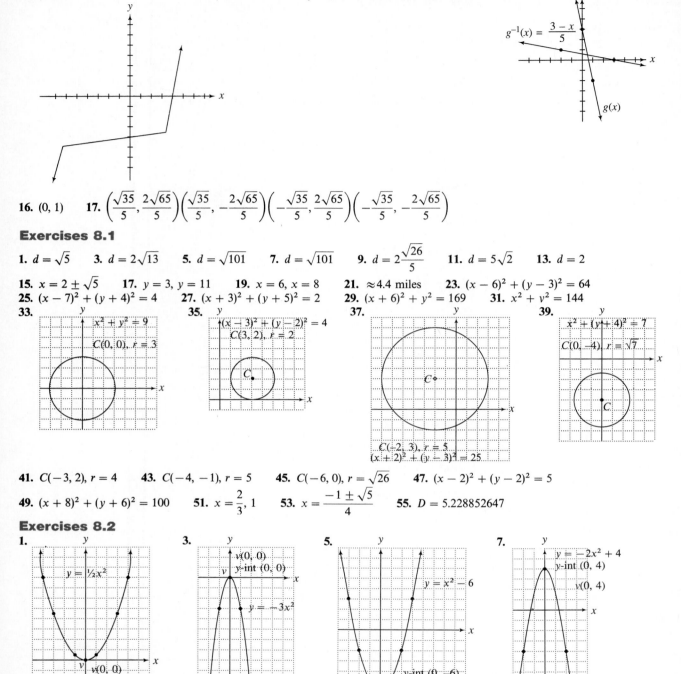

16. $(0, 1)$ **17.** $\left(\dfrac{\sqrt{35}}{5}, \dfrac{2\sqrt{65}}{5}\right)\left(\dfrac{\sqrt{35}}{5}, -\dfrac{2\sqrt{65}}{5}\right)\left(-\dfrac{\sqrt{35}}{5}, \dfrac{2\sqrt{65}}{5}\right)\left(-\dfrac{\sqrt{35}}{5}, -\dfrac{2\sqrt{65}}{5}\right)$

Exercises 8.1

1. $d = \sqrt{5}$ **3.** $d = 2\sqrt{13}$ **5.** $d = \sqrt{101}$ **7.** $d = \sqrt{101}$ **9.** $d = 2\dfrac{\sqrt{26}}{5}$ **11.** $d = 5\sqrt{2}$ **13.** $d = 2$

15. $x = 2 \pm \sqrt{5}$ **17.** $y = 3, y = 11$ **19.** $x = 6, x = 8$ **21.** ≈ 4.4 miles   **23.** $(x - 6)^2 + (y - 3)^2 = 64$
25. $(x - 7)^2 + (y + 4)^2 = 4$ **27.** $(x + 3)^2 + (y + 5)^2 = 2$ **29.** $(x + 6)^2 + y^2 = 169$ **31.** $x^2 + y^2 = 144$

33.   **35.**   **37.**   **39.**

41. $C(-3, 2), r = 4$ **43.** $C(-4, -1), r = 5$ **45.** $C(-6, 0), r = \sqrt{26}$ **47.** $(x - 2)^2 + (y - 2)^2 = 5$

49. $(x + 8)^2 + (y + 6)^2 = 100$ **51.** $x = \dfrac{2}{3}, 1$ **53.** $x = \dfrac{-1 \pm \sqrt{5}}{4}$ **55.** $D = 5.228852647$

Exercises 8.2

1.   **3.**   **5.**   **7.**

9.   **11.**   **13.**

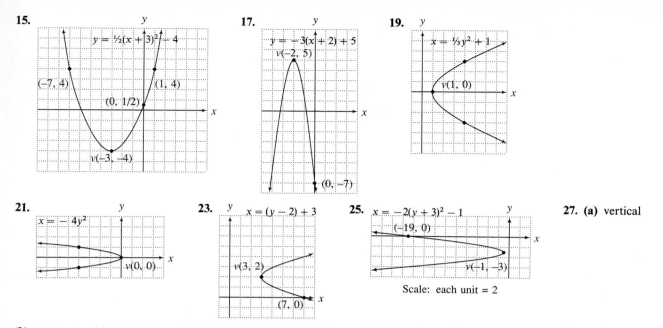

15. $y = \tfrac{1}{2}(x+3)^2 - 4$; $(-7, 4)$; $(0, 1/2)$; $(1, 4)$; $v(-3, -4)$

17. $y = -3(x+2)^2 + 5$; $v(-2, 5)$; $(0, -7)$

19. $x = \tfrac{1}{3}y^2 + 1$; $v(1, 0)$

21. $x = -4y^2$; $v(0, 0)$

23. $x = (y-2)^2 + 3$; $v(3, 2)$; $(7, 0)$

25. $x = -2(y+3)^2 - 1$; $(-19, 0)$; $v(-1, -3)$; Scale: each unit = 2

27. (a) vertical

(b) opens up **(c)** $v(-3, 1)$ **29. (a)** vertical **(b)** opens down **(c)** $v(1, -1)$ **31. (a)** horizontal **(b)** opens right
(c) $v(-2, -5)$ **33.** maximum profit = \$36,000, # items needed = 40   **35.** maximum profit = \$202,500, # items needed = 450

37. $y = -\dfrac{3}{2}\left(x - \dfrac{5}{2}\right)^2 + 36$; vertex (5/2 and 36); opens down; y-intercept $\left(0, \dfrac{213}{8}\right)$ **39.** $5x\sqrt{2x}$ **41.** $2x\sqrt{2} - 8\sqrt{2x}$

43. vertex $(-1.62, -5.38)$, y-intercept (-0.1312), x-intercepts $(0.020121947, -3.260121947)$

Exercises 8.3

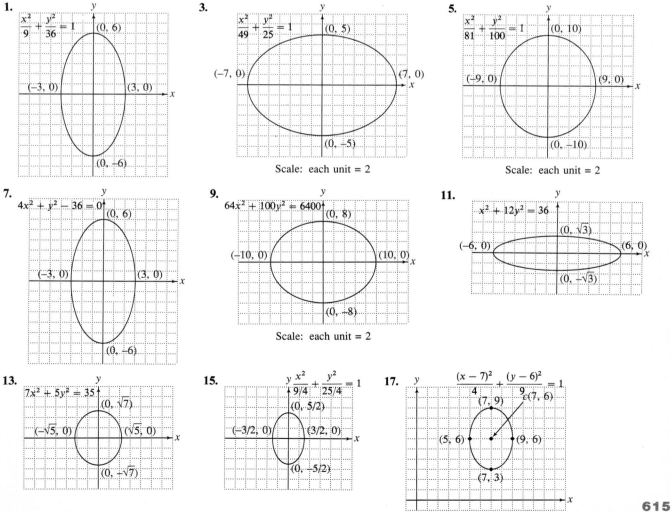

1. $\dfrac{x^2}{9} + \dfrac{y^2}{36} = 1$; $(0, 6)$; $(-3, 0)$; $(3, 0)$; $(0, -6)$

3. $\dfrac{x^2}{49} + \dfrac{y^2}{25} = 1$; $(0, 5)$; $(-7, 0)$; $(7, 0)$; $(0, -5)$; Scale: each unit = 2

5. $\dfrac{x^2}{81} + \dfrac{y^2}{100} = 1$; $(0, 10)$; $(-9, 0)$; $(9, 0)$; $(0, -10)$; Scale: each unit = 2

7. $4x^2 + y^2 - 36 = 0$; $(0, 6)$; $(-3, 0)$; $(3, 0)$; $(0, -6)$

9. $64x^2 + 100y^2 = 6400$; $(0, 8)$; $(-10, 0)$; $(10, 0)$; $(0, -8)$; Scale: each unit = 2

11. $x^2 + 12y^2 = 36$; $(0, \sqrt{3})$; $(-6, 0)$; $(6, 0)$; $(0, -\sqrt{3})$

13. $7x^2 + 5y^2 = 35$; $(0, \sqrt{7})$; $(-\sqrt{5}, 0)$; $(\sqrt{5}, 0)$; $(0, -\sqrt{7})$

15. $\dfrac{x^2}{9/4} + \dfrac{y^2}{25/4} = 1$; $(0, 5/2)$; $(-3/2, 0)$; $(3/2, 0)$; $(0, -5/2)$

17. $\dfrac{(x-7)^2}{4} + \dfrac{(y-6)^2}{9} = 1$; $c(7, 6)$; $(7, 9)$; $(5, 6)$; $(9, 6)$; $(7, 3)$

19. $\dfrac{(x+3)^2}{25} + \dfrac{(y-4)^2}{16} = 1$

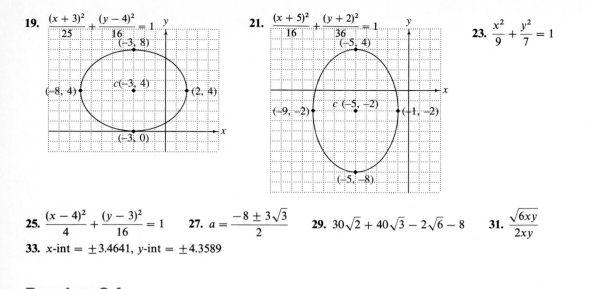

21. $\dfrac{(x+5)^2}{16} + \dfrac{(y+2)^2}{36} = 1$

23. $\dfrac{x^2}{9} + \dfrac{y^2}{7} = 1$

25. $\dfrac{(x-4)^2}{4} + \dfrac{(y-3)^2}{16} = 1$ **27.** $a = \dfrac{-8 \pm 3\sqrt{3}}{2}$ **29.** $30\sqrt{2} + 40\sqrt{3} - 2\sqrt{6} - 8$ **31.** $\dfrac{\sqrt{6xy}}{2xy}$

33. $x\text{-int} = \pm 3.4641,\ y\text{-int} = \pm 4.3589$

Exercises 8.4

1. **3.** **5.**

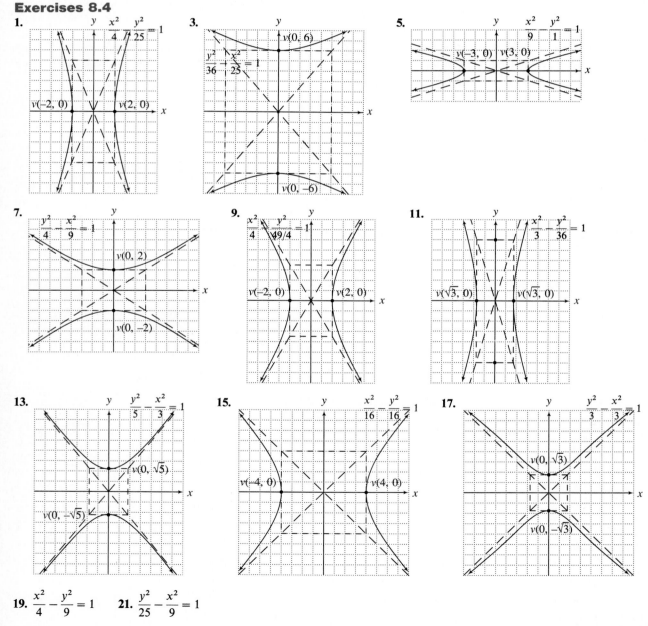

7. **9.** **11.**

13. **15.** **17.**

19. $\dfrac{x^2}{4} - \dfrac{y^2}{9} = 1$ **21.** $\dfrac{y^2}{25} - \dfrac{x^2}{9} = 1$

23. $\dfrac{(x-6)^2}{25} - \dfrac{(y-4)^2}{49} = 1$

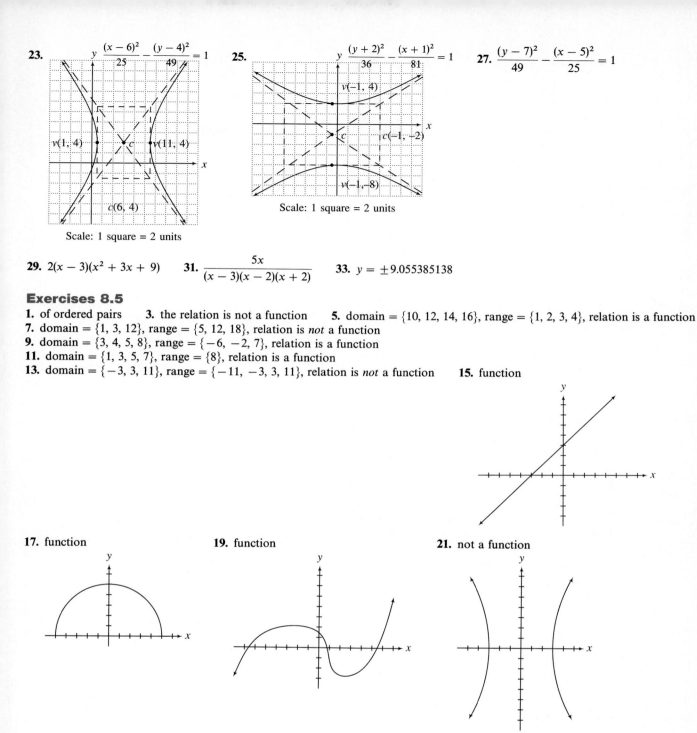

$v(1, 4)$ c $v(11, 4)$

$c(6, 4)$

Scale: 1 square = 2 units

25. $\dfrac{(y+2)^2}{36} - \dfrac{(x+1)^2}{81} = 1$

$v(-1, 4)$

c $c(-1, -2)$

$v(-1, -8)$

Scale: 1 square = 2 units

27. $\dfrac{(y-7)^2}{49} - \dfrac{(x-5)^2}{25} = 1$

29. $2(x-3)(x^2 + 3x + 9)$ **31.** $\dfrac{5x}{(x-3)(x-2)(x+2)}$ **33.** $y = \pm 9.055385138$

Exercises 8.5

1. of ordered pairs   **3.** the relation is not a function   **5.** domain = {10, 12, 14, 16}, range = {1, 2, 3, 4}, relation is a function
7. domain = {1, 3, 12}, range = {5, 12, 18}, relation is *not* a function
9. domain = {3, 4, 5, 8}, range = {−6, −2, 7}, relation is a function
11. domain = {1, 3, 5, 7}, range = {8}, relation is a function
13. domain = {−3, 3, 11}, range = {−11, −3, 3, 11}, relation is *not* a function   **15.** function

17. function   **19.** function   **21.** not a function

23. function   **25.** not a function   **27.** function

29. (a) $f(2) = 8$ **(b)** $f(-3) = -27$ **(c)** $f(0) = 0$ **31. (a)** $h\left(\dfrac{1}{3}\right) = -\dfrac{13}{3}$ **(b)** $h(-2) = -16$ **(c)** $h(0) = -6$

33. (a) $p(1) = -1$ **(b)** $p(-2) = 8$ **(c)** $r(3) = 36$ **35. (a)** $g(a) = 2a^2 - 3a + 4$ **(b)** $g(a+1) = 2a^2 - a + 3$
37. (a) $r(a) = a^2 + 6a + 9$ **(b)** $r(a-3) = a^2$ **39. (a)** $r(x+2) = x^2 + 10x + 25$ **(b)** $r(x) = x^2 + 6x + 9$

(c) $r(x+2) - r(x) = 4x + 16$ **41.** 4 **43.** $4x + 2h$ **45.** $A(2) = 20.5 \text{ ft}^2$, $A(5) = 15.625 \text{ ft}^2$, $A(8) = 13.0 \text{ ft}^2$ **47.** $\dfrac{4(x-1)}{x(x+2)}$

49. $x = 4$ **51.** $f(-2.36) = 28.9392$

Exercises 8.6

1. have same second coordinate **3.** $y = x$ **5.** yes **7.** no **9.** yes
11. yes **13.** no **15.** yes

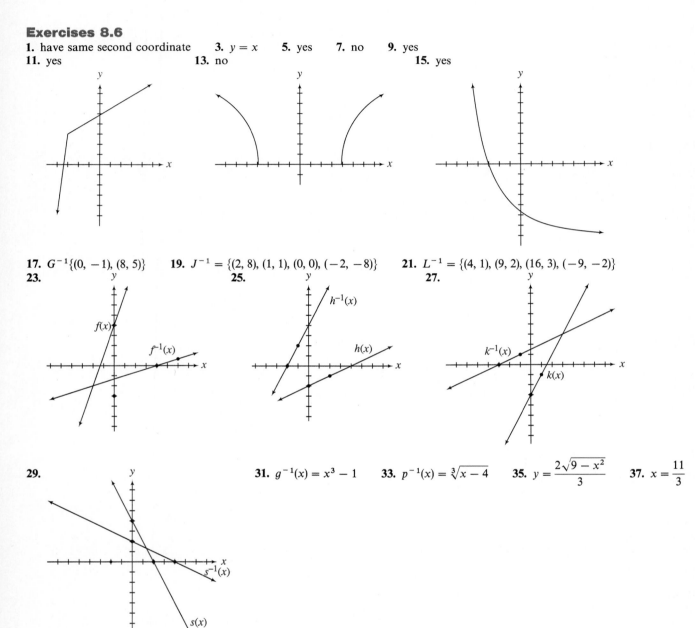

17. $G^{-1}\{(0, -1), (8, 5)\}$ **19.** $J^{-1} = \{(2, 8), (1, 1), (0, 0), (-2, -8)\}$ **21.** $L^{-1} = \{(4, 1), (9, 2), (16, 3), (-9, -2)\}$
23. **25.** **27.**

29. **31.** $g^{-1}(x) = x^3 - 1$ **33.** $p^{-1}(x) = \sqrt[3]{x - 4}$ **35.** $y = \dfrac{2\sqrt{9 - x^2}}{3}$ **37.** $x = \dfrac{11}{3}$

39. $x = -64$, $x = -27$ **41.** $f^{-1}(x) = 0.1931282 - 0.0519022x$

Exercises 8.7

1. $(1, 2)$ **3.** $(2, 0), (1, 1)$ **5.** $(-4, 5), (1, 0)$ **7.** $(3, 0), \left(-\dfrac{9}{5}, \dfrac{12}{5}\right)$ **9.** $(-4, 2), (4, -2)$ **11.** $\left(\dfrac{5}{2}, \dfrac{3}{2}\right)$

13. $\left(4 - 2\sqrt{2}, 2 + \sqrt{2}\right), \left(4 + 2\sqrt{2}, 2 - \sqrt{2}\right)$ **15.** $(1, 3), (-3, -1)$ **17.** $\left(\dfrac{\sqrt{30}}{3}, \pm\dfrac{\sqrt{21}}{3}\right), \left(-\dfrac{\sqrt{30}}{3}, \pm\dfrac{\sqrt{21}}{3}\right)$

19. $(3, \pm 2), (-3, \pm 2)$ **21.** $\left(\dfrac{4\sqrt{2}}{3}, \dfrac{2}{3}\right), \left(-\dfrac{4\sqrt{2}}{3}, \dfrac{2}{3}\right)$ **23.** $(1, \pm 2\sqrt{2}), (-1, \pm 2\sqrt{2})$ **25.** $y = \dfrac{10 \pm \sqrt{-68}}{4}$, no real sol.

27. $(0, \pm 3)$ **29.** one or two solutions. **31.** $(0, -6), \left(\dfrac{147}{29}, \dfrac{120}{29}\right)$ **33.** $\dfrac{x + y}{x^2 + xy + y^2}$ **35.** $x^2 + 1 + \dfrac{5}{x - 3}$

37. $x = 1.6392,\ y = 2.0244$ and $x = 0.1749,\ y = -0.6612$

Extra Practice: Exercises

Section 8.1 **1.** $\sqrt{65}$ **3.** $\sqrt{73}$ **5.** $\dfrac{\sqrt{5}}{2}$ **7.** $\dfrac{\sqrt{145}}{2}$ **9.** $\sqrt{33}$ **11.** 10 **13.** 1 **15.** $-6, 18$ **17.** $-3, -1$

19. ± 1 **21.** $(x - 5)^2 + (y - 1)^2 = 16$ **23.** $(x + 6)^2 + (y + 2)^2 = 9$ **25.** $(x + 5)^2 + (y - 7)^2 = 5$ **27.** $x^2 + (y + 4)^2 = 8$
29. $(x - L)^2 + (y - M)^2 = A^2$ **31.** **33.** $C(-5, -6), r = 4$ **35.** $C(0, 3), r = 2\sqrt{3}$

y $(x + 4)^2 + (y + 1)^2 = 25$
x
$C(4, -1), r = 5$

37. $C\left(-3, \dfrac{1}{2}\right), r = \dfrac{3}{2}$ **39.** $C(4, -0.2), r = \dfrac{3}{5}$ **41.** $C(-3, 4), r = 2$ **43.** $C(-5, 0), r = \sqrt{34}$ **45.** $C\left(-\dfrac{7}{2}, -2\right), r = \dfrac{\sqrt{73}}{2}$
47. $C(2, 3), r = 3$ ***Section 8.2*** **1.** vertical, up, $(0, 0)$ **3.** vertical, down, $(0, 0)$ **5.** vertical, up, $(0, 3)$
7. vertical, down, $(0, 4)$ **9.** vertical, up, $(1, 4)$ **11.** vertical, up, $(-4, -2)$ **13.** vertical, down, $(1, -3)$
15. horizontal, right, $(0, 0)$ **17.** horizontal, left, $(5, 0)$ **19.** horizontal, right, $(-3, -1)$ **21.** horizontal, right, $(6, -2)$
23. vertical, up, $(2, 0)$ **25.** horizontal, right, $(-2, 0)$ **27.** horizontal, right, $(0, 1)$ **29.** vertical, up, $(0, -2)$
31. **33.** $y = (x + 2)^2 + 3$, vertical, up, $(-2, 3)$ **35.** $y = -1(x - 3)^2 + 1$, vertical, down, $(3, 1)$

y
$v(2, 1)$
x
$(-2, 0)$

37. $x = (y - 4)^2 - 7$, horizontal, right, $(-7, 4)$ **39.** $x = \left(y - \dfrac{1}{2}\right)^2 - \dfrac{25}{4}$, horizontal, right, $\left(-\dfrac{25}{4}, \dfrac{1}{2}\right)$
41. $y = x^2 - 4$, vertical, up, $(0, -4)$ ***Section 8.3*** **1.** $(\pm 5, 0), (0, \pm 1)$ **3.** $(\pm 6, 0), (0, \pm 2)$ **5.** $(\pm 3\sqrt{2}, 0), (0, \pm 3)$

7. $(\pm \sqrt{3}, 0), (0, \pm 4)$ **9.** $(\pm 2\sqrt{2}, 0), (0, \pm \sqrt{7})$ **11.** $(\pm 1, 0), \left(0, \pm \dfrac{1}{2}\right)$ **13.** $(\pm 1, 0), \left(0, \pm \dfrac{1}{2}\right)$ **15.** $(\pm 2, 0), (0, \pm 4)$

17. $(\pm 3, 0), \left(0, \pm \dfrac{3\sqrt{3}}{2}\right)$ **19.** $\left(\pm \dfrac{1}{2}, 0\right), (0, \pm 1)$ **21.** $(\pm 2, 0), (0, \pm 3)$ **23.** $(0, 2), (3, 7), (6, 2), (3, -3), C = (3, 2)$
25. $(0, -5), (2, 1), (4, -5), (2, -11), C = (2, -5)$ **27.** $(-5, -3), (-3, 4), (-1, -3), (-3, -10), C = (-3, -3)$
29. $(-2, 2), (0, 5), (2, 2), (0, -1), C = (0, 2)$ **31.** $(-1, 1), (4, 4), (9, 1), (4, -2), C = (4, 1)$ **33.** $\dfrac{x^2}{3} + \dfrac{y^2}{64} = 1$

Section 8.4 **1.** horizontal, $(\pm 3, 0)$ **3.** horizontal, $(\pm 6, 0)$ **5.** vertical, $(0, \pm 3)$ **7.** vertical, $(0, \pm 3)$
9. horizontal, $(\pm 4, 0)$ **11.** vertical, $(0, \pm \sqrt{3})$ **13.** horizontal, $(\pm 4, 0)$ **15.** horizontal, $(\pm 5, 0)$ **17.** vertical, $(0, \pm \sqrt{5})$
19. horizontal, $(\pm 1, 0)$ **21.** vertical, $(0, \pm 3)$ **23.** vertical, $(0, \pm 4)$ **25.** horizontal, $(\pm 1, 0)$ **27.** horizontal, $(\pm 5, 0)$

29. **31.** $\dfrac{y^2}{36} - \dfrac{x^2}{49} = 1$ **33.** $(0, -5), (4, -5), C = (2, -5)$

y $\dfrac{x^2}{4} - \dfrac{y^2}{9} - 1 = 0$
$v(-2, 0)$ $v(2, 0)$
x

35. $(-4, 5), (-4, -7), C = (-4, -1)$ **37.** $(2, -6), (2, 0), C = (2, -3)$ **39.** $(2, 1), (2, -3), C = (2, -1)$

Section 8.5   **1.** $D = \{6, 7, 8, 9\}$, $R = \{0.1, 0.3, 0.5\}$, yes   **3.** $D = \{100, 20, 10\}$, $R = \{1, 2, 6, 5\}$, no
5. $D = \{-3, 3, 6\}$, $R = \{-2, 2, -4\}$, no   **7.** $D = \{4, 16, 8\}$, $R = \{-1, -3, -2\}$, yes   **9.** $D = \{0, 4, 5\}$, $R = \{0\}$, yes

11. $D = \{1, 2\}$, $R = \{0.2, 3\}$, yes   **13.** $D = \{0.1, 0.2\}$, $R = \left\{\dfrac{1}{2}, \dfrac{1}{3}\right\}$, yes   **15.** yes   **17. (a)** 8 **(b)** 4 **(c)** -2 **19. (a)** 10

(b) 6 **(c)** 15   **21. (a)** 16 **(b)** -16 **(c)** $16a^3$ **23. (a)** $4 - 2a$ **(b)** a^2 **(c)** $2a^2 + a$ **25. (a)** $\dfrac{13}{16}$ **(b)** $\dfrac{25}{9}$ **(c)** 0

27. (a) $-\dfrac{1}{2}a - \dfrac{1}{6}$ **(b)** $\dfrac{1}{3} - 2a$ **(c)** $10 - 2a$ **29. (a)** $4x^2 - 8x + 4$ **(b)** $x^2 - 4x + 4$ **(c)** $3x^2 - 4x$ **31.** $\dfrac{13}{3}$ **33.** 16

35. -4 **37.** $4x + 2h + 1$ **39.** $3x^2 + 3xh + h^2$ **Section 8.6**   **1.** yes   **3.** no   **5.** yes   **7.** no   **9.** yes   **11.** no
13. $H^{-1} = \{(1, 6), (2, 7), (-3, 8), (10, 10)\}$ **15.** $K^{-1} = \{(6, 1), (-5, -3), (7, -5), (1, 6)\}$
17. $M^{-1} = \{(-5, 0), (7, 3), (-8, 2), (8, -2)\}$ **19.** $S^{-1} = \{(-6, 2), (2, -6), (6, 5), (1, 1), (-1, 3)\}$

21. $g^{-1}(x) = \dfrac{x + 4}{3}$ **23.** $p^{-1}(x) = \dfrac{6x - 12}{5}$

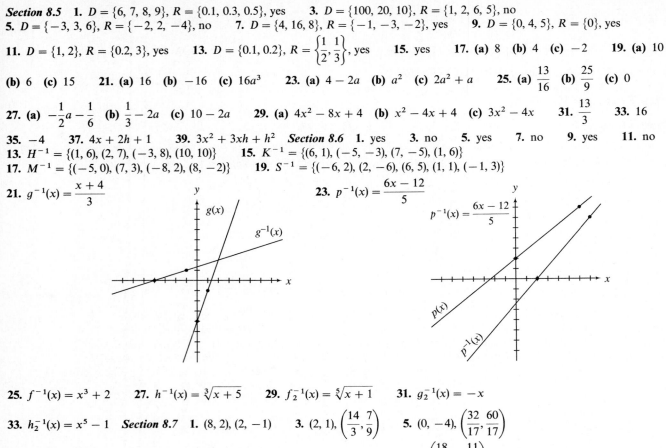

25. $f^{-1}(x) = x^3 + 2$ **27.** $h^{-1}(x) = \sqrt[3]{x + 5}$ **29.** $f_2^{-1}(x) = \sqrt[5]{x + 1}$ **31.** $g_2^{-1}(x) = -x$

33. $h_2^{-1}(x) = x^5 - 1$ **Section 8.7**   **1.** $(8, 2), (2, -1)$ **3.** $(2, 1), \left(\dfrac{14}{3}, \dfrac{7}{9}\right)$ **5.** $(0, -4), \left(\dfrac{32}{17}, \dfrac{60}{17}\right)$

7. $(2\sqrt{2}, -\sqrt{2}), (-2\sqrt{2}, \sqrt{2})$ **9.** no real sol.   **11.** $(3, 5), (5, 3)$ **13.** $(2, 1), \left(\dfrac{18}{5}, -\dfrac{11}{5}\right)$ **15.** $(4, -3), (-4, 3)$

17. $(-2, 2), (-10, 6)$ **19.** $(0, 5), (4, 3)$ **21.** $(2, -1), \left(\dfrac{1}{2}, -4\right)$ **23.** $\left(\dfrac{3}{2}, \pm\dfrac{1}{2}\right), \left(-\dfrac{3}{2}, \pm\dfrac{1}{2}\right)$ **25.** $(-4, 0)$

27. $(7, 2), (4, -1)$ **29.** $(2, \pm 1), (-2, \pm 1)$ **31.** $(1, \pm 3), (-1, \pm 3)$ **33.** no real sol.   **35.** $(\pm\sqrt{3}, -1), (\pm 2, 0)$

Review Problems Chapter 8
1. $\sqrt{41}$ **3.** $x^2 + (y + 7)^2 = 25$ **5.** $C(3, 4)$; $r = \sqrt{22}$ **7.**   **9.**

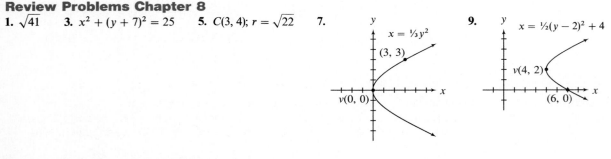

11. $x = (y - 4)^2 - 6$; $v = (-6, 4)$, right   **13.**

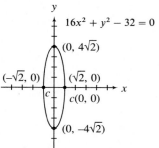

15. $C = (-5, -3); v = (-3, -3), (-7, -3), (-5, 2), (-5, -8)$ **17.**

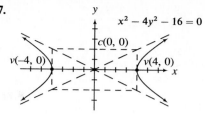

19. $(-5, 3), (-5, 1), C = (-5, 2)$ **21. (a)** $D = \{0, 3, 7\}$ **(b)** $R = \{-8, 3, 7, 8\}$ **(c)** no   **(d)** no   **23. (a)** $D = \left\{\dfrac{1}{2}, \dfrac{1}{4}, -\dfrac{1}{3}, 4\right\}$

(b) $R = \left\{2, 4, -3, \dfrac{1}{4}\right\}$ **(c)** yes   **(d)** yes   **25. (a)** $D = \{3, 2, 0, 1\}$ **(b)** $R = \{7, 1, -3\}$ **(c)** yes   **(d)** no

27. (a) no   **(b)** no   **29. (a)** yes   **(b)** no   **31. (a)** yes   **(b)** yes

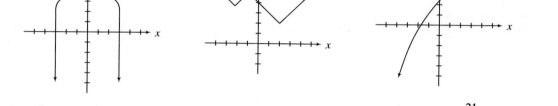

33. $B^{-1} = \{1, -10), (10, 1), (-7, 3), (3, 4)\}$ **35.** $g^{-1}(x) = 2 - x^3$ **37. (a)** -42 **(b)** $\dfrac{21}{8}$ **(c)** $8a^3 + 10a$ **39.** no real sol.

41. $(2, -1), (-2, 1), (1, -2), (-1, 2)$

Quiz Sections 8.1–8.4

1. $d = \sqrt{117}$ **2.** $(x - 5)^2 + (y + 7)^2 = 11$ **3.** $(x - 1)^2 + (y + 5)^2 = 36, C = (1, -5), r = 6$

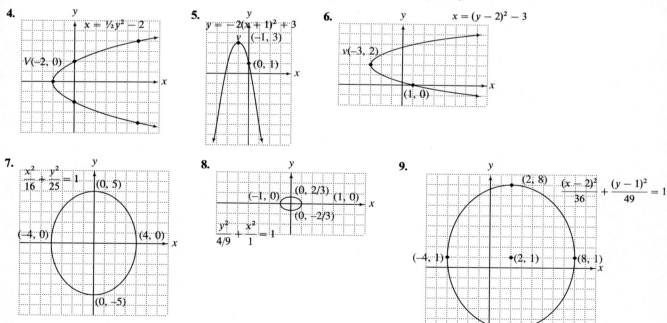

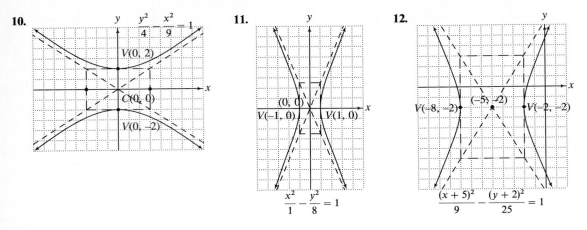

Quiz Sections 8.5–8.7

1. (a) $D = \left\{\dfrac{1}{2}, \dfrac{1}{3}, 0,\right\}$ **(b)** $R = \left\{\dfrac{1}{4}, \dfrac{1}{6}, 0, \dfrac{1}{8}\right\}$ **(c)** no **(d)** no **2. (a)** $D = \{-2, -7, 2, 7\}$ **(b)** $R = \{3, 18, -18\}$ **(c)** yes

(d) no **3. (a)** $D = \{12, -12, -3, 3\}$, **(b)** $R = \{0, 3, 12, -12\}$ **(c)** yes **(d)** yes **4. (a)** $D = \{3.6, 2.4, -4.8, -2.6\}$

(b) $R = \{1.2, 4.8, 2.2, 1.2\}$ **(c)** yes **(d)** yes **5. (a)** yes **(b)** no **6. (a)** no **(b)** no **7. (a)** yes **(b)** yes

8. $p(2) = 14$, $g(3) = 43$, $s(-2) = 6$ **9.** $p(-3) = -51$, $g(2) = 16$, $s\left(\dfrac{1}{2}\right) = \dfrac{19}{4}$ **10.** -5 **11.** 42 **12. (a)** $5a^2 + 12a - 1$

(b) $\dfrac{14 - a}{2}$ **13. (a)** $16a^3 - 2a$ **(b)** $5a^2 - 18a + 8$ **14.** -1 **15.** 3 **16.** $A^{-1} = \{(-5, 1), (-3, 2), (-2, 3), (6, -1)\}$

17. $B^{-1} = \{(5, 0), (6, -5), (7, 1), (1, 1)\}$ **18.** $f^{-1}(x) = \dfrac{4 - x}{3}$ **19.** $g^{-1}(x) = \sqrt[3]{x + 2}$ **20.** $(0, 1), (\sqrt{5}, 6), (-\sqrt{5}, 6)$

21. $(1, \pm2), (-1, \pm2)$ **22.** $(1, 4), (-1, 4), (2\sqrt{2}, \sqrt{2}), (-2\sqrt{2}, -\sqrt{2})$

Test Chapter 8

1. $\sqrt{185}$ **2.**

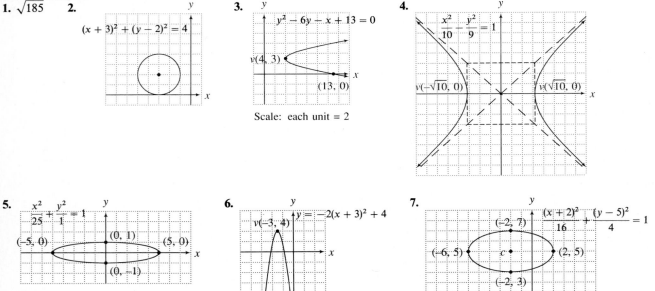

8.

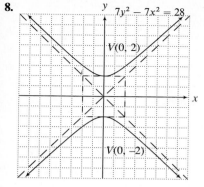

$7y^2 - 7x^2 = 28$

$V(0, 2)$

$V(0, -2)$

9. (a) $D = \{1, 2, -3\}$ **(b)** $R = \{1, 2, -3, -2\}$ **(c)** no **(d)** no **10. (a)** yes

(b) no **11.** $f(-2) = 20, f(1) = 5, f(a) = 3a^2 - 2a + 4, f(a + 2) = 3a^2 + 10a + 12$

12. $f^{-1} = \{(1.6, -2), (5.5, -1), (1.1, 3), (2, 1.6)\}$ **13.** $f^{-1}(x) = \dfrac{10x + 2}{5}$ **14.** $(0, 5), (-4, -3)$ **15.** $(1, 0), (-1, 0)$

16. $(\sqrt{3}, -\sqrt{3}), (-\sqrt{3}, \sqrt{3}), \left(\dfrac{\sqrt{6}}{2}, -\sqrt{6}\right), \left(-\dfrac{\sqrt{6}}{2}, \sqrt{6}\right)$

Cumulative Test Chapters 1–8

1. commutative property for multiplication **2.** -19 **3.** $8x + 12$ **4.** $p = \dfrac{A - 3bt}{rt}$ **5.** $(x + 5)(x^2 - 5x + 25)$

6. $\dfrac{3x + 18}{(x + 4)(x + 4)}$ **7.** $x = \dfrac{7}{2}$ **8.** $x = 4, y = -3, z = 1$ **9.** $2\sqrt{2x} - x\sqrt{2}$ **10.** $4\sqrt{3} + 6\sqrt{2} - \sqrt{6} - 3$ **11.** $3\sqrt{10}$

12.

$y = -\frac{1}{2}(x + 2)^2 - 3$

$v(-2, -3)$

$(0, -5)$

13.

$25x^2 + 25y^2 = 125$

$(0, \sqrt{5})$

$(\sqrt{5}, 0)$

Circle with radius $\sqrt{5}$

14.

$16x^2 - 4y^2 = 64$

$v(-2, 0)$ $v(2, 0)$

15.

$\dfrac{(x - 2)^2}{25} + \dfrac{(y - 3)^2}{16} = 1$

$(2, 7)$

$(-3, 3)$ $c(2, 3)$ $(7, 3)$

$(2, -1)$

16. (a) yes **(b)** yes **(c)** $A^{-1} = \{(6, 3), (8, 1), (7, 2), (4, 4)\}$ **17.** $f^{-1}(x) = \dfrac{x + 3}{7}$

18. (a) 22 **(b)** -168 **(c)** $40a^3 - 12a^2 - 6$ **19.** $(2, 8), (-1, 2)$ **20.** $\left(\dfrac{8}{3}, \pm\dfrac{2\sqrt{10}}{3}\right), \left(-\dfrac{8}{3}, \pm\dfrac{2\sqrt{10}}{3}\right)$

CHAPTER 9   Exponential and Logarithmic Functions

Pretest Chapter 9

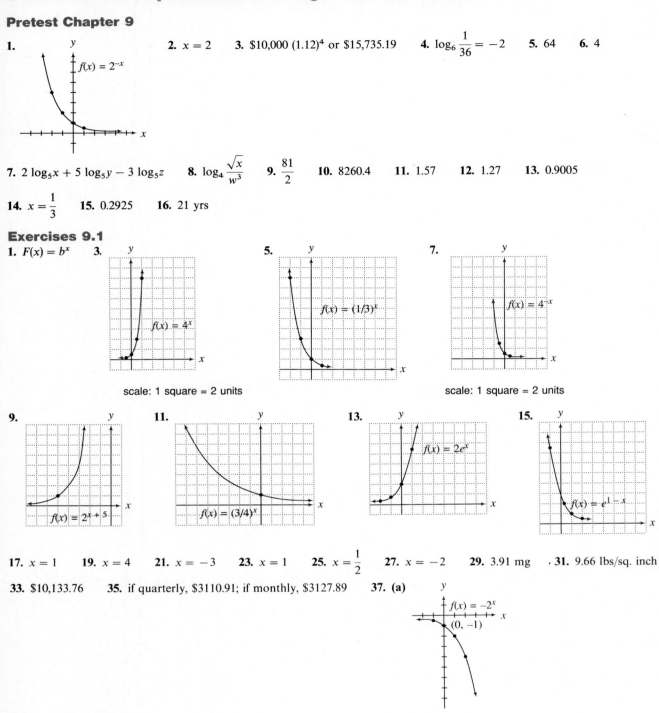

1. $f(x) = 2^{-x}$ **2.** $x = 2$ **3.** $10,000\ (1.12)^4$ or $15,735.19$ **4.** $\log_6 \dfrac{1}{36} = -2$ **5.** 64   **6.** 4

7. $2\log_5 x + 5\log_5 y - 3\log_5 z$ **8.** $\log_4 \dfrac{\sqrt{x}}{w^3}$ **9.** $\dfrac{81}{2}$ **10.** 8260.4   **11.** 1.57   **12.** 1.27   **13.** 0.9005

14. $x = \dfrac{1}{3}$ **15.** 0.2925   **16.** 21 yrs

Exercises 9.1

1. $F(x) = b^x$ **3.** $f(x) = 4^x$ scale: 1 square = 2 units   **5.** $f(x) = (1/3)^x$ **7.** $f(x) = 4^{-x}$ scale: 1 square = 2 units

9. $f(x) = 2^{x+5}$ **11.** $f(x) = (3/4)^x$ **13.** $f(x) = 2e^x$ **15.** $f(x) = e^{1-x}$

17. $x = 1$ **19.** $x = 4$ **21.** $x = -3$ **23.** $x = 1$ **25.** $x = \dfrac{1}{2}$ **27.** $x = -2$ **29.** 3.91 mg   **31.** 9.66 lbs/sq. inch

33. $10,133.76   **35.** if quarterly, $3110.91; if monthly, $3127.89   **37. (a)** $f(x) = -2^x$, $(0, -1)$

(b) In the first equation, 2 is raised to a power. In the second equation, -2 is raised to a power.
(c) The definition of $f(x) = b^x$ requires that $b > 0$.   **39.** 32,000 in 3 hr, 2,048,000 in 9 hr   **41.**

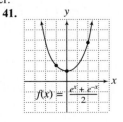

$f(x) = \dfrac{e^x + e^{-x}}{2}$

43. $x = -\dfrac{11}{4}$ **45.** $x = 1$ **47.** $f(1.63) = 23.59521283$, $f(2.95) = 88.32682408$, $f(-3.04) = 0.221140694$

Exercises 9.2

1. exponent   **3.** $x > 0$ **5.** $\log_4 64 = 3$ **7.** $\log_{10} 100 = 2$ **9.** $\log_5\left(\dfrac{1}{25}\right) = -2$ **11.** $\log_2 32 = 5$ **13.** $\log_e y = 3$

15. $3^2 = 9$ **17.** $5^4 = 625$ **19.** $10^3 = 1000$ **21.** $10^{-2} = 0.01$ **23.** $3^{-4} = \dfrac{1}{81}$ **25.** $e^5 = x$ **27.** $x = 16$

29. $x = \dfrac{1}{1000}$ **31.** $y = 4$ **33.** $y = -2$ **35.** $a = 2$ **37.** $a = 10$ **39.** $w = \dfrac{1}{3}$ **41.** $w = -1$ **43.** $w = 1000$

45. $w = \dfrac{1}{5}$ **47.** $w = e^4$ **49.** $x = 1$ **51.** $x = -3$ **53.** $x = 4$ **55.** $x = 2$ **57.** $x = \dfrac{1}{2}$

59.

Scale: 1 square = 2 units

61.

Scale: 1 square = 2 units

63.

65. pH $= 1$

67. $[\text{H}^+] = 10^{-9}$ **69.** $5^{\log_5 4} = y$, $\log_5 y = \log_5 4$, $y = 4$ **71.**

73. $m = \dfrac{1}{-5}$

75. $[\text{H}^+] = 5.011872 \times 10^{-9}$

Exercises 9.3

1. $\dfrac{1}{2}\log_5 x + 3\log_5 y$ **3.** $\log_7 2 + \log_7 x - \log_7 y$ **5.** $\log_2 7 + 3\log_2 x + 2\log_2 y - 5\log_2 z$ **7.** $\dfrac{1}{3}\log_b x - \dfrac{2}{3}\log_b y - \dfrac{1}{3}\log_b z$

9. $5 + \log_e x + 2\log_e y$ **11.** $\log_5 21x$ **13.** $\log_3\left(\dfrac{x^5}{7}\right)$ **15.** $\log_b \dfrac{\sqrt{x}\sqrt[3]{y}}{z^4}$ **17.** $\log_3 \sqrt{\dfrac{7}{xy}}$ **19.** 0 **21.** 1 **23.** 3

25. -4 **27.** $x = 4$ **29.** $x = \dfrac{1}{3}$ **31.** $x = 2$ **33.** $x = 2e^2$ **35.** $\log_{10} A = \log_{10} 10^4 + x\log 1.07$;

$\log_{10} A = 4 + x\log_{10} 1.07$; $x = \dfrac{\log_{10} A - 4}{\log_{10} 1.07}$ **37.** Let $\log_b M = x$, $\log_b N = y$. So, $b^x = M$, $b^y = N$, and $\dfrac{M}{N} = \dfrac{b^x}{b^y} = b^{x-y}$.

Thus, $\log_b \dfrac{M}{N} = \log_b b^{x-y}$, but $\log_b b^{x-y} = x - y$. Thus, $\log_b \dfrac{M}{N} = x - y$. Substitution for x, y, $\log_b \dfrac{M}{N} = \log_b M - \log_b N$

39. $4 + 2 = 6$ **41.** $A = 50.27$ sq. m   **43.** $x = 3$, $y = -2$

Exercises 9.4

1. 0.866877814 **3.** 0.551449998 **5.** 2.551449998 **7.** 5.096910013 **9.** -1.910094889 **11.** -0.050122296
13. Error. You cannot take the log of a negative number.   **15.** 1.450106836 **17.** 3.820322269 **19.** 61.09420249
21. 8519.223264 **23.** 2939679.609 **25.** 0.034300464 **27.** 0.000408037 **29.** 448.3322704 **31.** 1.726331664
33. 4.028916757 **35.** 11.82041016 **37.** -4.09234656 **39.** 2.189416395 **41.** 2.585709659 **43.** 11.02317638
45. 1202604.284 **47.** 0.878095431 **49.** 0.004086771 **51.** 1.466792181 **53.** 0.98247341 **55.** -1.151699337
57. 1.913507505 **59.** x represents the number that results when the base 10 is raised to an exponent, y. Ten to any power,

positive or negative, will always be a positive number.   **61.** 6.642564189 **63.** $x = 0$, $x = \dfrac{7}{17}$ **65.** $y = \dfrac{-2 \pm \sqrt{10}}{2}$

Exercises 9.5

1. $x = 1$ **3.** $x = 12$ **5.** $x = \dfrac{167}{61}$ **7.** $x = -\dfrac{28}{53}$, not a solution   **9.** $x = 4$, $x = -2$, not a solution

11. $x = 2$, $x = -\dfrac{1}{3}$, not a solution   **13.** $x = -5$, not a solution   **15.** $x = 1 + \sqrt{3}$, $x = 1 - \sqrt{3}$, not a solution

17. $x = 1.091329169$ **19.** $x = 0.365212389$ **21.** $x = 0.02915428$ **23.** $x = 5.128533874$ **25.** $x = 37.30969515$
27. $x = 3.610917913$ **29.** $x = 2.120263536$ **31.** 20 yr   **33.** 35 yr   **35.** 22 yr   **37.** 19 yr   **39.** 32 times greater
41. $7xy\sqrt{2x}$ **43.** $3\sqrt{2} + 4\sqrt{3} - \sqrt{6} - 4$ **45.** $x = 0.96394524$

Extra Practice: Exercises

Section 9.1   **1.**

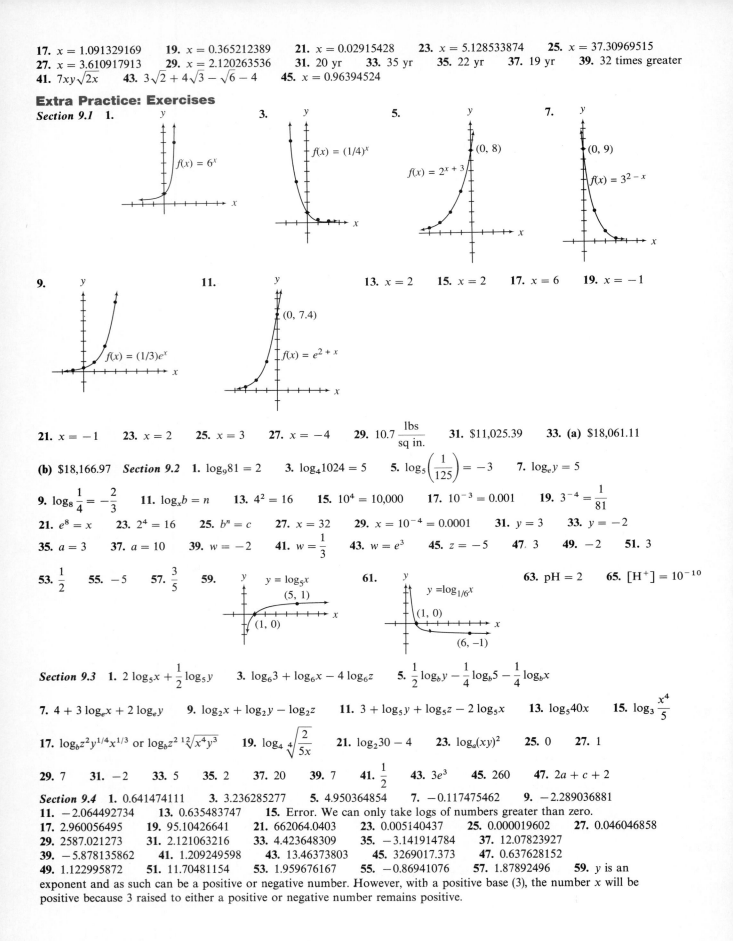

13. $x = 2$ **15.** $x = 2$ **17.** $x = 6$ **19.** $x = -1$

21. $x = -1$ **23.** $x = 2$ **25.** $x = 3$ **27.** $x = -4$ **29.** $10.7 \dfrac{\text{lbs}}{\text{sq in.}}$ **31.** \$11,025.39   **33. (a)** \$18,061.11

(b) \$18,166.97   *Section 9.2*   **1.** $\log_9 81 = 2$ **3.** $\log_4 1024 = 5$ **5.** $\log_5\left(\dfrac{1}{125}\right) = -3$ **7.** $\log_e y = 5$

9. $\log_8 \dfrac{1}{4} = -\dfrac{2}{3}$ **11.** $\log_x b = n$ **13.** $4^2 = 16$ **15.** $10^4 = 10{,}000$ **17.** $10^{-3} = 0.001$ **19.** $3^{-4} = \dfrac{1}{81}$

21. $e^8 = x$ **23.** $2^4 = 16$ **25.** $b^n = c$ **27.** $x = 32$ **29.** $x = 10^{-4} = 0.0001$ **31.** $y = 3$ **33.** $y = -2$

35. $a = 3$ **37.** $a = 10$ **39.** $w = -2$ **41.** $w = \dfrac{1}{3}$ **43.** $w = e^3$ **45.** $z = -5$ **47.** 3   **49.** -2 **51.** 3

53. $\dfrac{1}{2}$ **55.** -5 **57.** $\dfrac{3}{5}$ **59.**   **61.**   **63.** pH $= 2$ **65.** $[\text{H}^+] = 10^{-10}$

Section 9.3   **1.** $2\log_5 x + \dfrac{1}{2}\log_5 y$ **3.** $\log_6 3 + \log_6 x - 4\log_6 z$ **5.** $\dfrac{1}{2}\log_b y - \dfrac{1}{4}\log_b 5 - \dfrac{1}{4}\log_b x$

7. $4 + 3\log_e x + 2\log_e y$ **9.** $\log_2 x + \log_2 y - \log_2 z$ **11.** $3 + \log_5 y + \log_5 z - 2\log_5 x$ **13.** $\log_5 40x$ **15.** $\log_3 \dfrac{x^4}{5}$

17. $\log_b z^2 y^{1/4} x^{1/3}$ or $\log_b z^2 \sqrt[12]{x^4 y^3}$ **19.** $\log_4 \sqrt[4]{\dfrac{2}{5x}}$ **21.** $\log_2 30 - 4$ **23.** $\log_a (xy)^2$ **25.** 0   **27.** 1

29. 7   **31.** -2 **33.** 5   **35.** 2   **37.** 20   **39.** 7   **41.** $\dfrac{1}{2}$ **43.** $3e^3$ **45.** 260   **47.** $2a + c + 2$

Section 9.4   **1.** 0.641474111   **3.** 3.236285277   **5.** 4.950364854   **7.** -0.117475462 **9.** -2.289036881
11. -2.064492734 **13.** 0.635483747   **15.** Error. We can only take logs of numbers greater than zero.
17. 2.960056495   **19.** 95.10426641   **21.** 662064.0403   **23.** 0.005140437   **25.** 0.000019602   **27.** 0.046046858
29. 2587.021273   **31.** 2.121063216   **33.** 4.423648309   **35.** -3.141914784 **37.** 12.07823927
39. -5.878135862 **41.** 1.209249598   **43.** 13.46373803   **45.** 3269017.373   **47.** 0.637628152
49. 1.122995872   **51.** 11.70481154   **53.** 1.959676167   **55.** -0.86941076 **57.** 1.87892496   **59.** y is an
exponent and as such can be a positive or negative number. However, with a positive base (3), the number x will be
positive because 3 raised to either a positive or negative number remains positive.

Section 9.5   **1.** $\dfrac{31}{3}$ **3.** 9   **5.** 3   **7.** $\dfrac{\sqrt[3]{36}}{2}$ **9.** $\dfrac{7}{2}$ **11.** 4, 5   **13.** 2   **15.** $\dfrac{-3 + \sqrt{129}}{12}$ **17.** $\dfrac{17 + 3\sqrt{41}}{20}$

19. $\dfrac{3}{4}$ **21.** 50, -20 **23.** 2.402173503   **25.** -1.406307359 **27.** 3.543731421   **29.** 12.42513488

31. 3.258096538   **33.** 1.771956842   **35.** 1.313348026   **37.** $-\dfrac{5}{2}$ **39.** 10.87498135   **41.** 7.587824938

43. 26 yr   **45.** 23 yr   **47.** 17 yr   **49.** 23 yr

Review Problems Chapter 9

1.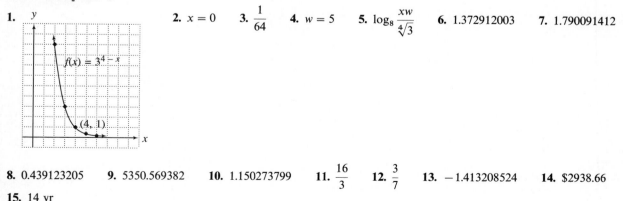

$f(x) = 4^{3 + x}$

$(-3, 1)$

3. 1   **5.** $10^{-3} = 0.001$ **7.** 2   **9.** 1   **11.** 0.001   **13.** 6   **15.** 3

17. $3 \log_2 x + \dfrac{1}{2} \log_2 y$ **19.** $\log_3 \dfrac{x\sqrt{w}}{2}$ **21.** 6   **23.** 25   **25.** -1.087777943 **27.** 6.688354714   **29.** 5.473947392

31. $x = \dfrac{34}{5}$ **33.** $x = 1$ **35.** 0.771243749   **37.** 2.331910758   **39.** \$6312.38   **41.** 50.1 times as much

Quiz Sections 9.1–9.3

1.

$f(x) = 2^{x - 3}$

$(3, 1)$

2. $x = -5$ **3.** \$3787.43   **4.** $\log_7\left(\dfrac{1}{49}\right) = -2$ **5.** $0.0001 = 10^{-4}$ **6.** $w = 4$

7. $x = 10^{-6}$ **8.** $w = 2$ **9.** $\log_6 2 + 3 \log_6 x - \log_6 5 - \dfrac{1}{2} \log_6 y$ **10.** $\log_5 \dfrac{2x}{\sqrt{z}}$ **11.** 3   **12.** $\dfrac{5}{2}$

Quiz Sections 9.4–9.5

1. 0.702430536   **2.** -2.663540266 **3.** 2.152924318   **4.** 11.95761129   **5.** 0.513673051   **6.** 4.015598116

7. 8.040813701   **8.** 92.19343574   **9.** 1.161834243   **10.** 6.68589442   **11.** $x = 2$ **12.** $x = \dfrac{10}{3}$

13. $x = 0.48490665$ **14.** -0.980192471 **15.** 14 yr   **16.** 35 yr

Test Chapter 9

1.

$f(x) = 3^{4 - x}$

$(4, 1)$

2. $x = 0$ **3.** $\dfrac{1}{64}$ **4.** $w = 5$ **5.** $\log_8 \dfrac{xw}{\sqrt[4]{3}}$ **6.** 1.372912003   **7.** 1.790091412

8. 0.439123205   **9.** 5350.569382   **10.** 1.150273799   **11.** $\dfrac{16}{3}$ **12.** $\dfrac{3}{7}$ **13.** -1.413208524 **14.** \$2938.66

15. 14 yr

Cumulative Test Chapters 1-9

1. 6   **2.** $x = \dfrac{H + 2ay}{3b}$ **3.** 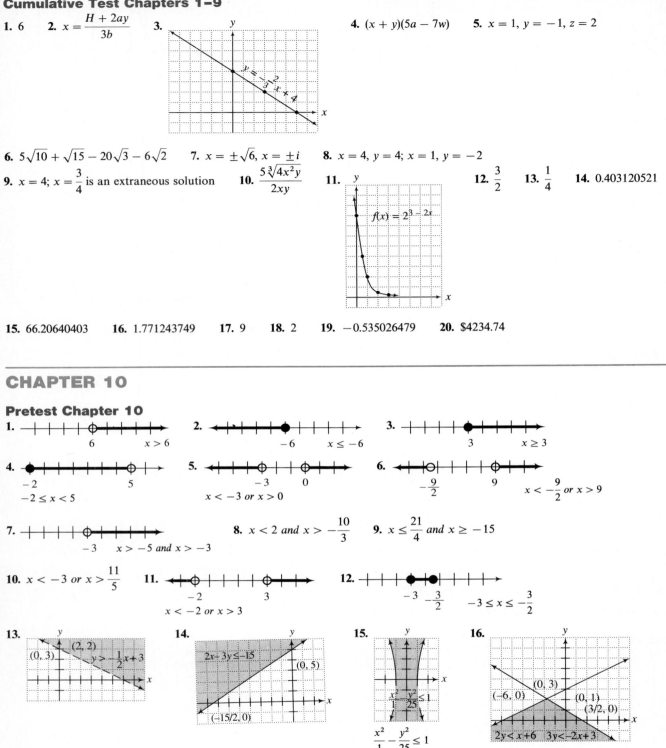   **4.** $(x + y)(5a - 7w)$ **5.** $x = 1, y = -1, z = 2$

6. $5\sqrt{10} + \sqrt{15} - 20\sqrt{3} - 6\sqrt{2}$ **7.** $x = \pm\sqrt{6}, x = \pm i$ **8.** $x = 4, y = 4; x = 1, y = -2$

9. $x = 4; x = \dfrac{3}{4}$ is an extraneous solution   **10.** $\dfrac{5\sqrt[3]{4x^2 y}}{2xy}$ **11.**   **12.** $\dfrac{3}{2}$ **13.** $\dfrac{1}{4}$ **14.** 0.403120521

15. 66.20640403   **16.** 1.771243749   **17.** 9   **18.** 2   **19.** -0.535026479 **20.** $4234.74

CHAPTER 10

Pretest Chapter 10

17.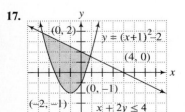

Exercises 10.1

1. True   **3.** >   **5.** <   **7.** >   **9.** >   **11.** <   **13.**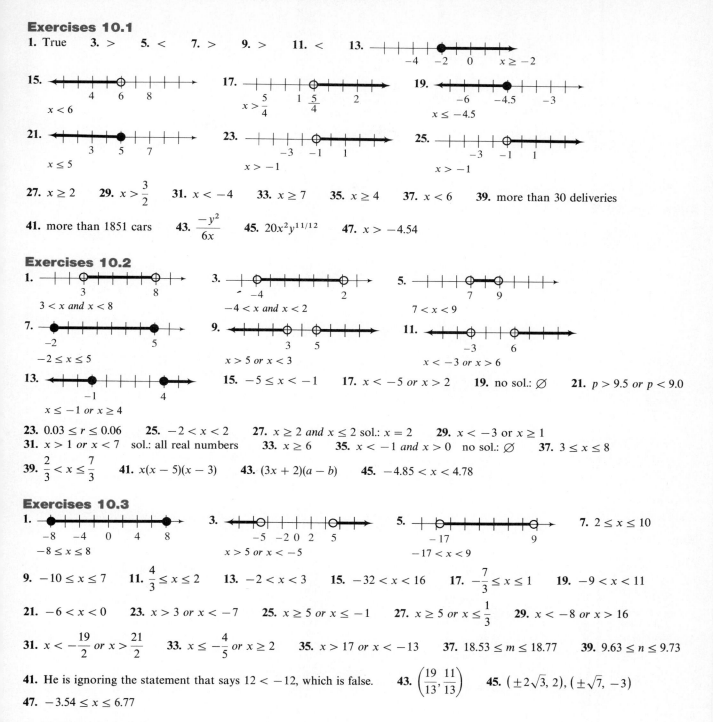
$x \geq -2$

15. $x < 6$ **17.** $x > \dfrac{5}{4}$ **19.** $x \leq -4.5$

21. $x \leq 5$ **23.** $x > -1$ **25.** $x > -1$

27. $x \geq 2$ **29.** $x > \dfrac{3}{2}$ **31.** $x < -4$ **33.** $x \geq 7$ **35.** $x \geq 4$ **37.** $x < 6$ **39.** more than 30 deliveries

41. more than 1851 cars   **43.** $\dfrac{-y^2}{6x}$ **45.** $20x^2 y^{11/12}$ **47.** $x > -4.54$

Exercises 10.2

1. $3 < x$ and $x < 8$ **3.** $-4 < x$ and $x < 2$ **5.** $7 < x < 9$

7. $-2 \leq x \leq 5$ **9.** $x > 5$ or $x < 3$ **11.** $x < -3$ or $x > 6$

13. $x \leq -1$ or $x \geq 4$ **15.** $-5 \leq x < -1$ **17.** $x < -5$ or $x > 2$ **19.** no sol.: $\varnothing$ **21.** $p > 9.5$ or $p < 9.0$

23. $0.03 \leq r \leq 0.06$ **25.** $-2 < x < 2$ **27.** $x \geq 2$ and $x \leq 2$ sol.: $x = 2$ **29.** $x < -3$ or $x \geq 1$
31. $x > 1$ or $x < 7$ sol.: all real numbers   **33.** $x \geq 6$ **35.** $x < -1$ and $x > 0$ no sol.: $\varnothing$ **37.** $3 \leq x \leq 8$
39. $\dfrac{2}{3} < x \leq \dfrac{7}{3}$ **41.** $x(x - 5)(x - 3)$ **43.** $(3x + 2)(a - b)$ **45.** $-4.85 < x < 4.78$

Exercises 10.3

1. $-8 \leq x \leq 8$ **3.** $x > 5$ or $x < -5$ **5.** $-17 < x < 9$ **7.** $2 \leq x \leq 10$

9. $-10 \leq x \leq 7$ **11.** $\dfrac{4}{3} \leq x \leq 2$ **13.** $-2 < x < 3$ **15.** $-32 < x < 16$ **17.** $-\dfrac{7}{3} \leq x \leq 1$ **19.** $-9 < x < 11$

21. $-6 < x < 0$ **23.** $x > 3$ or $x < -7$ **25.** $x \geq 5$ or $x \leq -1$ **27.** $x \geq 5$ or $x \leq \dfrac{1}{3}$ **29.** $x < -8$ or $x > 16$

31. $x < -\dfrac{19}{2}$ or $x > \dfrac{21}{2}$ **33.** $x \leq -\dfrac{4}{5}$ or $x \geq 2$ **35.** $x > 17$ or $x < -13$ **37.** $18.53 \leq m \leq 18.77$ **39.** $9.63 \leq n \leq 9.73$

41. He is ignoring the statement that says $12 < -12$, which is false.   **43.** $\left(\dfrac{19}{13}, \dfrac{11}{13}\right)$ **45.** $\left(\pm 2\sqrt{3}, 2\right), \left(\pm\sqrt{7}, -3\right)$
47. $-3.54 \leq x \leq 6.77$

Exercises 10.4

1. The critical points divide the number line into segments. All values of x in a given segment produce results that are greater than zero, or else all the values of x in a given segment produce results that are less than zero.

3. $-4 < x < 3$ **5.** $x < -4$ or $x > 6$ **7.** $-\dfrac{3}{2} < x < 1$

9. $x \leq -5$ or $x \geq -2$ **11.** $-\dfrac{1}{2} \leq x \leq 6$ **13.** $x = 3$

15. $x < \left(1 - \sqrt{5}\right)$ or $x > \left(1 + \sqrt{5}\right)$ Approx. $x < -1.2$ or $x > 3.2$ **17.** $3 - \sqrt{2} < x < 3 + \sqrt{2}$, Approx. $1.6 < x < 4.4$

19. $-5 < x < 4$ **21.** $-4 \le x \le \dfrac{1}{2}$ **23.** $x < \dfrac{-2}{3}$ or $x > \dfrac{3}{2}$ **25.** $x \le \dfrac{3 - \sqrt{5}}{4}$ or $x \ge \dfrac{3 + \sqrt{5}}{4}$, Approx. $x \le 0.2$ or $x \ge 1.3$

27. $-9 \le x \le 4$ **29.** real no. line has no intervals. solution: $\varnothing$ **31.** $(-5, 32), (-4, 21), (-3, 12), (-2, 5)$

33. (a) $\approx 11.5 < x < 208.5$ **(b)** \$122,000   **(c)** \$144,000   **35.** $x < -6$ or $-2 < x < 4$

37.   **39.**   **41.** $x > 0.3$ or $x < -0.7$

Exercises 10.5

1.   **3.**   **5.**   **7.**

9.   **11.**   **13.** pt. $(0, 0)$ is on the line   **15.**

17.   **19.**   **21.** circle   **23.** ellipse

Exercises 10.6

1.   **3.**   **5.**   **7.**

9.   **11.**   **13.**

15. $x = 3$ **17.** $(-0.9, 3.8), (2.3, -2.6)$

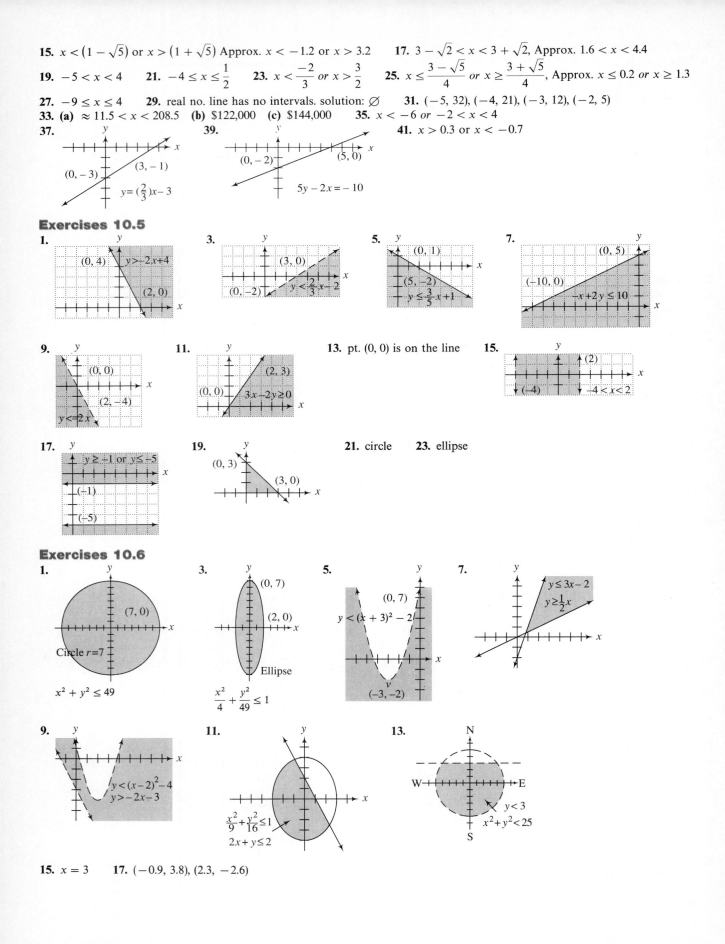

Section 10.1   **1.** <   **3.** <   **5.** >   **7.** >   **9.** >   **11.** <   **13.**

$x > 2$

15.

$x < 7$

17. $x \le -4$ **19.** $x > -12$ **21.** $x \le \dfrac{45}{4}$ **23.** $x \le \dfrac{55}{24}$ **25.** $x < \dfrac{22}{5}$ **27.** $x \ge 0$

29. $x \ge -\dfrac{19}{5}$ **31.** number of tables must be greater than 62

Section 10.2   **1.**

$4 < x$ and $x < 7$

3.

$4 < x \le 6.5$

5.

$x > 3$ or $x < -4$

7.

$x + 2 \ge 6$ or $x - 2 < -4$

9. $x < -1$ **11.** no sol. $\varnothing$ **13.** all real numbers   **15.** $x < -1$ **17.** no sol. $\varnothing$

Section 10.3   **1.** $x \ge 9$ or $x \le -9$ **3.** $-4 < x < 4$ **5.** $-15 < x < 3$ **7.** $-18 \le x \le 14$ **9.** $-1 \le x \le 9$

11. $-\dfrac{23}{5} \le x \le \dfrac{17}{5}$ **13.** $0 \le x \le \dfrac{10}{3}$ **15.** $-\dfrac{5}{2} < x < \dfrac{11}{2}$ **17.** $x > 8$ or $x < -8$ **19.** $x \ge 3$ or $x \le -7$

21. $x \ge 4$ or $x \le -\dfrac{2}{3}$ **23.** $x > 6$ or $x < -14$ **25.** $x \ge \dfrac{19}{2}$ or $x \le \dfrac{-17}{2}$ **27.** $x \le \dfrac{4}{5}$ or $x \ge \dfrac{8}{5}$ **29.** $x > \dfrac{31}{3}$ or $x < \dfrac{-1}{3}$

Section 10.4   **1.**

$-8 < x < 3$

3.

$3 > x$ or $x \ge 5$

5.

$4 < -x$ and $x \le 6$

7.

$x < -3$ or $x > 3$

9. $x < -6$ or $x > 5$ **11.** $-5 < x < -3$ **13.** all real numbers   **15.** $1 \le x \le \dfrac{3}{2}$

17. $x < 2$ or $x > 5$ **19.** $x \le -2$ or $x \ge \dfrac{1}{2}$ **21.** $x < 0$ or $x > 6$ **23.** $-\dfrac{4}{3} < x < 5$ **25.** $-2 \le x \le \dfrac{1}{5}$

27. $x \le \dfrac{1}{3}$ or $x \ge \dfrac{1}{2}$ **29.** $x \le \dfrac{4}{3}$ or $x \ge \dfrac{10}{3}$ **31.** $-\dfrac{5}{4} \le x \le \dfrac{3}{8}$ **33.** $x < -6$ or $1 < x < 4$

Section 10.5   **1.**

$2y < -x - 2$

3.

$2y < 3x - 6$

5.

$x + y \ge 7$

7.

$y \le 2x + 10$

9.

$x \le 6$

Section 10.6   **1.**

$y \ge (x - 2)^2 + 1$

3.

$(0, 2)$

$x^2 + (y - 2)^2 \le 36$

5.

$\dfrac{x^2}{9} - \dfrac{y^2}{4} \le -1$

7.

$x^2 + 9y^2 \le 9$

9.

$y = 3x$ $y = x$

$3x - y > 0$
$x < y$

11.

$2x - y \le 1$
$3x + y \ge 4$

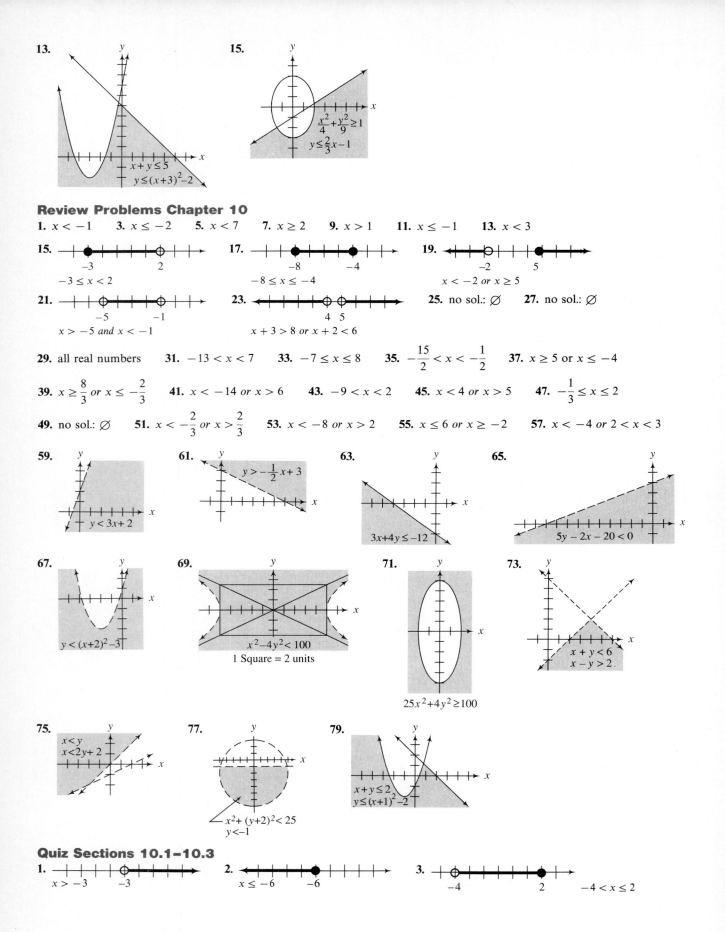

13.

$x + y \le 5$
$y \le (x+3)^2 - 2$

15.

$\dfrac{x^2}{4} + \dfrac{y^2}{9} \ge 1$
$y \le \dfrac{2}{3}x - 1$

Review Problems Chapter 10

1. $x < -1$ **3.** $x \le -2$ **5.** $x < 7$ **7.** $x \ge 2$ **9.** $x > 1$ **11.** $x \le -1$ **13.** $x < 3$

15. $-3 \le x < 2$

17. $-8 \le x \le -4$

19. $x < -2 \text{ or } x \ge 5$

21. $x > -5 \text{ and } x < -1$

23. $x + 3 > 8 \text{ or } x + 2 < 6$

25. no sol.: $\varnothing$ **27.** no sol.: $\varnothing$

29. all real numbers   **31.** $-13 < x < 7$ **33.** $-7 \le x \le 8$ **35.** $-\dfrac{15}{2} < x < -\dfrac{1}{2}$ **37.** $x \ge 5 \text{ or } x \le -4$

39. $x \ge \dfrac{8}{3} \text{ or } x \le -\dfrac{2}{3}$ **41.** $x < -14 \text{ or } x > 6$ **43.** $-9 < x < 2$ **45.** $x < 4 \text{ or } x > 5$ **47.** $-\dfrac{1}{3} \le x \le 2$

49. no sol.: $\varnothing$ **51.** $x < -\dfrac{2}{3} \text{ or } x > \dfrac{2}{3}$ **53.** $x < -8 \text{ or } x > 2$ **55.** $x \le 6 \text{ or } x \ge -2$ **57.** $x < -4 \text{ or } 2 < x < 3$

59. $y < 3x + 2$

61. $y > -\dfrac{1}{2}x + 3$

63. $3x + 4y \le -12$

65. $5y - 2x - 20 < 0$

67. $y < (x+2)^2 - 3$

69. $x^2 - 4y^2 < 100$
1 Square = 2 units

71. $25x^2 + 4y^2 \ge 100$

73. $x + y < 6$
$x - y > 2$

75. $x < y$
$x < 2y + 2$

77. $x^2 + (y+2)^2 < 25$
$y < -1$

79. $x + y \le 2$
$y \le (x+1)^2 - 2$

Quiz Sections 10.1–10.3

1. $x > -3$

2. $x \le -6$

3. $-4 < x \le 2$

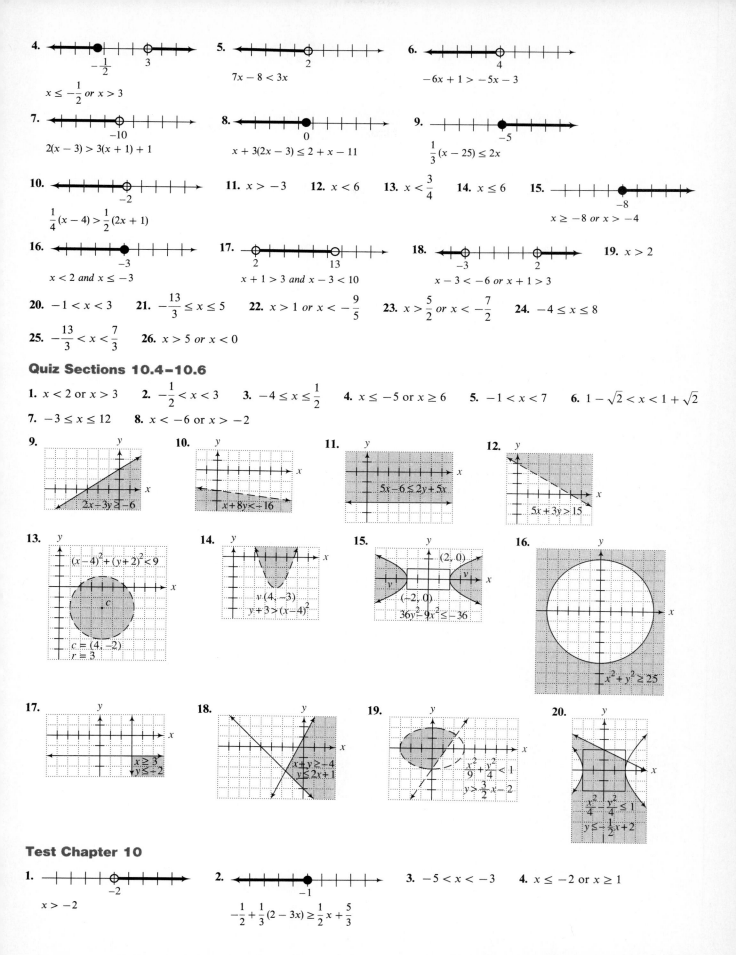

4. $x \le -\dfrac{1}{2}$ or $x > 3$

5. $7x - 8 < 3x$

6. $-6x + 1 > -5x - 3$

7. $2(x - 3) > 3(x + 1) + 1$

8. $x + 3(2x - 3) \le 2 + x - 11$

9. $\dfrac{1}{3}(x - 25) \le 2x$

10. $\dfrac{1}{4}(x - 4) > \dfrac{1}{2}(2x + 1)$

11. $x > -3$ **12.** $x < 6$ **13.** $x < \dfrac{3}{4}$ **14.** $x \le 6$ **15.** $x \ge -8$ or $x > -4$

16. $x < 2$ and $x \le -3$

17. $x + 1 > 3$ and $x - 3 < 10$

18. $x - 3 < -6$ or $x + 1 > 3$

19. $x > 2$

20. $-1 < x < 3$ **21.** $-\dfrac{13}{3} \le x \le 5$ **22.** $x > 1$ or $x < -\dfrac{9}{5}$ **23.** $x > \dfrac{5}{2}$ or $x < -\dfrac{7}{2}$ **24.** $-4 \le x \le 8$

25. $-\dfrac{13}{3} < x < \dfrac{7}{3}$ **26.** $x > 5$ or $x < 0$

Quiz Sections 10.4–10.6

1. $x < 2$ or $x > 3$ **2.** $-\dfrac{1}{2} < x < 3$ **3.** $-4 \le x \le \dfrac{1}{2}$ **4.** $x \le -5$ or $x \ge 6$ **5.** $-1 < x < 7$ **6.** $1 - \sqrt{2} < x < 1 + \sqrt{2}$

7. $-3 \le x \le 12$ **8.** $x < -6$ or $x > -2$

9. $2x - 3y \ge -6$

10. $x + 8y < -16$

11. $5x - 6 \le 2y + 5x$

12. $5x + 3y > 15$

13. $(x - 4)^2 + (y + 2)^2 < 9$ $c = (4, -2)$ $r = 3$

14. $(4, -3)$ $y + 3 > (x - 4)^2$

15. $(2, 0)$ $(-2, 0)$ $36y^2 - 9x^2 \le -36$

16. $x^2 + y^2 \ge 25$

17. $x \ge 3$ $y \le 2$

18. $x + y \ge -4$ $y \le 2x + 1$

19. $\dfrac{x^2}{9} + \dfrac{y^2}{4} < 1$ $y > \dfrac{3}{2}x - 2$

20. $\dfrac{x^2}{4} - \dfrac{y^2}{4} \le 1$ $y \le -\dfrac{1}{2}x + 2$

Test Chapter 10

1. $x > -2$

2. $-\dfrac{1}{2} + \dfrac{1}{3}(2 - 3x) \ge \dfrac{1}{2}x + \dfrac{5}{3}$

3. $-5 < x < -3$ **4.** $x \le -2$ or $x \ge 1$

5. $-\dfrac{15}{7} \le x \le 3$ **6.** $x < -\dfrac{8}{3}$ or $x > 2$ **7.** $-2 < x < 4$ **8.** $-\dfrac{2}{3} \le x \le 4$

9. **10.** **11.** **12.**

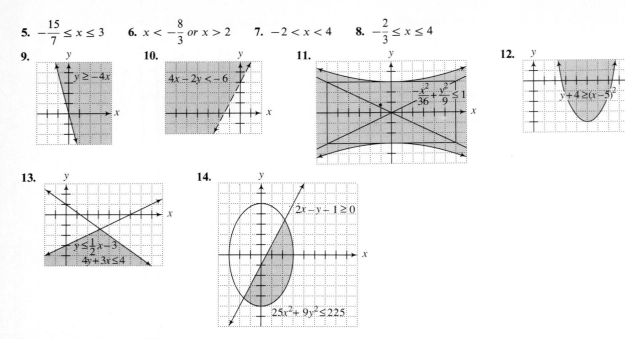

13. **14.**

Cumulative Test Chapters 1–10

1. $\dfrac{-x^2}{3y^7}$ **2.** $x = 2A - y$ **3.** $3(x + 3)(x^2 - 3x + 9)$ **4.** $x = 15$ **5.** **6.** 144 sq. meters

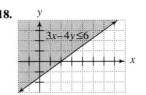

7. $x = 2,\ y = -1,\ z = 3$ **8.** $x = \dfrac{-7 \pm \sqrt{73}}{6}$ **9.** $x = 3$ **10.** $-7\sqrt{2x}$ **11.** $x > -10$ -10

12. $x \le 4$ 4 **13.** $-2 < x < 4$ **14.** $x \le -9$ or $x \ge -2$ **15.** $-20 < x < 12$

16. $x < -\dfrac{7}{3}$ or $x > 5$ **17.** $x < -\dfrac{1}{2}$ or $x > 3$ **18.** **19.**

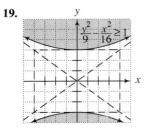

20.

PRACTICE FINAL EXAMINATION

Chapter 1 **1.** 4 **2.** $\dfrac{9x^2}{4y^2}$ **3.** $-a^2 - 10ab - a$ **4.** $y = -30$ **5.** $C = \dfrac{5F - 160}{9}$ ***Chapter 2*** **6.**

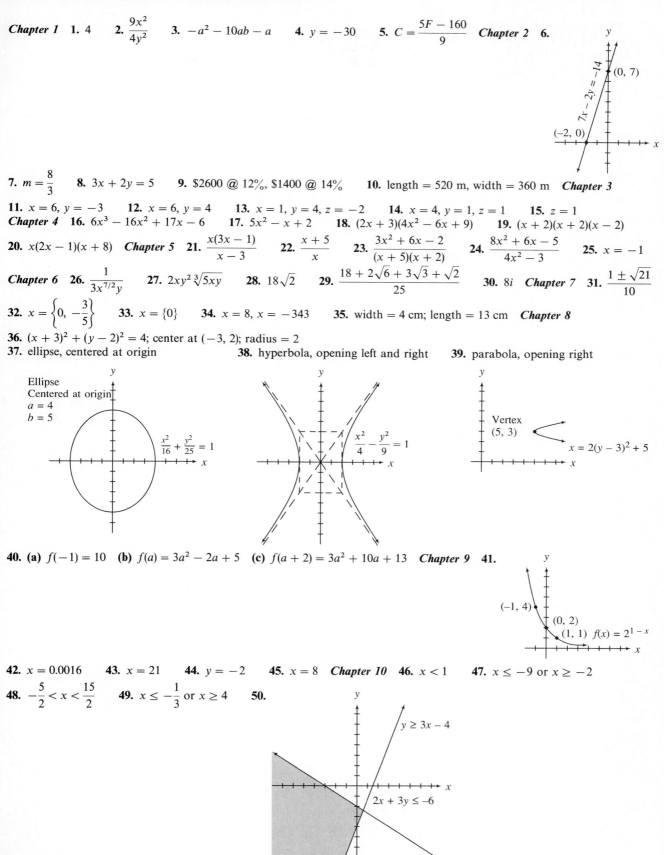

7. $m = \dfrac{8}{3}$ **8.** $3x + 2y = 5$ **9.** \$2600 @ 12%, \$1400 @ 14% **10.** length = 520 m, width = 360 m ***Chapter 3***

11. $x = 6$, $y = -3$ **12.** $x = 6$, $y = 4$ **13.** $x = 1$, $y = 4$, $z = -2$ **14.** $x = 4$, $y = 1$, $z = 1$ **15.** $z = 1$

Chapter 4 **16.** $6x^3 - 16x^2 + 17x - 6$ **17.** $5x^2 - x + 2$ **18.** $(2x + 3)(4x^2 - 6x + 9)$ **19.** $(x + 2)(x + 2)(x - 2)$

20. $x(2x - 1)(x + 8)$ ***Chapter 5*** **21.** $\dfrac{x(3x - 1)}{x - 3}$ **22.** $\dfrac{x + 5}{x}$ **23.** $\dfrac{3x^2 + 6x - 2}{(x + 5)(x + 2)}$ **24.** $\dfrac{8x^2 + 6x - 5}{4x^2 - 3}$ **25.** $x = -1$

Chapter 6 **26.** $\dfrac{1}{3x^{7/2}y}$ **27.** $2xy^2 \sqrt[3]{5xy}$ **28.** $18\sqrt{2}$ **29.** $\dfrac{18 + 2\sqrt{6} + 3\sqrt{3} + \sqrt{2}}{25}$ **30.** $8i$ ***Chapter 7*** **31.** $\dfrac{1 \pm \sqrt{21}}{10}$

32. $x = \left\{0, -\dfrac{3}{5}\right\}$ **33.** $x = \{0\}$ **34.** $x = 8$, $x = -343$ **35.** width = 4 cm; length = 13 cm ***Chapter 8***

36. $(x + 3)^2 + (y - 2)^2 = 4$; center at $(-3, 2)$; radius = 2

37. ellipse, centered at origin **38.** hyperbola, opening left and right **39.** parabola, opening right

40. (a) $f(-1) = 10$ (b) $f(a) = 3a^2 - 2a + 5$ (c) $f(a + 2) = 3a^2 + 10a + 13$ ***Chapter 9*** **41.**

42. $x = 0.0016$ **43.** $x = 21$ **44.** $y = -2$ **45.** $x = 8$ ***Chapter 10*** **46.** $x < 1$ **47.** $x \le -9$ or $x \ge -2$

48. $-\dfrac{5}{2} < x < \dfrac{15}{2}$ **49.** $x \le -\dfrac{1}{3}$ or $x \ge 4$ **50.**

APPENDIX A   On Variation

Exercises
1. $y = 1.6$ **3.** $y = 40.5$ **5.** 576 seconds   **7.** $y = 8.3$ **9.** $y = 47.4$ **11.** $p = 24$ lbs   **13.** $y = 120$
15. $y = 126.3$ **17.** 240 kg

Index